Legacy of Lexington

Kathleen H. Kirsan

ISBN: 978-0-5785-0361-5

Published in the United States of America

"The Stone which the builders rejected has become the Cornerstone.
This is the Lord's doing, and it is marvelous in our eyes."

Psalm 118:22-23

Contents

Preface

This book explores the depth of athletic talent to be found in our North American sport horse bloodlines. The focus of this study is through the lens of the American sport horse breeder rather than from the Thoroughbred perspective. However, it is based on the belief that the racehorse is not only essential in our sport horse recipes, but that it is the key ingredient for our success.

The sport horse breeders on this continent need to be retold about the outstanding quality sport genetics that reside in our North American breeds. For after forty years of the 'warmblood invasion,' it is not just the flood of foreign equine stock that has overwhelmed us, but more importantly it is the European mindset. An unfortunate consequence of this era of European indoctrination is that today most equestrians in North America believe all the important sport lines originate in Europe.

One fable that arose in this period was that the only Thoroughbred lines suitable in warmblood and sport horse breeding were those that were stamina-bred. This teaching, combined with the false judgment rendered on the American Thoroughbred—that it is a 'sprint only' breed, and is therefore not suitable for use in sport horse breeding—has taken a toll on our own estimation of our domestic sport horse. These doctrines, which have become imbedded in the minds of the North American sport horse breeder and enthusiast, are not based on fact.

I can see this pervasive thinking coloring even the contributions of intelligent American writers, who after years of brainwashing merely repeat the European rote. For instance, how many of the articles on the important bloodlines in show jumping ever mention Fair Play or his amazing son Man O' War? Or how many of you have seen the Domino line proclaimed as a premier source of sport talent? But I am sure you can repeat Cottage Son, Courville, Ladykiller, Orange Peel, etc. in your sleep. It is hard to explain this—except that we have allowed the sport horse 'experts' from Europe to dictate to us their versions of sport reporting, and perhaps more to the point, we have been negligent in presenting the North American contributions to sport ourselves. The result is after years of silence on the premier American sport bloodlines we have collectively forgotten our native sport sources, even when they are powering the bloodlines of the international champions.

This situation was evident to me after I had conducted an evaluation of the top performers in the Olympic-style sport (Hall of Fame inductees) and after researching and writing *North American Sport Horse Breeder* and several articles for my website (see Appendix E). It was then I realized the scope of this omission—it is glaring—but worse it is costing us breeders ever year that we fail to recognize the genetic treasure in our own backyard. On the other hand, if we can understand what our breeds are made of genetically, then we will be able to comprehend what the recent equine DNA studies have been declaring to us: that the qualities relevant for sport success abound in the sound athletic base our North American breeds are built on. American breeders—this is your heritage—some of the most enduring and powerful purveyors of sport in the world are our own.

The story of Lexington, his accomplishments, his far reaching genetic gifts and his spot in equine history epitomizes the American experience. As you follow with me the Lexington Legacy down through sport history, I believe you will be astounded at how far ranging and significant is his influence. It is a huge genetic footprint that he, his close relatives, and peers have made and continue to make not just in racing but in all international sport.

Kathleen Kirsan, 2014

Acknowledgments

Thanks especially to my biggest fan and supporter of my work Karrie Danekas—as always, it wouldn't happen without you.

And to my friend and the trainer of my horses: Claire King, thanks for your skill and love in training them, but also for your candid opinions, which have helped me in polishing this manuscript. Thanks also to my 'ex' Jody Kirsan for putting up with my reading sections of this manuscript to him, and for his helpful insights.

Tisk Quirk, one of America's greatest sport equine photographers, has allowed me to reproduce two of her historical photos of sport stars—thank you, Tish.

My gratitude and admiration to the Keeneland Association and the Keeneland Library for being such magnificent resources for the student of the horse, and their generosity in presenting and preserving the photographical collections of C. C. Cook, Skeet Meadors, and Bert Morgan and others for the public's use.

As always, thanks to the Thoroughbred pedigree experts Ken McLean, Edwin Anthony, and Les Brinsfield for allowing me to quote you.

Thanks to the Thoroughbred Racing Association for the publications it provides license-free for our use.

Thanks to the New York Public Library for making available in digital form its collections including the horse racing cigarette trading cards and the woodcuts of Alexander Anderson.

Thanks to Wiki Commons for their continual dedication to providing the public access to some rare and even unique public domain images.

Copyrighted Work

USET's *Great Horses of the United States Equestrian Team*; the USET graciously gave me permission to quote from their copyrighted book.

Simon Morris has generosity allowed me once again to present my pedigrees in his copyrighted TesioPower format.

The Thoroughbred pedigree experts Edwin Anthony, Ken McLean, and Les Brinsfield, have allowed me to use quotations from their copyrighted work.

Tish Quirk has given her permission to reproduce her historical copyrighted photos of Keen and Gem Twist at the height of their careers. The photo of Gem Twist especially is possibly the most artistically beautiful photo of a show jumper ever made, so thank you Tish for letting me reproduce your masterpiece.

Louise Robson has generously shared her years of experience of developing OTTBs into top dressage competitors.

Part I

The Making of the Ultimate Distance Racehorse

Chapter 1

Without Flaw

The majority of domestic sport horse breeders are not as well versed in Thoroughbred bloodlines as their Thoroughbred racehorse breeder counterparts. I know I am not, but I have found that once I gained an understanding of the history of our sport horse breeds and their bloodlines, that knowledge dramatically altered not only the way I viewed our North American breeds, but also the practice of breeding itself.

Parole, an early example of the American Thoroughbred, born in 1873. This gelding was an accomplished distance racer who would one day travel to England and beat the invincible Isonomy, a feat that was unimaginable to the British, but Parole was just a harbinger of things to come. —image found in *Racing in America*.

Because the racehorse, particularly the Thoroughbred, is such an important portion of sport aptitude and historically is such an essential portion of our best-performed North American sport horses (see Part IV and Appendix E), we should at least have a basic knowledge of our uniquely North American Thoroughbred. How else will we be able to use the marvelous resource of our domestic Thoroughbred to our advantage in our sport-horse breeding programs if we don't comprehend its important bloodlines for our goals?

In researching our North American Thoroughbred I discovered the most valuable strains to make dominant for my personal sport success, and in addition, I got the answer to some nagging questions that were in my mind from my warmblood-breeding era. For instance, I often wondered why there were not more American lines in the new 'international horse.' The answer was, first of all, there are more of them than I recognized; second, the international sport horse is a very new concept, and there was very little inter-breeding between continents until the twentieth century, and thirdly, our Thoroughbred horse was banned from international breeding for the first half of the twentieth century by the British Jockey Club. Yes, it is true, and this full first part of the book will give you the story on this event, but more important to us as breeders, it will explain to you exactly what it was about the American Thoroughbred that made it such a threat to Anglo breeding establishment.

> "No horse or mare can, after this date, be considered as eligible for admission unless it can be traced **without flaw** on both sire's and dam's side of the pedigree to horses and mares themselves already accepted in the earlier volumes of the book"(GSB 1913; emphasis mine).

The book referred to in the above quotation is the General Stud Book (Weatherby's) of the English Thoroughbred, and the English Jockey Club passed this rule unanimously in May of 1913. This regulation, popularly known as the 'Jersey Act,' slammed the door shut on the majority of American Thoroughbreds that could be allowed admission in the English Stud Book. England is the creator of the Thoroughbred breed, and therefore they control the qualifications of the breed. For the first forty years of its existence, the American Thoroughbred had been accepted into the GSB (General Stud Book), but in 1913 it was refused entry on the basis that it had 'impure' bloodlines. According to the English Jockey Club, there were certain bloodlines in the American Thoroughbred that were 'flawed'.

The American horses were still allowed to race in England, but they could not breed there or anywhere else and have their stock accepted into the General Stud Book; this ruling diminished their worth instantly. That was not the half of it, for it was because of this regulation the American Thoroughbred became a pariah in every country that raised or raced Thoroughbreds, because none of a country's stock containing American lines would be eligible for the General Stud Book, making them of significantly less commercial value. For admission into the English studbook a horse had to meet their qualifications, but as it has turned out the English Jockey Club standards are not static; they can be and have been adjusted by political policies over the years. Our American Thoroughbred met the standards to be called 'Thoroughbred' from 1868 until 1913—so what occurred to change its status?

A lot of stupid laws and regulations get passed every year in every country—in Thoroughbred racing history this particular rule had far-reaching consequences, not just for the American breeder; it eventually hurt England's and Ireland's own interests. The real shame of this law is that it remained in force until 1949—that's thirty-six years (read more on the Jersey Act in Appendix A).

However, there is a flip side not apparent at the time, an unforeseen result of this isolation: the American Thoroughbred over time became very strong in its uniquely American lines, because its best lines were forced to stay at home, and it turned out that those very 'flawed' bloodlines carried something extremely precious for sport performance, which would have been diluted without the reinforcement that resulted from the close breeding this segregation imposed. So ultimately the rule meant to harm the American breeder and our Thoroughbred Industry—and make no mistake, that was its intent—nonetheless was in the end a factor in our Thoroughbred becoming the most valuable in the world.

Lexington RH –etching from painting by Troye as it appeared in the "Spirit of the Times".

For now, let me introduce you to the stallion Lexington RH, for it was he and his close relatives and offspring who were the real targets of this rule. What about this bloodline made the English racing establishment adopt a 'kill it before it multiplies' attitude? It is the essence of Lexington RH that is the real story.

Lexington RH 1850:

Lexington RH is a pivotal horse in world equine history. He was born in 1850, and as our English cousins pointed out so strongly, he was not of purely English Thoroughbred ancestry—this was because he was an American Running Horse (the American Thoroughbred would not be a breed of its own until 1868, when separate performance standards—classic races—were adopted along with specific pedigree qualifications, which was at that time five generations of English blood). In the beginning of the *American Stud Book* (S. D. Bruce's—1868), the policy was that any horse eligible for the American book was automatically accepted into the *English Stud Book* and vice versa. All that changed once the quality of the American breed became evident (see Appendix D for more on American breed development).

When Lexington RH died in 1875, B. G. Bruce said in the "Kentucky Live Stock Record":

> "…Lexington, the most remarkable horse this country if not the world, has ever seen. He was not a passing meteor that rushes through the air, dazzling our eyes with its brilliant light, leaving little or no impression, but a blazing sun whose influence interpenetrated and has become identified with all our stock. No horse was his equal upon the American Turf, and none compare with him as a stallion…"

As Mr. Bruce had said then, so we find even today one hundred seventy-five years later: Lexington RH is still the essence of the American Thoroughbred, both literally by his multiple lines in our pedigrees, and symbolically he represents what makes the American Thoroughbred unique. In understanding Lexington RH, we will come to comprehend the full value of our native racehorse.

By Lexington's birth America had its own established racehorse breed for two hundred twenty-five years—it was called the Running Horse. Lexington RH was a member of our original racehorse breed that began in 1624 (see Appendix D, and read a full history of our Running Horse in *North American Sport Horse Breeder*).

It is true that by his era there were many English Thoroughbreds bred in the US—whether bred from two Thoroughbreds imported from England or descended exclusively from horses of strictly English Thoroughbred blood. Lloyds Traveller 1763, Lees Mark Anthony 1762, Symes Wildair 1776, and Sir Archy 1805 are prominent examples of these horses, and our distance strain of Running Horse usually had by Lexington's birth a significant amount of English Thoroughbred blood; however, this did not make those racers English Thoroughbred or even American Thoroughbred, and we find in the fastest racers of this period that it is especially the dam lines that remained of Running Horse ancestry. (The pre-Thoroughbred English racehorse was the English Running Horse). So our distance racer—often referred to as a long runner—was still of our domestic Running Horse breed with specific sires added over the years to enhance certain traits. In the early days, one of those factors was to add height to our much shorter Running Horse (13.3 to 14.2 hands). Equally important was the skeletal structure changes certain Oriental sires brought in (Places White Turk and Godolphin Arabian) to the English racer. Besides height and overall size (the English Running Horse was as short as the American) it was the laid-back shoulder and the high powerful hindquarter that had enabled the breed to move with power and extension and therefore a greater stride. This structure, combined with the amazing speed that was present from the Hobby genes resident in the English Running Horse, created the greatest racer in the world. We in the American colonies received those frame adjustments more from the English Thoroughbred imports then from direct infusion of Turcoman and Barb strains. On the other hand, we were already loaded with the speed of the Hobby—actually the American speed base probably had more variation than that which is found in the English racehorse population, and our small fast racehorse was more than a match for any racing breed—then or now.

These points may seem like trivial details, but because it was the Running Horse strains that were the basis of the ban on American racehorses, it is crucial we understand the differences. When you read about stellar individuals of our pre-Thoroughbred racehorse you will find them commonly referred to as 'Thoroughbred' in many texts and online, which is not accurate; it should be 'thoroughbred' if this term is used at all—for our original racehorse was not of the Thoroughbred breed. Actually our Running Horse developed at the same time as the English Thoroughbred (really thirty-five years earlier if you want to split hairs) **from the same mare base**, but the English added Oriental sires while we (with a few Barb exceptions) did not. Also, our original racehorse was so well bred and talented that even in our humble colonial state, this breed was already the best in the world in several categories (pacing racer, sprint racer, saddle horse) as well as being the only breed able to give its cousin the English Thoroughbred (mid-1700s) a legitimate challenge in distance racing (sometimes beating it). What you probably did not know was it was just one hundred years after (mid-1800s) that the American Running Horse was also

The American Running Horse, as depicted in a print made from a wood engraving by early American artist Alexander Anderson.

the undisputed ruler of true distance racing in the world.

In England it was only when they differentiated between their native Running Horse with pedigree requirements and different racing standards that their Thoroughbred was born (1670). (However, the breed title: 'Thoroughbred' was only assumed in the mid-1700s—one hundred years later.) A similar scenario developed here; our Thoroughbred did not become a separate breeding population until 1868 when we adopted the classic race standard, along with pedigree requirements of strictly English lineage for five generations.

Breeds are usually organized by specific performance criteria and/or specified parentage. As the English racing establishment pointed out so dramatically, many of our best and fastest racehorses were not exclusively of English Thoroughbred ancestry (neither were many of theirs for that matter.)

The second most important point for you to grasp in order to understand our original racehorse is that, contrary to the common assumption, our colonial American racehorse breeders were not ignorant, illiterate, or unschooled in the breeding science and advancements of the day—quite the opposite—even in earliest times they were of the highest class of privilege and education. When they created this breed, it was intentionally and selectively-bred from the fastest Hobby and Running Horse imports (see Appendix D). These horses were carefully chosen, purchased, and then shipped over to the Colonies by wealthy plantation owners specifically to breed racehorses from. They were valuable and high-class stock, well-worth the expense to ship across the ocean. But before we continue on let us examine exactly what constitutes a 'Thoroughbred.'

What is a Thoroughbred?

The original meaning of the term 'thoroughbred' was 'well-bred' in that it was related to animals selectively bred from superior ancestors, and it was applied to all domestic livestock—that means sheep, cattle, and hogs as well as horses. The English racehorse promoters appropriated this term later on (mid-1700s) for their selectively bred classic-distance racehorse.

The English Thoroughbred became a breed of its own when separate performance standards and pedigree requirements were met. Alexander MacKay-Smith has clearly delineated with his impeccable research and presentation what the English Thoroughbred is derived from in his 2000 masterpiece: *Speed and the Thoroughbred*. He has shown us that it is made up of three key ingredients:

- The Irish Hobby—provided the true source of speed and genetic base of the early English racehorse stud broodmare bands (English Running Horse).

- The Barb—provided some height and stamina, usually present from a sire.

- The Turcoman—provided height and stamina essentially through the 'Old Turk,' Places White Turk, and then, one hundred years later, from one other prepotent individual—the Godolphin Arabian—came the distinctive laid-back shoulder and high rump.

However, the speed travelled up the dam-lines, and the modern DNA studies have confirmed this (Bower et al and Hill et al).

Spanker 1670 is the acknowledged first Thoroughbred; until his birth it was the English Running Horse (Hobby and Barb genetics) that was the English racehorse breed—a fantastic sprint racer, it was also a gaited horse. Spanker is by D'Arcy's Yellow

Turk out of Old Peg 1655. The Yellow Turk was a domestically bred horse sired by the imported (1657) horse known as Place's White Turk out of an un-named D'Arcy Royal Mare (Hobby-based broodmare band). His dam Old Peg is also known as 'Old Morocco Mare,' and she is by the 1637 imported Morocco Barb out of Old Bald Peg (Hobby genetics). As you can see Spanker carries all three of the required strains, and his dam-lines are Hobby/Running Horse—the source of speed.

In England until 1666 most races run were sprints, which the Running Horse excelled at, and extreme distance races of up to twenty miles for the larger and slower English Charger or Hunter (these were tests for the conditioning of the Hunter, not speed races). King Charles changed all that along with which horses were bred to race when he established set racing standards in 1666 for heat racing that were usually three- or four-mile heat races; he provided written rules, and he actually rode in many of the meets himself. Over time an oval track became preferred so the entire race could be observed. The horses that were best at this race form were those of the above genetics. Spanker himself was the greatest four-mile heat racehorse of his day.

At the base of the English Thoroughbred you will find Spanker and his close relatives: Sister to Spanker, Young Bald Peg, and the 'Spanker Mare' who is by Spanker himself out of Old Peg (Spanker's dam). Young Bald Peg is out of Spanker's dam also, but is by Leedes Arabian—who is not an 'Arabian' but is by the same D'Arcys Yellow Turk as Spanker, therefore they are ½ brothers. Leedes Arabian is also the sire of the foundation mare Bay Peg who is out of Young Bald Peg. Other significant foundations of the English Thoroughbred, such as the Byerley Turk, were not imported either, as he is a domestic-bred descendant of the original Places White Turk (MacKay-Smith). As you can see this is a very tight gene pool.

The early racehorse studs were founded on Hobby and English Running Horse mares, and these are the true source of speed in the Thoroughbred. Unfortunately most of these early great Running Horse strains were lost during the English Civil War (1642-1660)—scattered or slaughtered—so it is only a very thin genetic thread that was saved in the form of Old Bald Peg and the D'Arcy Royal Mares (these mares were of Hobby/Running Horse blood, therefore a speed source). In the modern English studbook the mare families #1 through #15 all go back to these original mares, and it is they who are the source of the speed in the breed, not the Turk or Barb.

Also, another point of interest, the imported Godolphin Arabian 1724 and Darley Arabian 1700—both Turcoman Horses, not Arabian—are given in most accounts as foundation sires of the Thoroughbred; however, their progeny did not make an impact until several years after their import, so they are not when the Thoroughbred began (1670). Rather they instead were important typesetters imported fifty years after the breed commenced. Plus, in modern times it has been discovered that the Byerley Turk and the Leedes Arabian were bred in England, not imported—the Byerley Turk is by the Places White Turk out of a Hobby/Running Horse mare and Leedes Arabian is by D'Arcy's Yellow Turk (son of Places White Turk out of a Running Horse dam) presumably out of a Running Horse mare (MacKay-Smith *Speed and the Thoroughhred*).

––––––––––––––––––––

[Note: The modern English researcher James Hardiman has provided compelling evidence that the Yellow Turk was by the Tripoli Barb, and that Places White Turk was bred in England by the imported Moroccan Barb out of Old Bald Peg— meaning they were Barb or Barb/Running Horse combinations. If this is so then the Turcoman, which provided not only height, but the laid back shoulder, did not enter the gene pool until about 1720—therefore possibly pushing the true breed date up to 1720 from 1670—as all three elements (Barb, Running Horse and Turk) mixing is what provided the 'Thoroughbred'.]

Origin of Speed in the American Racehorse

Now, here is a key concept for North American breeders to take hold of on the sources of speed in all our racehorse breeds: the English Colonists who bred the foundation of our racehorse—the American Running Horse—got their original racing stock from the early studs in England before the English Civil War had eradicated them, and also directly from Ireland where the fastest speed strains originated from. The English Running Horse (Hobby-based), Scottish Galloway, and the Irish Hobby all became extinct by the end of the 1600s in the British Isles.

While the source of true speed in the British Isles was going extinct, we in the American Colonies were enjoying our domestic racehorse breed that sprang from those horses and their relatives. The pacing Rhode Island Plantation racer (Narragansett

Pacer) was becoming world-renown both as a premier pacing racehorse and exceptional saddle horse at the same time as the Maryland/Virginia breeders had produced a racehorse that excelled at all race lengths—sprint or four-mile heats, and in pace or gallop forms. Virginia perfected the sprinter first, but quickly followed with the distance racer and, after the American Revolution, saved the strains of pacing racehorse that had almost disappeared in the north. Therefore our domestic American mare families are a source of speed also, and actually may arise from a greater spectrum of the original Hobby gene pool than the English Thoroughbred possesses.

What happened when our fastest native racehorses met their near relatives that were imported in the mid-1700s from England? You will find the answers to this when you read about the breeding career of an imported 14 ¾-hand stallion named Janus (pedigree at chapter end). He impacted our racehorse and saddle horse population like few others (Fearnought, Diomed, and Messenger EH being the only other imported ones that produced this type of 'nick.') Look at his pedigree and read what I had to say about him in *North American Sport Horse Breeder*:

> **"Janus 1746:** 'The Janus stock exceeded all others in the United States for speed, durability, and uniformity of shape and were noted as the producers of more good saddle horses than any other stock. (Anderson).'
>
> "Janus put a profound and lasting type on our developing light horse breeds. His pedigree is also a window into the true beginnings of the English Thoroughbred. A study of his pedigree will explain this but here are a few things to notice: the full brother and sister Points/Bald Galloway 3x4 and the ¾ sisters Bay Peg and Betty Leedes 3x4. All of his fine Running Horse genetics were reinforced as more potency was built through the foundation mares Grey Whynot and Old Bald Peg, horses of ¾ Hobby/Running Horse blood, as is Hautboy the source of the large heart gene in the modern Thoroughbred (Haun). Another point of interest is Leedes Arabian, who as you can see is not an Arabian at all, but by a Barb sire, and possibly a Barb/RH dam. [error: Leedes Arabian is by the Yellow Turk out of a Running Horse dam (MacKay-Smith).]
>
> "It is no wonder then when Janus met our native Running Horse mares that he was an automatic nick and served as a consolidator of our native type while also contributing vigor as he carried the concentrated elements of our root stock in his background.
>
> "An early English Thoroughbred imported to this country in 1756, Janus was prepotent for sprinting speed, compact muscular conformation, and he was notable for transmitting the amble and pace as well as the trot to his descendants—clearly showing he was prepotent for the English Running Horse genes in his lineage rather than the Turkoman and Barb. When Janus's genes met our American Running Horse mares there was an explosion of potency and talent—as the English Running genes met their near relatives in our Running Horse. Janus is at the base of our Quarter Horse, Thoroughbred, and Standardbred, as well as the Plantation Horse and its descendant breeds. He reproduced his type consistently—sprint Running Horse form; that is, muscular, short-coupled, and high headed, with sprint speed and gaits.
>
> "Janus contained a genetic fabric almost free from defects, and he was inbred to with overall good results. When breeders structured pedigrees that contained inbreeding to Janus they were refocusing the extreme type and traits, leaving a lasting imprint on most of our American domestic breeds. Janus produced sprint distance winners, he was somewhat lacking in transmitting stamina. The import of Janus and the concentration of his bloodlines created a lasting type."

When we get to the horses of our Heroic Era of racing, we find that Janus is usually pretty far back, five to eight generations, but you will discover in a great many he is found on the dam-line, as he was most often bred to the Running Horse mares, and these mares are the purveyors of the speed. Also, Janus's offspring would have received his own Hobby/Running Horse speed gene—look at his pedigree (at chapter end); he would also pass on his dam's X chromosome, which was either from Bay Peg, Grey Whynot, or an unnamed Hobby, so these mares would receive Janus's speed gene and sex-linked traits as well as receiving speed from their own dams. (To understand how to 'read' pedigrees see Appendix B: Evaluating Pedigrees).

Janus, imported in 1757, would have been mated with our mares who had already been selectively bred for speed for one hundred years—just like his ancestors (very few of his mates were imported English TB mares for two reasons: very few English TB mares had been imported by then, and also because he stood in the quarter racing district where the mare base was American Running Horse almost exclusively). Enthusiasm for the 'Janus breed' inspired pedigree revisionists to rewrite American lines with multiple lines of Janus; in many cases five or six crosses are attributed to him, totally impossible by the time and place, so they were barely concealed frauds (see Appendix C for some of those).

In the first hundred years 1624-1730, the American Running Horse was developed, performance tested, and enjoyed to the utmost. It was a wonderful breed—renowned for its agreeable temperament, hardiness, gentle saddle gaits, and its astounding speed and stamina. Horse racing was our first national sport. The breeders of the racehorse strains perfected their racing capabilities with selective breeding to the best and fastest of their kind. By the end of those first hundred years the American Running Horse was the best pacing racer and the best sprint racer in the world, as well as being a premier distance racer and a saddle horse of high value. It was also the 'improver,' used on all our other breeds and types of horse.

When the English Thoroughbred arrived on our shores—just a dribble beginning in 1730, but more by the 1750s—certain individuals had tremendous success as typesetters on our native breed, horses such as Janus and Fearnought, and then later key sires like Medley, Shark, Messenger EH, and Diomed. There were other sires, but those who had the most success were prominent in old Hobby genetics, and when they met our racehorse broodmare bands who were heavy in Hobby genetics already, then history has shown us that the combination resulted in an explosion of athletic talent in speed and performance. Fearnought 1755 was an important factor in the development of both the distance racer and our Hunter Horse as he imparted height as well as speed.

At the time of the first wave of imports of English Thoroughbreds to North America, the English racing establishment was already headed to a change in the performance standards for their breed. A new racing test was developed of a shorter racing distance that was run once around a track—no heats. This form eventually became known as classic racing, and the St. Leger was initiated in 1776 at two miles, the Epsom Oaks in 1779 at 1 ½ miles, and the Epsom Derby in 1780 at 1 ½ miles—in this country this new race form was called 'dash' racing.

However, here in the States we continued right along with **all** the racing standards we had used to test our breed before the Thoroughbred arrived, which included ¼-mile sprints as well as the two- to four-mile heat race form, and these were run at the gallop or the pace, and later on (1800s) at the trot. We did not adopt the classic race standard until after our Civil War—1868 to be exact. It was in that hundred years between 1760 and 1860 that America perfected the four-mile heat racer.

Historically wars have had a tremendous impact on our equine populations; the entire world was essentially a horse society until the 1900s, and we all went to war on the horse, so whenever and wherever war was waged the horse populations were decimated—often along with the records of their ancestry. This is what had happened during the English Civil War and the wars in Ireland, and the majority of horses along with their records paid the price. We are left with scant information from the Sedbury, Helmsley, and Tutbury studs of England as well as the Desmond, Ossory, and Kildare studs of Ireland, which are the origin of the speed mares. Here in the US our Revolution had this same effect, especially in the northeast and mid-Atlantic region, and then our Civil War wiped out entire families of important racing and sport stock along with the memories of their roots, especially in the south.

Popular opinion and fads also take their toll on which records are preserved. In England the glamour of 'Oriental' sires and their promotion by their leaders resulted in the English Running Horse being discarded as 'common.' And because of this bias the pedigrees were expunged of this strain, ultimately resulting in the revered English Stud Book being loaded with bogus 'Arabian' names and invented ancestry in candidates vying for inclusion in the book.

We were no different, as our first 'official' racehorse studbook (Edgar's) was 'ethnically cleansed' of its domestic mare families and English Thoroughbred lineage substituted where none existed (see Appendix C for a list of colonial horses with questionable parentage). A good example of this is the English imported (1748) mare Mary Gray, whose exaggerated progeny list was detected by John Wallace, Fairfax Harrison, and Alexander MacKay-Smith. In Edgar's studbook, Mary Gray is claimed to be the dam of at least eleven offspring by Jolly Roger, something that is impossible by time and where he stood. John Wallace traced the rewriting of these and other made-up pedigrees, many in the old Quarter racing district, to a time when the full English Thoroughbreds were competing at race meets with the new hybrid American TB/RH racers. When it became clear to the English Thoroughbred importers and breeders that those 'mongrel-bred' racers were beating them regularly, they changed the race rules to allow only those horses who had 'pure' English bloodlines (sound familiar?). Wallace says from that moment on, the dam-lines were changed to fictitious English lines. Mary Gray was a well-documented imported English mare, so she was regularly substituted in dam-lines; however, when it became noticed that the progeny claims for Mary Gray were excessive and impossible in many cases, then the practice was switched to putting an equally fictitious, generic but harder to dispute, 'imported English mare' instead.

Other scholars, including Fairfax Harrison, observed the same practice—that bogus 'English mares' were invented for the dam-lines of great Running Horse racers such as Budd, Spider, Fancy, Sweet Mary (on Boston's dam-line), Caelia, Shad, Jupiter, Smiling Poll, and others (see Appendix C).

In addition, MacKay-Smith has pointed out that there was also an excessive use of Janus to fill out lineages. Janus stood in many different locations in the sprint breeding area, and because of the places he stood and at which time, then many of those claims of Janus parentage are impossible frauds. Plus MacKay-Smith found other pedigrees that were attributed to imported English sires that are also totally unreliable because of date and place (see Appendix C for a partial list of known colonial horses with made-up lineages). But the pedigree revisionists did not stop there. They went so far in this farce that some of the proper English sires, stated as serving our mares here, had never even been in America. And of course it has come to light that many, many of the imported English horses to this country came with 'beefed-up' lineages—what a mess!

A rare photo of Lexington RH, taken by James Mullen. It was one of a pair of nearly identical images meant to be viewed through a stereotype viewer. Look at his strong legs and feet, low cannons, strong hip and shoulder. —image courtesy of Wiki Commons

Our dedicated scholars (Farschler, Wallace, Harrison, Weeks, MacKay-Smith) along the way have alerted us to our true sport heritage, but it is only now with the recent work by the geneticist's Bower and Hill along with their research teams that we realize the scope of what was lost. (DNA studies have uncovered that the 'speed gene' came from the early English studs of the pre-Thoroughbred that were based on the Irish Hobby). It is our duty now, and also should be our joy, to rediscover our true equine sport roots, because we will find we are blessed, in spite of our wars and prejudices, to still have a strong connection to a genetic well of sport excellence—right here and now, on this continent.

So let's recap all this—by the mid-1600s in England King Charles had changed the popularity of the race standards from the sprints and twenty-mile stamina tests to heat race form. Long before the English Thoroughbred arrived here we enthusiastically adopted the new English race form—first in the New York Colony at the Hempstead Plain racecourse in 1665. The craze spread quickly to the other Colonies—to Virginia in 1677, and when in the mid-1700s we received our initial colonial stock of English Thoroughbreds, many were champion four-mile heat racers, but this also coincided with the shift in England to its new performance test: the classic race form. America **did not** adopt the classic form until one hundred years later.

It was in those hundred years—approximately 1760-1860—that America developed the greatest distance racehorse the world has ever seen. Extreme versatility was resident in our native breed, as examples of individuals that paced in one race and either trotted or galloped in another were not uncommon (the great racer Planet RH could race and win at both the trot or gallop), and we found some could win in a sprint contest as easily as a four-mile heat race (such as the colonial era Fearnought's son Barleysides RH, and a famous racer of the early 1800s: Monsieur Tonson RH 1822—see Chapter 4), and it didn't seem to matter if the races were ridden or driven either. Lady Suffolk AT 1833 for instance set the world record of her day at the trot both ridden and under harness—she was the first horse to do the trotted mile in 2:30—in both forms.

Lexington RH however was the pinnacle of distance heat racing, both as a racer and as a stallion. He set a world record for the fastest four-mile, and he was the top sire for a world record sixteen years—even during the time when many of his offspring were lost in the Civil War carnage. Since then no other horse has bested his stallion record, and his genetics have provided the racing and greater sport world with consistent speed and stamina. He is truly a contender for the greatest horse of all time.

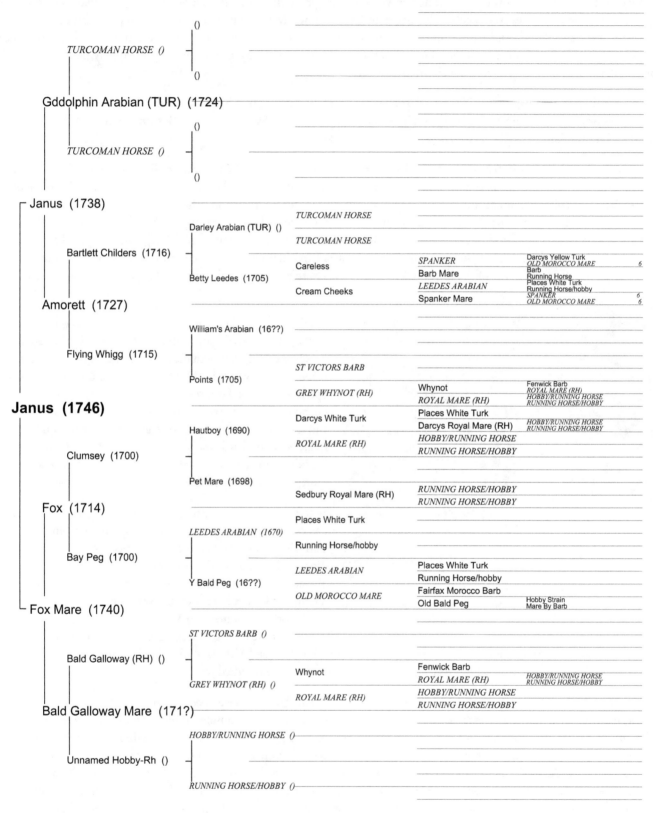

Janus 1746

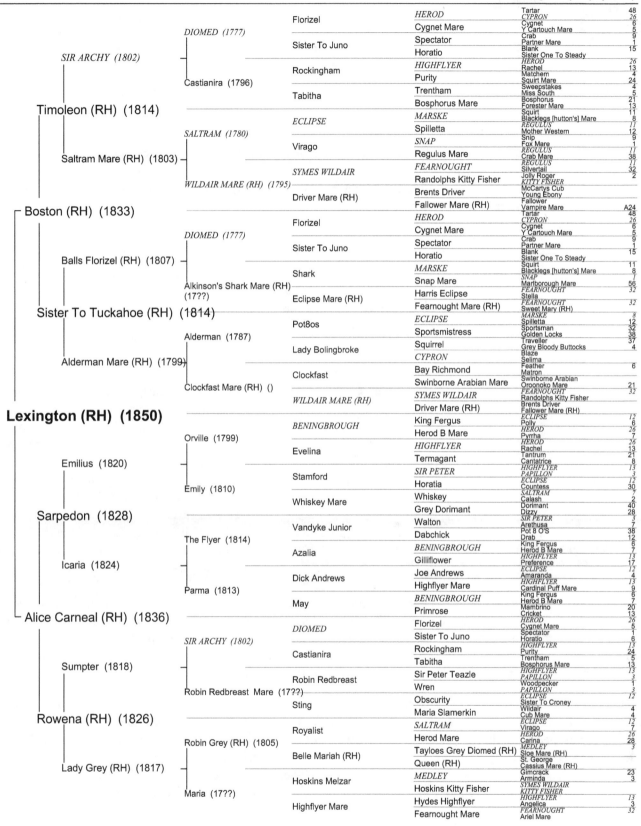

Lexington (RH) (1850)

- **Boston (RH) (1833)**
  - **Timoleon (RH) (1814)**
    - **SIR ARCHY (1802)**
      - DIOMED (1777)
        - Florizel
          - HEROD — Tartar 48, CYPRON 26
          - Cygnet Mare — Cygnet 6, Y Cartouch Mare 5
        - Sister To Juno
          - Spectator — Crab 9, Partner Mare 1
          - Horatio — Blank 15, Sister One To Steady
      - Castianira (1796)
        - Rockingham
          - HIGHFLYER — HEROD 26, Rachel 13
          - Purity — Matchem 4, Squirt Mare 24
        - Tabitha
          - Trentham — Sweepstakes 4, Miss South 5
          - Bosphorus Mare — Bosphorus 21, Forester Mare 13
    - **Saltram Mare (RH) (1803)**
      - SALTRAM (1780)
        - ECLIPSE
          - MARSKE — Squirt 11, Blacklegs [hutton's] Mare 8
          - Spilletta — REGULUS 11, Mother Western 12
        - Virago
          - SNAP — Snip 9, Fox Mare 1
          - Regulus Mare — REGULUS 11, Crab Mare 38
      - WILDAIR MARE (RH) (1795)
        - SYMES WILDAIR
          - FEARNOUGHT — REGULUS 11, Silvertail 32
          - Randolphs Kitty Fisher — Jolly Roger 2, KITTY FISHER
        - Driver Mare (RH)
          - Brents Driver — McCartys Cub, Young Ebony
          - Fallower Mare (RH) — Fallower, Vampire Mare A24
  - **Sister To Tuckahoe (RH) (1814)**
    - **Balls Florizel (RH) (1807)**
      - DIOMED (1777)
        - Florizel
          - HEROD — Tartar 48, CYPRON 26
          - Cygnet Mare — Cygnet 6, Y Cartouch Mare 5
        - Sister To Juno
          - Spectator — Crab 9, Partner Mare 1
          - Horatio — Blank 15, Sister One To Steady
      - Alkinson's Shark Mare (RH) (17??)
        - Shark
          - MARSKE — Squirt 11, Blacklegs [hutton's] Mare 8
          - Snap Mare — SNAP 7, Marlborough Mare 56
        - Eclipse Mare (RH)
          - Harris Eclipse — FEARNOUGHT 32, Stella
          - Fearnought Mare (RH) — FEARNOUGHT 32, Sweet Mary (RH)
    - **Alderman Mare (RH) (1799)**
      - Alderman (1787)
        - Pot8os
          - ECLIPSE — MARSKE 8, Spilletta 12
          - Sportsmistress — Sportsman 32, Golden Locks 38
        - Lady Bolingbroke
          - Squirrel — Traveller 37, Grey Bloody Buttocks 4
          - CYPRON — Blaze, Selima
      - Clockfast Mare (RH) ()
        - Clockfast
          - Bay Richmond — Feather 6, Matron
          - Swinborne Arabian Mare — Swinborne Arabian, Oroonoko Mare 21
        - WILDAIR MARE (RH)
          - SYMES WILDAIR — FEARNOUGHT 32, Randolphs Kitty Fisher
          - Driver Mare (RH) — Brents Driver, Fallower Mare (RH)
- **Alice Carneal (RH) (1836)**
  - **Sarpedon (1828)**
    - **Emilius (1820)**
      - Orville (1799)
        - BENINGBROUGH
          - King Fergus — ECLIPSE 12, Polly 6
          - Herod B Mare — HEROD 26, Pyrrha 7
        - Evelina
          - HIGHFLYER — HEROD 26, Rachel 13
          - Termagant — Tantrum 21, Cantatrice 8
      - Emily (1810)
        - Stamford
          - SIR PETER — HIGHFLYER 13, PAPILLON 3
          - Horatia — ECLIPSE 12, Countess 30
        - Whiskey Mare
          - Whiskey — SALTRAM 7, Calash 2
          - Grey Dorimant — Dorimant 40, Dizzy 28
    - **Icaria (1824)**
      - The Flyer (1814)
        - Vandyke Junior
          - Walton — SIR PETER 3, Arethusa 7
          - Dabchick — Pot 8 O'S 38, Drab 12
        - Azalia
          - BENINGBROUGH — King Fergus 6, Herod B Mare 7
          - Gilliflower — HIGHFLYER 13, Preference 17
      - Parma (1813)
        - Dick Andrews
          - Joe Andrews — ECLIPSE 12, Amaranda 4
          - Highflyer Mare — HIGHFLYER 13, Cardinal Puff Mare 9
        - May
          - BENINGBROUGH — King Fergus 6, Herod B Mare 7
          - Primrose — Mambrino 20, Cricket 13
  - **Rowena (RH) (1826)**
    - **Sumpter (1818)**
      - SIR ARCHY (1802)
        - DIOMED
          - Florizel — HEROD 26, Cygnet Mare 5
          - Sister To Juno — Spectator 1, Horatio 6
        - Castianira
          - Rockingham — HIGHFLYER 13, Purity 24
          - Tabitha — Trentham 5, Bosphorus Mare 13
      - Robin Redbreast Mare (17??)
        - Robin Redbreast
          - Sir Peter Teazle — HIGHFLYER 13, PAPILLON 3
          - Wren — Woodpecker 1, PAPILLON 3
        - Sting
          - Obscurity — ECLIPSE 12, Sister To Croney
          - Maria Slamerkin — Wildair 4, Cub Mare 4
    - **Lady Grey (RH) (1817)**
      - Robin Grey (RH) (1805)
        - Royalist
          - SALTRAM — ECLIPSE 12, Virago 7
          - Herod Mare — HEROD 26, Carina 28
        - Belle Mariah (RH)
          - Tayloes Grey Diomed (RH) — MEDLEY 3, Sloe Mare (RH)
          - Queen (RH) — St. George, Cassius Mare (RH)
      - Maria (17??)
        - Hoskins Melzar
          - MEDLEY — Gimcrack 23, Arminda 3
          - Hoskins Kitty Fisher — SYMES WILDAIR, KITTY FISHER
        - Highflyer Mare
          - Hydes Highflyer — HIGHFLYER 13, Angelica 3
          - Fearnought Mare — FEARNOUGHT 32, Ariel Mare

Lexington RH 1850

Chapter 2

The Flaw

"It is recognized the world over, and has been recognized for generations, that the Thoroughbred, and the running horse even before he came to be known as the Thoroughbred, has been the most important source of improvement of various types and breeds of light horses. This is not conjecture, but a matter of historical record." (Thoroughbred Racing Association 1944)

So what was the 'flaw' all about? We will discuss the true reasons for the ban on American horses in Chapter 8, but here we will look at the alleged deficit in Lexington's pedigree. Just what was wrong with it? The point that was ruled on by the English establishment as what was wrong with Lexington RH and his close relatives, and used as the basis to exclude them from their breeding populations, was actually what was best about them. Their speed genes were passed down to them by both American and English Running Horse bloodlines.

Colonial Running Horse race, performed at a 'speeding ground' (an area cleared for racing with posts marking the start and finish), depicted in a print from a wood engraving by early American artist Alexander Anderson. Our colonial racehorses were a carrier of the speed gene.

If you look at Lexington's pedigree, you will see I have identified him as an American Running Horse. When you pull up his pedigree online and elsewhere, you will **not** find him identified as a Running Horse (RH) in most versions of his lineage; instead he is usually said to be a Thoroughbred. This label is not correct, as the English so dramatically pointed out—Lexington RH and his peers had bloodlines that hadn't seen the British Isles since before the Thoroughbred came into being. Long before the English Thoroughbred landed on our shores (one hundred twenty-five years later) the American Colonists had developed their first rate race-horse from the early racing stock they had imported from England and Ireland. These were not Thoroughbred horses; the Thoroughbred did not become a breed until 1670 in England, and the colonies did not receive any of them until almost eighty years after that. In addition, the fact of an American horse having an English Thoroughbred dam or sire did not then, and certainly does not now, make them of the Thoroughbred breed—as the English Jockey Club has so strongly declared. The racing stock our colonial racehorse breeders imported was of the original pre-Thoroughbred racehorse breed.

The English Thoroughbred itself developed from this same earlier racehorse breed in the British Isles: the English Running Horse and its extremely fast cousin the Irish Hobby. These horses were small (14 hands or under), and they were gaited horses that possessed a wonderful temperament along with vast reservoirs of speed. **There was no horse breed that was faster in the known world at the time**. In England, it was on this base in the mid-1600s that a few Barb and Turcoman stallions were crossed in to improve height and increase stride. Those that proved the most capable in the new race form of heat racing were selectively bred to form the new "Thoroughbred"—although this breed title was not added until one hundred years after the breed was formed.

Much confusion has been caused in succeeding generations of breeders by the mislabeling of many of the early English Thoroughbred ancestors as 'Arabian' or 'Turk' or 'Barb' when in fact they were domestically bred. As we saw in the previous chapter, the Hobby/Running Horse was the base, especially the mare base, with only a few Barbs added over the years. However the most dramatic change was through **one** individual sire: Places White Turk, who gave them height, stamina, and greater stride, and then through one other typesetter one hundred years later: the Godolphin Arabian (another Turk). The Leedes Arabian and Byerley Turk were not imported, but domestically bred from the White Turk and his son the Yellow Turk—out of Running Horse/Hobby mares.

The American colonies had committed racehorse breeders who imported selected individuals from the pre-Thoroughbred racer: the English Running Horse, Scottish Galloway, and Irish Hobby (all closely related regional populations of this racehorse). By 1624 in Virginia, and twenty years later in the Rhode Island Plantations, they had already set performance standards of sprint and mile-long pacing races and were selectively breeding for racing—the new breed was the American Running Horse, and it traveled by ship regularly to race in both areas. In 1665 in the New York Colony the new English form of heat racing was introduced and caught on quickly, spreading along with the racers to all the colonies. However it was still our undiluted Colonial breed that was performance tested in all these forms—galloping and pacing races of all distances from sprints to four-mile heat contests. **Places White Turk was not even imported into England until 1657, so up until that time the English racehorse breed and our own were of identical genetics**. Our stock then came from the pre-Thoroughbred racer, the Hobby and English Running Horse—which includes of course the Scottish Galloway—all closely related breeding populations.

Our original racehorse breed was not only exceptionally fast and bred primarily for racing, but it was docile and exceedingly comfortable to ride and therefore became the preferred saddle horse as well. These were gaited horses, and eventually by the crossing in of other breeds some strains developed a trot, and many were dual-gaited. Therefore they became a pacing, trotting, and galloping race breed, equally desired as fine saddle horses and later as fine harness horses. By the mid-1700s a branch of our racehorse had perfected the distance heat racing, and by the early 1800s they had surpassed any previous breed in their perfection of this race form. Lexington RH 1850 was born at the pinnacle of this development.

An Englishman visiting America before our Revolution describes the American Running Horse breed as such: "…indeed, nothing can be more elegant and beautiful than the horse had here, either for the Turf, the field, the road or the coach…" (*Tour of the United States of America* J.F.D. Smythe).

Three of Lexington's four grandparent's dam-lines are of the Running Horse breed. His sire Boston RH actually has Running Horse dams ruling both his parent's dam-lines. His best son Lexington RH has as third-dam the Running Horse Lady Grey, who like Boston RH has Running Horse on both of her parent's dam-lines also. This makes up the Running Horse dam-lines found in Lexington RH; and these were the elements identified as his flaw, and it is the reason promoted to ban American horses (see Appendix A for three articles about the Jersey Act—written while it was still in force in 1944, 1947, and at its rescinding in 1949).

Here is an interesting point on those flawed Lexington RH lines: one of those Running Horse mares is English—not American. Calista (ERH) is believed to be an imported (in utero) Running Horse because her dam was a race mare who was not descended from the Oriental horses. Her dam was named when she arrived here Byrd's Express 1756, but she has no parentage identified (Hervey); either it was lost or more likely it was suppressed. You might as well ask yourself why an American breeder would pay to import an expensive mare if she had no documentation of her lineage. The answer is they would not—importing English horses was an expensive practice, and no one would purchase and ship a horse from England if it was not of top class. What we do know is this mare's daughter Calista ERH was a progenitor of immense speed as she also provided us with one of Fearnought's fastest sons: Dandridges Fearnought RH. She had the speed, what she lacked was the parentage to be classified English Thoroughbred.

Calista ERH is found on both sides of Lexington's lineage. In England, the only horses with true speed were the Hobby/Running Horse and its descendant the Thoroughbred. Calista ERH did not trace back to the approved Thoroughbred ancestors, but she possessed speed, and she obviously could pass on great speed—therefore she had to be a descendant of the English Running Horse or Irish Hobby breed. **There was no other horse in the British Isles that was fast—none,** just those and its descendant the Thoroughbred. It is probable she was ineligible for the studbook because she did not possess any 'Oriental' blood (Places White Turk, Godolphin Arabian, etc.) that was required in the new Thoroughbred breed. In her day, fast or not, the Running Horse was out of fashion.

Lexington's third-dam was the American Running Horse Lady Grey 1817. This mare carries another line of the same Calista ERH and another American Running Horse line (Cassius Mare RH) through her sire Robin Grey RH 1805. Notice also the many lines of Regulus—whose dam Grey Robinson is a daughter of Bald Galloway (a Scottish Galloway stallion), and that another daughter of his, Roxanna, is found in the taproot mare Kitty Fisher—whose traditional parentage has been also found to 'be wanting' (Appendix C). Yet the historical fact is, with all those 'flawed' lines in his lineage, **Lexington RH stands alone—he produced more top quality racehorses of both sexes than any other stallion—EVER—then or now** (Faversham/Rasmussen).

History has demonstrated that both Lexington RH and his sire Boston RH produced the best racehorses in the world. They broke all the records, and their progeny also won races not only in this country but abroad as well, and they established important racing families wherever their blood was concentrated. They also carried the blood of the best English Thoroughbred horses of their day such as Diomed, Saltram, Medley, Highflyer, Beningbrough, and others. In most accounts when scholars try to explain the origin of their immeasurable athletic talents and potency they will invariably point to those proper English lines as the source. Or in the case of Lexington RH and Boston RH specifically they most often point to the proper English sire of many of their mates: Glencoe, as the reason they were so good—completely discounting the speed contribution of our native Running Horse. But no one tries to explain then why, if it was only those wonderful English TB lines that provided racing class, why did these sires exceed all others who carried **only** those proper English bloodlines in this country and more importantly elsewhere? All the good English Thoroughbreds of their day carried those same English lines—it was the English-bred Glencoe daughter Pocahontas that was powering the best English bloodlines. So then the American combinations should be lesser in ability if that was the only factor—after all they had 'mongrel' damlines, so how could they match and exceed the better and purer-bred English Thoroughbreds? Once the American racehorse traveled to England to race—mid-1800s—the progeny of these sires and their close relatives demonstrated that their class could not be discounted, as many times they trounced those same peerless specimens on their own turf (see Chapter 8)—at the same time creating amazing blood dynasties that still power both racing and sport today, everywhere. It is the 'why' of this legacy that we want to understand.

[Note: There is an interesting study found in Rommy Faversham's and Leon Rasmussen's text *Inbreeding to Superior Female Families*. Wherein they list the dam-sires of Lexington's best racing progeny. They found fifty-seven exceptional stakes racers and used them to determine which combinations worked. Only about 30% were by Glencoe dams—70% were from other dam-sires. Glencoe with sixteen daughters is surely significant, but other sires tally well also, such as Yorkshire with eleven, and Albion with six, plus there were thirteen other dam-sires that provided the winners in conjunction with Lexington RH. This study reveals that the Glencoe factor is not quite the dramatic dominance in breeding we have been told. Lexington RH (and his sire Boston RH) was clearly able to produce the best racers of his day with a variety of dam-sires. Glencoe, make no mistake, is one of the greatest sires ever, and his daughters being mated to Lexington RH and Boston RH was one of the most fortunate combinations in racing history; however he is not the reason Lexington RH and his sire Boston RH were world beaters on the track and at stud. For instance, one of the greatest racing sons of Lexington RH is Duke of Magenta, and he is not by a Glencoe dam—his dam-sire is Yorkshire.]

The great Running Horse four-mile-heat race mare Fashion 1837 at stud. — etching found in *American Thoroughbred* by Trentham.

A look at the mare who beat Lexington's sire Boston RH in a match race, Fashion RH, shows us the same pattern: wonderful English Thoroughbred bloodlines, but her dam, the famous taproot mare Bonnets O' Blue RH, carries two lines of the Mark Anthony Mare (RH) on her dam-lines—the Flaw.

Modern scientific studies of the equine genome are providing us with big clues on this mystery. In our day it has been discovered that the speed gene in the Thoroughbred came from a mare in the early English studs, not from the Oriental foundation sires or 'Arabians'—which the scientists discovered do not carry it at all. In England with the great success of their new 'thoroughbred' breeding program, the native English

Running Horse fell out of favor—the breeders and public believed all that was good in their new racehorse breed came from the very glamorous imported Oriental sires. They did not realize that the speed came only from their native racer and was improved in distance racing expression when combined with the laid-back shoulder that allowed more extension and the additional height and overall size that the import provided. They gave credit only to the imported stock and distained their native breed. This attitude was unfortunate—as the Running Horse was used less and less, it was thought of as 'common' and fell out of favor. Then came the English Civil War, and the remaining studs of the native English racer were sacked, scattered, and destroyed. Very few of the English Running Horses survived.

In our modern times it has been discovered that other factors besides the speed came from those same native mares, such as the large heart gene which also travels up those same dam-lines (Haun). So then, if you can connect the dots, you will realize that the early American Running Horse was from those same pre-Thoroughbred mares—in fact, it may even carry a larger quantity of those important mare-lines in its lineages than the English TB that arose from just these few individuals who survived their Civil War eradication of the breed. The American Colonies got multiple shipments of those horses **before** they were destroyed in the English domestic conflict, and in Virginia there were multiple shipments that came directly from the Irish studs—the origin of the speed to the English Running Horse.

The Duke of Magenta, a son of Lexington RH out of a mare with a quarter racing dam-line. —from a painting by Henry Stull.

One of Lexington's best sons, Duke of Magenta 1875, is a case in point. During his racing years, his dam-line was remodeled so that he appeared more English than he was. It is in modern times only that his true dam-line has been recovered (when Vosborough wrote his *Racing in America* in 1922, he reported the rumor that Luzborough may not be the correct third-dam-sire, and in our day this has been verified by MacKay-Smith). His third-dam Minerva Anderson RH (foundation mare of female Thoroughbred family A11) is actually heavy in the early typesetters for the Quarter Horse breed! Her sire is not the English sire Luzborough as so often reported; rather she is by Big Printer RH, a son of the famous Printer who transferred the 'bull-dog' form to his descendants. Big Printer's dam is descended from the pacing Running Horse Blackburns Whip. The fourth dam, Sir Charles Mare RH is the daughter of a Celebrated Quarter Race Mare: Brimmer Quarter Mare RH (and the great four-miler Sir Charles RH). Duke of Magenta was the best racehorse of 1878, and he won eleven of twelve starts including the Preakness, Belmont, Withers, and Travers stakes races.

So then, the difference in the super racers and sires, descendants of Boston RH and Lexington RH such as Iroquois, Foxhall, and Parole (Chapter 8), from the quality English Thoroughbred of the late 1870-80s, was that they carried the undisturbed Running Horse dam-lines. It was 'the Flaw' itself that made them the best in the world—that is why the English were in a panic. The true reason our horses were rejected by the British wasn't because our pathetic Colonial-based racing stock was inferior in ability to their pristine breed, it was the opposite: our domestic American Running Horse lines were producing better racers than theirs.

Another fact to absorb is that after the Revolution, the mid-Atlantic area—from the start a premier breeding area—became the major producer of superior racing stock. New England's racing industry never recovered from the war and the urbanization that had occurred. Our racehorse was selectively bred for pacing and galloping speed at both sprint and distance racing; it always had stamina. Since earliest colonial times sprint racing was a favored pastime, and there were many breeding studs for sprint specialists in the southern Virginia, northern North Carolina area. This is where imported Janus stood, as he produced mostly sprint offspring and became valued as a strong typesetter where this race form was popular.

Visiting Englishman J. F. D. Smythe said of these horse races, "…they are much attached to quarter-racing, which is always a match between two horses, to run one quarter of a mile straight out, being—in extension of speed, and they have a breed that performs it with astonishing velocity, beating every other for that distance, with great ease, but they have no bottom."

This area then became a repository for sprint speed, and in hindsight we can see this was a most fortunate occurrence, as the speed gene is also a sprint gene (studies by Dr. Mim Bower and Dr. Emmiline Hill). Without this pocket of sprint selection the great carriers of the speed gene may have been lost, as once the English Thoroughbred Fearnought arrived (imported 1767) the craze of 'English heat-racing' threatened to eliminate the sprinter and his blood. Happily however, that did not happen, and our distance stars that set records often had a dam-line that went straight back to those sprint specialists.

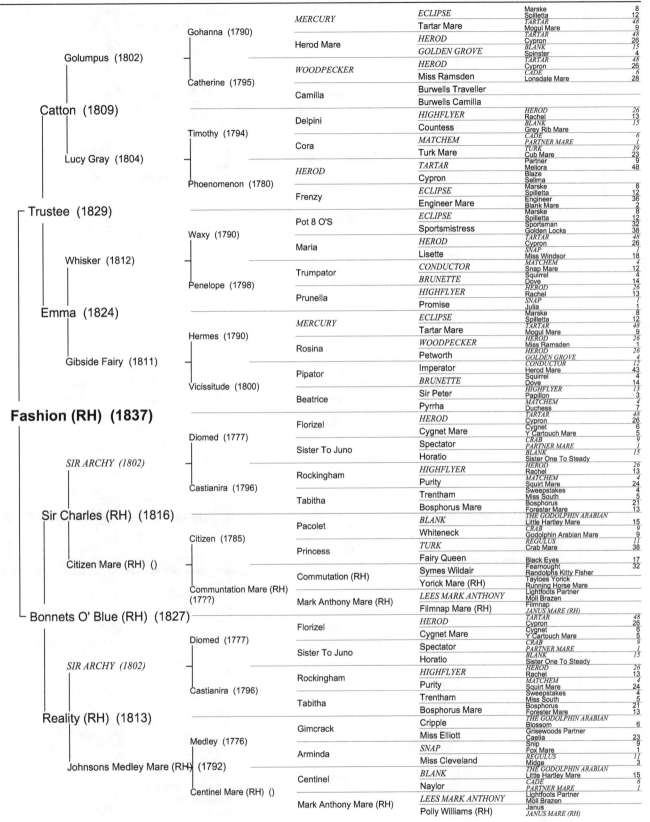

Fashion RH 1837

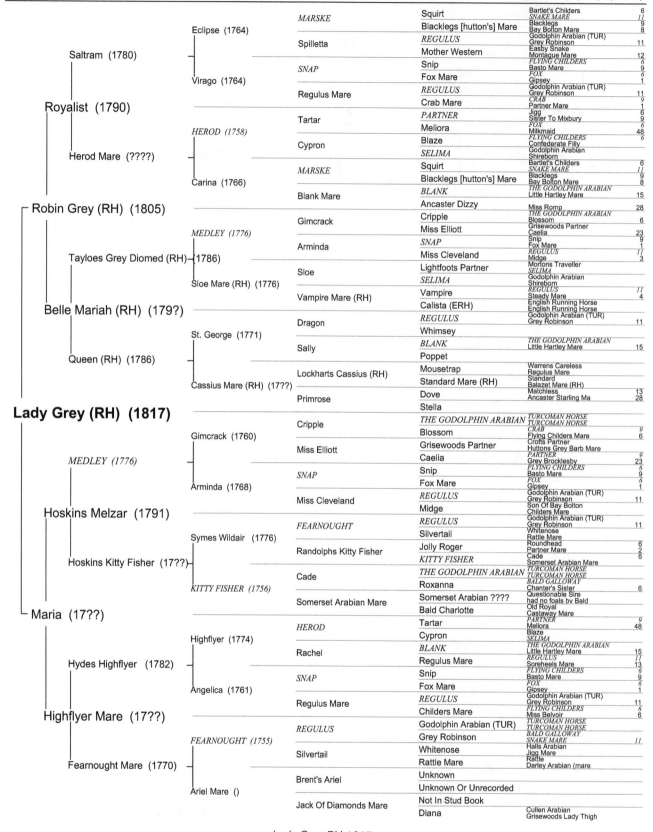

Lady Grey RH 1817

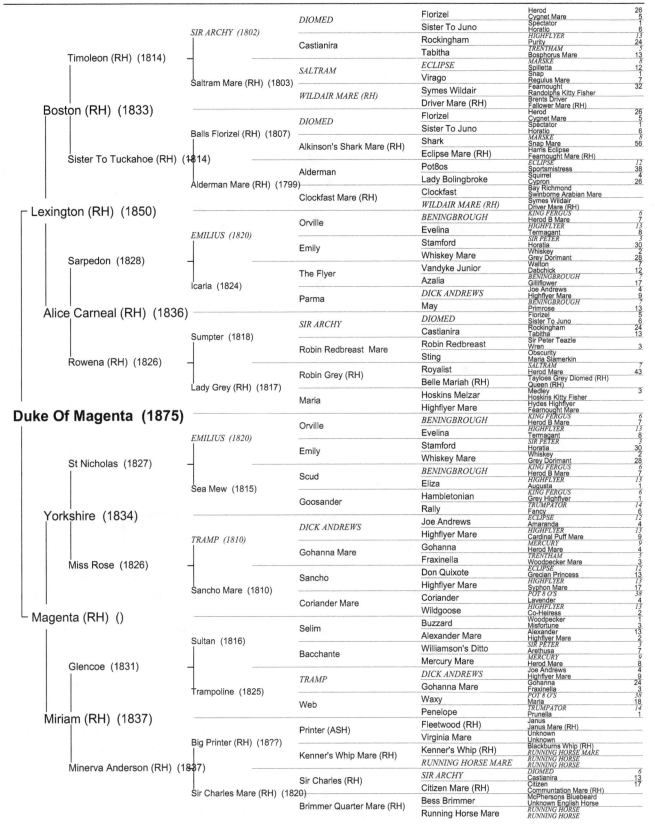

Duke of Magenta 1878

Chapter 3

Pinnacle of Stamina

The 1842 four-mile heat match race between Boston and Fashion, from an early lithograph by H.R. Robinson.

So let's look at what the fuss resulting in the Jersey Act was all about a little closer. We can begin with the greatest racer of the 1800s: Boston RH 1833 (sire of Lexington RH). He is rated not just the **best** racer of the 1800s, but he also led the sires list three times. He won forty-one of forty-five races (he was second twice and third once) and thirty of them were four-mile heats, he was tempestuous and difficult, but nearly unbeatable. His only real defeat was from one of the greatest female racers of that era: Fashion RH. His racing reputation was such that eventually by 1840 more and more tracks were barring him from running, plus he was going blind, so he was put to stud. He returned to race a few times in the fall of 1841; one of those races was with his nemesis Fashion RH, who defeated him. He went back to stud for the 1842 season and returned to challenge Fashion RH again in the fall. Fashion RH prevailed again, although it is debatable if this was an even contest as Boston RH severely injured his hip on a pole in the running and had to walk in. The race however, between Boston RH and Fashion RH, is one of the most famous of the North-South match races, and whatever the outcome, the seventy-thousand-plus spectators were watching the most extraordinary athletes of their day. Boston RH raced four more times that fall, winning three, and then he was retired at age ten for good.

Both of Boston's dam-lines trace to the same high quality race mare: Wildair Mare RH ~1795, whose dam-line goes back to a Running Horse mare from the early 1700s named Calista ERH, and then the records fail. However, as we discussed in Chapter 2, Calista is an English Running Horse.

Early American records are as spotty as those in England and Ireland, and often the best we can do is ascertain that the ancestor was a racing horse from our original Running Horse breed. This lack of continuous records is frustrating, especially as we know now that it was these same mares who provided the speed gene, and to hit a dead end in records on both sides of the Atlantic is disappointing. Boston's best son, Lexington RH, also carries this same line through his dam. Plus, we are discovering in our day that many apparently full lineages of exclusively English blood are entirely fabricated. Of the thirty-nine American Thoroughbred dam-line families, only six originate with a British TB mare (and some of those are

Boston 1833 —from painting by Troye.

questionable also)—the other thirty-three are from our native American Running Horse dams—most from our sprint breeding area. Seeing these families were identified and numbered for the very fact that it was those families that were producing the best runners—this then should speak for itself: it was our native RH that provided the speed.' (Appendix C).

Perhaps the dam-line of Balls Florizel RH (Boston's dam-sire) is a perfect example for us, as it goes back to a winning sprint-racer Running Horse mare: Sweet Mary 1766. Other lineage had traditionally been applied to Sweet Mary's daughter Fearnought Mare, but it is now known that the sprint racer Sweet Mary RH is her true mother. Sweet Mary RH herself is one of the very few who escaped Edgar's cleansing of native strains from his studbook—possibly because she was such a good racer. Also unusual is we know a little about her appearance; she is documented as being a grey mare of 14.3 hands with exceptional refinement and beauty. Besides her appearance in the Fearnought Mare RH pedigree, she is believed to be the dam of the great colonial racer Paddy Whack RH, and another good sprinter Chickey Mogg RH, as well as the taproot mare for the later Quarter Horse breed: Miss Alsup RH. We can thank Alexander MacKay-Smith and the Quarter Horse historian Robert Denhardt for their painstaking research that determined her true lineage.

As a sire Boston RH was a smashing success, and at age seventeen in 1849—even though completely blind and crippled—he sired his two best sons: Lecomte RH (aka Lecompte) and Lexington RH. Another of his offspring, Nina RH (a fantastic heat racer herself) produced the versatile champion Planet RH, a winning racer at both the trot and gallop, and some say he preferred to race at the trot. Another of Nina's notable sons is Algerine, found in Rhoda B, the mare who produced the European classic winners Orby and Rhodora. Boston RH was also a great sire of trotters. We find that a racehorse sire having Running Horse bloodlines, when mated with mares who have them also, can produce gaited saddle horses, as well as horses that can race at the trot or the pace. The early English import Janus is a famous example of this, as he produced great gallopers, great sprint racers, gaited saddle horses, and sometimes pacing racers when bred to American mares. Another is the later imported Messenger EH, who most probably had a largely ERH dam-line (see Appendix C).

There may also be another source responsible for Boston's trot genetics. Boston RH carries three lines of the mare Cypron 7x6x5—she is the dam of Herod and Lady Bolingbroke. Cypron is a daughter of Blaze, a stallion who is documented to be a prime transmitter of trot mechanics, as he is not only the sire of Old Shales the founder of the trotting Hackney breed, but also is strong in Mambrino and his son Messenger EH, the foundations of our American Trotter breed. Both Lexington RH and Lecomte RH carry over twenty lines of Cypron (Blaze daughter) within ten generations—this is a significant background build-up of a mare.

[Blaze is an example of pedigree fudging—even now modern day revisionists are attempting to supply Oriental ancestry for his dam-lines that are English Running Horse. (See Appendix C.)]

Boston's only real rival in racing, the mare Fashion RH, is the product of another great Running Horse mare line. Her dam, Bonnets o' Blue RH, and her granddam, Reality RH, are famous mares who created maternal dynasties of racers, and their dam-line goes straight back to Polly Williams RH, who was a celebrated quarter-mile race mare. This is where it gets really frustrating, though, as Fashion RH was a great racer—one of the best ever—but only a fair producer. Her dam was terrific in both categories as was her granddam, and then of course great granddam Polly Williams RH was also—who like Sweet Mary RH was one of the very few Quarter Racing Running Horses Edgar didn't erase from his stud-book; all were exceptional racers and broodmares of excellence. Polly Williams RH was by Janus out of a Janus mare (inbred to Janus 1x2), whose dam is unrecorded. But there the trail ends, because it was not fashionable to record the native strains, and Edgar purposely eliminated them and sometimes brazenly substituted fictitious English parentage. At least here, he left it blank, but that leaves us with not knowing where the true power is coming from—other than from our sprinting studs of colonial days.

This is not all the difficulty either, for later on when the breeders who were enamored of the English Thoroughbred started limiting the inclusion of racers that had 'American lines' from the races, then pedigree revisers got busy again substituting respectable English ancestors for the unwanted American lines, so that their fast racers could qualify. The progeny record of the imported Mary Gray is one that is documented as being expanded to have multiple sons and daughters entirely fabricated (see Appendix C).

This happened in England also—all those Barbs, Arabians, and Turks with no parentage listed are often now being discovered (through DNA) to be English-bred. Very few real Orientals were imported, and it is now known they might label a horse 'Barb' if it had a Barb anywhere in its parentage, or Turk for the same reason, and of course 'Arabian' after a name was usually pure fantasy. It is a shame. For us in this case, other than knowing Polly Williams's dam was a running horse mare bred to Janus—that's it. With what we know now about the power in the dam-lines—mtDNA and all that, which demonstrates that the real talent here came up that dam-line—it is also proven because generation after generation it continued to produce the best racing mares and broodmares.

"If we were to compare the English with the American methods of manufacturing pedigrees, it would be hard to determine which was the more shamefully dishonest" (Henry William Herbert, 1857).

The fantastic racer Fashion RH was not quite up to the quality of her dam-line in her produce. Some were good racers and decent producers, but the comet had truly begun to burn itself out. With no new strong Running Horse blood added, and being bred back almost exclusively to imported English sires who were by her era even further away from their speed roots (six or more generations), on the whole her offspring lacked the ability to pass on that breath-taking speed that she and her ancestors possessed in abundance. She is a classic illustration of what can happen with continual outcrossing: eventually there will be little of the original talent evident in the offspring (see Appendix B).

It was left then for the original descendants of the other great American four-milers, who were bred back to other contaminated bloodlines, to keep the spark alive.

Boston's two best sons, Lecomte RH and Lexington RH, were racing rivals, and both marvels; however, Lexington RH ended up besting Lecomte RH not just in racing (beat him twice—lost to him once), when he set the world record for the fastest four mile, but also as a sire—no horse in history can top his record. The difference in their pedigrees—both by Boston RH, but Lecomte's dam was Reel, who is often called the broodmare of the century (1800s); she is a daughter of Glencoe out of an English TB dam. Lexington's dam was Alice Carneal RH, a mare of ¾ top English TB blood, but the difference was her dam-line was both English and American Running Horse—the speed source.

Another great example of an early nineteenth century Running Horse sire and typesetter is Orphan RH 1810, by Balls Florizel RH out of Fair Rachel RH, who are ¾ siblings 1x1—extreme genetic concentration—the great Boston RH has Balls Florizel RH as his dam-sire. Orphan RH proved to be both a pronounced racer and an important sire. He will be found in the pedigree of the major typesetter Vandal RH as third-dam-sire (Chapter 7).

Nevertheless, it is a racing contemporary of Orphan RH who provides us with the best example of the power of the Running Horse for speed, soundness, and racing class. It is ironic as well, as the sire of this racer, the American-bred Sir Archy—with his pristine English pedigree, along with his record as a premier four-miler and the best sire of his day—should have his best racing son out of a fourteen-hand pacing Saddle Horse mare. Unfortunately this son of Sir Archy was gelded primarily because of his thoroughly American dam-line—what a blunder! Walk-in-the-Water RH 1813 is remembered and celebrated as the horse who won more races, traveled further back and forth on foot to them (From North Carolina all through the South to Mississippi and North through Tennessee and Kentucky, over and over, until he was nineteen), and he ran more accumulated miles than any other racehorse—probably still today (Hervey).

It was said by Allan Jones Davies, who stood Sir Archy for much of his stud career, that Walk-in-the-Water RH was the most remarkable racehorse in America, "...winning more races at a great variety of distances and at a greater age than any horse in the world."

Turf historian William Robertson reports, "...the old campaigner ranged so far afield as Natchez, traveling on foot from meeting to meeting, winning race after race, and conceding weight to rival after rival."

His dam, Dongolah Mare ASA, was a mere 14 hands tall. She was by Mark Anthony out of a Saddle Horse dam who was a natural pacer. His sire was Sir Archy, the premier distance sire of the time. As a racehorse Walk-in-the-Water RH stands way above the others. Unfortunately, that is all that is known about possibly **the greatest racehorse in the world for all time**. He raced until he was nineteen years old, beating the best of his day everywhere he went. His record of miles run, races won, and miles traveled to the meets, and soundness, I believe is still unsurpassed (MacKay-Smith, Robertson).

[Note: our first American foundation movement in equine breeding sought to preserve the attributes of our native Running Horse. This movement arose when the breeders became alarmed at the result they were seeing from the practice of over-breeding with the popular English Thoroughbred. Generation after generation of English Thoroughbred added to our domestic racehorse breed caused some of the Running Horse's best-loved traits to go dormant: comfortable saddle gaits, sprinting speed, pacing speed, hardiness, and sweet temperament. This project, which began in Virginia and North Carolina around 1800, succeeded in preserving the sweet temperament along with sprint and pacing lines of the Running Horse racer, and a new breed was formed from those lines that had the best saddle traits: the Plantation Horse, soon to be called the American Saddle Horse. This movement also preserved the pacing racer and the sprint racer bloodlines. Dongolah Mare ASA is an early example of this saddle horse type, bred in North Carolina; she was an un-sullied American Running Horse, a breed that was always dual-talented: a wonderful saddle horse as well as a fast racer. (See Appendix D for an outline of American sport breed development.)]

Here is what Henry Wm. Herbert, a recognized English expert and writer on the equestrian, reported on the American Horse when he came to America in the early 1800s:

> "On my first arrival in this country, when the eye is more awake to distinctions, than after it has become used by years of acquaintance to what it has daily before it, and forgetful of what it has ceased to see, I was particularly struck by the fact that the American general horse, as compared with the English horse, was inferior in height of the forehand, in the loftiness and thinness of the withers, and in the setting on and carriage of the neck and crest, while he was superior in the general development of his quarters, in the letdown of his hams, and in his height behind, and farther remarkable for his formation, approaching to what is often seen in the Irish horse, and known as the 'goose-rump'...Another point in which the American horse of all conditions differs extremely, and here, most advantageously, from the European animal, is his greater surefootedness, and freedom from the dangerous and detestable vice of stumbling...must be added his extreme good temper and docility, in which he unquestionably excels any other horse in the world...the young horse in Europe is, in nine cases out of ten, particularly if he has any pure blood in his veins, a wild, headstrong, ungovernable and almost indomitable savage." (*Frank Forester's Horse and Horsemanship of the United States and British Provinces of North America*)

What these extreme athletes are made of are the very best English Thoroughbred lines of the day—along with distinct American Running Horse dam-lines (the Flaw). They were superb racers and progenitors—the greatest of their era.

If you ask most people familiar with Thoroughbred bloodlines which horse was the greatest of the 1800s, almost 100% of them will say St. Simon—I thought so also until I did my own research. But I have found he cannot hold a candle to Lexington RH; both are great racehorses, and St. Simon retired unbeaten (dash racing), but Lexington RH set a **world** record in four-mile heat racing. St. Simon was top sire in England a whopping nine years, but that pales beside Lexington's sixteen times—once again a **world** record that has never been broken, which doesn't take into account the scores of his offspring who never lived to race as they were taken during the Civil War and never returned. So move over St. Simon, you do not deserve the top slot; it belongs to an American Running Horse named Lexington RH.

Now getting back to the period of 1750-1850, I don't want to leave the impression that pure English bloodlines could not go the distance—that would not be true, because many, many racers of pure English TB blood ran well at four miles (Sir

Archy 1805 is a great example), and we imported many of the greatest four-milers that England had; this was at the time when the English had begun to switch to classic distance racing, so they were discarding the four-milers. However in England, by the early 1800s, after fifty years of selection for the new dash form (classic racing), the English racehorse had changed its type; their breed had become a classic distance specialist. In America we found that those later imports of English horse were not of the quality of the earlier heat racers, as they not only lacked stamina, but were displaying more unsoundness, and unfortunately they passed these traits on.

Nonsensical as it was, this difference in race form selection produced in the English racing establishment a condescending attitude toward the American breed. "There has always been an engrained confidence in the minds of all Englishmen in the superiority of their thoroughbreds and their turf methods" (Lyman Weeks 1898). Or as reported in the Thoroughbred Record in 1881 just prior to Iroquois winning their Derby, "For some years many have contended that the best American colt was a stone or fourteen pounds inferior to the best English colts." This arrogance, seen as a challenge by the Americans, ultimately resulted in the American's taking their home-breds to England to test their mettle against the mother country's breed in the mid and late 1800s. The English truly believed the American horse to be a second-rate breed, and that our race tests were not legitimate contests for class, so they never condescended to bring their horses to our country to compete. However, America had always imported English horses, so the American breeder of the 1800s was familiar with their capacities on the turf, and generally found that they didn't have much stamina and were less sound when compared to our breed. Occasionally in the era just preceding the appearance of the American-breds on English tracks (1856), an English editorial on racing would suggest that American stock could be used to invigorate the 'tired English blood' (1830 Quarterly Review). In mid-century some suggested that they could bring in some American stock to improve soundness and endurance—but those editorials were few and far between. Generally, the English racehorse industry was blind to the quality found in the American-bred.

While at home, a horse was not considered first-rate unless it could run a four-mile heat race, and even repeat the performance in the same week. To us in our modern racing scene this is an astounding level of performance, almost unimaginable after one hundred sixty years of classic racing here. But the American distance racer of this time did it easily, and then often came back in a few days to do it again—it is difficult to even imagine this quality of athlete in our modern day experience (see Chapter 5 for a description of a five-heat race that tested the limitations of our phenomenal breed).

In the 1800s England was also using a handicap system—weight for age, as well as the tests of one to two miles—run once, this was a totally a different criterion from our program. Americans felt the 'weight for age' practice combined with the shortened 'dash' form would result in a lesser racer, and there was much discussion on this subject, the majority of breeders feeling it would actually encourage the breeding of an inferior racer as it penalized the good runners and allowed poorer performers to win (how right they turned out to be!). At the time the English had an edge on speed for shorter distances, as our sprinters were already delegated to the western frontier races (Quarter Horse), while our long runner excelled at distance speed and stamina.

So it was that the English were taken by such surprise, when suddenly they discovered that the American racehorse could hold its own against their superior stock when we began to bring over a few to race against theirs—just a few at first (Ten Broeck 1856), but later came more, until in the early 1880s the American-bred cleaned up the classic races, both in France and England, in a such a devastating fashion, that it humiliated their industry.

The full proof of the quality of our American product of that era is that, from those few individual American horses with strong RH genes that made it into the GSB before they were barred (1913), came some of the best and most enduring of England's, France's, and even Germany's bloodlines—this is the legacy of Lexington RH that we will explore in later sections of this book.

Many, I am sure, will dispute my statements on this—however history has declared its hard facts: many of the best modern bloodlines of Europe arose from the contaminated bloodlines of our Running Horse that slipped into the gene pool before they were banned. It was these carriers of the Flaw that were endowed with such tremendous racing prowess that they threatened to overwhelm the English racing and breeding interests by the turn of the century. Plus we have learned through wonderful modern day genetic and scientific evaluations that the important sport traits of the large heart, efficient respiratory conversion, and speed reside in those distained lines. With just that short window, from after our Civil War until the turn of the century, and with relatively few American-breds who made their way to England to race, the quality of those racers threatened the English racing industry so much that they determined to wall them out.

It was the genetic ingredients of our racehorse, plus the standard of the four-mile heat test used for breeding selection, that produced **racehorses of such quality that they have never been equaled in the succeeding one hundred fifty years.** In my day people are decrying the lack of stamina and soundness in the modern Thoroughbred (see Chapter 27 for more on the soundness crisis). Perhaps we should take a lesson from history and strive to cull unsound lines, change our selection criteria, and build up the lines born of our Heroic Age in the background of our lineages—then we will see what we are looking for, a superb sport horse of immense talent and soundness. It is not too late, the genetics are still there, we just have to target them and reconcentrate them until they reach critical mass (see Appendix B—Evaluating Pedigrees).

[In Part III you will find some examples of modern progenitors that—whether through accident or design—have amassed quantities of those genes, and their performance at both race and stud surprised many.]

It may help our perspective on our unique American Thoroughbred to view an outline of breed development.

Outline of American Thoroughbred Development:

1611-1660s: the American racehorse (RH) was developed from imported Irish Hobby and English Running Horse genetics—these were the carriers of the speed gene in both America and the British Isles.

1660-1730: virtually no new stock was received from the British Isles, with trade restrictions partially to blame. However, America did adopt the heat race form starting in 1665—this was raced with our native racehorse. All colonies were involved in racing; it was our major colonial recreation.

1730-1770: the first wave of the new English Thoroughbreds was imported, mostly of Godolphin Arabian lines, the premier source of the laid-back shoulder and height. This period is also when the English switch to the 'dash' race standard occurred, changing their breed selection criteria.

1770-1783: virtually no new importations of English horses—trade restrictions, heavy tax levies, and finally the Revolution.

1783-1806: second wave of English Thoroughbreds arrive, many of the Darley line, inspiring complaints by breeders that the quality was not as good as the first imports—excepting Diomed and Messenger EH.

1806-1830: trade embargoes and unrest with England create very little importation of English TBs (only two English sires are listed as imported in this period).

1830-present: this period saw the beginning of third wave of English Thoroughbreds—noticeably less in quality. There were multiple complaints about the unsoundness, bad temperament, and lack of stamina issues.

1856-1913: the American Running Horses, and then the new Thoroughbreds, first appeared to race in Europe. Some of those American horses were retained for breeding and were entered into the GSB, leaving a lasting imprint. The shock of the quality and racing superiority of our native racer stunned the British—causing waves of more restrictive rules made for entry into the GSB, until finally a new edict was drafted that banned the majority of American horses.

1868: the American Thoroughbred is established as a separate breed from its parent Running Horse, with a classic race performance standard and pedigree requirement of five generations of strictly English Thoroughbred blood. (The American Trotter had formed its own registry the year before, and the Saddle Horses had specialized from 1800, but the pacing Running Horse racer continued on. The American Quarter Horse had specialized in sprint racing and cattle work by this period also—see Appendix D for more on this.)

1913-1949: the American Thoroughbreds were banned in International breeding with the Jersey Act in place— they were virtually imprisoned at home. The American racing industry was severely curtailed with the worth of its stock dropping immediately, and it was forced to adjust its domestic structure to survive. Eventually it became a healthy operation, not needing international exposure and sales to survive—it was self-supporting, and by the end of this period it was thriving and the envy of the racing world.

1949-1975: GSB reopened to American Thoroughbreds, but very few venture out to race abroad. Those who do—Sir Ivor, Habitat, Roberto, Never Bend, etc—display their devastating superiority. This period also marks the beginning of the English and Irish raids on the American TB yearling sales.

1970-present: the second invasion of American Thoroughbreds into the International arena proves they are still the best racehorse in the world.

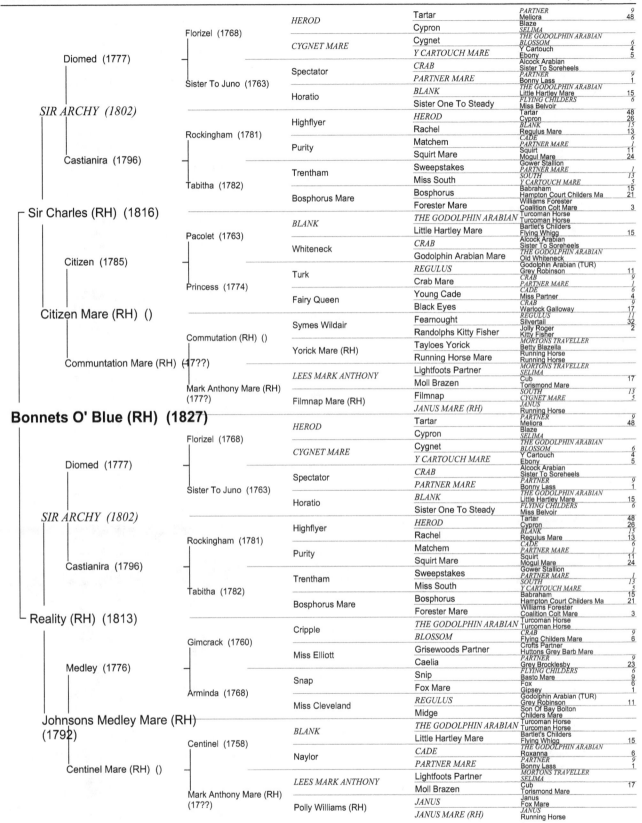

			PARTNER	9
		HEROD	Tartar	Meliora	48

Bonnets O' Blue RH 1827

Boston (RH) (1833)

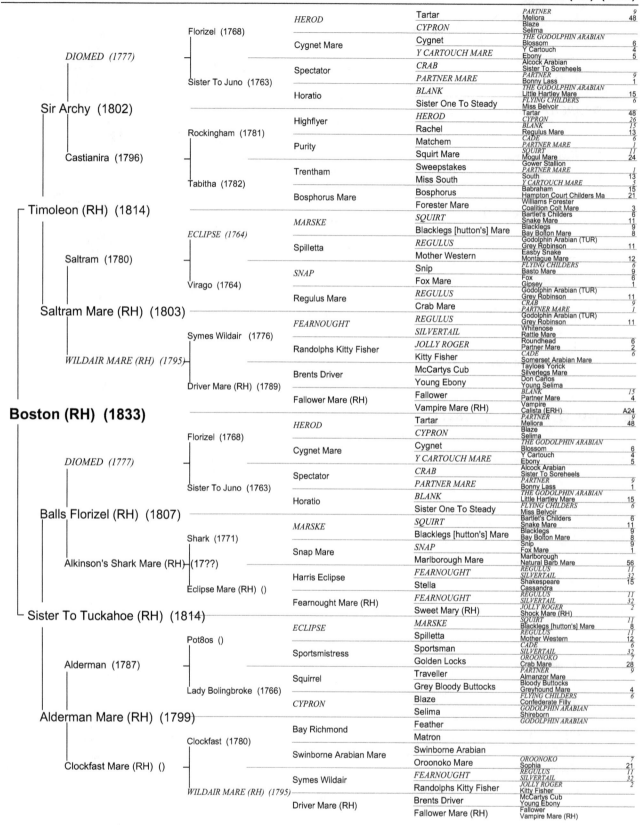

				Tartar	*PARTNER* 9 / Meliora 48
			HEROD	*CYPRON*	Blaze / Selima
		Florizel (1768)	Cygnet Mare	Cygnet	*THE GODOLPHIN ARABIAN* / Blossom 6
	DIOMED (1777)			*Y CARTOUCH MARE*	Y Cartouch 4 / Ebony 5
			Spectator	*CRAB*	Alcock Arabian / Sister To Soreheels
		Sister To Juno (1763)		*PARTNER MARE*	*PARTNER* 9 / Bonny Lass 1
Sir Archy (1802)			Horatio	*BLANK*	*THE GODOLPHIN ARABIAN* / Little Hartley Mare 15
				Sister One To Steady	*FLYING CHILDERS* 6 / Miss Belvoir
			Highflyer	*HEROD*	Tartar 48 / *CYPRON* 26
		Rockingham (1781)	Rachel	*BLANK* 15 / Regulus Mare 13
	Castianira (1796)		Purity	Matchem	*CADE* 6 / *PARTNER MARE* 1
				Squirt Mare	*SQUIRT* 11 / Mogul Mare 24
		Tabitha (1782)	Trentham	Sweepstakes	Gower Stallion / *PARTNER MARE* 1
				Miss South	South 13 / *Y CARTOUCH MARE* 5
			Bosphorus Mare	Bosphorus	Babraham 15 / Hampton Court Childers Ma 21
Timoleon (RH) (1814)				Forester Mare	Williams Forester / Coalition Colt Mare 3
			MARSKE	*SQUIRT*	Bartlet's Childers 6 / Snake Mare 11
		ECLIPSE (1764)	Blacklegs [hutton's] Mare	Blacklegs 9 / Bay Bolton Mare 8
			Spilletta	*REGULUS*	Godolphin Arabian (TUR) / Grey Robinson 11
	Saltram (1780)			Mother Western	Easby Snake / Montague Mare 12
			SNAP	Snip	*FLYING CHILDERS* 6 / Basto Mare 9
		Virago (1764)		Fox Mare	Fox 6 / Gipsey 1
			Regulus Mare	*REGULUS*	Godolphin Arabian (TUR) / Grey Robinson 11
Saltram Mare (RH) (1803)				Crab Mare	*CRAB* 9 / *PARTNER MARE* 1
			FEARNOUGHT	*REGULUS*	Godolphin Arabian (TUR) / Grey Robinson 11
		Symes Wildair (1776)		*SILVERTAIL*	Whitenose / Rattle Mare
			Randolphs Kitty Fisher	*JOLLY ROGER*	Roundhead 6 / Partner Mare 2
	WILDAIR MARE (RH) (1795)		Kitty Fisher	*CADE* 6 / Somerset Arabian Mare
			Brents Driver	McCartys Cub	Tayloes Yorick / Silverlegs Mare
		Driver Mare (RH) (1789)	Young Ebony	Don Carlos / Young Selima
			Fallower Mare (RH)	Fallower	*BLANK* 15 / Partner Mare 4
				Vampire Mare (RH)	Vampire / Calista (ERH) A24
Boston (RH) (1833)			*HEROD*	Tartar	*PARTNER* 9 / Meliora 48
				CYPRON	Blaze / Selima
		Florizel (1768)	Cygnet Mare	Cygnet	*THE GODOLPHIN ARABIAN* / Blossom 6
	DIOMED (1777)			*Y CARTOUCH MARE*	Y Cartouch 4 / Ebony 5
			Spectator	*CRAB*	Alcock Arabian / Sister To Soreheels
		Sister To Juno (1763)		*PARTNER MARE*	*PARTNER* 9 / Bonny Lass 1
			Horatio	*BLANK*	*THE GODOLPHIN ARABIAN* / Little Hartley Mare 15
Balls Florizel (RH) (1807)				Sister One To Steady	*FLYING CHILDERS* 6 / Miss Belvoir
			MARSKE	*SQUIRT*	Bartlet's Childers 6 / Snake Mare 11
		Shark (1771)	Blacklegs [hutton's] Mare	Blacklegs 9 / Bay Bolton Mare 8
			Snap Mare	*SNAP*	Snip 9 / Fox Mare 1
	Alkinson's Shark Mare (RH) (17??)		Marlborough Mare	Marlborough / Natural Barb Mare 56
			Harris Eclipse	*FEARNOUGHT*	*REGULUS* 11 / *SILVERTAIL* 32
		Eclipse Mare (RH) ()		Stella	Shakespeare 15 / Cassandra
			Fearnought Mare (RH)	*FEARNOUGHT*	*REGULUS* 11 / *SILVERTAIL* 32
Sister To Tuckahoe (RH) (1814)				Sweet Mary (RH)	*JOLLY ROGER* 2 / Shock Mare (RH)
			ECLIPSE	*MARSKE*	*SQUIRT* 11 / Blacklegs [hutton's] Mare 8
		Pot8os ()	Spilletta	*REGULUS* 11 / Mother Western 12
			Sportsmistress	Sportsman	*CADE* 6 / *SILVERTAIL* 32
	Alderman (1787)			Golden Locks	*OROONOKO* 7 / Crab Mare 28
			Squirrel	Traveller	*PARTNER* 9 / Almanzor Mare
		Lady Bolingbroke (1766)		Grey Bloody Buttocks	Bloody Buttocks / Greyhound Mare 4
			CYPRON	Blaze	*FLYING CHILDERS* 6 / Confederate Filly
Alderman Mare (RH) (1799)				Selima	*GODOLPHIN ARABIAN* / Shireborn
			Bay Richmond	Feather	*GODOLPHIN ARABIAN*
		Clockfast (1780)	Matron	
			Swinborne Arabian Mare	Swinborne Arabian	
	Clockfast Mare (RH) ()		Oroonoko Mare	*OROONOKO* 7 / Sophia 21
			Symes Wildair	*FEARNOUGHT*	*REGULUS* 11 / *SILVERTAIL* 32
		WILDAIR MARE (RH) (1795)	Randolphs Kitty Fisher	*JOLLY ROGER* 2 / Kitty Fisher
			Brents Driver	McCartys Cub / Young Ebony
		Driver Mare (RH)	Fallower Mare (RH)	Fallower / Vampire Mare (RH)

Boston RH 1833

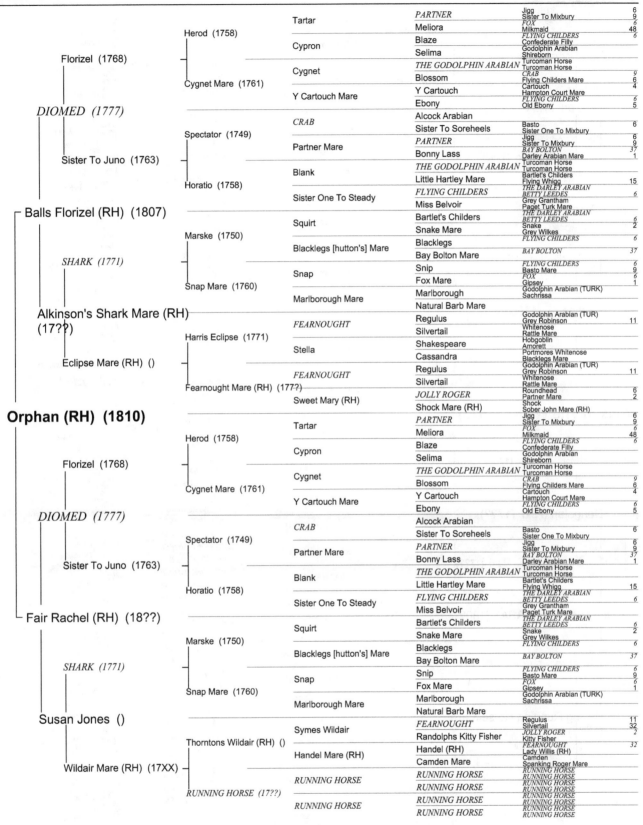

Orphan RH 1810

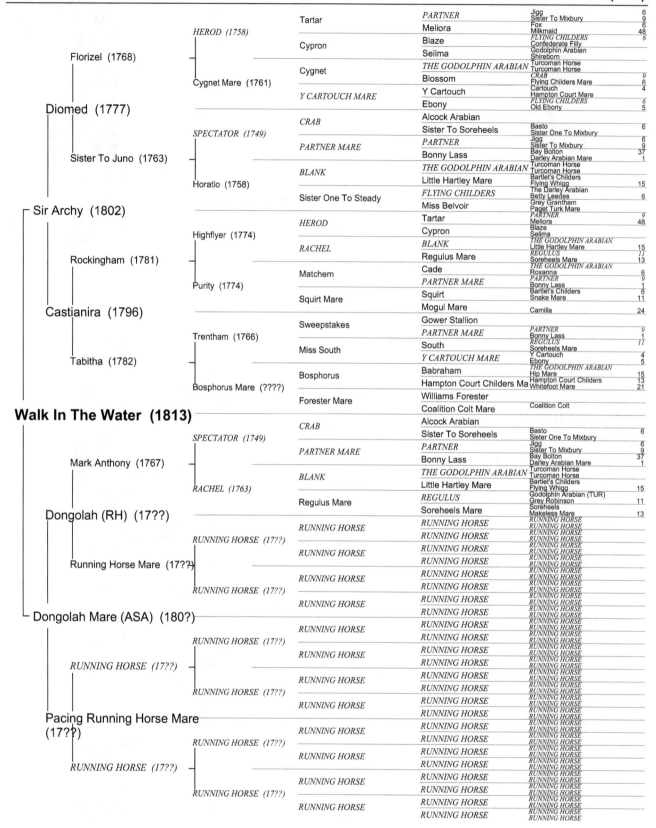

Pedigree of **Walk In The Water (1813)**

- **Sir Archy (1802)**
  - **Diomed (1777)**
    - Florizel (1768)
      - *HEROD (1758)*
        - Tartar
          - *PARTNER* — Jigg 6, Sister To Mixbury 9
          - Meliora — Fox 6, Milkmaid 48
        - Cypron
          - Blaze — *FLYING CHILDERS* 6, Confederate Filly
          - Selima — Godolphin Arabian, Shireborn
      - Cygnet Mare (1761)
        - Cygnet
          - *THE GODOLPHIN ARABIAN* — Turcoman Horse, Turcoman Horse
          - Blossom — *CRAB* 9, Flying Childers Mare 6
        - *Y CARTOUCH MARE*
          - Y Cartouch — Cartouch 4, Hampton Court Mare
          - Ebony — *FLYING CHILDERS* 6, Old Ebony 5
    - Sister To Juno (1763)
      - *SPECTATOR (1749)*
        - *CRAB*
          - Alcock Arabian
          - Sister To Soreheels — Basto 6, Sister One To Mixbury
        - *PARTNER MARE*
          - *PARTNER* — Jigg 6, Sister To Mixbury 9
          - Bonny Lass — Bay Bolton 37, Darley Arabian Mare 1
      - Horatio (1758)
        - *BLANK*
          - *THE GODOLPHIN ARABIAN* — Turcoman Horse, Turcoman Horse
          - Little Hartley Mare — Bartlet's Childers, Flying Whigg 15
        - Sister One To Steady
          - *FLYING CHILDERS* — The Darley Arabian, Betty Leedes 6
          - Miss Belvoir — Grey Grantham, Paget Turk Mare
  - **Castianira (1796)**
    - Rockingham (1781)
      - Highflyer (1774)
        - *HEROD*
          - Tartar — *PARTNER* 9, Meliora 48
          - Cypron — Blaze, Selima
        - *RACHEL*
          - *BLANK* — *THE GODOLPHIN ARABIAN*, Little Hartley Mare 15
          - Regulus Mare — *REGULUS* 11, Soreheels Mare 13
      - Purity (1774)
        - Matchem
          - Cade — *THE GODOLPHIN ARABIAN*, Roxanna 6
          - *PARTNER MARE* — *PARTNER* 9, Bonny Lass 1
        - Squirt Mare
          - Squirt — Bartlet's Childers 6, Snake Mare 11
          - Mogul Mare — Camilla 24
    - Tabitha (1782)
      - Trentham (1766)
        - Sweepstakes
          - Gower Stallion
          - *PARTNER MARE* — *PARTNER* 9, Bonny Lass 1
        - Miss South
          - South — *REGULUS* 11, Soreheels Mare
          - *Y CARTOUCH MARE* — Y Cartouch 4, Ebony 5
      - Bosphorus Mare (????)
        - Bosphorus
          - Babraham — *THE GODOLPHIN ARABIAN*, Hip Mare 15
          - Hampton Court Childers Ma — Hampton Court Childers 13, Whitefoot Mare 21
        - Forester Mare
          - Williams Forester
          - Coalition Colt Mare — Coalition Colt
- **Walk In The Water (1813)**
- **Dongolah Mare (ASA) (180?)**
  - Mark Anthony (1767)
    - *SPECTATOR (1749)*
      - *CRAB*
        - Alcock Arabian
        - Sister To Soreheels — Basto 6, Sister One To Mixbury
      - *PARTNER MARE*
        - *PARTNER* — Jigg 6, Sister To Mixbury 9
        - Bonny Lass — Bay Bolton 37, Darley Arabian Mare 1
    - *RACHEL (1763)*
      - *BLANK*
        - *THE GODOLPHIN ARABIAN* — Turcoman Horse, Turcoman Horse
        - Little Hartley Mare — Bartlet's Childers, Flying Whigg 15
      - Regulus Mare
        - *REGULUS* — Godolphin Arabian (TUR), Grey Robinson 11
        - Soreheels Mare — Soreheels, Makeless Mare 13
  - **Dongolah (RH) (17??)**
    - Running Horse Mare (17??)
      - *RUNNING HORSE (17??)*
        - *RUNNING HORSE* — *RUNNING HORSE*, *RUNNING HORSE*
        - *RUNNING HORSE* — *RUNNING HORSE*, *RUNNING HORSE*
      - *RUNNING HORSE (17??)*
        - *RUNNING HORSE* — *RUNNING HORSE*, *RUNNING HORSE*
        - *RUNNING HORSE* — *RUNNING HORSE*, *RUNNING HORSE*
  - *RUNNING HORSE (17??)*
    - *RUNNING HORSE (17??)*
      - *RUNNING HORSE* — *RUNNING HORSE*, *RUNNING HORSE*
      - *RUNNING HORSE* — *RUNNING HORSE*, *RUNNING HORSE*
    - *RUNNING HORSE (17??)*
      - *RUNNING HORSE* — *RUNNING HORSE*, *RUNNING HORSE*
      - *RUNNING HORSE* — *RUNNING HORSE*, *RUNNING HORSE*
  - **Pacing Running Horse Mare (17??)**
    - *RUNNING HORSE (17??)*
      - *RUNNING HORSE* — *RUNNING HORSE*, *RUNNING HORSE*
      - *RUNNING HORSE* — *RUNNING HORSE*, *RUNNING HORSE*
    - *RUNNING HORSE (17??)*
      - *RUNNING HORSE* — *RUNNING HORSE*, *RUNNING HORSE*
      - *RUNNING HORSE* — *RUNNING HORSE*, *RUNNING HORSE*

Walk in the Water RH 1813

Chapter 4

Performance in the Heroic Age

"…the accepted American standard of excellence, races among mature horses over heroic distance of 4-miles, in which to establish superiority it was necessary to win two heats or else distance all opponents" (*The History of Thoroughbred Racing in America* by Wm. Robertson).

The famous North/South four-mile heat match race of the top race mares Peytona and Fashion RH held on May 13, 1845, at Union racecourse. —Artist C. Severn, lithograph by Currier.

Performance testing is the benchmark of sport horse validation. It is the tool we use to define and develop our sport breeds. In America for the two hundred years from 1665 until after the Civil War was an era in racing referred to as the 'Heroic Era' by scholars such as William Robertson and John Hervey, where it was the distance racing branch of our Running Horse breed that was tested by heat racing; the ultimate contest is the four-mile heat race.

In those two hundred years we developed the greatest distance racehorse the world has ever seen and set records that have never been broken in the succeeding one hundred fifty years. Lexington RH, born in 1850, along with some of his relatives and competitors, are the height of this period of selection. The bloodlines developed then are still powering our sport breeds today.

We began this racing form in 1665 when the English-appointed governor of the New York Colony, Richard Nicolls, set up a two-mile oval racecourse and instituted heat racing in concert with what his monarch King Charles was doing in England. With silver plate prizes and annual meets, it was an immediate success, and it kicked off a racing mania of its own. In America the new "King's Plate" race form was performed with our Running Horse breed—there were no English Thoroughbreds at that time, and none got to America until one hundred years later.

In England this type of race also became known as 'King's Plate,' and with the King's participation and promotion it quickly became the new racing standard. The heat race form then became the performance test for the new breed that was bred from the special new Turk/Barb/Running Horse combinations; this was the birth of the English Thoroughbred. The horses raced were usually at least five years old.

However, this race form stayed in place in England only for one hundred years. During that time our American Colonist's discontent with their English government was growing, and finally by 1776 their oppressive rule became so intolerable the

Colonies revolted. This same year—1776—the English had set a new performance test for the English Thoroughbred when the first of the classic races was established (St. Leger). At this time the new classic distance tested English racehorse began being called the "Thoroughbred". This was a drastic change in breed testing, and of course over time it resulted in a horse with different traits. The new classic race was run once—no heats—at distances of one to two miles and was at first run exclusively with three-year-olds, but later even with two-year-olds. Americans regarded the new classic form with a critical eye. The idea of racing young horses so severely was considered brutal by most American horsemen. In America we referred to this new English standard as 'dash' racing.

Also, by this era Americans were already becoming concerned with standardizing racing—up until then there was no way to ascertain that a champion had been tested by a consistent measure. Racetracks in various colonies, whether oval or straight, might differ in actual length by many yards, so that a winner of a race of four miles might actually have raced only 3 ¾ miles; therefore there was no way to truly compare performance. So the movement began to standardize track lengths and layouts, and the issues of footing and timing were also being discussed. By the late 1700s the Americans had adopted the new French invention of a stopwatch that measured fractions of time up to 1/16 of a second. In the early 1800s the preferred surfacing of those tracks became a groomed dirt surface on an oval track—often referred to as a 'skinned' track. This then produced a consistency in the testing of our racehorse. Whether racing in Virginia or New Orleans or New York, they could evaluate and compare the horse's performance much more accurately. These improvements also contributed to the refining of our distance racer.

There were general rules for heat racing: usually at least two heats were run (eight miles), and the winner was the best two out of three. There was a fairly consistent rest period between heats (although local officials could adjust the rules). Generally, a four-mile heat had a thirty-minute rest between heats, a three-mile heat race had a twenty-minute rest period, and a two-mile had a fifteen-minute rest. The exception to the number of heats was when a competitor was 'distanced' by his rival. There was a fairly consistent rule about 'distancing' employed at most tracks, whereas a horse lagging behind at the finish line was eliminated from further heats. These distances were marked out on the course and were generally: four-mile had one hundred seventy yard rule, three-mile had one hundred thirty yard, two-mile had ninety yard, and one-mile had fifty yards as the cut-off point.

In America heat racing was usually done with horses five years old and older—some notable horses ran into their late teens still sound. The starting age was set not just because only a mature horse was strong enough, but it also took years to condition the racers properly for their extreme test. The early years of a potential long distance heat racer were spent in testing of heat races of one to three miles before they were judged to be ready for the four-mile competition.

The greatest racetracks of the day used for four-mile heats were Metaire in New Orleans, Union in New York, Newmarket Course and Tree Hill in Virginia, and Washington Course in South Carolina. Racers would travel on foot to these meets from New York to New Orleans.

When a horse was at the top of his heat form they were sometimes raced in more than one of these contests in the same week, and depending on the number of contestants, a race could extend from two heats (eight miles) to three (twelve miles), four (sixteen miles), and at times five heats (twenty miles) before a winner was declared (read an account of twenty-mile race in the next chapter). It stretches our comprehension of this level of athlete when we realize they raced only after they traveled **on their own power** to the meet. It is documented that one horse, Monsieur Tonson RH, traveled twelve hundred miles to his next contest. The horse breed that resulted from this two-hundred-year period of extreme performance trying and selection procedure was the pinnacle of speed combined with distance and soundness. **There has never been another breed like them.**

Certain English Thoroughbreds were strong typesetters in our distance racer. Of the early imports Fearnought especially was a great distance racing sire-line, a grandson of the Godolphin Arabian (Turcoman Horse—not Arabian) who was the genetic transmitter of the high withers with laid-back shoulder form that allowed great extension in the front and a high powerful rump that powered the movement; these offspring had a huge stride that just ate up the track. Then after the Revolution, a few more imports with strong genetics for staying distance entered the gene pool: the small grey Medley, the very fast Shark, and the best of that era was Diomed (see Chapter 6). Leviathan was another with an immense stud record, but most of his stock was destroyed during the Civil War. Other imported horses just did not produce as well, but these sires were generally bred to our American Running Horse dams—many of which were already accomplished sprint or pacing racers (speed horses).

But not all the important typesetters were English-bred horses. Our native racer had always produced superior racing genetics, so if we take the time to really look at what is dominant in the winners we get a real surprise sometimes. [Note—there is an outline of the origin and establishment of our American breeds in Appendix D, because our four-mile-heat racer is found in many of our other breeds; it may help your understanding to refer to this outline and the breed abbreviations used here as you follow the text.]

I knew Blackburns Whip RH was an important typesetter in our other premier sport breeds when I wrote about him in *North American Sport Horse Breeder.* But it is only in building out the pedigrees of the stars of the four-mile heat racing that I find this pacing RH consistently in the top racers, often appearing on the dam-sire or close to the front of the pedigree, or even doubled up. This indicates he is an important ancestor for not only our gaited saddle horses, sprint racers, and pacing racers, but he is also an example of those rare race stallions that could transfer speed along with large measures of soundness and stamina—he is possibly one of the greatest typesetting stallions in sport of all times. His ability to produce top saddle horses illustrates his dominance in good movement and ride-ability, as well as the speed he was so famous for—what a wonderful stallion!

A. Buford, who stood Blackburns Whip RH as a stallion in Kentucky, advertises him as:

"..beautiful mahogany bay, full fifteen and a half hands high [15.2] and for beauty of form, he is considered by the best judges a superior horse. As to walking, trotting, pacing and running I defy the state to produce his equal.

"Whip is also more distinguished for his colts than any horse in Kentucky. They are superior for running also for the harness or saddle and for the high price they command at market…"(Advertisement placed in "The Reporter" 4/15/1822).

George Kinney, like Nearco, carries both Lexington RH and Blackburns Whip RH on his dam-line. —image found in the "Thoroughbred Record" 1900

Blackburns Whip RH—a documented transmitter of speed at all distances—is also found in other important bloodlines in our long racer, such as the racer George Kinney 1878 through his dam the good mare Kathleen RH by Lexington RH who traces to Blackburns Whip RH through Miss Obstinate RH. He is also found via Miss Obstinate RH in Maiden RH another daughter of Lexington RH, she has him through the sire of her third-dam Jenny Slamerkin RH: Tiger RH, and as we will see Maiden RH is also the dam of the super racer Parole (Chapter 8) who beat the best England had, and also the third dam of Sibola, who sits on the Thoroughbred 'sire of the century' Nearco's dam-line. Did you ever imagine that the pillar of modern Thoroughbred racing, Nearco, not only carries the RH Lexington but has a pacing RH dam-line? What's more is that this same Sibola sits on the dam-line of many important *German* Derby winners, such as Neckar and others. The great Lexington RH son Duke of Magenta carries him also. He is also found in Aerolite RH and her full sister Idlewild RH—their fourth dam-sire. Aerolite RH is the dam of Spendthrift and Fellowcraft, therefore is found in the Fair Play and Hamburg dynasties. He is found as the third dam-sire of Virgil RH as well.

This same stallion—Blackburns Whip RH—contributed heavily to our QH breed and is found 2x4 in Harry Bluff RH the sire of the famous Steel Dust and in Old Printer also. Wherever speed and athleticism was needed—the sire Blackburns Whip RH filled the bill. His son Young Whip RH was a celebrated distance heat-racer, winning seven of eight starts, and in those seven wins he never lost a heat! Other notable sons are Kenner's Whip RH, Whip RH, Paragon RH, and Whipster RH.

This is what I wrote about Blackburns Whip RH in *North American Sport Horse Breeder*:

> "This stallion can serve as an example of the quality Maryland-and-Virginia bred pacing Running Horses that were exported to the western states and territories to both race and improve the type of our developing light horse breeds. By this era the frontier was western Kentucky, Tennessee, Missouri, and surrounding areas. We are fortunate to have pretty reliable information on him with much of it well documented, as many of his contemporaries such as Tom Hal and Cockspur have little reliable information on their ancestors. So Blackburns Whip can show us how the talented and typesetting Native American Woods Horses (RH) of this era were being bred.

> "Blackburns Whip is found at the base of most of our later developing breeds of American Saddle Horse, Quarter Horse, and Standardbred, especially in the pacing lines. He goes by many names: Cooks Whip, Youngs Whip, and Kentucky Whip—all these are the same horse.

> "His sire is the imported English Thoroughbred Whip, and he is out of the American Running Horse Speckleback. We have seen this phenomenon many times: an English Thoroughbred is imported and when bred to a Running Horse dam they produce gaited progeny, but the mating with our Running Horse caused dominance with the background English Running Horse and Hobby lines that are behind Regulus, Crab, and Blaze. All of these great English sires are heavy in Hobby background bloodlines. When these English genetics met their close cousin strains, a prepotency in Hobby type was produced.

> "Blackburns Whip was a strong typesetter of fast pacing racers and athletic saddle horses with comfortable gaits; he is easily found in the pedigrees of the Standardbred, Quarter Horse, Saddlebred, Tennessee Walker, Missouri Fox Trotter, and others" (*North American Sport Horse Breeder*, Appendix C).

When Blackburns Whip RH was mated with Jane Hunt RH 1796—a running horse mare who heads a maternal dynasty through her granddaughter Jenny Slamerkin RH who is 2x3 to her through a son and a daughter—they produced Tiger RH and Little Tiger RH, great sires and transmitters of extreme speed. Robert Denhardt in his important work *Foundation Dams of the American Quarter Horse* reports that both of these sons of Blackburns Whip RH were outstanding horses that transmitted great reservoirs of early speed.

Jane Hunt RH was a beautiful bay mare, superior racer, and broodmare; she is classified by Ellen Parker as a '*reine-de-course*' (see note below), because through her daughter Jenny Slamerkin RH she reigns over a family of broodmare superiority. Inbreeding combined with the practice of sex-balancing, especially through close siblings, is the most powerful structure we can build into our pedigrees (see Evaluating Pedigrees Appendix B). Jenny is 2x3 to Jane Hunt RH sex-balanced who is by the Blackburns Whip RH son Tiger RH 1812. From this mare descend a family of sport royalty. She is the third dam of La Henderson RH, a Lexington RH daughter, from whom descend five *reines-de-course* including Little Hut, Lodge, and Savage Beauty. Jenny is the third-dam of the Lexington RH daughter Maiden RH, who sits on the dam-line of Catnip. We will discuss Catnip's descendants in a few other chapters (16 and 17), suffice to say now that she rules over an Italian and German dynasty through Nogara, Nervasa, and Nella Da Gubbio, and through the *reine* Louise T (she is seventh dam) there are nine *reine-de-course* descending from her. This is a maternal bloodline of immense power.

[Note: *reine-de-course* is a title given by the Thoroughbred expert Ellen Parker for the list of key broodmares of the Thoroughbred breed; she is the creator of this list as well as its sustainer and publisher. Another important list for the Thoroughbred breed is the '*chefs-de-race*' list; this one was conceived and is published by Dr. Steve Roman, and it identifies the key Thoroughbred sires listed according to the race-length capabilities of their offspring. Throughout this book the key broodmares and sires often have earned this designation. You will find these complete lists online: www.reines-de-course.com and www.chefs-de-race.com]

I have found that the breeding of Tiger RH is often confused in print; whether this was an intentional deception when pedigrees were being spiffed-up in the early 1800s I can't yet determine. You may find in many texts that mention him, or more usually Jane Hunt RH and her offspring, that the sire of Tiger RH is often misprinted as imported Whip, who is actually his grandsire, his sire is the RH Blackburns Whip. This mistake, which hides the Running Horse contribution, multiplies down through the years. So that his granddaughter, the great broodmare Jenny Slamerkin RH appears in most publications to be solely of English Thoroughbred blood, and Jane Hunt RH, who is inbred to Jenny Slamerkin RH 2x3, is also put forth as of strictly English lines; however her sire Paragon is also a Running Horse.

Sir Archy —etching from painting, found in Spirit of the Times.

That is just the tip of the iceberg in pedigree revision and racing lore. Her descendant, Miss Obstinate RH, who is of the A4 family, then appears to be a pure English family—which is far from the truth. Miss Obstinate RH—who is heralded as the strongest branch of the Cub Mare line—is in fact made up of Running Horse speed lines (dam-lines), both English and American. The Cub Mare was an early English Thoroughbred mare imported by James Delancey along with Wildair and Lath. They are often spoken of as the pillars of the American Thoroughbred. John Hervey said of the Cub Mare: "...the most prolific producer of stakes winners in the American matriarchy," and of Miss Obstinate RH he says, "...the most famous and productive modern branch of the Cub Mare family." Miss Obstinate RH is the sixth dam of Catnip and is found in the great modern racers and producers: Brians Time, Shareef Dancer, Runaway Groom, and probably the most famous, the American-bred stallion Habitat (who was exported to England and became a great sire there). By the way, the second most productive branch of the Cub Mare family is Lady Rosebery who is by a Lexington RH son, Kingfisher RH. So you can see the discounting of our native breed is pretty comprehensive.

Another giant of our Heroic Age is one I am sure you are all familiar with: Sir Archy 1805, and he was the premier distance line of his time. Like his contemporary Blackburns Whip RH 1805 (premier speed line), Sir Archy permeates the background of all our sport and saddle breeds. Sir Archy was bred in America out of two English Thoroughbreds: the typesetter Diomed and the good producer Castianira. He is considered the foundation sire of the later formed American Thoroughbred. Sir Archy was a terrific four-miler, but it is his record at stud that surpasses most others—as he was inbred to in a manner that very few sires had success in, except perhaps individuals like the earlier Janus. Sir Archy was bred to his own daughters and ½ sisters regularly—with fantastic results. It was rare to find a fast horse in his era that did not carry his line, usually in multiples. Check out Fashion RH's pedigree in the previous chapter, her dam is 2x2 to him.

Sir Archy's best son was Sir Charles RH, a foremost four-miler and a great sire; he is found not only in our Thoroughbred lines, but also was a major contributor to the Standardbred, Quarter Horse, and our saddle horse breeds. Sir Charles RH is another example of the move to clean up our mongrel bloodlines, and it turns out the version of his lineage that was published in the American Stud Book (S.D. Bruce 1868), with his third dam Dare Devil Mare being of strictly good English blood, traveling right back to the English mare Jenny Dismal is not correct. His third dam is actually a Running Horse by Mark Anthony, and the line goes back to a quarter racing American Running Horse mare by Janus. The movement to become more 'English' must have been very powerful, because we find that Col. William Ransom, a man of unimpeachable stature in the racing industry of the day, who stood Sir Charles RH for most of his stud career, disputed the remodeled pedigree strongly. Then Benjamin Tayloe—another representative of an impeccable racing family—published Sir Charles's true pedigree. For all that, somehow, the revisionists got the upper hand, and the 'improved' pedigree was entered

Sir Charles RH, notice his riding horse conformation—he became an important sire of saddle horses as well as racers. —an engraving found in the American Turf Register and Sporting Magazine

Maria West RH —etching found in the 'Thoroughbred Record' from a painting by Troye

in the American studbook. The one posted here is the correct version; Sir Charles RH is an American Running Horse, not a Thoroughbred.

Sir Charles RH, a 15.3-hand chestnut, produced over twenty four-mile heat racers, some of the most well-known are Trifle RH, and Bonnets o' Blue RH, Collier RH, and the great sire Wagner RH—he is a **genetic giant**.

Sir Charles's daughter Trifle RH was inbred 2x2 to Sir Archy and was a mere 14.2 hands tall—thus her name. Nonetheless, she was a star racer of three- and four-mile heat races, with a record of nineteen wins and five seconds in twenty-four starts. Her daughter Gloriana RH was a good producer with four important offspring who were full siblings: the brothers Jack Malone RH, Pat Malloy RH, and Lanigan RH, plus their sister Miss Peyton RH. Her full sister Rosalee Somers RH is the dam of the great sire Revenue RH, who fathered Planet RH. This is a top sport line.

Sir Charles RH has a younger full brother, Marion RH 1820, who was also a great racer and sire, and to have both of these giants in the back of your pedigrees is powerful. Marion's greatest offspring was his daughter Maria West RH 1827, who was out of the good broodmare Ella Crump RH 1807 (foundation mare of A1 family), and she became a terrific broodmare. This is where it really gets interesting for students of breeding theory, for Maria West's best progeny was a stallion named Wagner RH, and he is by Sir Charles RH. That makes the full brothers Sir Charles RH and Marion RH 1x2! But that is not all, Wagner RH went on to be a good sire, and his best offspring is a taproot mare named Pekina ASA, who established a strong family in our saddle horse breeds. She is dam of the great Peavine ASA and Dave Akin ASA, both legendary sires. Pekina ASA (see pedigree) is by Wagner RH out of Collier Mare RH—Collier RH is another son of Sir Charles RH, which makes Pekina ASA 2x2x3 to Sir Charles RH/Marion RH—and in addition she is out of Blackburns Whip Mare RH. This puts Sir Charles RH and his full brother on a par genetically with their sire Sir Archy and the earlier Janus, all of them stallions that could stand up to such close inbreeding and produce the very finest horses time after time. Can this level of inbreeding sustain itself? I guess it can, for I have found in my database an excellent broodmare Miss Graves ASA; she is by Dave Akin ASA out of a Peavine mare, making Pekina ASA 2x3. Miss Graves ASA is the dam of Highland Denmark ASA, a very good saddle horse sire. This may be a big reach, but I will risk it because beautiful movement in gaits is a legacy of our pacing RH lines. It is interesting that the good sire Collier RH is also out of a Blackburns Whip RH daughter, and then his daughter Pekina ASA is out of another Blackburns Whip RH daughter, and they both are legendary purveyors of beautiful movement. Is it just a coincidence then that Nearco, remarkable for his smooth fluid motion, carries this same transmitter of excellent movement in his dam-line? Just some-

36

Henry RH —from a painting by Troye

Etching of American Eclipse RH —made from a painting by Mr. Fisher of Boston and engraved by Messrs. Capewell and Kimmel.

thing for you to think about, so that when you search for sources of dressage prospects it just might occur to you that the American breeds have a far richer genetic base for these traits than those farm/coach horse descendant breeds you have been using.

At age thirty, just before he died, the long-lived Diomed produced an amazing race mare in Haynie's Maria 1808, who, like her ½ brother Sir Archy, is exclusively of English Thoroughbred blood. She easily beat both mares and colts; she was a stellar four-miler, and she too gives us a big surprise, as she was also a champion sprinter—what a mare! It is not possible to overestimate the influence of Diomed—he is a genetic giant in American pedigrees (see Chapter 22 for a modern day dynasty built on his genes—I think it will surprise you.)

In sporting contests it was not too long before a great rivalry developed between the north and south breeders, which culminated in a series of match races. The first was a meet between the eight-year-old American Eclipse RH (15.2 hands) the pride of the north and the four-year-old Henry RH (14.3 hands), the southern entry (see pedigree) was drafted to replace Sir Charles RH, the great Sir Archy son, who broke down before the race. Henry (RH) was bred 2x2 to Diomed.

His opponent was American Eclipse RH, by the good sire Duroc RH, a son of Diomed—it is interesting that the dam of American Eclipse RH is a daughter of the imported typesetter and part-TB Messenger (EH). Messenger EH is a horse that has long been promoted as a full Thoroughbred, which he could not be. The evidence instead points to the fudged areas of his pedigree being carriers of strong concentrations of English Running Horse blood—as well as other foreign elements—talent does not drop from the sky, and speed at the mid-gaits came from the Running Horse, not the newer Thoroughbred. After reviewing all the evidence, including the exhaustive investigation done by John H. Wallace into Messenger's true lineage, it is blatantly obvious that he has strong Running Horse lines in him, as the fast trot (straight forward versus the high flexion of the slow trot form) originated with the pacing Running Horse (see *North American Sport Horse Breeder* for a full discussion of Messenger EH and his true parentage and Appendix C). Of further interest is that American Eclipse's Running Horse lines are all English—from Calista ERH and Messenger EH.

Henry RH won the first heat, but Eclipse RH took the next two—there were 60,000 spectators to this race held on Long Island, it is estimated twenty-thousand of them were Henry's fans that traveled from the south. The Turf historian William Richardson states that New York City itself had only one hundred fifty thousand residents at the time, so you can see this was an important event. Match races became the most attended sporting events of the era, even with the attendants traveling long distances by horseback or carriage.

American Eclipse RH had a few fantastic daughters; Ariel RH was one of the best racers, male or female of her day or any day; she won forty-two of fifty-seven starts, many of them four-mile heats. The American Turf Register in 1834 reported this about Ariel RH:

> "Ariel certainly ranks with the best horses of any age or clime. To adapt the language of a valued correspondent, 'we doubt whether any horse of any region ever did more good running, attended with such exhaustive and constant travel.' From reference to English works and to our own pages, we find no account of any horse that has either run or won as many races. In her last campaign in the 'race-horse region', she ran and won thirty-six miles in fifteen days: the first race, four-mile heats at Norfolk, beating horses of high reputation, and winning the second heat in 7m 43s; the next race of three-mile heats, at Broad Rock, where at four heats, the last in 5m 47s; she beat the 'crack nags' of Virginia; and the third, another race of four-mile heats, and in extraordinary time. On the eighth day thereafter she was beaten, the four-mile heats, by a very superior three-year-old; an excellent race; yet, in the two consecutive weeks, immediately succeeding, she won two more races....In the aggregate, taking into view speed, bottom, and durability; amount of running, travel, and of sums 'lost and won' on her, we think Ariel stands unrivalled."

American Eclipse RH is found easily in the stars of the Heroic Era in the lines of Aerolite RH, Enquirer RH, and Virgil RH for instance—usually as a dam-sire. Perhaps his best daughter was Black Maria RH, who also beat just about any horse she raced against. She was the winner of the famous four-mile heat race against Trifle RH and other top race mares, which actually went for five heats—a total of twenty miles (read a contemporary account of that race in the next chapter). Black Maria RH had a full sister and brother, Bay Maria RH and Shark RH, and all three were excellent producers.

Bay Maria RH, full sister to Black Maria RH and Shark RH, was an excellent broodmare. —from a painting by Troye

Another fine example of the four-miler is Washington RH 1819, and like Boston RH he is a son of Timoleon RH out of a RH dam. He was rated the best three-year-old of his crop. Both his dam-lines are Running Horse, Calista (ERH) from Timoleon RH and American Running Horse Yorick Mare. Distance heat racing was in its heyday from 1800-50, and then it began its slow decline in popularity, with the ravages of the studs and stock from the Civil War basically finishing it off.

But throughout this time unrest with the English continued, with embargos on shipping imposed on both sides, and between 1806 through 1830 virtually no new English Thoroughbred blood entered our racing population. Resistance to the English way of doing things ran high at this time, and the racing establishment made a point of not adopting the classic race form, so the American breeder continued the perfection of the heat-racing specialist.

The American distance racehorse developed largely on its own again until shipping reopened in the 1830s. Even then it was a rare horse that could seriously challenge our distance stars. Once the floodgates for British imports opened again, we can see the evidence of their other bloodlines in our later heat-racer, but most of those newer imports were not real stamina horses, having a hundred years of dash racing selection behind them; they were classic distance stars and were less sound also.

On the other hand, England had little firsthand knowledge of the quality of our racehorse, as very few American horses were imported into England until well after our Civil War. The attrition rate in our racing populations was tremendous during that war, and still being a horse society it took years to build back even the utility horses needed. Also we had switched our breed performance testing to the English version, and the heat race contesting of our racer was gradually being abandoned. Further, we kept crossing in English classic length horses so that our horse began accelerating in the downward slide in stamina and soundness. We recognized by 1882 that this practice was hurting our racehorse population.

> "If we will take an intelligent and unprejudiced view of the present condition of the American Turf, we will find that the tendency is to breed the flash and speedy horse at the expense of the stout and enduring one. We have nearly abolished heat races except over short courses, and under this false system of dash races over short courses, we are sacrificing the staying powers of our horses to speed. We are following too much in the steps of the English, discarding to a great extent our stoutest and most enduring horses for those possessed of extraordinary speed"(Thoroughbred Record 1882).

It is in this same period, after the Civil War in the last quarter of the century, in which we were sending our racehorses to England and elsewhere in Europe to compete, and it was those flawed strains that still were close enough to those of our pre-Civil War distance racers that proved they possessed devastating speed combined with immense stamina in measures that the English racer no longer had. It wasn't long then before objections and then moves were made to limit the American imports.

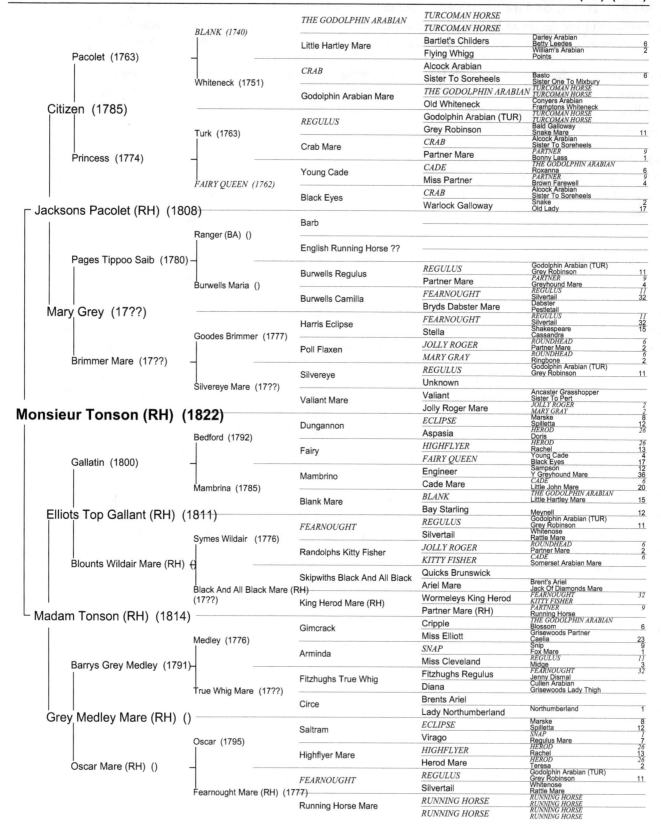

Monsieur Tonson (RH) (1822)

- **Jacksons Pacolet (RH) (1808)**
  - **Citizen (1785)**
    - **Pacolet (1763)**
      - *BLANK (1740)*
        - *THE GODOLPHIN ARABIAN* — *TURCOMAN HORSE* / *TURCOMAN HORSE*
        - Little Hartley Mare — Bartlet's Childers (Darley Arabian / Betty Leedes 6) / Flying Whigg (William's Arabian / Points 2)
      - Whiteneck (1751)
        - *CRAB* — Alcock Arabian / Sister To Soreheels (Basto 6 / Sister One To Mixbury)
        - Godolphin Arabian Mare — *THE GODOLPHIN ARABIAN* (*TURCOMAN HORSE* / *TURCOMAN HORSE*) / Old Whiteneck (Conyers Arabian / Framptons Whiteneck)
    - **Princess (1774)**
      - Turk (1763)
        - *REGULUS* — Godolphin Arabian (TUR) (*TURCOMAN HORSE* / *TURCOMAN HORSE*) / Grey Robinson (Bald Galloway / Snake Mare 11)
        - Crab Mare — *CRAB* (Alcock Arabian / Sister To Soreheels) / Partner Mare (*PARTNER* 9 / Bonny Lass 1)
      - *FAIRY QUEEN (1762)*
        - Young Cade — *CADE* (*THE GODOLPHIN ARABIAN* 6 / Roxanna) / Miss Partner (*PARTNER* 9 / Brown Farewell 4)
        - Black Eyes — *CRAB* (Alcock Arabian / Sister To Soreheels) / Warlock Galloway (Snake 2 / Old Lady 17)
  - **Mary Grey (17??)**
    - **Pages Tippoo Saib (1780)**
      - Ranger (BA) ()
        - Barb —
        - English Running Horse ?? —
      - Burwells Maria ()
        - Burwells Regulus — *REGULUS* (Godolphin Arabian (TUR) / Grey Robinson 11) / Partner Mare (*PARTNER* 9 / Greyhound Mare 4)
        - Burwells Camilla — *FEARNOUGHT* (*REGULUS* 11 / Silvertail 32) / Bryds Dabster Mare (Dabster / Pestletail)
    - **Brimmer Mare (17??)**
      - Goodes Brimmer (1777)
        - Harris Eclipse — *FEARNOUGHT* (*REGULUS* 11 / Silvertail 32) / Stella (Shakespeare 15 / Cassandra)
        - Poll Flaxen — *JOLLY ROGER* (*ROUNDHEAD* 6 / Partner Mare 2) / *MARY GRAY* (*ROUNDHEAD* 6 / Ringbone 2)
      - Silvereye Mare (17??)
        - Silvereye — *REGULUS* (Godolphin Arabian (TUR) / Grey Robinson 11) / Unknown
        - Valiant Mare — Valiant (Ancaster Grasshopper / Sister To Pert) / Jolly Roger Mare (*JOLLY ROGER* 2 / *MARY GRAY* 2)

- **Elliots Top Gallant (RH) (1811)**
  - **Gallatin (1800)**
    - Bedford (1792)
      - Dungannon — *ECLIPSE* (Marske 8 / Spilletta 12) / Aspasia (*HEROD* 26 / Doris)
      - Fairy — *HIGHFLYER* (*HEROD* 26 / Rachel 13) / *FAIRY QUEEN* (Young Cade 4 / Black Eyes 17)
    - Mambrina (1785)
      - Mambrino — Engineer (Sampson 12 / Y Greyhound Mare 36) / Cade Mare (*CADE* 6 / Little John Mare 20)
      - Blank Mare — *BLANK* (*THE GODOLPHIN ARABIAN* / Little Hartley Mare 15) / Bay Starling (Meynell 12)
  - **Blounts Wildair Mare (RH) ()**
    - Symes Wildair (1776)
      - *FEARNOUGHT* — *REGULUS* (Godolphin Arabian (TUR) / Grey Robinson 11) / Silvertail (Whitenose / Rattle Mare)
      - Randolphs Kitty Fisher — *JOLLY ROGER* (*ROUNDHEAD* 6 / Partner Mare 2) / *KITTY FISHER* (*CADE* 6 / Somerset Arabian Mare)
    - Black And All Black Mare (RH) (17??)
      - Skipwiths Black And All Black — Quicks Brunswick / Ariel Mare (Brent's Ariel / Jack Of Diamonds Mare)
      - King Herod Mare (RH) — Wormeleys King Herod (*FEARNOUGHT* 32 / *KITTY FISHER*) / Partner Mare (RH) (*PARTNER* 9 / Running Horse)

- **Madam Tonson (RH) (1814)**
  - **Barrys Grey Medley (1791)**
    - Medley (1776)
      - Gimcrack — Cripple (*THE GODOLPHIN ARABIAN* / Blossom 6) / Miss Elliott (Grisewoods Partner / Caelia 23)
      - Arminda — *SNAP* (Snip 9 / Fox Mare 1) / Miss Cleveland (*REGULUS* 11 / Midge 3)
    - True Whig Mare (17??)
      - Fitzhughs True Whig — Fitzhughs Regulus (*FEARNOUGHT* 32 / Jenny Dismal) / Diana (Cullen Arabian / Grisewoods Lady Thigh)
      - Circe — Brents Ariel / Lady Northumberland (Northumberland 1)
  - **Grey Medley Mare (RH) ()**
    - **Oscar Mare (RH) ()**
      - Oscar (1795)
        - Saltram — *ECLIPSE* (Marske 8 / Spilletta 12) / Virago (*SNAP* 1 / Regulus Mare 7)
        - Highflyer Mare — *HIGHFLYER* (*HEROD* 26 / Rachel 13) / Herod Mare (*HEROD* 26 / Teresa 2)
      - Fearnought Mare (RH) (1777)
        - *FEARNOUGHT* — *REGULUS* (Godolphin Arabian (TUR) / Grey Robinson 11) / Silvertail (Whitenose / Rattle Mare)
        - Running Horse Mare — *RUNNING HORSE* (*RUNNING HORSE* / *RUNNING HORSE*) / *RUNNING HORSE* (*RUNNING HORSE* / *RUNNING HORSE*)

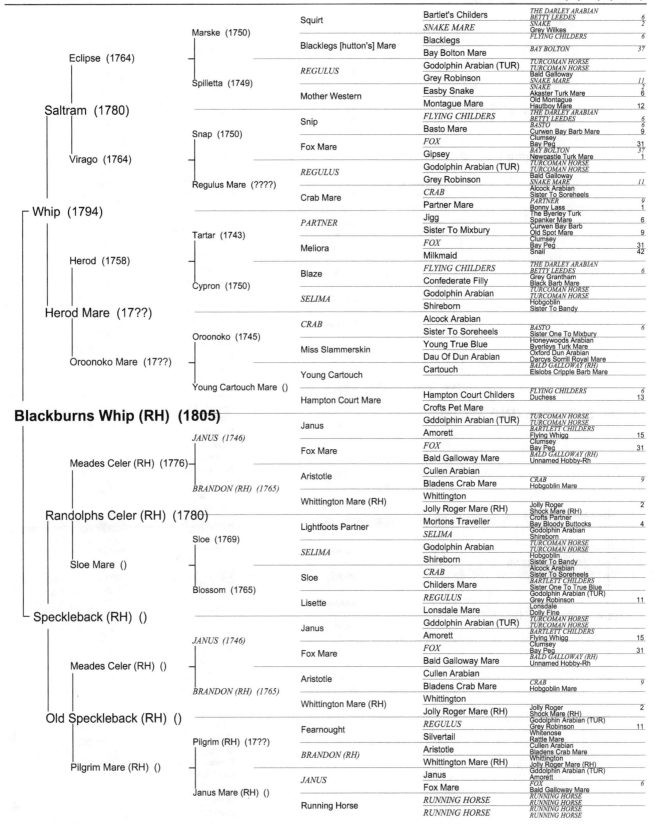

Blackburns Whip (RH) (1805)

Whip (1794)

- **Saltram (1780)**
  - Eclipse (1764)
    - Marske (1750)
      - Squirt
        - Bartlet's Childers — *THE DARLEY ARABIAN* / *BETTY LEEDES* 6 ; *SNAKE* 2
        - *SNAKE MARE* — *SNAKE* / Grey Wilkes
      - Blacklegs [hutton's] Mare
        - Blacklegs — *FLYING CHILDERS* 6
        - Bay Bolton Mare — *BAY BOLTON* 37
    - Spilletta (1749)
      - *REGULUS*
        - Godolphin Arabian (TUR) — *TURCOMAN HORSE* / *TURCOMAN HORSE*
        - Grey Robinson — Bald Galloway / *SNAKE MARE* 11
      - Mother Western
        - Easby Snake — *SNAKE* 2 / Akaster Turk Mare 6
        - Montague Mare — Old Montague / Hautboy Mare 12
  - Virago (1764)
    - Snap (1750)
      - Snip
        - *FLYING CHILDERS* — *THE DARLEY ARABIAN* / *BETTY LEEDES* 6
        - Basto Mare — *BASTO* 6 / Curwen Bay Barb Mare 9
      - Fox Mare
        - *FOX* — Clumsey / Bay Peg 31
        - Gipsey — *BAY BOLTON* 37 / Newcastle Turk Mare 1
    - Regulus Mare (????)
      - *REGULUS*
        - Godolphin Arabian (TUR) — *TURCOMAN HORSE* / *TURCOMAN HORSE*
        - Grey Robinson — Bald Galloway / *SNAKE MARE* 11
      - Crab Mare
        - *CRAB* — Alcock Arabian / Sister To Soreheels
        - Partner Mare — *PARTNER* 9 / Bonny Lass 1

Herod Mare (17??)

- **Herod (1758)**
  - Tartar (1743)
    - *PARTNER*
      - Jigg — The Byerley Turk / Spanker Mare 6
      - Sister To Mixbury — Curwen Bay Barb / Old Spot Mare 9
    - Meliora
      - *FOX* — Clumsey / Bay Peg 31
      - Milkmaid — Snail 42
  - Cypron (1750)
    - Blaze
      - *FLYING CHILDERS* — *THE DARLEY ARABIAN* / *BETTY LEEDES* 6
      - Confederate Filly — Grey Grantham / Black Barb Mare
    - *SELIMA*
      - Godolphin Arabian — *TURCOMAN HORSE* / *TURCOMAN HORSE*
      - Shireborn — Hobgoblin / Sister To Bandy
- **Oroonoko Mare (17??)**
  - Oroonoko (1745)
    - *CRAB*
      - Alcock Arabian — *BASTO* 6
      - Sister To Soreheels — Sister One To Mixbury
    - Miss Slammerskin
      - Young True Blue — Honeywoods Arabian / Byerleys Turk Mare
      - Dau Of Dun Arabian — Oxford Dun Arabian / Darcys Sorrill Royal Mare
  - Young Cartouch Mare ()
    - Young Cartouch
      - Cartouch — *BALD GALLOWAY (RH)* / Elslobs Cripple Barb Mare
    - Hampton Court Mare
      - Hampton Court Childers — *FLYING CHILDERS* 6 / Duchess 13
      - Crofts Pet Mare

Blackburns Whip (RH) (1805)

Speckleback (RH) ()

- **Randolphs Celer (RH) (1780)**
  - Meades Celer (RH) (1776)
    - *JANUS (1746)*
      - Janus
        - Gddolphin Arabian (TUR) — *TURCOMAN HORSE* / *TURCOMAN HORSE*
        - Amorett — *BARTLETT CHILDERS* / Flying Whigg 15
      - Fox Mare
        - *FOX* — Clumsey / Bay Peg 31
        - Bald Galloway Mare — *BALD GALLOWAY (RH)* / Unnamed Hobby-Rh
    - *BRANDON (RH) (1765)*
      - Aristotle
        - Cullen Arabian
        - Bladens Crab Mare — *CRAB* 9 / Hobgoblin Mare
      - Whittington Mare (RH)
        - Whittington
        - Jolly Roger Mare (RH) — Jolly Roger 2 / Shock Mare (RH)
  - Sloe Mare ()
    - Sloe (1769)
      - Lightfoots Partner
        - Mortons Traveller — Crofts Partner / Bay Bloody Buttocks 4
        - *SELIMA* — Godolphin Arabian / Shireborn
      - *SELIMA*
        - Godolphin Arabian — *TURCOMAN HORSE* / *TURCOMAN HORSE*
        - Shireborn — Hobgoblin / Sister To Bandy
    - Blossom (1765)
      - Sloe
        - *CRAB* — Alcock Arabian / Sister To Soreheels
        - Childers Mare — *BARTLETT CHILDERS* / Sister One To True Blue
      - Lisette
        - *REGULUS* — Godolphin Arabian (TUR) / Grey Robinson 11
        - Lonsdale Mare — Lonsdale / Dolly Fine
- **Old Speckleback (RH) ()**
  - Meades Celer (RH) ()
    - *JANUS (1746)*
      - Janus
        - Gddolphin Arabian (TUR) — *TURCOMAN HORSE* / *TURCOMAN HORSE*
        - Amorett — *BARTLETT CHILDERS* / Flying Whigg 15
      - Fox Mare
        - *FOX* — Clumsey / Bay Peg 31
        - Bald Galloway Mare — *BALD GALLOWAY (RH)* / Unnamed Hobby-Rh
    - *BRANDON (RH) (1765)*
      - Aristotle
        - Cullen Arabian
        - Bladens Crab Mare — *CRAB* 9 / Hobgoblin Mare
      - Whittington Mare (RH)
        - Whittington
        - Jolly Roger Mare (RH) — Jolly Roger 2 / Shock Mare (RH)
  - Pilgrim Mare (RH) ()
    - Pilgrim (RH) (17??)
      - Fearnought
        - *REGULUS* — Godolphin Arabian (TUR) / Grey Robinson 11
        - Silvertail — Whitenose / Rattle Mare
      - *BRANDON (RH)*
        - Aristotle — Cullen Arabian / Bladens Crab Mare
        - Whittington Mare (RH) — Whittington / Jolly Roger Mare (RH)
    - Janus Mare (RH) ()
      - *JANUS*
        - Janus — Gddolphin Arabian (TUR) / Amorett
        - Fox Mare — *FOX* 6 / Bald Galloway Mare
      - Running Horse
        - *RUNNING HORSE* — *RUNNING HORSE* / *RUNNING HORSE*
        - *RUNNING HORSE* — *RUNNING HORSE* / *RUNNING HORSE*

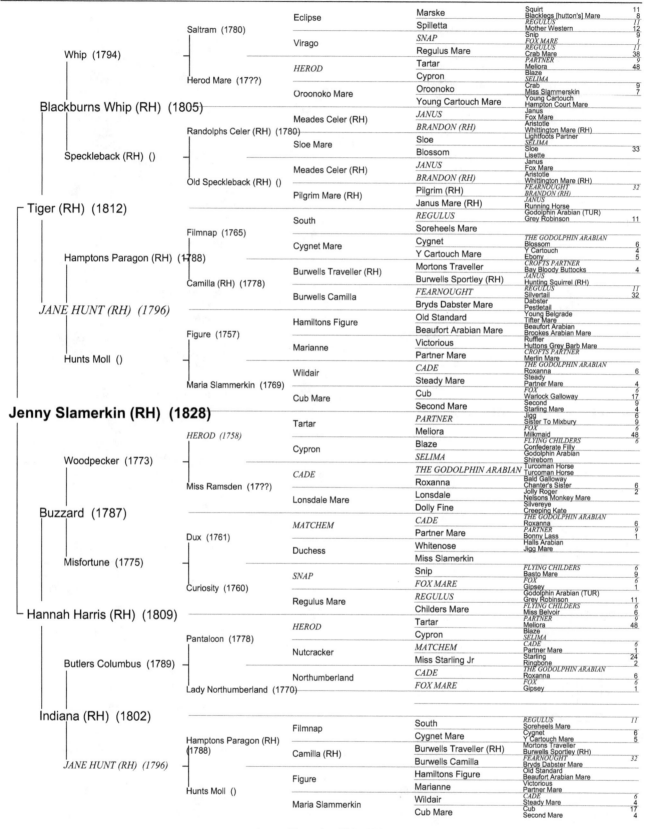

- **Jenny Slamerkin (RH) (1828)**
  - **Tiger (RH) (1812)**
    - Blackburns Whip (RH) (1805)
      - Whip (1794)
        - Saltram (1780)
          - Eclipse
            - Marske
              - Squirt — 11
              - Blacklegs [hutton's] Mare — 8
            - Spilletta
              - *REGULUS* — 11
              - Mother Western — 12
          - Virago
            - *SNAP*
              - Snip — 9
              - *FOX MARE* — 1
            - Regulus Mare
              - *REGULUS* — 11
              - Crab Mare — 38
        - *HEROD* Mare (17??)
          - *HEROD*
            - Tartar
              - *PARTNER* — 9
              - Meliora — 48
            - Cypron
              - Blaze
              - *SELIMA*
          - Oroonoko Mare
            - Oroonoko
              - Crab — 9
              - Miss Slammerskin — 7
            - Young Cartouch Mare
              - Young Cartouch
              - Hampton Court Mare
    - Speckleback (RH) ()
      - Randolphs Celer (RH) (1780)
        - Meades Celer (RH)
          - *JANUS*
            - Janus
            - Fox Mare
          - *BRANDON (RH)*
            - Aristotle
            - Whittington Mare (RH)
        - Sloe Mare
          - Sloe
            - Lightfoots Partner
            - *SELIMA*
          - Blossom
            - Sloe — 33
            - Lisette
      - Old Speckleback (RH) ()
        - Meades Celer (RH)
          - *JANUS*
            - Janus
            - Fox Mare
          - *BRANDON (RH)*
            - Aristotle
            - Whittington Mare (RH)
        - Pilgrim Mare (RH)
          - Pilgrim (RH)
            - *FEARNOUGHT* — 32
            - *BRANDON (RH)*
          - Janus Mare (RH)
            - *JANUS*
            - Running Horse
    - Hamptons Paragon (RH) (1788)
      - Filmnap (1765)
        - South
          - *REGULUS*
            - Godolphin Arabian (TUR)
            - Grey Robinson — 11
          - Soreheels Mare
        - Cygnet Mare
          - Cygnet
            - *THE GODOLPHIN ARABIAN*
            - Blossom — 6
          - Y Cartouch Mare
            - Y Cartouch — 4
            - Ebony — 5
      - Camilla (RH) (1778)
        - Burwells Traveller (RH)
          - Mortons Traveller
            - *CROFTS PARTNER*
            - Bay Bloody Buttocks — 4
          - Burwells Sportley (RH)
            - *JANUS*
            - Hunting Squirrel (RH)
        - Burwells Camilla
          - *FEARNOUGHT*
            - *REGULUS* — 11
            - Silvertail — 32
          - Bryds Dabster Mare
            - Dabster
            - Pestletail
  - *JANE HUNT (RH) (1796)*
    - Figure (1757)
      - Hamiltons Figure
        - Old Standard
          - Young Belgrade
          - Tifter Mare
        - Beaufort Arabian Mare
          - Beaufort Arabian
          - Brookes Arabian Mare
      - Marianne
        - Victorious
          - Ruffler
          - Huttons Grey Barb Mare
        - Partner Mare
          - *CROFTS PARTNER*
          - Merlin Mare
    - Hunts Moll ()
      - Maria Slammerkin (1769)
        - Wildair
          - *CADE*
            - *THE GODOLPHIN ARABIAN*
            - Roxanna — 6
          - Steady Mare
            - Steady
            - Partner Mare — 4
        - Cub Mare
          - Cub
            - *FOX* — 6
            - Warlock Galloway — 17
          - Second Mare
            - Second — 9
            - Starling Mare — 4

- **Jenny Slamerkin (RH) (1828)**
  - **Buzzard (1787)**
    - Woodpecker (1773)
      - *HEROD (1758)*
        - Tartar
          - *PARTNER*
            - Jigg — 6
            - Sister To Mixbury — 9
          - Meliora
            - *FOX* — 6
            - Milkmaid — 48
        - Cypron
          - Blaze
            - *FLYING CHILDERS* — 6
            - Confederate Filly
          - *SELIMA*
            - Godolphin Arabian
            - Shireborn
      - Miss Ramsden (17??)
        - *CADE*
          - *THE GODOLPHIN ARABIAN*
            - Turcoman Horse
            - Turcoman Horse
          - Roxanna
            - Bald Galloway
            - Chanters Sister — 6
        - Lonsdale Mare
          - Lonsdale
            - Jolly Roger — 2
            - Nelsons Monkey Mare
          - Dolly Fine
            - Silvereye
            - Creeping Kate
    - Misfortune (1775)
      - Dux (1761)
        - *MATCHEM*
          - *CADE*
            - *THE GODOLPHIN ARABIAN*
            - Roxanna — 6
          - Partner Mare
            - *PARTNER* — 9
            - Bonny Lass — 1
        - Duchess
          - Whitenose
            - Halls Arabian
            - Jigg Mare
          - Miss Slammerkin
      - Curiosity (1760)
        - *SNAP*
          - Snip
            - *FLYING CHILDERS* — 6
            - Basto Mare — 9
          - *FOX MARE*
            - *FOX* — 6
            - Gipsey — 1
        - Regulus Mare
          - *REGULUS*
            - Godolphin Arabian (TUR)
            - Grey Robinson — 11
          - Childers Mare
            - *FLYING CHILDERS* — 6
            - Miss Belvoir — 6
  - **Hannah Harris (RH) (1809)**
    - Butlers Columbus (1789)
      - Pantaloon (1778)
        - *HEROD*
          - Tartar
            - *PARTNER* — 9
            - Meliora — 48
          - Cypron
            - Blaze
            - *SELIMA*
        - Nutcracker
          - *MATCHEM*
            - *CADE* — 6
            - Partner Mare — 1
          - Miss Starling Jr
            - Starling — 24
            - Ringbone — 2
      - Lady Northumberland (1770)
        - Northumberland
          - *CADE*
            - *THE GODOLPHIN ARABIAN*
            - Roxanna — 6
          - *FOX MARE*
            - *FOX* — 6
            - Gipsey — 1
    - Indiana (RH) (1802)
      - Hamptons Paragon (RH) (1788)
        - Filmnap
          - South
            - *REGULUS* — 11
            - Soreheels Mare
          - Cygnet Mare
            - Cygnet — 6
            - Y Cartouch Mare — 5
        - Camilla (RH)
          - Burwells Traveller (RH)
            - Mortons Traveller
            - Burwells Sportley (RH)
          - Burwells Camilla
            - *FEARNOUGHT* — 32
            - Bryds Dabster Mare
      - *JANE HUNT (RH) (1796)*
        - Figure
          - Hamiltons Figure
            - Old Standard
            - Beaufort Arabian Mare
          - Marianne
            - Victorious
            - Partner Mare
        - Hunts Moll ()
          - Maria Slammerkin
            - Wildair
              - *CADE* — 6
              - Steady Mare — 4
            - Cub Mare
              - Cub — 17
              - Second Mare — 4

Jenny Slamerkin RH 1823

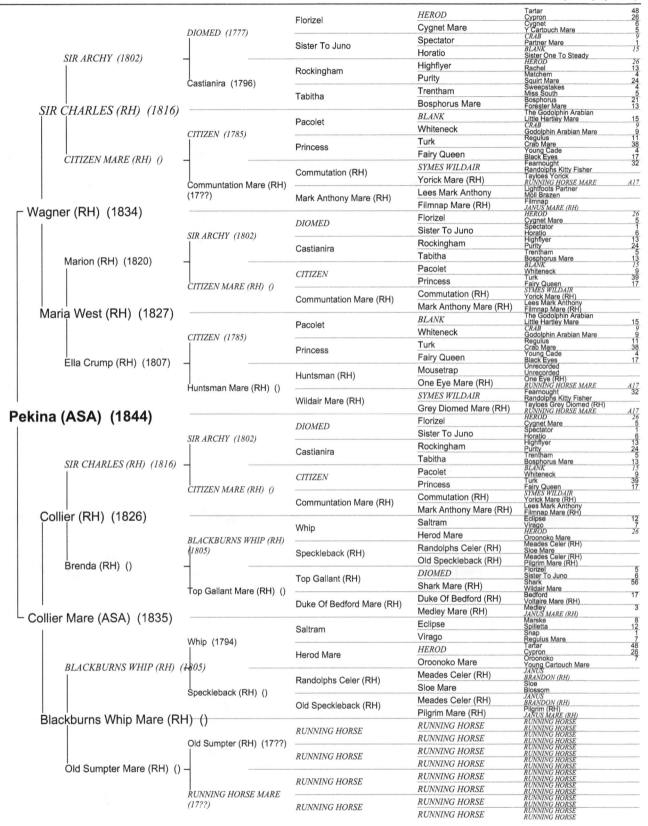

Pekina (ASA) 1844

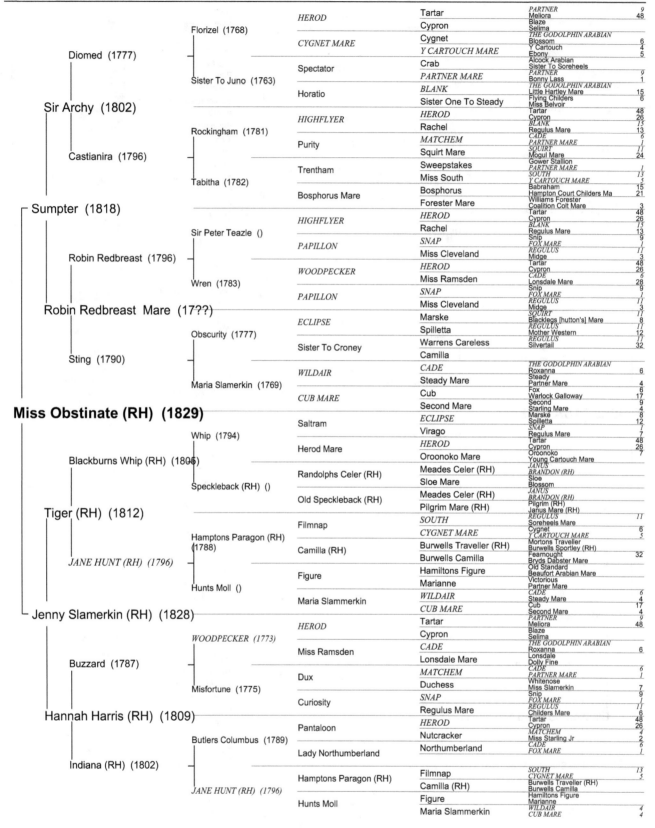

Miss Obstinate RH 1829

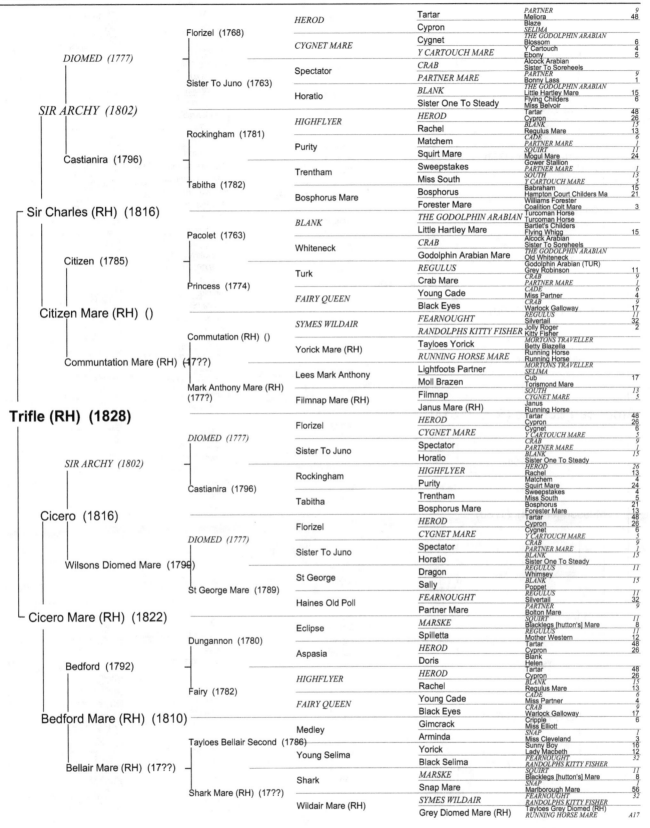

Trifle RH 1828

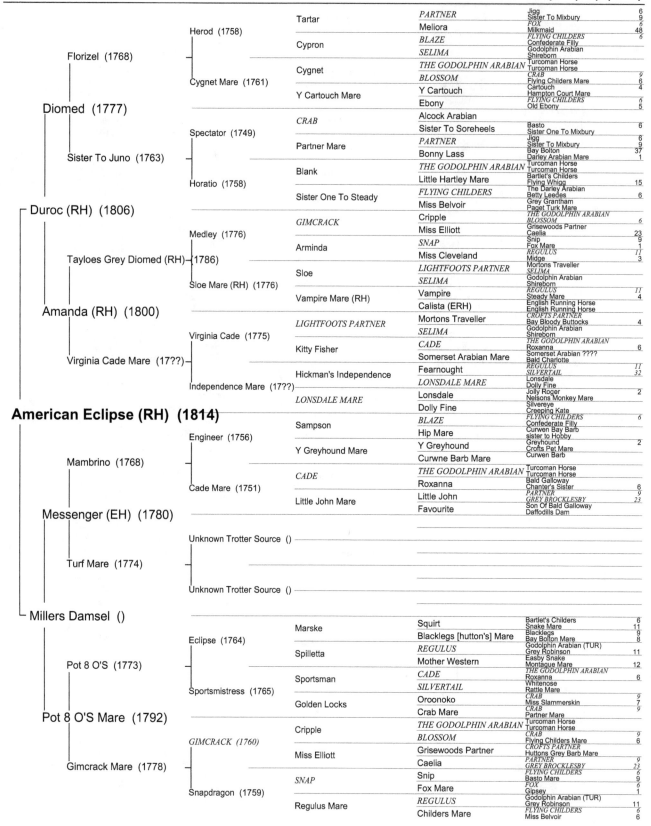

Diomed (1777)			
Florizel (1768)	Herod (1758)	Tartar	*PARTNER* — Jigg 6 / Sister To Mixbury 9
			Meliora — *FOX* 6 / Milkmaid 48
		Cypron	*BLAZE* — *FLYING CHILDERS* 6 / Confederate Filly
			SELIMA — Godolphin Arabian / Shireborn
	Cygnet Mare (1761)	Cygnet	*THE GODOLPHIN ARABIAN* — Turcoman Horse / Turcoman Horse
			BLOSSOM — *CRAB* 9 / Flying Childers Mare 6
		Y Cartouch Mare	Y Cartouch — Cartouch 4 / Hampton Court Mare
			Ebony — *FLYING CHILDERS* 6 / Old Ebony 5
Sister To Juno (1763)	Spectator (1749)	*CRAB*	Alcock Arabian
			Sister To Soreheels — Basto 6 / Sister One To Mixbury
		Partner Mare	*PARTNER* — Jigg 6 / Sister To Mixbury 9
			Bonny Lass — Bay Bolton 37 / Darley Arabian Mare 1
	Horatio (1758)	Blank	*THE GODOLPHIN ARABIAN* — Turcoman Horse / Turcoman Horse
			Little Hartley Mare — Bartlet's Childers / Flying Whigg 15
		Sister One To Steady	*FLYING CHILDERS* — The Darley Arabian / Betty Leedes 6
			Miss Belvoir — Grey Grantham / Paget Turk Mare

Duroc (RH) (1806)

Amanda (RH) (1800)			
Tayloes Grey Diomed (RH) (1786)	Medley (1776)	*GIMCRACK*	Cripple — *THE GODOLPHIN ARABIAN* / *BLOSSOM* 6
			Miss Elliott — Grisewoods Partner / Caelia 23
		Arminda	*SNAP* — Snip 9 / Fox Mare 1
			Miss Cleveland — *REGULUS* 11 / Midge 3
	Sloe Mare (RH) (1776)	Sloe	*LIGHTFOOTS PARTNER* — Mortons Traveller / *SELIMA*
			SELIMA — Godolphin Arabian / Shireborn
		Vampire Mare (RH)	Vampire — *REGULUS* 11 / Steady Mare 4
			Calista (ERH) — English Running Horse / English Running Horse
Virginia Cade Mare (17??)	Virginia Cade (1775)	*LIGHTFOOTS PARTNER*	Mortons Traveller — *CROFTS PARTNER* / Bay Bloody Buttocks 4
			SELIMA — Godolphin Arabian / Shireborn
		Kitty Fisher	*CADE* — *THE GODOLPHIN ARABIAN* / Roxanna 6
			Somerset Arabian Mare — Somerset Arabian ???? / Bald Charlotte
	Independence Mare (17??)	Hickman's Independence	Fearnought — *REGULUS* 11 / *SILVERTAIL* 32
			LONSDALE MARE — Lonsdale / Dolly Fine
		LONSDALE MARE	Lonsdale — Jolly Roger 2 / Nelsons Monkey Mare
			Dolly Fine — Silvereye / Creeping Kate

American Eclipse (RH) (1814)

Mambrino (1768)			
Engineer (1756)		Sampson	*BLAZE* — *FLYING CHILDERS* 6 / Confederate Filly
			Hip Mare — Curwen Bay Barb / sister to Hobby
		Y Greyhound Mare	Y Greyhound — Greyhound 2 / Crofts Pet Mare
			Curwne Barb Mare — Curwen Barb
Cade Mare (1751)		*CADE*	*THE GODOLPHIN ARABIAN* — Turcoman Horse / Turcoman Horse
			Roxanna — Bald Galloway / Chanter's Sister 6
		Little John Mare	Little John — *PARTNER* 9 / *GREY BROCKLESBY* 23
			Favourite — Son Of Bald Galloway / Daffodills Dam

Messenger (EH) (1780)

Turf Mare (1774)	Unknown Trotter Source ()
	Unknown Trotter Source ()

Pot 8 O'S (1773)			
Eclipse (1764)	Marske	Squirt — Bartlet's Childers 6 / Snake Mare 11	
		Blacklegs [hutton's] Mare — Blacklegs 9 / Bay Bolton Mare 8	
	Spilletta	*REGULUS* — Godolphin Arabian (TUR) / Grey Robinson 11	
		Mother Western — Easby Snake / Montague Mare 12	
Sportsmistress (1765)	Sportsman	*CADE* — *THE GODOLPHIN ARABIAN* / Roxanna 6	
		SILVERTAIL — Whitenose / Rattle Mare	
	Golden Locks	Oroonoko — *CRAB* 9 / Miss Slammerskin 7	
		Crab Mare — *CRAB* 9 / Partner Mare	

Millers Damsel ()

Pot 8 O'S Mare (1792)			
GIMCRACK (1760)	Cripple	*THE GODOLPHIN ARABIAN* — Turcoman Horse / Turcoman Horse	
		BLOSSOM — *CRAB* 9 / Flying Childers Mare 6	
	Miss Elliott	Grisewoods Partner — *CROFTS PARTNER* / Huttons Grey Barb Mare	
		Caelia — *PARTNER* 9 / *GREY BROCKLESBY* 23	
Snapdragon (1759)	*SNAP*	Snip — *FLYING CHILDERS* 6 / Basto Mare 9	
		Fox Mare — *FOX* 6 / Gipsey 1	
	Regulus Mare	*REGULUS* — Godolphin Arabian (TUR) / Grey Robinson 11	
		Childers Mare — *FLYING CHILDERS* 6 / Miss Belvoir 6	

American Eclipse RH 1814

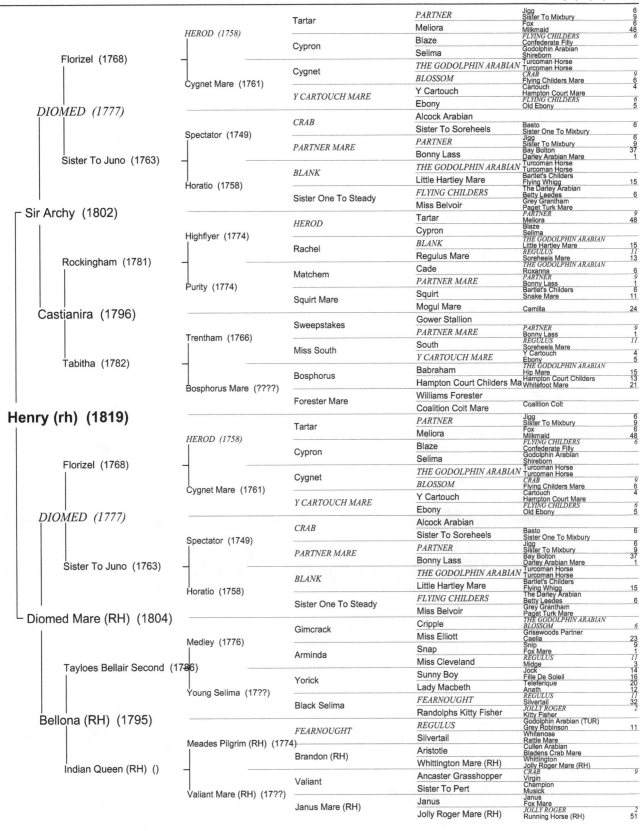

Henry RH 1819

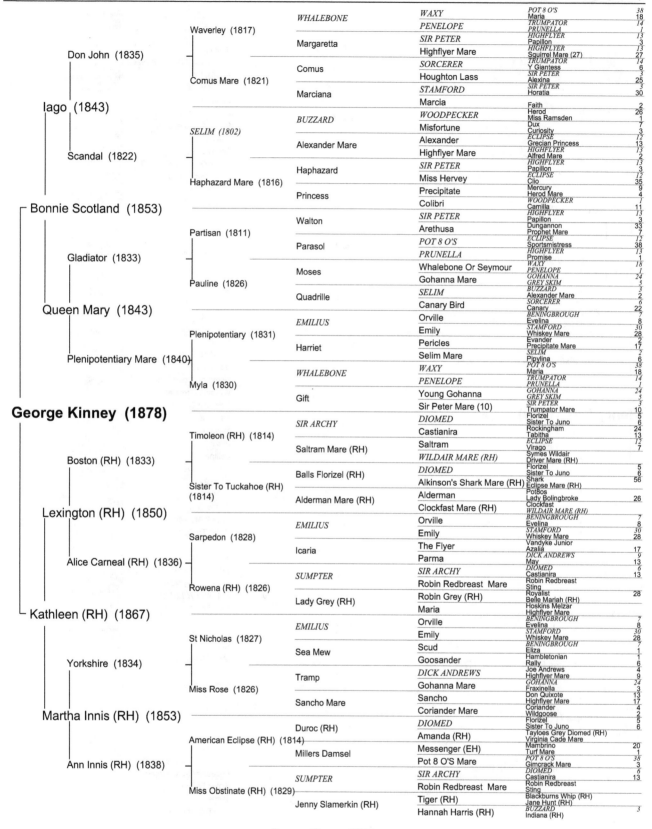

George Kinney 1878

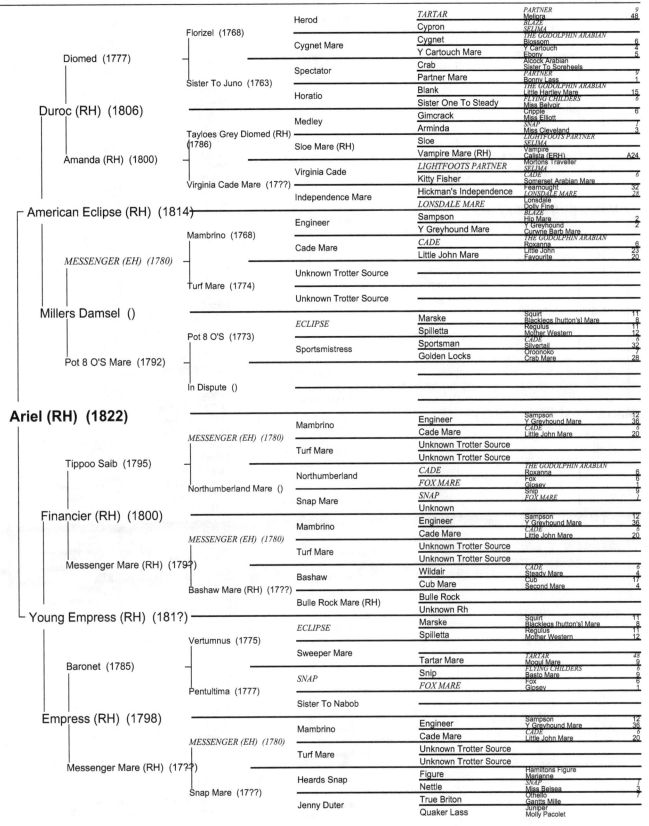

Ariel (RH) (1822)

- **American Eclipse (RH) (1814)**
  - Duroc (RH) (1806)
    - Diomed (1777)
      - Florizel (1768)
        - Herod
          - *TARTAR* — *PARTNER* 9 / Meliora 48
          - Cypron — *BLAZE* / *SELIMA*
        - Cygnet Mare
          - Cygnet — *THE GODOLPHIN ARABIAN* / Blossom 6
          - Y Cartouch Mare — Y Cartouch 4 / Ebony 5
      - Sister To Juno (1763)
        - Spectator
          - Crab — Alcock Arabian / Sister To Soreheels
          - Partner Mare — *PARTNER* 9 / Bonny Lass 1
        - Horatio
          - Blank — *THE GODOLPHIN ARABIAN* / Little Hartley Mare 15
          - Sister One To Steady — *FLYING CHILDERS* 6 / Miss Belvoir
    - Amanda (RH) (1800)
      - Tayloes Grey Diomed (RH) (1786)
        - Medley
          - Gimcrack — Cripple 6 / Miss Elliott
          - Arminda — *SNAP* 1 / Miss Cleveland 3
        - Sloe Mare (RH)
          - Sloe — *LIGHTFOOTS PARTNER* / *SELIMA*
          - Vampire Mare (RH) — Vampire / Calista (ERH) A24
      - Virginia Cade Mare (17??)
        - Virginia Cade
          - *LIGHTFOOTS PARTNER* — Mortons Traveller / *SELIMA*
          - Kitty Fisher — *CADE* 6 / Somerset Arabian Mare
        - Independence Mare
          - Hickman's Independence — Fearnought 32 / *LONSDALE MARE* 28
          - *LONSDALE MARE* — Lonsdale / Dolly Fine
  - Millers Damsel ()
    - MESSENGER (EH) (1780)
      - Mambrino (1768)
        - Engineer
          - Sampson — *BLAZE* 2 / Hip Mare 2
          - Y Greyhound Mare — Y Greyhound / Curwne Barb Mare
        - Cade Mare
          - *CADE* — *THE GODOLPHIN ARABIAN* / Roxanna 6
          - Little John Mare — Little John 23 / Favourite 20
      - Turf Mare (1774)
        - Unknown Trotter Source
        - Unknown Trotter Source
    - Pot 8 O'S Mare (1792)
      - Pot 8 O'S (1773)
        - *ECLIPSE*
          - Marske — Squirt 11 / Blacklegs [hutton's] Mare 8
          - Spilletta — Regulus 11 / Mother Western 12
        - Sportsmistress
          - Sportsman — *CADE* 6 / Silvertail 32
          - Golden Locks — Oroonoko 7 / Crab Mare 28
      - In Dispute ()

- **Young Empress (RH) (181?)**
  - Financier (RH) (1800)
    - Tippoo Saib (1795)
      - *MESSENGER (EH) (1780)*
        - Mambrino
          - Engineer — Sampson 12 / Y Greyhound Mare 36
          - Cade Mare — *CADE* 6 / Little John Mare 20
        - Turf Mare
          - Unknown Trotter Source
          - Unknown Trotter Source
      - Northumberland Mare ()
        - Northumberland
          - *CADE* — *THE GODOLPHIN ARABIAN* 6 / Roxanna 6
          - *FOX MARE* — Fox / Gipsey 1
        - Snap Mare
          - *SNAP* — Snip 9 / *FOX MARE* 1
          - Unknown
    - Messenger Mare (RH) (179?)
      - *MESSENGER (EH) (1780)*
        - Mambrino
          - Engineer — Sampson 12 / Y Greyhound Mare 36
          - Cade Mare — *CADE* 6 / Little John Mare 20
        - Turf Mare
          - Unknown Trotter Source
          - Unknown Trotter Source
      - Bashaw Mare (RH) (17??)
        - Bashaw
          - Wildair — *CADE* 6 / Steady Mare 4
          - Cub Mare — Cub 17 / Second Mare 4
        - Bulle Rock Mare (RH)
          - Bulle Rock
          - Unknown Rh
  - Empress (RH) (1798)
    - Baronet (1785)
      - Vertumnus (1775)
        - *ECLIPSE*
          - Marske — Squirt 11 / Blacklegs [hutton's] Mare 8
          - Spilletta — Regulus 11 / Mother Western 12
        - Sweeper Mare
          - Tartar Mare — *TARTAR* 48 / Mogul Mare 9
      - Pentultima (1777)
        - *SNAP*
          - Snip — *FLYING CHILDERS* 6 / Basto Mare 9
          - *FOX MARE* — Fox / Gipsey 1
        - Sister To Nabob
    - Messenger Mare (RH) (17??)
      - *MESSENGER (EH) (1780)*
        - Mambrino
          - Engineer — Sampson 12 / Y Greyhound Mare 36
          - Cade Mare — *CADE* 6 / Little John Mare 20
        - Turf Mare
          - Unknown Trotter Source
          - Unknown Trotter Source
      - Snap Mare (17??)
        - Heards Snap
          - Figure — Hamiltons Figure / Marianne
          - Nettle — *SNAP* 1 / Miss Belsea 3
        - Jenny Duter
          - True Briton — Othello 7 / Gantts Mille
          - Quaker Lass — Juniper / Molly Pacolet

Ariel RH 1822

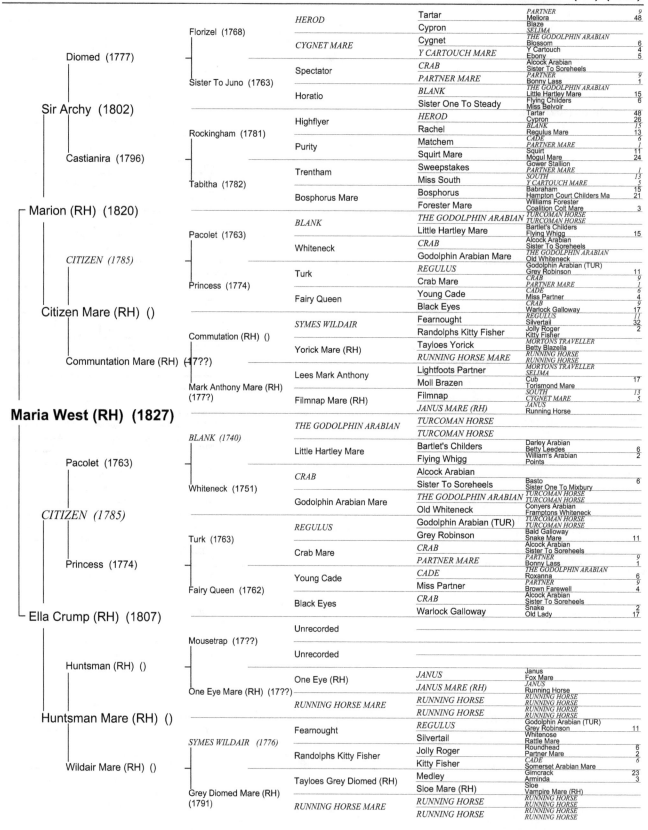

Maria West RH 1827

Chapter 5

The Famous Twenty-Mile Race

The diminutive (14.2) Trifle RH—a daughter of Sir Charles RH, she is one of the greatest race mares there has ever been. —from a painting by Troye

Before we visit the results of the American Running Horse and American Thoroughbred traveling to England and France to test their mettle against their peers, I should provide an example that illustrates in detail what two hundred years of performance testing and selective breeding for heat racing had produced at its height. There is no better proof of the racing merit found in our Heroic Era Running Horse, then the stamina, speed, soundness and above all the heart, found in the glorious mares in following race.

Eighteen years before the birth of Lexington RH there was a race that pushed the limits of our Running Horse beyond anything we can comprehend today. This race was not only of unimaginable duration but it was run in the heaviest going possible—a rain-soaked track, which means they had to work much harder to even gallop. This is possibly the greatest test of endurance, speed, and pluck there has ever been, and as you will see, it was really beyond what should have been expected of any race-horse (as reported in the American Turf Register and Sporting Magazine in 1832.)

"After the horses were brought upon the ground, much anxiety was exhibited as to the event of the coming con-test; and the interesting little Trifle appeared to be the favorite among the betters, as well as the spectators, — five to four, Trifle against the field, was current betting; and five to three, Trifle against Black Maria, were repeatedly offered and refused. Indeed, this offspring of the far-famed Lady Lightfoot seemed to have but few friends or well-wishers, comparatively speaking; and bets were repeatedly offered that she would not take a heat. Prepossessions, in favor of the Southern mare, appeared to exist among a decided majority of the spectators; and, as she was foaled 'south of Mason and Dixon's line,' it seemed a matter of course that she was to win. Indeed, if unfailing spirits, beauty of form, and a peculiar quietness of manner, could supply the defect of size, Trifle would not be considered as such in anything but *name*. She is racehorse in every sense of the word, but a racehorse of the smallest pattern—not over fourteen hands and a half high—of just proportions, undoubted bottom, and considerable power. Her color a bright chestnut, with a blaze, indicating spirit and blood.

"Black Maria, in size and general appearance, is in all respects unlike her rival, as is well known to Southern, as well as Northern sportsmen. Her color is indicated by her name; and her great size, strength and stride, show her a worthy daughter of a noble sire. Indeed, in her the blood of Eclipse and Lady Lightfoot are in no way disgraced, as this race will most fully prove.

"Lady Relief and Slim were almost unknown to fame; but certain individuals present were aware that the former had, upon a previous occasion, won the last half of sixteen miles; and they looked for sport, unexpected by others, if it should happen that the first heats were not taken either by Trifle or Maria. The latter, it was known, had the foot of Relief; as they met on the first of the month at Poughkeepsie, and contended together for the three-mile purse, which was taken by Maria with great ease. As the trumpet sounded for the horses to come up to the starting-post, they severally appeared, exhibiting their various tempers by their individual behavior. Black Maria—who had the inside track—showed neither alarm nor anxiety. She was as calm and unimpassioned as if she had been a mere spectator; and this coldness of demeanor won no 'golden opinions' among the lookers-on. Trifle exhibited high spirits, brought down to their proper level by judicious breaking and training. A slight tremor ran through her frame; and an impatient lifting of the fore foot, now and then, showed that she was alive to the coming struggle.

"Lady Relief, on the contrary, was all fire and animation—ready to break away from her groom, and dash through all obstacles for the sake of victory.

"Slim exhibited an impatient spirit, and seemed, by her anxiety, to show herself a descendant from that Childers who always ran—at least on our course—without whip or spur.

"At the tap of the drum the four went off together, Relief taking the lead within the first quarter, closely followed by Slim, then by Trifle, and last, but not *least*, by Black Maria. The first mile indicated a *waiting race,* as all the riders had their horses under the hardest pull; each seeming desirous that his antagonists should take the lead. Trifle, impatient at such *trifling,* began to make play, and this aroused Black Maria, who was trailing along quietly, behind the whole. With a few huge strides, she brought herself up to the front, passed the whole before she came to the judge's stand, followed closely by the gallant Trifle, who 'stuck to' her like an accompanying phantom. At the beginning of the third mile the leading nags made play, and during the whole of it Maria held the lead, followed closely by Trifle; while Relief and Slim were—and, as we believe, *not* willingly—at a most respectable distance in the rear.

"After passing the judge's stand and entering upon the fourth mile, and after compassing the turn, upon the southerly side of the course, Trifle 'made a dash' at Maria, and ran her so hard down the descending ground upon the straight side, that her stable antagonist—perhaps not unwillingly—gave up the track, which was taken by the Southern lady, and kept, with apparent ease, round the turn, until you come to that part of the course which looks up toward the judge's stand. Here, at a moment when all opinions had given Trifle the heat, as a 'safe thing that could not be missed", Maria 'went at her', and, before you could count one, she shot by Trifle like an arrow, and won the heat with ease; there being a considerable gap between herself and Trifle, and a much greater one between the latter and the hindmost horses.

"Here then was disappointment on all sides. Black Maria, that was not 'to take a heat', or who, at all events, had not *foot* enough to brush with the speedy little Trifle, had beat the field, in the last quarter, in what she was not supposed to possess, namely, *speed.* Indeed, we think that the rider of Trifle, committed a mistake in making his dash at Maria at the beginning of the fourth mile. As he had commenced a trailing race, his obvious policy was to wait until he came to the last turn; then run up to his antagonist upon ground where he had a decided advantage, from the size and form of his horse, and finally make 'his run' upon the straight side, coming in. Had he followed this course in the first heat—as he did in the second—we might possibly have had a different tale to tell; for his little nag obeys the spur well, and is a hard one to beat upon a brush. But, by running *at* Maria on the northerly side of the course, he distressed his mare, enabled his antagonist to come round him at the very moment when he was least prepared for it. The result has already been shown. Time, first heat, 8:06.

The incredible Black Maria RH (15.3 hands), a daughter of American Eclipse RH and Lady Lightfoot RH is a contender for the greatest racehorse—male or female, of all time. —from a painting by Troye

"It may be here remarked, that in consequence of the rains, which had prevailed for several days previous to the race, the course, although good, was unusually heavy; so much so, as to make a difference of several seconds, probably, in the *time* of a four-mile heat. The top of the ground was not perfectly firm, and, consequently, the foothold of the horses was yielding and insecure. On a hard track, the time of each heat would have been considerably reduced.

"Notwithstanding the unexpected success of Maria, she seemed still to have but few *real* admirers; although her owner and his friends stood manfully by her, and kept their spirits up to the betting point. Trifle was still the favorite, and it was a settled thing 'at all events', that Maria was not to 'win the money'. Lady Relief, at this moment, had not attracted much attention, except from one circumstance. Her saddle—which was a very small one— slipped from under her rider, who, nevertheless—as his girths had not parted—stoutly kept his seat upon her *bare back*—his feet in the stirrups, with the saddle before him! It was observed, however, that she ran with great spirit; and what she *might do*, the wise ones could not tell.

"At the start for the second heat Black Maria appeared calm—as is usual with her—while Trifle and Lady Relief were all animation. They went off as if this heat was to be won by *running*, instead of waiting, as in the first heat; Relief taking the lead, followed by Slim, then by Trifle, while Black Maria brought up the rear. Ere they had accomplished one mile, however, Trifle had passed Relief and Slim, while Black Maria, taking advantage of the raising ground, as you come up to the judge's stand, thundered by them all, with her long strides, and took up her station in front, closely followed by Trifle, whilst the others again dropped behind. Indeed, the pace at which they were running seemed so unreasonable to Miss Slim, that she concluded that she would not keep such company any longer; and, as she could not run away from them by pursuing her course upon the track, she very wisely abandoned it altogether, at the end of the third—seventh—mile, and quietly walked off the course. Maria, in the mean time, led Trifle, with apparent ease, round the second, third, and fourth miles, until you come to the 'run in.' And here her rider, instead of giving her the 'persuaders', to make 'assurance doubly sure', turned his head round to look for his antagonist; and he was not long in finding her; for Trifle, close at his heels, went at him up the straight side, whip and spur, gradually gaining at every step. Maria's rider begins to 'look wild'. She is at her throat-latch, and the judge's stand not six feet off. She makes a desperate effort, and head and head they pass the stand a *dead heat!* Time, 7:55.

"Here, again, all were at fault. One party were crying out to the rider of Maria, 'Why did you not stir yourself! One blow of the whip, before you came to the distance post, would have won the race.' 'I had no whip, sir; Maria won't bear it. It *discourages* her. She must run under a pull, with the spur as an admonisher.' Again a thousand rumors were afloat. Trifle was as gay as a bird—in no way distressed. She had *posed* the 'big un', who looked, as imagination said, 'both sick and sorry.' It was a 'safe thing', and 'Black Maria can't win—she's done up'—went round like wild fire, from mouth to mouth.

"In the mean time, Lady Relief was little thought of; but a Jerseyman was heard to say, 'We'll show 'em some of the Eclipse *pluck* yet, before we've done.' At the sounding of the trumpet for the third heat, Trifle and Relief came up in great spirits, while Black Maria seemed in no way ambitious of another trial. But she's always cool; and, as her mode of starting is reluctant and slow, nothing can be safely argued from her spirits.

"At the tap of the drum, Trifle and Relief went off from the score, leaving Maria some distance behind. In the course of the first mile, however, she lessened the gap between herself and the leading horses, and got well up to them. But it would not do; she could not pass—'What horse is that leading there? Surely it can't be Lady Relief! It is, upon my soul! The Jersey mare's ahead!' And, sure enough, so she was. The nag that had attracted so little notice, as neither to be heard nor cared for, had taken the lead upon the fourth mile; and away she ran, keeping the track in spite of them all, until you come within the distance pole, on the last quarter's stretch. And while she was leading, well ahead, from some unaccountable circumstance the boy pulled her up at once, and Trifle shot by and won the heat. Time, 8:18.

"Black Maria was 'well up' during the whole race, but she now fell into complete disfavor; and 'she's done up'—'an even bet she don't come again'—went round the field with great confidence. It is the writer's opinion, that Relief could have taken the heat if she had been urged up the judge's stand, and that she *ought* to have won it. As it was, Trifle, who well deserved her honors and the admiration of her friends, had been victorious. She had run twelve miles, winning the twelfth; and the little game creature appeared fresh as ever. It was *now* settled that she was to win the money; although it be that Relief, who was fast rising in favor, might make her 'run for it.' Indeed, the latter did not seem in full vigor until she had run two heats; and now her nostrils opened, and she pawed the ground, as if just brought upon the course.

"They saddled for the fourth heat; and here is to be a struggle until sixteen miles from the beginning are accomplished. Black Maria is in no way distressed, Relief full of spirit, but 'Trifles to win the money.' Off they go; Relief takes the lead, followed by Trifle, and then the black. Miles are passed over, and yet Relief is ahead—'How is this? Can't Trifle pass? Is the Jersey mare ahead?—She is, indeed; and ahead like to be. A better, truer, tougher, and more spirited piece of stuff never came from the loins of old Eclipse. She takes the track from the score. Trifle goes at her, but 'can't do it'—Three miles and a half are accomplished, and Black Maria has passed Trifle, and is close at the heels of Jersey. Now they come up the straight side. The black is at her, and Relief takes the whip like a glutton. Maria comes and laps her—she's at her shoulder; but they pass the stand, and Relief takes the heat by a neck. Time, 8:39.

"'Huzza for Jersey!' rings over the course; and a look of pity is cast upon the gallant little Trifle, who had done her utmost— 'Black Maria won't come again,' says a wise one, with a knowing look. 'I don't know that,' says a Yorker. 'If she had run twenty yards *farther*, she would have taken the heat.' 'She is distressed,' is the reply. 'Distressed! *May be she is.* I saw her lay her ears back, and lash out with her hind feet, after the boy dismounted from the sixteen miles, as if her sinews were of whipcord.'

"Here was an interesting point, *five* heats, in all, were to be run, and twenty miles to be passed over. 'The like was never seen on this course before.' Says a Long Islander. 'Bottom's the word—how go the bets?' 'At a stand still. Trifle's distressed; but Lady Relief has more life in her than any thing that ever ran sixteen miles before.'

"Up they come for a fifth heat; Relief all fire, Trifle very sorry, and Black Maria now begins to *paw the ground!* This she had not done before. Off they go; Relief ahead, Trifle after her, and Black Maria allowing no gap. She sticks to them like a spirit; and in the nineteenth mile the gallant little Trifle is reluctantly compelled to give it up. The Eclipse mares are obstinately determined to 'play out the play,' and the little chestnut is taken off the track, completely, 'done up.' Now comes a struggle, for the honors of a twentieth mile, between two half sisters—whalebone both—and 'never give it up' 's the word. Black Maria pushes up the straight side, as you enter upon the fourth—twentieth—mile, with a stride that counts terribly upon the steps of the Lady, who has relief now in nothing but name. The black is so close upon her, that she almost touches her heels. She pushes round the turn and goes at her on the straight side, like a quarter horse. They brush down the straight side with invincible courage; but that long untiring stride is too much for Relief. Maria gives her the go by, takes the track—keeps it in spite of all exertions—leads round the turn, and thunders up toward the judge's stand, hard in hand, untouched by whip or spur—passes the goal for the twentieth time, and wins the race. Time, 8:47.

"Neither of the Eclipse mares appeared much distressed, and they ran the last mile with the greatest spirit and stoutness. Relief is a nag of the most extraordinary *bottom*. She seems to become fresher after twelve miles, and then runs off gay as a lark. As for Black Maria, she is literally 'too fast for the speedy, and too strong for the

KATHLEEN H. KIRSAN

stout.' She ran the twentieth mile with a freshness and vigor that surprised every body, and the spectators at last *actually conceded* that she is '*game*'.! That she can conquer either Relief or Trifle at two heats, in a match, there can be no manner of doubt; and that she is a 'hard one to beat' in any race, even by a *field,* all sportsmen must now believe. She ran at her antagonists *every heat,* and at last let them know what it was to run for the honors of a twentieth mile!"

That twenty-mile contest was certainly the race of the century—possibly of any century—and was a feat very few of even the best Heroic Era racers would have been able to complete. After the race the gallant and exhausted Lady Relief RH came down with a respiratory illness she could not fight off and was dead within two weeks. Trifle RH was lamed from her effort and took almost to the end of the following season to recover—which she did, and then went on to win many more heat races. Incredibly, Black Maria RH took only a few months to regain her form, and in the spring came back to racing to win again. Needless to say, this test was beyond the typical four-mile heat race, which usually was done by the third heat, and very rarely went on for a fourth. A five-heat race was thankfully a very rare occurrence.

In comparison, I can't help remembering the wonder I felt watching (on television) as Secretariat won his Triple Crown—it was such a fantastic display of athletic superiority that it inspired awe in all who saw it. It was forty years ago that we watched our hero Secretariat distance his opponents by thirty-one lengths in that historic Belmont race in 1973, and overcome with the emotion of the moment the people at Belmont Park, almost to a one, were on their feet, many with tears streaming down their faces, as he made the run for home—knowing they were watching something superlative and rare. Yet one hundred forty years before that race, three mares—one of them just 14.2 hands tall—raced an incredible twenty miles in heavy going, nearly ten times the distance we watched in 1973. It may be beyond our abilities to imagine this as our trials for our racers are so different today, but this really happened back in 1832. What amazing creatures they were!

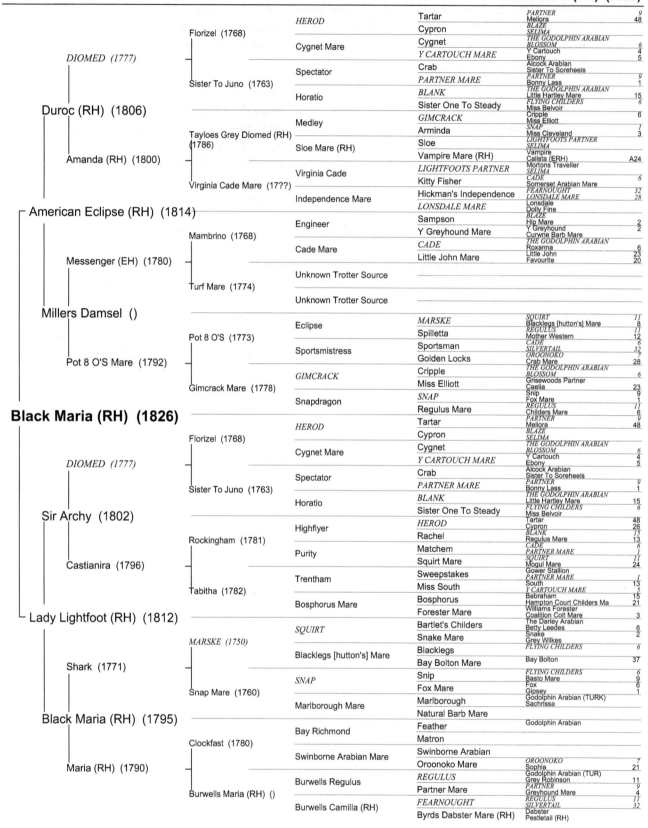

Black Maria (RH) (1826)

- **American Eclipse (RH) (1814)**
  - Duroc (RH) (1806)
    - DIOMED (1777)
      - Florizel (1768)
        - HEROD
          - Tartar — PARTNER 9, Meliora 48
          - Cypron — BLAZE, SELIMA
        - Cygnet Mare
          - Cygnet — THE GODOLPHIN ARABIAN, BLOSSOM 6
          - Y CARTOUCH MARE — Y Cartouch 4, Ebony 5
      - Sister To Juno (1763)
        - Spectator
          - Crab — Alcock Arabian, Sister To Soreheels
          - PARTNER MARE — PARTNER 9, Bonny Lass 1
        - Horatio
          - BLANK — THE GODOLPHIN ARABIAN, Little Hartley Mare 15
          - Sister One To Steady — FLYING CHILDERS 6, Miss Belvoir
    - Amanda (RH) (1800)
      - Tayloes Grey Diomed (RH) (1786)
        - Medley
          - GIMCRACK — Cripple 6, Miss Elliott
          - Arminda — SNAP 1, Miss Cleveland 3
        - Sloe Mare (RH)
          - Sloe — LIGHTFOOTS PARTNER, SELIMA
          - Vampire Mare (RH) — Vampire, Calista (ERH) A24
      - Virginia Cade Mare (17??)
        - Virginia Cade
          - LIGHTFOOTS PARTNER — Mortons Traveller, SELIMA
          - Kitty Fisher — CADE 6, Somerset Arabian Mare
        - Independence Mare
          - Hickman's Independence — FEARNOUGHT 32, LONSDALE MARE 28
          - LONSDALE MARE — Lonsdale, Dolly Fine
  - Millers Damsel ()
    - Messenger (EH) (1780)
      - Mambrino (1768)
        - Engineer
          - Sampson — BLAZE, Hip Mare 2
          - Y Greyhound Mare — Y Greyhound 2, Curwne Barb Mare
        - Cade Mare
          - CADE — THE GODOLPHIN ARABIAN, Roxanna 6
          - Little John Mare — Little John 23, Favourite 20
      - Turf Mare (1774)
        - Unknown Trotter Source
        - Unknown Trotter Source
    - Pot 8 O'S Mare (1792)
      - Pot 8 O'S (1773)
        - Eclipse
          - MARSKE — SQUIRT 11, Blacklegs [hutton's] Mare 8
          - Spilletta — REGULUS 11, Mother Western 12
        - Sportsmistress
          - Sportsman — CADE 6, SILVERTAIL 32
          - Golden Locks — OROONOKO, Crab Mare 28
      - Gimcrack Mare (1778)
        - GIMCRACK
          - Cripple — THE GODOLPHIN ARABIAN, BLOSSOM 6
          - Miss Elliott — Grisewoods Partner, Caelia 23
        - Snapdragon
          - SNAP — Snip 9, Fox Mare 1
          - Regulus Mare — REGULUS 11, Childers Mare 6
- **Lady Lightfoot (RH) (1812)**
  - Sir Archy (1802)
    - DIOMED (1777)
      - Florizel (1768)
        - HEROD
          - Tartar — PARTNER 9, Meliora 48
          - Cypron — BLAZE, SELIMA
        - Cygnet Mare
          - Cygnet — THE GODOLPHIN ARABIAN, BLOSSOM 6
          - Y CARTOUCH MARE — Y Cartouch 4, Ebony 5
      - Sister To Juno (1763)
        - Spectator
          - Crab — Alcock Arabian, Sister To Soreheels
          - PARTNER MARE — PARTNER 9, Bonny Lass 1
        - Horatio
          - BLANK — THE GODOLPHIN ARABIAN, Little Hartley Mare 15
          - Sister One To Steady — FLYING CHILDERS 6, Miss Belvoir
    - Castianira (1796)
      - Rockingham (1781)
        - Highflyer
          - HEROD — Tartar 48, Cypron 26
          - Rachel — BLANK 15, Regulus Mare 13
        - Purity
          - Matchem — CADE 6, PARTNER MARE 1
          - Squirt Mare — SQUIRT 11, Mogul Mare 24
      - Tabitha (1782)
        - Trentham
          - Sweepstakes — Gower Stallion, PARTNER MARE 1
          - Miss South — South 13, Y CARTOUCH MARE 5
        - Bosphorus Mare
          - Bosphorus — Babraham 15, Hampton Court Childers Ma 21
          - Forester Mare — Williams Forester, Coalition Colt Mare 3
  - Black Maria (RH) (1795)
    - Shark (1771)
      - MARSKE (1750)
        - SQUIRT
          - Bartlet's Childers — The Darley Arabian, Betty Leedes 6
          - Snake Mare — Snake 2, Grey Wilkes
        - Blacklegs [hutton's] Mare
          - Blacklegs — FLYING CHILDERS 6
          - Bay Bolton Mare — Bay Bolton 37
      - Snap Mare (1760)
        - SNAP
          - Snip — FLYING CHILDERS 6, Basto Mare 9
          - Fox Mare — Fox 6, Gipsey 1
        - Marlborough Mare
          - Marlborough — Godolphin Arabian (TURK)
          - Natural Barb Mare — Sachrissa
    - Maria (RH) (1790)
      - Clockfast (1780)
        - Bay Richmond
          - Feather — Godolphin Arabian
          - Matron
        - Swinborne Arabian Mare
          - Swinborne Arabian
          - Oroonoko Mare — OROONOKO 7, Sophia 21
      - Burwells Maria (RH) ()
        - Burwells Regulus
          - REGULUS — Godolphin Arabian (TUR), Grey Robinson 11
          - Partner Mare — PARTNER 9, Greyhound Mare 4
        - Burwells Camilla (RH)
          - FEARNOUGHT — REGULUS 11, SILVERTAIL 32
          - Byrds Dabster Mare (RH) — Dabster, Pestletail (RH)

Black Maria RH 1826

Chapter 6

Anatomy of Speed Combined with Stamina

Every good sport horse breeder knows it is only through careful selective breeding combined with performance testing that consistency and excellence are produced. In the era between the Revolution and Civil War, roughly 1783-1861, the American breeders produced such a prepotency in athletic talent that the modern typesetters for our greatest light horse breeds were formed then, and not just our racehorse breeds of Thoroughbred, Standardbred, and Quarter Horse, but also our premier light horse breeds of Morgan, Saddlebred, Tennessee Walker, and Missouri Fox Trotter. Individual horses like Figure RH 1789, Jane Hunt RH 1796, Tom Hal RH 1802, Blackburns Whip RH 1805, Cockspur RH 1805, Sir Archy 1805, Copperbottom RH 1809, Orphan RH 1810, Old Pacing Pilot RH 1823, Bonnets o' Blue RH 1827, Maria West RH 1827, Copper Bottom RH 1828, Black Hawk MO 1833, Boston RH 1833, Bald Stockings RH 1837, Steel Dust RH 1843, Hambletonian AT 1849, Gaines Denmark ASA 1851, Lecomte RH 1850, Vandal RH 1850, Lexington RH 1850, and Gibsons Tom Hal RH 1865; all of them set a prepotent type of athleticism, stamina, and speed.

An English horse expert and well-known writer of the period concluded his description of the American Horse of his time (early 1800s) as:

> "And I must say, in conclusion, that I consider the general horse of America superior, not in blood or in beauty, but decidedly in hardihood to do and to endure, in powers of travel, in speed, in docility and in good temper, to any other race of general horse in the known world," (Henry Wm Herbert 1857).

The greatest racehorses of their era competing together in the Baltimore Special 1877 at Pimlico track: Parole, Ten Broeck, and Tom Ochltree; the first two are out of Lexington RH dams and the latter is by Lexington RH—Currier & Ives 1877

Boston RH 1833 was the product of John Wickham of Richmond VA, and he came to be known as the 'greatest racehorse of the nineteenth century,' and considering this period includes the 'Heroic Era' of four-mile heat racing, this then is no small assessment. In most accounts when you read about Boston RH, even though he and his offspring were the target of the Jersey Act, it is still his English ancestors that are pointed to as the source of his amazing ability. He ran forty-five races and won forty-one of them; thirty-one were four-mile heat races, and besides being blind, he was retired sound. He had wonderful legs and feet. But is the crediting of his talent exclusively to his English Thoroughbred ancestors just?

The pedigree is the map of the genetics—if it is accurate. I can't recall how many times I have had to redo Boston's pedigree, trying to get it right enough to study. For instance, it is only recently that his dam-sire's, Balls Florizel, true dam line has become known (MacKay-Smith), tracing right back to documented sprint RH racers from the early Virginia studs. (I actually still had the pedigree of Lexington RH wrong in this same bloodline when I printed it in my first book—revised in 2014). In addition to this, Lexington's dam Alice Carneal RH, who has proven to be one of the greatest broodmares of her day, has many lines that cannot be traced back to the GSB or to identified American sources—they just end with an imported horse with no known ancestry or the Colonial Quarter racing studs with no name assigned to the mare.

With both British and American bloodlines, once you travel back to the mid-1700s accuracy in pedigrees become very shaky, and if you study into the late 1600s then all bets are off. Recently we have been startled to learn that several of the 1800s entries are also of fictitious parentage. Our American Race-Turf Register 1833 by Edgar, along with Weatherby's General Stud Book, is full of inaccuracies—especially in the early lines. We have been aware of the shortcomings in Edgar's book for quite some time, but the mapping of the equine genome in our day has revealed that the revered GSB has numerous errors in its early pedigrees. In that era, circa 1800, when breeders were trying to form registers, the records submitted to them by personages hoping to get their stock included were often not correct. Whether they relied on stud advertisements for stallions who had fictitious parentage, or if they beefed up the lineages themselves when they found there was no record of ancestry or when their true ancestors would not qualify; the result is we can be fairly certain that nearly all early studbooks are suspect (See Appendix C for a partial list of horses with incorrect parentage).

So where does that leave us? First of all, in our time, there are dedicated scholars who are trying to assign the correct parentage by using both genetics and with newly found records that can be verified—it is a grueling task, but happily they seem to be making some progress. For instance, it turns out that the old rumor that the typesetter Bend Or 1877 is really a different horse than thought may indeed be true (Hill and Bower mtDNA studies—see Appendix C). But on the whole, we will have to accept that we can only deal in generalities for the early records. So in the British pedigrees—once we get to the early racehorse studs—in most cases we have to assume that the broodmares are of Hobby/English Running Horse breeding, as that was what was used to produce the fastest racehorses. Here in the US we too in most cases will have to assume that it was our Hobby-based Running Horse that was bringing in the speed. We don't usually have the names of the early horses, but we do know in many cases where they came from and what their performance was (see *North American Sport Horse Breeder* for more on this). With the new DNA discoveries that determined speed in the racehorse and other important sport-related factors came from those early mares, we can at least feel that we have some solid ground to stand on with this.

Many of the great early English Thoroughbred bloodlines such as Regulus, Marske, Herod, Blaze, Snap, Partner, Crab, Blank, Cade, Snake, Squirt, and others are all strong in those early English RH/Hobby genetics especially from the dam—but those mares are usually un-named. In America we are finding that our best racers often have a dam line that travels back to some speedy sprint mare from our early racehorse studs as well. It has turned out that our scholars John Wallace and Alexander MacKay-Smith were dead-on in their research, although nearly a century apart, yet they both came to the same conclusion—the speed in our sport breeds came from those early gaited mares. It is a shocker to realize that our best horse breeds started out with small (13.2 to 14.2-hand) gaited horses, and that those tiny steeds packed such a powerful genetic punch because they carried excellent sport characteristics such as the speed gene. Then with the addition of key Turcoman and Barb strains, usually through a sire, which gave a skeletal structure difference—height (15 to 16 hands) along with a laid-back shoulder, which when combined with the Hobby speed and resiliency provided us with the base genetics for the taller, more athletic horses we enjoy today.

In America, the English TB combined with our Running Horse produced our modern Thoroughbred. But just being an imported English TB did not do the trick. It was certain strains of the English TB that worked—others did not, and some even lessened the sport ability in our native breed. So this is what we want to look at—what worked and why?

The best way to do this is to examine the pedigree structure of the great producers and racers. So it would be productive to look at Boston RH and his relatives, which should tell us what we need to know.

We already discussed the great typesetters Janus and Fearnought; one of the other great typesetters of our Heroic Era is an imported English Thoroughbred named Diomed. As a racer in England he won four-mile heat races, but because he was born just as the new classic race form was adopted he also ran in those, and he won a few times, including the first running of the English Derby. Here in America he stood above his peers—his quality and his ability to nick with our racing population was unmatched except perhaps by the earlier Janus and Fearnought. This is what I had to say about him in *North American Sport Horse Breeder*:

"**Diomed (TB) 1777:** Although he was born in 1777, it was twenty-one years later that his bloodline reached America. Diomed stood stud in America from 1798 to 1808 when he died at age thirty-one. A 15.3 chestnut with a compact frame, he was a great racehorse having won the first running of the Epsom Derby, and also a four-mile heat race (King's Plate) while carrying 168 lbs. He was a good sire in England and left a lasting legacy in his son Grey Diomed and a maternal dynasty from his daughter Young Giantess. Yet, he still wasn't popular with the English breeders. Some said that his sons could be high-strung and stubborn; even Weatherby described him as a 'bad-foal getter', plus his fertility waned while there.

"So he was sold to John Hoomes and arrived at Bowling Green, KY to stand stud at age twenty-one. He was an immediate sensation—producing great racers, saddle horses, and hunters. He sired the greatest racehorses of both sexes of his era: Sir Archy and Haynie's Maria, who was conceived when he was thirty.

"His pedigree is a lovely, potent design, with consistent sex balancing of all its prominent lines: Crab, Partner, Flying Childers, and Godolphin Arabian. It also has powerful background influences from multiple lines of the ¾ siblings Jigg/Cream Cheeks 5x7x8x9x7x5x6, plus the full siblings Points/Bald Galloway 6x6. This is a quality sire's pedigree.

"He arrived at a time period where American breeders were complaining of the poor results they were getting from other of the imported Thoroughbreds. The breeders were lamenting that the English Thoroughbred of their day was a far cry in value from the likes of Fearnought and Janus.

"Then Diomed arrived, and at twenty-one years of age provided the breeders with a dynasty of excellence when he was bred to our Running Horses. Why was he so much better than his imported Thoroughbred stallion peers? It is partly because he was from the earlier era, he was born in 1777, so his genetics were closer to our American Running Horse base, plus he was extremely well bred—with sex-balanced duplications and strong background lines that were potent sources of Hobby/Running Horse genes. So Diomed was a nick with our American mares, producing great stallion sons such as Sir Archy—the foundation sire of the American Thoroughbred—plus the dynasty building sires Duroc and Balls Floziel. His get were also sought after by the breeders of hunters and saddle horses, because he was consistently giving stamina, soundness, and brilliance. He was a sensation, and his genetics rejuvenated the genetic strengths in our native Running Horse."

Diomed 1777, a typesetter for the great distance racers of the 1800s. — from a painting by George Stubbs

Boston RH carries Diomed 3x3—this is one of the strongest genetic powers in him, and because it is through sons only (Sir Archy and Balls Florizel RH) he did not receive the sex-linked material of Diomed, only some performance and physical structure elements, but with a horse of Diomed's caliber that is plenty.

One thing I have noticed just recently in viewing Diomed's pedigree is the ¾ siblings Blaze/Sister One to Steady 4x3. In these older pedigrees, because the roots of the Thoroughbred are so narrow, you will find many common ancestors. Look to see how many lines of Flying Childers, Leedes Arabian, etc. that Diomed has, for instance—and of Spanker, and his dam Old Peg. Diomed is loaded with the early Thoroughbred components (Chapter 1 and 2). However—for the full power to reach the horse, there must be a closer focal point (see Evaluating Pedigrees in Appendix B). In Diomed's case we have a clear-cut focus point in those ¾ siblings. Blaze, by the way, is a known transmitter of trotting stamina and form. Both of these siblings refocus the speed from the Hobby dam-lines. Please note that modern day revisionists are trying to enlarge the background of Blaze's dam, Grey Grantham Dam, by putting in 'Oriental' lines that do not belong there—therefore making it more 'thoroughbred.' Within the next decade or so I believe we will see a lot of this type of revision being repealed as the DNA studies progress. Speed (especially at the trot and pace) did not come from the Oriental lines.

In Boston's pedigree you will also see a prominent placement of Eclipse 1756 4x5—possibly the greatest English Thoroughbred of the 1700s. However, like Diomed, Eclipse is here only by sons, so he doesn't transmit the sex-linked qualities—seeing Eclipse is out of a daughter of Regulus, a documented carrier of the large heart gene, this is a loss. But the powerful skeletal frame, sturdy legs and feet that he raced on may have come to Boston RH from both these genetic giants.

Studying Boston's pedigree we see then that the sex-linked traits he surely possessed such as large heart and respiratory efficiency would have come from others. However we do find that the good sire Snap is here through daughters, and better yet travels on dam-lines, so he was able to transmit these factors. There is also the good American-bred sire Symes Wildair bringing in the benefit of top-rate English broodmare Kitty Fisher 1756, whose sire Cade carries a dam-line saturated in early Hobby/English Running Horse blood: Bald Galloway/Spanker Mare, and these lines would have transferred their sex-linked material straight down to Kitty Fisher and on to Boston RH as she sits on his dam-line. Kitty Fisher, along with Selima, are possibly the highest class English mares imported to this country; however her traditionally given ancestry has been seriously challenged (see Appendix C). Take a moment to view the pedigrees of Snap and Kitty Fisher—they are very close to the beginnings of the English Thoroughbred, and even though I have not been able to build out all the lines you can see the strong Hobby/Running Horse base they are built on—these horses nicked tightly with our American Running Horse.

Boston's two best sons: Lecomte RH and Lexington RH were born in his last crop—1850. We always get clues on what works from examining the best offspring of a great sire. Lecomte RH was out of Reel—an American-bred daughter of Glencoe. Reel—an absolutely top-class mare—is considered by some to be the best American broodmare of the 1800s, plus she was a fabulous four-mile heat racer as well. However, Reel is strictly of English Thoroughbred lines, and her sire Glencoe is one of the main typesetters of this era.

A short bio of Glencoe 1831 from *North American Sport Horse Breeder*:

The genetic giant Glencoe—possibly the greatest broodmare sire ever. — etching found in *Famous Horses*, Taunton

"**Glencoe 1831:** An imported English Thoroughbred, Glencoe was an outstanding racehorse, but it is his genetic legacy that has made his lasting fame. Influential on both sides of the Atlantic, he is considered by many of the Thoroughbred experts to be the greatest broodmare sires of all time, and one of his daughters, Pocahontas, is rated the most significant mare in the last two hundred years. All of his daughters are valuable.

"Glencoe's pedigree is a study in close sibling relationships, for instance, while I found only one full sibling group in his front lineage, the sisters Curiosity/Virago, he carries twenty different ¾ sibling groupings and nineteen of ⅞ siblings—one of which, Curiosity/Papillon is 93% related—and so combined with Virago makes a triplicate of virtual full sisters. This is an inbred pattern of extreme genetic power.

"Other genetic power is coming from a strong filly factor of Blank daughters, and Glencoe's second dam is Web who is the full sister to Whalebone and Whisker, Derby winners found in multiples in the Thoroughbred population, so he provided the key sex balance for the power genetics of his day also.

"Glencoe daughters, mated with American Running Horses Boston and his son Lexington, created one of the greatest nicks of racehorse breeding. Those progeny are the backbone of the fastest modern Thoroughbred bloodlines."

Glencoe's pedigree is an illustration of critical mass that we can use for our study, but I am more focused on the elements he transferred to his daughters right now—please note the FEMALE emphasis of his pedigree—all those close sisters. It is saturation, plus he provided the female element (Web) for the key power bloodline of the day (Whisker/Whalebone). Those of you who want to build up female influences in your herd—Glencoe's pedigree is the ultimate template for you to study.

Lecomte RH, one of great racers and sires of the Heroic Age. A son of Boston RH, he was second only to his ½ brother Lexington RH—it appears Lecomte RH physically takes more after his sire Boston RH, whereas Lexington RH appears to resemble his dam more. —engraving by W. Ford Atwood, found in *Famous Horses* 1877

The second dam of Glencoe, Web 1808, delivers a tremendous bonus to his career as a stallion. Her third dams, of both sire and dam, are Lisette and Promise. These mares are very closely related, both being by Snap. Snap 1750 I have noticed is often found by daughters in the good racers and producers, so he may be an example of a very strong broodmare sire himself—transmitting high-class sex-linked material. His pedigree reveals that he is a powerful conduit of old Hobby/Running Horse lines. We see Snap lines in Boston RH also coming through to their daughters through Saltram and Shark—important imported sires in the 1700s. The nick Boston RH and Glencoe enjoyed may rely partially on this build-up of Snap.

Boston's son Lexington RH was the racing rival of his brother Lecomte RH—they were the best of their era—and possibly of any era since. Like Affirmed and Alydar, or the rivals Sunday Silence and Easy Goer in our modern day, they raced each other neck and neck, and with their closely matched talents, the outcome of their meets was always a cliffhanger. But in the end Lexington RH proved the mightier of the two both in racing and in breeding. This then is a big clue for us also.

Mr J. B. Pryor in 1863, who was a former trainer of Lexington RH, reported in a letter from England when he was asked to recount Lexington's racing ability:

"No horse was ever his match or ever could race with him after a half mile. Lexington was not fit to run when Lecomte beat him, he was full of cold, and even then, after having caught Lecomte and had him beat, the boy stopped him, thinking that he had gone four miles. Lexington, when right, was a distance better than any horse I ever saw run in America four-mile heats, and I have seen all the best horses run in England five years, and there is not a horse that he could not beat four miles. There are horses here that might beat or race with him two miles, but none four. He could go faster at the end of four miles then most horses can a half mile. I have been training horses thirty years, and am positive that Lexington is the best racehorse I ever saw in any country…"(from correspondence reported in the Thoroughbred Record.)

Nevertheless, the influence of Lecomte RH should not be disregarded. He was a great sire and will be found in very many lineages, often in conjunction with Lexington RH and Glencoe lines—where his presence adds complexity to the genetics as well

The ill-fated Pryor RH, he along with Lecomte RH, were two of the best four-milers of their time. It was a terrible tragedy that both succumbed to illness while in England and died there. Image from *Racing in America*.

as racing class. He might have left an even larger genetic footprint, but it was his misfortune to be among several horses shipped to England by Mr. Richard Ten Broeck for racing and breeding in 1856. Within a year, he along with his stable mates became seriously ill, and tragically, he along with another top American racer, Pyror RH, died there; some reports state that the illness arose from appalling stable conditions.

Now Boston RH has some nice female influences, but his leading genetic power is MALE—that means his sons will usually be better than his daughters. You'd think that Lecomte RH, because he is out of a Glencoe mare that he would ultimately win the day in class between the two super stars. But that wasn't the case. Excellent as he was in both categories—that is, as a sire and racer, his brother proved even better. The Lexington RH/Glencoe nick proved also to be the ultimate in racing success (such as seen powering Parole, Americus (Lady Josephine), Spendthrift, Hindoo, Bramble, Domino, and Nearco for instance).

Lexington RH was the dam-sire of both Parole and the great Ten Broeck (named for Mr. Ten Broeck). Parole is discussed in Chapter 8; Ten Broeck was a great racehorse, and like Parole, he was out of a daughter of Lexington RH. In 1876 Ten Broeck raced a four-mile dash (not heats) against Fellowcraft—who was also out of a daughter of Lexington RH. Fellowcraft won, setting a record of 7:15 ¾. Ten Broeck also broke the record for a one-mile dash at 1:39 ¾. As you can see straight dashes—not heats—were by the late 1800s already getting a strong hold in the American racing scene.

On Lexington's ability to get good foals, and especially because it was widely predicted by the pundits of the day that he would fail at stud, B. G. Bruce said in the 'Thoroughbred Record' on July 9, 1875:

> "His distinguished sons and daughters have adorned every page of racing chronicles since their first appearance in the record, the true test of merit, assigns him first position, a fame of his own creation. Besides what has sprung from his own loins, other stallions are now making their reputation from his daughters, the Lexington blood nicking with everything with which it has been crossed….As a race-horse he stands preeminently the best this country ever produced; as a stallion he must take the foremost rank in the world."

Let's see what it was that Lexington's dam added that tipped the balance in his class—keeping in mind that several of her bloodlines are unverified. Bred by Elisha Warfield, Alice Carneal was a very moderate racer and ended up as a broodmare at R. A. Alexander's stud operation. She is said to have been a nervous and difficult mare. (Tesio probably would have liked Alice as she was a mare with an excess of nervous energy—high-strung and so excitable she would worry herself out of condition before the race even started. She was a great racehorse that seldom had the composure to succeed, yet she still managed to win two out of eight starts.) There has to be something good running in her veins because she is the dam of ten offspring, and besides the superstar Lexington RH, she also produced the great racers Umpire RH (exported to England and then Russia) and the race mare Rescue RH, who is found in the pedigree of Rhoda B, plus several other good broodmares, including Lavender, who produced the Kentucky Derby winner Baden Baden, and the great racer Dublin, winner of the Saratoga Cup and Jockey Club Handicap.

[Note: Rhoda B carries Lexington RH and Rescue RH, a son and daughter out of Alice Carneal, therefore this is a 'filly factor' of the superior mare Alice Carneal—read more about Rhoda B in Chapter 8 and 15.]

Alice Carneal RH adds to the maleness of Boston RH with another line of a Sir Archy son—but she also provides a huge female strength through the Robin Redbreast Mare, which through her sire is 2x2 to Sir Peter and his 7/8 sister Wren, who are both out of this same Papillon (daughter of Snap) who is part of the power configuration in Glencoe, and Alice Carneal RH refocuses it through these ⅞ siblings who are 6x7x5x5 in his dam (no wonder Lexington RH nicked so well

Alice Carneal RH, the dam of Lexington RH. The saying, "great dams make great stallions" is proven here in Alice Carneal. For it was what she carried in her genes when combined with Boston's that trumped what was brought in by Lecomte's excellent dam Reel. Lexington RH physically resembles his dam more than his sire.

with Glencoe); therefore it reactivated and brought this saturation of female lines forward. I think this might after all be the key—the Sir Peter/Wren power (Papillon) —because it is one of his strongest pedigree dominances. In Alice Carneal through Wren there is a clear X chromosome path to her second dam Rowena, providing all her sex-linked material right to the front. This combination in the Lexington RH/Glencoe matings provides an avenue of connection right into the full sister power in Glencoe, creating a nick of immense power. Lexington RH also brings in another line of the key imported English mare Kitty Fisher 1756, as well as another line of the English Running Horse mare Calista ERH found on both Timoleon's and Robin Grey's dam-line. Lexington's lines of Sweet Mary RH and the Cassius Mare RH all connect back to the Colonial Virginia Running Horse studs that were based on high-quality Hobby genetics. Lexington's footprint is huge in the modern race and sport horse, even with the banning of his bloodlines worldwide, along with the loss of many of his best offspring during the Civil War. Still he rises like a phoenix, and one hundred fifty years later he still holds the world record as a sire.

Both Lecomte RH and Lexington RH have a tremendous build-up of the Blaze daughter Cypron—over twenty lines in ten generations. This is not that unusual as she is the dam of Herod, who is everywhere in the TB, but the difference here is the line of her daughter: Lady Bolingbroke that they both carry (found in Boston's dam: Sister to Tuckahoe RH). The representation of Cypron in these stars by both a son and a daughters is what we call a filly factor (a pedigree design found in the best stallions and mares—see Appendix B—Evaluating Pedigrees), and because there are twenty lines of her it is one of immense power. See also how many of these key individuals in her lineage are of partial fabricated ancestry in Appendix C—Blaze, Kitty Fisher etc. (It was fashionable to hide the Running Horse bloodlines at that time).

[Blaze, whose dam's lineage can not be traced, is the foundation sire of both the Hackney breed, through his son Old Shales and grandson Useful Cub, and of our American Trotter through his great-grandson Messenger. Blaze was not a full Thoroughbred, and he and his offspring—all crossed with Thoroughbreds, retained a propensity to trot and—his descendants often could race at both the trot and gallop, and they also became a valued line for stage coach horses!]

Lexington's blood comes down to us through multiple daughters who are the dams of modern dynasty builders: Hira RH dam of Himyar, Florence dam of Hindoo, Bay Flower RH dam of Bramble, Aerolite RH dam of Spendthrift et al, and Lida RH dam of Enquirer RH the sire of Mannie Grey—through them he pretty much dominates the important American TB families. Therefore like Glencoe, Lexington RH was a premier broodmare sire.

The influence of Lexington's sons may not be as noticeable, but you will find lines of his good sons Kentucky RH, Asteroid RH, Ten Broeck, and Duke of Magenta in important horses. Those key sires aside, there are two of his other sons who became stallions of immense influence. First there is Norfolk RH, out of a Glencoe mare whose dam was an inbred RH, and he was a very good racer, beating his ¾ brother Kentucky RH. Norfolk RH was also a good sire, with stakes-winning offspring such as Prince of Norfolk, El Rio Rey, Flood, and others, but it was his son Emperor of Norfolk, a great stakes winner himself, who sired Americus, the stallion who powers the Lady Josephine dynasty in England. Americus is inbred to Norfolk RH and his full sister The Nun RH 3x3. The other son that seems to be most commonly seen in pedigrees is

Longfellow RH 1867—a great racer and sire after the Civil War.
—photo from the "Thoroughbred Record"

War Dance RH, as he is the dam-sire of Mannie Gray, the dam of Domino et al, and she is also the dam of Lady Reel who is the dam of Hamburg. **Lexington RH saturates the background of the American Thoroughbred.**

Lexington RH is our primary focus in this book, because he is everywhere in the American Thoroughbred, and he is usually present with double digit multiple lines in horses by the twentieth century. Nonetheless, I don't want to downplay the importance of the other stars of this period, such as American Eclipse RH, who is found regularly, and who is a fine source of stamina, soundness, and speed.

Another individual you will surely find from this era in your background lines is the great racer Longfellow RH 1867, a son of Leamington out of Nantura RH, with multiple lines of Sir Archy as well as American Eclipse RH in the third generation. W. S. Vosborough writing about Longfellow: "Beyond question the most celebrated horse of the decade was Longfellow…his entire career was sensational, extravagant stories of his prowess were frequent, and people seemed to regard him as a superhorse."

Longfellow RH was a huge dark brown horse—almost 17 hands—with a white blaze and white hind socks. He inspired awe and when he ran his stride was measured at twenty-six feet. It took him a while to grow into himself, so he wasn't started until the end of his third year. In his first outing he was beat by Enquirer RH (sire of Mannie Gray), but after that he racked up an impressive winning streak of five straight victories. He raced against Preakness RH for the Monmouth Cup—2 ½ miles—and won, and at Saratoga he beat the Lexington RH son Kingfisher RH. The greatest racer of his day was Harry Bassett RH, another Lexington RH son, and a match race was inevitable between these two titans of the turf. It was set for the next running of the Monmouth Cup, and Longfellow RH lost a shoe during the race and lost to Harry by a length. Longfellow RH then retired to stud. He became a great sire, leading the sire's list in 1891 with Freeland, Leonatus, Thora, Longstreet, and many other notable racers. His nemesis is Harry Bassett RH, who was perhaps the greatest racer of that post-Civil War period, yet he was a poorer sire (see illustration of Harry Bassett RH in Chapter 36).

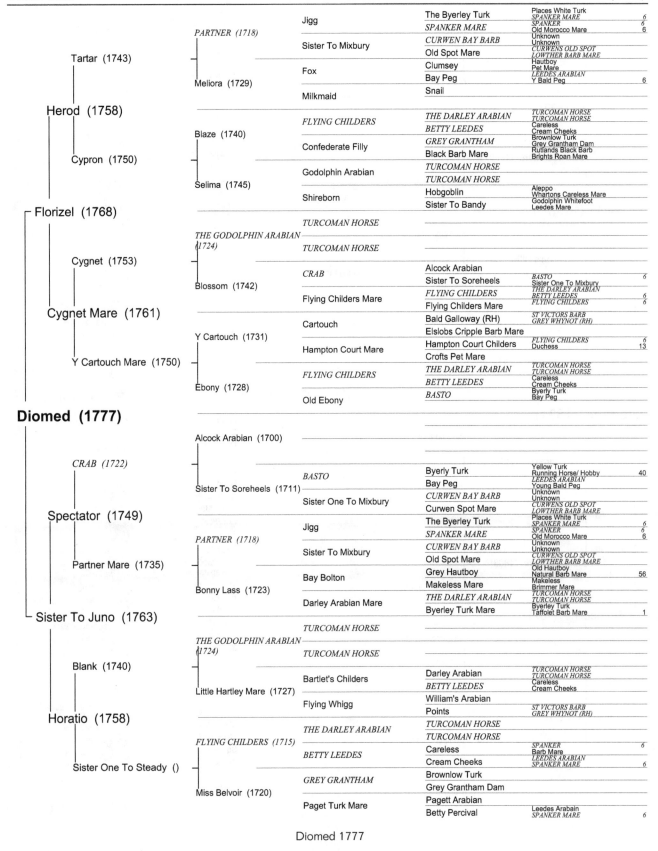

Diomed (1777)

Herod (1758)

Tartar (1743)

PARTNER (1718)

Jigg — The Byerley Turk — Places White Turk / *SPANKER MARE* 6 / *SPANKER* 6 / Old Morocco Mare 6

Sister To Mixbury — *CURWEN BAY BARB* — Unknown / Unknown / Old Spot Mare — *CURWENS OLD SPOT* / *LOWTHER BARB MARE*

Meliora (1729)

Fox — Clumsey — Hautboy / Pet Mare / Bay Peg — *LEEDES ARABIAN* / Y Bald Peg 6

Milkmaid — Snail

Cypron (1750)

Blaze (1740)

FLYING CHILDERS — *THE DARLEY ARABIAN* — TURCOMAN HORSE / TURCOMAN HORSE / *BETTY LEEDES* — Careless / Cream Cheeks

Confederate Filly — *GREY GRANTHAM* — Brownlow Turk / Grey Grantham Dam / Black Barb Mare — Rutlands Black Barb / Brights Roan Mare

Selima (1745)

Godolphin Arabian — TURCOMAN HORSE / TURCOMAN HORSE

Shireborn — Hobgoblin — Aleppo / Whartons Careless Mare / Sister To Bandy — Godolphin Whitefoot / Leedes Mare

Florizel (1768)

Cygnet (1753)

THE GODOLPHIN ARABIAN (1724) — TURCOMAN HORSE / TURCOMAN HORSE

Blossom (1742)

CRAB — Alcock Arabian / Sister To Soreheels — *BASTO* 6 / Sister One To Mixbury

Flying Childers Mare — *FLYING CHILDERS* — *THE DARLEY ARABIAN* 6 / *BETTY LEEDES* 6 / Flying Childers Mare — *FLYING CHILDERS*

Cygnet Mare (1761)

Y Cartouch (1731)

Cartouch — Bald Galloway (RH) — *ST VICTORS BARB* / *GREY WHYNOT (RH)* / Elslobs Cripple Barb Mare

Hampton Court Mare — Hampton Court Childers — *FLYING CHILDERS* 6 / Duchess 13 / Crofts Pet Mare

Y Cartouch Mare (1750)

Ebony (1728)

FLYING CHILDERS — *THE DARLEY ARABIAN* — TURCOMAN HORSE / TURCOMAN HORSE / *BETTY LEEDES* — Careless / Cream Cheeks

Old Ebony — *BASTO* — Byerly Turk / Bay Peg

Diomed (1777)

Spectator (1749)

CRAB (1722)

Alcock Arabian (1700)

Sister To Soreheels (1711)

BASTO — Byerly Turk — Yellow Turk / Running Horse/ Hobby 40 / Bay Peg — *LEEDES ARABIAN* / Young Bald Peg

Sister One To Mixbury — *CURWEN BAY BARB* — Unknown / Unknown / Curwen Spot Mare — *CURWENS OLD SPOT* / *LOWTHER BARB MARE*

Partner Mare (1735)

PARTNER (1718)

Jigg — The Byerley Turk — Places White Turk / *SPANKER MARE* 6 / *SPANKER* 6 / Old Morocco Mare 6

Sister To Mixbury — *CURWEN BAY BARB* — Unknown / Unknown / Old Spot Mare — *CURWENS OLD SPOT* / *LOWTHER BARB MARE*

Bonny Lass (1723)

Bay Bolton — Grey Hautboy — Old Hautboy / Natural Barb Mare 56 / Makeless Mare — Makeless / Brimmer Mare

Darley Arabian Mare — *THE DARLEY ARABIAN* — TURCOMAN HORSE / TURCOMAN HORSE / Byerley Turk Mare — Byerley Turk / Taffolet Barb Mare 1

Sister To Juno (1763)

Blank (1740)

THE GODOLPHIN ARABIAN (1724) — TURCOMAN HORSE / TURCOMAN HORSE

Little Hartley Mare (1727)

Bartlet's Childers — Darley Arabian — TURCOMAN HORSE / TURCOMAN HORSE / *BETTY LEEDES* — Careless / Cream Cheeks

Flying Whigg — William's Arabian / Points — *ST VICTORS BARB* / *GREY WHYNOT (RH)*

Horatio (1758)

FLYING CHILDERS (1715)

THE DARLEY ARABIAN — TURCOMAN HORSE / TURCOMAN HORSE

BETTY LEEDES — Careless — *SPANKER* 6 / Barb Mare / Cream Cheeks — *LEEDES ARABIAN* / *SPANKER MARE* 6

Sister One To Steady ()

Miss Belvoir (1720)

GREY GRANTHAM — Brownlow Turk / Grey Grantham Dam

Pagett Turk Mare — Pagett Arabian / Betty Percival — Leedes Arabain / *SPANKER MARE* 6

Diomed 1777

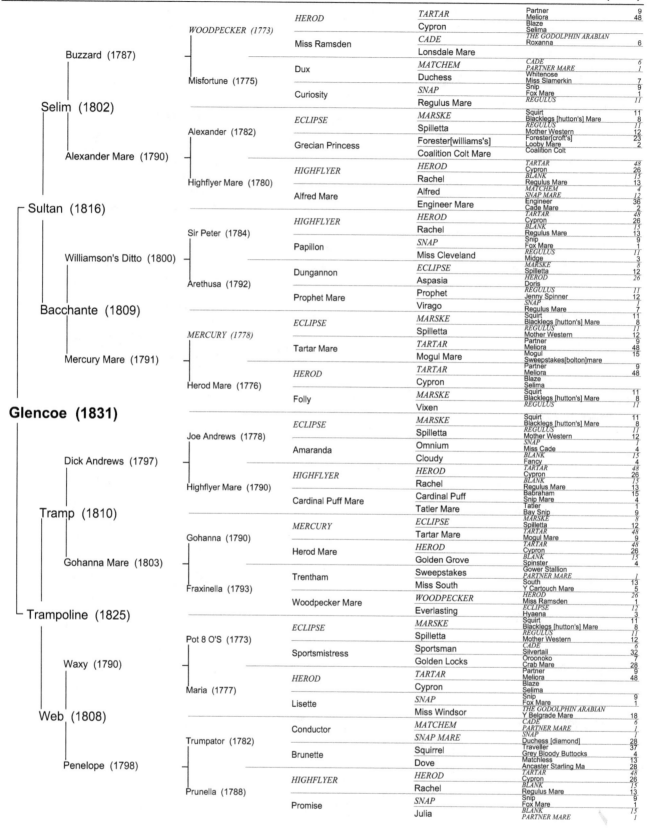

		HEROD	*TARTAR*	Partner 9
	WOODPECKER (1773)			Meliora 48
			Cypron	Blaze
Buzzard (1787)				Selima
		Miss Ramsden	*CADE*	*THE GODOLPHIN ARABIAN*
				Roxanna 6
			Lonsdale Mare	
		Dux	*MATCHEM*	*CADE* 6
	Misfortune (1775)			*PARTNER MARE* 1
			Duchess	Whitenose
Selim (1802)				Miss Slamerkin 7
		Curiosity	*SNAP*	Snip 9
				Fox Mare 1
			Regulus Mare	*REGULUS* 11
		ECLIPSE	*MARSKE*	Squirt 11
	Alexander (1782)			Blacklegs [hutton's] Mare 8
			Spilletta	*REGULUS* 11
				Mother Western 12
		Grecian Princess	Forester[williams's]	Forester[croft's] 23
				Looby Mare 2
Alexander Mare (1790)			Coalition Colt Mare	Coalition Colt
		HIGHFLYER	*HEROD*	*TARTAR* 48
	Highflyer Mare (1780)			Cypron 26
			Rachel	*BLANK* 15
				Regulus Mare 13
		Alfred Mare	Alfred	*MATCHEM* 4
				SNAP MARE 1
			Engineer Mare	Engineer 36
Sultan (1816)				Cade Mare 2
		HIGHFLYER	*HEROD*	*TARTAR* 48
	Sir Peter (1784)			Cypron 26
			Rachel	*BLANK* 15
				Regulus Mare 13
		Papillon	*SNAP*	Snip 9
				Fox Mare 1
			Miss Cleveland	*REGULUS* 11
Williamson's Ditto (1800)				Midge 3
		Dungannon	*ECLIPSE*	*MARSKE* 8
	Arethusa (1792)			Spilletta 12
			Aspasia	*HEROD* 26
				Doris
		Prophet Mare	Prophet	*REGULUS* 11
				Jenny Spinner 12
			Virago	*SNAP* 1
				Regulus Mare 7
		ECLIPSE	*MARSKE*	Squirt 11
	MERCURY (1778)			Blacklegs [hutton's] Mare 8
			Spilletta	*REGULUS* 11
				Mother Western 12
Bacchante (1809)		Tartar Mare	*TARTAR*	Partner 9
				Meliora 48
			Mogul Mare	Mogul 15
				Sweepstakes[bolton]mare
		HEROD	*TARTAR*	Partner 9
	Herod Mare (1776)			Meliora 48
			Cypron	Blaze
Mercury Mare (1791)				Selima
		Folly	*MARSKE*	Squirt 11
				Blacklegs [hutton's] Mare 8
			Vixen	*REGULUS* 11

Glencoe (1831)

		ECLIPSE	*MARSKE*	Squirt 11
	Joe Andrews (1778)			Blacklegs [hutton's] Mare 8
			Spilletta	*REGULUS* 11
				Mother Western 12
		Amaranda	Omnium	*SNAP* 1
				Miss Cade 4
			Cloudy	*BLANK* 15
Dick Andrews (1797)				Fancy 4
		HIGHFLYER	*HEROD*	*TARTAR* 48
	Highflyer Mare (1790)			Cypron 26
			Rachel	*BLANK* 15
				Regulus Mare 13
		Cardinal Puff Mare	Cardinal Puff	Babraham 15
				Snip Mare 4
			Tatler Mare	Tatler 1
Tramp (1810)				Bay Snip 9
		MERCURY	*ECLIPSE*	*MARSKE* 8
	Gohanna (1790)			Spilletta 12
			Tartar Mare	*TARTAR* 48
				Mogul Mare 9
		Herod Mare	*HEROD*	*TARTAR* 48
				Cypron 26
			Golden Grove	*BLANK* 15
Gohanna Mare (1803)				Spinster 4
		Trentham	Sweepstakes	Gower Stallion
	Fraxinella (1793)			*PARTNER MARE* 1
			Miss South	South 13
				Y Cartouch Mare 5
		Woodpecker Mare	*WOODPECKER*	*HEROD* 26
				Miss Ramsden 1
			Everlasting	*ECLIPSE* 12
				Hyaena 3
		ECLIPSE	*MARSKE*	Squirt 11
	Pot 8 O'S (1773)			Blacklegs [hutton's] Mare 8
			Spilletta	*REGULUS* 11
				Mother Western 12
		Sportsmistress	Sportsman	*CADE* 6
				Silvertail 32
			Golden Locks	Oroonoko 7
Trampoline (1825)				Crab Mare 28
		HEROD	*TARTAR*	Partner 9
	Maria (1777)			Meliora 48
			Cypron	Blaze
				Selima
		Lisette	*SNAP*	Snip 9
				Fox Mare 1
			Miss Windsor	*THE GODOLPHIN ARABIAN*
				Y Belgrade Mare 18
		Conductor	*MATCHEM*	*CADE* 6
Waxy (1790)	Trumpator (1782)			*PARTNER MARE* 1
			SNAP MARE	*SNAP* 1
				Duchess [diamond] 28
		Brunette	Squirrel	Traveller 37
				Grey Bloody Buttocks 4
			Dove	Matchless 13
Web (1808)				Ancaster Starling Ma 28
		HIGHFLYER	*HEROD*	*TARTAR* 48
	Prunella (1788)			Cypron 26
			Rachel	*BLANK* 15
				Regulus Mare 13
Penelope (1798)		Promise	*SNAP*	Snip 9
				Fox Mare 1
			Julia	*BLANK* 15
				PARTNER MARE 1

Glencoe 1831

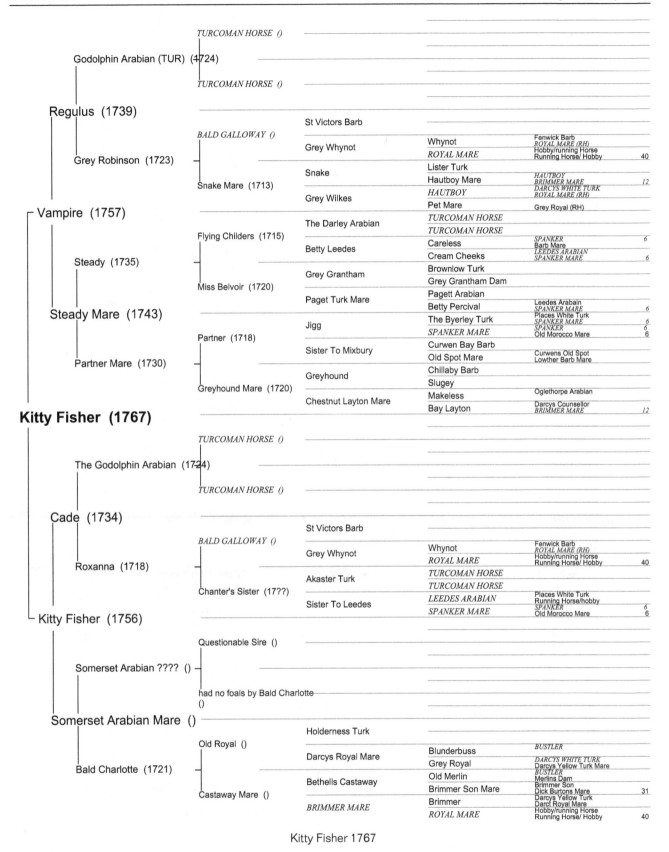

Kitty Fisher 1767

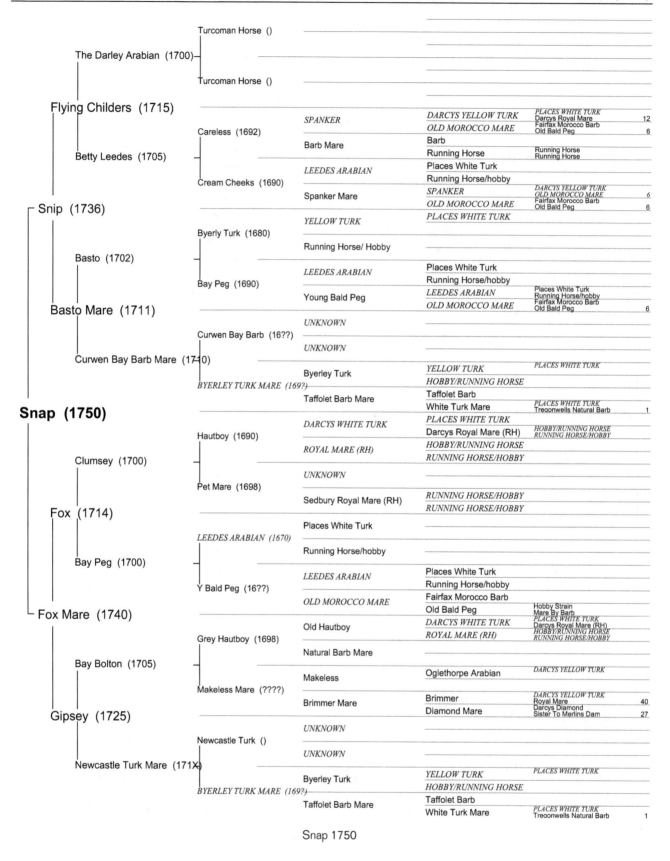

Snap 1750

Chapter 7

The Genetic Bedrock for Supreme Performance

The distance racing strain of our American racehorse had been performance tested by a four-mile heat race standard since 1665—therefore by the time of our Civil War our long-racer Running Horse had two hundred years of selective breeding and performance testing behind it. During the Civil War the 'dash' form supplanted the four-mile heat race in popularity. The bloodlines that survived the conflict, however, were the result of selection in breeding and performance for the heat racer, so they were the ultimate combination of speed, soundness, and stamina in the world. Therefore this breed of horse was able to travel elsewhere and race in two-mile contests day after day, as if they were warm-ups for the real event. The American horse was built upon the most powerful racing genetics there has ever been developed.

An undefeated racehorse, Asteroid RH 1861 is one of the many great four-mile racers produced by the Lexington/Glencoe 'nick'. —Wiki Commons public domain image, photographer James Mullen.

The bloodlines born of this period have driven the American Thoroughbred for generations; we will take a brief look at the main progenitors. The production of stamina racers reached its peak shortly before the Civil War, which decimated this horse industry. This time period was perilous for the horse; it was both the mode of all transport and was the vehicle of war. For example, the great four-mile racer Asteroid RH almost lost his life when he was stolen by band of plundering guerillas, and he was saved only when he was bargained back from them; some accounts say he was bought back for $250, others that he was traded back for two other horses. Either way, the thieves didn't know he was a famous racehorse (a Lexington RH son, Asteroid RH was a great racer, undefeated in all twelve of his starts) and the bargaining agent for the owners told them he was a pet horse of no practical use. Many of his contemporaries were not so fortunate and were killed, lamed, stolen, or lost during the conflict.

Great racers and sires were formed with combinations such as these (Glencoe/Lexington RH cross), as in Asteroid RH shown here; other examples are the great four-miler Kentucky RH 1861 and his full brother Daniel Boone RH both by Lexington RH out of the Glencoe daughter Magnolia, both stellar four-mile heat racers.

1861 must have been a banner year for Lexington RH, as not only were the champions Asteroid RH, Norfolk RH, and Kentucky RH born, but also the broodmare typesetter Aerolite RH. A daughter of Lexington RH out of Florence RH by Glencoe out of a RH mare, Aerolite RH also had as her third-dam a daughter of the pacing Running Horse Blackburns Whip (speed transmitter), whose impact in our racing industry is discussed in Chapter 4—therefore she is almost a full sister to Maiden RH who is found in both Parole and Catnip. Aerolite RH produced several offspring including four full brothers: Spendthrift, Fellowcraft, Rutherford, and Miser who provided a dynasty of great racing talent; the first two left

Spendthrift—the grandsire of Fair Play—is out of the Lexington RH daughter Aerolite RH, who also carries the pacing RH typesetter Blackburns Whip on her dam-line—making her a close relative to Maiden RH, the fourth dam of Nearco. —photographer unknown.

IDLEWILD.
Record—4 miles. (Centreville Course, L. I., June 25th, 1863,) 7:26].

The great race mare Idlewild RH, blind in one eye and racing against the boys, winning despite her handicap, is justly celebrated as the best heat racer during the Civil War—she is a full sister to Aerolite RH. —illustration found in *Famous Horses* 1877.

the greatest legacy. Spendthrift is the sire of Hastings—the sire of Fair Play and grandsire of Man O' War. His full brother Fellowcraft is the sire of Lady Reel, the dam of Hamburg. We will see in further chapters how these two lines intertwine to produce greatness. Aerolite RH can stand with Mannie Gray and Maggie B. B. RH as being a taproot mare of an important race and sport family.

Aerolite RH had a full sister who is rated one of the greatest racers of all time—Idlewild RH. She was blind in one eye, which caused her to bear out in her races, yet even with this disability she is rated the best racer of both sexes during the Civil War. It was her heart as well as her racing form that inspired her admirers. Her greatest race was a four-mile heat race run on June 25, 1863, where carrying more weight than her top male opponents (Jerome Edgar RH and Dangerous RH) she won, but only after a grueling duel for the lead with Jerome Edgar RH; the spectators were humbled by her display of courage, knowing that when she finally pulled away to win by two lengths it was on sheer grit alone. She was a good producer also; her son Wildidle RH won a four-mile heat race in the very fast time of 7:25 ½, and he was a good sire of first-class racers, and her daughter Fanchon RH was a formidable racer and producer also, for example she is the fourth dam of Sweep On, who is the second dam-sire of the great Miss Disco (dam of Bold Ruler).

By 1875 the south was recovering from the Civil War enough to start rebuilding her racehorse industry, and this reconstruction was looked on as a sign that our distance racehorse bloodlines would be preserved.

"The resuscitation of the Turf in the South is an excellent omen of its future prosperity of the Southerners for heat and distance races is a guarantee that breeders will have to look to bottom as well as speed as an element of success in a fair proportion of the races held in that section. If the prejudice against four mile heats as destructive of the stamina of the horse is well founded, give us at least two mile heats and four mile dashes. I would like to see a series of four mile dashes in the fall corresponding to the Cup races in the Spring, which are mostly two and one quarter miles. Let such champions as Fellowcraft, Wanderer and Katie Pease be encouraged by giving the widest field for the display of their peculiar excellence that of preserving to the bitter end—which forty years ago was, and until recently has been considered the highest attribute of the race-horse" (1875 "Thoroughbred Record" by Greysteel—believed to be S. D. Bruce).

From the inception of dash racing here, objections to the racing of two-year-olds were continual. The classic race practice required the racing of two and three year olds, and many of the breeders here believed that this would ruin their race horse breed, because the easier standard who allow horses with less athletic talents and even those with faults to compete (as youth often hid physical weaknesses) or it would damage potentially good racehorses by racing them at too young an age—damaging their joints and bones that had not finished growing. The Civil War had destroyed much of the infrastructure of four-mile heat industry, and there were not the resources available to rebuild it on the scale it enjoyed before the war began.The simple reality was it was less costly to run young horses and put on shorter races. There was also the breed requirements set by the British to be considered. The very fact that the American Thoroughbred was allowed to be called a 'Thoroughbred' was not just based on the performance test of the classic race that the English Jockey Club had used as its standard for one hundred years, and we adopted in 1868, but on the pedigree requirements of at least five generations of English Thoroughbred blood. If the breeders wanted their horses to be registered as Thoroughbred then they had to abide by the English rules.

[Note: Our new Thoroughbred (1868) was automatically accepted into the English Stud Book (and vice versa). However, you will see (Chapter 8) that once England experienced firsthand the true quality of our racehorse they started raising the studbook requirements: first to eight generations of purely English blood, but when that didn't block our stock they changed it to be that all lines must trace back to the individuals in the English studbook, no matter how distant—thereby walling out the American racer (Jersey Act).]

As mentioned above, right from the beginning of this change to the classic race standard, many here foresaw the effect this would have in downgrading our breed of horse—predicting that it would produce a more unsound horse that lacked stamina. But the four-mile heat race standard was an impossible practice to sustain after the Civil War, as most of the infrastructure and the privately funded studs (which had been centered in the south) were no longer in operation, and racing had become, by necessity, a more public affair.

That reality, combined with higher purses being offered for two-year-olds racing, hastened the loss of the talent and soundness of our magnificent pre-Civil War breed. Some individuals tried to restrain the decline of the performance standard. For instance, in 1900 at a Jockey Club meeting F. R. Hitchcock entered a possible amendment for vote that would forbid purses exceeding $1000 for two-year-old contests, but he was outvoted.

Perhaps the most powerful voice against this practice of racing two-year-olds ironically came in 1899 from the owner of the highest two-year-old money earner: James Keene—owner of Domino—when he said he believed that two-year-old racing should be abolished. "I do not see how any sane man who knows anything about the turf can think otherwise. There should be no racing two-year-olds for big stakes allowed, at any rate before July 1."

After the war the Duke of Magenta 1878 was born—the star of the Lorillard stable (Chapter 2 and 6). His quality can best be understood in that he won a prestigious quadruplet of races: Belmont Stakes, Preakness Stakes, Travers, and Withers Stakes that has been won only by two other horses: Man O' War and Native Dancer. Therefore Duke of Magenta, a son of the RH Lexington, is on a level with Man O' War and Native Dancer. He has a dam-line that goes back to a short-racing Running Horse mare, Brimmer Quarter Mare.

The uniquely American lines of Boston RH, Lexington RH, Lecomte RH, American Eclipse RH, Blackburns Whip RH, Sir Charles RH, War Dance RH, and Vandal RH, along with the purely English lines of Sir Archy and Glencoe, were the sire-lines that powered the bloodlines of this Civil War period, and they produced the very best specimens of the four-mile-heat racer, plus they provided the genetic bedrock of all our sport horse breeds. Yes, not just in the Thoroughbred, because you will find these genetic giants in all the best American sport horse breeds. This is something the American breeder needs to understand: our best light horse breeds (the race breeds of Quarter Horse, Standardbred, and Thoroughbred) as well as our premier saddle breeds (Saddlebred, Tennessee Walker, and Missouri Fox Trotter) all directly descend from not only the original Hobby-based stock, but their genetics were all refocused again through the very best specimens of this heat-race period. That means you will find strong lines of Lexington RH, Vandal RH, American Eclipse RH, Blackburns Whip RH and the others in many of our great breeds. Our sport horses are all closely related, and unlike many foreign sport horse breeds that began with a cavalry, coach, or farm horse, **the American Horse was always a sport horse**—therefore its genetics are very valuable for our success in all our sport pursuits.

Boston RH produced several good trotters; for instance, there is the versatile champion Planet RH 1855, a son of the RH Revenue—an important conduit of Running Horse lines, out of the good race mare RH Nina (a Boston RH daughter);

Planet RH 1855 was considered a first-rate four-mile heat race-horse, and he loved to race at the trot also. —Wiki Commons public domain image, photographer James Mullen

Planet RH was able to race and win at both the trot and the gallop. Planet RH is rated the best four-miler in the period after Lexington RH raced and before the Civil War; nonetheless it is said that he actually preferred to race at the trot. Our Running Horse was an amazingly versatile sport performer. (The lines of closely related Boston RH, Lexington RH and Planet RH, plus American Eclipse RH are found also in the background of our American Standardbred. Lexington RH stood at R.A. Alexander's stud farm in Kentucky, which was one of the largerst breeders of both breeds of racer (Running Horse and Trotter) at the time, and Lexington RH was sometimes bred to trotter mares.)

At Planet's death the Kentucky Live Stock Record 1875 said, "Planet at a fee of $100 with return privileges was the leading money earner in American history, with $69,700. The last of the great ante-bellum champions, he had won 27 of his 31 races (some of them having consisted of more than one heat) and finished second in the other four. In 1875, at age 20, he was already established a very successful sire."

Glencoe is a premier broodmare sire-line, and his many daughters, especially those combined with Lexington RH and Boston RH lines are pure genetic gold in pedigrees. His fabulous daughter Reel was not only the dam of the champion Lecomte RH (out of a Boston RH mare), she also produced the top race mare Prioress—who was one of those who traveled to England and won, but Prioress unfortunately left no significant offspring. However, her dam Reel combined with Lexington RH gave us the important sire War Dance RH, who played a role in the later success of the typesetter Mannie Gray.

War Dance RH, a son of Lexington RH out of the English TB Reel, he is the dam-sire of Mannie Gray—the dam of Domino. He is also the ¾ genetic brother to Lecomte RH. —from a painting by Troye

Perhaps the greatest race mare produced by Glencoe was Peytona, a huge mare—16.2 hands—she was of full English Thoroughbred blood being out of Giantess, a daughter of imported Leviathan, and whose dam was a daughter of the domestic-bred Thoroughbred Sir Archy. She was one of the greatest four-mile racers of her day—beating the equally fantastic Fashion RH in their famous match race (illustration at beginning of Chapter 3). However Peytona broke down soon after (perhaps her great size was a factor) and was retired to stud. More misfortune came her way, as it was her fate to be purchased by A. Keene Richards for use in his infamous 'Arabian' experiments. Richards believed that the Arabian was the base of the Thoroughbred breed and the source of its speed (like thousands before and after him), so he went to Arabia twice to purchase their finest racing Arabians—believing this would upgrade his stock. He spent a lot of time and money on this theory, and he bought Peytona and her priceless genetics to breed to these Oriental sires—the result was very poor, and once again the Arabian myth was exposed as the fairy tale it is, but worse the great Peytona then left us no significant genetic legacy.

But Glencoe, usually remembered as a broodmare sire, also produced a great and important typesetting son in Vandal (RH) 1850—born the same year as Lexington RH and Lecomte RH, he is often mixed with them in the best performers of the day. Vandal RH inherited his sire's lordosis (sway-back), which seems to be transferred to Glencoe from his sire Sultan, and

KATHLEEN H. KIRSAN

Vandal RH: notice his sway-back, a trait that traveled down the genetic trial from Sultan his grandsire. —from a painting by Troye

he passed it on with some frequency. However, this conformation did not keep him (or his sire) from producing the highest class in racing. When you read about Vandal's breeding you will learn he is a son of Glencoe and his dam-sire is Tranby—an imported English Thoroughbred, but very little mention is made of his dam. In Vandal's case it might well be because she is an American Running Horse; nonetheless, take a look at his dam-line, because I found something very interesting there.

First, Vandal's second dam—the RH Lucilla 1837—carries the fuse that ignites the genetic dynamite in the English portion of the pedigree. Our distance Running Horse of the day usually had substantial amounts of English Thoroughbred bloodlines with all their best progenitors in evidence. Here in Vandal RH we see his background is overrun with lines of Eclipse—ten of them (6x7x6x6x7x6x7x7x7x7)—this is the equivalent of having Eclipse in the third generation. Knowing that adding multiple lines of an important ancestor builds dominance, then you can see from this design that it is a valuable tool that we can use ourselves in our breeding plans to target and build up the very best sport genes in the background lines, because if you get enough of them and provide a focal point closer up, then they can overpower the influence of the lesser horses closer up. (See Appendix B—Evaluating Pedigrees—this tool is one we can use in recapturing the benefits of our Heroic Era genes—Chapter 27).

Eclipse 1764 was the pinnacle of the English-breds and quite possibly their best ever. His pedigree is a 'who's who' of strong Hobby genetics. Vandal's sire—Glencoe—carries only sons of Eclipse, which limits the full expression. However it is Vandal's dam that brings in the much needed daughter line of Eclipse (Eclipse Mare). But that is not all, as it is what the second dam Lucilla (RH) carries that really sets this off, as the rarely seen full sister to Eclipse, Prosperine, is carried twice through her daughter Caelia—through Sir Solomon. This configuration produces an overriding dominance in Eclipse type with the extreme genetic power that only a full sibling configuration brings; try to see this—it is a valuable tool for your breeding success.

[Bringing the opposite sex elements of a dominant line that is present by only one sex results in a huge upgrading of talent. This is what has made the sires Teddy and Tracery so influential—they carry the rarely found daughter lines of the taproot mare Pocahontas, who is usually represented by her sons only—see Chapter 22 for another example of this power in La Troienne.]

However, even with all these lines of Eclipse/Prosperine, the sex-linked material does not make it through to Vandal RH (X chromosome)—Vandal RH gets that DNA material from his RH lines. His third dam Lucy RH is by the intensely inbred Orphan RH 1810 (see his pedigree in Chapter 4). His parents are ¾ siblings by Diomed out of the Running Horse dams Atkinsons Shark Mare 1785 and Susan Jones—both by Shark. Therefore, Balls Florizel RH is ¾ brother to Fair Rachel RH; this is a huge genetic concentration that surely influenced this sire's career. These lines through Orphan RH do keep an open X chromosome pathway.

Another factor in Vandal's success at stud is that he also carries the rarely seen Diomed daughter line of Fair Rachel RH (found in Orphan RH)—this is a key to his tremendous ability to nick with Lexington RH's and Boston RH's offspring.

If you flip to Chapter 8—to the pedigree of the superstar Foxhall—you will see how important a sire Vandal RH was in the production of stamina stars. In Foxhall he rules both dam-lines, which meant Lucy RH genetics are transferred to the mares Capitola RH and Mollie Jackson RH, and therefore from Orphan RH, to his daughter Lucy RH and so on to Vandal RH. There is something else significant in Foxhall—while you are still there I want you to notice that the dam of Lucy RH is Lucy Grey RH; follow the dam-sire Lexington's dam-line and there she is again—his third dam. With the line of Balls Florziel RH and his ¾ sister along with the additional lines of this important mare—it is plain to see why the lines of Vandal RH meshed so well with Lexington RH, because he was supplying all these missing sex-balances: Diomed, Eclipse, and Lady Grey RH. Vandal RH bloodlines are the perfect foil for those of Lexington RH, and Boston RH and Lecomte RH as well (see Understanding Pedigrees in Appendix B).

There is a jump in the Vandal RH line also, evidenced in his good son Votigeur RH, as he is the sire of the top performer Princeton, a winner of the ultimate American steeplechase—the Maryland Hunt Cup—three times! He is also the sire of Nora M, the dam of the Quarter Horse typesetter Peter McCue. Vandal RH also produced the good sire Virgil RH, who

Virgil RH, son of Vandal RH and sire of Hindoo, was underappreciated for much of his life, until the few progeny he had began to race; it was then he was finally valued as a sire. He was a great progenitor and is a valuable sport resource—besides speed and stamina, this line has a big jump—digital image courtesy of Encore Edition from a painting by Henry Stull.

you will find in many good sport horse lineages. Virgil RH was a versatile performer, able to win both as flat racer and a timber horse (jumper). Virgil's dam-line also carries a daughter of early pacing Running Horse Blackburns Whip (see Chapter 4).

The career of the versatile and underrated Virgil RH is interesting. A beautiful black horse and a sprinter, he won six out of eight races as a three-year-old. Then he became lame and was not raced again until he was six, and then it was hurdle races. Then after that assignment he was finally down-graded at age seven to driving in harness. Luckily, because his owner Mr. Sanford's stallions and mares were mostly by Lexington RH, he was sometimes used as an outcross stallion. However still not valued, he was shortly sold. But then a few of his offspring from those Lexington RH mares began racing, such as Vagrant, Virginius, and Virgil, and their stellar abilities caused Mr. Sanford to have second thoughts. Vagrant became a top racehorse, winning the 1876 Kentucky Derby, and his brother Virgil was also showing top form. Mr. Sanford then bought Virgil RH back—his throwaway stallion. Virgil's son Tremont was an undefeated racer, and his son Hindoo was the greatest racer of his day and heads an American dynasty of talent. "His get have won the Kentucky Derby three times since its inauguration in 1875—Vagrant in 1876, Hindoo in 1881, and Ben Ali in 1886" (Thoroughbred Record April 11, 1881).

This leads us to another significant sport line. When the line of Vandal RH is brought together in a pedigree that has Lexington RH, Lecomte RH, or their sire Boston RH, great and lasting power combinations are formed. One of the strongest was in Hindoo 1878, a son of Virgil RH out of a Lexington RH mare (see pedigree). Vandal's dam-line hooks right into the speed lines in Lexington RH—Balls Florizel RH and Lady Grey RH creating a rarely seen leading dominance in Running Horse lines. There is also a strong full sibling arrangement with Vandal RH supplying Web and two lines of her full brother Whisker arriving from the mare. This is the structure of a very potent stallion, and so he proved to be—Hindoo heads up one of the great American families forged during this era (see Chapters 9 and 10).

But before his wonderful stud career, Hindoo proved he was a racer of the highest class by winning his first seven starts as a two-year-old, and he continued his display of superior genetics at three when he won eighteen in a row including the Travers and Kentucky Derby, plus he won five of six races as a four-year-old. Performance is always an indicator of quality and in Hindoo's case he qualifies as one of the best racers of all time. He had a strong impact at stud, his best son Hanover is rated one of the greatest sires of his day or any day. Hanover's second dam Ella D RH is a daughter of Vandal RH—putting Vandal RH 3x3 sex-balanced on both the sire and dam-line—this is a sound line.

Another important American sport family began at this general time also—Bramble 1875, whose second dam Bay Flower RH is a daughter of Lexington RH. When he was mated to Roseville 1888, the result was Ben Brush; he is another stallion that was destined to head a dynasty. Roseville's second dam Elastic was by the Lexington RH son Kentucky RH. Doubling up on the Running Horse conduits of speed certainly seems to have proven itself as a road to success. Ben Brush is 4x5 to Lexington RH.

Bramble had the misfortune of being the racing contemporary of Duke of Magenta—who regularly beat him at three years old. The next year, however, the Duke had been shipped to England to race (although he did not race there as he became sick on the trip to England and later came home). But with Duke of Magenta out of the way Bramble easily won five cup races (2 ¼ miles), and all told as a four-year-old he won fifteen of twenty starts. He continued winning at five, then at six he broke down and was put to stud.

Just 15.2 hands, Bramble was a plain bay—no markings. A son of imported Bonnie Scotland (a producer of sprinters), it is said by many that his sire Bonnie Scotland contributes toughness and soundness to the American racer. However, while this assessment is repeated over and over again in Thoroughbred literature, I have also discovered that Bonnie Scotland was never sound himself and completely broke down at three years, ending his race career, and his son Bramble broke down too (*The Quarter Running Horse,* Robert Denhardt), however, Bramble's son Ben Brush is a very sound line. Bramble's top racers were Clifford and Ben Brush. Maybe the confusion on Bonnie Scotland's soundness is because his progeny were out

Kentucky RH was a Lexington RH son who was a great racehorse and good sire. This lovely image is from an aquatint done in 1867 by Knoedler from an original painting by Troye, and it shows us a common mode of transport in the background—six-horse coach.

of our own good tough running horse racers, giving him the reputation for soundness that perhaps really belongs to his mates instead.

There is another family that was created in this time frame that has made a huge footprint in our lineages and continues to power all forms of equine sport today, and this is the Mannie Gray family. Her dam Lizzie G RH 1867 is a carrier of a powerful maternal configuration of three lines of the super-mare Reel and her ¾ sister Judith. This configuration—2x3x3 to ¾ sisters, is refocused by the intense inbreeding to the ¾ brothers Lecomte RH/War Dance RH 1x2. This is the pedigree design of a typesetter with a capital 'T'—and one that works only if the individuals are the very best of sport and breeding stock. This is the case here (see Orphan RH for another typesetter of this intensity), and this line has powered generations. When Lizzie G RH was mated with Enquirer RH it accessed the leading inbreeding by bringing in a Lexington RH daughter Lida RH, which sex-balanced the two Lexington RH lines 3x3 and added to the immense consistency of type with the Lecomte RH line—they are ½ brothers. This is a genetic powerhouse, providing concentration of the very best distance racers ever. Mannie Gray produced three full siblings when mated with Himyar, who was out of another Lexington RH daughter—putting Lexington RH/Lecomte RH inbreeding 3x4x4x4. Who were these offspring? None other than Domino and his full sisters Correction and Mannie Himyar, the conduits of this immense power to our modern sport horse. The sire Himyar was a brilliant racer who kept running until he was six. He was a nervous horse and some said he lacked stamina—yet at four he won every race he started in. This bloodline Mannie Gray/Himyar has proven to be one of the most powerful in the world. See the Chapters 9 and 14 for an expanded discussion.

The debate was raging in the late 1800s through the early 1900s on which racehorse is the best, the American or the English or the French, and each side of this issue had some strong opinions. However, it appears that each side was content to just hold on to their domestic illusions except the Americans, who wanted to 'know' strongly enough to make the journey across the ocean to find the answer. So, it was only the Americans who transported their racers to England and France—not the other way around.

The leading American horse trainer Foxhall Daingerfield spoke out on this issue in April of 1904:

> "I believe that the American Thoroughbred and racehorse, *under equal condition,* is the peer of any breed on this earth. The truth or error of this opinion will probably never be demonstrated as the English, French and Australians will not send their horses to America to compete with us on our own soil—as we do ours to England and France—and the racing life of no horse is long enough to make an animal *quite* what he might have been in his native country— even if an expatriated horse does fully recover from the acclimating ordeal, which I seriously doubt, unless the change be made in extreme youth. Yet, despite all the disadvantages of us sending our untried youngsters to undergo this ordeal of acclimatization, while the English and the French rival is going uninterrupted in his development and his training—such horses as Foxhall, Iroquois, Don Fulano, Blue Grass, Cap and Bells, King Courier, Renssalear, Noonday, the two-year-old (weight for age) winner of the July Stakes, Running Stream, Brobinski, Lancashire, the Sweeper, and a host of others, give some evidence that under equal conditions American-bred horses could hold their own with the best English and French Thoroughbreds" (Thoroughbred Record).

The result of this quest was that the Americans did indeed come to really know that there was no better racehorse in the world than their own, and their own assessment was amplified by the reaction of the French, Irish and English, who were so threatened by their presence, their numbers, and above all their superiority, that it was not long before they were banned.

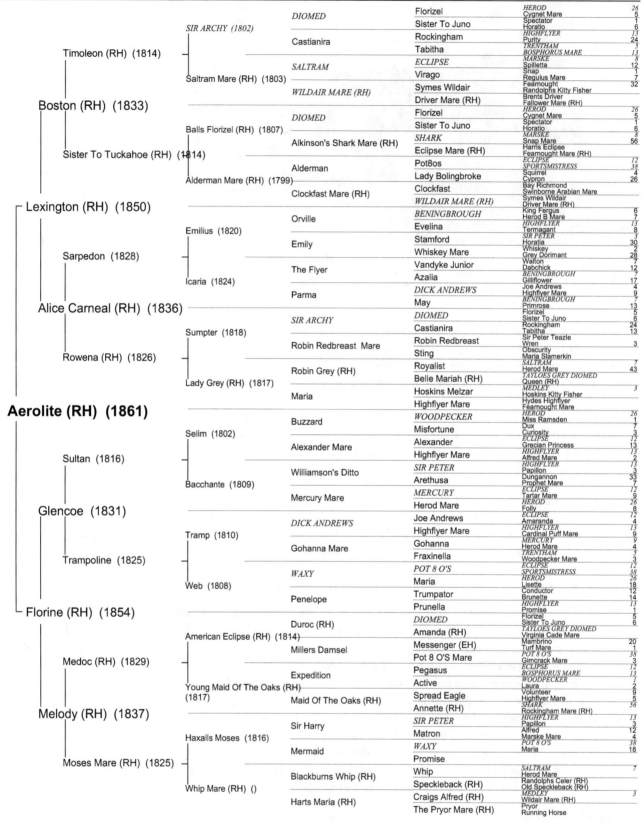

Aerolite (RH) (1861)

- **Lexington (RH) (1850)**
  - **Boston (RH) (1833)**
    - **Timoleon (RH) (1814)**
      - *SIR ARCHY (1802)*
        - *DIOMED*
          - Florizel — *HEROD* 26 / Cygnet Mare 5
          - Sister To Juno — Spectator 1 / Horatio 6
        - Castianira
          - Rockingham — *HIGHFLYER* 13 / Purity 24
          - Tabitha — *TRENTHAM* 5 / *BOSPHORUS MARE* 13
      - Saltram Mare (RH) (1803)
        - *SALTRAM*
          - *ECLIPSE* — *MARSKE* 8 / Spilletta 12
          - Virago — Snap 1 / Regulus Mare 7
        - *WILDAIR MARE (RH)*
          - Symes Wildair — Fearnought 32 / Randolphs Kitty Fisher
          - Driver Mare (RH) — Brents Driver / Fallower Mare (RH)
    - **Sister To Tuckahoe (RH) (1814)**
      - Balls Florizel (RH) (1807)
        - *DIOMED*
          - Florizel — *HEROD* 26 / Cygnet Mare 5
          - Sister To Juno — Spectator 1 / Horatio 6
        - Alkinson's Shark Mare (RH)
          - *SHARK* — *MARSKE* 8 / Snap Mare 56
          - Eclipse Mare (RH) — Harris Eclipse / Fearnought Mare (RH)
      - Alderman Mare (RH) (1799)
        - Alderman
          - Pot8os — *ECLIPSE* 12 / *SPORTSMISTRESS* 38
          - Lady Bolingbroke — Squirrel 4 / Cypron 26
        - Clockfast Mare (RH)
          - Clockfast — Bay Richmond / Swinborne Arabian Mare
          - *WILDAIR MARE (RH)* — Symes Wildair / Driver Mare (RH)
  - **Alice Carneal (RH) (1836)**
    - **Sarpedon (1828)**
      - Emilius (1820)
        - Orville
          - *BENINGBROUGH* — King Fergus 6 / Herod B Mare 7
          - Evelina — *HIGHFLYER* 13 / Termagant 8
        - Emily
          - Stamford — *SIR PETER* 3 / Horatia 30
          - Whiskey Mare — Whiskey 2 / Grey Dorimant 28
      - Icaria (1824)
        - The Flyer
          - Vandyke Junior — Walton 7 / Dabchick 12
          - Azalia — *BENINGBROUGH* 7 / Gilliflower 17
        - Parma
          - *DICK ANDREWS* — Joe Andrews 4 / Highflyer Mare 9
          - May — *BENINGBROUGH* 7 / Primrose 13
    - **Rowena (RH) (1826)**
      - Sumpter (1818)
        - *SIR ARCHY*
          - *DIOMED* — Florizel 5 / Sister To Juno 6
          - Castianira — Rockingham 24 / Tabitha 13
        - Robin Redbreast Mare
          - Robin Redbreast — Sir Peter Teazle / Wren 3
          - Sting — Obscurity / Maria Slamerkin
      - Lady Grey (RH) (1817)
        - Robin Grey (RH)
          - Royalist — *SALTRAM* 7 / Herod Mare 43
          - Belle Mariah (RH) — *TAYLOES GREY DIOMED* / Queen (RH)
        - Maria
          - Hoskins Melzar — *MEDLEY* 3 / Hoskins Kitty Fisher
          - Highflyer Mare — Hydes Highflyer / Fearnought Mare
- **Glencoe (1831)**
  - **Sultan (1816)**
    - Selim (1802)
      - Buzzard
        - *WOODPECKER* — *HEROD* 26 / Miss Ramsden 1
        - Misfortune — Dux 7 / Curiosity 3
      - Alexander Mare
        - Alexander — *ECLIPSE* 12 / Grecian Princess 13
        - Highflyer Mare — *HIGHFLYER* 13 / Alfred Mare 2
    - Bacchante (1809)
      - Williamson's Ditto
        - *SIR PETER* — *HIGHFLYER* 13 / Papillon 3
        - Arethusa — Dungannon 33 / Prophet Mare 7
      - Mercury Mare
        - *MERCURY* — *ECLIPSE* 12 / Tartar Mare 9
        - Herod Mare — *HEROD* 26 / Folly 8
  - **Trampoline (1825)**
    - Tramp (1810)
      - *DICK ANDREWS*
        - Joe Andrews — *ECLIPSE* 12 / Amaranda 4
        - Highflyer Mare — *HIGHFLYER* 13 / Cardinal Puff Mare 9
      - Gohanna Mare
        - Gohanna — *MERCURY* 9 / Herod Mare 4
        - Fraxinella — *TRENTHAM* 5 / Woodpecker Mare 3
    - Web (1808)
      - *WAXY*
        - POT 8 O'S — *ECLIPSE* 12 / *SPORTSMISTRESS* 38
        - Maria — *HEROD* 26 / Lisette 18
      - Penelope
        - Trumpator — Conductor 12 / Brunette 14
        - Prunella — *HIGHFLYER* 13 / Promise 1
- **Florine (RH) (1854)**
  - **Medoc (RH) (1829)**
    - American Eclipse (RH) (1814)
      - Duroc (RH)
        - *DIOMED* — Florizel 5 / Sister To Juno 6
        - Amanda (RH) — *TAYLOES GREY DIOMED* / Virginia Cade Mare
      - Millers Damsel
        - Messenger (EH) — Mambrino 20 / Turf Mare 1
        - Pot 8 O'S Mare — *POT 8 O'S* 38 / Gimcrack Mare 3
    - Young Maid Of The Oaks (RH) (1817)
      - Expedition
        - Pegasus — *ECLIPSE* 12 / *BOSPHORUS MARE* 13
        - Active — *WOODPECKER* 1 / Laura 2
      - Maid Of The Oaks (RH)
        - Spread Eagle — Volunteer 9 / Highflyer Mare 5
        - Annette (RH) — *SHARK* 56 / Rockingham Mare (RH)
  - **Melody (RH) (1837)**
    - Haxalls Moses (1816)
      - Sir Harry
        - *SIR PETER* — *HIGHFLYER* 13 / Papillon 3
        - Matron — Alfred 12 / Marske Mare 4
      - Mermaid
        - *WAXY* — *POT 8 O'S* 38 / Maria 18
        - Promise
    - Moses Mare (RH) (1825)
      - Blackburns Whip (RH)
        - Whip — *SALTRAM* 7 / Herod Mare
        - Speckleback (RH) — Randolphs Celer (RH) / Old Speckleback (RH)
      - Harts Maria (RH)
        - Craigs Alfred (RH) — *MEDLEY* 3 / Wildair Mare (RH)
        - The Pryor Mare (RH) — Pryor / Running Horse

Aerolite RH 1861

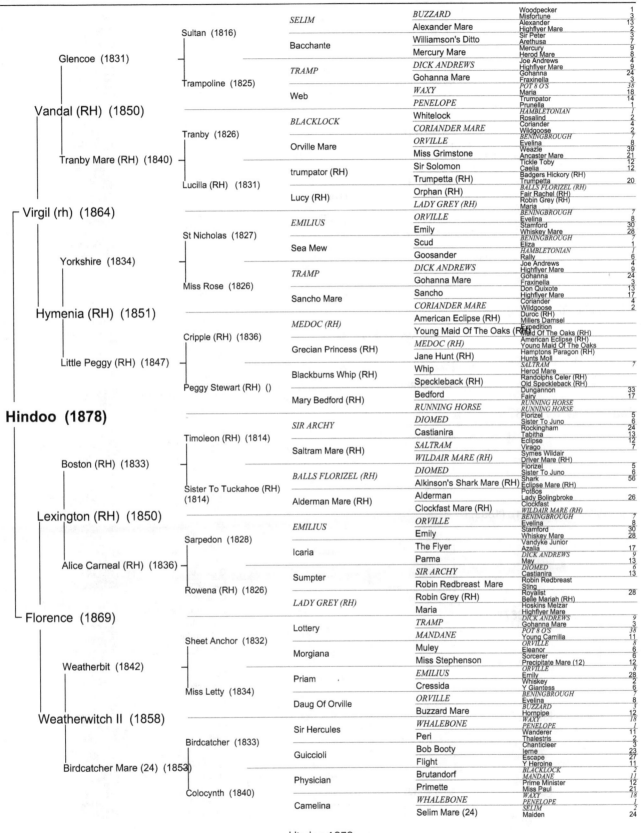

Hindoo 1878

Mannie Gray (1874)

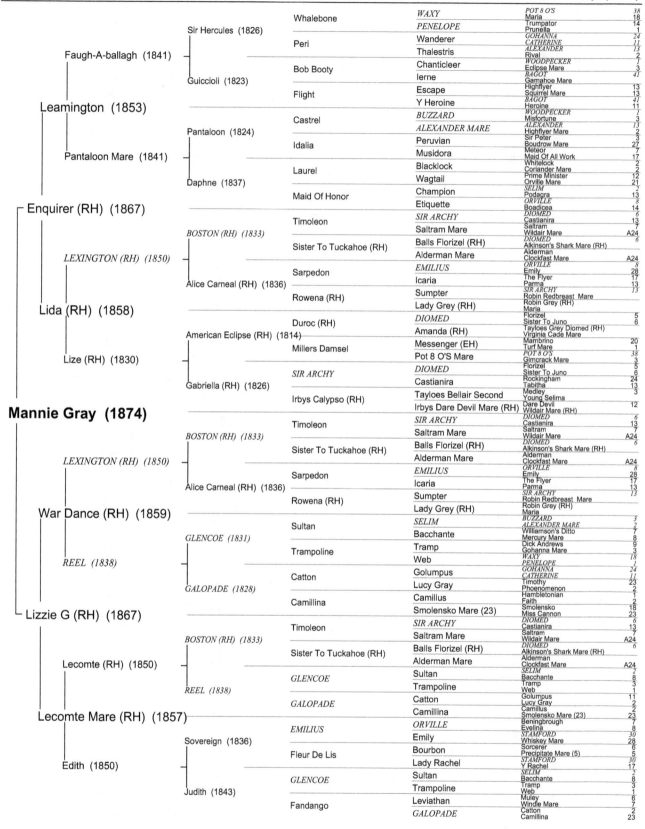

- **Mannie Gray (1874)**
  - **Enquirer (RH) (1867)**
    - Leamington (1853)
      - Faugh-A-ballagh (1841)
        - Sir Hercules (1826)
          - Whalebone
            - *WAXY* — *POT 8 O'S* 38 / Maria 18
            - *PENELOPE* — Trumpator 14 / Prunella 1
          - Peri
            - Wanderer — *GOHANNA* 24 / *CATHERINE* 11
            - Thalestris — *ALEXANDER* 13 / Rival 2
        - Guiccioli (1823)
          - Bob Booty
            - Chanticleer — *WOODPECKER* 1 / Eclipse Mare 3
            - Ierne — *BAGOT* 41 / Gamahoe Mare
          - Flight
            - Escape — Highflyer 13 / Squirrel Mare 13
            - Y Heroine — *BAGOT* 41 / Heroine 11
      - Pantaloon Mare (1841)
        - Pantaloon (1824)
          - Castrel
            - *BUZZARD* — *WOODPECKER* 1 / Misfortune 3
            - *ALEXANDER MARE* — *ALEXANDER* 13 / Highflyer Mare 2
          - Idalia
            - Peruvian — Sir Peter 3 / Boudrow Mare 27
            - Musidora — Meteor 17 / Maid Of All Work
        - Daphne (1837)
          - Laurel
            - Blacklock — Whitelock 2 / Coriander Mare
            - Wagtail — Prime Minister 12 / Orville Mare 21
          - Maid Of Honor
            - Champion — *SELIM* 2 / Podagra 13
            - Etiquette — *ORVILLE* 8 / Boadicea 14
    - Lida (RH) (1858)
      - *LEXINGTON (RH) (1850)*
        - *BOSTON (RH) (1833)*
          - Timoleon
            - *SIR ARCHY* — *DIOMED* 6 / Castianira 13
            - Saltram Mare — Saltram 7 / Wildair Mare A24
          - Sister To Tuckahoe (RH)
            - Balls Florizel (RH) — *DIOMED* 6 / Alkinson's Shark Mare (RH)
            - Alderman Mare — Alderman / Clockfast Mare A24
        - Alice Carneal (RH) (1836)
          - Sarpedon
            - *EMILIUS* — *ORVILLE* 8 / Emily 28
            - Icaria — The Flyer 17 / Parma 13
          - Rowena (RH)
            - Sumpter — *SIR ARCHY* 13 / Robin Redbreast Mare
            - Lady Grey (RH) — Robin Grey (RH) / Maria
      - Lize (RH) (1830)
        - American Eclipse (RH) (1814)
          - Duroc (RH)
            - *DIOMED* — Florizel 5 / Sister To Juno 6
            - Amanda (RH) — Tayloes Grey Diomed (RH) / Virginia Cade Mare
          - Millers Damsel
            - Messenger (EH) — Mambrino 20 / Turf Mare
            - Pot 8 O'S Mare — *POT 8 O'S* 38 / Gimcrack Mare 3
        - Gabriella (RH) (1826)
          - *SIR ARCHY*
            - *DIOMED* — Florizel 5 / Sister To Juno 6
            - Castianira — Rockingham 24 / Tabitha 13
          - Irbys Calypso (RH)
            - Tayloes Bellair Second — Medley 3 / Young Selima
            - Irbys Dare Devil Mare (RH) — Dare Devil 12 / Wildair Mare (RH)
  - **War Dance (RH) (1859)**
    - *LEXINGTON (RH) (1850)*
      - *BOSTON (RH) (1833)*
        - Timoleon
          - *SIR ARCHY* — *DIOMED* 6 / Castianira 13
          - Saltram Mare — Saltram 7 / Wildair Mare A24
        - Sister To Tuckahoe (RH)
          - Balls Florizel (RH) — *DIOMED* 6 / Alkinson's Shark Mare (RH)
          - Alderman Mare — Alderman / Clockfast Mare A24
      - Alice Carneal (RH) (1836)
        - Sarpedon
          - *EMILIUS* — *ORVILLE* 8 / Emily 28
          - Icaria — The Flyer 17 / Parma 13
        - Rowena (RH)
          - Sumpter — *SIR ARCHY* 13 / Robin Redbreast Mare
          - Lady Grey (RH) — Robin Grey (RH) / Maria
    - *REEL (1838)*
      - *GLENCOE (1831)*
        - Sultan
          - *SELIM* — *BUZZARD* 3 / *ALEXANDER MARE* 2
          - Bacchante — Williamson's Ditto 7 / Mercury Mare 8
        - Trampoline
          - Tramp — Dick Andrews 9 / Gohanna Mare 3
          - Web — *WAXY* 18 / *PENELOPE* 1
      - *GALOPADE (1828)*
        - Catton
          - Golumpus — *GOHANNA* 24 / *CATHERINE* 11
          - Lucy Gray — Timothy 23 / Phoenomenon 2
        - Camillina
          - Camillus — Hambletonian 1 / Faith 2
          - Smolensko Mare (23) — Smolensko 18 / Miss Cannon 23
  - **Lizzie G (RH) (1867)**
    - Lecomte (RH) (1850)
      - *BOSTON (RH) (1833)*
        - Timoleon
          - *SIR ARCHY* — *DIOMED* 6 / Castianira 13
          - Saltram Mare — Saltram 7 / Wildair Mare A24
        - Sister To Tuckahoe (RH)
          - Balls Florizel (RH) — *DIOMED* 6 / Alkinson's Shark Mare (RH)
          - Alderman Mare — Alderman / Clockfast Mare A24
      - *REEL (1838)*
        - *GLENCOE*
          - Sultan — *SELIM* 2 / Bacchante 8
          - Trampoline — Tramp 3 / Web 1
        - *GALOPADE*
          - Catton — Golumpus 11 / Lucy Gray 2
          - Camillina — Camillus 2 / Smolensko Mare (23) 23
    - Lecomte Mare (RH) (1857)
      - Sovereign (1836)
        - *EMILIUS*
          - *ORVILLE* — Beningbrough 7 / Evelina 8
          - Emily — *STAMFORD* 30 / Whiskey Mare 28
        - Fleur De Lis
          - Bourbon — Sorcerer 6 / Precipitate Mare (5) 5
          - Lady Rachel — *STAMFORD* 30 / Y Rachel 17
      - Edith (1850)
        - Judith (1843)
          - *GLENCOE*
            - Sultan — *SELIM* 2 / Bacchante 8
            - Trampoline — Tramp 3 / Web 1
          - Fandango
            - Leviathan — Muley 6 / Windle Mare 7
            - *GALOPADE* — Catton 2 / Camillina 23

Mannie Gray 1874

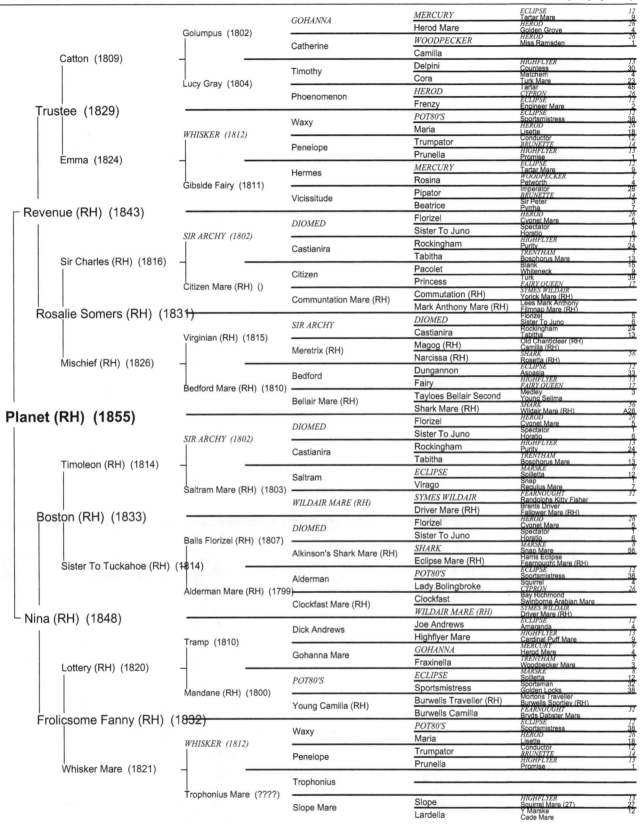

Planet RH 1855

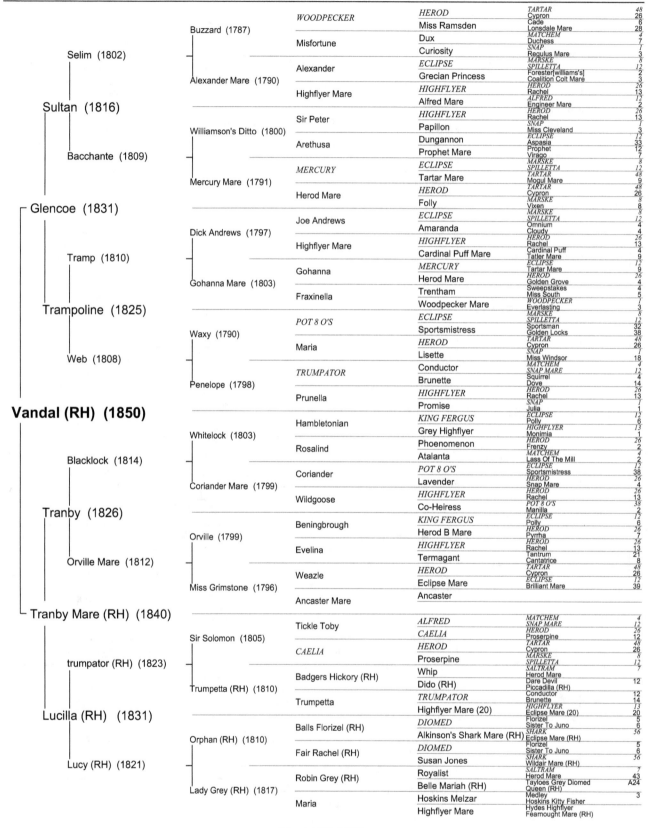

Left-side lineage:

- **Vandal (RH) (1850)**
  - Glencoe (1831)
    - Sultan (1816)
      - Selim (1802)
      - Bacchante (1809)
    - Trampoline (1825)
      - Tramp (1810)
      - Web (1808)
  - Tranby Mare (RH) (1840)
    - Tranby (1826)
      - Blacklock (1814)
      - Orville Mare (1812)
    - Lucilla (RH) (1831)
      - trumpator (RH) (1823)
      - Lucy (RH) (1821)

Sire/Dam (year)	Parent	Grandparent	Ancestor	#
Buzzard (1787)	*WOODPECKER*	*HEROD*	*TARTAR*	48
			Cypron	26
		Miss Ramsden	Cade	6
			Lonsdale Mare	28
	Misfortune	Dux	*MATCHEM*	4
			Duchess	7
		Curiosity	*SNAP*	1
			Regulus Mare	3
Alexander Mare (1790)	Alexander	*ECLIPSE*	*MARSKE*	8
			SPILLETTA	12
		Grecian Princess	Forester[williams's]	2
			Coalition Colt Mare	3
	Highflyer Mare	*HIGHFLYER*	*HEROD*	26
			Rachel	13
		Alfred Mare	*ALFRED*	12
			Engineer Mare	2
Williamson's Ditto (1800)	Sir Peter	*HIGHFLYER*	*HEROD*	26
			Rachel	13
		Papillon	*SNAP*	1
			Miss Cleveland	3
	Arethusa	Dungannon	*ECLIPSE*	12
			Aspasia	33
		Prophet Mare	Prophet	12
			Virago	7
Mercury Mare (1791)	*MERCURY*	*ECLIPSE*	*MARSKE*	8
			SPILLETTA	12
		Tartar Mare	*TARTAR*	48
			Mogul Mare	9
	Herod Mare	*HEROD*	*TARTAR*	48
			Cypron	26
		Folly	*MARSKE*	8
			Vixen	8
Dick Andrews (1797)	Joe Andrews	*ECLIPSE*	*MARSKE*	8
			SPILLETTA	12
		Amaranda	Omnium	4
			Cloudy	4
	Highflyer Mare	*HIGHFLYER*	*HEROD*	26
			Rachel	13
		Cardinal Puff Mare	Cardinal Puff	4
			Tatler Mare	9
Gohanna Mare (1803)	Gohanna	*MERCURY*	*ECLIPSE*	12
			Tartar Mare	9
		Herod Mare	*HEROD*	26
			Golden Grove	4
	Fraxinella	Trentham	Sweepstakes	4
			Miss South	5
		Woodpecker Mare	*WOODPECKER*	1
			Everlasting	3
Waxy (1790)	*POT 8 O'S*	*ECLIPSE*	*MARSKE*	8
			SPILLETTA	12
		Sportsmistress	Sportsman	32
			Golden Locks	38
	Maria	*HEROD*	*TARTAR*	48
			Cypron	26
		Lisette	*SNAP*	1
			Miss Windsor	18
Penelope (1798)	*TRUMPATOR*	Conductor	*MATCHEM*	4
			SNAP MARE	12
		Brunette	Squirrel	4
			Dove	14
	Prunella	*HIGHFLYER*	*HEROD*	26
			Rachel	13
		Promise	*SNAP*	1
			Julia	
Whitelock (1803)	Hambletonian	*KING FERGUS*	*ECLIPSE*	12
			Polly	6
		Grey Highflyer	*HIGHFLYER*	13
			Monimia	1
	Rosalind	Phoenomenon	*HEROD*	26
			Frenzy	2
		Atalanta	*MATCHEM*	4
			Lass Of The Mill	2
Coriander Mare (1799)	Coriander	*POT 8 O'S*	*ECLIPSE*	12
			Sportsmistress	38
		Lavender	*HEROD*	26
			Snap Mare	4
	Wildgoose	*HIGHFLYER*	*HEROD*	26
			Rachel	13
		Co-Heiress	*POT 8 O'S*	38
			Manilla	2
Orville (1799)	Beningbrough	*KING FERGUS*	*ECLIPSE*	12
			Polly	6
		Herod B Mare	*HEROD*	26
			Pyrrha	7
	Evelina	*HIGHFLYER*	*HEROD*	26
			Rachel	13
		Termagant	Tantrum	21
			Cantatrice	8
Miss Grimstone (1796)	Weazle	*HEROD*	*TARTAR*	48
			Cypron	26
		Eclipse Mare	*ECLIPSE*	12
			Brilliant Mare	39
	Ancaster Mare	Ancaster		
Sir Solomon (1805)	Tickle Toby	*ALFRED*	*MATCHEM*	4
			SNAP MARE	12
		CAELIA	*HEROD*	26
			Proserpine	12
	CAELIA	*HEROD*	*TARTAR*	48
			Cypron	26
		Proserpine	*MARSKE*	8
			SPILLETTA	12
Trumpetta (RH) (1810)	Badgers Hickory (RH)	Whip	*SALTRAM*	7
			Herod Mare	
		Dido (RH)	Dare Devil	12
			Piccadilla (RH)	
	Trumpetta	*TRUMPATOR*	Conductor	12
			Brunette	14
		Highflyer Mare (20)	*HIGHFLYER*	13
			Eclipse Mare (20)	20
Orphan (RH) (1810)	Balls Florizel (RH)	*DIOMED*	Florizel	5
			Sister To Juno	6
		Alkinson's Shark Mare (RH)	*SHARK*	56
			Eclipse Mare (RH)	
	Fair Rachel (RH)	*DIOMED*	Florizel	5
			Sister To Juno	6
		Susan Jones	*SHARK*	56
			Wildair Mare (RH)	
Lady Grey (RH) (1817)	Robin Grey (RH)	Royalist	*SALTRAM*	7
			Herod Mare	43
		Belle Mariah (RH)	Tayloes Grey Diomed	A24
			Queen (RH)	
	Maria	Hoskins Melzar	Medley	3
			Hoskins Kitty Fisher	
		Highflyer Mare	Hydes Highflyer	
			Feamought Mare (RH)	

Vandal RH 1850

Chapter 8

The Squeeze

Pierre Lorillard, American breeder, brought eight horses over to England to test them against their English cousins—one of those was a horse named Parole.

The squeeze on American bloodlines in England began earlier than the 1913 ruling of the Jersey Act. It all started with the stunning performance by an American-bred gelding Parole 1873. Up until this time very few American racehorses were seen in England—as we were recovering from our own Civil War and our horse industry had suffered greatly. This was still at the dawn of our American Thoroughbred breed, as the classic race standard and the new studbook with pedigree requirements was only adopted in 1868. At that time England and America had a reciprocal arrangement, in that any American racer that qualified for the American studbook was automatically accepted into the English book and vice versa. But that was before the English experienced the power and talent of our American breed firsthand.

The meeting of the American racer with its English counterpart began slowly and modestly. England, as mentioned before, did not care to condescend to compete with our horses—they truly believed that no other population of racer could ever approach theirs in class. But in America, by the mid-1800s, the breeders had been importing the English Thoroughbred for one hundred years, and they had already found by 1800 that the classic-tested version was lacking in stamina and soundness—and having adopted the classic form of racing in America in 1868, the American sportsmen were itching to test their stock against the best the English had, and they were willing to travel to England to try it.

Richard Ten Broeck in 1856 was the first to attempt this endeavor. With the financial backing of Frank Morris, he gathered together a few of his top racers and brought them to England. His string included Pryor RH (Glencoe son out of an American Eclipse RH dam), Prioress (Sovereign daughter), and the great four-miler Lecomte RH (Boston RH son). Tragedy struck almost immediately—first of all the horses had a hard time recovering from the trans-Atlantic trip and then adjusting to their new home, and then worse, the stable conditions were atrocious, and the trainer was negligent.

> "Disaster attended Mr. Ten Broeck's venture from the outset. His horses did not become acclimated, so as to make good running, they were not well cared for by the trainer, and the much-vaunted British love of fair play was scantily manifested towards them" (Lyman Weeks).

Within the first year all three top stars were seriously ill, and Lecomte RH and Pryor RH died. However, against all odds, the filly Prioress had recovered by late in the season, enough so that she was able to race in the Ceasarwitch—a two-mile/two-furlong race, with over thirty of England's finest, where she dead-heated for first with Queen Bess and El Harkim. This required a rerunning, and it was in this second round that she showed the true mettle of the American-bred when she bested her opponents by a length and half.

Ten Broeck stayed in England for several years, replacing his lost stock. Prioress was joined by other American horses such as Starke RH and Umpire RH, all of who won their share of races, and they stayed on to breed there. However, the English press of the period reports that the American-breds were not quite up to the English in class. Overall, Ten Broeck's horses, while not quite the smashing success he had hoped for (and having lost his best racers to illness), even with what he had left they had performed well enough that the British attitude toward the American-bred had shifted from a complete discounting to a reserved respect.

After Ten Broeck, not much went on with American horses racing in England then until 1875 when Mr. Sanford brought over a small string to try his luck. His group included three sons of Lexington RH: the two-year-olds Big Final and Brown Prince as well as the older stallion Preakness RH—a full brother to Big Final. Although his success was spotty also, he continued on until 1881. In 1876 he had a few victories including a stakes win by the young Big Final. In 1877 he had a notable winner in Brown Prince who won the Rowley Mile, and then he came in a game second to Chamant in the 2000 Guineas.

However, the big change occurred when the American sportsman Pierre Lorillard brought over eight of his racers in 1878. His string included Uncas (by Lexington RH), Friar (by Saxon out of Revenue RH dam), Boreas (by Saxon out of Lexington RH dam), Cherokee (by Saxon, out of Vandal RH line dam), Papoose (filly by Leamington out of Lexington RH dam), Nereid (all English bred), Geraldine (filly by Saxon out of Virgil RH dam), and Parole (full brother to Papoose) who was substituted for Duke of Magenta when he became ill. (Many of these sons and daughters of Lexington RH, Vandal RH and others, had qualified for inclusion in the new American studbook, and so they do not have RH after their names).

At home Parole had amassed several victories against the best of his class, including the great Pimlico race of 1877—the Baltimore Special (illustration at beginning of Chapter 6) —when he beat the best racers of his era: the Lexington RH son Tom Ochiltree and Ten Broeck. Bred by Pierre Lorillard, Parole was a son of imported Leamington out of Maiden RH (daughter of Lexington RH)—this mare is found also on the dam line of Nearco. He was a last-minute draft by Lorillard as he took the place of Lorillard's best racer, the Duke of Magenta, who had come down with a respiratory illness and therefore could not race.

The 'American Mule' Parole—he defeated the best the British had and did it in three races in less than a week. —etching by Henry Stull, found in *Famous Horses 1877*

Although Parole was brought to England with a group of excellent American racers by Pierre Lorillard in hopes of capturing a English victory, Lorillard's goals for victory did not rely on Parole who was now an older horse, rather he was only expected to be used in the pace setting and the work before the events. (By this time it was apparent that the younger horses had an easier time adjusting and recovering from the trip and the stress of being put into a new environment. So Parole's stellar race record aside, it was assumed he would not fully acclimatize—being six-years-old—so he was not expected to perform at top level.)

Before he was slated to race, the British enjoyed ridiculing Parole—calling him the 'Yankee Mule' in the newspapers. It wasn't his excellent race record that made them so smug; rather it was his breeding, which was all Running Horse on his dam side. To say the race was an upset is to put it too mildly. By the time of the race he was seven, yet the 'mule' Parole defeated the best English racehorse of the day, the famous and undefeated four-year-old Isonomy, in the 1879 running of Newmarket Handicap (Isonomy's only defeat). This outcome sent shock waves through the British press. But that was just for starters, for less than a week later Parole was entered in the prestigious City and Suburban Handicap against their proper English horses, and he won that as well, and then **on the very next day** he ran in the Great Metropolitan Handicap and won that also. His performance stunned the British, who were forced to eat several servings of humble pie. It wasn't just the fact that Parole polished off their best that stung; it was he did it in three major races within a week! The English racer could no longer perform like that as they no longer had the stamina that the selection for four-mile heat racing produces. Parole racked up a few more victories while he was there as well as some losses. No longer was he referred to in the press as the Yankee Mule, instead he was respectfully titled the 'Hero of Two Continents' (Vosborough). When he returned home, the gelding continued racing until he was twelve. His lifetime record is one hundred thirty-nine starts/fifty-nine wins (with this wonderful racing record we can safely assume that this is not just a bloodline of talent, but of extreme toughness and soundness as well).

It wasn't long after Parole that Lorillard had added a few more to his string—one of these was a horse named Iroquois. Perhaps Parole's performance could have been written off as a fluke, but then the American-bred Iroquois took both the English Derby and the St. Leger in 1881, and the American-bred could no longer be explained away. Iroquois was a registered American Thoroughbred, but he was out of a Running Horse dam—his entire bottom half was Running Horse;

The English Derby winner Iroquois.
—image from Thoroughbred Record

his second dam was a ½ sister to Lexington RH. His dam, Maggie B. B. RH, became a legendary producer, not just of Iroquois, but her daughter Jaconet produced Belmont Stakes winner Sir Dixon who became a very good sire, and her son Harold won the Preakness. In our time Maggie B.B. RH has become recognized as an important taproot mare, thanks to Ellen Parker (*reine-de-course*) for much of this, but back then Maggie B.B. RH was considered 'common' (more on Maggie B.B. RH in Chapters 9 and 11).

Both Parole and Iroquois are sons of the English Thoroughbred Leamington, and in most accounts that give an explanation for their success, the writers point to Leamington as the source of their racing class. Leamington was well-bred and a good classic distance racer; however his race record was both good and erratic, and he had only a fair stud record in England. He was sold to the US, and it was here that he made his mark. Rated as a horse with a delicate constitution, when he was bred to our more robust American mares he led the sire list four times. His best offspring such as Enquirer RH, Iroquois, Aristides, and others were possessed of Lexington RH or Boston RH dam-lines. Unfortunately, it is fairly certain that he also transmitted vascular weakness to his progeny as several had career-ending occurrences of ruptured arteries—that is, he produced bleeders. He was also noted as a transmitter of bad disposition: "But all the Leamington horses I have ever known were more or less vicious, whether sons or grandsons," (Hildalgo—TB Record).

We will see this tendency to value the English bloodlines while ignoring the American Running Horse contribution when we read about Lexington's stud career—many saying his success is due exclusively to the Glencoe mares he was bred to. But you will see (next chapter) that attitude just doesn't hold water—all of these—both English-bred and American-bred—were excellent racehorses, with great potency and racing genetics. Were Lexington RH and Boston RH and their like lesser horses than the English stallions of their day? Of course not, history has proven it is not so. As breeders we need to wake up and look clearly at the sources of genetic strength in our pedigrees.

"Foxhall proved himself to be a most wonderful animal, and actually and collaterally better at weight for age then the Derby winners—Bend Or and Iroquois." —quotation and illustration from *Famous Horses*, Taunton

Shortly after Lorillard's successes, another top American breeder, James Keene, got together a string of his racers and set up shop in England also, which included the incomparable Foxhall.

But in the late 1800s the situation kept heating up. It was bad enough to have Iroquois come in and win both the Derby and the St. Leger in 1881, but then there was the sensation Foxhall 1878, by King Alfonso (a stallion with an American Running Horse dam-line) out of Jamaica, a Lexington RH daughter. Foxhall raced and won in both France and England; he won the Paris Grand Prix 1881 then came to England and won the Grand Duke Michael Stakes, the prestigious Cesarewitch, the Select Stakes, and the Cambridgeshire—in the latter he trounced no other than the stellar Bend Or and Tristan, as well as other first-class racers. Although it now turns out that "Bend Or" was not Bend Or—he was instead a ringer called Tadcaster (see Appendix C). And there was no English bred sire here to point to in Foxhall—he is undeniably American bred on both sides of his pedigree.

Asmodeus of the London Standard said of Foxhall in November of 1881:

> "To look at Foxhall is a grand trial for any person who loves the thoroughbred…I think he is the handsomest horse I ever saw, and his most recent performances show us that he is as good as beautiful. I have not now the slightest hesitation in dubbing Foxhall the crack of the season, and I feel sure that over the course of the six furlongs or upwards he would beat his fellow-countryman Iroquois. It is not a little singular that the Americans should be represented by two such swell as Iroquois and Foxhall in one season."

And L. J. Jimmy in London reporting for the New York World said:

"Everybody now admits that Foxhall is the best three-year-old in the world."

Needless to say, from that point on the American-bred horse was seriously respected by the British, because between 1879 and 1882 sixteen home-breds won the most important races in England: Iroquois, Parole, Pappoose, Wallenstein, Foxhall, Bookmaker, Don Fulano, Merced, and Aristocrat were all big winners.

But after 1882 there was a lull in the American invasion. The American campaign of those years was a hard act to follow, first because of the cost and logistics of maintaining a stable in England. Plus there was another factor that arose. The British sportsmen started raiding the claiming races to buy up many American horses out of those races, and then return with them in English colors to win. One example of a 'claimed' racer was Passaic (by Longfellow RH out of Jury RH by Lexington RH), and he won the prestigious City and Suburban for his new English owner.

Some of the more independent breeders in England also reacted to the talent found in the American horses, not by shutting down, but by opening up, buying some breeding stock in spite of the disapproval of the racing establishment—that is before the Jersey Act squashed this movement. Here is an example: the good racehorse Preakness RH, a son of Lexington RH, was brought to England by Mr. Sanford and then was purchased by the Duke of Hamilton to stand as one of his stallions. Preakness RH, although a good racer and sire, didn't leave as much legacy as he might have because his breeding career was ended after he developed a vicious temperament that ultimately forced the Duke to have him shot.

W. S. Vosborough reports on Preakness in his 1922 *Racing in America:*

"When *Preakness* made his appearance at Baltimore for the Dinner Party Stakes of '70, people asked of Mr. Stanford 'expected to beat Foster with a cart-horse.' The track was fetlock deep in mud and the 'cart-horse' not only seemed at home in it but beat his field handily. It was his first race, as he had never started at two, and the race was late in October. An enormous colt he was, but people who called him a 'cart-horse' did not know that the family of his dam, Bay Leaf, was generally inclined to race best in flesh. But when the following spring he came out and won the Westchester Cup from Glenleg and Helmbold, he had fined down considerably. He soon after went amiss, as the horses of that family did when drawn fine, and only recovered in the autumn to win the Maturity Stakes at 3 miles. In 1872 he did little, having sustained an injury to his loin; but in 1873 and 1874 he began to play a prominent part in racing, carrying the high weights. In 1875, when eight years old, he seemed better than ever before, winning the Baltimore Cup with 131 pounds, and was third to Wildidle for the Fordham Handicap at Jerome Park, conceding 27 pounds to the winner._

Preakness RH, a son of Lexington RH who was sent to England to race when he was eight years old. —from an etching found in *Famous Horses 1877*

"The culmination of the career of Preakness in America was his dead heat with Springbok for the Saratoga Cup of '75. The field was perhaps the highest in point of quality that ever started for that historic event, Grindstead, Olitipa, Aaron Penington, Wildidle and Rutherford finishing behind the dead heaters. The same autumn Mr. Sanford sent Preakness and his entire stable to England. The old horse, however, was not what he had been. The Duke of Hamilton purchased him for the stud, where he sired Fiddler, the horse which defeated Foxhall for the Alexandra Plate. Preakness was a bay, son of Lexington and Bayleaf by Yorkshire, therefore a full brother to Bayonet and Beacon, but taller and more massive."

In the beginning of the post-Civil War era when American horses were entering into the English classic contests, most of the American runners were like Iroquois, in that they raced in England but then they returned home to breed.

However, not all of them did this; for instance there was Sibola whose second dam was Perfection, a full sister to Parole, and she won the 1899 running of the 1000 Guineas, and she was also entered into the GSB. An even earlier example is Umpire RH, bred by Richard Ten Broeck, an American breeder discussed previously, who regularly raced and bred in the British Isles; Umpire RH was entered into vol. X of the GSB. The Running Horse Umpire 1857 is by Lecomte RH, Lexington's greatest rival on the track and at stud, who is actually his ½ brother, and Umpire RH is out of the same dam as Lexington RH: Alice Carneal RH, and therefore he is a ¾ brother to Lexington RH. However it wasn't long before he was exported from England to Russia, but not before he sired a few foals in England.

One of those foals by Umpire RH was a filly named Wrangle, born in 1875, and she has an interesting history. When the English studbook was squeezing out the American lines, some of their own bloodlines couldn't meet the new guidelines either. A very good stallion named Shogun 1910 was one of those—his dam-line was unverified, so he was classified as a half-bred and used in the production of steeplechase racers, and while his progeny could race on the flat they could not be entered into the GSB. In 1919 he was bred to a mare named Finale 1908, whose second dam was Wrangle, the daughter of the American Running Horse Umpire—however, because Umpire RH had been accepted into the studbook years before the crackdown, this meant that Wrangle qualified for it also. The foal was a filly named Verdict 1920, who ironically was ineligible for the GSB, not because of the flawed American line, but because of the English unverified line from her sire Shogun. Verdict therefore was classified as half-bred. Verdict HB was a very good racer, but she also proved to be a great producer, as her daughter Quashed HB (also ineligible for the GSB) won the Oaks (Epsom) and then won the Ascot Gold Cup—against colts. (In modern times, after the repeal of the Jersey Act, many of these horses and others previously excluded were given their rightful place in the GSB).

Verdict HB 1920—a great English racer and broodmare who was a casualty of the Jersey Act, as her English sire's dam-line was unverified. Verdict is descended from Alice Carneal RH, the dam of Lexington RH—Thoroughbred Record.

Another English breeder, Lord William Beresford, owned several American-bred winners before the crackdown, including Diakka by The Sailor Prince out of Rizpah whose third dam was Maiden RH by Lexington RH. Beresford also owned the mare Jiffy II, also by The Sailor Prince, whose dam was 4x4 to Lexington RH; later he sold this mare to Federico Tesio. This mare was destined to play a role in Tesio's career as a breeder as she produced his first big winner: Fidia.

The next wave of 'Yankee mules' was brought into the British Isles by her own prodigal son and 'black sheep,' Richard Croker. Born in Ireland, Croker escaped the potato famine with his family by emigrating to New York. He was an enterprising guy, and after a series of short careers he entered politics. Croker quickly gained a reputation as a renegade, and he found his niche in the corrupt political machine of Tammany Hall in NY. He thrived there and rose to the top where he was given the nickname 'the Boss'. When the exposing of graft and other scandals brought down the Tammany group, it was then Croker hotfooted it back to Ireland. He brought with him some fine American-bred racehorses; included in them were two who made racing history through their progeny: Americus and Rhoda B.

Americus 1892, bred in California by 'Lucky' Baldwin, was originally named Rey de Carreras. He was a high-class sprint racer known for winning under heavy weights. Americus is inbred 2x2 to the full siblings The Nun RH and Norfolk RH, who are by Lexington RH out of Novice RH, a Glencoe daughter. Seeing the Lexington RH/Glencoe nick is possibly the greatest sport horse typesetting combination in sport history, Americus was a great carrier of extreme talent. But there is even more athletic dominance in his line, because Novice, the Glencoe daughter, is out of a Running Horse mare named Chloe Anderson who is 2x2 to full brothers Sir Archy of Montorio RH and Sir William of Transport RH, both by Sir Archy out of the great Running Horse broodmare Transport, present by a son and daughter—which insured the full potency rides through. Inbreeding to full siblings is one of the strongest genetic designs you can create in your lineages—here is Americus with two close to the front of the pedigree; he is extremely potent (see Appendix B—Evaluating Pedigrees).

Novice RH, dam of Norfolk RH and The Nun RH, is inbred to the full brothers Sir Archy of Montaro RH and Sir William of Transport RH—both by Sir Archy out of the RH mare Transport. —from a painting by Troye.

Americus raced in Britain, winning some sprints, but then he stood stud for only a few years in Ireland and was not used much; then he was sent to Italy for two years, and following that he came back for only a year to England before he was sold to Germany, where he died in 1910. Therefore his stud career was severely curtailed, and he left relatively few offspring (see Chapter 18 for his offspring in Germany).

Americus's pedigree is a map of massive genetic power—as it is 2x2 to the full siblings Norfolk RH/The Nun RH. Even with his very limited stud career, a few of his offspring produced a lasting and extremely deep footprint in the international Thoroughbred. Americus Girl, Lady Americus, Mrs. K, and a few others were enough to produce such significant racers and bloodstock that they imparted a change and upgrading to the British horse, of which the pinnacle is the Lady Josephine family. Lady Josephine was duly registered in the General Stud Book, and her descendants—especially through her daughters Mumtaz Mahal and Lady Juror—are the backbone of the modern English Thoroughbred: Nasrullah, Royal Charger, Mahmoud, Fair Trial, Sansonnet, Tudor Minstrel, and Riot are just some of this legacy. This is a speed line—whether sprint or classic length, it is known for its ability to pass on extreme speed.

Lesser known, but of interest to sport horse breeders, is the Americus daughter Alabama, who is out of Rhoda B; as she had a decent broodmare career in Germany—so you can keep an eye out for her in your sport horse lineages (see Chapter 18).

Another of Croker's imports was Rhoda B—also dam of Alabama mentioned above, an American-bred mare who started an English racing family through her son Orby, who is by the English sire Orme. Rhoda B is by Hanover (who heads up his own American family Chapters 9 and 10). Hanover carries a Lexington RH daughter, out of a mare who has Rescue RH and Nina RH—both by Boston RH and therefore ½ siblings to Lexington RH, so a saturation of Boston RH/Lexington RH type, with a tremendous filly factor of Alice Carneal RH 5x5 through both a son and a daughter. At long odds Orby won the English Derby, and then he won the Irish Derby as well. Then, this 'long shot' started an Anglo dynasty of racers and sires that includes the lines of The Boss 1910 and Gold Bridge 1929. Rhoda B also produced the fantastic race mare Rhodora who easily won the 1000 Guineas. "Rhodera was far and away the best filly in the Thousand…she won in a canter" (London June 8, 1908).

During this period the unease with these American race-stealers grew. However, all of the above and a few more made it in to the studbook before 1909 when rule #XXI was drafted limiting further registration to animals descended from individuals already in the studbook. This blocked some of the American lines, but allowed others like Nearco with the American mare Sibola on his dam-line to later be registered, and the descendants of Lady Josephine were all allowed as she was a 1908 studbook entry, as were those by Rhoda B and her son Orby. But other lines of Hanover (sire of Rhoda B), and of Americus and Lexington RH along with other American lines were excluded from the book.

'Still they Come', London Sportsman October 24, 1908:

> "English and Irish breeders are complaining of the American Invasion, and I do no wonder at it…during the past week we have seen seventy five American yearlings sold for fair prices, and the cry is—Still they come!…It is not, as a 'rule', judicious to suggest in the press to the Jockey Club stewards how they should or should not act, but on this subject I venture to submit for consideration that all American yearlings should be charged a much more substantial registration to qualify them to race in England…."

The writing was already on the wall by this point on how they were going to stem the American tide—that it would be by questioning the 'purity' of our bloodlines. The hypocrisy of this pretense was well apparent to the American owners and breeders, and they knew this was just a smoke screen. John Hervey writing under the name Salvador had this to say on the 'purity' of the English Stud Book:

"That the amount of myth perpetuated in the pages of Weatherby's is by no means small no reasonable being can deny…it is not both plausible and picturesque to believe that the Godolphin Arabian, Darley Arabian and the Byerly Turk were all lineal descendants in tail male of Pegasus himself? Whatever the first two were, we know that that Arabs they were not, nor is there any more credible testimony that the third was a Turk…"

Sir Martin 1906 raced and bred in England, and then he came home to stand stud. —photo by W. A. Rouch

But the tide of American-breds entering Europe kept rising. Starting right around the turn of the century (1900) other disturbing upsets were occurring with greater regularity when American-bred horses would win English contests. Sir Martin was a most unlucky American horse, having fallen in the Derby of 1909, of which it is generally conceded he would have won otherwise. "But for having a fall at Tattenham Corner, Sir Martin would have won the English Derby of 1909—at least that was the general opinion" (*Thoroughbred Types*). Sir Martin kept racing and next year proved his class, as we see reported from London on June 2, 1910, "There is much happiness among the Americans tonight. All are saying 'I told you so' for at last Sir Martin justified the claim of his American breeder Mr. John Madden. That good horse…trounced a brilliant field in the Coronation Cup at Epsom today…Sir Martin achieved his victory with so much ease that everyone sympathized with his present owner Mr. Louis Winans, for not gaining last year's Derby laurels."

"Rubio"
Grand National, 1908

Rubio 1908—he won the Aintree Grand National—another flawed American-bred. Cigarette trading cards were collected by the followers of horse racing with enthusiasm. —courtesy of the New York Public Library digital collection.

Sir Martin also won the Durham Stakes and Challenge Stakes while in England, and because of his successes John Madden repurchased him from Louis Winans and brought him home to stand stud. However, Sir Martin did leave some offspring in the British Isles, and you will come across them in English and Irish pedigrees from time to time. He also became a good sire in America; for instance he is the fifth dam-sire of Palace Music—the sire of the great Cigar.

Then, James Haggin's California-bred Rubio 1908 took the Aintree Grand National. Then August Belmont's Norman won the 2000 Guineas—both of these stars have Lexington RH mares on their dam-lines.

And then William Vandebilt's Northeast won the Grand Prix at Longechamp and took the fabulous purse of $80,000.

By then the anti-American racehorse campaign was heating up rapidly, and the final push to exclude our horses arrived when yet another ill-conceived rule was made; this time it was in America, when betting at racetracks was banned in New York in 1910. This rule had far-reaching consequences, because at that time New York was one of the largest centers of racing and breeding in America, plus it was a big buyer of Kentucky's bloodstock, so when betting at racetracks was banned it sent the entire domestic racing industry into a downward spiral, resulting eventually in racetracks closing. The American owners and the breeders then **increased** their exports to Europe to try to save their investments. For instance, H.B. Duryea moved his entire operation to France, and from there his Sweeper II came into England and took the 1911 running of the 2000 Guineas. Even though this rule was quickly repealed (in 1912), it had already resulted in the racing British Isles believing they would now be overwhelmed by the American horses, so they decided that strong and immediate action was necessary to stop the invasion, and hopefully finish off the breed as well (see Appendix A).

On December 10, 1910, Mr. Allison, the Special Commissioner of the London Sportsman, reported:

> "Let me state that a petition to the Jockey Club stewards has been prepared and is in course of signature by British and Irish breeders and owners of bloodstock, the object being to restrict the importation (for sale) of American yearlings and older racing stock...the petition referred to will be available for signature at the December Sales."

England was not alone in their desire to rid themselves of the American racers, for in Argentina on October 9, 1910, the American Thoroughbred was banned by the Buenos Aires Jockey Cup, when they ruled that their races were now only open to Argentina-bred horses.

It was apparent to the British since the time of Parole's upsets that most of the great American racers and stallions were descended from Lexington RH or his family, and they were winners wherever they went. Lexington RH and his 'ilk' were not of full English Thoroughbred blood. Therefore changing the studbook rules could take care of the problem of American Thoroughbreds overwhelming the English and Irish breeders and racers. The rules were changed to exclude any horse with the 'flaw' in its lineage—except for those already allowed into the studbook. Because Lexington RH is the equivalent in the American racehorse as Eclipse is in English pedigrees—in that he was the bedrock of top performance, therefore his bloodline and those of his near relatives were just about everywhere in the American racer—this then effectively slammed the door shut on the American racehorse and its bloodlines.

All this culminated in May of 1913—as reported in the Dublin Sport:

> "At the meeting of the Jockey Club Lord Villier said that "...the importance of the question became more apparent every year, because more horses were imported from America, and when the owners of doubtfully bred American horses saw horses of similar breeding in the Stud Book, they not unnaturally claimed the same privileges for their own horses...the idea of admitting animals of doubtful breeding, such as Colin and Americus, on their own performances, however brilliant, was entirely contrary to the whole principle of the Stud Book...whether in view of the fact that a new volume of the Stud Book will be published this year...that the last sentence of the first paragraph of the preface be added to, to read as follows: '..no horse or mare can, after this date, be considered as eligible for admission unless it can be traced without flaw on both sire's and dam's side of its pedigree to horses and mares themselves already accepted in earlier volumes of the book."

Thus the Jersey Act was enacted, and the American-bred was now a pariah in Thoroughbred breeding—worldwide. By phrasing the rule the way they did, it bypassed the ancestry of previously accepted horses like Sibola, Orby, Lady Josephine, Umpire RH, Starke RH, but still excluded all others that were carriers of Lexington RH and his relatives; all in all this was very surgically and effectively done.

Looking back on this event, American sportsman Ned Welch in 1946 recaps the actions and reactions that led to this punitive act:

> "Their success was sensational and set a pattern destined to be of far reaching influence, for it was to be followed in later years by a number of American owners that, between them, were to carry off, at one time and another, practically every one of the historic 'classics' of the British calendar, from the Derby down, also the great handicaps, cups, plates, etc., etc., until in sum total their showing became really wonderful when it was considered that they were just a little groups of invaders opposed by the entire strength of the British turf organization.

> "These horses, moreover, were American-bred, with very few exceptions, and their pedigrees showed elements that the British had allowed to die out at home and affected to look down upon as inferior...just as a member of the Jockey Club and House of Lords looked down upon their owners are plebian 'Yankees', whom they utterly despised and hated despicably.

> "Time passed and the resentment of the Jockey Club toward the horses from across the Atlantic and their prowess became deep-seated and embittered. It began, therefore, to cast about for means to rid itself of their unwelcome presence—made doubly unwelcome because a good many American strains of blood were being

taken up by less snobbish British breeders and beginning to crop up in the pedigrees of British-bred stakes horses and 'classic winners', thus demonstrating beyond fear of successful contradiction their value as outcrosses for the fashionable British blood-horses" (read the entire article in Appendix A).

The folly of the new rule became apparent almost immediately. In 1914—just a year after the rule change—Durbar II, a French-bred TB (H.B. Duryea) took the English Derby. Durbar's second dam Urania, who was not only a daughter of Hanover (by Hindoo out of Vandal RH daughter), but had an additional line of Lexington RH on her dam-line; there was no way around it: Durbar did not qualify under their new rules. Of course Durbar was entered into the French studbook.

Player Cigarette card depicting Durbar II.
—courtesy of NY Public Library digital collection

As time went on some of England's home-bred winners could not qualify either, including the sensational mare Quashed HB and her dam Verdict HB mentioned above. And it only got worse; the French typesetter Tourbillon and his fantastic offspring were ineligible, as was the American sire Fair Play and his great son Man O' War, and the German Derby winners descended from Grave and Gay, and on and on. By the end, 1948, England and Ireland were way behind the curve in racing class, and that fact and financial reality, combined with the strong French objection to participation in a studbook that barred the best racehorses—then, finally in 1949, the infamous Jersey Act was emasculated with a new rule that allowed most of the strains previously excluded to then be listed.

[Read more on the Jersey Act in Appendix A, articles written just before the Act was ended, one by Ned Welch in 1947 and the other an account by the Thoroughbred Racing Association (TRA) in 1944—they are a poignant recounting of the American breeder's experience of the Jersey Act and the worldwide results, plus the announcement in England of the repeal in 1949. These writings bring home to us how the American breeders felt about this rule, and the scope of damage that was done to our Thoroughbred Industry. It was a mean-spirited rule, which might have been excused as a knee-jerk reaction to the perceived unstoppable wave of superior American horses, except for the fact the American stables had mostly gone home after 1912 with the reopening of racing in New York, and they left fully by the 1920s, yet this rule remained in place for **36 years** (during which time America spent its resources and lives in defense of these same allies in two World Wars); therefore its true target cannot be hidden, it was plain to the breeders then and should be to us now, that its intent was to destroy the competition, the American Thoroughbred.]

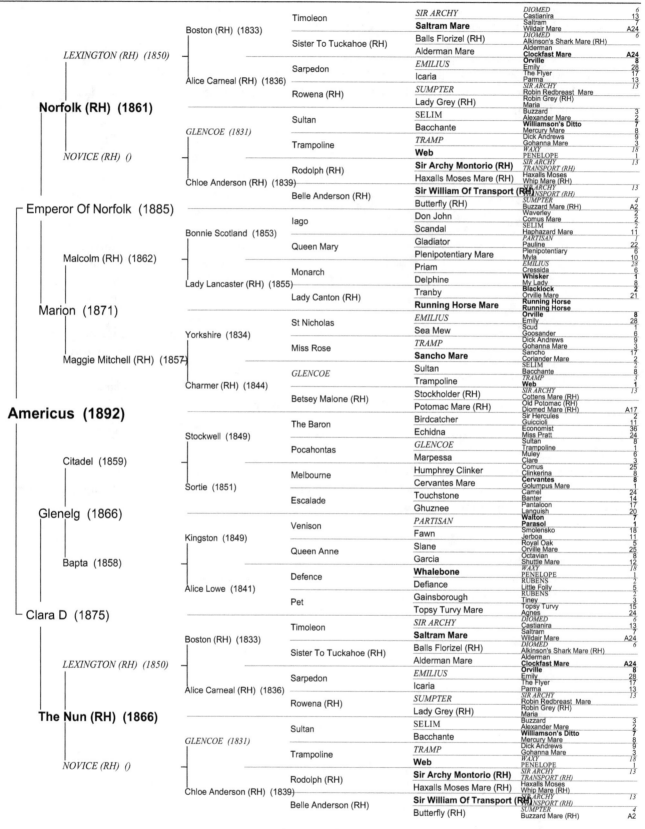

		Timoleon	*SIR ARCHY*	*DIOMED* 6
				Castianira 13
	Boston (RH) (1833)		**Saltram Mare**	Saltram 7
				Wildair Mare A24
		Sister To Tuckahoe (RH)	Balls Florizel (RH)	*DIOMED* 6
LEXINGTON (RH) (1850)				Alkinson's Shark Mare (RH)
			Alderman Mare	Alderman
				Clockfast Mare A24
		Sarpedon	*EMILIUS*	**Orville** 8
				Emily 28
	Alice Carneal (RH) (1836)		Icaria	The Flyer 17
				Parma 13
		Rowena (RH)	*SUMPTER*	*SIR ARCHY* 13
Norfolk (RH) (1861)				Robin Redbreast Mare
			Lady Grey (RH)	Robin Grey (RH)
				Maria
		Sultan	SELIM	Buzzard 3
				Alexander Mare 2
	GLENCOE (1831)		Bacchante	**Williamson's Ditto** 7
				Mercury Mare 8
		Trampoline	*TRAMP*	Dick Andrews 9
				Gohanna Mare 3
NOVICE (RH) ()			**Web**	*WAXY* 18
				PENELOPE 1
		Rodolph (RH)	**Sir Archy Montorio (RH)**	*SIR ARCHY* 13
	Chloe Anderson (RH) (1839)			*TRANSPORT (RH)*
			Haxalls Moses Mare (RH)	Haxalls Moses
				Whip Mare (RH)
		Belle Anderson (RH)	**Sir William Of Transport (RH)**	*SIR ARCHY* 13
				TRANSPORT (RH)
Emperor Of Norfolk (1885)			Butterfly (RH)	*SUMPTER* 4
				Buzzard Mare (RH) A2
		Iago	Don John	Waverley 2
				Comus Mare 2
	Bonnie Scotland (1853)		Scandal	SELIM 11
				Haphazard Mare
		Queen Mary	Gladiator	*PARTISAN* 1
				Pauline 22
Malcolm (RH) (1862)			Plenipotentiary Mare	Plenipotentiary 6
				Myla 10
		Monarch	Priam	*EMILIUS* 28
				Cressida 6
	Lady Lancaster (RH) (1855)		Delphine	**Whisker** 1
				My Lady 8
		Lady Canton (RH)	Tranby	**Blacklock** 21
Marion (1871)				Orville Mare
			Running Horse Mare	**Running Horse**
				Running Horse
		St Nicholas	*EMILIUS*	**Orville** 8
				Emily 28
	Yorkshire (1834)		Sea Mew	Scud 1
				Goosander 6
		Miss Rose	*TRAMP*	Dick Andrews 9
				Gohanna Mare 17
Maggie Mitchell (RH) (1857)			**Sancho Mare**	Sancho 2
				Coriander Mare 2
		Sultan	SELIM	Bacchante 8
	GLENCOE		Trampoline	*TRAMP* 3
				Web 1
	Charmer (RH) (1844)	Betsey Malone (RH)	Stockholder (RH)	*SIR ARCHY* 13
				Cottens Mare (RH)
			Potomac Mare (RH)	Old Potomac (RH)
Americus (1892)				Diomed Mare (RH) A17
		The Baron	Birdcatcher	Sir Hercules 2
				Guiccioli 11
	Stockwell (1849)		Echidna	Economist 36
				Miss Pratt 24
		Pocahontas	*GLENCOE*	Sultan 8
				Trampoline 1
Citadel (1859)			Marpessa	Muley 6
				Clare 3
		Melbourne	Humphrey Clinker	Comus 25
				Clinkerina 8
	Sortie (1851)		Cervantes Mare	**Cervantes** 8
				Golumpus Mare 1
		Escalade	Touchstone	Camel 24
				Banter 14
			Ghuznee	Pantaloon 17
Glenelg (1866)				Languish 20
		Venison	*PARTISAN*	**Walton** 7
				Parasol 1
	Kingston (1849)		Fawn	Smolensko 18
				Jerboa 11
		Queen Anne	Slane	Royal Oak 5
				Orville Mare 25
Bapta (1858)			Garcia	Octavian 8
				Shuttle Mare 12
		Defence	**Whalebone**	*WAXY* 18
				PENELOPE 1
	Alice Lowe (1841)		Defiance	RUBENS 2
				Little Folly 5
		Pet	Gainsborough	RUBENS 2
				Tiney 15
Clara D (1875)			Topsy Turvy Mare	Topsy Turvy 15
				Agnes 24
		Timoleon	*SIR ARCHY*	*DIOMED* 6
				Castianira 13
	Boston (RH) (1833)		**Saltram Mare**	Saltram 7
				Wildair Mare A24
		Sister To Tuckahoe (RH)	Balls Florizel (RH)	*DIOMED* 6
LEXINGTON (RH) (1850)				Alkinson's Shark Mare (RH)
			Alderman Mare	Alderman
				Clockfast Mare A24
		Sarpedon	*EMILIUS*	**Orville** 8
				Emily 28
	Alice Carneal (RH) (1836)		Icaria	The Flyer 17
				Parma 13
		Rowena (RH)	*SUMPTER*	*SIR ARCHY* 13
The Nun (RH) (1866)				Robin Redbreast Mare
			Lady Grey (RH)	Robin Grey (RH)
				Maria
		Sultan	SELIM	Buzzard 3
				Alexander Mare 2
	GLENCOE (1831)		Bacchante	**Williamson's Ditto** 7
				Mercury Mare 8
		Trampoline	*TRAMP*	Dick Andrews 9
				Gohanna Mare 3
NOVICE (RH) ()			**Web**	*WAXY* 18
				PENELOPE 1
		Rodolph (RH)	**Sir Archy Montorio (RH)**	*SIR ARCHY* 13
	Chloe Anderson (RH) (1839)			*TRANSPORT (RH)*
			Haxalls Moses Mare (RH)	Haxalls Moses
				Whip Mare (RH)
		Belle Anderson (RH)	**Sir William Of Transport (RH)**	*SIR ARCHY* 13
				TRANSPORT (RH)
			Butterfly (RH)	*SUMPTER* 4
				Buzzard Mare (RH) A2

Americus 1892

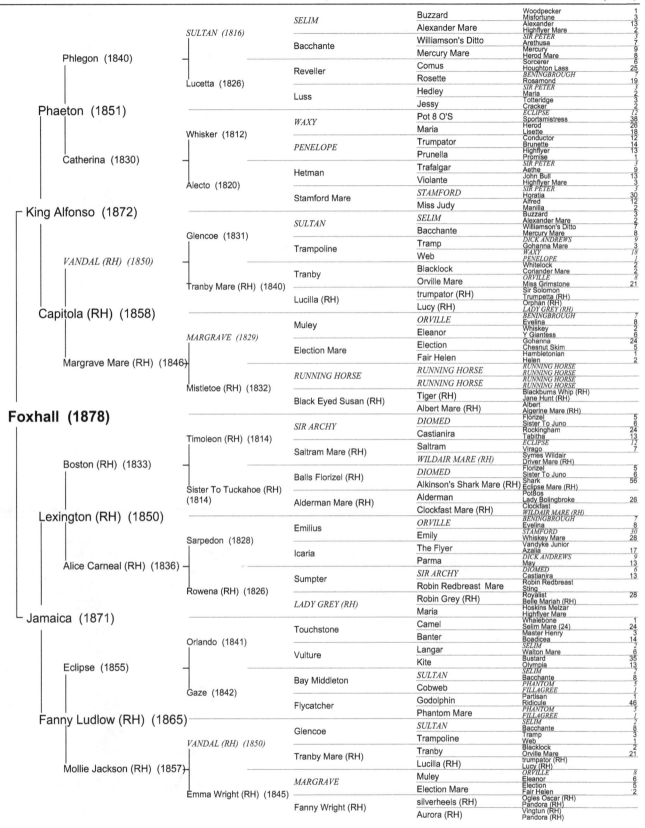

Foxhall (1878)

- **King Alfonso (1872)**
  - **Phaeton (1851)**
    - Phlegon (1840)
      - *SULTAN (1816)*
        - *SELIM*
          - Buzzard — Woodpecker 1, Misfortune 3
          - Alexander Mare — Alexander 13, Highflyer Mare 2
        - Bacchante
          - Williamson's Ditto — *SIR PETER* 3, Arethusa 7
          - Mercury Mare — Mercury 9, Herod Mare 8
      - Lucetta (1826)
        - Reveller
          - Comus — Sorcerer 6, Houghton Lass 25
          - Rosette — *BENINGBROUGH* 7, Rosamond 19
        - Luss
          - Hedley — *SIR PETER* 3, Maria 2
          - Jessy — Totteridge 3, Cracker 2
    - Catherina (1830)
      - Whisker (1812)
        - *WAXY*
          - Pot 8 O'S — *ECLIPSE* 12, Sportsmistress 38
          - Maria — Herod 26, Lisette 18
        - *PENELOPE*
          - Trumpator — Conductor 12, Brunette 14
          - Prunella — Highflyer 13, Promise 1
      - Alecto (1820)
        - Hetman
          - Trafalgar — *SIR PETER* 3, Aethe 9
          - Violante — John Bull 13, Highflyer Mare 3
        - Stamford Mare
          - *STAMFORD* — *SIR PETER* 3, Horatia 30
          - Miss Judy — Alfred 12, Manilla 2
  - **Capitola (RH) (1858)**
    - *VANDAL (RH) (1850)*
      - Glencoe (1831)
        - *SULTAN*
          - *SELIM* — Buzzard 3, Alexander Mare 2
          - Bacchante — Williamson's Ditto, Mercury Mare 8
        - Trampoline
          - Tramp — *DICK ANDREWS* 9, Gohanna Mare 3
          - Web — *WAXY* 18, *PENELOPE* 1
      - Tranby Mare (RH) (1840)
        - Tranby
          - Blacklock — Whitelock 2, Coriander Mare 2
          - Orville Mare — *ORVILLE* 8, Miss Grimstone 21
        - Lucilla (RH)
          - trumpator (RH) — Sir Solomon, Trumpetta (RH)
          - Lucy (RH) — Orphan (RH), *LADY GREY (RH)*
    - Margrave Mare (RH) (1846)
      - *MARGRAVE (1829)*
        - Muley
          - *ORVILLE* — *BENINGBROUGH* 7, Evelina 8
          - Eleanor — Whiskey 2, Y Giantess 6
        - Election Mare
          - Election — Gohanna 24, Chesnut Skim 5
          - Fair Helen — Hambletonian 1, Helen 2
      - Mistletoe (RH) (1832)
        - *RUNNING HORSE*
          - *RUNNING HORSE* — *RUNNING HORSE*, *RUNNING HORSE*
          - *RUNNING HORSE* — *RUNNING HORSE*, *RUNNING HORSE*
        - Black Eyed Susan (RH)
          - Tiger (RH) — Blackburns Whip (RH), Jane Hunt (RH)
          - Albert Mare (RH) — Albert, Algerine Mare (RH)

- **Jamaica (1871)**
  - **Lexington (RH) (1850)**
    - Boston (RH) (1833)
      - Timoleon (RH) (1814)
        - *SIR ARCHY*
          - *DIOMED* — Florizel 5, Sister To Juno 6
          - Castianira — Rockingham 24, Tabitha 13
        - Saltram Mare (RH)
          - Saltram — *ECLIPSE* 12, Virago 7
          - *WILDAIR MARE (RH)* — Symes Wildair, Driver Mare (RH)
      - Sister To Tuckahoe (RH) (1814)
        - Balls Florizel (RH)
          - *DIOMED* — Florizel 5, Sister To Juno 6
          - Alkinson's Shark Mare (RH) — Shark 56, Eclipse Mare (RH)
        - Alderman Mare (RH)
          - Alderman — Pot8os, Lady Bolingbroke 26
          - Clockfast Mare (RH) — Clockfast, *WILDAIR MARE (RH)*
    - Alice Carneal (RH) (1836)
      - Sarpedon (1828)
        - Emilius
          - *ORVILLE* — *BENINGBROUGH* 7, Evelina 8
          - Emily — *STAMFORD* 30, Whiskey Mare 28
        - Icaria
          - The Flyer — Vandyke Junior, Azalia 17
          - Parma — *DICK ANDREWS* 9, May 13
      - Rowena (RH) (1826)
        - Sumpter
          - *SIR ARCHY* — *DIOMED* 6, Castianira 13
          - Robin Redbreast Mare — Robin Redbreast, Sting
        - *LADY GREY (RH)*
          - Robin Grey (RH) — Royalist 28, Belle Mariah (RH)
          - Maria — Hoskins Melzar, Highflyer Mare
  - **Fanny Ludlow (RH) (1865)**
    - Eclipse (1855)
      - Orlando (1841)
        - Touchstone
          - Camel — Whalebone 1, Selim Mare (24) 24
          - Banter — Master Henry 3, Boadicea 14
        - Vulture
          - Langar — *SELIM* 2, Walton Mare 6
          - Kite — Bustard 35, Olympia 13
      - Gaze (1842)
        - Bay Middleton
          - *SULTAN* — *SELIM* 2, Bacchante 8
          - Cobweb — *PHANTOM* 5, *FILLAGREE* 1
        - Flycatcher
          - Godolphin — Partisan 1, Ridicule 46
          - Phantom Mare — *PHANTOM* 5, *FILLAGREE* 1
    - Mollie Jackson (RH) (1857)
      - *VANDAL (RH) (1850)*
        - Glencoe
          - *SULTAN* — *SELIM* 2, Bacchante 8
          - Trampoline — Tramp 3, Web 1
        - Tranby Mare (RH)
          - Tranby — Blacklock 2, Orville Mare 21
          - Lucilla (RH) — trumpator (RH), Lucy (RH)
      - Emma Wright (RH) (1845)
        - *MARGRAVE*
          - Muley — *ORVILLE* 8, Eleanor 6
          - Election Mare — Election 5, Fair Helen 2
        - Fanny Wright (RH)
          - silverheels (RH) — Ogles Oscar (RH), Pandora (RH)
          - Aurora (RH) — Vingtun (RH), Pandora (RH)

Foxhall 1878

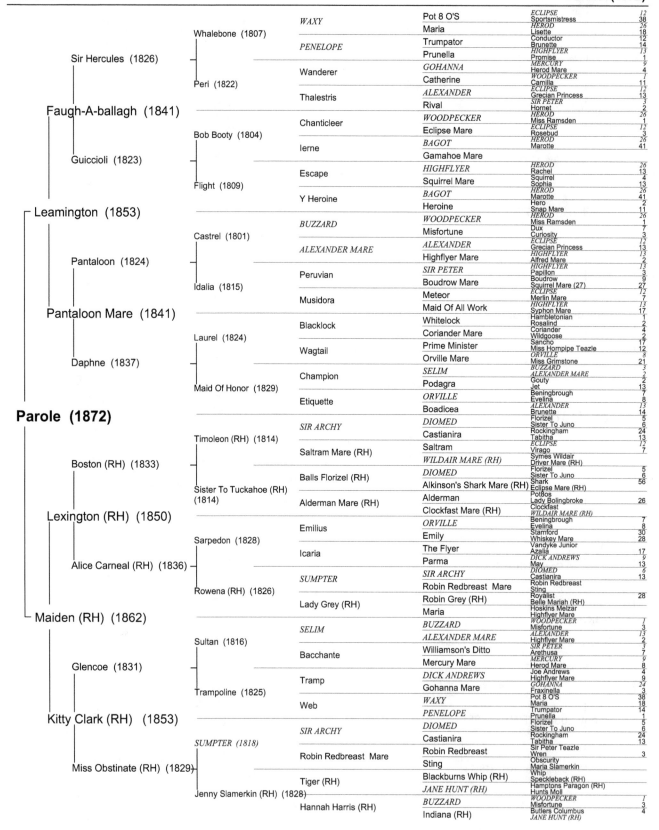

Parole 1872

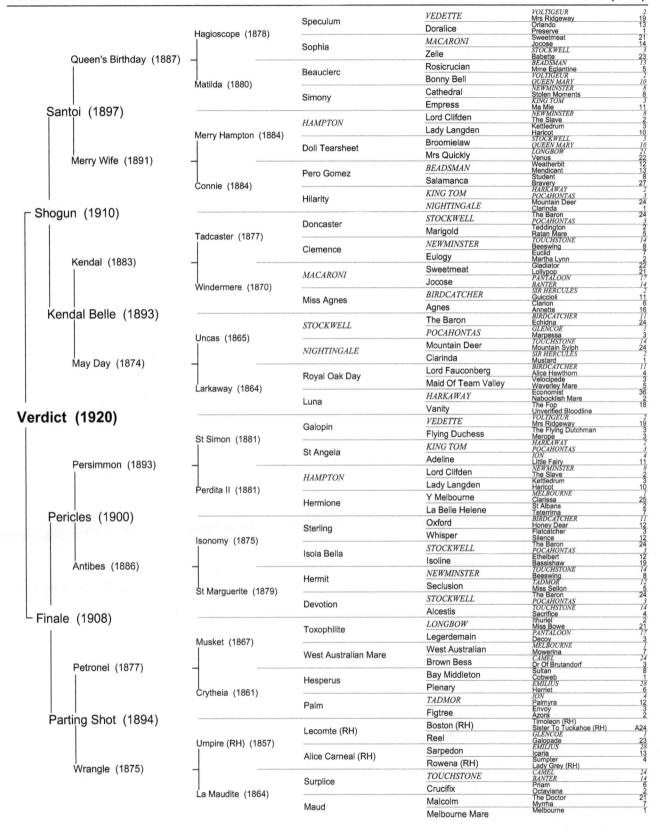

Verdict HB 1920

Part II

Foundations of the Modern Sport Performer

Chapter 9

Major American Families Emerge from the Heroic Era

As our Civil War ended and our country was immersed in rebuilding, five powerful racehorse families emerged out of the dust. These following five families have made an indelible mark on our modern sport and racehorses—providing the very best sport resources for the breeder then and now.

Our sport horse view of what constitutes a family is slightly different from what the Thoroughbred industry uses. You will often read in articles and books by Thoroughbred authorities that a famous sire-line has faded out—that it no longer has a representative in the modern era; for instance Lexington RH is lamented as no longer having a living representative (Faversham). What is typically being talked about is that there is no direct tail-male descendent. This way of looking at things is a tool that is expedient and simple, but it is far from accurate in showing us dominance. As we know Lexington RH and his relatives permeate the background bloodlines of all our American light horse breeds, as does Janus, Fearnought, Blackburns Whip RH, Sir Archy, American Eclipse RH, Boston RH, Glencoe, Vandal RH, and Diomed—they are the bedrock of the American sport horse. The same holds true to 'female families,' or dam-lines, when they are declared to have died out, or when attributing dominance to the female family, what they are looking at is the direct tail-female descent. The pedigree, and therefore the genetics, of a sport horse encompass far more than the direct tail-female or –male lines, and in many cases the true dominance in the lineage is not demonstrated by a representative in those lines (see Aspidistra in Chapter 21). It does not make sense to view the genetics from the pedigree this way exclusively, and throughout this book we will discuss the genetics as seen in the pedigree through the lens of what we can Tesio Methods—see Understanding Pedigrees—Appendix B. Statistically these factors have been shown to illustrate true dominance (Harper—*Thoroughbred Breeders Handbook*).

Hanover 1884, the best son of Hindoo, was banned as a 'half-breed,' yet he was a great racer and important stud; his bloodline is found behind many of the greatest sport horses of today—even in Europe. —image found in Thoroughbred Record

We look at those two tail lines as the providers of the Y and X chromosome material holding the sex-linked factors that travel on the X chromosome, plus the mtDNA, and while these factors are very important in our evaluations, they may not represent the true dominance in the pedigree. As far as sex-linked material goes—which is carried on the X chromosome—we tend to forget that a mare has two X chromosomes. One of the Xs comes up the dam-line; however at any point it may be replaced by that particular dam's sire's X, as each sire gives an X chromosome to his daughters. So the X the mare passes on to her foals may not be from her dam, it could be from her sire's dam. Try to see this; the X chromosome can be supplied from two sources in a mare whereas the mtDNA always comes up the tail-dam-line.

Each pedigree is an individual design, like a fingerprint, it differs from all others (except full siblings) in some ways. Dominance is built from concentration and empowering of the genetics, this can encompass the tail-female and tail-male lines or not. As breeders we need to examine the entire pedigree to understand the horse itself and to enable us to determine the best mates for our sport goals. In this book then we will not limit our view of the important horses to their tail-male line or their female family—it is too restrictive.

Enquirer RH—by Leaminton out of Lida RH, a Lexington RH daughter—was a great stallion from our Heroic Era; he is the sire of Mannie Gray and dam-sire of Domino. —from a painting by Troye

A good example of this is Mannie Gray—a genetic giant in our American bloodlines (pedigree at the end of Chapter 7), but when you read about her sources of quality, it is usually exclusively attributed to the three lines of the good mare Galopade through two different daughters 4x5x6 found in her dam Lizzie G RH, and sometimes mention is made she is by a son of the English sire Leamington. But did you ever read that she also is 3x3x3 to Lexington RH and his ½ brother Lecomte RH—sex-balanced—and that those sires influence three of the dam-lines? Or that her dam-sire is the Lexington RH son War Dance RH? This is a clear illustration for us, as this is a significant genetic configuration, and the line of Lexington's daughter in the sire Enquirer RH actually sits on his dam-line, so it would have provided one of Mannie Gray's two X chromosomes—therefore possibly half of the sex-linked traits; this then shows some of the limitations of the current popular method of pedigree evaluation.

We often can gain valuable insights from noting which offspring of a key sire or mare are the best—whether in performance or breeding—and then looking at their pedigrees to see which of the elements they built on from their parent. In Mannie Gray's case, her daughter Lady Reel gave us the key sire Hamburg. Lady Reel brought in three more lines of Lexington RH to add to Hanover's two; it is her strongest dominance. Three of Mannie Gray's offspring are full siblings: Domino/Correction/Mannie Himyar—these are all outstanding progenitors. What do they have in common? They all are by a sire—Himyar—that is out of a daughter of Lexington RH. Then that is the power they connected to in the dam so is the leading dominance in those individuals. These are Mannie Gray's best offspring—these are the ones who have made the strongest genetic impression on our sport horse lineages—and what do they build on? It is Lexington RH again!

Does that mean Galopade and her daughters are of no account? No, of course not, they are surely a large part of the reproductive and performance success of those horses and are the source of half of the X chromosomes—the sex-linked material—and they transfer the mtDNA, so then the Galopade family provides a very strong and potent design, and we know that building up mare lines is a proven way to success; my point is, this is not the full story. We will visit Mannie Gray and her outstanding progeny at the close of this discussion (Chapter 14). Also, because of the requirements to enter the English General Studbook and the various changes of their 'rules', many horses were left out of pedigrees intentionally or others substituted to make horses qualify for the strict pedigree guidelines, and many of these deceptions went undetected or were even ignored, resulting in whole sections of that revered studbook in our modern day being discovered to be in error (through DNA evaluations). Of course, most American horses could not qualify with the inception of the Jersey Act anyway. In America we experienced the same level of 'fudging' in Edgar's 1833 Race and Turf Register, where a great many pedigrees were 'enhanced' (falsified), while other American lines were expunged or not entered at all. (See Appendix C for a partial list of horses with erroneous parentage). The errors in our stud history were compounded when S. D. Bruce produced his *American Stud Book* (the first officially accepted book for the new Thoroughbred) —he just added information from Edgar's book without editing it.

In the English studbook a prominent example is Messenger EH—listed as a full Thoroughbred, which he is not (see *North American Sport Horse Breeder* for a discussion on this) —he is a significant bloodline in America because besides of his contribution to the American Trotter, and he has also left a strong legacy in the American Thoroughbred. One result of these revelations is we now know much of our 'common knowledge' on our racehorse breeds needs a reset. With each equine genome discovery in our day we are experiencing a remodel of our records and our beliefs, as previously unknown documentation or the mapping of the equine genome exposes the truth of the parentage.

The Five American Families that have Shaped Top Equine Sport Worldwide

1. Maggie B. B. RH 1867

Maggie B. B. RH.
–digital image provided by Encore Editions

Maggie, who is a mare with 'flawed' American lines in her pedigree, is a proven genetic powerhouse emerging from our Heroic Era of racing. Her unfashionable pedigree kept her from being fully appreciated until modern times. For instance, in our day, when Thoroughbred pedigree expert Ellen Parker devised the *reine-de-course* list, which identifies the important mares (blue hens), she discovered that Maggie B. B. RH deserves a rightful place as a formidable foundation mare (www.reines-de-course.com). Maggie B. B. RH's pedigree is found after Chapter 11.

Just as the American Thoroughbred was being organized (1868), the Running Horse Maggie B. B. RH was born (1867). She was by the good imported English sire Australian out of Magnolia RH, a Boston RH daughter, so technically (date of birth and parentage) she is a Running Horse.

[Note: It was only a portion of our original Running Horse breed that entered the 'Thoroughbred' studbook. Other branches of our racehorse specialized in different types of racing—pacing, trotting, sprint, and also as saddle horses—and we, breeders of sport horses, can exploit these other sources as well.]

It is interesting, that these parents of Maggie B. B. RH make her a close relative (¾) to the Aerolite RH/Spendthrift family. By anyone's standards she is an extraordinary mare, as she was a top class racer, winning three out of seven starts and placing second in the other four—racing against the best colts of her time. She then retired to stud and produced fifteen foals, three of them stakes winners: Harold 1876 won the Preakness, Iroquois 1877 won the English Derby and St. Leger (see Chapter 8), and Panique 1881 won the Belmont. Two of her daughters established strong American families, Jaconet (full sister to Iroquois and Harold) and Red-and-Blue (full sister to Panique). Maggie B. B. RH had four mates in her stud career: Leamington and Alarm produced the above named offspring, but her matings with Reform and Woodlands had mediocre results. Maggie had seven foals by Leamington, but all seemed to have some sort of physical weakness, and from this mating Lord Clifton, Pera, and Magnum Bonum were also unremarkable in racing or at stud—lacking the speed and vitality needed to succeed. Her daughter Francesca by Leamington was a decent mare, especially through her daughter Frances Hindoo, a good broodmare by Hindoo, from whom the great sire Rosemont descends. Jaconet—the great producer of her daughters, also by Leamington—actually had a condition commonly called 'big head'—usually caused by low levels of calcium. Plus the best racers of the seven offspring, Harold and Iroquois, were both retired after a burst artery rendered them less able to win from then on—symptomatic of bleeders—a trait coming from the delicate Leamington.

Alarm, although demonstrating his finely drawn conformation, appears overall to be sounder than Leamington.
—image from *Celebrated Horses*-Taunton 1888

The two by Alarm seemed sounder; however Panique had a reoccurring splint that caused him problems. Red-and-Blue was never raced.

We find that soundness issues increased in our racehorse population once the extreme testing of the heat race was abandoned. With a shorter test standard that was performed with younger stock (two- and three-year-olds), many weaknesses would be camouflaged by their youth—and might not show up until they were older or with those lesser demands put on the athlete, animals with lesser athleticism often bred on. Plus we were bringing in more English lines, which had a century of the easier performance testing behind them and were therefore from a breed that had more unsoundness and less stamina than our own.

In Maggie's case, when we look for a source of the weakness in her offspring, her sire imported Australian was one of the better English

Old Rosebud, Kentucky Derby winner, a descendant of Maggie B. B. RH by her grandson Uncle. —image from *Thoroughbred Types*

imports of his time, and he reliably transmitted speed with soundness, even though he had fertility problems. Her dam-sire Boston RH raced forty-five times, mostly in four-mile heat races, and except for being blind (which may have been caused by an infection) he retired sound. Glencoe, aside from being a transmitter of lordosis (sway-back) was a remarkably sound line also. The vascular weakness (burst artery during racing in two of her sons) then probably doesn't come from Boston RH, Australian, or Glencoe, and none of these progenitors can be deemed weak in the category of their progeny—all three are acknowledged sires of sound, resilient horses. So that leaves us with the English mates she was bred to.

Therefore **Maggie is the sound portion of her off-spring**—her mates appear to be who brought in weakness. Nevertheless, this bloodline went on to produce a dynasty of superior sport horses. History has demonstrated that it was her daughters who have provided her greatest legacy. Jaconet produced the great sire Sir Dixon (Belmont winner) and from her daughter The Niece (an exceptional broodmare) came several good broodmares as well as the good stallion Uncle, the sire of the Kentucky Derby winner Old Rosebud. Her daughter Red-and-Blue, when mated with Hindoo (another American dynasty starter), gave us the top broodmare full sisters Bonnie Blue and Sallie McClelland, who when mated to Sir Dixon (Jaconet son) produced the taproot mares Audience, Martha Gorman, and the leading money earner of 1901: Blue Girl—this combination positioned Maggie B. B. RH 3x3 and can stand for us as an illustration of critical mass.

In our modern day, we find it is especially the inbred lines of Maggie B. B. RH, such as found in Audience and Martha Gorman, that are the strongest—and each heads a maternal dynasty. Look for them, especially on your dam-line designs, as they are very potent.

When we examine Maggie B. B. RH's pedigree, we see her greatest genetic dominance is ruled by the full siblings Web/Whalebone/Whisker 4x5x6x5. Full siblings in a lineage often point to the strongest genetic power, and these three (and their five other full siblings) are the backbone of the English Thoroughbred; they are so often present they are called a 'standard pattern,' which means it is more common to have them in multiples than not to (see *North American Sport Horse Breeder* for a discussion on these siblings). The key to releasing their power—which is of the highest athletic type—is to have a clear conduit to the front of the pedigree, which Maggie B. B. RH does, as her dam Madeline RH provides an open conduit for the sister Web to travel on the X chromosome right to the front where she meets up with the lines of her full brother Whisker, especially the Whisker daughter who also travels on Australian's dam-line right down to Maggie B. B. RH. This position of the Whisker daughters is surely one of the reasons Australian was so successful as a sire, as he carries this strong filly factor of Whisker daughters close up 2x3, which would enhance his ability to produce high-class offspring (see Evaluating Pedigrees—Appendix B). Australian is one of the best English Thoroughbreds imported in his time, not only the sire of the great Maggie B. B. RH but also of Spendthrift and his three full siblings, who benefitted from having him as sire. Australian is 5x4x3 to the full siblings Whalebone/Whisker with sex-balanced lines, plus he carries the top broodmare Catherine 5x6 (another filly factor). Maggie's dam Madeline RH brought in the line of the full sister Web (from Glencoe), which activated this strength.

Today the strongest lines of Maggie B. B. RH are found in the full sisters Audience and Martha Gorman, who are 3x3 to her—these mares are daughters of Sallie McClelland, a Hindoo daughter. It is always instructive to see what changes in dominance occurred when a mating is very successful. So we will take a close look at what changed or was built on to get to the super mares Sallie McClelland and Bonnie Blue. When Maggie was bred to Alarm something very good happened, especially with the daughter of this mating: Red-and-Blue. We can see that the mating brought in another Glencoe daughter—making them 3x5, and Alarm carries two full sisters: Cobweb and Phantom Mare 4x4—these are filly factors, a configuration that statistically is found in the better broodmares and stallions, so this mating provided two (see Australian above), as well as a sex-balanced double of the good sire Touchstone, a colt factor, needed for top performance.

When Red-and-Blue was bred to Hindoo, more crucial interactions occurred as Hindoo provided the sex-balance for key bloodlines: a line of the Glencoe son Vandal RH balances the daughter lines; a Birdcatcher daughter balances the son in Alarm, and closest to the front is a Boston RH son, Lexington RH, to balance the daughter in Maggie B. B. RH—3x3. With this strong pedigree structure, these mares, Bonnie Blue and Sallie McClelland, were equipped to produce high-quality colts and fillies—and so they did (more on the Maggie B. B. RH family in Chapter 11). Through these mares come the strongest and soundest branch of this family.

---

2. Hindoo 1878

Hindoo—fantastic racer and sire.
—image from *Racing in America* by Vosborough

Hindoo (Hall of Fame inductee) was also born as our heat racing was fading into past history. By then we had adopted the English form of classic length race testing as our standard for our newly organized American Thoroughbred (1868). Heat racing still remained and was performed until the turn of the century, but it was not used as the measure for the newly formed American Thoroughbred. Instead it was replaced with the much easier classic race standard. Our distance Running Horse was distained then by the breeders who were trying to make their racing stock more acceptable to English standards. This era saw most of the other branches of our Running Horse specializing and organizing into breeds of their own. For instance, in 1867 the trotting racer branch of our Running Horse had organized its own registry (American Trotter) with a 2:40 mile standard. In this time frame we also find most of the sprint racers (Quarter Horses) had migrated to the West, and the pacing Running Horse racer had been pushed out of Kentucky and was centralized by then mostly in the Missouri, Indiana and Tennessee areas. The premier saddle horse branches of our Running Horse (Plantation Horses—American Saddle Horse) were specializing regionally and by gait type. (This is a unique and important factor that should not be ignored by the American breeder: all our premier sport horse sources emerged from our original Running Horse, and therefore they have a genetic affinity for each other as they sprang from a common background—not a utility horse or farm or coach horse, but a true sport horse.)

There were great economic factors as well that pushed the distance racing industry in the dash race direction; with pari-mutual betting providing funding for race meets and the industry, the days of the great breeders who were able to support huge racing stables such as Keene, Baldwin, Haggin, Alexander, Ransom, and Lorillard were past. Racing was a much more public event—local tracks were supported by public attendance not private subscription, and the tracks had also become standardized across the country. With betting it was of course economically more beneficial to be able to hold several (one heat or 'dash') one- or two-mile races in a day, rather than to stage the one four-mile heat race.

Hindoo was tested in classic distance contests, and he had thirty wins out of thirty-five starts. He left a lasting legacy through his son Hanover and his grandson Hamburg (Chapter 10). Plus his daughters Bonnie Blue, Sallie McClelland (out of the Maggie B. B. RH daughter Red-and-Blue), and Hindoo Rose (who is 1x2 to Hindoo) head important maternal lines. In addition, Hindoo's full sister Florida also produced well, and her daughter Firenzi 1884 was inducted into the Hall of Fame because of her forty-eight wins out of sixty-two starts. Obviously there is a strong combination of speed, stamina, and toughness in this line. A half-sister to Hindoo, Blue and White, can be found in the great stayer Olambala 1906.

Firenzi 1884, a daughter of Hindoo's full sister Florida, was a fantastic racer and a valuable horse for line-breeding with Hindoo. —image from *Racing in America*

Hindoo (pedigree in Chapter 7) comprised the best bloodlines of his era: he is by Virgil RH 1864 (Glencoe grandson) out of Florence (Lexington RH daughter), and he carries other important English Thoroughbred and American Running Horse bloodlines as well: Balls Florizel RH, Blackburns Whip RH, and Whalebone/Web.

When Hindoo was mated with the taproot mare Maggie B. B. RH it produced two fabulous mares: Bonnie Blue and Sallie McClelland. Bonnie Blue began a female dynasty, and her greatest racing daughter—Blue Girl—was inbred to Maggie B. B. RH 3x3; she was the best racing filly of 1901.

Nevertheless, as great as Bonnie Blue was, perhaps an even greater broodmare was her full sister Sallie McClelland, who when bred to Sir Dixon (Jaconet son) produced the mare Audience (which puts Maggie B.B. RH 3x3) who in turn became the dam of Whisk Broom II, a great racer and sire of the twentieth century. Notice the level of greatness achieved in both these breedings when the Maggie B. B. RH lines were positioned 3x3—this is not a coincidence. Whisk Broom II also carries Ben Brush, who is another conduit of the old heat racing power. We will find, when following these important American families down through time, that often the strongest of them was the result of inbreeding or mixing with one or more of these other families, which reinforces the Heroic Era genes. Whisk Broom's greatest honors were earned the same year as the Jersey Act: Handicap Triple Crown 1913, Older male 1913, Horse of the Year 1913, and he has been inducted into the Hall of Fame. (Naturally, crossing lines of Whisk Broom II with those of Hanover will also build up and sex-balance Hindoo lines).

Hindoo's greatest son was Hanover 1884, bred by Runnymeade Farm. He was then sold to the Dwyer brother's stable in NY. This stable was a legendary racing operation but was also noted for the severity of its schedule of meets—they were terribly hard on their horses, notorious for running them into the ground, and many good horses were lamed from the unrelenting regime of racing. There was no rest for a Dwyer horse; it was raced until it either went lame or started to lose, at which point it was sold.

Luckily for Hanover he was not their leading horse when he was two, so he was not tried as hard as some, and therefore had some time to grow into himself before the heavy trials began. By the time he was three it was his turn in the hot seat. He won seventeen consecutive races, and he won the Belmont Stakes by fifteen lengths. As it happened with many of the Dwyer horses, though, he went lame as a four-year-old. However, because Hanover was such a big earner for this stable, instead of selling him off they had his foot 'nerved' so he wouldn't feel the pain, and he was brought back as a five-year-old. He then won nine of seventeen races. He was a great weight carrier as well, and he raced against the best of his class. When he was retired at six he had raced fifty times with thirty-two wins, fourteen seconds, and two thirds. The Dwyer's did not breed, so he was sold to Milton Young of Kentucky. He became leading sire in America four consecutive years: 1885 through 1889.

Hanover is 3x3 to the important heat-racing sire Vandal RH, plus he carries other Running Horse lines (Ophelia RH and Lexington RH). Hanover is found not only in our American bloodlines but in the English and French racer as well—for instance, Rhoda B (dam of English and Irish Derby winner Orby and Alabama, a broodmare who stood in Germany), is by Hanover. Hanover is also found in the good French-bred sire Chicle and in the great French champion and English Derby winner Durbar II as well as the French mega-sire Tourbillon. Hanover stood in France for a while, as did his son Halma, so don't be surprised when you run across them in your European pedigrees.

3. Bramble 1875/ Ben Brush

The family of Ben Brush begins with Bramble, a modest horse, purchased for $450 as a yearling; he was a very good racer but clearly was second best to his peer Duke of Magenta, although he did beat him once. When the Duke was shipped to England to race (Chapter 8), Bramble then won fifteen races as a three-year-old.

He is considered a very good, but not great, racehorse. However, as a sire he excelled, and when he was bred to Roseville he produced Ben Brush 1893, who was destined to lead an important American family of racers including the mega-sires Broomstick and Sweep. Bramble also sired the good runners Prince of Melbourne and Clifford, who won forty-two races. This level of soundness combined with a high athleticism is what our Heroic Era racers produced.

Bramble 1875, a great racer and head of a family of top performance. —photographer unknown

Bramble was from the moderate, imported sprinter sire Bonnie Scotland; he did little in England in breeding, because he broke down at three, but he had success here in the New World—part of that might be attributed to not only the double of Whalebone, sex-balanced 4x4, but he also carries Parasol, Whalebone's ¾ genetic sister in the fourth—complexity in bloodlines is always a potent design. Also in America he is often found with his sisters Blinkhoolie and Bonnie Doon, which brings in the sex-linked factors and demonstrably provides an upgrade to his descendants. His dam is better bred than his sire, so doubling on her has proven the key to success with this line. Bonnie Scotland's bloodline is found in many Quarter Horse racers.

Bramble's best son, Ben Brush, was out of Roseville who brought in a half-sister to Bonnie Scotland—making them 2x4—reinforcing his dam Queen Mary, plus another daughter of Yorkshire 4x5 on both dam-lines, and a sex-balance in the Lexington RH son Kentucky RH for the Lexington RH daughter Bay Flower RH making them 3x4. Bramble's dam Ivy Leaf RH was by the great imported sire Australian out of Bay Flower RH (Lexington RH daughter), so she is a ¾ sister to the great Spendthrift (and Fellowcraft et al). Maggie B. B. RH is also closely related to Spendthrift. Seeing Spendthrift began an American family of excellence himself, this too then is a clue to a strong power in Bramble. Bramble's second dam Ivy Leaf RH and Ben Brush's third dam Elastic are closely related also. Ben Brush became an important sire of not only top racing class—surprisingly he is a sound line, even with that inbreeding to the unsound Bonnie Scotland and his ½ sister. He is known for passing on a bulky frame combined with very stout legs that can carry them well at speed, and we will continue on with the families by his sons Broomstick and Sweep in further chapters. Obviously his stout American lines prevailed in his genotype.

------

4. Aerolite 1861 RH/Spendthrift 1876 et al

Aerolite RH is a maternal genetic giant, like Maggie B. B. RH preceding and Mannie Gray following; she heads a family of excellence and had several full sibling progeny to carry it on: Spendthrift/Rutherford/Fellowcraft and Miser. These full brothers are by the good English sire Australian out of the Lexington RH daughter Aerolite RH, who also carries a line of Blackburns Whip RH. They are 6x5x4x5 to the full siblings Whalebone/Whisker/Web, plus they have a rarely seen ¾ sister Mermaid in the sixth—this is the strongest genetic factor in these horses. Of lesser input is the double of Emilius 4x5 and Sir Archy 5x6 since both are only by sons, which limits how much of the genes from a sire is passed on—it is always better to have a daughter or sister line along with the son.

Kingston 1884, a son of Spendthrift, was a great racer and sire, and his line is sound and tough. — image from *Racing in America*, Vosborough

Spendthrift was a great racer, but with perpetual sore feet he did much better in soft footing, although he still managed to win the Belmont Stakes and many other races; he raced in England as well. He was named Champion-Three-Year-Old colt in America and he was a major sire. One of his best offspring was the high-class stayer and good sire Kingston, who raced until he was ten—the greatest money earner of his day. Kingston had a full sister Question who was also a good racer. Kingston's and his sister's lineage changed the genetic focus of Spendthrift from the full siblings Whalebone et al by bringing in a ½ sister to West Australian making them 3x3, plus a sex-balance for the Touchstone line 3x4, and adding another Glencoe daughter—putting them 4x4 on both dam-lines. Also of interest to line-breeders is a lovely filly factor of a Marpessa son and daughter 4x4 from his dam—Marpessa is the dam of Pocahontas.

"Kingston was a beautiful brown horse, foaled in 1884 by Spendthrift, out of Kapanga by Victorious, and was a great racehorse and sire. In fact, he had the most remarkable career of any horse that ever raced in this country, and after nine years of successful and hard campaigning retired a perfectly sound horse"(Thoroughbred Record).

Kingston was a 15.3-hand brown with a star, noted for his great feet and legs; he was such a good racer that the Dwyer brothers bought him to get him out of Hanover's way. At three he won thirteen of eighteen races, at four he won ten of fourteen, at five he won fourteen of fifteen, and at six he won ten of ten—a wonderful record, and he was kept racing until he was ten and retired sound with a record of eighty wins out of one hundred thirty-eight starts. His preferred racing distance was a mile and a quarter.

Ballyhoo Bey, a good racer son of Kingston, like his dad he was tough and resilient.
—image from *Thoroughbred Types*

His jockey said "he was the gamest, most honest horse I ever rode." This line is very sound and tough.

A good son of Kingston was Ballyhoo Bey 1898, out of Ballyhoo, a daughter of Duke of Magenta. He raced in the US and was a stakes winner; his best race was in the Futurity Stakes of 1900.

As exceptional as Kingston was, Spendthrift is best known for his son Hastings, an extremely bad-tempered and even at times savage horse, who nonetheless was a good sprinter-miler and great weight carrier (140 lbs.) when they could get him to cooperate. Extremely talented, he had enough class to win the Belmont stakes even though it was beyond his best distance. He ran the good stayer Clifford (Bramble son mentioned above) to a dead heat in the Kearney Handicap. Like Kingston above Hastings carried a sister for Australian 2x4, another Glencoe daughter 3x4, but then he also had additional lines of the full siblings—two lines of Whalebone, a Whisker son, and a line of Web (their full sister)—building on the background power. The fourth sire of Australian is Comus, and Hastings's dam brings in his ½ sister Comus Mare on her dam-line; these are all powerful configurations. Hastings led the Sires List twice, and he heads a dynasty through his son Fair Play. Hastings is often found in top show jumpers.

Spendthrift's full brother Fellowcraft 1870 was the better racehorse, as he set records in four-mile heat races which included lowering his dam-sire Lexington's record by a ¼ second, and he is probably the next most commonly seen of the full siblings as he is the dam-sire of the great Hamburg. However, the other two are not unknown; Rutherford 1871 was a good (but not great) racer and a good sire with stakes winning offspring Solid Silver and Lucky B. The least regarded of the four is

Hastings—encore editions image by Henry Stull

Miser 1877, who still managed to sire some notable fillies: the full sisters Marquise 1893 and The Rose 1896, both stakes winners. The Rose was one of the American horses who raced in France (1911). Miser's best daughter, however, is Yorkville Belle 1889, a fantastic race mare who won twenty-one of thirty-seven starts, had six seconds and three thirds, and ended up being owned by Richard Croker of Americus fame (Chapter 8). She was the US champion filly at two and at three—an amazing racer. Yorkville Belle's dam was out of a daughter of Lexington RH—putting Lexington RH daughters 2x2. (We can see this racing prowess delivered by the inbreeding to Lexington RH daughters repeated in another great racer, the sensation Imp, found in Chapter 27).

---

5. Mannie Gray 1874/Domino 1891

Mannie Gray, her best producers are Domino, Correction, Mannie Himyar, and Lady Reel—the first three are full siblings. Mannie Gray produced six stakes winners. When I evaluated the bloodlines behind the members of our sporting Hall of Fames I found that the bloodline of Domino not only stands with Fair Play (descendant of Aerolite RH) as a powerful sport transmitter, but often surpasses him in his genetic footprint in our modern sport bloodlines (see Part III and Appendix E). Domino's full sister Correction was dam of the useful sire Yankee, who is a ¾ brother to Hamburg—they all have four lines of Lexington RH, six lines of Glencoe, and five lines of Boston RH—in seven generations. Mannie Himyar's daughter Adana gave us Ariel, a very good sire who is 4x2 to the full siblings Mannie Himyar and Domino, and as mentioned above Lady Reel is the dam of Hamburg, who carries much the same inbreeding as Yankee.

Himyar, the sire of the full siblings, was by Alarm out of a Lexington RH daughter. He was a nervous horse, but raced until he was six, and he was like his son Domino in that he was best at a mile. An excellent sire, for besides the famous three full siblings, he also established lasting influence through his son Plaudit, who is found easily in modern pedigrees through his descendant Questionnaire in *chef-de-race* Rough n' Tumble. For instance the magnificent Holy Bull has thirty-two lines of Himyar (Chapter 24).

Himyar—the sire of Domino, Correction, and Mannie Himyar (out of Mannie Gray) and the sire Plaudit—was an excellent racer also. He is a source of sport talent and is found to be a background dominance in Holy Bull. —image from the Thoroughbred Record

Domino 1891 was a great sprinter, but not just 'a' sprinter—he was possibly the best ever. He was called the 'Black Whirlwind,' and no one could touch him in a mile or under—no one. He has powered the best racers and sport horses for over a century—he is a **genetic giant** in every way. He and his full siblings are powered by 3x4x4 Lexington RH, 6x5x6x6 Glencoe, 4x5x5x5 Boston RH, 6x5x7x7x6 Emilius, and 6x4 Faugh-a-Ballah/Birdcatcher. He, being inbred to Lexington RH, is genetically similar to Americus who is inbred to Lexington RH 3x3 also, plus Hamburg who is 4x4x5x5 to Lexington RH, and the French full sisters Heldifann and Durban who carry eight lines of Lexington RH in seven generations, and the utterly fantastic Beaming Beauty who has nine lines of Lexington RH in seven generations 6x7x6x7x7x7x7x7x7 (and if we extend her lineage further we find she has seventeen Lexington lines in ten generations!)—all of those sources have made a lasting impact in racing class and sport on both sides of the Atlantic, as they are the foremost purveyors of speed and racing class in our modern horse. Combined in later pedigrees they produced an outstanding upgrade in performance.

The above outline of important American families is a very simplistic review, but hopefully we can begin to see patterns of greatness—that certain lines keep appearing in the champions of sport and stud, and, in spite of all efforts to eliminate from our pedigrees the 'Flaw' and its relatives, it is these bloodlines that carry strength in our Running Horse that prevail through the generations in the champions.

There is something else very interesting here for the student of pedigree structure. The pedigree expert and scientist Clive Harper found that when he applied scientific method to the evaluation of pedigree patterns he was able to develop statistics showing which pedigree designs produced more winners (*Thoroughbred Breeders Handbook*). He discovered that **inbreeding** to ¾ siblings produced sprint speed in racehorses—even if the individuals inbred to were stamina sires. Domino is certainly a good illustration of this finding as he is inbred to the ¾ brothers War Dance RH and Lecomte RH 3x4, as well as having Lexington RH daughters 3x3—War Dance RH is a son of Lexington RH and Lecomte RH is his ½ brother. This phenomenon was found to occur with inbreeding to Janus in the colonial era. Janus raced in four-mile heat races in England and in America, but when inbred to in the Colonies he produced sprinters, and it was found that the closer the inbreeding the shorter the distance they could race well.

Harper also found that inbreeding to full siblings produces both sprint and classic distance racers. Lucky Baldwin would have to agree with that as his Rey Del Carreras (Americus) was inbred to the full siblings The Nun RH and Norfolk RH, and he was the fastest horse he had ever seen. This horse was imported to England and renamed Americus and is behind two of the most successful English racing families: Mumtaz Mahal and Lady Juror. The Nun RH and Norfolk RH are by Lexington RH out of Novice RH, a Glencoe daughter—who is in-turn inbred to full brothers by Sir Archy out of Transport RH (See more on this and other factors in Evaluating Pedigrees in Appendix B).

So inbreeding to Lexington RH, the king of stayers (with or without Glencoe), when doubled or tripled in one to three generations produces extreme speed, if the siblings are ¾ related, then they seem to be strictly sprinters—no matter the distance capabilities of the line inbred to. With ½ siblings close up it produces speed, but can be of a greater distance—depending on the rest of the lineage patterns. We can see this repeated time and again—take the Domino son Ultimus, he is 2x2 to Domino, his son High Time is 2x3x3 to Domino. They are producers of extreme speed and are powerful conduits in our modern pedigrees. However **it is a mistake to assume that Domino et al produced only sprinters**; his most successful son Commando was not a sprinter, nor was his great classic racers Celt and Colin—speed obviously was always transmitted in great measure. Commando is line-bred (not inbred) 4x5x5x5x5 to Lexington RH, and he raced and won beyond a mile—as did his progeny.

For us, the sport horse breeders, we can be certain that **inbreeding concentrates whatever is there**, and we need to be aware there is usually also a weakness in lines as well as strengths, so we could bring those traits to the fore as well as the target sport abilities—Domino's line is notorious for sore feet in some of his descendants; this is not a 'given' however, as his full sister Correction did not appear to have sore feet—she won 38 races. In our racehorse the Domino line was usually tempered by the sound, tough lines of Ben Brush and Fair Play that he was usually mixed with. This is a line to treasure, not one to avoid. Also Domino died at age six, after producing only twenty foals. When weighing the soundness factor it helps to remember that most lines have a weakness; for instance St. Simon transmitted bad temperament and sickle hocks as well as speed at any distance, the icon Glencoe transmitted swayback to **some** of his offspring. Domino's descendants Black Toney and Sweep are extremely sound for instance (We will discuss the soundness issue in Chapter 27).

A second fact concerning speed that becomes hard to ignore is that some of the most powerful modern-day transmitters of speed in England can be found in the Lady Josephine family (Americus granddaughter) —in France it is the full sisters Durban/Heldifann and here in the USA it is the Domino family—all are almost identically concentrated to Lexington RH/Glencoe, sources of the highest-class speed within any distance. In Durban/Heldifann Lexington RH is 6x6x6x5x6x5x6x6, which is the equivalent of him sitting between the second and third generation; in Americus he is 3x3—the equivalent of the second generation, and in Domino Lexington RH is 3x4x4, once again the equivalent of him being in the second generation. Further Hamburg carries Lexington RH 4x4x5x5, which is the equivalent of him being once again between the second and third generation—all these genetic giants are very similar then in pedigree design and dominance.

These five major American families have bloodlines in common: four have Lexington RH close up—sometimes doubled. The exception is Maggie B. B. RH, who is out of a Boston RH daughter, therefore a sister to Lexington RH. Four examples have strong Glencoe components, and two carry Blackburns Whip RH close up—most of them also have concentrations of the English sires of the day also (especially the full sibling groups of Whalebone/Web et al and Birdcatcher/Faugh-a-Ballah), but remember the difference in the American racehorse—versus the English racer of the day—is the lines of our Running Horse it carries as well. I believe you will be surprised to discover how much of their genetics is powering the top sport horses of our day—not just here but worldwide. This is a fabulous genetic heritage of unsurpassed sport performance that was born in our Colonies and refined in our Heroic Era.

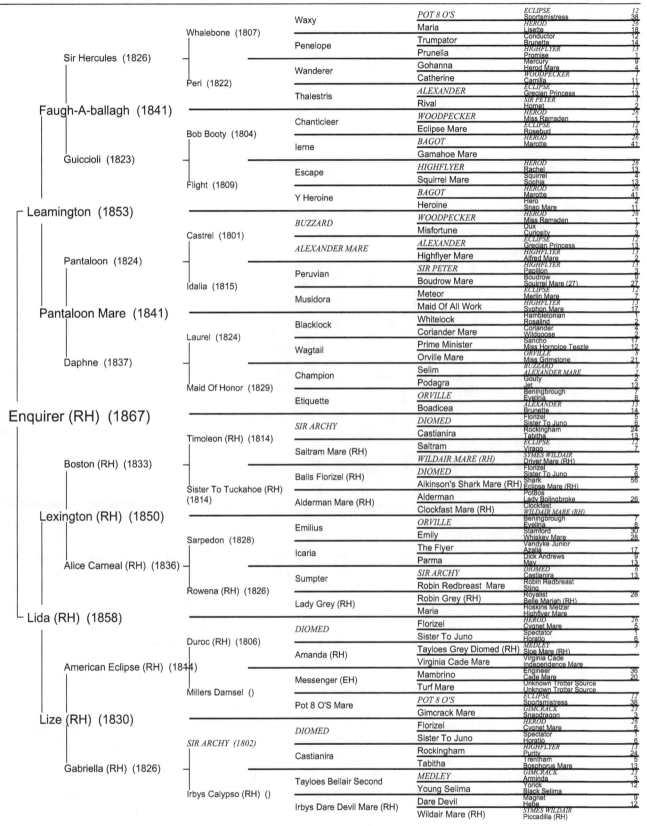

Enquirer RH 1867

Chapter 10

Hanover Sport Dynasty

Hanover—a fountainhead of sport performance in the USA and abroad as well.
—image found in *Racing in America*, Vosborough

So, let's begin by examining each American family a little closer, so you can recognize them and their descendants. Hanover 1884 (labeled a half-breed by the English) is the head of a sport dynasty that produced the very best—not only in America, but in spite of being a victim of the Jersey Act, his progeny have spread to England, France, and even Germany where they have left a lasting heritage of sport excellence.

Hanover was a star racer (Belmont Stakes 1887). He was champion horse at both two and three years; he won thirty-two of fifty starts, American Horse-of-the-Year 1887, was a Hall of Fame inductee, and his produce record ranks him as a sire of greatness—he led the sires list for four years. Obviously this is a very high-class bloodline, and one we want to increase in the background of our pedigrees. His proven ability to consistently transmit racing class prompted M. F. Dwyer (who had owned Hanover during his race career) in 1895 to purchase his entire crop of eight colts—sight unseen—to take to race in England. Being in England at the time, Dwyer sent an English stockman, Mr. Armstrong, to load and accompany the youngsters on their trip by sea to England without ever inspecting them—it was good enough for him that they were Hanover sons (Thoroughbred Review).

Hanover took a while to mature. As a two-year-old they had trouble getting him to run; he was sluggish, and they had to really ride him hard, with whip and spur, to get him out there. Yet for all that he still won enough to be named Champion Two-Year-Old. This performance is an indication of him being too young to start—still growing body and mind—because at three he appeared a different horse as he moved right out with enthusiasm, racing to the front and fighting to stay there; he did not like to be passed. He was also a wonderful sire leading the sires list in 1895-98.

Hanover is 3x3 to the Running Horse Vandal, plus he carries a Lexington RH daughter in the second, and the great broodmare Ophelia RH is his fourth-dam. His offspring were not eligible for the GSB because according to the new rules he was a half-breed. However his daughter Rhoda B was already included in the GSB, her son Orby had already won the English and Irish Derby, and her daughter Rhodora won the 1000 Guineas (we will discuss their impact in the English Thoroughbred in further chapters). Hanover can also be considered a jump transmitter.

Hanover Offspring

Hanover's son Halma 1892 is a Kentucky Derby winner who also sired a Derby winner: Alan-a-Dale. He did not remain in the US but was sent to France, and then in 1901 he was sold to Poland. His French-bred son Oversight won several stakes races in France: the Grand Prix de Saint-Cloud 1910 and others. You will find him then in the European pedigrees.

Hanover's son Blackstock 1899 produced the good sire Mentor, who in turn bred the important sire Wise Counsellor 1921, who carries seven lines of Lexington RH in six generations; Blackstock is the ¾ brother to Hamburg and therefore is valuable in line-breeding exercises.

Great Britain—a stakes winning son of The Commoner.
—photo by Stronmeyer, found in *Thoroughbred Types*

Hanover's son The Commoner 1892 is a full brother to Rhoda B, the dam of Orby (see Chapter 15). He was an important sire and great racer—winning eighteen stakes races. The Commoner is found repeatedly in the lineages of *reines*; for instance his daughter Grace Commoner is the second-dam of the *reine* Ruddy Light 1921, who in-turn is dam of the *reine* Chicleight, a daughter of Chicle who also brings in another line of both Hanover and Mannie Gray. Chicleight is dam of the *reine* Blue Delight, who in-turn is dam of the *reine* Real Delight—it is rare to find such a far-reaching maternal dynasty. The Commoner (pedigree) has strong filly factors from a sex-balanced double of Alice Carneal RH 4x4 and of the Orville Mare 6x7. He also had a good stakes winning son in the racer Great Britain. You find the line of Great Britian in the top international jumper Untouchable (see Chapter 32). Naturally, combining lines of The Commoner with those of Rhoda B, his full sister, will give a strong injection of class into the pedigree.

Hanover's son Abe Frank 1899 was another stakes winner, and although he was a sire with limited opportunities (stood in Texas) he exceeded expectations. He also stood as a Remount stallion, but his stud career was cut short when he was killed by lightning at age sixteen. He left good racers such as Viral, the top sprinter Closer, and the stakes winner Caluse; however, that fades beside his daughter Pan Zareta 1911 as she is one of the most amazing race fillies of all time.

The legend—Pan Zareta—one of the greatest sprint racers of all time, or quite possibly 'the best.' —image courtesy of Wiki Commons

Pan Zareta raced during the black out in America—often at the Juarez track in Mexico where betting was allowed. Bred in Texas by J. F. and H. S. Newman, in her short life she raced one hundred fifty-one times and won seventy-six, placed second thirty-one and third twenty-one times! She set several **world records** for speed at five furlongs; she was strictly a sprinter as her limit was ⅞ mile. She raced everywhere, all over the west from Juarez to Canada, and even in the east in Kentucky. After the ban was lifted she raced in New York. She is one of the all-time great racehorses, a sprinter, and an extremely fast starter like her uncle Hamburg; she was also a great weight carrier, once winning with 146 lbs.

Nelson C. Nye, in his 1973 book *Speed in the Quarter Horse,* made space to remember the greatest sprinter there ever was,

"Her uniqueness is incontestable. Far as I know she still holds three world's records and it appears extremely likely she will go on holding them forever. She carried 146 pounds and won with it, more weight than ever was carried on a track by any other mare in racing history, and she won more races than any other mare in world history, and she won more handicaps than any other horse that ever lived—stallion, mare or gelding. What she did in six years of sprinting makes the records of Citation, Equipoise, Sarazen, Hindoo, Stymie, Seabiscuit and that other great Texan—Assault—look pale indeed."

She is justly called 'the winningest race mare in all history.' It was a great tragedy when at age nine she died of pneumonia in her stall at the racetrack in New Orleans, so she never produced a foal. Pan Zareta is not only a granddaughter of Hanover, she is loaded with other flawed lines: Iroquois (Maggie B.B. RH son and English Derby winner); Jack Boston (Lexington RH son); and the great Shiloh RH (QH foundation sire). She is 5x5 to Lexington RH and 5x5 to Vandal RH. Even though she left no offspring, I believe we want to see how her pedigree was structured because with one hundred fifty-one races to her credit she still remained sound, a supreme athlete, and these traits are something we want to learn how to construct into our breeding designs. (See Chapter 31 for another horse descended from Abe Frank—it will surprise you.)

Tea Caddy 1913, out of Tea's Over, was a winner of many races and a line found in many jumpers. — image from *Thoroughbred Types*.

Hanover's daughter Tea's Over 1893, who carries four lines of Vandal RH and three of Lexington RH in five generations, had great success through her daughters. For instance, Tea Biscuit is granddam of none other than Seabiscuit, and another daughter is the great American-bred racing filly Reading 1918, who won on both the flat and steeplechase in the British Isles during the Jersey Act. Reading 1918 is inbred 3x3 Hanover. That is not all, from the Tea's Over daughter Toggery descends the international show jump champion Jet Run and the great sire Jamestown. Toggery is classified as a *reine* also, and besides those champions she gave us the full siblings Cri-de-Coeur/Mademoiselle Dazie/Tailor Maid. Tea's Over produced great sons as well: Ort Wells, Dick Welles, Dick Finnell, and Security—another is Tea Caddy, which is a line I have found in many show jumpers. He is also found in the elite mare Aspidistra.

Hanover's daughter Lady Sterling 1899 was also a top producer, including Triple Crown winner Sir Barton, her daughter Lady Doreen—who was a great producer also—and her son the great racer sire Sir Martin (who raced in England and France, winning several important stakes including the Coronation cup, and then stood in England in 1908—discussed in Chapter 8). Sir Barton 1916 was a fair sire, and you will find him in pedigrees such as in the champion Susan's Girl where he is the third dam-sire. He was later donated to the Remount, so he will also be found in western horse breeds. His description below is reminiscent of his grandsire Hanover.

"He was slow to mature, but no colt improved more than he,…[at 3] winning the Preakness, the Kentucky Derby, the Belmont and the Withers…not a tall horse (he stood scarcely 15.3 in training) Sir Barton was a sturdy one. So hearty a feeder was he, that his trainer often said "I have to almost kill him to get him fit" (*Thoroughbred Types*).

The tremendous vitality found in the males of this line is notable. Sir Barton, like his grandsire Hanover and his ½ brother Hamburg, was a voracious eater, and all of these fantastic racehorses thrived on work—it seemed the more the better.

Hanover's daughter Retained is second dam of the good sire Eternal, who like Sir Martin was a two-year-old champion.

Then there is Urania 1892, who is 3x3 to Lexington RH and 5x5x4 to Glencoe, who became ancestress of a top French dynasty that includes the Derby winner Durbar II and his daughter Durban who is 4x4 to Hanover. Durban became the dam of none other than Tourbillon (sire of Djebel, Donatella, Nerada (German), Timor, and the *reine-de-course* mare Tourzima). We will visit this French branch in its own chapter.

Hanover's son David Garrick 1897 became savage as he matured, although he did win the Champagne Stakes (2 ¼ miles) and in England won the Chester Cup (2 ¼ miles), but he was only a mediocre sire, and he was later gelded because of his bad disposition.

His son Ben Holladay 1893 was said to be a very tough stayer, winning the Morris Park Handicap and Telegraph stakes among others. He also has a good record as a sire; from his daughter Ophirdale descends the Triple Crown winner Whirl-away and his winning ½ brother Reaping Reward.

Another Hanover son, Handspring 1893, has five lines of Glencoe and two of Boston RH close up, and he was a good racer—a champion at two—but he had poor feet, which limited his racing career. His best son was Major Daingerfield 1899 who had twenty-one wins from ninety-six starts (raced for Dwyer Brothers) and was the top earner of 1902. Hand-spring was exported for stud duty in England, so he may pop up in the European lines from time to time.

But all these wonderful offspring were just a 'warm-up' for the massive genetic shadow thrown by Hamburg, who is Hanover's greatest son, who we will follow below.

Hamburg 1895

Hamburg. —image courtesy of Wiki Commons

Hamburg is about as good as it ever gets--a colossus among champions. He was a great weight carrier, and he was so full of energy and fire and so fast out of the starting gate the officials were often questioned about his time. He had a savage appetite, and they tried a muzzle and all sorts of tricks to slow him from wolfing down his food. He needed to be worked regularly, and he ran his best when he was kept in hard training—given too much time off he would become difficult.

"Hamburg was a glutton, both at feed and for work. No matter how hard he had been galloped, he ate so heartily and the repair of his tissue was so rapid that they soon found he required twice the work of the other horses" (Vosborough).

Hamburg was flashy; a bay with a blaze and two hind stockings, and his hind end was large and muscular like a Quarter Horse. He was a handful—not many could ride him, he would just buck them off, and while he was a true stayer he also possessed great speed. He won the 2 ¼-mile Brighton Cup by one hundred lengths, and he beat Kentucky Derby winner Plaudit in the Lawrence Realization and won multiple stakes races easily. He was a great sire producing twenty-seven stakes winners and Hamburg was the leading sire of 1905.

While his sire Hanover is powerfully bred with a sex-balanced double of Vandal RH 3x3, Hamburg's pedigree builds on the Lexington RH daughter Hanover carries: Florence, by bringing in three more lines—Aerolite RH, Lida RH, and War Dance RH—plus his ½ brother Lecomte RH, making them 4x5x5x5x6. Of those lines, Aerolite RH is ¾ brother to War Dance RH, and War Dance RH is ¾ brother to Lecomte Mare RH—all closely related lines brought in by his dam, and this concentration of genes can explain his high energy (mtDNA is from the dam).

Notice as we list some of his progeny how many of them or their best offspring build on the Flaw.

Hamburg produced good stakes-winning sons such as the gelding Borrow, who won stakes in England—including the prestigious Middle Park Plate—and when he was shipped home after the enactment of the Jersey Act, he won many more; he raced until he was eleven.

"Borrow was one of the horses that Mr. Whitney sent to England as a yearling in 1909, and the following year he won the Middle Park Plate—the greatest of English events for two-year-olds. He won several good races, and in 1914 when Mr. Whitney brought him home he signalized his return to his native land, though then six years old, by winning the Yonkers and Saratoga Handicaps. In 1915, he won the Kentucky Handicap at Louisville, the Ferry at Windsor, the Dominion at Fort Erie, and Municipal at Belmont Park. But his crowning triumph

Borrow 1908, gelding, was a stakes winner in England and in the US he ranks among the best racing geldings of all time. —image by C.C. Cook found in *Thoroughbred Types*

Artful 1902—a winner against top-class colts and fillies and beautiful as well. —image and quotation above from *Racing in America*

Hamburg Belle 1901—not as pretty as Artful but possessed of amazing speed and graceful action—she could beat them all at a mile or less, both colts and fillies, it did not matter—she won. —image found in *Racing in America*, Vosborough

was when, in 1917 and nine years old, he won the Brooklyn Handicap (117 lbs.), beating his stable companion Regret, Old Rosebud, Roamer, Boots, Stromboli and Omar Khayyim. He ran until eleven years old and left a name second to no horse of his era. He was one the greatest geldings of the Turf ranking with Parole and Stromboli" (*Thoroughbred Types*).

There were many other stakes winners from Hamburg's loins, such as Dandelion winner of the Dwyer, the Travers, Saratoga, and the Suburban, and his son Prince Eugene who won the Belmont.

But it is his daughters who are incomparable, both as racers and as breeders. There is Artful 1902, one of the most successful racing fillies ever. As a two-year-old she beat a field that included her brother Dandelion and the immortal Sysonby in the Futurity.

"When *Artful* won the Futurity of '04, following Hamburg Belle's victory of 1903, horsemen asked themselves if a Hamburg dynasty was about to overwhelm racing…Artful as a three-year-old (1905) ran only three times, and won each time. Two of them were sprints, but the third was more portentous—the Brighton Handicap, 103 pounds, at 1¼ miles—and against competition of the most formidable character: Beldame, 125 pounds, Ort Wells, 125 pounds, Delhi, 126 pounds—winners of the Realization, Suburban, Belmont, and Brooklyn…As she was dismissed as 'a mere sprinter', and it was agreed that 'if she can last the route she'll win, but it's long odds she can't.' But she did, winning by 2 lengths, Ort Wells second, Beldame third. And thus Artful retired in a blaze of glory" (*Racing in America* - Vosborough).

Artful did fairly well as a dam, especially from her daughter Paintbrush through whom she is ancestress of the good sire Runaway Groom, the sire of Cherokee Run, and the good sire Smarten.

Hamburg Belle 1901, another Hamburg daughter of top quality, "there have been few fillies of greater speed than *Hamburg Belle*. She was not a stayer, in the full sense of the term, but she had a turn of speed with which few could live, even at a mile" (Vosborough). As a two-year-old she beat the top colts Broomstick, Leonidus, Criterion, and Rosebud. She is remembered as the epitome of grace, as her movement and action was described as so light and smooth it could not 'break an egg.' She is found in the background of many stakes winners today, such as Successful Appeal.

But it is Frizette 1905 that is in a class of her own as both a stakes winner and dynasty creator. She has legendary status as a broodmare both here and in France. A flashy bay with a big blaze (like her sire), she was classified as a half-breed by the English Jockey Club as she was 5x5x6x6 to Lexington RH. Bred by James Keene, she was raced pretty hard with twenty-seven races as a three-year-old of which she won eight. She was bought by Herman Duryea and shipped to France with the rest of his breeding stock in 1908. She raced and won there before she was put to stud in 1909. After Duryea died, his widow carried on the stud, and she sold many of Frizette's offspring to Marcel Boussac—the great French breeder—and finally sold Frizette herself to him.

Frizette is a genetic giant who must be rated in significance and quality right up there with Pocahontas. She is the dam of three *reines-de-course*: Banshee, Frizeur, and Princess Palatine. Her other offspring, such as her stallion son Frizzle, or her other daughters Lespedeza, Ondulation, Durzetta, and Frizelle are only slightly below the other three superstars in potency. It is almost like you cannot lose with her, and she is on a par with La Troienne, Maggie B. B. RH, Mannie Gray—a super elite mare. Banshee is dam of the full sisters Durban/Heldifann who have created a maternal French dynasty that appears to have no end—they carry eight lines of Lexington RH in seven generations. Frizeur is dam of the super American producers Black Curl and Myrtlewood (see Chapter 21), plus Bluelarks, Janet Blair, and Pearl River. Frizette's daughter Princess Palatine continued a maternal dynasty through her daughter Valkyr, a daughter of Man O' War, who is rated a *reine* and produced a *reine* in Vicaress. You cannot lose with building up these lines in your horses.

We will carry on the discussion of Frizette's French-bred descendants in another chapter, but for now realize she is responsible for none other than Tourbillon, Diedene, Priam II, and Djeddah, and when her descendants Black Tarquin and My Babu took the English classics in the 1940s, it was a strong factor in ending the Jersey Act.

Frizeur's daughter Myrtlewood is a foundation mare of the modern American Thoroughbred with the good producers to her credit of Durazna, Miss Dogwood, Myrtle Charm, Vagrancy, Crepe Myrtle, the good sire Tiger, and Kentucky Derby winner Ferdinand.

Edwin Anthony, in his newest book *The American Thoroughbred,* provides multiple examples of how to concentrate Frizette in your pedigrees, listing among others: Quiet American, Unbridled, Fair Charmer (dam of Seattle Slew), Djeddan, Bernardini, Fappiano, and Distorted Humor.

Hamburg had some decent sons also, for example his son Burgomaster (full brother to the filly Jersey Lightning—the dam of Kentucky Derby winner Regret) was a good sire both here and then in South America. A tank of a horse, he did well at two but broke down at three—his weight being too much for his legs to carry at speed—and speedy he was. He was sent to South America to stud, but not before he left some progeny here.

Jersey Lightning 1905, who is 3x5 to War Dance RH and carries six lines of Lexington RH, is the dam of Kentucky Derby winner Regret—the first filly to win it. You will find Regret quite easily in the descendants of her granddaughter Sweet Sixteen. Regret has a full brother Thunderer, who was a good racer and fair sire.

Burgomaster—"Burgomaster was probably the largest and heaviest colt that has ever prevailed in great sweepstakes. Mr. Whitney bred him at his stud in New Jersey, and he was the best son of Hamburg." —photo and quotation found in *Thoroughbred Types.*

This is Burgomaster's good jumper son Burgoright. At 16.2 hands, and with his hunter build, he did well in the hunter show ring, but like a true Hamburg descendant he really loved to run, and he had his best victories racing over jumps—he won the Meadow Brook Point-to-Point and also the grueling Maryland Hunt Cup, and he loved to have competition, racing his hardest over the obstacles when someone was giving him a challenge. He was also field hunted for years—a very sound horse. — photo by Haas, found in *Thoroughbred Types.*

First filly to win the Kentucky Derby—Regret 1912—image by L. S. Sutcliff in *Thoroughbred Types*.

Thunderer, the full brother to Regret. —photo from *Thoroughbred Types*

Golden Broom "In action he was the reincarnation of Hamburg himself—low, close to the ground, the kind that steals away inches" —*Thoroughbred Types*

Biturica 1900 is yet another fantastic Hamburg daughter. When she was bred to the Domino son Disquise II, she produced the great champion Maskette 1906, who is 3x4 Mannie Gray and has seven lines of Lexington RH in seven generations. Biturica's daughter Bellisario is fifth-dam of the great modern sire Damascus.

Lady Hamburg 1908 was sent to England by her owner Mr. Whitney, and it was there she was bred to Spearmint, the result being the good sire Chicle (classified as a French-bred because she gave birth in France). Then she was bred to Sardanapale, and the result was Dis Donc, the sire of the great mare Top Flight. Chicle produced maternal dynasties through his daughters Chiclelight (*reine*), Goose Egg dam of Shut Out, and Panay from whom Rough n' Tumble descends, sire of Dr Fager, Minnesota Mac, and My Dear Girl—dam of In Reality.

Hamburg's daughter Courage 1912 produced Valorous when she was mated to the Domino-line stallion Pennant. Valorous is found frequently in top show jumpers (see Chapter 30).

Zuna was taken to France by Duryea, and while there she was bred to Sweeper II—the result was Golden Broom. He was a decent racehorse, but his career was curtailed as he was used mostly as workout partner for Man O' War. (He is found in jumpers also—see the pedigree of Almost Persuaded in Chapter 30.)

Hamburg's daughter Adriana 1905 out of Kildeer (who adds more Lexington RH, Glencoe, and Galopade) is the third-dam of the great Discovery (he will be discussed in Chapter 13).

Hamburg's daughter May Florence is dam of 1920 Kentucky Derby winner Paul Jones.

Hamburg's daughter Rosie O'Grady is considered a *reine*; she is out of Cherokee Rose II, and she was a very good stakes winner. She produced Erin and Potheen, mares from whom descends Ruffian, Icecapade and Buckfinder, and Bewitch. She is found also in Pine Bluff, Fusaichi Pegasus, Marias Mon, Intentionally, and Holy Bull.

The Hanover/Hamburg family throws a consistent type of strongly muscled horses, often with a powerful hind end—they are unlike the delicate Phalaris family which also throws a bulky form, in that the Hanover/Hamburgs are most usually supported by equally stout legs and on the whole are extremely sound line. The Ben Brush family is like this also, solid and sound.

Hamburg is a close relative to Blackstock and Domino, and like them he is a concentrated source of Lexington RH. His daughters are all genetically valuable. Hanover/Hamburg are prime sport lines with jumper traits, and they are also perfect candidates for eventing because they love to run—and surprisingly they are found in dressage stars also. Sport horse breeders, you cannot lose with building up this bloodline.

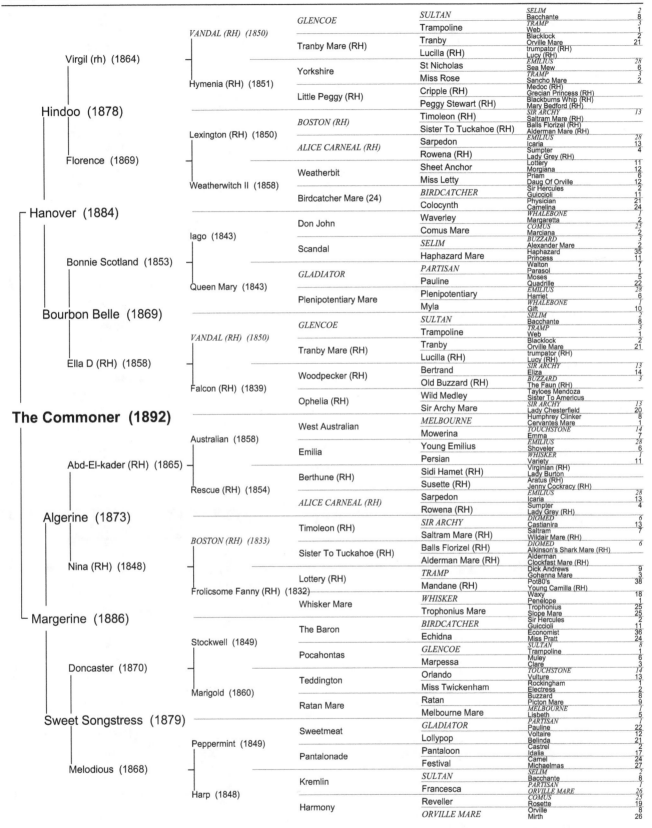

The Commoner 1892

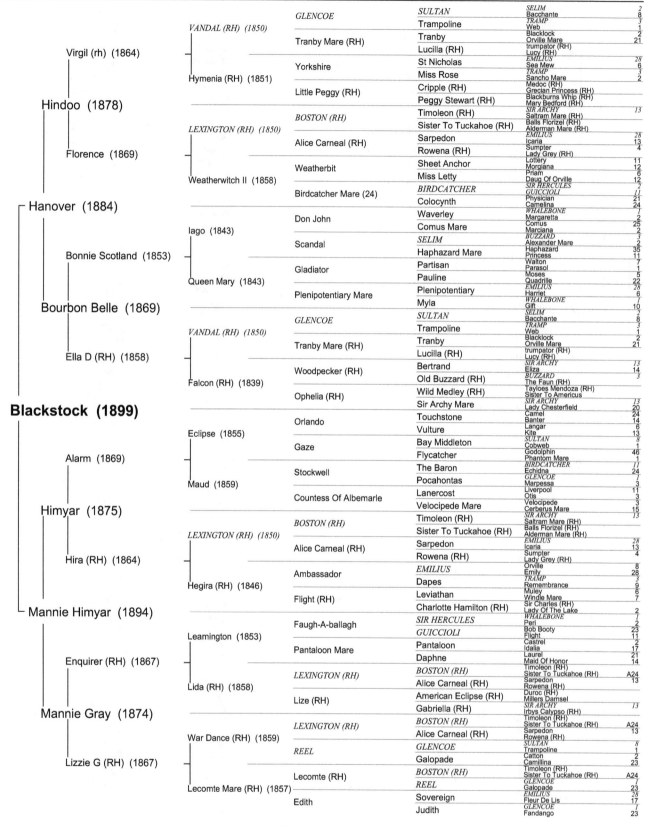

Blackstock 1899

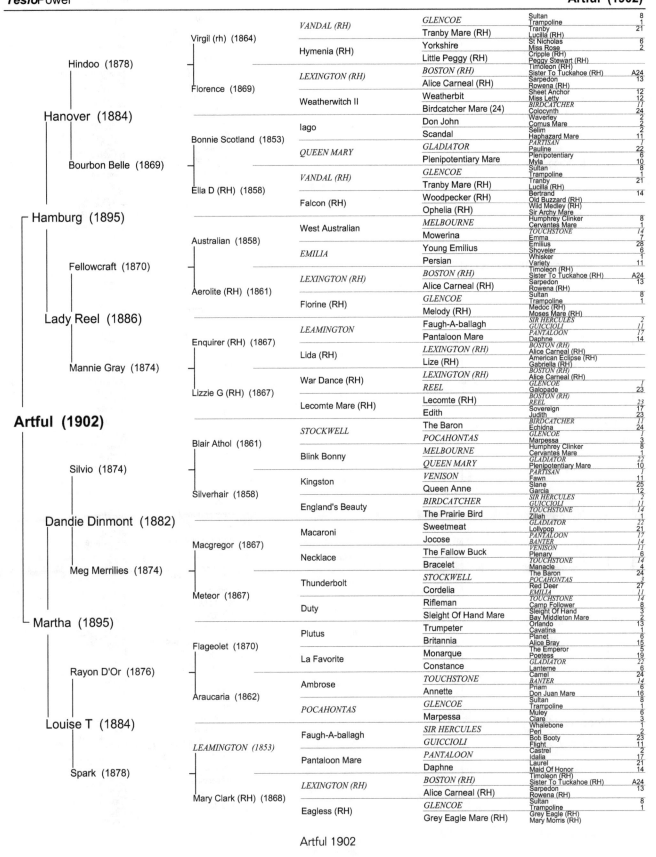

Artful 1902

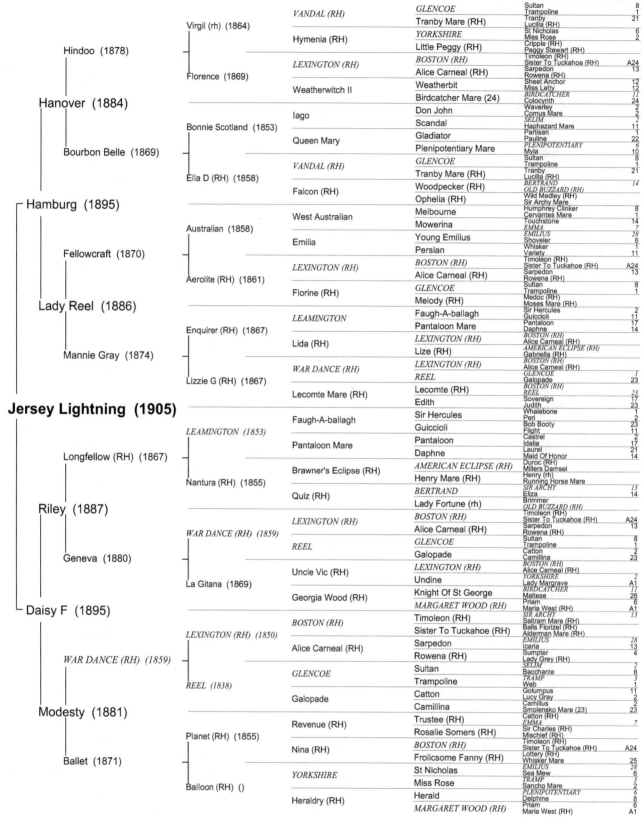

Jersey Lightning 1905

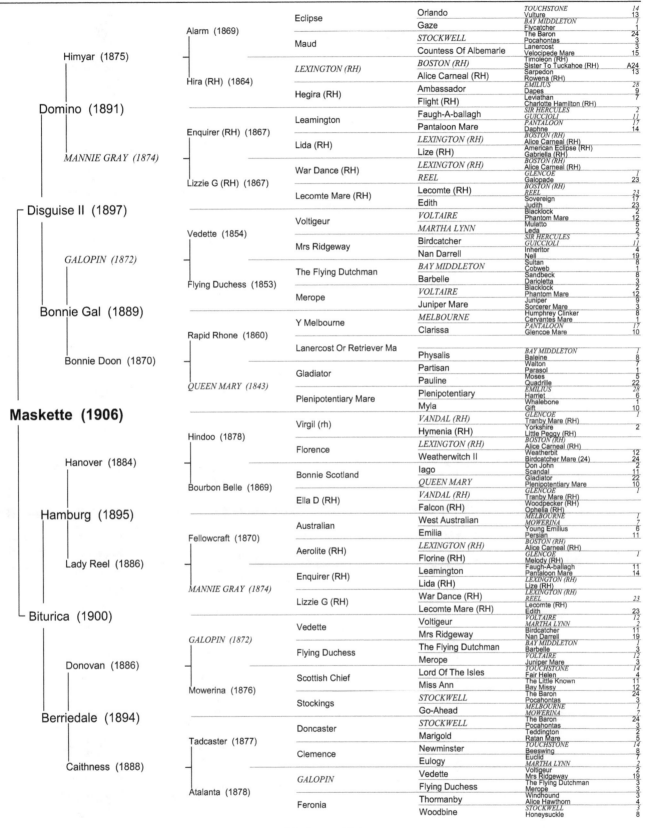

Maskette 1906

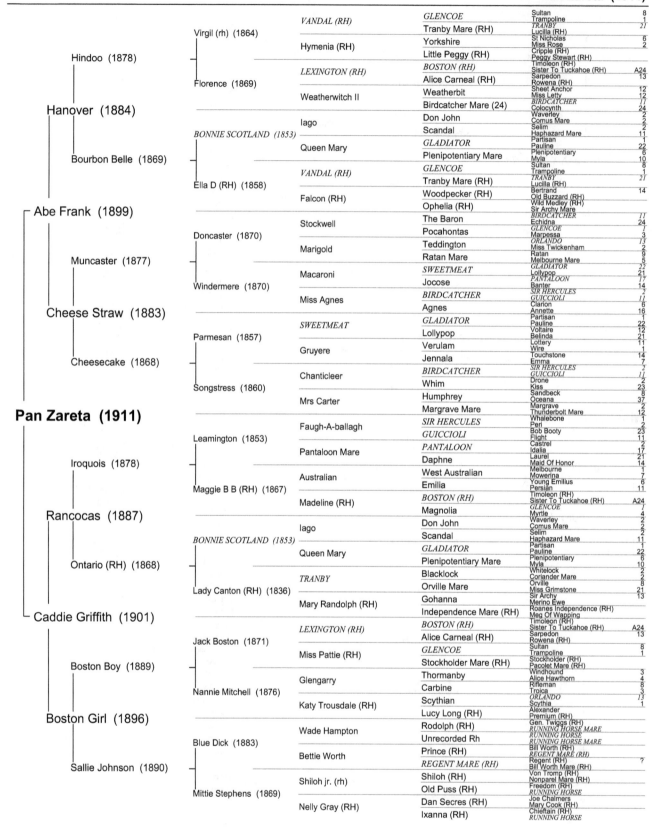

Pedigree of **Pan Zareta (1911)**

- **Hanover (1884)**
  - Hindoo (1878)
    - Virgil (rh) (1864)
      - *VANDAL (RH)*
        - *GLENCOE* — Sultan 8 / Trampoline 1
        - Tranby Mare (RH) — *TRANBY* 21 / Lucilla (RH)
      - Hymenia (RH)
        - Yorkshire — St Nicholas 6 / Miss Rose 2
        - Little Peggy (RH) — Cripple (RH) / Peggy Stewart (RH)
    - Florence (1869)
      - *LEXINGTON (RH)*
        - *BOSTON (RH)* — Timoleon (RH) / Sister To Tuckahoe (RH) A24
        - Alice Carneal (RH) — Sarpedon 13 / Rowena (RH)
      - Weatherwitch II
        - Weatherbit — Sheet Anchor 12 / Miss Letty 12
        - Birdcatcher Mare (24) — *BIRDCATCHER* 11 / Colocynth 24
  - Bourbon Belle (1869)
    - *BONNIE SCOTLAND (1853)*
      - Iago
        - Don John — Waverley 2 / Comus Mare 2
        - Scandal — Selim 2 / Haphazard Mare 11
      - Queen Mary
        - *GLADIATOR* — Partisan 1 / Pauline 22
        - Plenipotentiary Mare — Plenipotentiary 6 / Myla 10
    - Ella D (RH) (1858)
      - *VANDAL (RH)*
        - *GLENCOE* — Sultan 8 / Trampoline 1
        - Tranby Mare (RH) — *TRANBY* 21 / Lucilla (RH)
      - Falcon (RH)
        - Woodpecker (RH) — Bertrand 14 / Old Buzzard (RH)
        - Ophelia (RH) — Wild Medley (RH) / Sir Archy Mare

- **Muncaster (1877)**
  - Doncaster (1870)
    - Stockwell
      - The Baron — *BIRDCATCHER* 11 / Echidna 24
      - Pocahontas — *GLENCOE* 1 / Marpessa 3
    - Marigold
      - Teddington — *ORLANDO* 13 / Miss Twickenham 2
      - Ratan Mare — Ratan 9 / Melbourne Mare 5
  - Windermere (1870)
    - Macaroni
      - *SWEETMEAT* — *GLADIATOR* 22 / Lollypop 21
      - Jocose — *PANTALOON* 17 / Banter 14
    - Miss Agnes
      - *BIRDCATCHER* — *SIR HERCULES* 2 / *GUICCIOLI* 11
      - Agnes — Clarion 6 / Annette 16

- **Cheese Straw (1883)**
  - Parmesan (1857)
    - *SWEETMEAT*
      - *GLADIATOR* — Partisan 1 / Pauline 22
      - Lollypop — Voltaire 12 / Belinda 21
    - Gruyere
      - Verulam — Lottery 11 / Wire
      - Jennala — Touchstone 14 / Emma 7
  - Songstress (1860)
    - Chanticleer
      - *BIRDCATCHER* — *SIR HERCULES* 2 / *GUICCIOLI* 11
      - Whim — Drone 2 / Kiss 23
    - Mrs Carter
      - Humphrey — Sandbeck 8 / Oceana 37
      - Margrave Mare — Margrave 2 / Thunderbolt Mare 12

Left-hand lineage grouping:
- **Hindoo (1878)** → **Hanover (1884)**
- **Bourbon Belle (1869)** → **Hanover (1884)**
- **Hanover (1884)**, **Muncaster (1877)** → **Abe Frank (1899)**
- **Cheese Straw (1883)**, **Cheesecake (1868)**

- **Abe Frank (1899)** → **Pan Zareta (1911)**

- **Iroquois (1878)**
  - Leamington (1853)
    - Faugh-A-ballagh
      - *SIR HERCULES* — Whalebone 1 / Peri 2
      - *GUICCIOLI* — Bob Booty 23 / Flight 11
    - Pantaloon Mare
      - *PANTALOON* — Castrel 2 / Idalia 17
      - Daphne — Laurel 21 / Maid Of Honor 14
  - Maggie B B (RH) (1867)
    - Australian
      - West Australian — Melbourne 1 / Mowerina 7
      - Emilia — Young Emilius 6 / Persian 11
    - Madeline (RH)
      - *BOSTON (RH)* — Timoleon (RH) / Sister To Tuckahoe (RH) A24
      - Magnolia — *GLENCOE* 1 / Myrtle 4

- **Rancocas (1887)**
  - Ontario (RH) (1868)
    - *BONNIE SCOTLAND (1853)*
      - Iago
        - Don John — Waverley 2 / Comus Mare 2
        - Scandal — Selim 2 / Haphazard Mare 11
      - Queen Mary
        - *GLADIATOR* — Partisan 1 / Pauline 22
        - Plenipotentiary Mare — Plenipotentiary 6 / Myla 10
    - Lady Canton (RH) (1836)
      - *TRANBY*
        - Blacklock — Whitelock 2 / Coriander Mare 2
        - Orville Mare — Orville 8 / Miss Grimstone 21
      - Mary Randolph (RH)
        - Gohanna — Sir Archy 13 / Merino Ewe
        - Independence Mare (RH) — Roanes Independence (RH) / Meg Of Wapping

- **Boston Boy (1889)**
  - Jack Boston (1871)
    - *LEXINGTON (RH)*
      - *BOSTON (RH)* — Timoleon (RH) / Sister To Tuckahoe (RH) A24
      - Alice Carneal (RH) — Sarpedon 13 / Rowena (RH)
    - Miss Pattie (RH)
      - *GLENCOE* — Sultan 8 / Trampoline 1
      - Stockholder Mare (RH) — Stockholder (RH) / Pacolet Mare (RH)
  - Nannie Mitchell (1876)
    - Glengarry
      - Thormanby — Windhound 3 / Alice Hawthorn 4
      - Carbine — Rifleman 8 / Troica 3
    - Katy Trousdale (RH)
      - Scythian — *ORLANDO* 13 / Scythia 1
      - Lucy Long (RH) — Alexander / Premium (RH)

- **Boston Girl (1896)**
  - Sallie Johnson (1890)
    - Blue Dick (1883)
      - Wade Hampton
        - Rodolph (RH) — Gen. Twiggs (RH) / *RUNNING HORSE MARE*
        - Unrecorded Rh — *RUNNING HORSE* / *RUNNING HORSE MARE*
      - Bettie Worth
        - Prince (RH) — Bill Worth (RH) / *REGENT MARE (RH)*
        - *REGENT MARE (RH)* — Regent (RH) / Bill Worth Mare (RH) ?
    - Mittie Stephens (1869)
      - Shiloh jr. (rh)
        - Shiloh (RH) — Von Tromp (RH) / Nonparel Mare (RH)
        - Old Puss (RH) — Freedom (RH) / *RUNNING HORSE*
      - Nelly Gray (RH)
        - Dan Secres (RH) — Joe Chalmers / Mary Cook (RH)
        - Ixanna (RH) — Chieftain (RH) / *RUNNING HORSE*

- **Caddie Griffith (1901)** → **Pan Zareta (1911)**

Pan Zareta 1911

Chapter 11

Maternal Dynasty of Maggie B. B. RH

Maggie B. B. RH 1867 was ignored in the past when top foundation mares were honored because of her unfashionable pedigree, but today she has ascended to the position she deserves. Much of the credit for this belongs to Ellen Parker, so I urge you to visit her site www.reines-de-course.com for full information on the genetic relevance of not just Maggie B. B. RH but other important mares. For us, the sport horse breeders, we want to understand not only her long shadow in sport, but which descendants are potent carriers of her and other 'flawed' lines. Maggie B. B. RH is by the good Running Horse sire Enquirer out of a Boston RH daughter (who is out of a Glencoe mare). Maggie's pedigree shows us she is strong in the English full siblings: Whalebone/Whisker/Web—this is her genetic bedrock—and to this base was added the Boston RH/Glencoe nick. Because of the isolation brought on by the Jersey Act, it was those 'flawed' lines that were built upon in the succeeding generations that produced the best of her descendants. Maggie was herself a sound and talented racehorse, most of her progeny picked up some physical flaws through their imported sires (see Chapter 9).

If the Jersey Act had not been in place for thirty-six years we would probably not have the powerful American Thoroughbred families that we enjoy today; instead our TB would just be a decent population of purely English Thoroughbred lineage—nothing really special or superior. It wasn't just the fact of the Jersey Act either—even many of the American breeders looked down their noses at those stained American lines, believing the English propaganda that said they were impure therefore lesser horses. We in the sport horse world have been witnessing the same phenomenon with the perception even by Americans that the American sport breeds (including our TB—see Appendix E) are a lesser sport horse than the European brand—it is basically the same thing, repeated indoctrination twists our perception until we cannot see what is right in front of us.

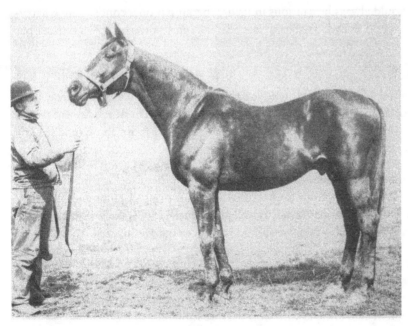

Sir Dixon 1885, Belmont winner and a son of the Maggie B. B. RH daughter Jaconet (Maggie B. B. RH on the dam-line is historically a winning recipe). — photographer unknown

Without the isolation forced on American breeders by the Jersey Act our great American world-beater bloodlines, with distinct genetic gains from our native racehorse breed (Running Horse), would have been watered down generation after generation—as they were in some cases (consider the breeding career of Fashion RH in Chapter 3) —by continually breeding back to strictly English lines. However, the Jersey Act forced incestuous breeding upon us, and the result was the greatest sport bloodlines in the world. These American families we are exploring can still provide us, the modern breeder, with sport power when we build them up to significant levels in our designs—even though they were born over a hundred years ago.

Taking up where we left off in Chapter 9, Maggie's daughters Jaconet and Red-and-Blue are genetic powerhouses, and both have achieved *reine* status for the excellence of their produce. Jaconet's strongest progeny are her son Sir

Dixon and her daughter The Niece. The Niece produced several good mares including Alarm Bell by Spendthrift RH, La Colonia and Nisbat by Hindoo, and Mantana and Matanza by Hanover—as you can see we are doubling and tripling up on the American families here. She also produced the good sire Uncle by Star Shoot, and he is the sire of Old Rosebud (Kentucky Derby winner), plus many good mares. One of them, Eventide out of Noontide by Colin (Domino son), produced Sunset Gun by Man O' War, who in turn produced Stop Watch the dam of Stymie. Another example is Uncle's daughter Hurakan, whose dam carries more Boston RH and Glencoe, and she is the dam of Stimulus, who is by the Domino son Commando and is inbred to Domino.

Sir Dixon by Billet was a good sire especially when he was bred back to other carriers of Running Horse lines; for instance his daughter Elusive out of Vega, a War Dance RH daughter out of a Planet RH dam, produced Petticoat when she was bred to Hamburg, who in-turn produced Frillery by Broomstick, and she in-turn produced the *reine* Frilette by Man O' War, who produced many good horses including Equestrian the sire of Stymie. If you follow that line down you can see that returning to sires of the other American families preserved the power, and the produce was always first class. The best of his offspring carry more of our native lines. It is interesting that Sir Dixon had at least eight offspring out of Hindoo mares, the good broodmares Dike, Marie Frances, Mariedna, Winifred A, Yankee Girl, and Kentucky Belle. Hindoo brings in the sex-balance of Lexington RH for her dam Madeline RH, a Boston RH daughter.

But it is Sir Dixon's two daughters out of the Red-and-Blue daughter Sallie McClelland that are off the charts in excellence—Audience and Martha Gorman are full sisters by Sir Dixon out of Sallie McClelland, and both established female dynasties of their own (*reines*). Their pedigree puts Maggie B. B. RH 3x3 on both dam-lines. They have concentrated the power of Maggie B. B. RH. This is extraordinary female power. These two sisters (daughters of Maggie B. B. RH) Red-and-Blue and Jaconet and their long-reaching impact on the American Thoroughbred, can stand as an illustration of what we can achieve when we build up female lines. We can make a point of building up these lines by targeting descendants who carry several of them.

With Martha Gorman it appears that her genetic gifts were saved and brought down to us today mainly through a mare named Seven Pines who is 3x3 to her—once again we can see that **inbreeding sets and preserves a type for us**. (Please notice how this reaches back and preserves the genetic power, as this tool can be used to build up dominance in the lines we desire from long ago—it shows that it is not impossible, and very well within our reach). Seven Pines's daughter Misty Isle is considered a *reine*, as is the great granddaughter Ole Liz. As you follow our American families it will become plain how lines that could have been lost through the generations are instead revitalized and empowered by an **inbred descendant**. We are often fearful of inbreeding, and we should always be cautious in its use, because it does concentrate whatever is there, and provides potency in all those traits—good or bad. That said, it is also the most powerful tool a breeder has for potency building, and it is the way we stamp a recognizable type on our herds.

We see a similar pattern of inbreeding in the fabulous broodmare sire Americus who is 2x2 to the full siblings Norfolk RH and The Nun RH, who in-turn are out of an inbred dam Novice RH, who is 3x3 to full brothers, whose dam Transport RH was an extraordinary broodmare in the midst of our Heroic Era. That the power concentrated in Americus was passed to his daughters and then their daughters through sex-linked characteristics cannot be denied. From those mares, Lady Juror and Mumtaz Mahal, came a modern day genetic bonanza in the British Thoroughbred.

With inbreeding, generally the individual inbred horse is not the best performer—more often they excel at stud duties, but may not be performance stars—although there are notable exceptions to this (the inbred offspring of Janus and Sir Archy offspring for instance, and of course inbred Americus was a great performer as well as producer.) So when we use it our first goal must be to set type, and then if we get top performance also then we should consider ourselves blessed.

But here we have the concentration put in place by Seven Pines and her descendants who have passed on Martha's gifts reliably. As the generations went on we can see that when a sire brought in additional lines of Maggie B. B. RH—as in the *reine* Ole Liz—another top broodmare was produced. Ole Liz's progeny were great grade I racers, and her full sister Bourbon Mist also transferred top class, such as her daughter Life's Magic who won over $2 million!

Sallie McClelland had a full sister—Bonnie Blue II 1891—who produced the top racing filly of her day: Blue Girl, who beat them all to earn her top Filly-of-the-Year award 1901. Jaconet produced well through other daughters: Intrepid is ranked a *reine* and gave us the great broodmares Sankara and Sanfara (*reines* also). When these lines met with Blue Larkspur—who carries Domino and Ben Brush (along with a great filly factor of Padua daughters)—one of the greatest modern mares came about: Alablue. Out of her daughter Mattie T comes the important *reine* Margaret Lawerence and her daughter Unerring. When these lines met up with Royal Charger, who carries Lexington RH in multiples through Catnip and Lady Josephine, then the great stakes winner Idun was produced, who at stud produced many jumpers in England.

The full sister to Martha Gorman, Audience, heads her own family, which includes the top performers Kentucky Derby winner Venetian Way and Top Flight, and from the Portage branch of her family comes good racer and sire Cozzene and the 1994 broodmare of the year Fall Aspen who was dam of Timber Country.

What happens when we use those who carry inbreeding to Maggie B. B. RH? I guess the best answer to that is Whisk Broom II, one of the most important sires of his time. He is out of Audience who is 3x3 to Maggie B. B. RH, and is by the Ben Brush son Broomstick, who builds on the Boston RH/Lexington RH portion of the dam's genes. When racing was restarted in New York in 1912, and American stables began slowly returning their stock back to the States, one of those racing stars brought back was Whisk Broom II who had raced and won in England.

> "Whisk Broom II was bred by Mr. H.P. Whitney, who sent the colt to England as a yearling to be trained by A. J. Joyner. He ran five races in 1909, winning the Prince of Wales Plate in York, and ran Lemberg to a neck in the Middle Park Plate and was beaten by him for the Dewhurst Plate. At three he ran third for the 2000, won the Trial at Ascot, second for the Craven, and won the Select at Newmarket, beating Dean Swift. As a four-year-old he won twice, and at five he won the Victoria Cup. He had proved one of the fleetest horses in England up to a mile, and had been very heavily handicapped, but he could not seem to prevail at longer distances" (Vosborough).

Whisk Broom II—home from England—is seen here winning the Suburban and setting a new record
for 2 minutes flat for 1 ¼ miles in 1913—that's over 37 mph! —photo by C. C. Cook

When he returned he also won the Metropolitan Handicap, then he set a track record when he won the Brooklyn Handicap, and just a week later while carrying the heavy weight of one hundred thirty-nine pounds he broke his own and Broomstick's record of 2:02 1/16 with two minutes flat. He was the first horse to win all three New York Handicap races, which in our day is called the Handicap Triple Crown, and this feat was only repeated fifty years later when Tom Fool took them all. Whisk Broom II was voted Horse-of-the-Year in 1913, and he is sire of the good racers Upset, Nedna, Whiskaway, Diavolo, Victorian, Whiskery, and John P. Grier (see Chapter 25). He is found continually in jumpers and eventing champions.

Perhaps the best example of the quality possible from building up of Whisk Broom II lines (and therefore Maggie B. B. RH) can be seen in the gelding John Henry 1975. His dam was Once Double by Double Jay out of Intent One is 3x5x5 to Whisk Broom

II through daughters; it is a shame he was gelded. John Henry raced eighty-three times, and won thirty-nine, came second fifteen times and third nine times, and he remained sound —what a wonderful racehorse. He earned over $6.5 million!

Martha Gorman (3x3 Maggie B. B. RH) proved to be a wonderful broodmare, not just of potent daughters as we saw above, but she also provided an important sire. Taken to France by J. E. Widener, she was bred to the French stallion Maintenon; the result of this joining was the good racehorse and sire Maintenant 1913. He won his first and only race, but it being the era of the Jersey Act he was brought home to the US to stand stud. His American-bred son, the good sire Haste, was out of Miss Malaprop, who was out of Correction (the full sister to Domino). Haste is the sire of the *reine* Seven Pines who is 3x3 to Martha Gorman therefore is 6x6x6x6 to Maggie B. B. RH (mentioned above). Another of his daughters is recognizable to most; this is Quickly, the dam of the Triple Crown Winner Count Fleet and his full brother Count Speed. Quickly's dam reinforces the Martha Gorman power by bringing in another line of Hindoo 5x5 through a Hanover daughter. Count Fleet is rated a *chef-de-race*, and he is a prime and enduring sport horse line, a factor in many top stamina lines as well.

Maintenant, born in France out of Martha Gorman, was brought to the US to stand stud. —photo from *Thoroughbred Types* by W. A. Rouch

Maggie B. B. RH, even in our day has far reaching power—especially when she is found on the dam-line. For instance, one of the greatest producing mares of modern times is Fall Aspen, and she is tail-female to Maggie through her granddaughter Audience. Crossing lines of Cozzene, Fall Aspen, and Count Fleet can build on this power.

You will still find the sons of Maggie B. B. RH such as Iroquois and Harold in modern pedigrees, but they have not bred on the way her daughters and granddaughters have—Maggie B. B. RH obviously has something very powerful in her mtDNA and sex-linked characteristics.

Count Fleet—a strong and sound line in sport horse breeding. —image courtesy of Keeneland Library

KATHLEEN H. KIRSAN

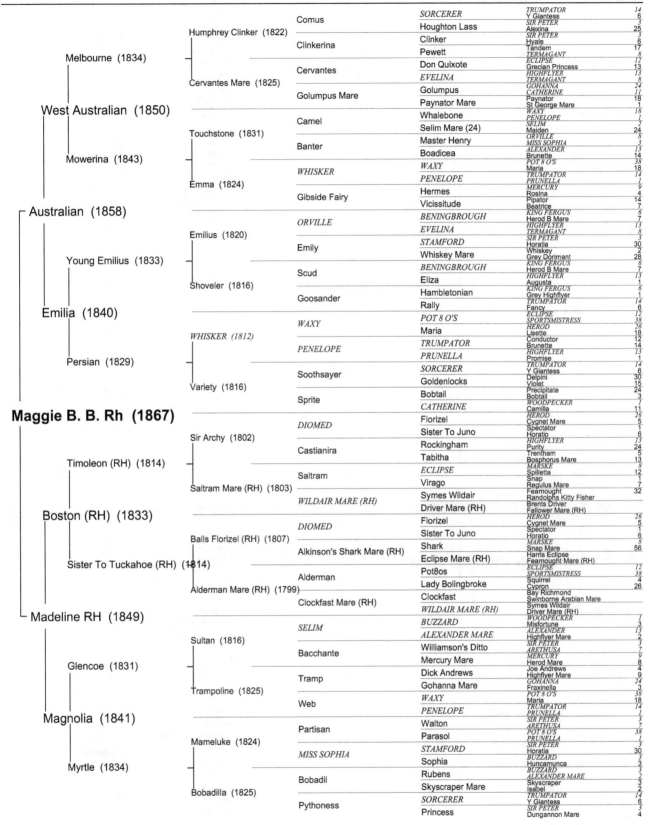

Maggie B.B. RH 1867

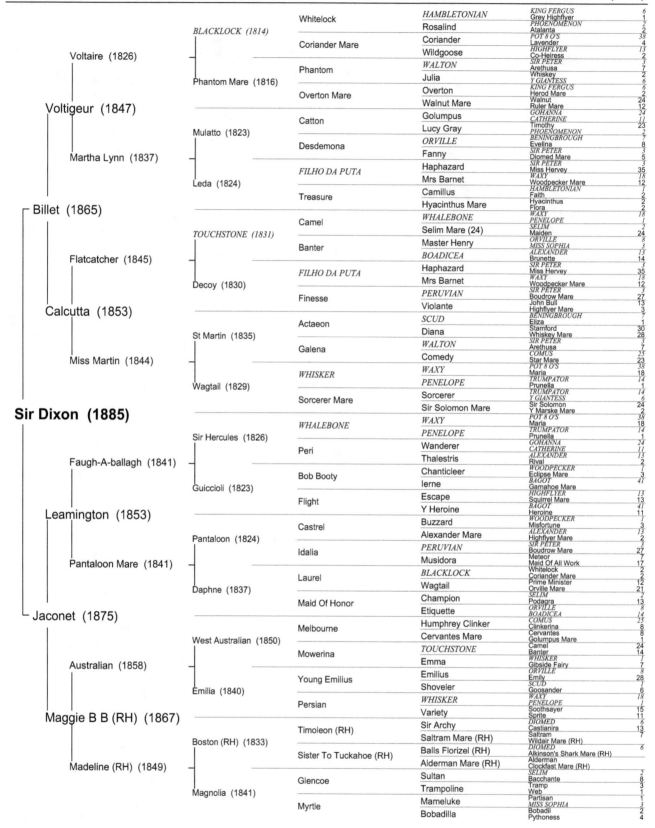

Sir Dixon (1885)

- Billet (1865)
  - Voltigeur (1847)
    - Voltaire (1826)
      - *BLACKLOCK (1814)*
        - Whitelock
          - *HAMBLETONIAN* — KING FERGUS 6 / Grey Highflyer 1
          - Rosalind — *PHOENOMENON* 2 / Atalanta 2
        - Coriander Mare
          - Coriander — *POT 8 O'S* 38 / Lavender 4
          - Wildgoose — *HIGHFLYER* 13 / Co-Heiress 2
      - Phantom Mare (1816)
        - Phantom
          - *WALTON* — SIR PETER 3 / Arethusa 7
          - Julia — Whiskey 2 / *Y GIANTESS* 6
        - Overton Mare
          - Overton — *KING FERGUS* 6 / Herod Mare 2
          - Walnut Mare — Walnut 24 / Ruler Mare 12
    - Martha Lynn (1837)
      - Mulatto (1823)
        - Catton
          - Golumpus — *GOHANNA* 24 / *CATHERINE* 11
          - Lucy Gray — Timothy 23 / *PHOENOMENON* 2
        - Desdemona
          - *ORVILLE* — BENINGBROUGH 7 / Evelina 8
          - Fanny — *SIR PETER* 3 / Diomed Mare 5
      - Leda (1824)
        - *FILHO DA PUTA*
          - Haphazard — *SIR PETER* 3 / Miss Hervey 35
          - Mrs Barnet — *WAXY* 18 / Woodpecker Mare 12
        - Treasure
          - Camillus — *HAMBLETONIAN* 1 / Faith 2
          - Hyacinthus Mare — Hyacinthus 2 / Flora 2
  - Flatcatcher (1845)
  - Calcutta (1853)
    - *TOUCHSTONE (1831)*
      - Camel
        - *WHALEBONE* — WAXY 18 / PENELOPE 1
        - Selim Mare (24) — *SELIM* 2 / Maiden 24
      - Banter
        - Master Henry — *ORVILLE* 8 / *MISS SOPHIA* 3
        - *BOADICEA* — ALEXANDER 13 / Brunette 14
    - Decoy (1830)
      - *FILHO DA PUTA*
        - Haphazard — *SIR PETER* 3 / Miss Hervey 35
        - Mrs Barnet — *WAXY* 18 / Woodpecker Mare 12
      - Finesse
        - *PERUVIAN* — SIR PETER 3 / Boudrow Mare 27
        - Violante — John Bull 13 / Highflyer Mare 3
    - Miss Martin (1844)
      - St Martin (1835)
        - Actaeon
          - *SCUD* — BENINGBROUGH 7 / Eliza 1
          - Diana — Stamford 30 / Whiskey Mare 28
        - Galena
          - *WALTON* — SIR PETER 3 / Arethusa 7
          - Comedy — *COMUS* 25 / Star Mare 23
      - Wagtail (1829)
        - *WHISKER*
          - *WAXY* — POT 8 O'S 38 / Maria 18
          - *PENELOPE* — TRUMPATOR 14 / Prunella 1
        - Sorcerer Mare
          - Sorcerer — *TRUMPATOR* 14 / *Y GIANTESS* 6
          - Sir Solomon Mare — Sir Solomon 24 / Y Marske Mare 2
- Jaconet (1875)
  - Leamington (1853)
    - Faugh-A-ballagh (1841)
      - Sir Hercules (1826)
        - *WHALEBONE*
          - *WAXY* — POT 8 O'S 38 / Maria 18
          - *PENELOPE* — TRUMPATOR 14 / Prunella 1
        - Peri
          - Wanderer — *GOHANNA* 24 / *CATHERINE* 11
          - Thalestris — *ALEXANDER* 13 / Rival 2
      - Guiccioli (1823)
        - Bob Booty
          - Chanticleer — *WOODPECKER* 1 / Eclipse Mare 3
          - Ierne — *BAGOT* 41 / Gamahoe Mare
        - Flight
          - Escape — *HIGHFLYER* 13 / Squirrel Mare 13
          - Y Heroine — *BAGOT* 41 / Heroine 11
    - Pantaloon Mare (1841)
      - Pantaloon (1824)
        - Castrel
          - Buzzard — *WOODPECKER* 1 / Misfortune 3
          - Alexander Mare — *ALEXANDER* 13 / Highflyer Mare 2
        - Idalia
          - *PERUVIAN* — SIR PETER 3 / Boudrow Mare 27
          - Musidora — Meteor 17 / Maid Of All Work 17
      - Daphne (1837)
        - Laurel
          - *BLACKLOCK* — Whitelock 2 / Coriander Mare 2
          - Wagtail — Prime Minister 12 / Orville Mare 21
        - Maid Of Honor
          - Champion — *SELIM* 2 / Podagra 13
          - Etiquette — *ORVILLE* 8 / *BOADICEA* 14
  - Maggie B B (RH) (1867)
    - Australian (1858)
      - West Australian (1850)
        - Melbourne
          - Humphrey Clinker — *COMUS* 25 / Clinkerina 8
          - Cervantes Mare — Cervantes 8 / Golumpus Mare 1
        - Mowerina
          - *TOUCHSTONE* — Camel 24 / Banter 14
          - Emma — *WHISKER* 1 / Gibside Fairy 7
      - Emilia (1840)
        - Young Emilius
          - Emilius — *ORVILLE* 8 / Emily 28
          - Shoveler — *SCUD* 1 / Goosander 6
        - Persian
          - *WHISKER* — WAXY 18 / PENELOPE 1
          - Variety — Soothsayer 15 / Sprite 11
    - Madeline (RH) (1849)
      - Boston (RH) (1833)
        - Timoleon (RH)
          - Sir Archy — *DIOMED* 6 / Castianira 13
          - Saltram Mare (RH) — Saltram 7 / Wildair Mare (RH)
        - Sister To Tuckahoe (RH)
          - Balls Florizel (RH) — *DIOMED* 6 / Alkinson's Shark Mare (RH)
          - Alderman Mare (RH) — Alderman / Clockfast Mare (RH)
      - Magnolia (1841)
        - Glencoe
          - Sultan — *SELIM* 2 / Bacchante 8
          - Trampoline — Tramp 3 / Web 1
        - Myrtle
          - Mameluke — Partisan 1 / *MISS SOPHIA* 3
          - Bobadilla — Bobadil 2 / Pythoness 4

Sir Dixon 1885

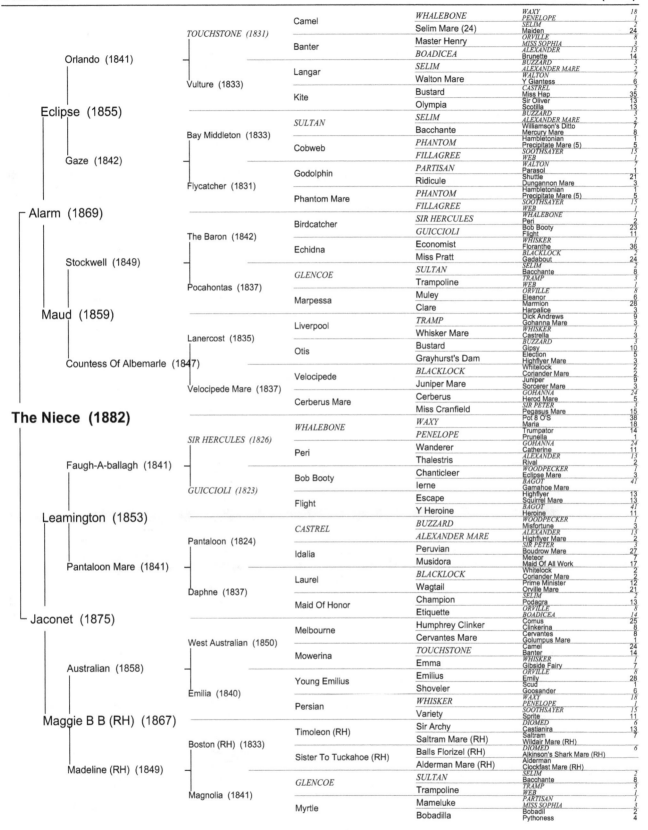

			Camel	*WHALEBONE*	*WAXY* 18 / *PENELOPE* 1
		TOUCHSTONE (1831)		Selim Mare (24)	*SELIM* 2 / Maiden 24
	Orlando (1841)		Banter	Master Henry	*ORVILLE* 8 / *MISS SOPHIA* 3
				BOADICEA	*ALEXANDER* 13 / Brunette 14
			Langar	*SELIM*	*BUZZARD* 3 / *ALEXANDER MARE* 2
Eclipse (1855)		Vulture (1833)		Walton Mare	*WALTON* 7 / Y Giantess 6
			Kite	Bustard	*CASTREL* 2 / Miss Hap 35
				Olympia	Sir Oliver 13 / Scotilla 13
			SULTAN	*SELIM*	*BUZZARD* 3 / *ALEXANDER MARE* 2
		Bay Middleton (1833)		Bacchante	Williamson's Ditto 7 / Mercury Mare 8
	Gaze (1842)		Cobweb	*PHANTOM*	Hambletonian 1 / Precipitate Mare (5) 5
				FILLAGREE	*SOOTHSAYER* 15 / WEB 1
		Flycatcher (1831)	Godolphin	*PARTISAN*	*WALTON* 7 / Parasol 1
				Ridicule	Shuttle 21 / Dungannon Mare 3
			Phantom Mare	*PHANTOM*	Hambletonian 1 / Precipitate Mare (5) 5
				FILLAGREE	*SOOTHSAYER* 15 / WEB 1
Alarm (1869)		The Baron (1842)	Birdcatcher	*SIR HERCULES*	*WHALEBONE* 1 / Peri 2
				GUICCIOLI	Bob Booty 23 / Flight 11
			Echidna	Economist	*WHISKER* 1 / Floranthe 36
	Stockwell (1849)			Miss Pratt	*BLACKLOCK* 2 / Gadabout 24
		Pocahontas (1837)	*GLENCOE*	*SULTAN*	*SELIM* 2 / Bacchante 8
				Trampoline	*TRAMP* 3 / WEB 1
			Marpessa	Muley	*ORVILLE* 8 / Eleanor 6
				Clare	Marmion 28 / Harpalice 3
Maud (1859)		Lanercost (1835)	Liverpool	*TRAMP*	Dick Andrews 9 / Gohanna Mare 3
				Whisker Mare	*WHISKER* 1 / Castrella 3
			Otis	Bustard	*BUZZARD* 3 / Gipsy 10
	Countess Of Albemarle (1847)			Grayhurst's Dam	Election 5 / Highflyer Mare 3
		Velocipede Mare (1837)	Velocipede	*BLACKLOCK*	Whitelock 2 / Coriander Mare 2
				Juniper Mare	Juniper 9 / Sorcerer Mare 3
			Cerberus Mare	Cerberus	*GOHANNA* 24 / Herod Mare 5
				Miss Cranfield	*SIR PETER* 15 / Pegasus Mare 3

The Niece (1882)

		SIR HERCULES (1826)	*WHALEBONE*	*WAXY*	Pot 8 O'S 38 / Maria 18
				PENELOPE	Trumpator 14 / Prunella 1
	Faugh-A-ballagh (1841)		Peri	Wanderer	*GOHANNA* 24 / Catherine 11
				Thalestris	*ALEXANDER* 13 / Rival 2
		GUICCIOLI (1823)	Bob Booty	Chanticleer	*WOODPECKER* 1 / Eclipse Mare 3
				Ierne	*BAGOT* 41 / Gamahoe Mare
Leamington (1853)			Flight	Escape	Highflyer 13 / Squirrel Mare 13
				Y Heroine	*BAGOT* 41 / Heroine 11
		Pantaloon (1824)	*CASTREL*	*BUZZARD*	*WOODPECKER* 1 / Misfortune 3
				ALEXANDER MARE	*ALEXANDER* 13 / Highflyer Mare 2
	Pantaloon Mare (1841)		Idalia	Peruvian	*SIR PETER* 3 / Boudrow Mare 27
				Musidora	Meteor 7 / Maid Of All Work 17
		Daphne (1837)	Laurel	*BLACKLOCK*	Whitelock 2 / Coriander Mare 2
				Wagtail	Prime Minister 12 / Orville Mare 21
			Maid Of Honor	Champion	*SELIM* 2 / Podagra 13
				Etiquette	*ORVILLE* 8 / *BOADICEA* 14
Jaconet (1875)		West Australian (1850)	Melbourne	Humphrey Clinker	Comus 25 / Clinkerina 8
				Cervantes Mare	Cervantes 8 / Golumpus Mare 1
	Australian (1858)		Mowerina	*TOUCHSTONE*	Camel 24 / Banter 14
				Emma	*WHISKER* 1 / Gibside Fairy 7
		Emilia (1840)	Young Emilius	Emilius	*ORVILLE* 8 / Emily 28
				Shoveler	Scud 1 / Goosander 6
			Persian	*WHISKER*	*WAXY* 18 / *PENELOPE* 1
				Variety	*SOOTHSAYER* 15 / Sprite 11
Maggie B B (RH) (1867)		Boston (RH) (1833)	Timoleon (RH)	Sir Archy	*DIOMED* 6 / Castianira 13
				Saltram Mare (RH)	Saltram 7 / Wildair Mare (RH)
			Sister To Tuckahoe (RH)	Balls Florizel (RH)	*DIOMED* 6 / Atkinson's Shark Mare (RH)
				Alderman Mare (RH)	Alderman / Clockfast Mare (RH)
	Madeline (RH) (1849)	Magnolia (1841)	*GLENCOE*	*SULTAN*	*SELIM* 2 / Bacchante 8
				Trampoline	*TRAMP* 3 / WEB 1
			Myrtle	Mameluke	*PARTISAN* 1 / *MISS SOPHIA* 3
				Bobadilla	Bobadil 2 / Pythoness 4

The Niece 1882

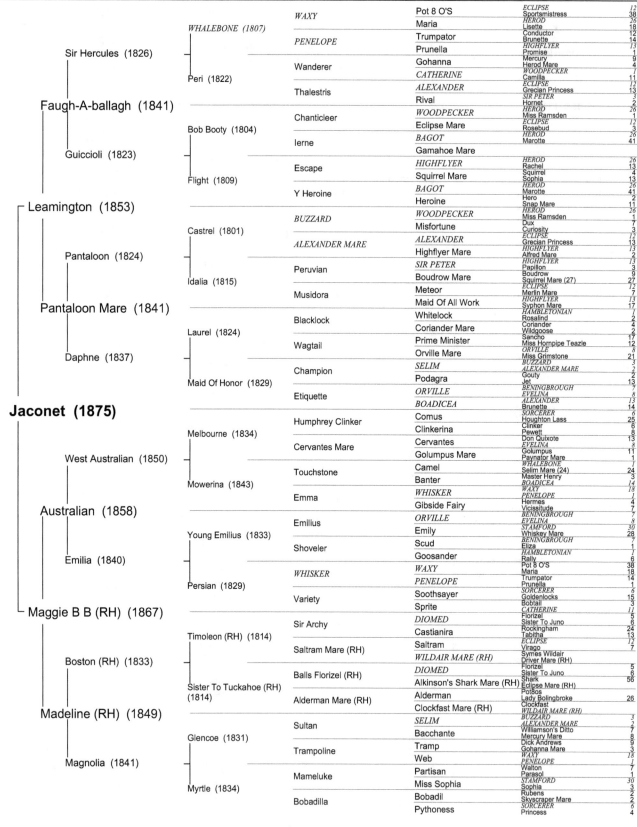

Jaconet (1875)

- **Faugh-A-ballagh (1841)**
  - Sir Hercules (1826)
  - Guiccioli (1823)
- **Leamington (1853)**
- **Pantaloon Mare (1841)**
  - Pantaloon (1824)
  - Daphne (1837)

- **Australian (1858)**
  - West Australian (1850)
  - Emilia (1840)
- **Maggie B B (RH) (1867)**
  - Boston (RH) (1833)
  - Madeline (RH) (1849)
  - Magnolia (1841)

WHALEBONE (1807)	WAXY	Pot 8 O'S	*ECLIPSE* 12 / Sportsmistress 38
		Maria	*HEROD* 26 / Lisette 18
	PENELOPE	Trumpator	Conductor 12 / Brunette 14
		Prunella	*HIGHFLYER* 13 / Promise 1
Peri (1822)	Wanderer	Gohanna	Mercury 9 / Herod Mare 4
		CATHERINE	*WOODPECKER* 7 / Camilla 11
	Thalestris	ALEXANDER	*ECLIPSE* 12 / Grecian Princess 13
		Rival	*SIR PETER* 3 / Hornet 2
Bob Booty (1804)	Chanticleer	WOODPECKER	*HEROD* 26 / Miss Ramsden 1
		Eclipse Mare	*ECLIPSE* 12 / Rosebud 3
	Ierne	BAGOT	*HEROD* 26 / Marotte 41
		Gamahoe Mare	
Flight (1809)	Escape	HIGHFLYER	*HEROD* 26 / Rachel 13
		Squirrel Mare	Squirrel 4 / Sophia 13
	Y Heroine	BAGOT	*HEROD* 26 / Marotte 41
		Heroine	Hero 2 / Snap Mare 11
Castrel (1801)	BUZZARD	WOODPECKER	*HEROD* 26 / Miss Ramsden 1
		Misfortune	Dux 7 / Curiosity 3
	ALEXANDER MARE	ALEXANDER	*ECLIPSE* 12 / Grecian Princess 13
		Highflyer Mare	*HIGHFLYER* 13 / Alfred Mare 2
Idalia (1815)	Peruvian	SIR PETER	*HIGHFLYER* 13 / Papillon 3
		Boudrow Mare	Boudrow 9 / Squirrel Mare (27) 27
	Musidora	Meteor	*ECLIPSE* 12 / Merlin Mare 7
		Maid Of All Work	*HIGHFLYER* 13 / Syphon Mare 17
Laurel (1824)	Blacklock	Whitelock	*HAMBLETONIAN* 1 / Rosalind 2
		Coriander Mare	Coriander 4 / Wildgoose 2
	Wagtail	Prime Minister	Sancho 17 / Miss Hornpipe Teazle 12
		Orville Mare	*ORVILLE* 8 / Miss Grimstone 21
Maid Of Honor (1829)	Champion	SELIM	*BUZZARD* 2 / *ALEXANDER MARE* 2
		Podagra	Gouty 2 / Jet 13
	Etiquette	ORVILLE	*BENINGBROUGH* 7 / *EVELINA* 8
		BOADICEA	*ALEXANDER* 14 / Brunette
Melbourne (1834)	Humphrey Clinker	Comus	*SORCERER* 6 / Houghton Lass 25
		Clinkerina	Clinker 6 / Pewett 8
	Cervantes Mare	Cervantes	Don Quixote 13 / *EVELINA* 8
		Golumpus Mare	Golumpus 11 / Paynator Mare 1
Mowerina (1843)	Touchstone	Camel	*WHALEBONE* 1 / Selim Mare (24) 24
		Banter	Master Henry 3 / *BOADICEA* 14
	Emma	WHISKER	*WAXY* 18 / *PENELOPE* 1
		Gibside Fairy	Hermes 4 / Vicissitude 7
Young Emilius (1833)	Emilius	ORVILLE	*BENINGBROUGH* 7 / *EVELINA* 8
		Emily	*STAMFORD* 30 / Whiskey Mare 28
	Shoveler	Scud	*BENINGBROUGH* 7 / Eliza 1
		Goosander	*HAMBLETONIAN* 1 / Rally 6
Persian (1829)	WHISKER	WAXY	Pot 8 O'S 38 / Maria 18
		PENELOPE	Trumpator 14 / Prunella 1
	Variety	Soothsayer	*SORCERER* 6 / Goldenlocks 15
		Sprite	Bobtail 3 / *CATHERINE* 11
Timoleon (RH) (1814)	Sir Archy	DIOMED	Florizel 5 / Sister To Juno 6
		Castianira	Rockingham 24 / Tabitha 13
	Saltram Mare (RH)	Saltram	*ECLIPSE* 12 / Virago 7
		WILDAIR MARE (RH)	Symes Wildair / Driver Mare (RH)
Sister To Tuckahoe (RH) (1814)	Balls Florizel (RH)	DIOMED	Florizel 5 / Sister To Juno 6
		Alkinson's Shark Mare (RH)	Shark 56 / Eclipse Mare (RH)
	Alderman Mare (RH)	Alderman	Pot8os / Lady Bolingbroke 26
		Clockfast Mare (RH)	Clockfast / *WILDAIR MARE (RH)*
Glencoe (1831)	Sultan	SELIM	*BUZZARD* 3 / *ALEXANDER MARE* 2
		Bacchante	Williamson's Ditto 7 / Mercury Mare 8
	Trampoline	Tramp	Dick Andrews 9 / Gohanna Mare 3
		Web	*WAXY* 18 / *PENELOPE* 1
Myrtle (1834)	Mameluke	Partisan	Walton 1 / Parasol 1
		Miss Sophia	*STAMFORD* 30 / Sophia 3
	Bobadilla	Bobadil	Rubens 2 / Skyscraper Mare 2
		Pythoness	*SORCERER* 6 / Princess 4

Jaconet 1875

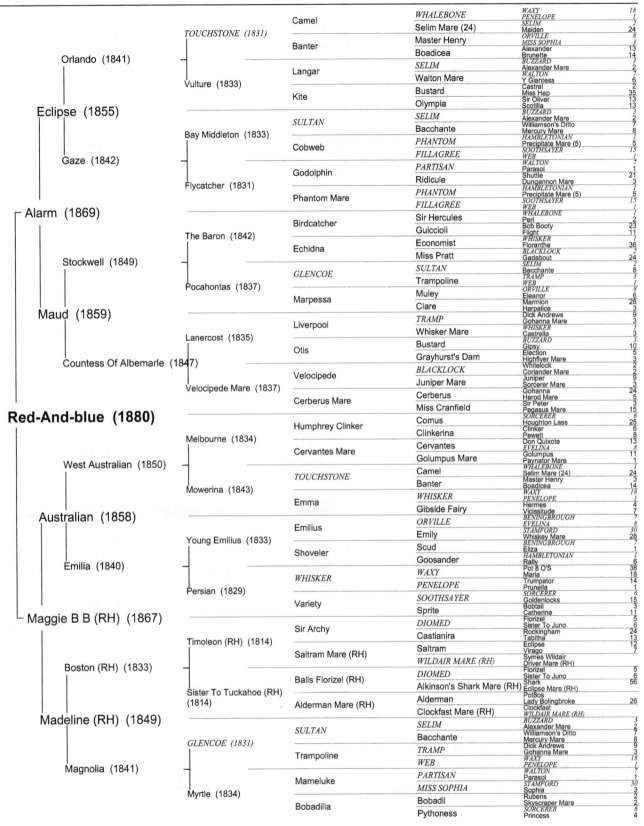

Red and Blue 1880

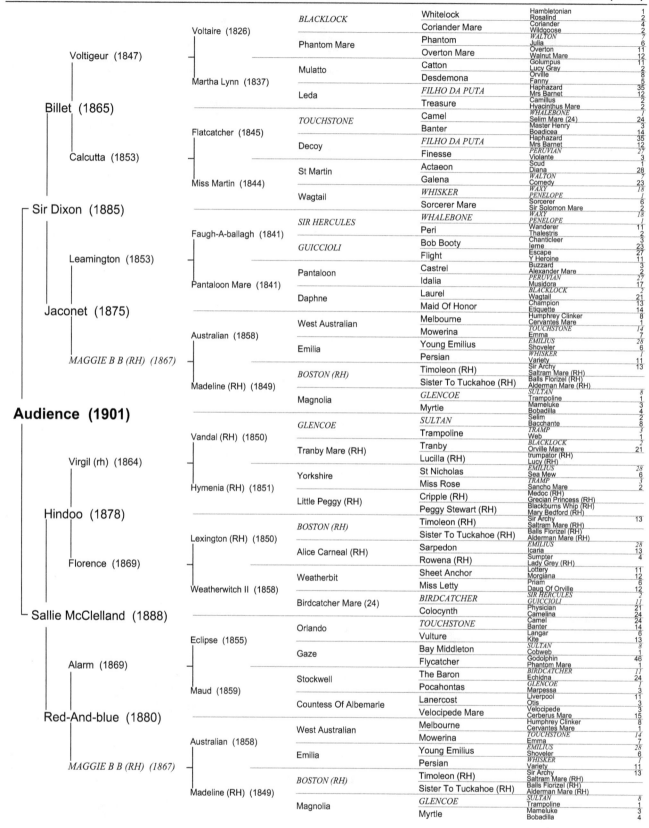

Audience 1901

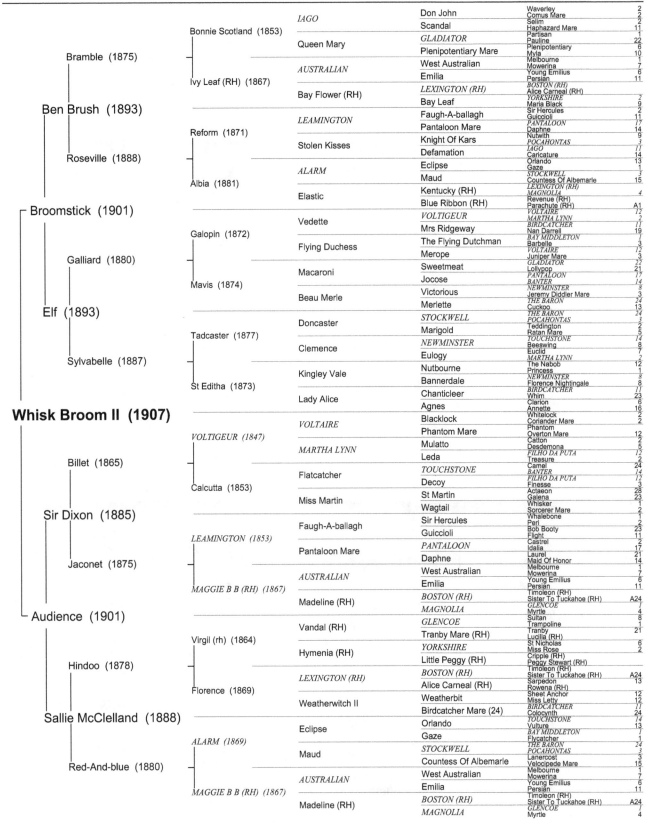

Whisk Broom II (1907)

- Broomstick (1901)
  - Ben Brush (1893)
    - Bramble (1875)
      - Bonnie Scotland (1853)
        - *IAGO*
          - Don John — Waverley 2 / Comus Mare 2
          - Scandal — Selim 2 / Haphazard Mare 11
        - Queen Mary
          - *GLADIATOR* — Partisan 1 / Pauline 22
          - Plenipotentiary Mare — Plenipotentiary 6 / Myla 10
      - Ivy Leaf (RH) (1867)
        - *AUSTRALIAN*
          - West Australian — Melbourne 1 / Mowerina 7
          - Emilia — Young Emilius 6 / Persian 11
        - Bay Flower (RH)
          - *LEXINGTON (RH)* — *BOSTON (RH)* / Alice Carneal (RH)
          - Bay Leaf — *YORKSHIRE* 2 / Maria Black 9
    - Roseville (1888)
      - Reform (1871)
        - *LEAMINGTON*
          - Faugh-A-ballagh — Sir Hercules 2 / Guiccioli 11
          - Pantaloon Mare — *PANTALOON* 17 / Daphne 14
        - Stolen Kisses
          - Knight Of Kars — Nutwith 9 / *POCAHONTAS* 3
          - Defamation — *IAGO* 11 / Caricature 14
      - Albia (1881)
        - *ALARM*
          - Eclipse — Orlando 13 / Gaze 1
          - Maud — *STOCKWELL* 3 / Countess Of Albemarle 15
        - Elastic
          - Kentucky (RH) — *LEXINGTON (RH)* / *MAGNOLIA* 4
          - Blue Ribbon (RH) — Revenue (RH) / Parachute (RH) A1
  - Elf (1893)
    - Galliard (1880)
      - Galopin (1872)
        - Vedette
          - *VOLTIGEUR* — *VOLTAIRE* 12 / *MARTHA LYNN* 2
          - Mrs Ridgeway — *BIRDCATCHER* 11 / Nan Darrell 19
        - Flying Duchess
          - The Flying Dutchman — *BAY MIDDLETON* 1 / Barbelle 3
          - Merope — *VOLTAIRE* 12 / Juniper Mare 3
      - Mavis (1874)
        - Macaroni
          - Sweetmeat — *GLADIATOR* 22 / Lollypop 21
          - Jocose — *PANTALOON* 17 / *BANTER* 14
        - Beau Merle
          - Victorious — *NEWMINSTER* 8 / Jeremy Diddler Mare 3
          - Merlette — *THE BARON* 24 / Cuckoo 13
    - Sylvabelle (1887)
      - Tadcaster (1877)
        - Doncaster
          - *STOCKWELL* — *THE BARON* 24 / *POCAHONTAS* 3
          - Marigold — Teddington 2 / Ratan Mare 5
        - Clemence
          - *NEWMINSTER* — *TOUCHSTONE* 14 / Beeswing 8
          - Eulogy — Euclid 7 / *MARTHA LYNN* 2
      - St Editha (1873)
        - Kingley Vale
          - Nutbourne — The Nabob 12 / Princess 1
          - Bannerdale — *NEWMINSTER* 8 / Florence Nightingale 8
        - Lady Alice
          - Chanticleer — *BIRDCATCHER* 11 / Whim 23
          - Agnes — Clarion 6 / Annette 16
- Audience (1901)
  - Sir Dixon (1885)
    - Billet (1865)
      - *VOLTIGEUR (1847)*
        - *VOLTAIRE*
          - Blacklock — Whitelock 2 / Coriander Mare 2
          - Phantom Mare — Phantom 12 / Overton Mare 2
        - *MARTHA LYNN*
          - Mulatto — Catton 5 / Desdemona 12
          - Leda — *FILHO DA PUTA* 12 / Treasure 2
      - Calcutta (1853)
        - Flatcatcher
          - *TOUCHSTONE* — Camel 24 / *BANTER* 14
          - Decoy — *FILHO DA PUTA* 12 / Finesse 3
        - Miss Martin
          - St Martin — Actaeon 28 / Galena 23
          - Wagtail — Whisker 1 / Sorcerer Mare 2
    - Jaconet (1875)
      - *LEAMINGTON (1853)*
        - Faugh-A-ballagh
          - Sir Hercules — Whalebone 1 / Peri 2
          - Guiccioli — Bob Booty 23 / Flight 11
        - Pantaloon Mare
          - *PANTALOON* — Castrel 2 / Idalia 17
          - Daphne — Laurel 21 / Maid Of Honor 14
      - *MAGGIE B B (RH) (1867)*
        - *AUSTRALIAN*
          - West Australian — Melbourne 1 / Mowerina 7
          - Emilia — Young Emilius 6 / Persian 11
        - Madeline (RH)
          - *BOSTON (RH)* — Timoleon (RH) / Sister To Tuckahoe (RH) A24
          - *MAGNOLIA* — *GLENCOE* 1 / Myrtle 4
  - Sallie McClelland (1888)
    - Hindoo (1878)
      - Virgil (rh) (1864)
        - Vandal (RH)
          - *GLENCOE* — Sultan 8 / Trampoline 1
          - Tranby Mare (RH) — Tranby 21 / Lucilla (RH)
        - Hymenia (RH)
          - *YORKSHIRE* — St Nicholas 6 / Miss Rose 2
          - Little Peggy (RH) — Cripple (RH) / Peggy Stewart (RH)
      - Florence (1869)
        - *LEXINGTON (RH)*
          - *BOSTON (RH)* — Timoleon (RH) / Sister To Tuckahoe (RH) A24
          - Alice Carneal (RH) — Sarpedon 13 / Rowena 13
        - Weatherwitch II
          - Weatherbit — Sheet Anchor 12 / Miss Letty 12
          - Birdcatcher Mare (24) — *BIRDCATCHER* 11 / Colocynth 24
    - Red-And-blue (1880)
      - *ALARM (1869)*
        - Eclipse
          - Orlando — *TOUCHSTONE* 14 / Vulture 13
          - Gaze — *BAY MIDDLETON* 1 / Flycatcher 1
        - Maud
          - *STOCKWELL* — *THE BARON* 24 / *POCAHONTAS* 3
          - Countess Of Albemarle — Lanercost 3 / Velocipede Mare 15
      - *MAGGIE B B (RH) (1867)*
        - *AUSTRALIAN*
          - West Australian — Melbourne 1 / Mowerina 7
          - Emilia — Young Emilius 6 / Persian 11
        - Madeline (RH)
          - *BOSTON (RH)* — Timoleon (RH) / Sister To Tuckahoe (RH) A24
          - *MAGNOLIA* — *GLENCOE* 1 / Myrtle 4

Whisk Broom II 1907

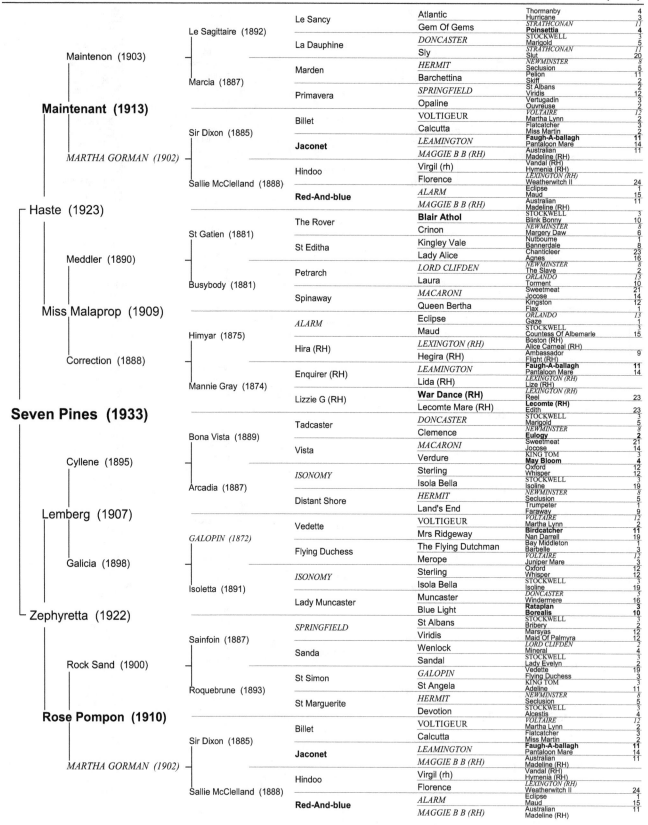

Maintenant (1913)
- Maintenon (1903)
  - Le Sagittaire (1892)
    - Le Sancy
      - Atlantic — Thormanby 4 / Hurricane 3
      - Gem Of Gems — *STRATHCONAN* 11 / **Poinsettia** 4
    - La Dauphine
      - *DONCASTER* — STOCKWELL 3 / Marigold 5
      - Sly — *STRATHCONAN* 11 / Slut 20
  - Marcia (1887)
    - Marden
      - *HERMIT* — *NEWMINSTER* 8 / Seclusion 5
      - Barchettina — Pellon 11 / Skiff 2
    - Primavera
      - *SPRINGFIELD* — St Albans 2 / Viridis 12
      - Opaline — Vertugadin 3 / Ouvreuse 2
- *MARTHA GORMAN (1902)*
  - Sir Dixon (1885)
    - Billet
      - VOLTIGEUR — *VOLTAIRE* 12 / Martha Lynn 2
      - Calcutta — Flatcatcher 3 / Miss Martin 2
    - **Jaconet**
      - *LEAMINGTON* — **Faugh-A-ballagh** 11 / Pantaloon Mare 14
      - *MAGGIE B B (RH)* — Australian 11 / Madeline (RH)
  - Sallie McClelland (1888)
    - Hindoo
      - Virgil (rh) — Vandal (RH) / Hymenia (RH)
      - Florence — *LEXINGTON (RH)* / Weatherwitch II 24
    - **Red-And-blue**
      - *ALARM* — Eclipse 1 / Maud 15
      - *MAGGIE B B (RH)* — Australian 11 / Madeline (RH)

Haste (1923)
- Meddler (1890)
  - St Gatien (1881)
    - The Rover
      - **Blair Athol** — STOCKWELL 3 / Blink Bonny 10
      - Crinon — *NEWMINSTER* 8 / Margery Daw 6
    - St Editha
      - Kingley Vale — Nutbourne 1 / Bannerdale 8
      - Lady Alice — Chanticleer 23 / Agnes 16
  - Busybody (1881)
    - Petrarch
      - *LORD CLIFDEN* — *NEWMINSTER* 8 / The Slave 2
      - Laura — *ORLANDO* 13 / Torment 10
    - Spinaway
      - *MACARONI* — Sweetmeat 21 / Jocose 14
      - Queen Bertha — Kingston 12 / Flax 1
- Miss Malaprop (1909)
  - Himyar (1875)
    - *ALARM*
      - Eclipse — *ORLANDO* 13 / Gaze 1
      - Maud — STOCKWELL 3 / Countess Of Albemarle 15
    - Hira (RH)
      - *LEXINGTON (RH)* — Boston (RH) / Alice Carneal (RH)
      - Hegira (RH) — Ambassador 9 / Flight (RH)
  - Mannie Gray (1874)
    - Enquirer (RH)
      - *LEAMINGTON* — **Faugh-A-ballagh** 11 / Pantaloon Mare 14
      - Lida (RH) — *LEXINGTON (RH)* / Lize (RH)
    - Lizzie G (RH)
      - **War Dance (RH)** — *LEXINGTON (RH)* / Reel 23
      - Lecomte Mare (RH) — **Lecomte (RH)** / Edith 23

Seven Pines (1933)
- Lemberg (1907)
  - Cyllene (1895)
    - Bona Vista (1889)
      - Tadcaster
        - *DONCASTER* — STOCKWELL 3 / Marigold 5
        - Clemence — *NEWMINSTER* 8 / **Eulogy** 2
      - Vista
        - *MACARONI* — Sweetmeat 21 / Jocose 14
        - Verdure — KING TOM 3 / **May Bloom** 4
    - Arcadia (1887)
      - *ISONOMY*
        - Sterling — Oxford 12 / Whisper 12
        - Isola Bella — STOCKWELL 3 / Isoline 19
      - Distant Shore
        - *HERMIT* — *NEWMINSTER* 8 / Seclusion 5
        - Land's End — Trumpeter 1 / Faraway 9
  - Galicia (1898)
    - *GALOPIN (1872)*
      - Vedette
        - VOLTIGEUR — *VOLTAIRE* 12 / Martha Lynn 2
        - Mrs Ridgeway — **Birdcatcher** 11 / Nan Darrell 19
      - Flying Duchess
        - The Flying Dutchman — Bay Middleton 1 / Barbelle 3
        - Merope — *VOLTAIRE* 12 / Juniper Mare 3
    - Isoletta (1891)
      - *ISONOMY*
        - Sterling — Oxford 12 / Whisper 12
        - Isola Bella — STOCKWELL 3 / Isoline 19
      - Lady Muncaster
        - Muncaster — *DONCASTER* 5 / Windermere 16
        - Blue Light — **Rataplan** 3 / **Borealis** 10
- Zephyretta (1922)
  - Rock Sand (1900)
    - Sainfoin (1887)
      - *SPRINGFIELD*
        - St Albans — STOCKWELL 3 / Bribery 2
        - Viridis — Marsyas 12 / Maid Of Palmyra 12
      - Sanda
        - Wenlock — *LORD CLIFDEN* 2 / Mineral 4
        - Sandal — STOCKWELL 3 / Lady Evelyn 2
    - Roquebrune (1893)
      - St Simon
        - *GALOPIN* — Vedette 19 / Flying Duchess 3
        - St Angela — KING TOM 3 / Adeline 11
      - St Marguerite
        - *HERMIT* — *NEWMINSTER* 8 / Seclusion 5
        - Devotion — STOCKWELL 3 / Alcestis 4
  - **Rose Pompon (1910)**
    - Sir Dixon (1885)
      - Billet
        - VOLTIGEUR — *VOLTAIRE* 12 / Martha Lynn 2
        - Calcutta — Flatcatcher 3 / Miss Martin 2
      - **Jaconet**
        - *LEAMINGTON* — **Faugh-A-ballagh** 11 / Pantaloon Mare 14
        - *MAGGIE B B (RH)* — Australian 11 / Madeline (RH)
    - *MARTHA GORMAN (1902)*
    - Sallie McClelland (1888)
      - Hindoo
        - Virgil (rh) — Vandal (RH) / Hymenia (RH)
        - Florence — *LEXINGTON (RH)* / Weatherwitch II 24
      - **Red-And-blue**
        - *ALARM* — Eclipse 1 / Maud 15
        - *MAGGIE B B (RH)* — Australian 11 / Madeline (RH)

Seven Pines 1933

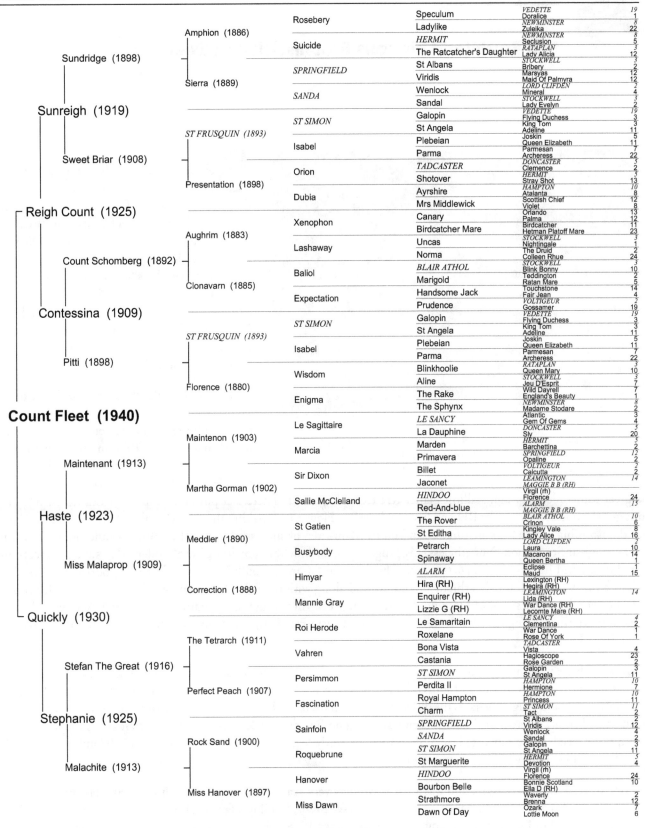

Count Fleet 1940

Chapter 12

Ben Brush (and his sons Broomstick and Sweep)

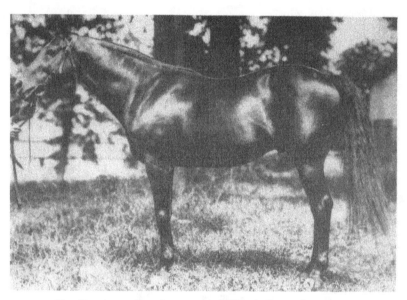

Ben Brush, modern day conduit of Heroic Era performance.
—image from Thoroughbred Record

Ben Brush 1893 heads a sport dynasty, one of the five principal American families that arose from the four-mile heat era. Like most American Thoroughbreds, Ben Brush has strong English Thoroughbred bloodlines; in them I have found three separate groups of full siblings: the brothers Selim/Castrel 5x6, the full siblings Touchstone and his sister Pasquinade 6x6, and the ever present Whalebone/Whisker 6x6x7x6. Full siblings are indicators of genetic power. Also notable is the ½ sister to Bonnie Scotland, Defamation, making them 2x4.

Of course, Ben Brush is also a product of our Heroic Era, so he is a carrier of strong American bloodlines such as Revenue RH, sire of the fourth-dam Blue Ribbon RH—who goes straight back to Ella Crump RH, the A1 maternal family. Revenue RH is also the sire of the great four-mile racer and stallion Planet RH (see Chapter 7). There is a powerful double of Lexington RH also, through his good son Kentucky RH and his daughter Bay Flower RH making them 3x4—ruling both dam-lines. Notice that the Running Horse lines are often found on the dam-lines of successful horses. Ben Brush would not then qualify for the English Stud Book. Nonetheless, his progeny are an indelible portion of the modern-day superior racers and sport horses, and he has rated a *chef-de-race*. This bloodline transfers bulk in muscle, but is supported by stout legs; therefore this is a sound, tough, athletic bloodline, and along with the Fair Play family were key ingredients for mixing with the very fast but less sound Domino dynasty (sore feet). All through the duration of the Jersey Act, with the continual importation of English sires, it still was the Ben Brush, Fair Play, and Domino lines that produced the majority of winners (TRA).

(Many soundness issues in the modern day TB are attributed to the influx of sires with tremendous muscling but on delicate legs—this has proven a design for disaster. Ben Brush was a bulky horse, and he passed this trait on, but he was also incredibly sound and tough—what is the difference between his bulky line and that of Phalaris's bulk? Look at his legs; they are short and stout, whereas the Phalaris family is racing on fine delicate legs. Bulk is a good trait as it supplies muscular power, but it needs to be supported by proportionately sturdy legs to remain sound. The Hanover/Hamburg family also generally provided bulk with strong underpinnings.)

Ben Brush raced until he was four and was a stakes winner every year, and he led the sires list in 1909. He produced excellent offspring—his daughter Idle Fancy is rated as a *reine-de-course*, heading a family of superior stock. When she was bred to Ultimus (inbred to Domino) she produced Ultimate Fancy 1918, who when bred to imported Wrack produced Fancy Racket 1925. Her greatest offspring resulted from her being bred to Bubbling Over, such as Hildene—not only a great broodmare (*reine*) but one of the most powerful female lines today. Hildene 1938 is 4x4 to Ben Brush and 5x6x6x5x5 to Domino. Hildene also produced the notable stallions First Landing, Third Brother, and Hill Prince (see Chapter 21).

Ben Brush's daughter Belgravia was a top broodmare also; she is the dam of the dynasty creator Black Toney and his ¾ sister Bonnie Mary 1917. This line is found everywhere good sport horses are, Europe as well as America. Black Toney is sire of the important stallions Black Servant (sire of Blue Larkspur), Brokers Tip, Baladier, and Bimelech—who are plentiful especially in American pedigrees. His daughter Bridal Colors is the dam of Relic, by the Man O' War son War Relic, this sire stood in the US where he gave us the great racer and sire Olden Times, but he also has huge footprint in Europe. He stood in France and gave them Mystic II, who turned out to be a premier sire of show jumpers including the famous Springer and Springdale. Relic's daughter Relance heads a French dynasty that includes the *chef-de-race*, Reliance, Relko, and the good sire Match—these are all great stamina lines. Relic is also the sire of Pericles, a bloodline of note in the Dutch Warmblood. In England he produced the good sire Buisson Ardent among others.

Relic has fifteen lines of Lexington RH in ten generations. Plus his background power is refocused close up, not just through the ¾ brothers Man O' War/Friar Rock 2x3, but there is the interesting position of Domino and his ¾ sister Quesal 6x5x5, and there is also a fortunate full sibling configuration of the good English lines of Cremorne/Mabille 6x6. This is a very powerful pedigree, and the design explains his far-reaching potency. Once again this is a clear illustration of the power that is produced when our Heroic Era bloodlines are mixed together, we have not only Ben Brush, but three lines of Himyar (Domino, Quesal) and Fair Play.

Ben Brush's sons were both excellent stakes winners and sires, such as his son the good sire Delhi, with offspring like the good sire Dominant (out of Domino line) and the good mare Idle Dell (also with Domino line). But it is his two sons Sweep and Broomstick who rewrote racing history and remain today dominant bloodlines—they are both rated *chef-de-race*. If you breed racehorses or sport horses you will find these lines usually in multiples.

Broomstick 1901

Broomstick, exceptional racer and sire.
—photo by W. A. Rouch found in *Thoroughbred Types*

When Joe Estes, a top writer and expert on the Thoroughbred rated the *chef* Broomstick for the record, he declared that whichever measure you use that this stallion must be rated very high, because besides being the leading sire three times, he was never lower than tenth in seventeen years—an extraordinary record (Bloodhorse).

At this stage in our study we will be finding that many of the significant offspring of a key sire or dam are the result of the re-entry of other of our American family bloodlines. As we saw in the previous chapter, the great sire and typesetter Whisk Broom II is by Broomstick, but out of Audience who is 2x2 to Maggie B. B. RH. Broomstick's full sister Matinee gave us the good mare Idle Hour, plus when Matinee was sent to France she produced the good sire Rialto 1920, a son of the English-bred but French-born Chicle, who himself is out of a Hamburg mare, and when Spendthrift (War Relic) and Domino (Ultimus) were added to Ben Brush lines you saw some of the results above. In our modern day pedigree building—if we want to capture the stamina, speed, and soundness of our Heroic Era—it is individuals like these we will want to build into our pedigree. We can actually thank the poor sportsmanship of the British for some of this quality, because by them banishing our lines from the rest of the racing world it forced us to keep them at home and therefore reconcentrate them. What they designed to harm our breeding industry, and it did in the short run—our breeders of the day suffered greatly and many were ruined—it has, however, ended up providing the bedrock of our power today (see Chapters 15 and 23).

Broomstick's daughter Rowes Bud 1917 is out of the *reine* Cherokee Rose who is by Peter Pan (Domino line), yet another illustration of this concentrating Heroic Era genes, for when she was bred to Chicle (out of a Hamburg mare) she produced Rosebloom 1932, and when this daughter was bred to imported Sir Gallahad she produced a mare named Fragrance 1942, who in turn produced by the inbred sire Eight Thirty a great mare named Rare Perfume (also a full sister Early Bloom). Rare Perfume is a broodmare with a powerful legacy; her stallion son Jaipur by Nasrullah has been a modern sire of note. But it is her daughter Rare Treat by inbred Stymie who is the second dam of Be My Guest, a significant stallion— the first to stand for the new Coolmore stud in Ireland. Be My Guest carries the ¾ sister to Rosebloom: Mother Goose (*reine*) on his sire's (Northern Dancer) dam-line, which makes them 4x5. Be My Guest produced great flat racers and superior jumpers. His son Assert won the French and the Irish Derby (I hope you are noticing how valuable the inbred carriers of these lines became in the production of the top racers and breeding stock—look for them when you are stacking your genetic decks),

Wildair 1917, son of Broomstick, "Wildair is the colt that made Man O' War run a mile in 1:35 for the Withers Stakes of 1920, and at the same meeting (Belmont Park) he won the Metropolitan Handicap" — photo by W.A. Rouch, quotation from *Thoroughbred Types*

Cudgel 1914 was a top class racehorse. "Cudgel was, perhaps, the best racehorse that appeared between the era of Sysonby and that of Man O' War. He defeated all the best horses of his era," —*Thoroughbred Types*

Broomstick's son Wildair was a first-class racer, and as you can see a lovely looking horse, and he was a decent sire as well, with winning offspring such as Canter 1923.

The good sire Bostonian 1924, a Broomstick son who is out of Yankee Maid—a product of Peter Pan (Domino) with Hindoo and Maggie B. B. RH. Whenever you find Sir Dixon and Ben Brush in the same pedigree as you do here, this puts the ¾ siblings Kentucky RH and Madeline RH (Boston RH line) together—here they are 4x5. Bostonian's daughter Fiji by imported Bull Dog (Teddy line) produced the good mare Isolde, who is the dam of the great racer and good sire Dark Star 1950 (he won Kentucky Derby and is the horse who gave Native Dancer his only defeat). Born just as the Jersey Act had been lifted, Dark Star produced the *reine* Hidden Talent out of a Nasrullah dam. She gave us the *reine* Turn to Talent (by Turn To) and the good mare Too Bald (inbred to Nasruallah 2x3), a good racer who produced five stakes winners. When Dark Star was seventeen he was sent to France, so you will find some French progeny also.

Then there is Broomstick's daughter Regret 1912, who was the first mare to win the Kentucky Derby, she is out of the Hamburg mare Jersey Lightning, who is 4x5x6 to the Lexington RH son War Dance RH, as is her full brother Thunderer—he also was a good racer and sire.

Even Broomstick's son Cudgel, who was out of a purely English dam, when he was bred to a mare carrying Maggie B.B. RH he produced the useful sire Milkman, who in-turn, when he was bred to the Bubbling Over daughter Agnes Star, he begat the *reine* Cottage Cheese. Bubbling Over is out of a Sweep daughter, and he is 4x5x5x5 to Domino and his ½ sister Lady Reel.

And then there is Frillery, the great mare by yet another daughter of Hamburg. Some of Broomstick's offspring were taken to Europe during the New York blackout. His son Sweeper II was taken as a yearling to France by Duryea, and then while racing for France in 1911 he won the 2000 Guineas in England. He later became the sire of the great broodmares (*reines*) Frizeur 1916 and Ondulation 1920, both of these mares are out of Frizette—a Hamburg daughter, therefore they are built on the Flaw. He had other great daughters such as Dustpan II out of Banshee—a Frizette daughter who won the French 1000 Guineas, as well as Sweepless out of another Hamburg daughter: Artless. He also produced the good sire Golden Broom out of another Hamburg daughter Zuna, he carries five lines of Lexington RH.

"Both as a racehorse and sire, Broomstick has made a named surpassed by no other American Thoroughbred of his generation. A winner of fourteen races…As a sire, Broomstick soon began to scatter his image on the land. Three times he led the 'Winning Sires' (1913, 1914 and 1915)…"(*Thoroughbred Types*).

Frizette-Frizeur-Frilette-Frillery-Frizelle

I don't know about you, but I am getting confused by the multitudes of important mares with similar names: Frizette and Frizeur, both *reines*, and am having trouble keeping them straight. So I looked them up, and then saw one of the reasons why I was having a problem. There are two *reines* with almost identical names: Frizette, by Hamburg born in 1905, and the other is Frizeur 1916 is by Sweeper out of the 1905 Frizette, but then there is even a third *reine* with a similar name: Frilette by Man O' War born in 1924.

Frizette 1905 is a mega-*reine,* if I can invent a term, she left massive families in both America and France—her shadow is huge: there is her *reine* daughter Banshee (who in-turn produced Durban, Heldifann, Dust Pan II, and Sheba); then there is Frizette's stallion son Frizzle who provides a sex-balance when brought into your pedigrees (see how important his line is in the pedigree of the *reine* Aspidistra in Chapter 21). Also valuable are Frizette's daughters the three full sisters by Rabelais: Durzetta, Frizelle, and Lespedeza, plus Princess Palatine (*reine*), Ondulation, and another *reine* daughter Frizeur (see Chapter 10). Her family is still one of the most powerful in the breed worldwide.

Frizeur 1916 by Sweeper out of Frizette, and she also is a *reine* and gave us the American family of Black Curl, granddam of the Kentucky Derby winner and very good sire Jet Pilot, as well as the super *reine* Myrtlewood.

Frilette 1924, is also a *reine*, she is by Man O' War, out of Frillery 1913—who is by Broomstick out of Petticoat by Hamburg out of Elusive, who is by Sir Dixon out of Vega by War Dance RH—you can't get more American than this mare! She is 4x5 to the full brothers Spendthrift/Fellowcraft, sex-balanced; she is 5x7 to War Dance RH, and she is 6x7x7x7x6 Lexington RH.

But the confusion does not stop with these great producers, as there are two other mares with a name that begins with 'Fri' who are also closely related and almost as important as the broodmares above. There is Frillery 1913, who besides being the dam of Frilette (above) is also the dam of Equestrian, the sire of Stymie who in turn is the sire of Rare Treat (discussed above) and a *reine* Lipstick. She is the dam of the good mare Jabot who is in-turn the dam of the good sire Counterpoint, who in-turn produced the *reine* Allemande, plus her daughter Halcyon Days by Halcyon (Broomstick son), who in-turn produced Sunlight by Count Fleet (who brings in Maggie B. B. RH through Martha Gorman), and Sunlight is the dam of the great racer and sire Tompion, a son of Tom Fool. Tompion is 3x4 to the full brothers Pharamond/Sickle; he is 4x5 to the full brothers Sunreigh and Sun Briar, and he is 6x4x6 to Broomstick.

But then there is still another: Frizelle 1922. She is a daughter of Frizette by Durbar, so is inbred to Hanover 3x4 and St. Simon 4x4; she too is a significant producer. She was bred by Marcel Boussac, and she is a ¾ sister to Durban the dam of Tourbillon—so a candidate for line-breeding (Chapter 16).

Sweep 1907

The *chef-de-race* Sweep was bred by the legendary breeder James Keene. He began as a champion at two and stayed at the top through his third year winning both the US titles for champion colt as a two and as a three-year-old. Many horses are good racers but lack the prepotency to pass on their talents consistently. Here is where Sweep stands above most others—he was a fantastic sire—he is a **genetic giant**.

Sweep—contender for greatest broodmare sire ever—is genetic gold in your pedigrees. —photo found in *Thoroughbred Types*

Although Sweep's greatest legacy is through his daughters, he also provided the racing world with good colts. The Porter 1915, was a good racer, winning three out of five starts when he was two, and his performance was what first alerted the industry that Sweep might be a significant sire. The Porter continued racing successfully at three, winning the Baltimore Handicap and others against high-class colts. A small compact horse like his sire, he proved to be a good sire as well. He is the sire of the *reine* Two Bob.

The Porter 1915, a good son of Sweep.
—photo by L. S. Sutcliffe

That was a good start, but the next year saw a couple of other significant sons arrive. Eternal 1916 was a very fast horse, and he did well in heavy track conditions—winning the Hopeful Stakes—and when he was three he took the Brooklyn Handicap. Like his sire he was not too large and of compact build. His dam brought in a line of Hanover. He was a fairly good sire, with notable offspring such as Ariel and Okapi.

Born in the same year (1916) was probably the best of Sweep's sons: Sweep On (pedigree), a stakes winner who was very fast. He is interesting to us genetically as his fourth dam is Fanchon RH, a daughter of Idlewild RH (the full sister to Aerolite RH), plus his dam brings in a ¾ brother, Falsetto, to Mannie Gray—surely these features helped in his impact as a sire. His daughter Sweep Out is the second dam of none other than the mare Ellen Parker calls "Queen Mother"; this is Miss

KATHLEEN H. KIRSAN

Sweep On 1916, perhaps the best son of Sweep, was a high-class racehorse and a sire of note. —photo by W. A. Rouch

Disco whose progeny record is 'off the charts' as she is the dam of Bold Ruler and his five full siblings by Nasrullah, plus an important mare by Tom Fool: Foolish One.

Yet, with all those good sons to carry on his name, Sweep's greatest contribution to our sport sources is through his daughters. Like the great broodmare sire Discovery or Hamburg, having a Sweep daughter or two in your designs is almost a guarantee of success. Sweep transfers the large heart gene to his daughters. Here are a few of his most famous daughters:

La Chica—dam of the foundation mare Miyako by John P. Grier (see pedigree), who is the granddam of the *chef-de-race* Native Dancer, plus she is dam of Planetoid who is dam of the modern megamare Grey Flight (*reine*), herself dam of two *reines*: Misty Morn and Clear Ceiling.

Miyako is inbred 3x4 to Ben Brush and is 3x4 to Pink Domino.

Washoe Belle—another foundation mare, dam of the *reine* Ruddy Light who is dam of the *reine* Chicleight, who is dam of the *reine* Blue Delight, who is dam of the *reine* Real Delight; this is extraordinary maternal power, and her descendants include the *chefs* Alydar and T.V. Lark plus the good sire Forward Pass.

The superlative War Admiral—one of the greatest horses of all times, superior racer and sire. He is out of a Sweep dam. —image courtesy of Keeneland Library, photographer C. C. Cook

Beaming Beauty—who is 3x4x4x4 to Domino and his ½ sister Lady Reel and who carries nine lines of Lexington RH in seven generations; she is a foundation mare of extreme potency. Her daughter Bar Nothing produced the filly Blade of Time who in turn produced the *reine* Kerala, who is the dam of Damascus, the mega-sire. Plus her son Bubbling Over is a great sire—his son Burgoo King won the Kentucky Derby, and his daughter Hildene is a *reine* of great influence (discussed above); his daughter Baby League is also a *reine* and dam of the world beater Busher, her full sister Striking (*reine*), and their full brother Mr. Busher—to combine these ingredients in our modern pedigrees is a recipe for success, such as we see demonstrated by Seattle Slew's dam My Charmer and the recent Belmont and Preakness winner California Chrome (see Chapter 21 and 26 for more on her).

Brushup—the dam of the *chef-de-race* War Admiral—Triple Crown winner, and one of the greatest dam-sires of all time (six *reines*: Beltshazar, Busanda, Portage, Striking, Searching, and Iron Maiden) he transfers great speed and the large heart gene. There are also four full sisters to War Admiral.

Dustwhirl—dam of Whirlaway, another Triple Crown winner and good sire.

Brush Along—dam of the national show jumper champion and sire Holystone 1931 (Man O' War son).

All of Sweep's daughters are valuable in pedigrees today. Realize he is the dam-sire of two Triple Crown winners: War Admiral and Whirlaway, and second dam-sire of Native Dancer, Bubbling Over, and Damascus. Also of those greats just mentioned, three have earned *chef* status: War Admiral, Native Dancer, and Damascus—it *does* not get any better than this. He is without doubt one of the greatest broodmare sires ever; over the years his bloodline has risen to a height of influence few ever reach. In addition he is a documented carrier of the large heart gene, and obviously he transfers speed as well, plus this bloodline is sound.

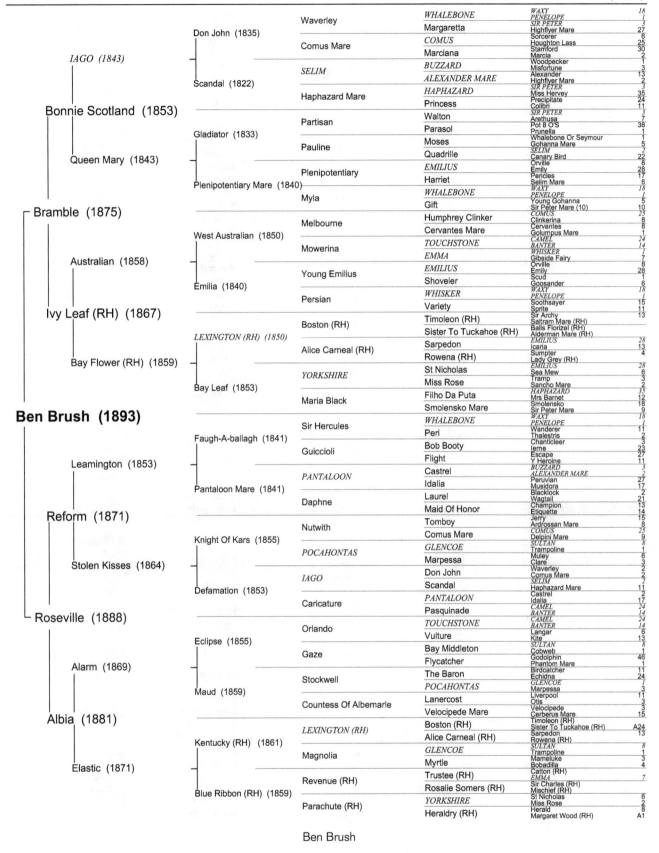

Ben Brush (1893)

Bramble (1875)

Bonnie Scotland (1853)
- *IAGO (1843)*
  - Don John (1835)
    - Waverley
      - WHALEBONE — WAXY 18 / PENELOPE 1
      - Margaretta — SIR PETER 3 / Highflyer Mare 27
    - Comus Mare
      - COMUS — Sorcerer 6 / Houghton Lass 25
      - Marciana — Stamford 30 / Marcia 2
  - Scandal (1822)
    - SELIM
      - BUZZARD — Woodpecker 1 / Misfortune 3
      - ALEXANDER MARE — Alexander 13 / Highflyer Mare 2
    - Haphazard Mare
      - HAPHAZARD — SIR PETER 3 / Miss Hervey 35
      - Princess — Precipitate 24 / Colibri 11
- Queen Mary (1843)
  - Gladiator (1833)
    - Partisan
      - Walton — SIR PETER 3 / Arethusa 7
      - Parasol — Pot 8 O'S 38 / Prunella 1
    - Pauline
      - Moses — Whalebone Or Seymour 1 / Gohanna Mare 5
      - Quadrille — SELIM 2 / Canary Bird 22
  - Plenipotentiary Mare (1840)
    - Plenipotentiary
      - EMILIUS — Orville 8 / Emily 28
      - Harriet — Pericles 17 / Selim Mare 6
    - Myla
      - WHALEBONE — WAXY 18 / PENELOPE 1
      - Gift — Young Gohanna 5 / Sir Peter Mare (10) 10

Ivy Leaf (RH) (1867)
- Australian (1858)
  - West Australian (1850)
    - Melbourne
      - Humphrey Clinker — COMUS 25 / Clinkerina 8
      - Cervantes Mare — Cervantes 8 / Golumpus Mare 1
    - Mowerina
      - TOUCHSTONE — CAMEL 24 / BANTER 14
      - EMMA — WHISKER 1 / Gibside Fairy 7
  - Emilia (1840)
    - Young Emilius
      - EMILIUS — Orville 8 / Emily 28
      - Shoveler — Scud 1 / Goosander 6
    - Persian
      - WHISKER — WAXY 18 / PENELOPE 1
      - Variety — Soothsayer 15 / Sprite 11
- Bay Flower (RH) (1859)
  - *LEXINGTON (RH) (1850)*
    - Boston (RH)
      - Timoleon (RH) — Sir Archy 13 / Saltram Mare (RH)
      - Sister To Tuckahoe (RH) — Balls Florizel (RH) / Alderman Mare (RH)
    - Alice Carneal (RH)
      - Sarpedon — EMILIUS 28 / Icaria 13
      - Rowena (RH) — Sumpter 4 / Lady Grey (RH)
  - Bay Leaf (1853)
    - *YORKSHIRE*
      - St Nicholas — EMILIUS 28 / Sea Mew 6
      - Miss Rose — Tramp 3 / Sancho Mare 2
    - Maria Black
      - Filho Da Puta — HAPHAZARD 35 / Mrs Barnet 12
      - Smolensko Mare — Smolensko 18 / Sir Peter Mare 9

Roseville (1888)

Reform (1871)
- Leamington (1853)
  - Faugh-A-ballagh (1841)
    - Sir Hercules
      - WHALEBONE — WAXY 18 / PENELOPE 1
      - Peri — Wanderer 11 / Thalestris 2
    - Guiccioli
      - Bob Booty — Chanticleer 3 / Ierne 23
      - Flight — Escape 27 / Y Heroine 11
  - Pantaloon Mare (1841)
    - *PANTALOON*
      - Castrel — BUZZARD 3 / ALEXANDER MARE 2
      - Idalia — Peruvian 27 / Musidora 17
    - Daphne
      - Laurel — Blacklock 21 / Wagtail 13
      - Maid Of Honor — Champion 13 / Etiquette 14
- Stolen Kisses (1864)
  - Knight Of Kars (1855)
    - Nutwith
      - Tomboy — Jerry 15 / Ardrossan Mare 8
      - Comus Mare — COMUS 25 / Delpini Mare 9
    - *POCAHONTAS*
      - GLENCOE — SULTAN 8 / Trampoline 1
      - Marpessa — Muley 6 / Clare 3
  - Defamation (1853)
    - *IAGO*
      - Don John — Waverley 2 / Comus Mare 2
      - Scandal — SELIM 2 / Haphazard Mare 11
    - Caricature
      - PANTALOON — Castrel 2 / Idalia 17
      - Pasquinade — CAMEL 24 / BANTER 14

Albia (1881)
- Alarm (1869)
  - Eclipse (1855)
    - Orlando
      - TOUCHSTONE — CAMEL 24 / BANTER 14
      - Vulture — Langar 6 / Kite 13
    - Gaze
      - Bay Middleton — SULTAN 8 / Cobweb 1
      - Flycatcher — Godolphin 46 / Phantom Mare 1
  - Maud (1859)
    - Stockwell
      - The Baron — Birdcatcher 11 / Echidna 24
      - POCAHONTAS — GLENCOE 1 / Marpessa 3
    - Countess Of Albemarle
      - Lanercost — Liverpool 11 / Otis 3
      - Velocipede Mare — Velocipede 3 / Cerberus Mare 15
- Elastic (1871)
  - Kentucky (RH) (1861)
    - *LEXINGTON (RH)*
      - Boston (RH) — Timoleon (RH) / Sister To Tuckahoe (RH) A24
      - Alice Carneal (RH) — Sarpedon / Rowena (RH) 13
    - Magnolia
      - GLENCOE — SULTAN 8 / Trampoline 1
      - Myrtle — Mameluke 3 / Bobadilla 4
  - Blue Ribbon (RH) (1859)
    - Revenue (RH)
      - Trustee (RH) — Catton (RH) / EMMA 7
      - Rosalie Somers (RH) — Sir Charles (RH) / Mischief (RH)
    - Parachute (RH)
      - YORKSHIRE — St Nicholas 6 / Miss Rose 2
      - Heraldry (RH) — Herald 8 / Margaret Wood (RH) A1

Ben Brush

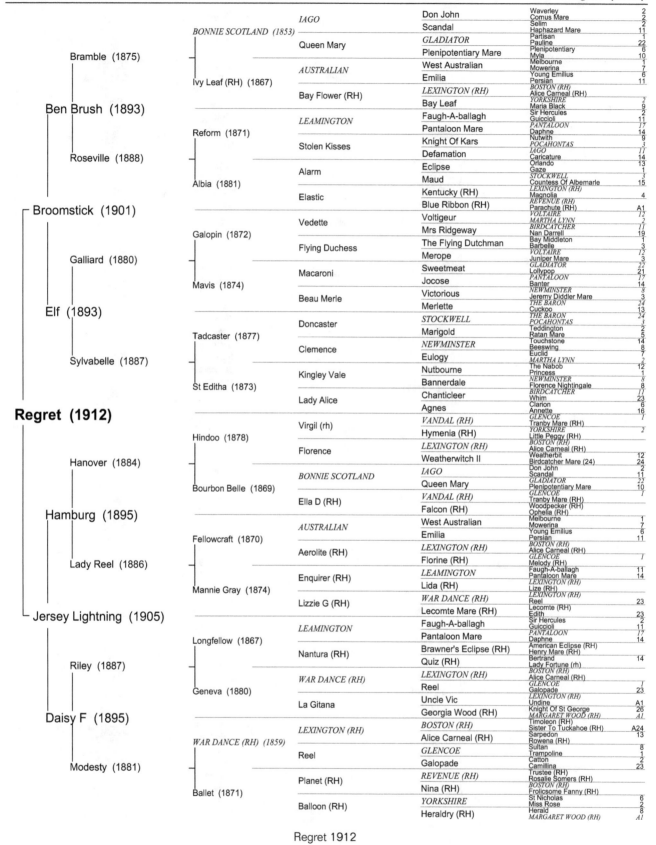

Regret 1912

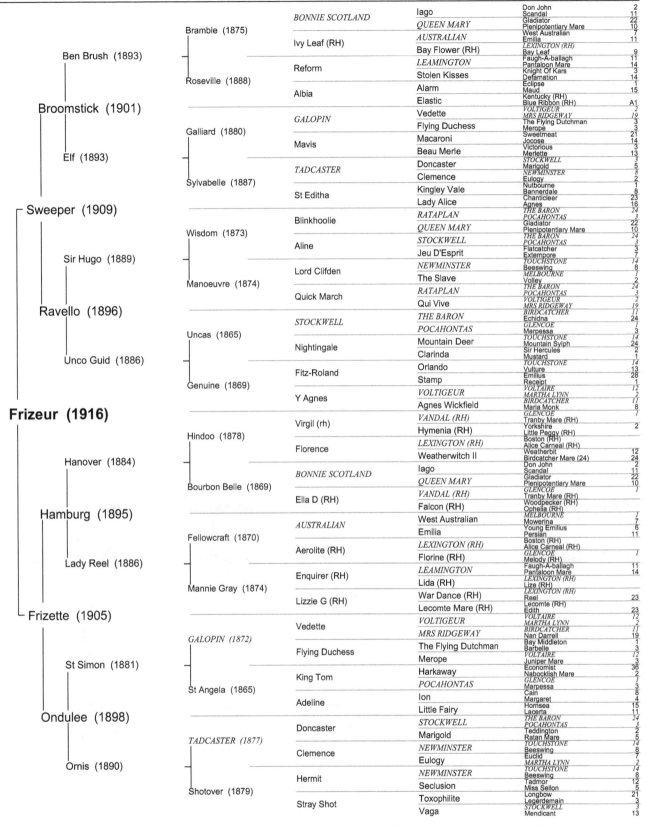

Frizeur 1916

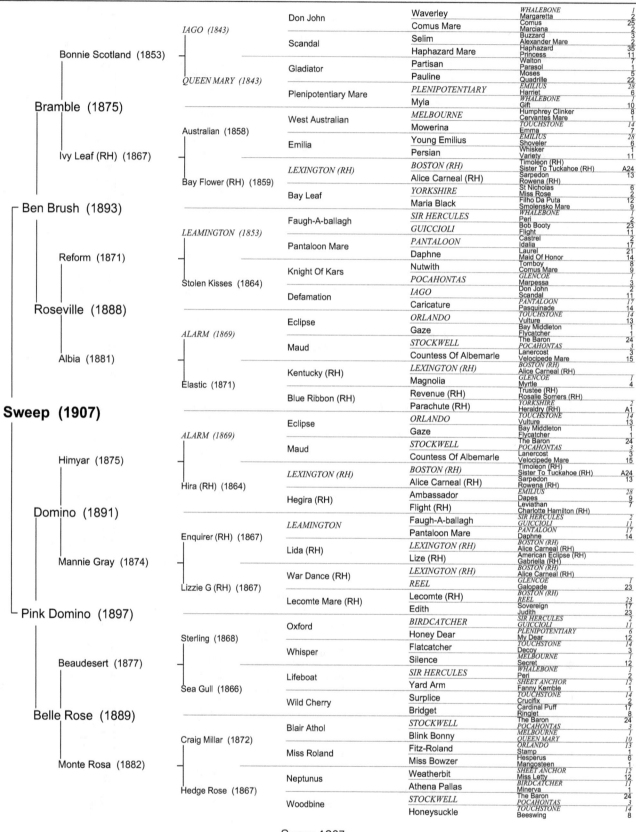

Sweep 1907

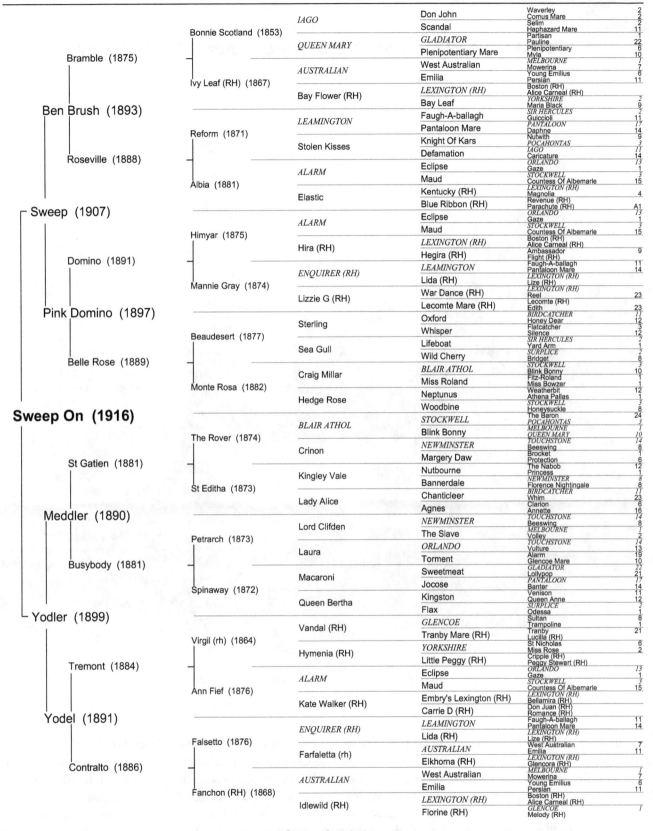

Left ancestry column:

- Ben Brush (1893)
  - Bramble (1875)
  - Roseville (1888)
- Sweep (1907)
  - Domino (1891)
  - Pink Domino (1897)
    - Belle Rose (1889)
- **Sweep On (1916)**
  - St Gatien (1881)
  - Meddler (1890)
    - Busybody (1881)
  - Yodler (1899)
    - Tremont (1884)
    - Yodel (1891)
      - Contralto (1886)

Detailed pedigree:

Bonnie Scotland (1853)	IAGO	Don John	Waverley 2 / Comus Mare 2
		Scandal	Selim 2 / Haphazard Mare 11
	QUEEN MARY	GLADIATOR	Partisan 1 / Pauline 22
		Plenipotentiary Mare	Plenipotentiary 6 / Myla 10
Ivy Leaf (RH) (1867)	AUSTRALIAN	West Australian	MELBOURNE 1 / Mowerina 7
		Emilia	Young Emilius 6 / Persian 11
	Bay Flower (RH)	LEXINGTON (RH)	Boston (RH) / Alice Carneal (RH)
		Bay Leaf	YORKSHIRE 2 / Maria Black 9
Reform (1871)	LEAMINGTON	Faugh-A-ballagh	SIR HERCULES 2 / Guiccioli 11
		Pantaloon Mare	PANTALOON 17 / Daphne 14
	Stolen Kisses	Knight Of Kars	Nutwith 9 / POCAHONTAS 3
		Defamation	IAGO 11 / Caricature 14
Albia (1881)	ALARM	Eclipse	ORLANDO 13 / Gaze 1
		Maud	STOCKWELL 3 / Countess Of Albemarle 15
	Elastic	Kentucky (RH)	LEXINGTON (RH) / Magnolia 4
		Blue Ribbon (RH)	Revenue (RH) / Parachute (RH) A1
Himyar (1875)	ALARM	Eclipse	ORLANDO 13 / Gaze 1
		Maud	STOCKWELL 3 / Countess Of Albemarle 15
	Hira (RH)	LEXINGTON (RH)	Boston (RH) / Alice Carneal (RH)
		Hegira (RH)	Ambassador 9 / Flight (RH)
Mannie Gray (1874)	ENQUIRER (RH)	LEAMINGTON	Faugh-A-ballagh 11 / Pantaloon Mare 14
		Lida (RH)	LEXINGTON (RH) / Lize (RH)
	Lizzie G (RH)	War Dance (RH)	LEXINGTON (RH) / Reel 23
		Lecomte Mare (RH)	Lecomte (RH) / Edith 23
Beaudesert (1877)	Sterling	Oxford	BIRDCATCHER 11 / Honey Dear 12
		Whisper	Flatcatcher 3 / Silence 12
	Sea Gull	Lifeboat	SIR HERCULES 2 / Yard Arm 1
		Wild Cherry	SURPLICE 2 / Bridget 8
Monte Rosa (1882)	Craig Millar	BLAIR ATHOL	STOCKWELL 3 / Blink Bonny 10
		Miss Roland	Fitz-Roland 1 / Miss Bowzer 1
	Hedge Rose	Neptunus	Weatherbit 12 / Athena Pallas 1
		Woodbine	STOCKWELL 3 / Honeysuckle 8
The Rover (1874)	BLAIR ATHOL	STOCKWELL	The Baron 24 / POCAHONTAS 3
		Blink Bonny	MELBOURNE 1 / QUEEN MARY 10
	Crinon	NEWMINSTER	TOUCHSTONE 14 / Beeswing 8
		Margery Daw	Brocket 1 / Protection 6
St Editha (1873)	Kingley Vale	Nutbourne	The Nabob 12 / Princess 1
		Bannerdale	NEWMINSTER 8 / Florence Nightingale 8
	Lady Alice	Chanticleer	BIRDCATCHER 11 / Whim 23
		Agnes	Clarion 6 / Annette 16
Petrarch (1873)	Lord Clifden	NEWMINSTER	TOUCHSTONE 14 / Beeswing 8
		The Slave	MELBOURNE 1 / Volley 2
	Laura	ORLANDO	TOUCHSTONE 14 / Vulture 13
		Torment	Alarm 19 / Glencoe Mare 10
Spinaway (1872)	Macaroni	Sweetmeat	GLADIATOR 22 / Lollypop 21
		Jocose	PANTALOON 17 / Banter 14
	Queen Bertha	Kingston	Venison 11 / Queen Anne 12
		Flax	SURPLICE 2 / Odessa 1
Virgil (rh) (1864)	Vandal (RH)	GLENCOE	Sultan 8 / Trampoline 1
		Tranby Mare (RH)	Tranby 21 / Lucilla (RH)
	Hymenia (RH)	YORKSHIRE	St Nicholas 6 / Miss Rose 2
		Little Peggy (RH)	Cripple (RH) / Peggy Stewart (RH)
Ann Fief (1876)	ALARM	Eclipse	ORLANDO 13 / Gaze 1
		Maud	STOCKWELL 3 / Countess Of Albemarle 15
	Kate Walker (RH)	Embry's Lexington (RH)	LEXINGTON (RH) / Bellamira (RH)
		Carrie D (RH)	Don Juan (RH) / Romance (RH)
Falsetto (1876)	ENQUIRER (RH)	LEAMINGTON	Faugh-A-ballagh 11 / Pantaloon Mare 14
		Lida (RH)	LEXINGTON (RH) / Lize (RH)
	Farfaletta (rh)	AUSTRALIAN	West Australian 7 / Emilia 11
		Elkhorna (RH)	LEXINGTON (RH) / Glencora (RH)
Fanchon (RH) (1868)	AUSTRALIAN	West Australian	MELBOURNE 1 / Mowerina 7
		Emilia	Young Emilius 6 / Persian 11
	Idlewild (RH)	LEXINGTON (RH)	Boston (RH) / Alice Carneal (RH)
		Florine (RH)	GLENCOE 1 / Melody (RH)

Sweep On 1916

Chapter 13

Fountainhead of Sport Performance - Aerolite RH Family

Man O' War 1917 is one of the most gifted and enduring of sport horse performance lines in the world, in spite of being born during the Jersey Act and therefore banned from international breeding as 'half-bred'. This line is still potent today—in racing producing stamina and soundness, in sport it is perhaps the greatest transmitter of jump out there. —photo by L.S. Sutcliff.

Soundness, stamina, and jump ability are just a few of attributes that come down to us from Aerolite RH family. The Lexington RH daughter Aerolite RH, who we outlined in Chapter 9, was an unraced filly, but she heads a family of racing and sport superiority. Reams of paper have been used in documenting and celebrating the English female families—Brown Bess, Queen Mary, Pilgrimage, Pocahontas, etc. It is time we woke up and started celebrating our own fantastic mare families, such as Aerolite RH, Frizette, Mannie Gray, and Maggie B.B. RH, as we will here. The most famous branch of this is seen in Fair Play, as even in our time his descendants are strong transmitters of the very best in sport performance, and we will visit them shortly. But first, let's look at those other lesser-known descendants of Aerolite RH. For example, seldom seen or talked about are her daughter lines, or it may be that they just go unnoticed in the background of our lineages. Realize a large number of her descendents are unrecorded because of the chaos of the Civil War; however because

KATHLEEN H. KIRSAN

this mare and her family are so influential we should try to identify those modern horses descended from her daughters so we can create a strong filly factor structure in the background of our designs (see Appendix B), or recognize one if it is there already—such as multiple lines of Aerolite RH and her full sister Idlewild RH.

Aerolite's offspring

Aerolite's daughter Platina 1869 interests me partly because she is a daughter of the great four-miler Planet RH (Chapter 7). She was a pretty handy racer herself, and in 1872 she won the Harper Stakes and came in second to Alarm in the Saratoga Dash—this proves her racing class, as imported Alarm was a top sprinter winning all his races that year. She was inbred to Boston RH 3x3 through both a son and a daughter. In her stud career it appears she was bred exclusively to Ten Broeck (Lexington RH son) and Longfellow RH (Leamington son out of an American Eclipse RH dam). I find her in the pedigree of the good broodmare Frances McClelland (daughter of Sallie McClelland—Maggie B.B. RH line). Platina had seven named foals, two who were good racing geldings, one stallion Con Cregan, and four daughters, Sallie M—through whom the great show jumper Holystone and his full sister Thirty Knots descends, who is 4x4 to Aerolite RH—plus Lenora Morris, Georgia A, and Secret.

Another daughter of Aerolite RH, Jersey Bell, had six named foals: two colts, Kingcraft and Macbeth, and four daughters, Amabel, Favorite, Jersey Girl, and Jersey Lass. All her offspring were out of Australian sons. Her daughter Favorite was a stakes winner, and Favorite's daughter Mary Malloy produced Kentucky Derby winner Pink Star—who was gelded at four years because of his bad disposition. Favorite had a son Favor who was kept as a stallion.

Aerolite's daughter Addie C by King Alfonso (sire of Foxhall, see Chapter 8) produced the stallion Chant, who won the Kentucky Derby and several other stakes, but even though he raced sixty-three times with twenty-two wins, fifteen seconds, and six thirds, he was not highly regarded—pretty tough standards! Addie C produced another stallion named Chorister; he is found in the pedigree of the Hall of Fame show jumper Nautical (Chapter 30).

Morvich—he's linebred 5x5 to the Idlewild RH son Wildidle. —photo by W.A. Rouch

Aerolite's full sister Idlewild RH (see Chapter 8) was a great racehorse who also left some legacy at stud; for instance, from her daughter Fanchon RH she is tail-female ancestress of the Sweep son, Sweep On, who in-turn produced Sweep Out who is the second-dam of Miss Disco and her full brother Loser Weeper, a good stakes winner (see previous chapter). Miss Disco is immortal as she is the dam of the *chef* Bold Ruler. Idlewild's great racing son Wildidle left some legacy also; for instance the decent sire Morvich is 5x5 to him sex-balanced. Poor Morvich, he was underrated his whole life, sold and resold multiple times even though he was a winner at two, and at three he won the Kentucky Derby—even though it was beyond his best distance—which shows tremendous heart. For us he is a valuable line to use for reinforcing this family.

My point here is that even though much of the documentation of the produce of her children was lost (Civil War), still all the female lines of this family are out there, and their inclusion in your background lineages would be helpful. However, even though we may not have noticed them, it appears we usually will carry them anyway, seeing that Bold Ruler is almost everywhere in the American Thoroughbred, so just with a line of him you can be sure you have the female side of the Aerolite RH family covered.

But Aerolite RH is most well known as a producer of high-quality stallions, so we find her most commonly through her sons. Aerolite RH produced four significant sons (Chapters 7 and 8), and even the two 'lesser' regarded—Miser and Rutherford—left good offspring. Miser, who was blind in one eye completely and partially in the other, was viewed as the poorest specimen of the line. Yet when mated with great race mare Thora he produced the racing phenomenon Yorkville Belle 1898. Vosborough reports: "Yorkville Belle takes rank with Ruthless, Miss Woodford, Ferida, Firenzi, Wanda, and Thora as one of the great mares in that they went out of their class and defeated the colts."

The sensational racer Yorkville Belle 1889, a daughter of Miser (Aerolite RH son and full brother to Spendthrift)—notice the flaxen in her tail; this trait comes from her sire. She is inbred 3 x3 to Lexington RH through daughters. —image found in *Racing in America* 1922

Fellowcraft will be commonly found, as he is the dam-sire of Hamburg, a genetic giant discussed in Chapters 9 and 11. For instance if you have a line of the *chef* Discovery—one of the greatest broodmare sires of all time (dam-sire of the *chef* Native Dancer, the *chef* Bold Ruler, Hasty Road, and Traffic Judge)—then you have brought together the full brothers Fellowcraft and Spendthrift 4x5, Fellowcraft through a daughter and Spendthrift through a son, obviously one of the power configurations in this top racer and sire.

But the major branch of this family is through Spendthrift, especially through his hard to control son Hastings. As you would expect in a sire who leaves a huge legacy, Hastings's pedigree shows up several strong potencies. Hastings carries sex-balanced lines of the ever-present full siblings Whisker/Whalebone/Web 6x5x6x6x6x7. He carries a sex-balanced double of the good sire West Australian 2x4, and like Glencoe and Australian he has a very powerful set of filly factors: Glencoe daughters 5x4, Birdcatcher daughters 3x5, and a double of the mare Lollypop 5x5. (Filly factors are statistically proven to be a significant design in the best stallions and mares—see Appendix B for more on this.)

Nonetheless, a problem arises in our study because of the uncertain parentage of his dam, the imported Cinderella—is she by Tomahawk or by Blue Ruin? Usually she is recorded as by Tomahawk, who was the last to breed her during that heat, but would it change the dynamic genetic components if Blue Ruin was the true sire? The Birdcatcher and West Australian doubles are untouched by the change, but the Lollypop double and the Glencoe filly factor are. In the Blue Ruin version a ¾ brother to Lollypop is brought in: Charles XII on Blue Ruin's dam-line, plus a double of Venison 6x6 through sons.

Discovery 1931 carries Hamburg on his dam-line, plus the full brothers Fellowcraft and Spendthrift; he is a chef-de-race for stamina and also one of the most valued broodmare sires of the breed. —photo by Joe Fleischer for *Who's Who in Thoroughbred Racing*.

Hastings is notorious for his excitable nature and pure viciousness; he truly was a danger to his riders and handlers, and they would only go into his stall or paddock with a club in hand for protection. When he was at stud they ended up constructing an enclosed passage that went from his stall to his paddock, so that the stable hands were out of the reach of his teeth and leg. If pedigree structure is any indicator at all, and of course I believe it is, I hoped I would find a definitive indicator of bad temper in one over the other. However, in both we have a reinforcement of the Lollypop line which is often believed to be the source of the bad attitude. In Tomahawk version Cinderella has Lollypop 4x4; in the Blue Ruin version she is 4x4 to Lollypop and her ¾ brother Charles XII, which doubles up on her second-dam Wagtail, who in-turn is inbred 2x3 to Trumpator. This also brings in a double of Venison through sons—and I just don't know enough about these English lines to make a guess on whether they transmitted temperament problems. Perhaps it is the fact of concentrating strong female pedigree elements that elevates the energy production from mtDNA. Ann Bowling

Flittergold, a great racer and very sound, and a sire of stakes winners—he is the full brother to Fair Play. —photo by W.A. Rouch

King James, a son of Plaudit—good racer and sire. —image found in *Thoroughbred Types*

Friar Rock 1913, a ¾ genetic brother to Man O' War, is a key line in sport horse pedigrees. —photo found in *Thoroughbred Types*.

referred to mtDNA as the 'metabolic power station' as it controlled muscle metabolism (*Horse Genetics*). Hopefully in our day the scientists working on the equine genome will discover how this 'super-charged' energy level occurs. High concentrations (inbreeding) on the dam-lines have often been suspected of producing a high-strung temperament, although it is not the only flag we find for this (see Stymie below).

There are many great sires who were so high-strung that they often lost races they would otherwise have won. The modern day mega-sire Nasrullah comes to mind: he descends from Lady Josephine from the inbred Americus line whom his sire Nearco engages with another line of Lexington—that said his high-strung disposition is usually attributed to his dam-sire Blenheim. But Hastings obviously had such high levels of energy he was uncontrollable—and in this factor they are very similar—Nasrullah just couldn't contain his energy level, and evidently neither could Hastings. Hastings' racing class is represented by the full siblings in the fourth through seventh generation: Whalebone/Whisker etc. and his West Australian double—these are English bloodlines of the highest racing class.

Cinderella produced other good stakes winners such as Foreigner, Ferrier, and Handsome. But second to Hastings she is best remembered as the dam of the great sire and Kentucky Derby winner Plaudit. One of his sons, King James, was an important sire (see pedigree). Notice he is inbred to Himyar, who is also the sire of Domino. He is the great-grandsire of Questionnaire, the sire of Rough n' Tumble, a sire who has been sort of a 'long shot' but in spite of his perceived poor chances he has made himself a solid name in the modern racers—reaching *chef* status in our day (see Chapter 24).

Hastings regularly begat stakes winners such as Gunfire, Masterman, Nantor, Amicitia, Fire Eater, Lord of the Isle, and Mizzie, year after year. But when Hastings was bred to imported mare Fairy Gold he hit the jackpot with the great mare Golden View, plus a top stayer and good sire in Flittergold, and then in the super-star Fair Play, who is rated a *chef-de-race* (stamina). Because this mating was such an outstanding example we would like to understand the genetics of it. But here we run into a great difficulty again, because the sire of Fairy Gold is recorded as Bend Or, one of the most venerated English stallions of the last century—the sire of Ormonde and Bona Vista and half of the magical Bend Or/Macaroni nick. So it is a huge shock to learn Fairy Gold's parentage is incorrect. The mapping of the equine genome has benefitted the equine industry in many ways, and hopefully it will continue to do so. One of the things it is doing is exposing the incorrect lineages of some very famous horses. It was a big upset when the geneticists discovered that many of the elite mare families of the English TB were in fact in error, and now they say that the old rumor about Bend Or, that he might be another horse could well be true. Bend Or was a great racer winning ten of fourteen starts, and his importance to the English TB as a sire is massive. But now it turns out he is not who they thought, and he is in fact a horse called Tadcaster—who was switched for him in training—a ringer!

So here we are, with one of the greatest American Thoroughbred families, of proven enduring class and relevance—Fair Play—and we cannot be certain of his parentage, not because the Civil War destroyed the records or because the country bumpkin colonial breeders couldn't read or write, but because the creators of the 'purebred' Thoroughbred couldn't keep their records straight or police their own industry.

Fairy Gold was the dam of another American sire of significance: Friar Rock, who is also a great staying racer and sire; he is sire of the key broodmares Black Curl and Friars Carse as well as the important sire Pilate—making them also casualties of this pedigree mess. The *reine-de-course* Friars Carse (see pedigree) is dam of four full siblings: the good mares (all of them *reines*) War Kilt, Anchors Ahead, and Speed Boat, but also the mega-sire War Relic. This is across the board excellence (100%) that occurred when her genetics were crossed with Man O' War—obviously we should strive to build this super bloodline up in our lineages.

[Note: War Relic was **not** rated as a top racer or sire during his era; it is now only in hindsight we can see his tremendous genetic shadow.]

 Friars Carse has several strong filly factors: Tadcaster daughters 2x3, War Dance RH daughters 5x6, plus the full siblings St. Simon/Angelica through daughters 5x6, plus she carries the very rarely seen Wire, a full sibling to the common Whalebone/Whisker/Web lines—this is an extremely powerful broodmare pedigree and can serve as a template for those of us who want to learn how to design good broodmare breedings.

Both Tadcaster and Bend Or are sons of Doncaster, so the discrepancy is in their dams. Tadcaster is out of Clemence, not Rouge Rose. I devoted a whole chapter to Fair Play and his sport dynasty in *North American Sport Horse Breeder*, but now have to supply his corrected pedigree for you.

The Tetrarch—inbred 3x3 to the full siblings Tadcaster/Clemintina, he is a nick with the Fair Play line, because Fair Play carries the sex-balance. Both have produced lasting sport horse dynasties—Thoroughbred Record.

The *chef-de-race* of stamina, Fair Play—notice the high head and neck carriage, and fine jump hip—these horses can fly over obstacles—Wiki commons picture

The Tadcaster/Bend Or mix-up is going to produce a tidal wave of discussion in the years to come. In our focus—the sport horse—there is another notable stallion affected strongly by the Bend Or/Tadcaster switch. This horse, another *chef-de-race*, is a known source of speed and is also found consistently in jump pedigrees. The great sire and a formidable sport line even today, The Tetrarch (English Thoroughbred), a talented racer, was sub-fertile, that is, he produced few foals, and had poor front legs. We can see, in the corrected pedigree, where The Tetrarch's genetic power comes from, as he is really 3x3 to Tadcaster and his full sister Clementina! All other potencies in his lineage take a backseat to this configuration. Tadcaster in The Tetrarch is through his son Bona Vista, and Clementina is through a son also: Le Samaritain. This surely explains his lasting influence in modern pedigrees—even being sub-fertile, his few offspring were sensational; however this design is a male-leaning pedigree. In Fair Play Tadcaster is carried by a daughter—Fairy Gold. When The Tetrarch and Fair Play meet in a pedigree—as I found they often do in top sport horses (see Appendix E) —it provides the needed female balance. For instance look at the pedigree of the good sire Pilate 1928; he is a valuable resource because he is the sire of the Hall of Famer and *chef* Eight Thirty, Platter, and others. Pilate is by Friar Rock out of The Tetrarch daughter Herodias—obviously the full sibling Tadcaster/Clementina configuration 3x6x5 dominates his genetics!

Because the Bend Or/Tadcaster controversy has been settled by mtDNA, I am going to assume Fair Play's dam-sire is Tadcaster. But that still leaves the uncertainty about Cinderella's sire—is it Tomahawk or is it Blue Ruin as many think? That part of the mystery has not been unraveled yet, so I will give you two versions of his pedigree here, both with Tadcaster, one with Tomahawk and another with Blue Ruin. Don't take a sigh of relief yet—because Lollypop's (remember her?) sire is in dispute also.

KATHLEEN H. KIRSAN

Seeing as Fairy Gold, her sons Friar Rock and Fair Play, and of course Fair Play's son Man O' War, are pillars of the modern American TB, we would like to have accurate information in their pedigrees. We will just do the best we can for now with what has been discovered, and be hopeful more mysteries will be solved by the scientists who have been working so hard on this. I think you'll agree that the more we know about the genetics of our sport horse stock, the more productive our decisions in breeding can be.

Fair Play created a dynasty with wonderful sons and daughters, who are found everywhere in the American Thoroughbred—they are a reliable source of stamina, soundness, and tremendous athletic ability, which includes a first class jump along with reservoirs of speed. Mad Hatter, Chance Play, Chance Shot, Etoile Filante, Oval, Display/Discovery, and of course Man O' War are a few of the representatives of this line that we want to build up in our breeding designs—they are as close to a guarantee of top sport performance you will find in any bloodline the world over. If you are wondering why they are not more prevalent in the pedigrees of sport performers worldwide it is because of the Jersey Act—those lines were deemed 'half-bred,' so until after the 1950 they were seldom seen in European lineages (See Chapters 32, 33, and 34 for the jumpers from this line).

Fair Play stock, on the whole, is typical of stayers: slow to mature, performing their best at age three and beyond—very few will win at two (see Stymie below). In the 1940s, when Joe Estes reviewed the impact of the Fair Play for Bloodhorse, he said Fair Play was not a great sire of two-year-olds; instead it was his three-year-olds and beyond who broke all records. Fair Play, his son Man O' War, and his grandson Discovery are all rated *chef-de-race* for stamina transmission.

In Estes's research he determined that the other notable sires of this same time period are in order of relevance: Black Toney, Bull Dog, High Time, Equipoise, and Pennant—note all but Bull Dog (Teddy line) are American lines, and all four of those other important sires descend from Domino (next chapter).

The line of Fair Play not only produced the best late-maturing racehorses, it transmitted a tremendous jump and is found consistently in the top international level jumpers. America had a thriving jump, hunt, and steeplechase industry at home during its ban from international breeding. For instance, great breeders such as Joseph E. Widener, J. H. Whitney (and his wife Liz), and Marion DuPont had huge studs devoted to the jumper in all its forms, producing great jumpers and racers such as Battleship, Annapolis, Neji, Great War, and Holystone (see Chapter 33). When the American 'half-breeds' ventured to England to race and compete in the Hunter Sports (jumping, steeplechasing) before and during the Jersey Act, they very often won.

When looking to double up and increase these proven lines for top performance and soundness in sport, it is wonderful to find individuals who are already inbred to these lines. I am going to bring to your attention three individuals who concentrate the Man O' War/Fair Play lines (with or without other dominances) that you can be on the alert for in your efforts to capture the essence of American speed, jump ability, and soundness combined with stamina.

Stymie, inbred to Man O' War, Colin, and Broomstick, is potent, talented, and sound. —sketch by C.W. Anderson made for *Who's Who in Thoroughbred Racing*

First is Stymie, whose name means to block or thwart, and it was a name that proved prophetic for his racing career. Stymie had a very difficult temperament, irascible, and unruly, so he was hard to train and nearly impossible to race—there we are with that 'super-charged' energy again. He never won a race at two or three years old. Hirsch Jacobs, who must have seen something in him, because he claimed him for a mere $1500. Jacob's vision and patience paid off, for at age four Stymie began to bloom and plowed through race after race in first-class company. This was in 1945, and even with our government shutting down racing for four months (due to war), Stymie won eight major races and was second four times and third in four others—an impressive record by any standards. He was voted US Champion-Handicap-Horse, and Horse-of-the-Year.

Stymie kept right on winning at age five when he won seven more (plus five seconds, four thirds). At six he won seven more handicaps (five seconds, two thirds), and at seven years he won three, was second in three, and was third in two. At eight years he fractured his seismoid bone and was retired. He was the leading money winner of his era—in one hundred thirty-one starts, he won thirty-five, came second in thirty-three, and was third in twenty-eight for a total of $918,485 (in 1947)—obviously a fantastic feat.

Stymie was out of two inbred parents; his sire Equestrian was 3x3 to Broomstick through daughters and had the maternal dynasty founder Frilette (see Chapter 11) on his dam-line. His dam Stop Watch is 3x5 to Colin (Domino son), sex-balanced, plus with her third-dam Noontide is inbred herself to Domino 2x3. As noted in Chapter 11, Stymie carries two strong conduits straight back to Maggie B. B. RH (The Niece and Sir Dixon). No wonder he could not contain his energy—he was extremely inbred to the best American bloodlines there are: Broomstick 4x4, Man O' War 3x3, and Colin (Domino) 3x5. Stymie has twenty-nine lines of Lexington RH.

As a stayer he was pretty typical in that he did not reach his full ability until he was four. For us, the sport horse breeders, he is a genetic gold mine of our Heroic Era bloodlines.

A second example of concentration in these desired elements is the mare Nothirdchance; plus she is a key bloodline in a number of different pedigree designs for the sex-balance she provides, as she is out of a Blue Larkspur son, when his greatest imprint is most usually found through his excellent daughters. Her sire Blue Swords was a top racer, second best to Triple Crown winner Count Fleet in 1943, who is found quite often in top jump pedigrees (Bold Minstrel, for example). Blue Swords has a full sister Blue Haze who is found in classic pedigrees also, including the good sire Ajhal. Also Blue Swords's second dam-sire is the inbred High Time, who is inbred to Domino 2x3x3, and we will enlarge on the importance of this line in the next chapter. Here however, it is Nothirdchance's double of Man O' War 3x4 through daughters that interests us—as she brings the Man O' War influence forward: speed, stamina, athleticism, and soundness.

As a broodmare Nothirdchance excelled. She has several stakes winning progeny. For instance, her daughter Be Suspicious 1963 was a fair winner, plus she also became a good broodmare: Blue Coast, Suspicious Native, Secret Scheme, and Half and Half. Nothirdchance's daughter Treachery 1960 was exceptional, racing for five years with a total of one hundred five starts and ending with $182,071 in earnings—her best distance being a mile. Treachery is by Promised Land 1954 who brings in more Domino through inbred Stimulus and The Porter, plus a line of Whisk Broom II (Hanover and Maggie B.B. RH lines) and a line of Mumtaz Mahal—who is a carrier of Lexington RH lines—bringing home to us our own blood. Another of her offspring is the good racer Ala Toby who won twelve of twenty races, who is by Olympian (a rarely seen Domino son). Nothirdchance has twenty lines of Lexington RH.

Hail to Reason—out of Nothirdchance, a *chef-de-race*, far sounder than his sire. —image courtesy of Keeneland Library, Bert Morgan collection

Even with all those good daughters, Nothirdchance has achieved broodmare immortality because she is the dam of the mega-sire Hail to Reason 1958, whose genetic influence continues to grow worldwide even today. When you read about the *chef-de-race* Hail to Reason, his racing career—Champion Juvenile of 1960—and he also led the sires list in 1970 and was sire of the great Roberto (1972 Epsom Derby), who is also classified as a *chef*. The emphasis is placed on the Phalaris line as he is by the good but unsound Royal Charger son Turn-To, who is inbred to Pharos 3x3, sex-balanced. This configuration is powerful and was surely powering Turn-To himself. When Nothirdchance, who is inbred to Man O' War 3x3, was mated with Turn-To, a fortunate inbreeding design was found of an equally inbred sire and dam in different bloodlines, which has proven to be a tremendously successful pattern. But that is not all, as other genetic interactions occurred, such as the Maid of the Mist offspring Craig an Eran and Hamoaze 4x5—a filly factor, Swynford son and daughter 4x4, and another Plucky Liege son putting Sir Gallahad and Admiral Drake 3x3.

Hail to Reason is an exceptionally potent sire with these new strengths combined with the immense inbreeding resident in the parents. He could have success with many different mares—and he has—he is one of the most significant sires of the twentieth century. Turn-To also returned to America some lines of Lexington RH—through Catnip and Lady Josephine. All this adds to genetic affinity; however by concentrating Pharos and Swynford there is more unsoundness also that can pop up now in this line: forelegs, tendon issues (Phalaris), and joints (John O' Gaunt—sire of Swynford). Read more on unsoundness in Chapter 27. Both Americus (behind Lady Josephine) and Domino (behind High Time, Blue Larkspur, Supremus) are inbred to Lexington RH. Hail to Reason is found in super-sires Roberto (*chef*), Seattle Slew (*chef*), Bold Reasoning, Lemon Drop Kid, Jacinto, and Sunday Silence. He also had two full sister daughters who have both earned *reine* status: Admiring and Priceless Gem. There is a strong lesson for us in this breeding history that we can emulate in our programs. A prime example of the power generated in doubling up on these concentrated carriers (Hail to Reason and Stymie) is the mare Regal Gleam 1964, as she is the second dam of the French Derby winner and top European sire Caerleon 1980—see his pedigree after Chapter 20.

Often we are leery of inbreeding, but look at how this was done—the mare had strong inbred elements, and then she was mated with a sire with equally potent inbred elements in different lines, so it provided strong concentration in top quality genes but also worked as somewhat of an outcross providing some hybrid vigor. The great Holstein show jump sire Landgraf I was bred like this—two inbred parents, inbred in different lines—and his genetic reach, like Hail to Reason, seems to have no end.

The magnificent Eight Thirty winning the Suburban Handicap in 1940—he was bred by George Widener. —photo from *Who's Who in Thoroughbred Racing*

A third genetic powerhouse is the *chef-de-race* Eight Thirty; he is one you might want to build up and combine with his ¾ genetic relative War Relic (or with any of his *reine* sisters: Anchors Ahead, War Kilt, or Speedboat). Eight Thirty 1936 was an excellent racer, winning sixteen of twenty-seven starts with three seconds and five thirds and earnings of $155,475—he was a stayer of high class. His vitality is demonstrated not just by performance in sport and stud, but also in that he lived until twenty-nine. Like the great sire War Relic, Eight Thirty is inbred to the ¾ brothers Man O' War and Friar Rock—these are tough, sound staying bloodlines. Eight Thirty has eleven lines of Lexington RH.

His sire Pilate is by Friar Rock out of Herodias, a The Tetrarch daughter. If you remember from our previous discussion, all these lines are affected by the Bend Or-Tadcaster mix up. Happily, as we discussed, this combination gives full sibling strength of Tadcaster and his sister Clementina 4x6x6x6. This configuration is very potent and will rule genotype for generations. But that is not all, because as in Nothirdchance, Eight Thirty carries the highly inbred High Time as well—he is the dam-sire—which puts Domino 5x5x4 here. Therefore Eight Thirty is powered equally by Tadcaster/Clementina and Domino. (Once again the same pattern of inbreeding in two different lines.)

Eight Thirty produced many good racers; twenty-four of whom raced over one hundred times! One even raced two hundred twenty-two times! This is an incredible indicator of soundness and resiliency—elements we would want to load into our sport product.

His best racing son was Sailor, also an important sire, he won twelve of twenty-one starts (second three times, third once), and he won $321,075—all while racing against greats like Nashua, Swaps, Traffic Judge, and Summer Tan. He sired the US champion sprinter Ahoy, and the Hall of Fame mare Bowl of Flowers—dam of the good sire Whiskey Road. He is also the third dam-sire of the sensational modern sire Distorted Humor (see Chapter 27).

Another good Eight Thirty son is Bolero 1946, who set several world records as a sprinter and sired many stakes winners.

His daughter Rare Perfume raced one hundred one times and is the dam of the great producer Rare Treat who is by Stymie—they are both rated *reine-de-course*. Rare Treat (fifty-two lines of Lexington RH) is a great producer and is the dam of What a Treat 1962, champion three-year-old filly and the dam of the Coolmore stood stallion Be My Guest—who in turn is sire of Assert—winner of both the Irish and French Derby. Eight Thirty's bloodline is one to treasure in sport horse breeding as well, as he was repeatedly in the top show jumpers (see Chapter 34).

All these lines were created while the draconian Jersey Act was in force.

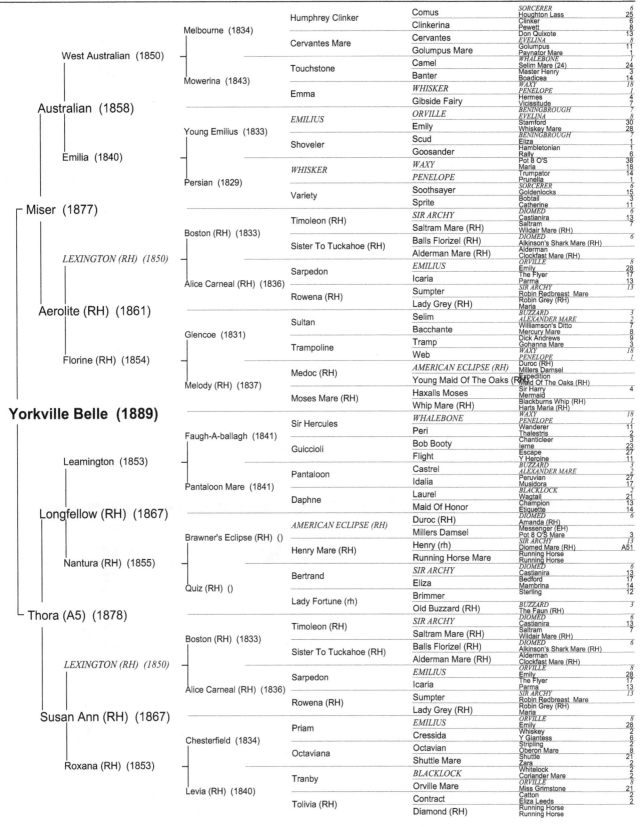

Yorkville Belle 1889

Fanchon (RH) (1868)

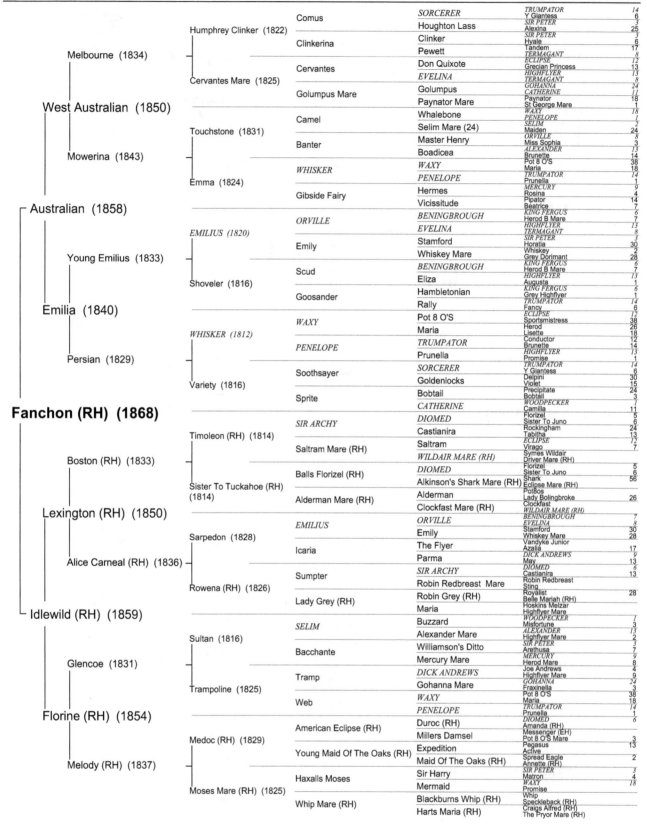

- **Australian (1858)**
  - West Australian (1850)
    - Melbourne (1834)
      - Humphrey Clinker (1822)
        - Comus
          - SORCERER — TRUMPATOR 14 / Y Giantess 6
          - Houghton Lass — SIR PETER 3 / Alexina 25
        - Clinkerina
          - Clinker — SIR PETER 3 / Hyale 6
          - Pewett — Tandem 17 / TERMAGANT 8
      - Cervantes Mare (1825)
        - Cervantes
          - Don Quixote — ECLIPSE 12 / Grecian Princess 13
          - EVELINA — HIGHFLYER 13 / TERMAGANT 8
        - Golumpus Mare
          - Golumpus — GOHANNA 24 / CATHERINE 11
          - Paynator Mare — Paynator 18 / St George Mare 1
    - Mowerina (1843)
      - Touchstone (1831)
        - Camel
          - Whalebone — WAXY 18 / PENELOPE 1
          - Selim Mare (24) — SELIM 2 / Maiden 24
        - Banter
          - Master Henry — ORVILLE 8 / Miss Sophia 3
          - Boadicea — ALEXANDER 13 / Brunette 14
      - Emma (1824)
        - WHISKER
          - WAXY — Pot 8 O'S 38 / Maria 18
          - PENELOPE — TRUMPATOR 14 / Prunella 1
        - Gibside Fairy
          - Hermes — MERCURY 9 / Rosina 4
          - Vicissitude — Pipator 14 / Beatrice 7
  - Emilia (1840)
    - Young Emilius (1833)
      - EMILIUS (1820)
        - ORVILLE
          - BENINGBROUGH — KING FERGUS 6 / Herod B Mare 7
          - EVELINA — HIGHFLYER 13 / TERMAGANT 8
        - Emily
          - Stamford — SIR PETER 3 / Horatia 30
          - Whiskey Mare — Whiskey 2 / Grey Dorimant 28
      - Shoveler (1816)
        - Scud
          - BENINGBROUGH — KING FERGUS 6 / Herod B Mare 7
          - Eliza — HIGHFLYER 13 / Augusta 1
        - Goosander
          - Hambletonian — KING FERGUS 6 / Grey Highflyer 1
          - Rally — TRUMPATOR 14 / Fancy 6
    - Persian (1829)
      - WHISKER (1812)
        - WAXY
          - Pot 8 O'S — ECLIPSE 12 / Sportsmistress 38
          - Maria — Herod 26 / Lisette 18
        - PENELOPE
          - TRUMPATOR — Conductor 12 / Brunette 14
          - Prunella — HIGHFLYER 13 / Promise 1
      - Variety (1816)
        - Soothsayer
          - SORCERER — TRUMPATOR 14 / Y Giantess 6
          - Goldenlocks — Delpini 30 / Violet 15
        - Sprite
          - Bobtail — Precipitate 24 / Bobtail 3
          - CATHERINE — WOODPECKER 11 / Camilla
- **Idlewild (RH) (1859)**
  - Lexington (RH) (1850)
    - Boston (RH) (1833)
      - Timoleon (RH) (1814)
        - SIR ARCHY
          - DIOMED — Florizel 5 / Sister To Juno 6
          - Castianira — Rockingham 24 / Tabitha 13
        - Saltram Mare (RH)
          - Saltram — ECLIPSE 12 / Virago 7
          - WILDAIR MARE (RH) — Symes Wildair / Driver Mare (RH)
      - Sister To Tuckahoe (RH) (1814)
        - Balls Florizel (RH)
          - DIOMED — Florizel 5 / Sister To Juno 6
          - Alkinson's Shark Mare (RH) — Shark 56 / Eclipse Mare (RH)
        - Alderman Mare (RH)
          - Alderman — Pot8os / Lady Bolingbroke 26
          - Clockfast Mare (RH) — Clockfast / WILDAIR MARE (RH)
    - Alice Carneal (RH) (1836)
      - Sarpedon (1828)
        - EMILIUS
          - ORVILLE — BENINGBROUGH 7 / EVELINA 8
          - Emily — Stamford 30 / Whiskey Mare 28
        - Icaria
          - The Flyer — Vandyke Junior / Azalia 17
          - Parma — DICK ANDREWS 9 / May 13
      - Rowena (RH) (1826)
        - Sumpter
          - SIR ARCHY — DIOMED 6 / Castianira 13
          - Robin Redbreast Mare — Robin Redbreast / Sting
        - Lady Grey (RH)
          - Robin Grey (RH) — Royalist 28 / Belle Mariah (RH)
          - Maria — Hoskins Melzar / Highflyer Mare
  - Florine (RH) (1854)
    - Glencoe (1831)
      - Sultan (1816)
        - SELIM
          - Buzzard — WOODPECKER 1 / Misfortune 3
          - Alexander Mare — ALEXANDER 13 / Highflyer Mare 2
        - Bacchante
          - Williamson's Ditto — SIR PETER 3 / Arethusa 7
          - Mercury Mare — MERCURY 9 / Herod Mare 8
      - Trampoline (1825)
        - Tramp
          - DICK ANDREWS — Joe Andrews 4 / Highflyer Mare 9
          - Gohanna Mare — GOHANNA 24 / Fraxinella 3
        - Web
          - WAXY — Pot 8 O'S 38 / Maria 18
          - PENELOPE — TRUMPATOR 14 / Prunella 1
    - Melody (RH) (1837)
      - Medoc (RH) (1829)
        - American Eclipse (RH)
          - Duroc (RH) — DIOMED 6 / Amanda (RH)
          - Millers Damsel — Messenger (EH) / Pot 8 O'S Mare 3
        - Young Maid Of The Oaks (RH)
          - Expedition — Pegasus 13 / Active
          - Maid Of The Oaks (RH) — Spread Eagle 2 / Annette (RH)
      - Moses Mare (RH) (1825)
        - Haxalls Moses
          - Sir Harry — SIR PETER 3 / Matron 4
          - Mermaid — WAXY 18 / Promise
        - Whip Mare (RH)
          - Blackburns Whip (RH) — Whip / Speckleback (RH)
          - Harts Maria (RH) — Craigs Alfred (RH) / The Pryor Mare (RH)

Fanchon RH 1868

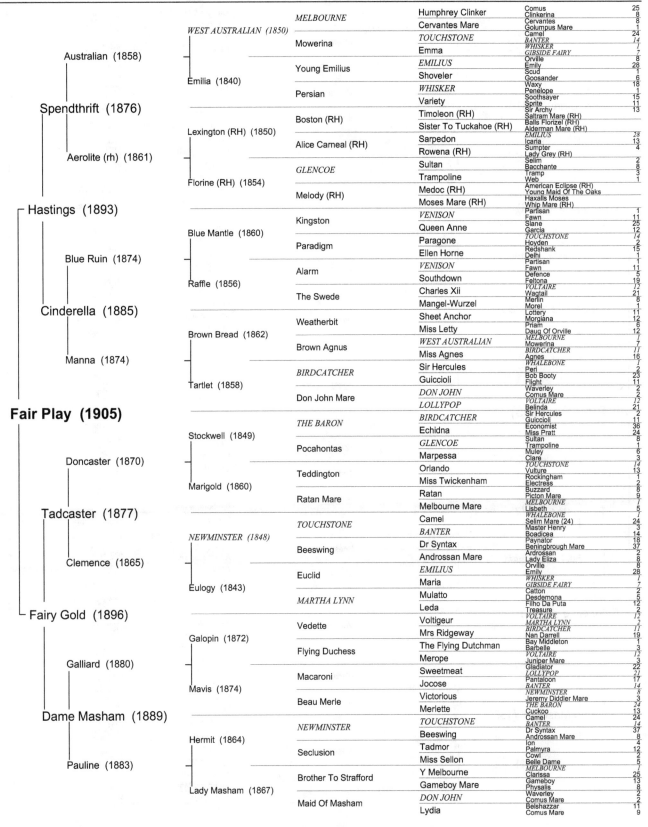

Fair Play (1905)

- **Hastings (1893)**
  - **Spendthrift (1876)**
    - Australian (1858)
      - WEST AUSTRALIAN (1850)
        - MELBOURNE
          - Humphrey Clinker — Comus 25, Clinkerina 8
          - Cervantes Mare — Cervantes 8, Golumpus Mare 1
        - Mowerina
          - TOUCHSTONE — Camel 24, BANTER 14
          - Emma — WHISKER 1, GIBSIDE FAIRY 7
      - Emilia (1840)
        - Young Emilius
          - EMILIUS — Orville 8, Emily 28
          - Shoveler — Scud 1, Goosander 6
        - Persian
          - WHISKER — Waxy 18, Penelope 1
          - Variety — Soothsayer 15, Sprite 11
    - Aerolite (rh) (1861)
      - Lexington (RH) (1850)
        - Boston (RH)
          - Timoleon (RH) — Sir Archy 13, Saltram Mare (RH)
          - Sister To Tuckahoe (RH) — Balls Florizel (RH), Alderman Mare (RH)
        - Alice Carneal (RH)
          - Sarpedon — EMILIUS 28, Icaria 13
          - Rowena (RH) — Sumpter 4, Lady Grey (RH)
      - Florine (RH) (1854)
        - GLENCOE
          - Sultan — Selim 2, Bacchante 8
          - Trampoline — Tramp 3, Web 1
        - Melody (RH)
          - Medoc (RH) — American Eclipse (RH), Young Maid Of The Oaks
          - Moses Mare (RH) — Haxalls Moses, Whip Mare (RH)
  - **Cinderella (1885)**
    - Blue Ruin (1874)
      - Blue Mantle (1860)
        - Kingston
          - VENISON — Partisan 1, Fawn 11
          - Queen Anne — Slane 25, Garcia 12
        - Paradigm
          - Paragone — TOUCHSTONE 14, Hoyden 2
          - Ellen Horne — Redshank 15, Delhi 1
      - Raffle (1856)
        - Alarm
          - VENISON — Partisan 1, Fawn 11
          - Southdown — Defence 5, Feltona 19
        - The Swede
          - Charles Xii — VOLTAIRE 12, Wagtail 21
          - Mangel-Wurzel — Merlin 8, Morel 1
    - Manna (1874)
      - Brown Bread (1862)
        - Weatherbit
          - Sheet Anchor — Lottery 11, Morgiana 12
          - Miss Letty — Priam 6, Daug Of Orville 12
        - Brown Agnus
          - WEST AUSTRALIAN — MELBOURNE 1, Mowerina 7
          - Miss Agnes — BIRDCATCHER 11, Agnes 16
      - Tartlet (1858)
        - BIRDCATCHER
          - Sir Hercules — WHALEBONE 1, Peri 2
          - Guiccioli — Bob Booty 23, Flight 11
        - Don John Mare
          - DON JOHN — Waverley 2, Comus Mare 2
          - LOLLYPOP — VOLTAIRE 12, Belinda 21
- **Fairy Gold (1896)**
  - **Tadcaster (1877)**
    - Doncaster (1870)
      - Stockwell (1849)
        - THE BARON
          - BIRDCATCHER — Sir Hercules 2, Guiccioli 11
          - Echidna — Economist 36, Miss Pratt 24
        - Pocahontas
          - GLENCOE — Sultan 8, Trampoline 1
          - Marpessa — Muley 6, Clare 3
      - Marigold (1860)
        - Teddington
          - Orlando — TOUCHSTONE 14, Vulture 13
          - Miss Twickenham — Rockingham 1, Electress 2
        - Ratan Mare
          - Ratan — Buzzard 8, Picton Mare 9
          - Melbourne Mare — MELBOURNE 1, Lisbeth 5
    - Clemence (1865)
      - NEWMINSTER (1848)
        - TOUCHSTONE
          - Camel — WHALEBONE 1, Selim Mare (24) 24
          - BANTER — Master Henry 3, Boadicea 14
        - Beeswing
          - Dr Syntax — Paynator 18, Beningbrough Mare 37
          - Androssan Mare — Ardrossan 2, Lady Eliza 8
      - Eulogy (1843)
        - Euclid
          - EMILIUS — Orville 8, Emily 28
          - Maria — WHISKER 1, GIBSIDE FAIRY 7
        - MARTHA LYNN
          - Mulatto — Catton 2, Desdemona 5
          - Leda — Filho Da Puta 12, Treasure 2
  - **Dame Masham (1889)**
    - Galliard (1880)
      - Galopin (1872)
        - Vedette
          - Voltigeur — VOLTAIRE 12, MARTHA LYNN 2
          - Mrs Ridgeway — BIRDCATCHER 11, Nan Darrell 19
        - Flying Duchess
          - The Flying Dutchman — Bay Middleton 1, Barbelle 3
          - Merope — VOLTAIRE 12, Juniper Mare 3
      - Mavis (1874)
        - Macaroni
          - Sweetmeat — Gladiator 22, LOLLYPOP 21
          - Jocose — Pantaloon 17, BANTER 14
        - Beau Merle
          - Victorious — NEWMINSTER 8, Jeremy Diddler Mare 3
          - Merlette — THE BARON 24, Cuckoo 13
    - Pauline (1883)
      - Hermit (1864)
        - NEWMINSTER
          - TOUCHSTONE — Camel 24, BANTER 14
          - Beeswing — Dr Syntax 37, Androssan Mare 8
        - Seclusion
          - Tadmor — Ion 4, Palmyra 12
          - Miss Sellon — Cowl 5, Belle Dame
      - Lady Masham (1867)
        - Brother To Strafford
          - Y Melbourne — MELBOURNE 1, Clarissa 25
          - Gameboy Mare — Gameboy 13, Physalis 8
        - Maid Of Masham
          - DON JOHN — Waverley 2, Comus Mare 2
          - Lydia — Belshazzar 11, Comus Mare 9

Fair Play 1905

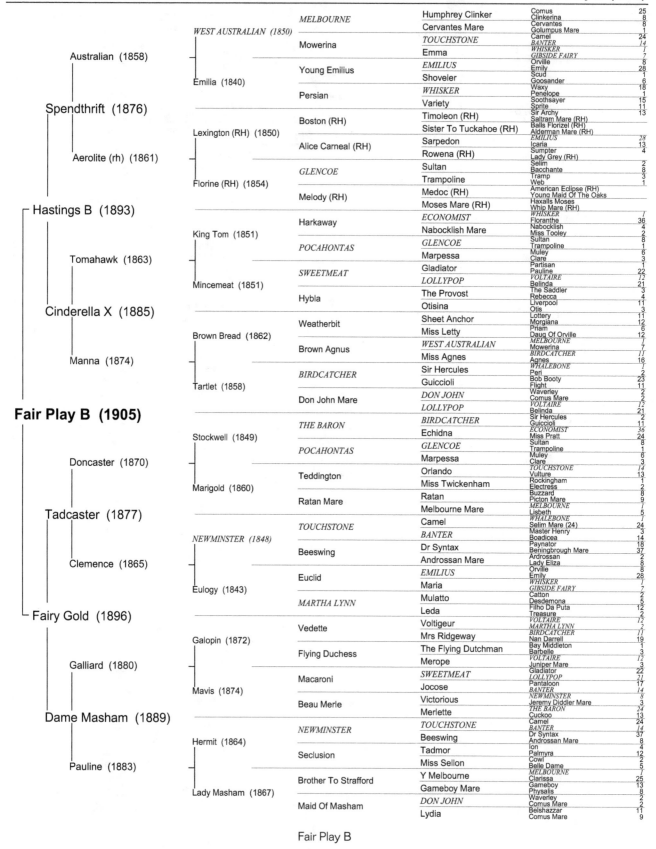

			Comus	25
		MELBOURNE	Humphrey Clinker	Clinkerina	8
	WEST AUSTRALIAN (1850)			Cervantes	6
			Cervantes Mare	Golumpus Mare	1
Australian (1858)				Camel	24
		Mowerina	*TOUCHSTONE*	*BANTER*	14
			Emma	*WHISKER*	1
				GIBSIDE FAIRY	7
Spendthrift (1876)	Emilia (1840)		*EMILIUS*	Orville	8
		Young Emilius		Emily	28
			Shoveler	Scud	1
				Goosander	6
		Persian	*WHISKER*	Waxy	18
				Penelope	1
			Variety	Soothsayer	15
				Sprite	11
Aerolite (rh) (1861)			Timoleon (RH)	Sir Archy	13
		Boston (RH)		Saltram Mare (RH)	
	Lexington (RH) (1850)		Sister To Tuckahoe (RH)	Balls Florizel (RH)	
				Alderman Mare (RH)	
		Alice Carneal (RH)	Sarpedon	*EMILIUS*	28
				Icaria	13
			Rowena (RH)	Sumpter	4
				Lady Grey (RH)	
Hastings B (1893)			Sultan	Selim	2
		GLENCOE		Bacchante	8
	Florine (RH) (1854)		Trampoline	Tramp	3
				Web	1
		Melody (RH)	Medoc (RH)	American Eclipse (RH)	
Tomahawk (1863)				Young Maid Of The Oaks	
			Moses Mare (RH)	Haxalls Moses	
				Whip Mare (RH)	
		Harkaway	*ECONOMIST*	*WHISKER*	1
				Floranthe	36
	King Tom (1851)		Nabocklish Mare	Nabocklish	4
				Miss Tooley	2
Cinderella X (1885)		POCAHONTAS	GLENCOE	Sultan	8
				Trampoline	1
			Marpessa	Muley	6
				Clare	3
		SWEETMEAT	Gladiator	Partisan	1
				Pauline	22
Manna (1874)	Mincemeat (1851)		*LOLLYPOP*	*VOLTAIRE*	12
				Belinda	21
		Hybla	The Provost	The Saddler	3
				Rebecca	4
			Otisina	Liverpool	11
				Otis	3
Fair Play B (1905)		Weatherbit	Sheet Anchor	Lottery	11
				Morgiana	12
	Brown Bread (1862)		Miss Letty	Priam	6
				Daug Of Orville	12
		Brown Agnus	WEST AUSTRALIAN	*MELBOURNE*	1
				Mowerina	1
			Miss Agnes	*BIRDCATCHER*	11
Doncaster (1870)				Agnes	16
		BIRDCATCHER	Sir Hercules	*WHALEBONE*	1
				Peri	2
	Tartlet (1858)		Guiccioli	Bob Booty	23
				Flight	11
		Don John Mare	DON JOHN	Waverley	2
				Comus Mare	2
Tadcaster (1877)			LOLLYPOP	*VOLTAIRE*	12
				Belinda	21
		THE BARON	BIRDCATCHER	Sir Hercules	2
				Guiccioli	11
	Stockwell (1849)		Echidna	*ECONOMIST*	36
				Miss Pratt	24
Clemence (1865)		POCAHONTAS	GLENCOE	Sultan	8
				Trampoline	1
			Marpessa	Muley	6
				Clare	3
		Teddington	Orlando	*TOUCHSTONE*	14
				Vulture	13
	Marigold (1860)		Miss Twickenham	Rockingham	1
				Electress	2
Fairy Gold (1896)		Ratan Mare	Ratan	Buzzard	8
				Picton Mare	9
			Melbourne Mare	*MELBOURNE*	1
				Lisbeth	5
		TOUCHSTONE	Camel	*WHALEBONE*	1
	NEWMINSTER (1848)			Selim Mare (24)	24
		BANTER	Master Henry	3
			Boadicea	14
Galliard (1880)		Beeswing	Dr Syntax	Paynator	18
				Beningbrough Mare	37
			Androssan Mare	Ardrossan	2
				Lady Eliza	8
	Eulogy (1843)	Euclid	*EMILIUS*	Orville	8
				Emily	28
			Maria	*WHISKER*	1
				GIBSIDE FAIRY	7
		MARTHA LYNN	Mulatto	Catton	2
				Desdemona	5
			Leda	Filho Da Puta	12
				Treasure	12
Dame Masham (1889)		Vedette	Voltigeur	*VOLTAIRE*	12
				MARTHA LYNN	1
	Galopin (1872)		Mrs Ridgeway	*BIRDCATCHER*	11
				Nan Darrell	19
		Flying Duchess	The Flying Dutchman	Bay Middleton	1
				Barbelle	3
			Merope	*VOLTAIRE*	12
				Juniper Mare	3
		Macaroni	SWEETMEAT	Gladiator	22
				LOLLYPOP	21
Pauline (1883)	Mavis (1874)		Jocose	Pantaloon	17
				BANTER	14
		Beau Merle	Victorious	*NEWMINSTER*	8
				Jeremy Diddler Mare	3
			Merlette	*THE BARON*	24
				Cuckoo	13
		NEWMINSTER	TOUCHSTONE	Camel	24
	Hermit (1864)			*BANTER*	14
			Beeswing	Dr Syntax	37
				Androssan Mare	8
		Seclusion	Tadmor	Ion	4
				Palmyra	12
			Miss Sellon	Cowl	2
				Belle Dame	5
	Lady Masham (1867)	Brother To Strafford	Y Melbourne	*MELBOURNE*	1
				Clarissa	25
			Gameboy Mare	Gameboy	13
				Physalis	8
		Maid Of Masham	DON JOHN	Waverley	2
				Comus Mare	2
			Lydia	Belshazzar	11
				Comus Mare	9

Fair Play B

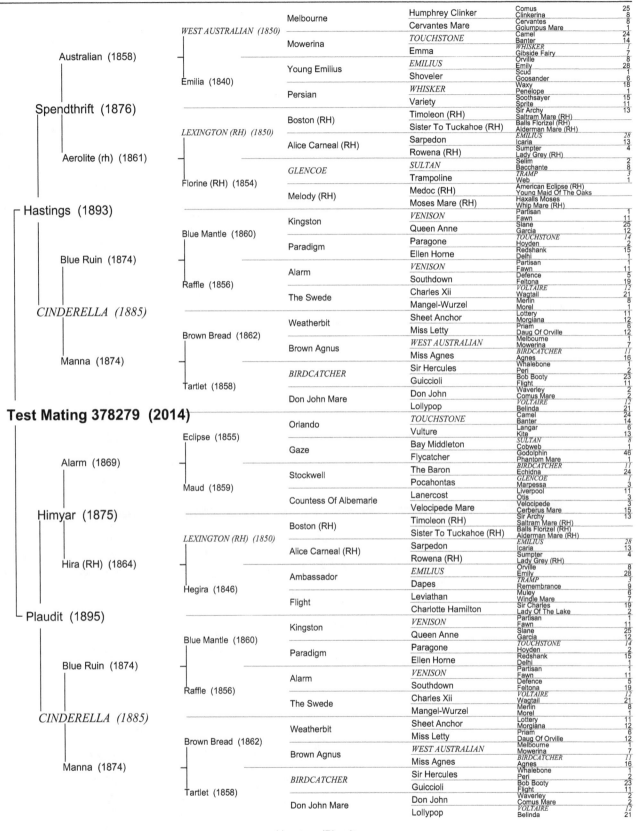

Hastings/Plaudit

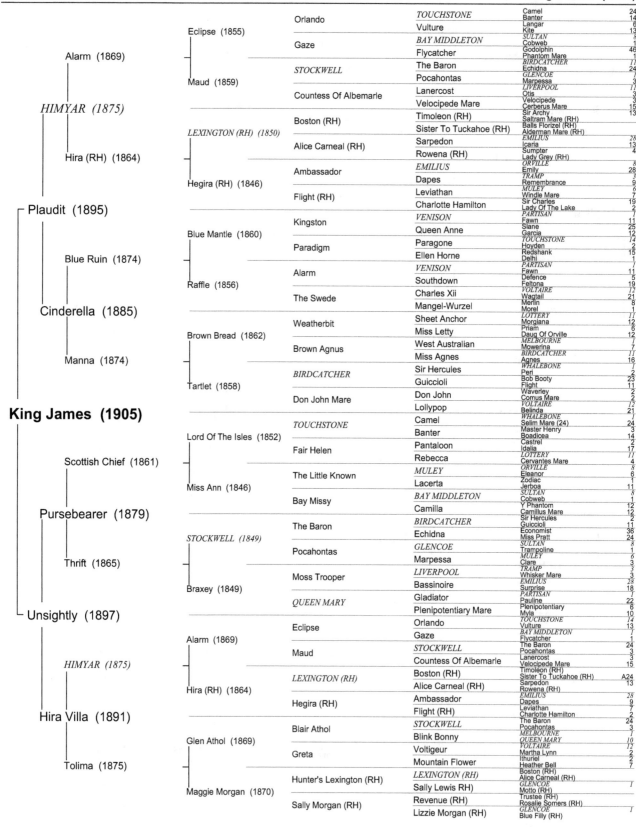

King James 1905

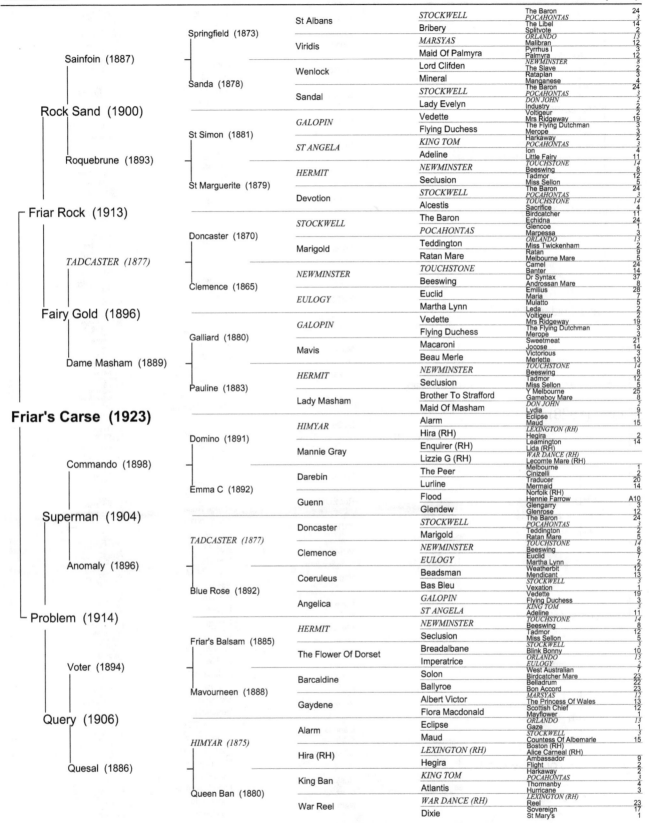

Friar's Carse (1923)

- **Friar Rock (1913)**
  - **Rock Sand (1900)**
    - Sainfoin (1887)
      - Springfield (1873)
        - St Albans
          - STOCKWELL — The Baron 24 / POCAHONTAS 3
          - Bribery — The Libel 14 / Splitvote 2
        - Viridis
          - MARSYAS — ORLANDO 13 / Malibran 12
          - Maid Of Palmyra — Pyrrhus I 3 / Palmyra 12
      - Sanda (1878)
        - Wenlock
          - Lord Clifden — NEWMINSTER 8 / The Slave 2
          - Mineral — Rataplan 3 / Manganese 4
        - Sandal
          - STOCKWELL — The Baron 24 / POCAHONTAS 3
          - Lady Evelyn — DON JOHN 2 / Industry 2
    - Roquebrune (1893)
      - St Simon (1881)
        - GALOPIN
          - Vedette — Voltigeur 19 / Mrs Ridgeway 3
          - Flying Duchess — The Flying Dutchman 3 / Merope 3
        - ST ANGELA
          - KING TOM — Harkaway 2 / POCAHONTAS 3
          - Adeline — Ion 4 / Little Fairy 11
      - St Marguerite (1879)
        - HERMIT
          - NEWMINSTER — TOUCHSTONE 14 / Beeswing 8
          - Seclusion — Tadmor 12 / Miss Sellon 5
        - Devotion
          - STOCKWELL — The Baron 24 / POCAHONTAS 3
          - Alcestis — TOUCHSTONE 14 / Sacrifice 4
  - **Fairy Gold (1896)**
    - TADCASTER (1877)
      - Doncaster (1870)
        - STOCKWELL
          - The Baron — Birdcatcher 11 / Echidna 24
          - POCAHONTAS — Glencoe 1 / Marpessa 3
        - Marigold
          - Teddington — ORLANDO 13 / Miss Twickenham 2
          - Ratan Mare — Ratan 9 / Melbourne Mare 5
      - Clemence (1865)
        - NEWMINSTER
          - TOUCHSTONE — Camel 24 / Banter 14
          - Beeswing — Dr Syntax 37 / Androssan Mare 8
        - EULOGY
          - Euclid — Emilius 28 / Maria 7
          - Martha Lynn — Mulatto 5 / Leda 2
    - Dame Masham (1889)
      - Galliard (1880)
        - GALOPIN
          - Vedette — Voltigeur 19 / Mrs Ridgeway 3
          - Flying Duchess — The Flying Dutchman 3 / Merope 3
        - Mavis
          - Macaroni — Sweetmeat 21 / Jocose 14
          - Beau Merle — Victorious 3 / Merlette 13
      - Pauline (1883)
        - HERMIT
          - NEWMINSTER — TOUCHSTONE 14 / Beeswing 8
          - Seclusion — Tadmor 12 / Miss Sellon 5
        - Lady Masham
          - Brother To Strafford — Y Melbourne 25 / Gameboy Mare 8
          - Maid Of Masham — DON JOHN 2 / Lydia 9
- **Problem (1914)**
  - **Superman (1904)**
    - Commando (1898)
      - Domino (1891)
        - HIMYAR
          - Alarm — Eclipse 1 / Maud 15
          - Hira (RH) — LEXINGTON (RH) 2 / Hegira 14
        - Mannie Gray
          - Enquirer (RH) — Leamington / Lida (RH)
          - Lizzie G (RH) — WAR DANCE (RH) / Lecomte Mare (RH)
      - Emma C (1892)
        - Darebin
          - The Peer — Melbourne 1 / Cinizelli 2
          - Lurline — Traducer 20 / Mermaid 14
        - Guenn
          - Flood — Norfolk (RH) / Hennie Farrow A10
          - Glendew — Glengarry 3 / Glenrose 12
    - Anomaly (1896)
      - TADCASTER (1877)
        - Doncaster
          - STOCKWELL — The Baron 24 / POCAHONTAS 3
          - Marigold — Teddington 2 / Ratan Mare 5
        - Clemence
          - NEWMINSTER — TOUCHSTONE 14 / Beeswing 8
          - EULOGY — Euclid 7 / Martha Lynn 2
      - Blue Rose (1892)
        - Coeruleus
          - Beadsman — Weatherbit 12 / Mendicant 13
          - Bas Bleu — STOCKWELL 3 / Vexation 1
        - Angelica
          - GALOPIN — Vedette 19 / Flying Duchess 3
          - ST ANGELA — KING TOM 3 / Adeline 11
  - **Query (1906)**
    - Voter (1894)
      - Friar's Balsam (1885)
        - HERMIT
          - NEWMINSTER — TOUCHSTONE 14 / Beeswing 8
          - Seclusion — Tadmor 12 / Miss Sellon 5
        - The Flower Of Dorset
          - Breadalbane — STOCKWELL 3 / Blink Bonny 10
          - Imperatrice — ORLANDO 13 / EULOGY 2
      - Mavourneen (1888)
        - Barcaldine
          - Solon — West Australian 7 / Birdcatcher Mare 23
          - Ballyroe — Belladrum 22 / Bon Accord 23
        - Gaydene
          - Albert Victor — MARSYAS 13 / The Princess Of Wales 13
          - Flora Macdonald — Scottish Chief 12 / Mayflower 1
    - Quesal (1886)
      - HIMYAR (1875)
        - Alarm
          - Eclipse — ORLANDO 13 / Gaze 1
          - Maud — STOCKWELL 3 / Countess Of Albemarle 15
        - Hira (RH)
          - LEXINGTON (RH) — Boston (RH) / Alice Carneal (RH)
          - Hegira — Ambassador 9 / Flight 2
      - Queen Ban (1880)
        - King Ban
          - KING TOM — Harkaway 2 / POCAHONTAS 3
          - Atlantis — Thormanby 4 / Hurricane 3
        - War Reel
          - WAR DANCE (RH) — LEXINGTON (RH) 23 / Reel
          - Dixie — Sovereign 17 / St Mary's 1

Friars Carse 1923

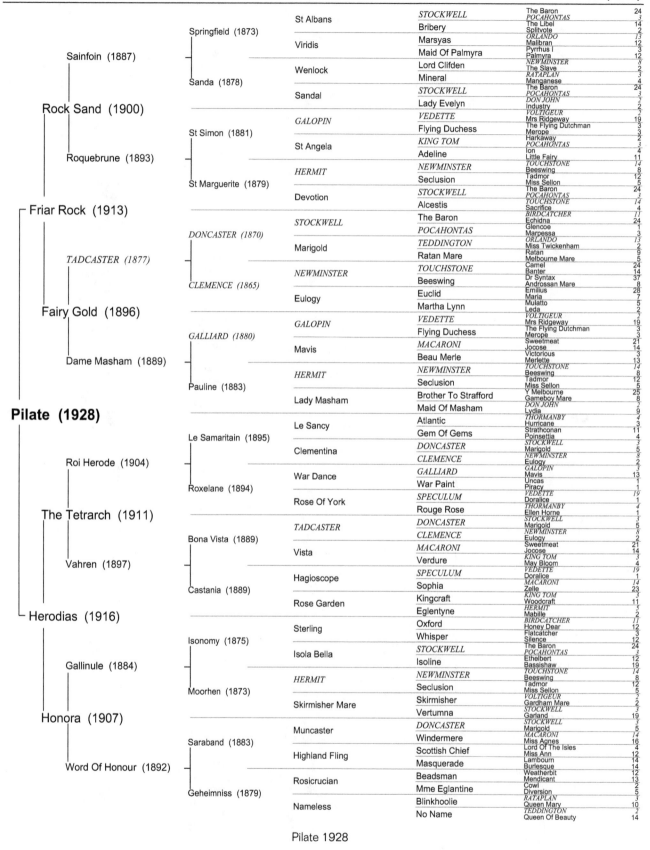

Pilate (1928)

- **Friar Rock (1913)**
  - **Rock Sand (1900)**
    - **Sainfoin (1887)**
      - Springfield (1873)
        - St Albans — *STOCKWELL* (The Baron 24, *POCAHONTAS* 3), Bribery (The Libel 14, Splitvote 2)
        - Viridis — Marsyas (*ORLANDO* 13, Malibran 12), Maid Of Palmyra (Pyrrhus I 3, Palmyra 12)
      - Sanda (1878)
        - Wenlock — Lord Clifden (*NEWMINSTER* 8, The Slave 2), Mineral (*RATAPLAN* 3, Manganese 4)
        - Sandal — *STOCKWELL* (The Baron 24, *POCAHONTAS* 3), Lady Evelyn (*DON JOHN* 2, Industry 2)
    - **Roquebrune (1893)**
      - St Simon (1881)
        - *GALOPIN* — *VEDETTE* (*VOLTIGEUR* 2, Mrs Ridgeway 19), Flying Duchess (The Flying Dutchman 3, Merope 3)
        - St Angela — *KING TOM* (Harkaway 2, *POCAHONTAS* 3), Adeline (Ion 4, Little Fairy 11)
      - St Marguerite (1879)
        - *HERMIT* — *NEWMINSTER* (*TOUCHSTONE* 14, Beeswing 8), Seclusion (Tadmor 12, Miss Sellon 5)
        - Devotion — *STOCKWELL* (The Baron 24, *POCAHONTAS* 3), Alcestis (*TOUCHSTONE* 14, Sacrifice 4)
  - **Fairy Gold (1896)**
    - **TADCASTER (1877)**
      - *DONCASTER* (1870)
        - *STOCKWELL* — The Baron (*BIRDCATCHER* 11, Echidna 24), *POCAHONTAS* (Glencoe 1, Marpessa)
        - Marigold — *TEDDINGTON* (*ORLANDO* 13, Miss Twickenham 2), Ratan Mare (Ratan 9, Melbourne Mare 5)
      - *CLEMENCE* (1865)
        - *NEWMINSTER* — *TOUCHSTONE* (Camel 24, Banter 14), Beeswing (Dr Syntax 37, Androssan Mare 8)
        - Eulogy — Euclid (Emilius 28, Maria 7), Martha Lynn (Mulatto 5, Leda 2)
    - **Dame Masham (1889)**
      - *GALLIARD* (1880)
        - *GALOPIN* — *VEDETTE* (*VOLTIGEUR* 2, Mrs Ridgeway 19), Flying Duchess (The Flying Dutchman 3, Merope 3)
        - Mavis — *MACARONI* (Sweetmeat 21, Jocose 14), Beau Merle (Victorious 3, Merlette 13)
      - Pauline (1883)
        - *HERMIT* — *NEWMINSTER* (*TOUCHSTONE* 14, Beeswing 8), Seclusion (Tadmor 12, Miss Sellon 5)
        - Lady Masham — Brother To Strafford (Y Melbourne 25, Gameboy Mare 8), Maid Of Masham (*DON JOHN* 2, Lydia 9)

- **Herodias (1916)**
  - **The Tetrarch (1911)**
    - **Roi Herode (1904)**
      - Le Samaritain (1895)
        - Le Sancy — Atlantic (*THORMANBY* 4, Hurricane 3), Gem Of Gems (Strathconan 11, Poinsettia 4)
        - Clementina — *DONCASTER* (*STOCKWELL* 3, Marigold 5), *CLEMENCE* (*NEWMINSTER* 8, Eulogy 2)
      - Roxelane (1894)
        - War Dance — *GALLIARD* (*GALOPIN* 3, Mavis 13), War Paint (Uncas 1, Piracy 1)
        - Rose Of York — *SPECULUM* (*VEDETTE* 19, Doralice 1), Rouge Rose (*THORMANBY* 4, Ellen Horne 1)
    - **Vahren (1897)**
      - Bona Vista (1889)
        - *TADCASTER* — *DONCASTER* (*STOCKWELL* 3, Marigold 5), *CLEMENCE* (*NEWMINSTER* 8, Eulogy 2)
        - Vista — *MACARONI* (Sweetmeat 21, Jocose 14), Verdure (*KING TOM* 3, May Bloom 4)
      - Castania (1889)
        - Hagioscope — *SPECULUM* (*VEDETTE* 19, Doralice 1), Sophia (*MACARONI* 14, Zelle 23)
        - Rose Garden — Kingcraft (*KING TOM* 3, Woodcraft 11), Eglentyne (*HERMIT* 5, Mabille)
  - **Honora (1907)**
    - **Gallinule (1884)**
      - Isonomy (1875)
        - Sterling — Oxford (*BIRDCATCHER* 11, Honey Dear 12), Whisper (Flatcatcher 3, Silence 12)
        - Isola Bella — *STOCKWELL* (The Baron 24, *POCAHONTAS* 3), Isoline (Ethelbert 12, Bassishaw 19)
      - Moorhen (1873)
        - *HERMIT* — *NEWMINSTER* (*TOUCHSTONE* 14, Beeswing 8), Seclusion (Tadmor 12, Miss Sellon 5)
        - Skirmisher Mare — Skirmisher (*VOLTIGEUR* 2, Gardham Mare 5), Vertumna (*STOCKWELL* 3, Garland 19)
    - **Word Of Honour (1892)**
      - Saraband (1883)
        - Muncaster — *DONCASTER* (*STOCKWELL* 3, Marigold 5), Windermere (*MACARONI* 14, Miss Agnes 16)
        - Highland Fling — Scottish Chief (Lord Of The Isles 4, Miss Ann 12), Masquerade (Lambourn 14, Burlesque 14)
      - Geheimniss (1879)
        - Rosicrucian — Beadsman (Weatherbit 12, Mendicant 13), Mme Eglantine (Cowl 2, Diversion 5)
        - Nameless — Blinkhoolie (*RATAPLAN* 3, Queen Mary 10), No Name (*TEDDINGTON* 2, Queen Of Beauty 14)

Pilate 1928

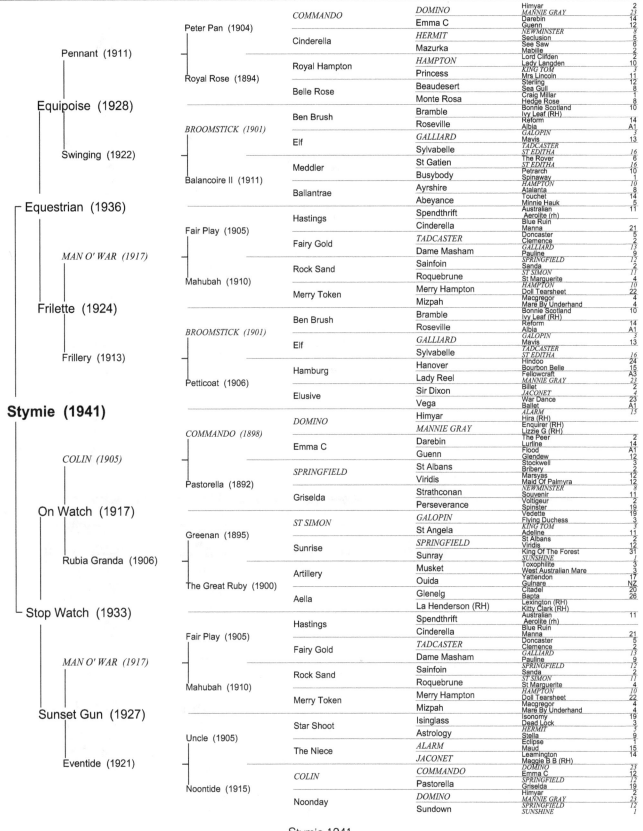

Stymie (1941)

Equestrian (1936)				
Equipoise (1928)	Pennant (1911)	Peter Pan (1904)	COMMANDO	DOMINO — Himyar 2 / *MANNIE GRAY* 23
				Emma C — Darebin 14 / Guenn 12
			Cinderella	*HERMIT* — *NEWMINSTER* 8 / Seclusion 5
				Mazurka — See Saw 6 / Mabille 2
		Royal Rose (1894)	Royal Hampton	*HAMPTON* — Lord Clifden 2 / Lady Langden 10
				Princess — *KING TOM* 3 / Mrs Lincoln 11
			Belle Rose	Beaudesert — Sterling 12 / Sea Gull 8
				Monte Rosa — Craig Millar 1 / Hedge Rose 8
	Swinging (1922)	*BROOMSTICK (1901)*	Ben Brush	Bramble — Bonnie Scotland 10 / Ivy Leaf (RH)
				Roseville — Reform 14 / Albia A1
			Elf	*GALLIARD* — *GALOPIN* 3 / Mavis 13
				Sylvabelle — *TADCASTER* / *ST EDITHA* 16
		Balancoire II (1911)	Meddler	St Gatien — The Rover 6 / *ST EDITHA* 16
				Busybody — Petrarch 10 / Spinaway 1
			Ballantrae	Ayrshire — *HAMPTON* 10 / Atalanta 8
				Abeyance — Touchet 14 / Minnie Hauk 5
Frilette (1924)	*MAN O' WAR (1917)*	Fair Play (1905)	Hastings	Spendthrift — Australian 11 / Aerolite (rh)
				Cinderella — Blue Ruin / Manna 21
			Fairy Gold	*TADCASTER* — Doncaster 5 / Clemence 2
				Dame Masham — *GALLIARD* 13 / Pauline 9
		Mahubah (1910)	Rock Sand	Sainfoin — *SPRINGFIELD* 12 / Sanda 2
				Roquebrune — *ST SIMON* 11 / St Marguerite 4
			Merry Token	Merry Hampton — *HAMPTON* 10 / Doll Tearsheet 22
				Mizpah — Macgregor 4 / Mare By Underhand 4
	Frillery (1913)	*BROOMSTICK (1901)*	Ben Brush	Bramble — Bonnie Scotland 10 / Ivy Leaf (RH)
				Roseville — Reform 14 / Albia A1
			Elf	*GALLIARD* — *GALOPIN* 3 / Mavis 13
				Sylvabelle — *TADCASTER* / *ST EDITHA* 16
		Petticoat (1906)	Hamburg	Hanover — Hindoo 24 / Bourbon Belle 15
				Lady Reel — Fellowcraft A3 / *MANNIE GRAY* 23
			Elusive	Sir Dixon — Billet 2 / *JACONET* 4
				Vega — War Dance 23 / Ballet A1
Stop Watch (1933)				
On Watch (1917)	*COLIN (1905)*	*COMMANDO (1898)*	*DOMINO*	Himyar — *ALARM* 15 / Hira (RH)
			MANNIE GRAY	Enquirer (RH) / Lizzie G (RH)
			Emma C	Darebin — The Peer 2 / Lurline 14
				Guenn — Flood A1 / Glendew 12
		Pastorella (1892)	*SPRINGFIELD*	St Albans — Stockwell 3 / Bribery 2
				Viridis — Marsyas 12 / Maid Of Palmyra 12
			Griselda	Strathconan — *NEWMINSTER* 8 / Souvenir 11
				Perseverance — Voltigeur 2 / Spinster 19
	Rubia Granda (1906)	Greenan (1895)	*ST SIMON*	*GALOPIN* — Vedette 19 / Flying Duchess 3
			St Angela	*KING TOM* 3 / Adeline 11
			Sunrise	*SPRINGFIELD* — St Albans 2 / Viridis 12
				Sunray — King Of The Forest 31 / *SUNSHINE* 1
		The Great Ruby (1900)	Artillery	Musket — Toxophilite 3 / West Australian Mare
				Ouida — Yattendon 17 / Gulnare NZ
			Aella	Glenelg — Citadel 20 / Bapta 26
				La Henderson (RH) — Lexington (RH) / Kitty Clark (RH)
Sunset Gun (1927)	*MAN O' WAR (1917)*	Fair Play (1905)	Hastings	Spendthrift — Australian 11 / Aerolite (rh)
				Cinderella — Blue Ruin / Manna 21
			Fairy Gold	*TADCASTER* — Doncaster 5 / Clemence 2
				Dame Masham — *GALLIARD* 13 / Pauline 9
		Mahubah (1910)	Rock Sand	Sainfoin — *SPRINGFIELD* 12 / Sanda 2
				Roquebrune — *ST SIMON* 11 / St Marguerite 4
			Merry Token	Merry Hampton — *HAMPTON* 10 / Doll Tearsheet 22
				Mizpah — Macgregor 4 / Mare By Underhand 4
	Eventide (1921)	Uncle (1905)	Star Shoot	Isinglass — Isonomy 19 / Dead Lock 3
				Astrology — *HERMIT* 5 / Stella 9
			The Niece	*ALARM* — Eclipse 1 / Maud 15
				JACONET — Leamington 14 / Maggie B B (RH)
		Noontide (1915)	*COLIN*	*COMMANDO* — *DOMINO* 23 / Emma C 12
				Pastorella — *SPRINGFIELD* 12 / Griselda 19
			Noonday	*DOMINO* — Himyar 2 / *MANNIE GRAY* 23
				Sundown — *SPRINGFIELD* 12 / *SUNSHINE* 1

Stymie 1941

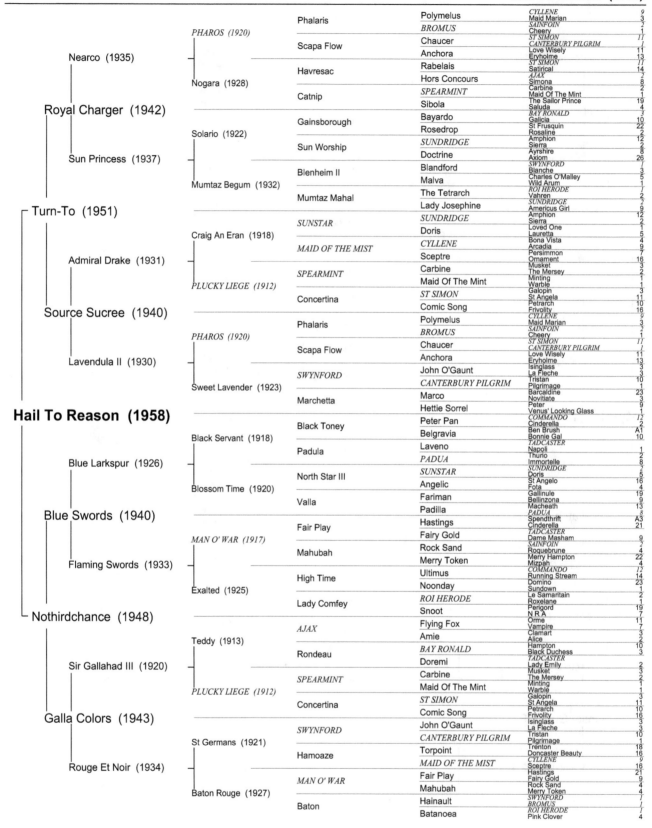

Hail To Reason (1958)

Nearco (1935)

Royal Charger (1942)

Sun Princess (1937)

Turn-To (1951)

Admiral Drake (1931)

Source Sucree (1940)

Lavendula II (1930)

Blue Larkspur (1926)

Blue Swords (1940)

Flaming Swords (1933)

Nothirdchance (1948)

Sir Gallahad III (1920)

Galla Colors (1943)

Rouge Et Noir (1934)

PHAROS (1920)	Phalaris	Polymelus	CYLLENE 9 / Maid Marian 3
		BROMUS	SAINFOIN 2 / Cheery 1
	Scapa Flow	Chaucer	ST SIMON 11 / CANTERBURY PILGRIM 1
		Anchora	Love Wisely 11 / Eryholme 13
Nogara (1928)	Havresac	Rabelais	ST SIMON 11 / Satirical 14
		Hors Concours	AJAX 2 / Simona 8
	Catnip	SPEARMINT	Carbine 2 / Maid Of The Mint
		Sibola	The Sailor Prince 19 / Saluda
Solario (1922)	Gainsborough	Bayardo	BAY RONALD 4 / Galicia 10
		Rosedrop	St Frusquin 22 / Rosaline 2
	Sun Worship	SUNDRIDGE	Amphion 12 / Sierra 2
		Doctrine	Ayrshire 8 / Axiom 26
Mumtaz Begum (1932)	Blenheim II	Blandford	SWYNFORD 7 / Blanche 3
		Malva	Charles O'Malley 5 / Wild Arum 1
	Mumtaz Mahal	The Tetrarch	ROI HERODE 1 / Vahren 2
		Lady Josephine	SUNDRIDGE 2 / Americus Girl 9
Craig An Eran (1918)	SUNSTAR	SUNDRIDGE	Amphion 12 / Sierra 2
		Doris	Loved One 1 / Lauretta 5
	MAID OF THE MIST	CYLLENE	Bona Vista 4 / Arcadia 9
		Sceptre	Persimmon 7 / Ornament 16
PLUCKY LIEGE (1912)	SPEARMINT	Carbine	Musket 3 / The Mersey 2
		Maid Of The Mint	Minting 1 / Warble 1
	Concertina	ST SIMON	Galopin 3 / St Angela 11
		Comic Song	Petrarch 10 / Frivolity 16
PHAROS (1920)	Phalaris	Polymelus	CYLLENE 9 / Maid Marian 3
		BROMUS	SAINFOIN 2 / Cheery 1
	Scapa Flow	Chaucer	ST SIMON 11 / CANTERBURY PILGRIM 1
		Anchora	Love Wisely 11 / Eryholme 13
Sweet Lavender (1923)	SWYNFORD	John O'Gaunt	Isinglass 3 / La Fleche 10
		CANTERBURY PILGRIM	Tristan 1 / Pilgrimage
	Marchetta	Marco	Barcaldine 23 / Novitiate 3
		Hettie Sorrel	Peter 9 / Venus' Looking Glass 1
Black Servant (1918)	Black Toney	Peter Pan	COMMANDO 12 / Cinderella 2
		Belgravia	Ben Brush A1 / Bonnie Gal 10
	Padula	Laveno	TADCASTER 1 / Napoli 2
		PADUA	Thurio / Immortelle 8
Blossom Time (1920)	North Star III	SUNSTAR	SUNDRIDGE 2 / Doris 5
		Angelic	St Angelo 16 / Fota 4
	Valla	Fariman	Gallinule 19 / Bellinzona 13
		Padilla	Macheath / PADUA A3
MAN O' WAR (1917)	Fair Play	Hastings	Spendthrift 3 / Cinderella 21
		Fairy Gold	TADCASTER / Dame Masham 9
	Mahubah	Rock Sand	SAINFOIN 2 / Roquebrune 4
		Merry Token	Merry Hampton 22 / Mizpah 4
Exalted (1925)	High Time	Ultimus	COMMANDO 12 / Running Stream 14
		Noonday	Domino 23 / Sundown 1
	Lady Comfey	ROI HERODE	Le Samaritain 2 / Roxelane 19
		Snoot	Perigord 7 / N R A
Teddy (1913)	AJAX	Flying Fox	Orme 11 / Vampire 7
		Amie	Clamart 3 / Alice
	Rondeau	BAY RONALD	Hampton 10 / Black Duchess 3
		Doremi	TADCASTER / Lady Emily 2
PLUCKY LIEGE (1912)	SPEARMINT	Carbine	Musket 3 / The Mersey 2
		Maid Of The Mint	Minting 1 / Warble 1
	Concertina	ST SIMON	Galopin 3 / St Angela 11
		Comic Song	Petrarch 10 / Frivolity 16
St Germans (1921)	SWYNFORD	John O'Gaunt	Isinglass 3 / La Fleche 10
		CANTERBURY PILGRIM	Tristan 1 / Pilgrimage
	Hamoaze	Torpoint	Trenton 18 / Doncaster Beauty 16
		MAID OF THE MIST	CYLLENE 9 / Sceptre 16
Baton Rouge (1927)	MAN O' WAR	Fair Play	Hastings 21 / Fairy Gold 9
		Mahubah	Rock Sand 4 / Merry Token 4
	Baton	Hainault	SWYNFORD 1 / BROMUS 1
		Batanoea	ROI HERODE 1 / Pink Clover 4

Hail to Reason 1958

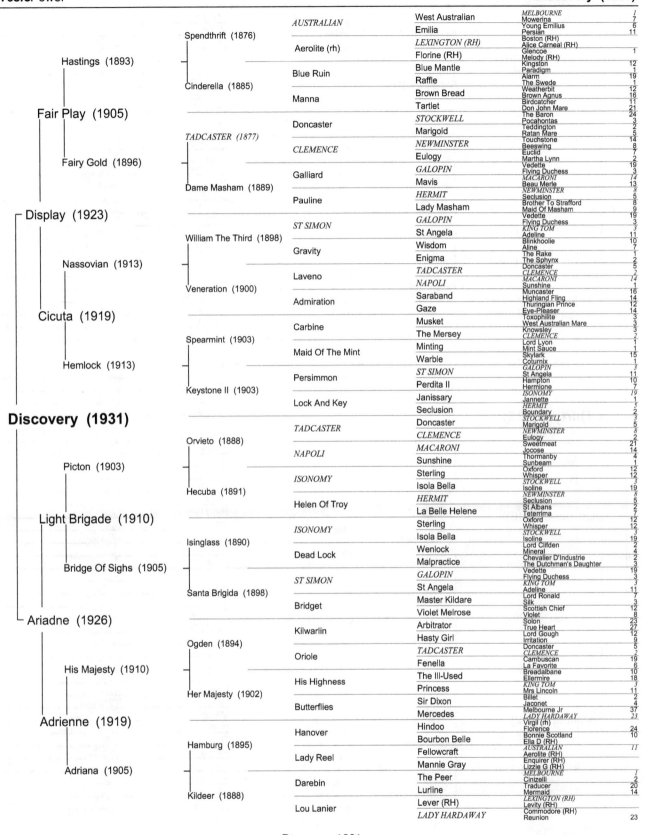

Discovery 1931

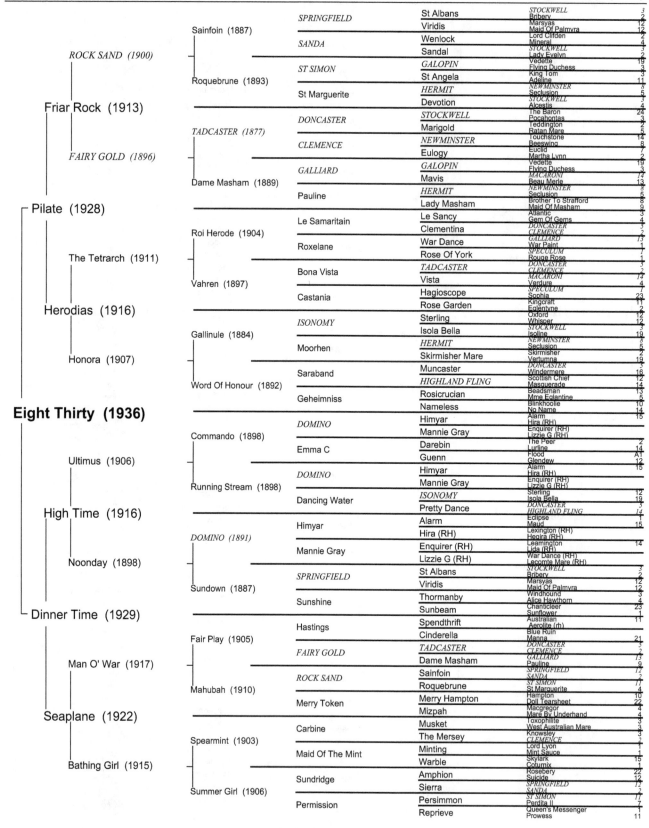

Eight Thirty 1936

Chapter 14

Mannie Gray and the Black Whirlwind

The Black Whirlwind Domino,
—from a painting by Gean Smith

I f we listen to the conventional wisdom fed to us—the North American sport horse breeders—by the European warmblood gurus, we would never expect to find the king of sprinters, Domino, behind our top sport horses. We have been told over and over that only stamina-bred Thoroughbreds are appropriate for sport horse breeding. Yet, when I did my own research I found that both sprint and stamina types powered the best lines, and not just in America, as Europe is loaded with them as well, with sprint horses producing high-quality sport horses (Nasrullah, Abernant, Tudor Minstrel, etc.).

For instance, one notable bloodline found in successful sport horses in all countries is The Tetrarch, which with his corrected pedigree (Bend Or controversy—see Chapter 13 and Appendix C) is revealed to be 3x3 to the full siblings Clementina/Tadcaster. This configuration, according to the statistics developed by Clive Harper, indicates a horse that can transmit speed at both sprint and classic lengths—so he did. He was a good racer himself but had to retire early with unsound legs. He left a dynasty of superior sport stock, in spite of his fertility and soundness problems. He is considered a source of speed—not stamina.

However it was twenty years before The Tetrarch was born that the speed demon called the Black Whirlwind burst upon the American racing scene. This is Domino, and he too was a confirmed sprinter-miler, and in spite of chronic sore feet he kept racing, and he won nineteen of his twenty-five starts. Bred by Baruch Thomas he was a racing phenomenon right from the start—with blistering sprint speed that none could match, he was truly unbeatable at eight furlongs or less. On Domino's death (July 29, 1897) the "Thoroughbred Record" reported:

"He was probably the fastest racehorse American turfmen have ever seen, and certainly during his career on the turf there was no other horse which could live with him in a contest of speed. His style of action was bold and dashing, smothering his field with a burst of speed which defied restraint. He would go to the front; difficulty of placing him was perhaps the cause of the suspicion that he could not go a distance. No horse on earth could sustain his flight of speed for a long distance, and efforts to reserve it necessitated such strong restraint as to choke him. He was a wonderful weight carrier, and at distances up to a mile no horse could approach him."

His contribution to sport is staggering and is still growing today, which is all the more remarkable as he sired only two small crops of foals before his early death at age six from spinal meningitis. Kept as a private stallion by James Keene, his first crop was only six foals, and his second fourteen. Nine of his offspring were sons, but four were gelded, and one died. Three of the remaining sons are found easily in your pedigrees. Far and away his best son was Commando. His son Disguise II 1867 is distant second, but then there is the even more rarely seen Olympian 1868.

When The Blood-Horse published their retrospective of 1916-1940 (*A Quarter-Century of American Racing and Breeding* 1941) it tabulated statistics of all manner and categories of racehorses—this publication is handy for our study as it covers almost the entire duration of the Jersey Act. One such list was of the stallions with the highest percentage of stakes winners. All lists like this attempt to quantify talent and to separate and identify the best horses, but all are limited in their scope by the nature of their strict selection criteria. In this list for instance Fair Play's percentage is skewed because it is taken from total foals, and his daughters rarely raced, so his total percent was possibly halved. But still we find it is valuable tool. Traditionally any horse with a percentage of 10% stakes winners or higher is considered a great sire—it is extremely rare to find a stallion with 20% or over. I have put the results of that survey in chart form for you to view, with the horse's sire-line or power bloodline noted as well.

Great Thoroughbred Sires 1916 – 1940

Sire (bloodline)	percent of stakes winners
Domino (Mannie Gray/Himyar)	42%
Commando (Domino)	37%
Broomstick (Ben Brush)	24.6%
Black Toney (Domino/Ben Brush)	18%
Fair Play (Spendthrift)	18%
Man O' War (Fair Play)	17%
Pennant (Commando/Domino)	16%
Bull Dog (Teddy)	15%
Sickle (Phalaris)	15%
Celt (Commando/Domino)	15%
Colin (Commando/Domino)	14%
Chicle (Spearmint/Carbine/Hamburg)	13%
High Time (inbred to Domino)	13%
St. Germans (Swynford/Cyllene)	13%
The Finn (Isonomy)	13%
Star Shoot (Isonomy/Hermit)	12%
Sweep (Domino/Ben Brush)	12%
Sun Briar (Galopin/Hermit)	12%
Uncle (Maggie B.B. RH)	12%
Equipoise (Domino/Ben Brush)	12%

All of these sires fall into the great sire category as they produced over 10% stakes winners. As anyone can see Domino and his descendants are far and away the majority of the important racers' bloodlines; therefore the Dominos obviously are the vastly superior hereditary transmitters of speed—no other source comes close to him.

Domino 1891, the greatest influence for speed in the world.—Thoroughbred Record

Colin, an undefeated racehorse, is one of the many sons of Domino that is rated a 'great' sire; he had 14% stakes winners—Thoroughbred Record

Usually it is assumed that Domino is not just a speed line, but strictly a sprinter line—this is not accurate. (The newly discovered 'speed gene' is also a 'sprint gene', but not only sprinters carry it, what we call a stayer today may carry it as well, as long as one parent contributes a 'speed gene' to the offspring, while the other one may not carry or transfer it. Domino always passed on speed to all his offspring, but depending on the contribution of the mare the distance racing capacity of the offspring could vary.) As the Thoroughbred pedigree expert Les Brinsfield has pointed out, Domino, the king of sprinters, passed on speed at all distances. While the highest profile examples of this are the classic distance champions Celt and Colin—we would call them stayers today. The sprint speed transmission comes through strongly concentrated with his inbred descendants, such as High Time, Ultimus, and Supremus.

During the term of the Jersey Act, which the above statistics represent, America imported many English sires, and they often led the sires list for a time. But as we discussed in previous chapters, they did not always breed on, and usually in spite of their popularity and number of high quality mares bred to them they have pretty abysmal standings. It is far and away Domino who produced the high-class racers, with Ben Brush and Fair Play coming on strong, and Maggie B. B. RH (born thirty years before the rest) making a showing also. Hermit lines made their mark, as did Isonomy, Teddy, Phalaris, Spearmint, Carbine, Swynford, Cyllene, and Galopin—the best of the foreign lines. But their numbers do not seem so impressive beside Domino—actually no other comes close to him and his progeny, and when we realize how short his life was—six years, and also his best stallion son Commando died young, leaving only twenty and twenty-four progeny respectively, then we begin to realize just how special their genetics are—**their potency for class and speed are unmatched**. Just like a comet, soaring through the sky, Domino's life shone bright and brief. But his legacy continues to grow today.

Domino is found consistently, usually in multiples, in the race and sport champions of today. He is the most potent carrier of Lexington's genetics in America as he has them 3x4x4, plus a line of the ½ brother Lecomte in the fourth generation. All of those lines are through daughters, and they rule every X chromosome pathway in his pedigree. It is clear then that it is Lexington RH (and his sire Boston) once again behind this fountain of speed. Domino is closely related to Hamburg who is 4x4x5x5 to Lexington RH, to Durban/Heldifann et al who are 7x6x7x6x7x7x8x8 to Lexington RH and Americus is 3x3 to Lexington RH, so they can be combined in pedigrees with his lines for more concentration and complexity. His only real rivals for top sport bloodlines in America are Fair Play and Broomstick, and truly they are a distant second. What a wonder.

[Note: the top mare Beaming Beauty 1917 trumps the Lexington RH potency of Durban/Heldifann, as she is 3x4x4x4 to Domino/Lady Reel, she has seventeen lines of Lexington RH in ten generations—see Chapter 21.]

Mannie Gray produced two full sisters to Domino: Mannie Himyar, the dam of Ariel, dam of Blackstock who is the sire of Wise Counsellor; and Correction, the fantastic racer. Correction was the older sister to Domino, and because of her magnificent sprint feats on the track—winning thirty-eight times—the industry was already looking at her younger brother to see what he could do. Correction is the dam of the good sire Yankee (found in Jack High), and she is the second dam of Haste, the dam-sire of Count Fleet. Yankee was a fair racer, winning the Futurity at two, but he was

Yankee 1899—seen here giving the photographer the 'hairy eyeball'. He did not have the best disposition as he was very high-strung, yet he is still a valuable bloodline for us today. —photo found in *Thoroughbred Types*

'heavily topped' and broke down at three—a son of Hanover, who often transmitted big, beefy frames. His temperament left much to be desired also, as he was very high-strung, but maybe this isn't so surprising when we look at his pedigree structure: he was 4x4 Vandal RH, 4x4x5x5 Lexington RH, plus 4x5 the ¾ brothers War Dance RH/Lecomte RH—definitely a super-charged lineage.

It always pays to do your research—such as that done by the Aussie Thoroughbred experts Rommy Faversham and Leon Rasmussen (*Inbreeding to Superior Females* 1999) in which they determined that only 30% of the Lexington's top racing offspring could be attributed to Glencoe. This is a significant amount, but it is not definitive, and certainly not enough to credit Glencoe with the breeding success of the Running Horse Lexington. Don't misunderstand me, in my opinion Glencoe is a genetic giant, and one of the greatest broodmares sires in racing history—and this 'nick' was surely one of the most powerful and fortunate in racing history. My point is that Lexington RH, and sire Boston RH, both, are equally **genetic giants**, and Lexington RH has his own superb record as a broodmare sire.

This is demonstrated nowhere as strongly as in Domino and his full siblings. The X chromosome of Domino's dam is Lizzie G RH, who is strongly ruled by Glencoe, but Mannie Gray's other X chromosome comes from Lida RH, and it is all American Running Horse: Lexington RH, American Eclipse RH/Irbys Calypso RH—this is the dam-line of the great sire Enquirer RH, sire of Mannie Gray. Plus Himyar, who is Domino's sire but also the sire of his full sisters Correction and Mannie Himyar, would transfer one of those mare's X chromosome to his daughters through his dam Hira RH—another Lexington RH daughter. So for Domino it is only a 50% chance that Glencoe daughters are ruling his sex-linked traits (large heart, respiratory) and in his full sisters it is only a 33% chance. Correction was one of the greatest sprinters of her day, winning thirty-eight races, and she was sound. Speed can be transmitted equally by both sexes and so the first rate speed of Himyar certainly transferred to Domino as well as his sisters.

Speed transmitters are not just found in English bloodlines—if that was the case they would have had no problem dominating our racehorses consistently—then and now. Our American Running Horse descends from the same original carriers of the speed gene that the English Thoroughbred descends from—the Hobby-based racers. I think this is probably a large part of the confusion the scholars have found when trying to explain away the superior racing class shown by our 'mongrel' racers—they are not mongrels at all; they come from the same source of speed as the English breed, and actually may carry more variety in it (see Chapter 1 and 2).

We can see some of this in the legacy of Domino. His best son Commando was a pronounced speedster, a classic race winner, and sire, and he far outclasses the other sons in produce. His breeder James Keene believed it was necessary to add English Thoroughbred to his stock, and he imported English-bred mares to breed to his homegrown stallions—therefore you will find the vast majority of the stock bred by Keene to be out of strictly English Thoroughbred dams. One rare exception to this is Commando, as his dam is American-bred, and she adds two more lines of Lexington RH. One of those additional Lexington RH lines is the great sire and racer Norfolk RH who provides an automatic nick for his descendants with the Lady Josephine family which carries him and his full sister The Nun through Americus. The second best son Disquise II is out of an English dam-line, as is most of the other produce of Domino. As Commando is dramatically the superior to the other two Domino stallions, we must look to his dam and therefore once again find there is a strong case for the Running Horse leading the genetics.

As mentioned before, the great pedigree expert Clive Harper applied scientific methods to the evaluation of pedigree patterns and gave us statistics on which patterns produce a higher percentage of good horses (see Appendix B). He also made some other interesting discoveries, one of which is that inbreeding can produce speed in racehorses, even if the individual inbred to is a stamina source. We can stand Domino as the ultimate example of Harper's findings as he is inbred so strongly to Lexington RH—the king of stayers. But across the pond as well, we find the speed source Americus, inbred also to Lexington RH, brings in extreme speed to his granddaughter Lady Josephine (see next chapter).

The evidence of Domino—in that he is living proof (as was Americus) of the principle identified by Clive Harper: that concentrating Lexington RH lines (stamina racer) produces sprinting speed appears to go against the science of our day. The newly discovered speed gene by Bower et al 2010 and Hill et al 2012, with the more recent developments outlined by Petersen et al in 2014 show that the speed gene is a sprint gene and that they assume it was caused by a mutation, and that it entered the gene pool through one individual. And when they tested the fastest sprinting racehorse breed: the American

Quarter Horse and its near relative the American Paint Horse, these findings were confirmed, as 89% of the population is homozygous for the gene.

The speed gene is also known as 'myostatin gene' and 'ECA18', which reflects its placement in the equine genome. They also found that the high incidence of this gene correspond to a higher level of Type 2B muscle fiber (fast contracting—bulky muscle), and with a conformation of the short, compact, muscular form that the Quarter Horse is famous for. This form if you flip back to Chapter 1 you will see in the woodcut done of the American Running Horse by Alexander Anderson, that this form is reminiscent of our original Running Horse as well.

The evidence they have found then seems to contradict the findings of Clive Harper (also a scientist) whereas he found that inbreeding to individual horses often produces sprinting speed—whether the horse is a sprinter or a stayer—he found it did not matter, and if the inbreeding was to full siblings then it produces fast horses at sprint and classic distance. Multiple lines of a horse in the background of a pedigree he found produced stayers---stamina racers, once again no matter the distance talent of the duplicated horse. And there is no denying that inbreeding to the King of Stayers: Lexington RH resulted in sprinting speed in Americus and Domino. So what are we to make of all this?

First we must remember that the research on the genetic traits in the horse is not finished, plus the Horse Genome Project has made a statement that they believe there is more than one speed gene, and more than one group of traits that produce speed in the horse. Therefore, both schools of research are then right, and ground breaking, and valuable for the sport horse breeder, but we can also look ahead to more genetic revelations to come—it isn't complete.

Commando—Domino's best stallion son— carries seven lines of Lexington RH in seven generations. —image from Thoroughbred Record

Domino's best stallion son Commando, not only won the Belmont Stakes, but he sired two Belmont winners: Colin (undefeated racehorse) and Peter Pan, and as Les Brinsfield, well-known pedigree consultant, has pointed out, in our day we would be hailing Commando as a great 'stamina' line. I have to say that this only confirms Clive Harper's findings—that inbreeding concentrates whatever is there—if it is speed then the tight designs (3x3 or closer) can produce great speed at short distances, whereas the looser designs (4x4 or further) would transfer speed at longer distances.

Domino was a pure sprinter himself, and he was bred 3x4x4 to Lexington RH—the king of stayers. Then his son Commando added two more lines of Lexington RH, but the pattern was then 4x5x5x5x5—he exhibited tremendous speed, but at longer distances (Belmont Stakes). On the other hand is High Time who is inbred 2x3x3 to Domino—he was able to win only one sprint at two, running out of steam by four furlongs. This is reminiscent to what the colonial breeders discovered when they inbred to Janus closely they found that the speed was there but would burn itself out in just three furlongs, which is too soon to be of any racing worth. However, they found when they held the inbreeding back just a little they got the great racers they were looking for.

In his first crop of six foals, Domino produced a mare named Pink Domino 1897; she had some notable daughters such as Sweepaway (found in Spring Run—dam of Red God), Curiosity (found in the great sire John P. Grier), and Swan Song—the sister to the great sire Sweep. Pink Domino's son Sweep (by Ben Brush) is one of the greatest sire-lines of the twentieth century, a carrier of the large heart, dam-sire of two Triple Crown winners: Whirlaway and War Admiral, and sire of the good sire The Porter and the dynasty-creating mare Beaming Beauty, dam of Bubbling Over—this is a hard-to-match genetic legacy.

Luke McLuke—a son of the inbred Ultimus.
—photo by L.S. Sutcliffe

High Time—the most concentrated source of
Domino as he is 3x3x2, sex-balanced to him—in
spite of reservations in using such an inbred sire,
has proved he is an extremely valuable source of
speed and sport talent.—Wiki Commons picture

"Sarazen's history reads like a romance. His dam
was a mare of no record and was purchased in a
half-hearted way by Mr. M. E. Johnston for the
incredibly small sum of $37.50. She was then
bred free of charge to High Time, a horse held in
so little esteem that it was impossible to obtain a
stud fee for his services. He had won one race as
a two-year-old in very fast time but beat a poor
field and soon faded away. Yet, from this union
came Sarazen, a colt unbeaten as a two-year-old
and at three champion racehorse of that year and
top weight for the handicap of 1925," —photo
and quotation from *Thoroughbred Types*

Also in Domino's first crop was the good sire Disguise II—out of an English dam, he raced in England, was third in the English Derby, and won the Jockey Club Stakes (stamina races). He became a good sire; his daughters especially have proved outstanding, such as Maskette—a good stakes winner, she is 3x3 to Mannie Gray—and there is also Miss Puzzle and Court Dress who are exceptional. This era is when James Keene maintained a stable in England. Disguise's son Iron Mask was a good racer also, winning stakes in England, and Disguise's daughter Cap and Bells, out of an English dam, was taken to England to race where she stunned the British by winning the English Oaks.

Domino produced a good broodmare in Running Stream, whose greatest offspring is the highly inbred Ultimus, whose genetic footprint grows even today; however he also can pass on sore feet. From the Ultimus daughter Fancy Racket descends the great modern *reine-de-course* Hildene. From Ultimus' son Luke McLuke descends the modern typesetter of the Quarter Horse: Three Bars and the *reine-de-course* Nellie Flag who is found in multiple winners. Ultimus' daughter Sweetheart is also a *reine-de-course* who produced the good mare Appeal, the *reine* Warrior Lass (by Man O' War), and the great sire Case Ace (Teddy son), who when bred to a Man O' War dam gave us the *reine* Ace Card, plus the *reine* Raise You by a Man O' War son (American Flag), and she is the dam of Raise a Native, who in-turn gave us Alydar, Exclusive Native, Majestic Prince, and Mr. Prospector! Ultimus' son Stimulus produced the *reine* Bourtai, the good mare Broad Ripple—dam of Shimmer who is dam of Nantallah, the sire of Ridan, Mocassin, Lt. Stevens, and Thong; plus the good mare Hug Again. Then there is the Ultimus son Supremus who you will run into in the best pedigrees also, and through Supremus' *reine* daughter Alcibiades come the great mares Lithe, Sparta, and Salamina, plus the super-sire Menow—the sire of the *chef* Tom Fool.

From Domino's 1898 daughter Noonday, not only does the great Stymie (Chapter 12) descend, but the most inbred sire to Domino: High Time (3x3x2 to Domino). From High Time's daughter Dinner Time descends the great stayer and sire Eight Thirty, and from Eight Thirty's daughter Exalted comes Blue Swords and Blue Haze (Chapter 12). High Time is also the sire of the great stakes winner Sarazen. Contrary to all we usually assume about inbred horses, we find that High Time is also a significant jump sire; he popped up as a constant in Birdsall's work (see Chapter 34).

A son of High Time, the gelding Sarazen lacked size and quality—being rangy and angluar, and he was a nervous horse, who nonetheless moved with perfection and could race under any conditions and win—fast track or slow, muddy going, and they say when he galloped no horse could catch him. He won twenty-seven of fifty-five starts, was Horse-of-the-Year and Champion Three-Year-Old in 1924, Horse-of-the-Year and Champion Handicap Horse in 1925, and in 1926 he also earned Champion-Handicap-Horse title—now that is racing class! The funny thing is he was almost was not born at all, as few would patronize his extremely inbred sire, but for Mrs. Daingerfield, who believed in High Time, and it was she who authorized Dr. Marcus Johnston to buy five mares to breed to High Time at no charge. One of those mares was mares was Rush Box.

For students of breeding, here again is an example of the spectacular success that can be achieved when two inbred horses are crossed. High Time was 3x3x2 to Domino, and the dam Rush Box was 4x4 to the full siblings Angelica/St. Simon. This is a recipe we keep finding in the best horses. This little mare—rated of no value—Rush Box is now listed as a *reine*.

But the greatest of Domino's offspring is Commando 1898, who was underrated when he started his two-year season, but he surprised them all and won the Champion-Two-Year-Old colt title. He then won the Belmont Stakes at three, and he retired to be a tremendous sire, but he also died young like his sire, from sepsis caused from an infected foot—see Chapter 27 for unsoundness in the bloodlines—the great Native Dancer, who is 5x6x5 to Domino, retired with abscessed feet. In just 2 ½ crops of foals—crop meaning a year's produce, Commando dominated racing and then breeding. His great son Peter Pan was born in 1904; he became the sire of dynasty heads Black Toney and Pennant. Peter Pan, like his sire Commando, was the best stallion son of his sire. He was a racehorse of high class, winning ten races at two, and taking the Belmont, Dwyer, and other stakes at three. As a stallion he excelled; his son Tryster and his daughter Prudery were respectively the Champion Colt and Filly of 1920, and other greats followed such as the good sire Peter Hastings and wonderful daughters Cherokee Rose II (*reine*), Yankee Maid, Verdure, Snooze, Panoply, and Flyatit.

Peter Pan 1904—the most successful of Commando's stallion sons. —photo by W.A. Rouch

Colin 1905—one of the all-time greats—was an unbeaten racehorse and a great sire as well; he produced 14% stakes winners. —photo by W. A. Rouch

In 1905 Commando gave the world Colin—an undefeated champion racer. He is a powerful classic winner, including the Belmont Stakes where he beat the legend Fair Play by a neck. He raced in England and stood stud there, but he was sent home shortly as the English ignored him—this was on the eve of the Jersey Act. Nonetheless, he still became a sire of note (14% stakes winners) with good sons like Neddie and On Watch and daughters such as Noontide and Slow and Easy. That same year the great Celt was born also, a classic winner and wonderful sire with 15% stakes winners. Born the same year, 1905 was the lesser known stakes winner Transvaal—a ¾ brother to Pennant.

As modern day sport horse breeders we want to be able to build up this line quickly and easily in our backgrounds. The best way to our goals is to identify the carriers who are inbred to Domino and his relatives. Luckily, Domino and his close relatives have ample descendants who are strongly line-bred or inbred to them.

Perhaps an excellent example of an inbred carrier of Domino is the Commando son Hippodrome, who is 2x2 to Domino, and through his daughter Bellasario—who also brings in the closely related Hamburg line—when she was bred to Sweep who is out of Pink Domino, the amazing broodmare *reine* Beaming Beauty was born (read more about her in Chapter 21).

Ultimus, rated as a *chef-de-race*, he as discussed above, is also inbred to Domino and he has multiple daughters and two of his sons are commonly found in pedigrees: Supremus and Stimulus. Plus keep your eye out for the great speed transmitter High Time, who is by Ultimus out of a Domino mare—2x3x3 to Domino. There is some unsoundness in the Domino line, usually in the front feet. His successful career as a sire benefitted hugely when both he and his descendants were bred to horses of the sound Fair Play and Ben Brush lines. But not all lines of Domino carry a weakness.

His full sister Correction was very sound and had immense talent. His grandson Sweep is another one of those very sound lines—he is by Ben Brush—and Sweep is dam-sire of one of the greatest broodmare sires of all time: War Admiral, who is by Man O' War (Fair Play line).

Then there is the *chef-de-race* Black Toney 1911, a Peter Pan son out of a Ben Brush mare, and this line is powerful for the sport horse breeder today. This line is also sound. A stakes winner and good sire, Black Toney 1911 still did not make the spectacular splash that other of his tribe did. Yet as the years went by his bloodline stands as a conduit of the best in Domino without the weakness. This branch of the Domino line is continually found in top sport horses (Chapter 34).

Black Toney—an important bloodline for the sport horse breeder.
—photo by L.S. Sutcliffe

Black Toney was sired by Peter Pan, Commando's best son whose dam is a loosely bred English TB imported by Keene: Cinderella (this is a different Cinderella from one who is the dam of Hastings). Black Toney's dam Belgravia was a daughter of Ben Brush, so she adds two more lines of Lexington RH to the five in Commando making seven lines of Lexington RH in seven generations for Black Toney. Her dam is English (as that was Keene's practice), but that English mare brings something very profitable for a breeding animal: she is 4x4 to the good English mare Queen Mary, by a son and a daughter, therefore a filly factor (see Appendix B)—plus Queen Mary is 4x4 to the full sisters Gohanna Mare and Young Gohanna. This mare is powerful, and this strong 'filly factor' (see Appendix B) certainly helped Black Toney's career as a top stallion. His grandson Blue Larkspur, who heads his own dynasty, also carries an instructive pedigree design in the benefit of doubling up on mares.

At stud Black Toney shone, especially as a producer of two-year-olds. One of his best racers is the Hall of Fame inductee Black Gold 1921 who won eighteen of his thirty-five starts including four Derby Stakes in four different states—a feat few others have achieved (Kentucky Derby, Louisiana Derby, Chicago Derby, and Ohio Derby). On the smaller side, Black Gold was notable for his toughness and resiliency.

Black Toney also sired another Kentucky Derby winner and good sire Broker's Tip, and you can easily find him in To Market—to whom Spectacular Bid was inbred to 3x3.

Black Servant—a lovely looking horse who was known for his smooth, fluid movement. —photo by W. A. Rouch

His elegant son Black Servant 1918 was also a stakes winner, and his movement was light and fluid, plus he has become immortal as he is the sire of Blue Larkspur.

But it is the Black Servant son Blue Larkspur, a *chef* who has become a pillar of modern racing and sport breeding. A conduit of the large heart gene, he also transmitted some of the elegance of his bloodline with fluid motion along with sport ability. It is interesting in a reflection of what Black Toney's dam contributed genetically, that Blue Larkspur's dam also brought in a second line of the mare Padua, making her 3x4, through two different daughters on both dam-lines—this mare also carries full sisters 4x5: Vulture and Lady Moore Carew; this is a demonstration for us that doubling up on mares in our designs—especially in potential breeding stock—is a proven road to success. Like Sweep and War Admiral, he is an exceptional broodmare sire. You will find him in such greats as Buckpasser and the versatile international jumper and eventing champion Bold Minstrel.

Some of the greatest racers and breeders of our modern day are combinations that include Black Toney or Blue Larkspur with Sweep and War Admiral, especially those that also bring in La Troienne—see Chapter 22 to find out what that mare carried that set off our Heroic Era genes so well. If you want class and performance in your foals take a lesson from history and make sure you have created dominance in your background with some strong lines of Domino mixed with Fair Play and Ben Brush in the lineages of your herd.

Blue Larkspur is a modern day genetic giant; he reliably transmitted great athleticism, the large heart, and good movement. —image courtesy of Keeneland Library

Lexington RH is the essence of the American Thoroughbred—he is found everywhere there is excellence in sport. It was his descendant Domino who is inbred to Lexington RH 3x3x4 who holds the same position in his era. Domino, as well as Lexington RH, is the essence of the American Thoroughbred.

Now let's look at what was happening with the Heroic Era bloodlines that were trapped in Europe during the Jersey Act.

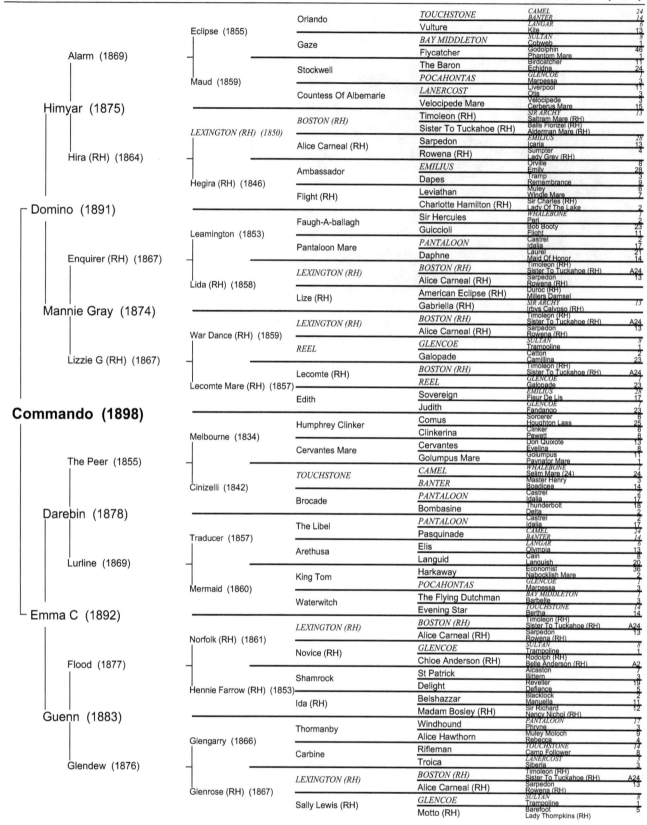

Commando 1898

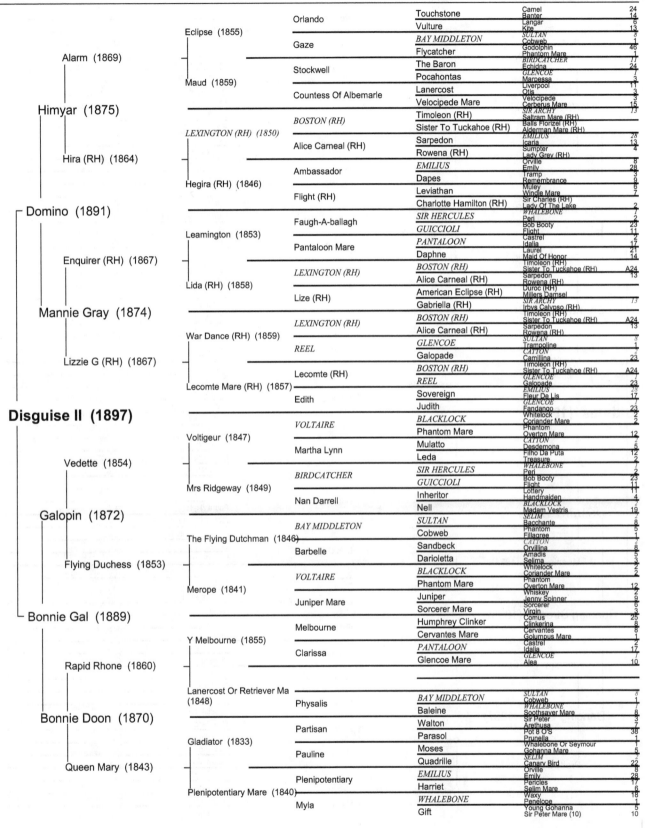

			Touchstone	Camel 24
		Orlando		Banter 14
			Vulture	Langar 6
	Eclipse (1855)			Kite 13
			BAY MIDDLETON	SULTAN 8
		Gaze		Cobweb 1
			Flycatcher	Godolphin 46
Alarm (1869)				Phantom Mare 1
			The Baron	BIRDCATCHER 11
		Stockwell		Echidna 24
	Maud (1859)		Pocahontas	GLENCOE 7
				Marpessa 3
		Countess Of Albemarle	Lanercost	Liverpool 11
Himyar (1875)				Otis 3
			Velocipede Mare	Velocipede 3
				Cerberus Mare 15
			Timoleon (RH)	SIR ARCHY 13
		BOSTON (RH)		Saltram Mare (RH)
			Sister To Tuckahoe (RH)	Balls Florizel (RH)
	LEXINGTON (RH) (1850)			Alderman Mare (RH)
			Sarpedon	EMILIUS 28
		Alice Carneal (RH)		Icaria 13
Hira (RH) (1864)			Rowena (RH)	Sumpter 4
				Lady Grey (RH)
			EMILIUS	Orville 8
		Ambassador		Emily 28
	Hegira (RH) (1846)		Dapes	Tramp 3
				Remembrance 9
			Leviathan	Muley 6
		Flight (RH)		Windle Mare 7
			Charlotte Hamilton (RH)	Sir Charles (RH)
				Lady Of The Lake 2
			SIR HERCULES	WHALEBONE 7
		Faugh-A-ballagh		Peri 2
			GUICCIOLI	Bob Booty 23
Domino (1891)	Leamington (1853)			Flight 11
			PANTALOON	Castrel 2
		Pantaloon Mare		Idalia 17
			Daphne	Laurel 21
				Maid Of Honor 14
			BOSTON (RH)	Timoleon (RH)
		LEXINGTON (RH)		Sister To Tuckahoe (RH) A24
			Alice Carneal (RH)	Sarpedon 13
Enquirer (RH) (1867)	Lida (RH) (1858)			Rowena (RH)
			American Eclipse (RH)	Duroc (RH)
		Lize (RH)		Millers Damsel
			Gabriella (RH)	SIR ARCHY 13
				Irbys Calypso (RH)
			BOSTON (RH)	Timoleon (RH)
		LEXINGTON (RH)		Sister To Tuckahoe (RH) A24
			Alice Carneal (RH)	Sarpedon 13
	War Dance (RH) (1859)			Rowena (RH)
			GLENCOE	SULTAN 8
		REEL		Trampoline 1
Mannie Gray (1874)			Galopade	CATTON 23
				Camillina
			BOSTON (RH)	Timoleon (RH)
		Lecomte (RH)		Sister To Tuckahoe (RH) A24
	Lecomte Mare (RH) (1857)		REEL	GLENCOE 7
				Galopade 23
			Sovereign	EMILIUS 28
		Edith		Fleur De Lis 17
Lizzie G (RH) (1867)			Judith	GLENCOE 7
				Fandango 23

Disguise II (1897)

			BLACKLOCK	Whitelock 2
		VOLTAIRE		Coriander Mare 2
			Phantom Mare	Phantom 12
	Voltigeur (1847)			Overton Mare
			Mulatto	CATTON 2
		Martha Lynn		Desdemona 5
			Leda	Filho Da Puta 12
Vedette (1854)				Treasure 2
			SIR HERCULES	WHALEBONE 7
		BIRDCATCHER		Peri 2
			GUICCIOLI	Bob Booty 23
	Mrs Ridgeway (1849)			Flight 11
			Inheritor	Lottery 4
		Nan Darrell		Handmaiden
			Nell	BLACKLOCK 2
				Madam Vestris 19
			SULTAN	SELIM 8
		BAY MIDDLETON		Bacchante 5
			Cobweb	Phantom 1
Galopin (1872)	The Flying Dutchman (1846)			Filagree
			Sandbeck	CATTON 2
		Barbelle		Orvillina 8
			Darioletta	Amadis 3
				Selima 2
			BLACKLOCK	Whitelock 2
		VOLTAIRE		Coriander Mare 2
			Phantom Mare	Phantom 12
	Merope (1841)			Overton Mare
			Juniper	Whiskey 2
		Juniper Mare		Jenny Spinner 9
Flying Duchess (1853)			Sorcerer Mare	Sorcerer 6
				Virgin 3
			Humphrey Clinker	Comus 25
		Melbourne		Clinkerina 8
			Cervantes Mare	Cervantes 8
	Y Melbourne (1855)			Golumpus Mare 1
			PANTALOON	Castrel 2
		Clarissa		Idalia 17
			Glencoe Mare	GLENCOE 7
Bonnie Gal (1889)				Alea 10
	Lanercost Or Retriever Ma (1848)			
			BAY MIDDLETON	SULTAN 8
		Physalis		Cobweb 1
			Baleine	WHALEBONE 7
Rapid Rhone (1860)				Soothsayer Mare 8
			Walton	Sir Peter 3
		Partisan		Arethusa 37
	Gladiator (1833)		Parasol	Pot 8 O'S 38
				Prunella 1
			Moses	Whalebone Or Seymour 1
		Pauline		Gohanna Mare 5
Bonnie Doon (1870)			Quadrille	SELIM 8
				Canary Bird 22
			EMILIUS	Orville 8
		Plenipotentiary		Emily 28
			Harriet	Pericles 17
	Plenipotentiary Mare (1840)			Selim Mare 6
			WHALEBONE	Waxy 18
		Myla		Penelope 1
Queen Mary (1843)			Gift	Young Gohanna 5
				Sir Peter Mare (10) 10

Disguise II 1897

Ultimus (1906)

- **Commando (1898)**
  - *DOMINO (1891)*
    - Himyar (1875)
      - Alarm (1869)
        - Eclipse
          - *ORLANDO* — *TOUCHSTONE* 14 / Vulture 13
          - Gaze — Bay Middleton 1 / Flycatcher 1
        - Maud
          - *STOCKWELL* — The Baron 24 / *POCAHONTAS* 3
          - Countess Of Albemarle — Lanercost 3 / Velocipede Mare 15
      - Hira (RH) (1864)
        - *LEXINGTON (RH)*
          - *BOSTON (RH)* — Timoleon (RH) / Sister To Tuckahoe (RH) A24
          - Alice Carneal (RH) — Sarpedon 13 / Rowena (RH)
        - Hegira (RH)
          - Ambassador — Emilius 28 / Dabes 9
          - Flight (RH) — Leviathan 7 / Charlotte Hamilton (RH)
    - Mannie Gray (1874)
      - Enquirer (RH) (1867)
        - Leamington
          - *FAUGH-A-BALLAGH* — *SIR HERCULES* 2 / *GUICCIOLI* 11
          - Pantaloon Mare — *PANTALOON* 17 / Daphne 14
        - Lida (RH)
          - *LEXINGTON (RH)* — *BOSTON (RH)* / Alice Carneal (RH)
          - Lize (RH) — American Eclipse (RH) / Gabriella (RH)
      - Lizzie G (RH) (1867)
        - War Dance (RH)
          - *LEXINGTON (RH)* — *BOSTON (RH)* / Alice Carneal (RH)
          - *REEL* — *GLENCOE* 1 / Galopade 23
        - Lecomte Mare (RH)
          - Lecomte (RH) — *BOSTON (RH)* / *REEL* 23
          - Edith — Sovereign 17 / Judith 23
  - **Emma C (1892)**
    - Darebin (1878)
      - The Peer (1855)
        - *MELBOURNE*
          - Humphrey Clinker — Comus 25 / Clinkerina 8
          - Cervantes Mare — Cervantes 8 / Golumpus Mare 1
        - Cinizelli
          - *TOUCHSTONE* — Camel 24 / Banter 14
          - Brocade — *PANTALOON* 17 / Bombasine 2
      - Lurline (1869)
        - Traducer
          - The Libel — *PANTALOON* 17 / Pasquinade 14
          - Arethusa — Elis 13 / Languid 20
        - Mermaid
          - King Tom — Harkaway 2 / *POCAHONTAS* 3
          - Waterwitch — The Flying Dutchman 3 / Evening Star 14
    - Guenn (1883)
      - Flood (1877)
        - Norfolk (RH)
          - *LEXINGTON (RH)* — *BOSTON (RH)* / Alice Carneal (RH)
          - Novice (RH) — *GLENCOE* 1 / Chloe Anderson (RH) A2
        - Hennie Farrow (RH)
          - Shamrock — St Patrick 3 / Delight 5
          - Ida (RH) — Belshazzar / Madam Bosley (RH) 11
      - Glendew (1876)
        - Glengarry
          - Thormanby — Windhound 3 / Alice Hawthorn 4
          - Carbine — Rifleman 8 / Troica 3
        - Glenrose (RH)
          - *LEXINGTON (RH)* — *BOSTON (RH)* / Alice Carneal (RH)
          - Sally Lewis (RH) — *GLENCOE* 1 / Motto (RH)
- **Running Stream (1898)**
  - *DOMINO (1891)*
    - Himyar (1875)
      - Alarm (1869)
        - Eclipse
          - *ORLANDO* — *TOUCHSTONE* 14 / Vulture 13
          - Gaze — Bay Middleton 1 / Flycatcher 1
        - Maud
          - *STOCKWELL* — The Baron 24 / *POCAHONTAS* 3
          - Countess Of Albemarle — Lanercost 3 / Velocipede Mare 15
      - Hira (RH) (1864)
        - *LEXINGTON (RH)*
          - *BOSTON (RH)* — Timoleon (RH) / Sister To Tuckahoe (RH) A24
          - Alice Carneal (RH) — Sarpedon 13 / Rowena (RH)
        - Hegira (RH)
          - Ambassador — Emilius 28 / Dabes 9
          - Flight (RH) — Leviathan 7 / Charlotte Hamilton (RH)
    - Mannie Gray (1874)
      - Enquirer (RH) (1867)
        - Leamington
          - *FAUGH-A-BALLAGH* — *SIR HERCULES* 2 / *GUICCIOLI* 11
          - Pantaloon Mare — *PANTALOON* 17 / Daphne 14
        - Lida (RH)
          - *LEXINGTON (RH)* — *BOSTON (RH)* / Alice Carneal (RH)
          - Lize (RH) — American Eclipse (RH) / Gabriella (RH)
      - Lizzie G (RH) (1867)
        - War Dance (RH)
          - *LEXINGTON (RH)* — *BOSTON (RH)* / Alice Carneal (RH)
          - *REEL* — *GLENCOE* 1 / Galopade 23
        - Lecomte Mare (RH)
          - Lecomte (RH) — *BOSTON (RH)* / *REEL* 23
          - Edith — Sovereign 17 / Judith 23
  - **Dancing Water (1887)**
    - Isonomy (1875)
      - Sterling (1868)
        - Oxford
          - *BIRDCATCHER* — *SIR HERCULES* 2 / *GUICCIOLI* 11
          - Honey Dear — Plenipotentiary 6 / My Dear 12
        - Whisper
          - Flatcatcher — *TOUCHSTONE* 14 / Decoy 3
          - Silence — *MELBOURNE* / Secret 12
      - Isola Bella (1868)
        - *STOCKWELL*
          - The Baron — *BIRDCATCHER* 11 / Echidna 24
          - *POCAHONTAS* — *GLENCOE* 1 / Marpessa 3
        - Isoline
          - Ethelbert — *FAUGH-A-BALLAGH* 11 / Espoir
          - Bassishaw — The Prime Warden 17 / Miss Whinney 19
    - Pretty Dance (1878)
      - Doncaster (1870)
        - *STOCKWELL*
          - The Baron — *BIRDCATCHER* 11 / Echidna 24
          - *POCAHONTAS* — *GLENCOE* 1 / Marpessa 3
        - Marigold
          - Teddington — *ORLANDO* 13 / Miss Twickenham 2
          - Ratan Mare — Ratan 9 / Melbourne Mare 5
      - Highland Fling (1869)
        - Scottish Chief
          - Lord Of The Isles — *TOUCHSTONE* 14 / Fair Helen 4
          - Miss Ann — The Little Known 11 / Bay Missy 12
        - Masquerade
          - Lambourn — Loup-Garou 4 / Pantaloon Mare 14
          - Burlesque — *TOUCHSTONE* 14 / Maid Of Honor 14

Ultimus 1906

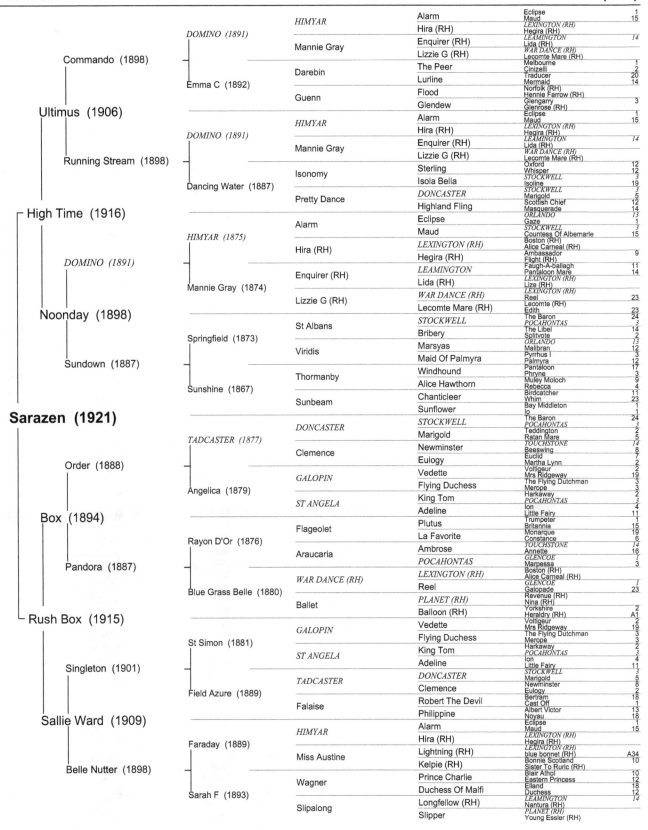

Commando (1898)	DOMINO (1891)	HIMYAR	Alarm	Eclipse 1 / Maud 15
			Hira (RH)	LEXINGTON (RH) / Hegira (RH)
		Mannie Gray	Enquirer (RH)	LEAMINGTON 14 / Lida (RH)
			Lizzie G (RH)	WAR DANCE (RH) / Lecomte Mare (RH)
	Emma C (1892)	Darebin	The Peer	Melbourne 1 / Cinizelli 2
			Lurline	Traducer 20 / Mermaid 14
		Guenn	Flood	Norfolk (RH) / Hennie Farrow (RH)
			Glendew	Glengarry 3 / Glenrose (RH)
Ultimus (1906)	DOMINO (1891)	HIMYAR	Alarm	Eclipse 1 / Maud 15
			Hira (RH)	LEXINGTON (RH) / Hegira (RH)
		Mannie Gray	Enquirer (RH)	LEAMINGTON 14 / Lida (RH)
			Lizzie G (RH)	WAR DANCE (RH) / Lecomte Mare (RH)
	Dancing Water (1887)	Isonomy	Sterling	Oxford 12 / Whisper 12
Running Stream (1898)			Isola Bella	STOCKWELL 3 / Isoline 19
		Pretty Dance	DONCASTER	STOCKWELL 3 / Marigold 5
			Highland Fling	Scottish Chief 12 / Masquerade 14
High Time (1916)	HIMYAR (1875)	Alarm	Eclipse	ORLANDO 13 / Gaze 1
			Maud	STOCKWELL 3 / Countess Of Albemarle 15
		Hira (RH)	LEXINGTON (RH)	Boston (RH) / Alice Carneal (RH)
			Hegira (RH)	Ambassador 9 / Flight (RH)
DOMINO (1891)	Mannie Gray (1874)	Enquirer (RH)	LEAMINGTON	Faugh-A-ballagh 11 / Pantaloon Mare 14
			Lida (RH)	LEXINGTON (RH) / Lize (RH)
		Lizzie G (RH)	WAR DANCE (RH)	LEXINGTON (RH) / Reel 23
			Lecomte Mare (RH)	Lecomte (RH) 23 / Edith 24
Noonday (1898)	Springfield (1873)	St Albans	STOCKWELL	The Baron 24 / POCAHONTAS 3
			Bribery	The Libel 14 / Splitvote 2
		Viridis	Marsyas	ORLANDO 13 / Malibran 12
			Maid Of Palmyra	Pyrrhus I 12 / Palmyra 12
Sundown (1887)	Sunshine (1867)	Thormanby	Windhound	Pantaloon 17 / Phryne 3
			Alice Hawthorn	Muley Moloch 9 / Rebecca 4
		Sunbeam	Chanticleer	Birdcatcher 11 / Whim 23
			Sunflower	Bay Middleton 1 / Io
Sarazen (1921)	TADCASTER (1877)	DONCASTER	STOCKWELL	The Baron 24 / POCAHONTAS 3
			Marigold	Teddington 2 / Ratan Mare 5
		Clemence	Newminster	TOUCHSTONE 14 / Beeswing 8
			Eulogy	Euclid 7 / Martha Lynn 2
Order (1888)	Angelica (1879)	GALOPIN	Vedette	Voltigeur 2 / Mrs Ridgeway 19
			Flying Duchess	The Flying Dutchman 3 / Merope 3
		ST ANGELA	King Tom	Harkaway 2 / POCAHONTAS 3
			Adeline	Ion 4 / Little Fairy 11
Box (1894)	Rayon D'Or (1876)	Flageolet	Plutus	Trumpeter 1 / Britannia 15
			La Favorite	Monarque 19 / Constance 6
		Araucaria	Ambrose	TOUCHSTONE 14 / Annette 16
			POCAHONTAS	GLENCOE 1 / Marpessa 3
Pandora (1887)	Blue Grass Belle (1880)	WAR DANCE (RH)	LEXINGTON (RH)	Boston (RH) / Alice Carneal (RH)
			Reel	GLENCOE 1 / Galopade 23
		Ballet	PLANET (RH)	Revenue (RH) / Nina (RH)
			Balloon (RH)	Yorkshire 2 / Heraldry (RH) A1
Rush Box (1915)	St Simon (1881)	GALOPIN	Vedette	Voltigeur 2 / Mrs Ridgeway 19
			Flying Duchess	The Flying Dutchman 3 / Merope 3
		ST ANGELA	King Tom	Harkaway 2 / POCAHONTAS 3
			Adeline	Ion 4 / Little Fairy 11
Singleton (1901)	Field Azure (1889)	TADCASTER	DONCASTER	STOCKWELL 3 / Marigold 5
			Clemence	Newminster 8 / Eulogy 2
		Falaise	Robert The Devil	Bertram 18 / Cast Off 1
			Philippine	Albert Victor 13 / Noyau 18
Sallie Ward (1909)	Faraday (1889)	HIMYAR	Alarm	Eclipse 1 / Maud 15
			Hira (RH)	LEXINGTON (RH) / Hegira (RH)
		Miss Austine	Lightning (RH)	LEXINGTON (RH) / blue bonnet (RH) A34
			Kelpie (RH)	Bonnie Scotland 10 / Sister To Ruric (RH)
Belle Nutter (1898)	Sarah F (1893)	Wagner	Prince Charlie	Blair Athol 10 / Eastern Princess 12
			Duchess Of Malfi	Elland 18 / Duchess 12
		Slipalong	Longfellow (RH)	LEAMINGTON 14 / Nantura (RH)
			Slipper	PLANET (RH) / Young Essler (RH)

Sarazen 1925

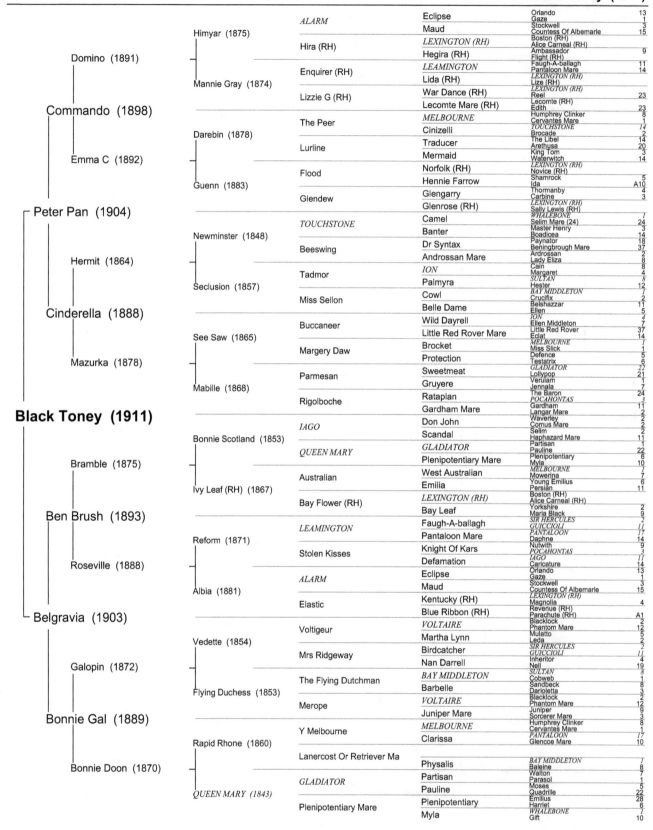

Left-hand descent:

- Commando (1898)
  - Domino (1891)
  - Emma C (1892)
- Peter Pan (1904)
- Hermit (1864)
- Cinderella (1888)
- Mazurka (1878)
- **Black Toney (1911)**
- Bramble (1875)
- Ben Brush (1893)
- Roseville (1888)
- Belgravia (1903)
- Galopin (1872)
- Bonnie Gal (1889)
- Bonnie Doon (1870)

Pedigree columns:

Gen 1	Gen 2	Gen 3	Gen 4	#	#
Himyar (1875)	*ALARM*	Eclipse	Orlando / Gaze	13	1
		Maud	Stockwell / Countess Of Albemarle	3	15
	Hira (RH)	*LEXINGTON (RH)*	Boston (RH) / Alice Carneal (RH)		
		Hegira (RH)	Ambassador / Flight (RH)	9	
Mannie Gray (1874)	Enquirer (RH)	*LEAMINGTON*	Faugh-A-ballagh / Pantaloon Mare	11	14
		Lida (RH)	*LEXINGTON (RH)* / Lize (RH)		
	Lizzie G (RH)	War Dance (RH)	*LEXINGTON (RH)* / Reel		23
		Lecomte Mare (RH)	Lecomte (RH) / Edith		23
Darebin (1878)	The Peer	*MELBOURNE*	Humphrey Clinker / Cervantes Mare	8	1
		Cinizelli	*TOUCHSTONE* / Brocade	14	2
	Lurline	Traducer	The Libel / Arethusa	14	20
		Mermaid	King Tom / Waterwitch	3	14
Guenn (1883)	Flood	Norfolk (RH)	*LEXINGTON (RH)* / Novice (RH)		
		Hennie Farrow	Shamrock / Ida	5	A10
	Glendew	Glengarry	Thormanby / Carbine	4	3
		Glenrose (RH)	*LEXINGTON (RH)* / Sally Lewis (RH)		
Newminster (1848)	*TOUCHSTONE*	Camel	*WHALEBONE* / Selim Mare (24)	1	24
		Banter	Master Henry / Boadicea	3	14
	Beeswing	Dr Syntax	Paynator / Beningbrough Mare	18	37
		Androssan Mare	Ardrossan / Lady Eliza	2	8
Seclusion (1857)	Tadmor	*ION*	Cain / Margaret	8	4
		Palmyra	*SULTAN* / Hester	8	12
	Miss Sellon	Cowl	*BAY MIDDLETON* / Crucifix	1	1
		Belle Dame	Belshazzar / Ellen	11	5
See Saw (1865)	Buccaneer	Wild Dayrell	*ION* / Ellen Middleton	4	7
		Little Red Rover Mare	Little Red Rover / Eclat	37	14
	Margery Daw	Brocket	*MELBOURNE* / Miss Slick	1	1
		Protection	Defence / Testatrix	5	6
Mabille (1868)	Parmesan	Sweetmeat	*GLADIATOR* / Lollypop	23	21
		Gruyere	Verulam / Jennala	1	7
	Rigolboche	Rataplan	The Baron / *POCAHONTAS*	24	3
		Gardham Mare	Gardham / Langar Mare	11	2
Bonnie Scotland (1853)	*IAGO*	Don John	Waverley / Comus Mare	2	2
		Scandal	Selim / Haphazard Mare	2	11
	QUEEN MARY	*GLADIATOR*	Partisan / Pauline	1	22
		Plenipotentiary Mare	Plenipotentiary / Myla	6	10
Ivy Leaf (RH) (1867)	Australian	West Australian	*MELBOURNE* / Mowerina	1	7
		Emilia	Young Emilius / Persian	6	11
	Bay Flower (RH)	*LEXINGTON (RH)*	Boston (RH) / Alice Carneal (RH)		
		Bay Leaf	Yorkshire / Maria Black	2	9
Reform (1871)	*LEAMINGTON*	Faugh-A-ballagh	*SIR HERCULES* / *GUICCIOLI*	2	11
		Pantaloon Mare	*PANTALOON* / Daphne	17	14
	Stolen Kisses	Knight Of Kars	Nutwith / *POCAHONTAS*	9	3
		Defamation	*IAGO* / Caricature	11	14
Albia (1881)	*ALARM*	Eclipse	Orlando / Gaze	13	1
		Maud	Stockwell / Countess Of Albemarle	3	15
	Elastic	Kentucky (RH)	*LEXINGTON (RH)* / Magnolia		4
		Blue Ribbon (RH)	Revenue (RH) / Parachute (RH)		A1
Vedette (1854)	Voltigeur	*VOLTAIRE*	Blacklock / Phantom Mare	2	12
		Martha Lynn	Mulatto / Leda	5	2
	Mrs Ridgeway	Birdcatcher	*SIR HERCULES* / *GUICCIOLI*	2	11
		Nan Darrell	Inheritor / Nell	4	19
Flying Duchess (1853)	The Flying Dutchman	*BAY MIDDLETON*	*SULTAN* / Cobweb	8	1
		Barbelle	Sandbeck / Darioletta	8	3
	Merope	*VOLTAIRE*	Blacklock / Phantom Mare	2	12
		Juniper Mare	Juniper / Sorcerer Mare	9	3
Rapid Rhone (1860)	Y Melbourne	*MELBOURNE*	Humphrey Clinker / Cervantes Mare	8	1
		Clarissa	*PANTALOON* / Glencoe Mare	17	10
	Lanercost Or Retriever Ma		*BAY MIDDLETON* / Baleine	1	8
		Physalis			
QUEEN MARY (1843)	*GLADIATOR*	Partisan	Walton / Parasol	7	1
		Pauline	Moses / Quadrille	5	22
	Plenipotentiary Mare	Plenipotentiary	Emilius / Harriet	28	6
		Myla	*WHALEBONE* / Gift	1	10

Black Toney 1911

Chapter 15

A Catholic Horse Wins the English Derby

In 1907, the unthinkable happened; an Irish-trained horse, Orby, won the English Derby. Worse, he was owned by the outcast Richard Croker. Although born in Ireland, Croker had become an American citizen. His infamy as a crooked politician in America resulted in him being barred admission into the Jockey Club in both England and Ireland. But he kept on entering their good races with his horses anyway. When Croker was refused the right of entry to the Newmarket facility for training, he asked in writing for a reason. The British Jockey Club responded: "The Jockey Club will remind you that the training grounds at Newmarket are the private property of the Jockey Club and that no one is allowed to train on the grounds unless permission is first asked and received. I am directed by the Stewards to inform you that they do not wish you to have your horses trained at Newmarket."

What a comeuppance it was then to have this disreputable and banished interloper enter the Derby and then win it. The insult was increased as Croker's horse Orby was ridden by an American jockey, Johnny Rieff, and was out an American-bred dam. Could it get any worse? Well as a matter of fact, yes, it could, and there were several more chapters of this notorious string of horses that were to be written into the annals of England's racing history.

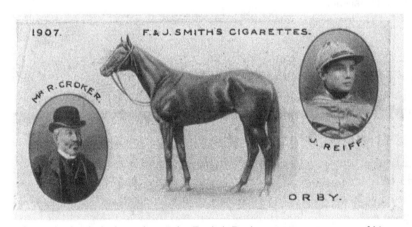

Orby, the 'catholic horse' won the English Derby. —image courtesy of New York Public Library Digital Collection, Arent's Cigarette Collection

How could this horror upon the English racing industry have occurred? Here is the short version: leaving America before he could be indicted for corruption, the Irish-born Croker came home to Ireland with a few American-bred horses. One of these was a mare named Rhoda B, a daughter of the great American stallion Hanover, out of a dam by Algerine, who was a close relative to Lexington RH, with a double of his dam Alice Carneal RH. Croker bred Rhoda B to the great English sire Orme (sire of Flying Fox), and in 1904 a colt was born whom he named Orby. In 1907, the long shot—100 to 9 Orby—won the English Derby (obviously without the benefit of training at Newmarket), soundly defeating the favorite Slieve Gallon who had already won the 2000 Guineas. Orby instantly became a national hero to the Irish; they proudly called him the 'catholic horse,' and at home in Ireland after the Derby he raced to a victory in the Irish Derby as well.

"Richard Croker's chestnut colt Orby by Orme—Rhoda B by Hanover, own the English Derby at Epsom on Wednesday. The victory was clean cut, Orby finishing two lengths in front of Colonel Baruch's Wool Winder, which was a half-length infront of Captain Greer's Slieve Gallon…."("Thoroughbred Record" June 8, 1907).

But that was not all this American-bred Hanover daughter Rhoda B produced, because when she was bred to St. Frusquin she foaled the 1000 Guineas winner Rhodora. Rhodora was also of the highest racing class, but left little legacy as she died fairly young giving birth to foal by her brother Orby. Rhoda B's record as a broodmare with two stakes winners of the highest class from different sires indicates that she carried some significant genes. Looking at her lineage we can clearly see the source: she is

3x4 to Boston RH through a son and daughter, she is 3x3 to Vandal RH sex-balanced lines also, and she carried a powerful filly factor of Alice Carneal RH 4x4—this is the best the American Heroic Era had to offer in strong formations.

Orby, often characterized as a 'poor' Derby winner, has left a notable legacy in the British Isles, and his offspring were allowed into the General Stud Book because Orby had already been entered in to the GSB—just before the Jockey Club banned horses with American bloodlines. Orby's spectacular victory was not a fluke, as his son Grand Parade (also owned by Croker) won the 1919 running of the Derby also. Grand Parade was a successful sire and is found in many English pedigrees. Grand Parade is the sire of Nella da Gubbio, the head of a maternal dynasty in German sport (see Chapter 18). However, this lack-luster Derby winner Orby has now risen to the level of the prime English sires such as Hyperion, Tudor Minstrel, Nasrullah, as he too is rated a *chef-de-race*, as is his grandson Sir Cosmo.

Player's Cigarettes

"Grand Parade" Derby, 1919

Grand Parade, the Derby winning son of Orby. —NYPL digital image

Orby produced other notable offspring, such as his daughter Diadem who was a good stakes winner, running until she was six. Diadem left many progeny including a stallion son Diophon who is 2x2 to Orby, and he too left many offspring, for instance he is second dam-sire of the great *chef-de-race* Noholme II, who not only brings in another line of Orby 5x5x5, but his half-sister Topiary (the dam of Tracery). Orby's son Flying Orb sired many offspring and is often seen in classic pedigrees. Orby provided bloodlines found in the British sport horse also—his son O'Donoghue 1918 stood for the National Hunt and was a noted sire of steeplechase, hunt, and jumper horses of talent.

Possibly his most often seen son in pedigrees is The Boss, as he is sire of the *chef* Sir Cosmo, a good sprint racer, who has achieved immortality because he is the broodmare sire of the American-bred mega-sire (*chef*) Round Table and his full sister Monarchy. Round Table won forty-three of sixty-three starts—winning $1,749,869. Round Table was US Champion Turf horse in 1957, 1958, and 1959. He was US Champion-Male-Handicap-Horse in 1958 and 1959, American Horse-of-the-Year 1958, and the Leading sire in 1972—it doesn't get much better than this.

The Boss also sired Golden Boss, the sire of Gold Bridge, who provides Orby with possibly his longest genetic shadow. French-bred Gold Bridge is inbred to him 3x3. I do wish one of those lines was through a daughter, as being both by sons they will not transfer all the good traits that is associated with this line. But Gold Bridge will live on in the pedigrees of great horses for generations because he is the sire of the great *reine* Rough Shod II. Rough Shod was by Gold Bridge out of Dalmary—the ⅞ sister to Blenheim—she was destined to head a dynasty in America that has spread throughout the world.

Rough Shod II was purchased by A. B. Hancock in England for his Kentucky stud; Hancock also bought Knight Daughter at this same time (dam of Round Table). Rough Shod produced a great mare in Gambetta who was by My Babu—a stallion who won the 2000 Guineas and other important stakes in England but was not eligible for the GSB because his grandsire Tourbillon is out of Durban, so he is loaded with Lexington RH lines (he also had Lady Josephine close up—more American 'stain'). His victory and that of Black Tarquin (American dam-line) in the same year (1948) helped repeal the Jersey Act as the French were fed up with their best racehorses being excluded. Gambetta was a stakes winner and a great broodmare. Her daughter Gamely won $574,961, and her daughter Staretta won $145,297. But Rough Shod's greatest achievement as a broodmare was to produce four full siblings by Nantallah. (Nantallah brings in multiple Heroic Era genes, not just through Catnip and Lady Josephine, but also a line of Durbar, three lines of Domino, and even Maggie B. B. RH through The Niece). These offspring are Ridan, Lt. Stevens, Thong, and Moccasin (pedigree). Ridan was a great runner and a good sire. His brother Lt. Stevens was also a stakes winner and a good broodmare sire. Thong, a good racer, was an even better broodmare (*reine*), producing the likes of Thatch by Forli (inbred 4x4 to Lady Josephine). Forli was destined to be an Irish champion and good European sire, so he is easy to find in English and Irish pedigrees. Thong also foaled King Pellinore by Round Table, a good classic racer in Europe, who did even better in America; he is a noted broodmare sire also.

Thong foaled other greats such as Lisadell, Espadrille, Pump, but it is her *reine-de-course* daughter Special—also by Forli—who hit the big time with her son Nureyev, champion racehorse and sire (*chef*). His ¾ sisters Bound and Number are also both stakes winners and good producers. Then there is Special's daughter Fairy Bridge (also a *reine*)—who even equals her dam's record as a broodmare as she is the dam of the *chef-de-race* Sadlers Wells (and his full brothers Fairy Bridge and Tate Gallery, plus their full sister Puppet Dance—who is sure to become very valuable in later line-breeding—see Chapter 24 for more on this). Seeing Sadlers Wells is possibly the greatest stallion that ever stood in Europe, this then is no small thing.

However, certainly on a par with Thong is her full sister Moccasin, as she was a top racer winning $388,075 and earning the Horse-of-the-Year title as well. As a broodmare she produced seven stakes winners out of nine foals, including the important sire Apalachee, who has also achieved *chef* status. This is tremendous maternal power.

[Note: with the multiples of *chef* and *reine* awards here, and in other chapters that outline the descendants of our Heroic Era genetic carriers, one may tend to start to view the *chef* and *reine* rating as common place. This is far from the truth, as it is a very exclusive club—only the very best sires and dams make it to this status; it is the highest honor a thoroughbred sire or dam can reach, as it recognizes their history as genetic transmitters of the most excellent racing traits.]

With just these four full siblings and their ½ sister Gambetta (also a *reine*), with their descendants, the breeder has enough to build top performance through line-breeding to create greatness for years to come—this family is a line-breeders dream, with multiple full siblings—they are all of top quality.

Orby's daughter Orlass, out of Simon Lass, won the 1951 Oaks and produced numerous good offspring—she carries St. Simon/Angelica 3x3—a recipe that has proven extremely successful. We see this fortunate genetics providing top quality in her daughter Lost Soul, who produced a great mare in Phase, who we find easily in English pedigrees. For instance, Phase was bred six times to Nearco, which brings in more of the American lines—nicking with what Orby carries. I have run into Phase in sport horse breeding in the good line of Hethersett, who carries her daughter Netherton Maid (*reine*). The interesting thing is that the sire of Hethersett is High Lupus who is inbred to Tourbillon, whose dam is inbred to Hanover, and one of those lines of Hamburg is out of Lady Reel who is by Fellowcraft (Aerolite RH—Lexington daughter RH) and out of Mannie Gray—the dam of Domino. This puts these American lines in concentration. Further, Netherton Maid is also a daughter of Nearco, so she already carries the Lexington RH daughter Maiden RH and a line of Blackburns Whip RH. The great Hanoverian dressage performer and sire Welthrum has Nevado as his dam-sire. Nevado is a son of Hethersett and is out of yet another daughter of Nearco—Neara. Not only then does Neara add more Lexington RH/Blackburns Whip RH through Nearco, but Neara's dam is descended from Orby also. Who ever imagined that the very essence of German dressage, Weltruhm, had so many American Running Horse bloodlines? But that is just the tip of the iceberg (see Chapter 18 for other strong American lines in Germany), even the Holstein typesetter Ladykiller has Orby in him, his dam-sire Loaningdale is out of Perfection—an Orby daughter. Orby is definitely one of those 'hidden' sources of American lines in the European sport horse (Chapter 29). Not a bad record for such a 'poor' Derby winner.

Lady Josephine

Sire of Americus: Emperor of Norfolk.
—image from "Thoroughbred Record"

Right before the Jersey Act crashed down upon the American international market, a few of the progeny of an even more significant sire made it into the GSB. This was Americus, a very close relative to Domino—his contemporary—and his life and influence is eerily similar to Domino; like mirror images their genetics improved the Thoroughbred and the sport horse on both sides of the Atlantic by quantum leaps out of relatively few offspring.

Americus was by the Emperor of Norfolk, who is considered the best horse Lucky Baldwin had, as he was one of America's fastest racehorses in an era where there still was plenty of real competition. "Emperor of Norfolk was a great two-year-old and a still greater three-year-old" ('Thoroughbred Record' December 21, 1907). He was foaled when his sire Norfolk was twenty-two years old.

Norfolk 1891, one of the greatest sons of Lexington RH, is most often seen in English lineages because he is the grandsire of Americus. —image from *Racing In America*

Americus was brought into Ireland by Richard Croker, and he was a talented sprint racehorse, but it is as a sire that he has earned a prominent place in Thoroughbred history. Nevertheless, it was against great odds that his line has survived, and it is only because of its undeniable merits that it has lived on in the unwelcoming Anglo environment. Americus was undervalued as a sire and received very few opportunities to breed, as he was largely ignored by the breeders in the British Isles, and unfortunately, like Domino, he died fairly young. The Americus bloodline was banned from the General Stud Book as a 'half-bred'.

Americus, never fully utilized by our British cousins, passed away in 1910. At his death, the "Horse and Hound" on April 23, 1910 said:

"Americus died at Hoppegarten Stud last week, having been sold by Mr. Croker to the Germans for 'L 1000' in September 1908, did a lot of traveling in his life. Bred in the United States in 1892, after showing himself a racehorse of exceptional speed in his own country, where as a two-year-old he won three races, and the next year ten, including the Flying Stakes and Atlantic Stakes, he came over here to run unsuccessfully as a four-year-old…"(the next year fully acclimated he did win three).

"Americus won the Riddlesdown Plate and Southdown Plate, winning the later by eight lengths from Milford. Then he was put to stud, only to be trained again in 1899, when he won the Charlwood Handicap, and the next year won the Eton Handicap at Windsor; and although failing to score in 1901, the same year his two-year-old son Gladwin won a couple of races. Americus showed a lot of his old speed, especially at the July Cup at Newmarket…in 1902 Americus once more took up stud duties, and having been leased for the seasons of 1906 and 1907 to Italy, then returned to cover in Ireland, and remained there, until going to Germany in 1908. He was a fine looking bay horse by Emperor of Norfolk (son of Norfolk and Miriam), out of Clara D., by Glenleg, from The Nun, by Lexington. Winners by Americus in England and Ireland include such speedy racers as the lovely Americus Girl, Gladwin, Golden Rod, Illinois, Jack Snipe and Rhododendron…"

This attitude toward American-bred stallions is not an isolated case; for example, it was only a short time later that the Brits made the same mistake with American-bred Tracery, as he was undervalued also by them, and shortly they sold him to Argentina. However, in Tracery's case, they realized their error in time to buy him back—after three years. For Americus it was too late—he was dead.

It was when his daughter Americus Girl began racing and winning that the Anglos realized that they might have overlooked something valuable, but by that time he was in Germany and died there in 1910 (see Chapter 18 for more on Americus in Germany). Americus Girl won five of her six starts as a two-year-old, but then continued on winning at three, four, and five, often carrying heavy weights. All told in twenty-nine starts she won twelve—a very impressive record.

Americus had some other stars that hit the racing scene, such as Americus Lady who won the Coventry Stakes at two. His daughter Mrs K became a good broodmare producing, among other good horses, the mare Shyness who in-turn produced the great broodmare Slow and Easy by Colin (Domino line), who is dam of the good mares Easy Lass (dam of Coaltown) and Always, plus the good stallion Easy Mon.

Another daughter of Americus, Caspia, is dam of 1000 Guineas winner Glaspia who is the dam of the stakes winner Grand Glacier (pedigree). He has a wonderful lineage as he is 3x3 to Hanover daughters—a strong filly factor—plus he has three strong full sibling configurations: St. Simon/Angelica 4x4x5, Norfolk RH/The Nun RH 5x5, and Hermit/Chanoinesse 6x5x6. Caspia is out of Halma, a Hanover daughter who is out of a Longfellow RH daughter. Americus's daughter Yankee, when mated with Orby, produced Glen Cairn (pedigree), a good stallion and sire of three full siblings, the champion Anna Marrone, the good racer and broodmare Catherine Marrone, and their brother Joe Marrone—who went to England but his progeny could not be entered into the GSB (his dam added four lines of Lexington RH along with other RH lines) as he was labeled as a half-breed.

Americus had good sons also, such as Golden Rod, sire of Irish Oaks winner Golden Maid. But of all of these great and good offspring, it is Americus Girl who stands above the rest—she has made Thoroughbred breeding history by providing the strongest dam-line in England in the twentieth century. When bred to the good English sire Sundridge she produced a filly named Lady Josephine, a Coventry stakes winner, who altered the course of British racing. Lady Josephine's strongest dominances are from two full sibling configurations: the Pocahontas sons Stockwell/Rataplan are 5x6x5x6x6, and they are usually credited by writers as the explanation for her lasting influence. Surely those Pocahontas sons are a significant portion of her genetic strength. However, equally strong—that means dominant—is the 4x4 placement of the full siblings Norfolk RH/The Nun RH—further The Nun RH rules one of Lady Josephine's X chromosomes. Adding to this potency is their dam Novice RH, whose dam Chloe Anderson RH is inbred 2x2 to full brothers by Sir Archy out of Transport RH. Curiously, this extremely potent configuration is very seldom (if ever) mentioned in the explaining the genetic power of this pillar of English racing. By their placement and numbers these sibling groups are equally dominant. Shouldn't these Lexington RH offspring be given the credit they are due for the tremendous potency found in this mare line? Especially seeing the dam of those two, Novice RH, is a ½ sister to Pocahontas—thereby providing the needed sex-balance for the Pocahontas's sons.

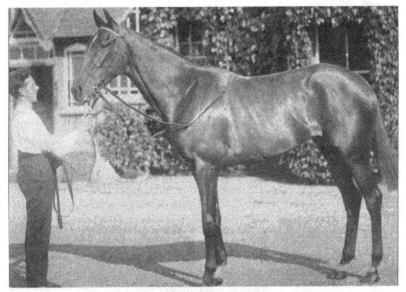

Lady Josephine 1912—one of the most significant English mares of the twentieth century is inbred 5x5 to Lexington RH. —TB Record

The *reine-de-course* Lady Josephine is a legend in Thoroughbred breeding, and all her progeny are valuable, even her least daughter Joyous, by Gay Crusader, was a good broodmare in Ireland.

Then there is her daughter Lady Juror by Son-in-Law, a stakes winning stayer. Lady Juror ('reine') also became an elite broodmare—she is the dam of Fair Trial, his ⅞ sister Riot, and the *reine* Sansonnet. Fair Trial, a sprinter of class, is also an important sire producing among others the great Court Martial, a modern pillar of the English TB (*chef*—sprint). Interesting for sport horse breeders is his son Courville—one of those jump transmitters found in warmbloods who is consistently identified by the European sport writers as a jump line. Riot produced the good mares Climax and Commotion. Commotion won the Oaks and produced well at stud including the great Hyperion son Aristophanes.

Then there is Sansonnet, by Sansovino, who is immortal as the dam of the great Tudor Minstrel. Tudor Minstrel is lauded as possibly the best miler to date; he is also a strong and powerful sire producing the great sire Sing Sing, the *reine* Mixed Marriage, and the great mare What a Treat, out of a Stymie mare (dam of Be My Guest). An interesting point for the sport horse breeders: the great dressage sire Lauries Crusador, who descends from Tudor Minstrel, carries at least twenty lines of Lexington RH, four of Blackburns Whip RH, and one of Hanover, and only two of those Lexington RH lines are through Tudor Minstrel. It is a startling revelation to find so many American Running Horse lines coming into the European warmblood product through the Trojan Horse of the English Thoroughbred before the Jersey Act.

Lady Juror retains the same dominance as her dam plus adds a strong filly factor from a son and daughter of the mare Seclusion 5x7. With Fair Trial, new powerful dominances are added to what his dam brought in the full siblings Sierra/Sainfoin 4x4, plus Rattlewings/Galliard 6x6 and some more Stockwell/Rataplan lines as well—he is a very potent sire.

If Lady Juror isn't fantastic enough—her ½ sister Mumtaz Mahal throws an even larger influence. A great racer, Mumtaz Mahal was definitely a sprinter, and it is often said she may be the fastest filly ever—although I believe our own Pan Zareta has her beat. Either way she was extremely fast; she is nicknamed the 'flying filly', and while our Pan Zareta left no offspring—England's Mumtaz Mahal has rewritten the studbook of racing with her progeny; she of course is a *reine*. She is dam of important sires Furrokh Siyar, Mizra II, French-bred Nizami (sire of the *reine* Grey Flight—see Chapter 21), and Badruddin (dam of Perfume II, the dam of My Babu). But like her mom it is her daughters who are the most influential.

Mumtaz Mahal 1921—one of the fastest horses ever. She has created a maternal dynasty of immense influence. —Thoroughbred Record.

Mah Mahal—also a *reine*—is the dam of Mah Iran who is the dam of the great champion Migoli; Mah Mahal is also the dam of the good sire Pherozshah and the dynasty builder Mahmoud, the English Derby winner and one of the greatest sires of twentieth century (*chef*), who came to America to stand stud, the first to return to us the Americus line. Her daughter Rustom Mahal is the dam of the good sire Kurdistan and the important sire Abernant (*chef*), a sprinter often found in sport horse pedigrees. It is Mumtaz Mahal's daughter Mumtaz Begum, only a moderate racer, who is off the charts as a producer (*reine-de-course*) with wonderful mares such as Sun Princess, the dam of Royal Charger; Malindi, a *reine* and dam of the important but unsound sire Prince Taj; and Malindi's full sister Rivaz. But her greatest fame is that she is the dam of the *chef-de-race* Nasrullah, who may end up being the most significant sire of the last fifty years. In international sport horse breeding he has no competition for the top title, he is found more often than any other line (Birdsall). It is significant that the best offspring of Mumtaz Begum are by Nearco, who brings in an additional line of Lexington RH on his dam-line, causing a nick with the Lexington RH double on the dam-line.

If you ever needed an example of the power of full sibling configurations in your pedigrees, than Mumtaz Mahal can prove this to you. Her pedigree dominances are: Clementina/Tadcaster 4x4, Norfolk RH/The Nun RH 5x6, and Stockwell/Rataplan 6x7x6x7x6x6x7x6x7x7.

It is ironic that in England during much of the Jersey Act Lady Josephine was rated the #1 most influential horse—right through 1930 (Faversham). In America her lines through Nasrullah/Mahmoud/Royal Charger made her very prominent here in the States from 1960 through 1980. British bloodstock historians downplay Orby's significance—saying he is only of fair class in Derby winners and sires—even though he produced a Derby winner and earned the elusive *chef-de-race* title. However they are at a loss to explain the reach of Americus, and therefore they seldom mention him at all when writing about their pride in Lady Josephine. Indeed, when Lady Josephine is discussed and her astounding influence as a foundation mare—possibly "the" foundation mare of the modern English TB—not one of them has credited any of her potency and enduring power to her dam-sire with his inbreeding to the full siblings Norfolk RH/The Nun RH. Yet, for all that, many will concede that the breeding performance of both Orby and Americus was largely responsible for the panic that led to the Jersey Act.

Those two lines, Orby and some of the progeny of Americus, were already in the GSB before 1913. What happened to American lines in Great Britain after that? Many American breeders had purchased or leased stables and stud farms in England and Ireland (and France) and invested heavily in their industries. The ban on racing in New York was lifted in 1912, so many of those American operations, after a short while, packed it all up and came home—it made no financial sense to stay there. You will find traces of the American-bred in the Half-Bred Stud Book—commonly called National Hunt horses. American-breds such as Sir Martin, Colin, Peter Pan, Sweep, Yankee, Hastings, Hamburg, and Hanover all left legacies, especially in hunt and steeplechase records.

Sir Martin 1906 for instance was a huge producer of National Hunt horses, with multiple winners of flat, steeplechase, and hurdle races. Why was he classified a half-bred? Because his dam was by Hanover, who is inbred to Vandal RH, plus carries lines of Lexington RH and Blackburns Whip RH. Hanover himself is well represented in the Half-bred studbook, for instance his daughter Mary Hanover was a celebrated producer of flat and jump horses in Britain. Sir Martin produced a fine sport horse in his daughter Reading. She was out of Tea Biscuit. If that name sounds familiar to you it is because she is the dam of Seabiscuit's sire Hard Tack, and she—Tea's Biscuit, dam of Hard Tack—ended up in England also. Reading 1918 was a great racer; she won three flat races, six hurdle races, and three steeplechases. She is inbred 3x3 to Hanover.

Sir Martin was a good stakes winner at home; he was rated the top US juvenile male of 1908, and then he was shipped to England that fall. He raced in both France and England as well, winning thirteen of thirty-two starts which includes the prestigious Coronation Cup. He stood there for a while and then was brought home to stand stud.

The Cad, a Hunter owned by Harry W. Smith, competed regularly in Ireland and at home—for fifteen years! —image from *Thoroughbred Types*

Prior to the Jersey Act, it wasn't just the full Thoroughbreds that competed and won all over Ireland and Britain; it was our Hunter Horses as well (see David Gray in Chapter 35 for an example). For an example here, the American sportsman Harry W. Smith competed regularly in Ireland on his home-bred Hunters. Such as The Cad pictured here, he is a Hunter-bred Lexington RH grandson, and with Smith he raced in steeplechase and participated in Hunter competitions for fifteen years in the late 1800s through the early-1900s in Ireland as well as at home. He may not be very pretty, but he was very athletic and sound.

Some other American-breds came to Britain during the Jersey Act—still banned as half-breds, they performed well but were barred from the GSB. A good example is Picric 1914, a mare bred by Foxhall Keene; she was taken to England/Ireland in 1923 and was a good producer. Her dam Gingham is by Domino. The mare Swinging Glance 1916 by Sweep was exported also in 1923, and she and her daughter Look Up by Ultimus (*chef*) produced well there—she is 3x3x4 to Domino. Look Up won two races, was second three times, and third in one. These mares are the second and third dams of the great stallion Roman.

Nonetheless, during the Jersey Act very few American-breds were found there. Evidently it was not too long after this that the Brits forgot why they put the Jersey Act in place, because according to Tony Morris (*Thoroughbred Stallions*) they were totally taken by surprise when Sir Ivor and those after him began appearing in Britain in the 1960s-70s. Sport horse breeders who wondered why they didn't find evidence of our great sport producers such as Fair Play and Black Toney for example in the European stars may now understand why. Did the absence of American lines from the greater European sport product make our American sport stars any less in ability and talent? No, in fact it is just the opposite.

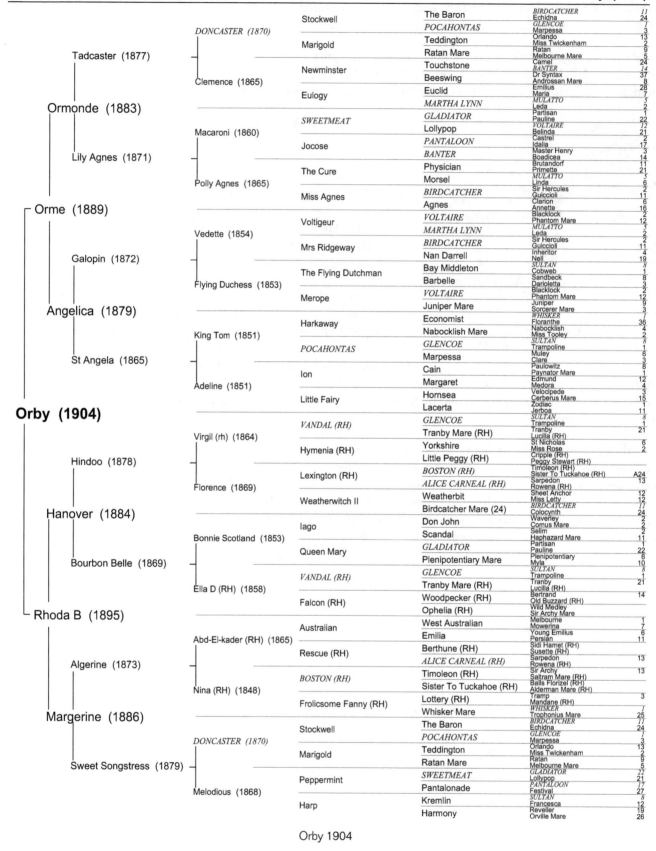

			Stockwell	The Baron	*BIRDCATCHER* 11 / Echidna 24
	DONCASTER (1870)			*POCAHONTAS*	*GLENCOE* 1 / Marpessa 3
			Marigold	Teddington	Orlando 13 / Miss Twickenham 2
Tadcaster (1877)				Ratan Mare	Ratan 9 / Melbourne Mare 5
			Newminster	Touchstone	Camel 24 / *BANTER* 14
	Clemence (1865)			Beeswing	Dr Syntax 37 / Androssan Mare 8
			Eulogy	Euclid	Emilius 28 / Maria 7
Ormonde (1883)				*MARTHA LYNN*	*MULATTO* 5 / Leda 2
		SWEETMEAT	*GLADIATOR*		Partisan 1 / Pauline 22
	Macaroni (1860)		Lollypop		*VOLTAIRE* 12 / Belinda 21
		Jocose	*PANTALOON*		Castrel 2 / Idalia 17
Lily Agnes (1871)			*BANTER*		Master Henry 3 / Boadicea 14
		The Cure	Physician		Brutandorf 11 / Primette 21
	Polly Agnes (1865)		Morsel		*MULATTO* 5 / Linda 6
		Miss Agnes	*BIRDCATCHER*		Sir Hercules 2 / Guiccioli 11
			Agnes		Clarion 6 / Annette 16
		Voltigeur	*VOLTAIRE*		Blacklock 2 / Phantom Mare 12
	Vedette (1854)		*MARTHA LYNN*		*MULATTO* 5 / Leda 2
		Mrs Ridgeway	*BIRDCATCHER*		Sir Hercules 2 / Guiccioli 11
Orme (1889)			Nan Darrell		Inheritor 4 / Nell 19
		The Flying Dutchman	Bay Middleton		*SULTAN* 8 / Cobweb 1
	Flying Duchess (1853)		Barbelle		Sandbeck 8 / Darioletta 3
		Merope	*VOLTAIRE*		Blacklock 2 / Phantom Mare 12
Galopin (1872)			Juniper Mare		Juniper 9 / Sorcerer Mare 3
		Harkaway	Economist		*WHISKER* 1 / Floranthe 36
	King Tom (1851)		Nabocklish Mare		Nabocklish 4 / Miss Tooley 2
		POCAHONTAS	*GLENCOE*		*SULTAN* 8 / Trampoline 1
Angelica (1879)			Marpessa		Muley 6 / Clare 3
		Ion	Cain		Paulowitz 8 / Paynator Mare 1
	Adeline (1851)		Margaret		Edmund 12 / Medora 4
		Little Fairy	Hornsea		Velocipede 3 / Cerberus Mare 15
St Angela (1865)			Lacerta		Zodiac 11 / Jerboa 11
		VANDAL (RH)	*GLENCOE*		*SULTAN* 8 / Trampoline 1
	Virgil (rh) (1864)		Tranby Mare (RH)		Tranby 21 / Lucilla (RH)
		Hymenia (RH)	Yorkshire		St Nicholas 6 / Miss Rose 2
Orby (1904)			Little Peggy (RH)		Cripple (RH) / Peggy Stewart (RH)
		Lexington (RH)	*BOSTON (RH)*		Timoleon (RH) / Sister To Tuckahoe (RH) A24
	Florence (1869)		*ALICE CARNEAL (RH)*		Sarpedon 13 / Rowena (RH)
Hindoo (1878)		Weatherwitch II	Weatherbit		Sheet Anchor 12 / Miss Letty 12
			Birdcatcher Mare (24)		*BIRDCATCHER* 11 / Colocynth 24
		Iago	Don John		Waverley 2 / Comus Mare 2
	Bonnie Scotland (1853)		Scandal		Selim 2 / Haphazard Mare 11
		Queen Mary	*GLADIATOR*		Partisan 1 / Pauline 22
Hanover (1884)			Plenipotentiary Mare		Plenipotentiary 6 / Myla 10
		VANDAL (RH)	*GLENCOE*		*SULTAN* 8 / Trampoline 1
	Ella D (RH) (1858)		Tranby Mare (RH)		Tranby 21 / Lucilla (RH)
		Falcon (RH)	Woodpecker (RH)		Bertrand 14 / Old Buzzard (RH)
Bourbon Belle (1869)			Ophelia (RH)		Wild Medley / Sir Archy Mare
		Australian	West Australian		Melbourne 1 / Mowerina 7
	Abd-El-kader (RH) (1865)		Emilia		Young Emilius 6 / Persian 11
		Rescue (RH)	Berthune (RH)		Sidi Hamet (RH) / Susette (RH)
Rhoda B (1895)			*ALICE CARNEAL (RH)*		Sarpedon 13 / Rowena (RH)
		BOSTON (RH)	Timoleon (RH)		Sir Archy 13 / Saltram Mare (RH)
	Nina (RH) (1848)		Sister To Tuckahoe (RH)		Balls Florizel (RH) / Alderman Mare (RH)
		Frolicsome Fanny (RH)	Lottery (RH)		Tramp 3 / Mandane (RH)
Algerine (1873)			Whisker Mare		*WHISKER* 1 / Trophonius Mare 25
		Stockwell	The Baron		*BIRDCATCHER* 11 / Echidna 24
	DONCASTER (1870)		*POCAHONTAS*		*GLENCOE* 1 / Marpessa 3
		Marigold	Teddington		Orlando 13 / Miss Twickenham 2
Margerine (1886)			Ratan Mare		Ratan 9 / Melbourne Mare 5
		Peppermint	*SWEETMEAT*		*GLADIATOR* 22 / Lollypop 21
	Melodious (1868)		Pantalonade		*PANTALOON* 17 / Festival 27
Sweet Songstress (1879)		Harp	Kremlin		*SULTAN* 8 / Francesca 12
			Harmony		Reveller 19 / Orville Mare 26

Orby 1904

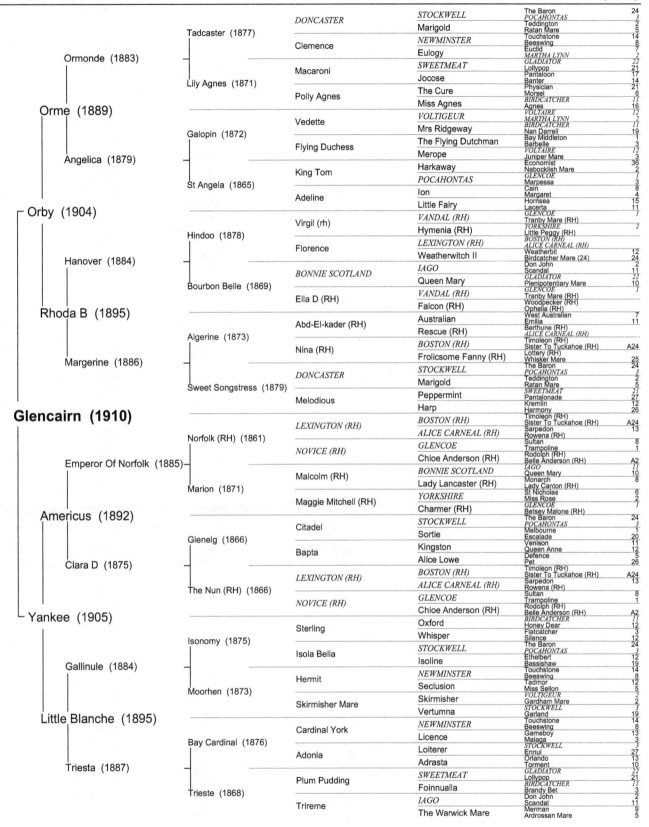

Glen Cairn 1910

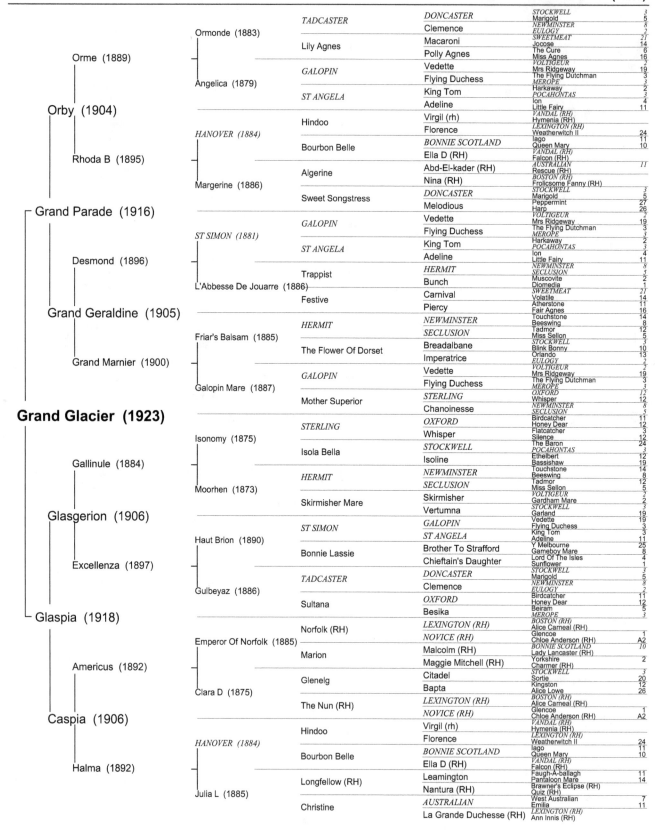

Grand Glacier (1923)

Grand Parade (1916)
- Orby (1904)
  - Orme (1889)
  - Rhoda B (1895)
- Grand Geraldine (1905)
  - Desmond (1896)
  - Grand Marnier (1900)

Glaspia (1918)
- Glasgerion (1906)
  - Gallinule (1884)
  - Excellenza (1897)
- Caspia (1906)
  - Americus (1892)
  - Halma (1892)

Orme (1889)
- Ormonde (1883)
  - TADCASTER
    - DONCASTER — *STOCKWELL* 3 / Marigold 5
    - Clemence — *NEWMINSTER* 8 / *EULOGY* 2
  - Lily Agnes
    - Macaroni — *SWEETMEAT* 21 / Jocose 14
    - Polly Agnes — The Cure 6 / Miss Agnes 16
- Angelica (1879)
  - GALOPIN
    - Vedette — *VOLTIGEUR* 2 / Mrs Ridgeway 19
    - Flying Duchess — The Flying Dutchman 3 / *MEROPE* 3
  - ST ANGELA
    - King Tom — Harkaway 2 / *POCAHONTAS* 3
    - Adeline — Ion 4 / Little Fairy 11

Rhoda B (1895)
- HANOVER (1884)
  - Hindoo
    - Virgil (rh) — *VANDAL (RH)* / Hymenia (RH)
    - Florence — *LEXINGTON (RH)* / Weatherwitch II 24
  - Bourbon Belle
    - BONNIE SCOTLAND — Iago 11 / Queen Mary 10
    - Ella D (RH) — *VANDAL (RH)* / Falcon (RH)
- Margerine (1886)
  - Algerine
    - Abd-El-kader (RH) — *AUSTRALIAN* / Rescue (RH) 11
    - Nina (RH) — *BOSTON (RH)* / Frolicsome Fanny (RH)
  - Sweet Songstress
    - DONCASTER — *STOCKWELL* 3 / Marigold 5
    - Melodious — Peppermint 27 / Harp 26

Desmond (1896)
- ST SIMON (1881)
  - GALOPIN
    - Vedette — *VOLTIGEUR* 2 / Mrs Ridgeway 19
    - Flying Duchess — The Flying Dutchman 3 / *MEROPE* 3
  - ST ANGELA
    - King Tom — Harkaway 2 / *POCAHONTAS* 3
    - Adeline — Ion 4 / Little Fairy 11
- L'Abbesse De Jouarre (1886)
  - Trappist
    - HERMIT — *NEWMINSTER* 8 / *SECLUSION* 5
    - Bunch — Muscovite 2 / Diomedia 1
  - Festive
    - Carnival — *SWEETMEAT* 21 / Volatile 14
    - Piercy — Atherstone 11 / Fair Agnes 16

Grand Marnier (1900)
- Friar's Balsam (1885)
  - HERMIT
    - NEWMINSTER — Touchstone 14 / Beeswing 8
    - SECLUSION — Tadmor 12 / Miss Sellon 5
  - The Flower Of Dorset
    - Breadalbane — *STOCKWELL* 3 / Blink Bonny 10
    - Imperatrice — Orlando 13 / *EULOGY* 2
- Galopin Mare (1887)
  - GALOPIN
    - Vedette — *VOLTIGEUR* 2 / Mrs Ridgeway 19
    - Flying Duchess — The Flying Dutchman 3 / *MEROPE* 3
  - Mother Superior
    - STERLING — *OXFORD* 12 / Whisper 12
    - Chanoinesse — *NEWMINSTER* 8 / *SECLUSION*

Gallinule (1884)
- Isonomy (1875)
  - STERLING
    - OXFORD — Birdcatcher 11 / Honey Dear 12
    - Whisper — Flatcatcher 3 / Silence 12
  - Isola Bella
    - STOCKWELL — The Baron 24 / *POCAHONTAS* 3
    - Isoline — Ethelbert 12 / Bassishaw 19
- Moorhen (1873)
  - HERMIT
    - NEWMINSTER — Touchstone 14 / Beeswing 8
    - SECLUSION — Tadmor 12 / Miss Sellon 5
  - Skirmisher Mare
    - Skirmisher — *VOLTIGEUR* 2 / Gardham Mare
    - Vertumna — *STOCKWELL* 3 / Garland 19

Excellenza (1897)
- Haut Brion (1890)
  - ST SIMON
    - GALOPIN — Vedette 19 / Flying Duchess 3
    - ST ANGELA — King Tom / Adeline 11
  - Bonnie Lassie
    - Brother To Strafford — Y Melbourne 25 / Gameboy Mare 8
    - Chieftain's Daughter — Lord Of The Isles 4 / Sunflower 1
- Gulbeyaz (1886)
  - TADCASTER
    - DONCASTER — *STOCKWELL* 3 / Marigold 5
    - Clemence — *NEWMINSTER* 8 / *EULOGY* 2
  - Sultana
    - OXFORD — Birdcatcher 11 / Honey Dear 12
    - Besika — Beiram 5 / *MEROPE* 3

Americus (1892)
- Emperor Of Norfolk (1885)
  - Norfolk (RH)
    - LEXINGTON (RH) — *BOSTON (RH)* / Alice Carneal (RH)
    - NOVICE (RH) — Glencoe 1 / Chloe Anderson (RH) A2
  - Marion
    - Malcolm (RH) — *BONNIE SCOTLAND* 10 / Lady Lancaster (RH)
    - Maggie Mitchell (RH) — Yorkshire 2 / Charmer (RH)
- Clara D (1875)
  - Glenelg
    - Citadel — *STOCKWELL* 3 / Sortie 20
    - Bapta — Kingston 12 / Alice Lowe 26
  - The Nun (RH)
    - LEXINGTON (RH) — *BOSTON (RH)* / Alice Carneal (RH)
    - NOVICE (RH) — Glencoe 1 / Chloe Anderson (RH) A2

Halma (1892)
- HANOVER (1884)
  - Hindoo
    - Virgil (rh) — *VANDAL (RH)* / Hymenia (RH)
    - Florence — *LEXINGTON (RH)* / Weatherwitch II 24
  - Bourbon Belle
    - BONNIE SCOTLAND — Iago 11 / Queen Mary 10
    - Ella D (RH) — *VANDAL (RH)* / Falcon (RH)
- Julia L (1885)
  - Longfellow (RH)
    - Leamington — Faugh-A-ballagh 11 / Pantaloon Mare 14
    - Nantura (RH) — Brawner's Eclipse (RH) / Quiz (RH)
  - Christine
    - AUSTRALIAN — West Australian 7 / Emilia 11
    - La Grande Duchesse (RH) — *LEXINGTON (RH)* / Ann Innis (RH)

Grand Glacier 1923

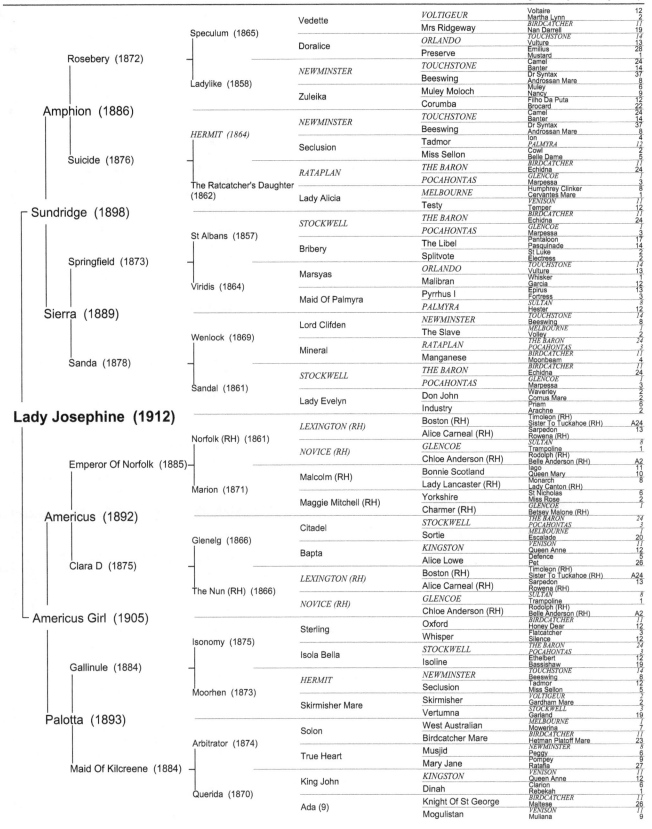

Lady Josphine 1912

Mumtaz Mahal (1921)

The Tetrarch (1911)

- **Roi Herode (1904)**
  - **Le Samaritain (1895)**
    - Le Sancy (1884)
      - Atlantic
        - THORMANBY — Windhound 3 / Alice Hawthorn 4
        - Hurricane — Wild Dayrell 7 / Midia 3
      - Gem Of Gems
        - Strathconan — NEWMINSTER 8 / Souvenir 11
        - Poinsettia — Y Melbourne 25 / LADY HAWTHORN 4
    - Clementina (1880)
      - DONCASTER
        - STOCKWELL — THE BARON 24 / POCAHONTAS 3
        - Marigold — Teddington 2 / Ratan Mare 5
      - CLEMENCE
        - NEWMINSTER — Touchstone 14 / Beeswing 8
        - Eulogy — Euclid 7 / Martha Lynn 2
  - **Roxelane (1894)**
    - War Dance (1887)
      - Galliard
        - Galopin — VEDETTE 19 / Flying Duchess 3
        - Mavis — MACARONI 14 / Beau Merle 13
      - War Paint
        - Uncas — STOCKWELL 3 / Nightingale 1
        - Piracy — Buccaneer 14 / Newminster Mare 1
    - Rose Of York (1880)
      - SPECULUM
        - VEDETTE — VOLTIGEUR 2 / Mrs Ridgeway 19
        - Doralice — ORLANDO 13 / Preserve 1
      - Rouge Rose
        - THORMANBY — Windhound 3 / Alice Hawthorn 4
        - Ellen Horne — Redshank 15 / Delhi 1

- **Vahren (1897)**
  - **Bona Vista (1889)**
    - Tadcaster (1877)
      - DONCASTER
        - STOCKWELL — THE BARON 24 / POCAHONTAS 3
        - Marigold — Teddington 2 / Ratan Mare 5
      - CLEMENCE
        - NEWMINSTER — Touchstone 14 / Beeswing 8
        - Eulogy — Euclid 7 / Martha Lynn 2
    - Vista (1879)
      - MACARONI
        - Sweetmeat — Gladiator 22 / Lollypop 21
        - Jocose — Pantaloon 17 / Banter 14
      - Verdure
        - KING TOM — Harkaway 2 / POCAHONTAS 3
        - May Bloom — NEWMINSTER 8 / LADY HAWTHORN 4
  - **Castania (1889)**
    - Hagioscope (1878)
      - SPECULUM
        - VEDETTE — VOLTIGEUR 2 / Mrs Ridgeway 19
        - Doralice — ORLANDO 13 / Preserve 1
      - Sophia
        - MACARONI — Sweetmeat 21 / Jocose 14
        - Zelle — STOCKWELL 3 / Babette 23
    - Rose Garden (1878)
      - Kingcraft
        - KING TOM — Harkaway 2 / POCAHONTAS 3
        - Woodcraft — VOLTIGEUR 2 / Venison Mare 11
      - Eglentyne
        - HERMIT — NEWMINSTER 8 / Seclusion 5
        - Mabille — Parmesan 7 / Rigolboche 2

Mumtaz Mahal (1921)

Lady Josephine (1912)

- **Sundridge (1898)**
  - **Amphion (1886)**
    - Rosebery (1872)
      - SPECULUM
        - VEDETTE — VOLTIGEUR 2 / Mrs Ridgeway 19
        - Doralice — ORLANDO 13 / Preserve 1
      - Ladylike
        - NEWMINSTER — Touchstone 14 / Beeswing 8
        - Zuleika — Muley Moloch 9 / Corumba 22
    - Suicide (1876)
      - HERMIT
        - NEWMINSTER — Touchstone 14 / Beeswing 8
        - Seclusion — Tadmor 12 / Miss Sellon 5
      - The Ratcatcher's Daughter
        - RATAPLAN — THE BARON 24 / POCAHONTAS 3
        - Lady Alicia — Melbourne 1 / Testy 12
  - **Sierra (1889)**
    - Springfield (1873)
      - St Albans
        - STOCKWELL — THE BARON 24 / POCAHONTAS 3
        - Bribery — The Libel 14 / Splitvote 2
      - Viridis
        - Marsyas — ORLANDO 13 / Malibran 12
        - Maid Of Palmyra — Pyrrhus I 3 / Palmyra 12
    - Sanda (1878)
      - Wenlock
        - Lord Clifden — NEWMINSTER 8 / The Slave 2
        - Mineral — RATAPLAN 3 / Manganese 4
      - Sandal
        - STOCKWELL — THE BARON 24 / POCAHONTAS 3
        - Lady Evelyn — Don John 2 / Industry 2

- **Americus Girl (1905)**
  - **Americus (1892)**
    - Emperor Of Norfolk (1885)
      - Norfolk (RH)
        - LEXINGTON (RH) — Boston (RH) / Alice Carneal (RH)
        - NOVICE (RH) — Glencoe 1 / Chloe Anderson (RH) A2
      - Marion
        - Malcolm (RH) — Bonnie Scotland 10 / Lady Lancaster (RH)
        - Maggie Mitchell (RH) — Yorkshire 2 / Charmer (RH)
    - Clara D (1875)
      - Glenelg
        - Citadel — STOCKWELL 3 / Sortie 20
        - Bapta — KINGSTON 12 / Alice Lowe 26
      - The Nun (RH)
        - LEXINGTON (RH) — Boston (RH) / Alice Carneal (RH)
        - NOVICE (RH) — Glencoe 1 / Chloe Anderson (RH) A2
  - **Palotta (1893)**
    - Gallinule (1884)
      - Isonomy
        - Sterling — Oxford 12 / Whisper 12
        - Isola Bella — STOCKWELL 3 / Isoline 19
      - Moorhen
        - HERMIT — NEWMINSTER 8 / Seclusion 5
        - Skirmisher Mare — Skirmisher 5 / Vertumna 19
    - Maid Of Kilcreene (1884)
      - Arbitrator
        - Solon — West Australian 7 / Birdcatcher Mare 23
        - True Heart — Musjid 6 / Mary Jane 27
      - Querida
        - King John — KINGSTON 12 / Dinah 1
        - Ada (9) — Knight Of St George 26 / Mogulistan 9

Mumtaz Mahal 1921

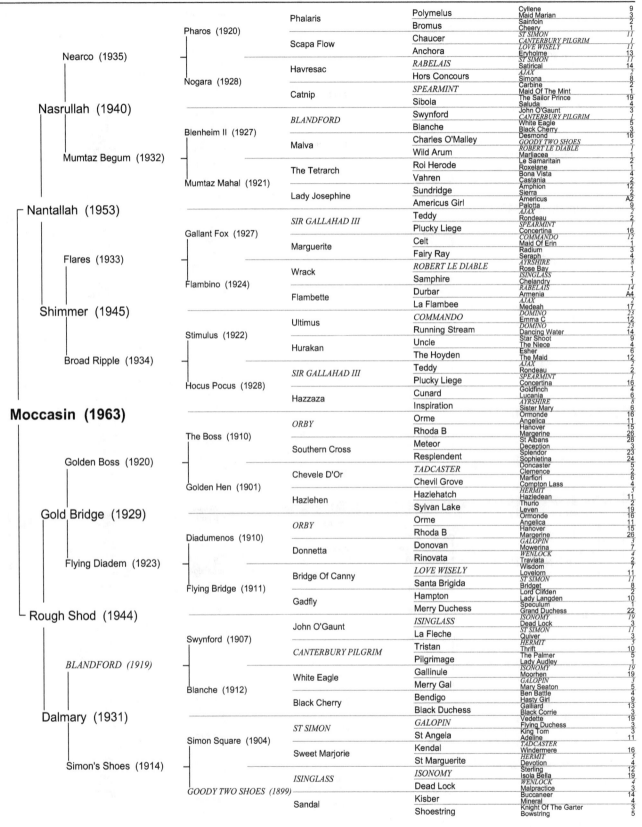

		Phalaris	Polymelus	Cyllene	9
				Maid Marian	3
	Pharos (1920)		Bromus	Sainfoin	1
				Cheery	1
Nearco (1935)		Scapa Flow	Chaucer	*ST SIMON*	11
				CANTERBURY PILGRIM	1
			Anchora	*LOVE WISELY*	11
				Eryholme	13
		Havresac	*RABELAIS*	*ST SIMON*	11
	Nogara (1928)			Satirical	14
			Hors Concours	*AJAX*	2
				Simona	8
		Catnip	*SPEARMINT*	Carbine	2
				Maid Of The Mint	1
Nasrullah (1940)			Sibola	The Sailor Prince	19
				Saluda	4
		BLANDFORD	Swynford	John O'Gaunt	3
				CANTERBURY PILGRIM	1
	Blenheim II (1927)		Blanche	White Eagle	5
				Black Cherry	3
		Malva	Charles O'Malley	Desmond	16
Mumtaz Begum (1932)				*GOODY TWO SHOES*	5
			Wild Arum	*ROBERT LE DIABLE*	1
				Marliacea	1
	Mumtaz Mahal (1921)	The Tetrarch	Roi Herode	Le Samaritain	2
				Roxelane	1
			Vahren	Bona Vista	4
				Castania	2
Nantallah (1953)		Lady Josephine	Sundridge	Amphion	12
				Sierra	A2
			Americus Girl	Americus	9
				Palotta	2
		SIR GALLAHAD III	Teddy	*AJAX*	2
				Rondeau	2
	Gallant Fox (1927)		Plucky Liege	*SPEARMINT*	1
				Concertina	16
		Marguerite	Celt	*COMMANDO*	12
Flares (1933)				Maid Of Erin	1
			Fairy Ray	Radium	3
				Seraph	4
		Wrack	*ROBERT LE DIABLE*	*AYRSHIRE*	8
				Rose Bay	1
	Flambino (1924)		Samphire	*ISINGLASS*	3
				Chelandry	1
		Flambette	Durbar	*RABELAIS*	14
Shimmer (1945)				Armenia	A4
			La Flambee	*AJAX*	2
				Medeah	17
		Ultimus	*COMMANDO*	*DOMINO*	23
				Emma C	12
	Stimulus (1922)		Running Stream	*DOMINO*	23
				Dancing Water	14
		Hurakan	Uncle	Star Shoot	9
				The Niece	4
			The Hoyden	Esher	6
Broad Ripple (1934)				The Maid	12
		SIR GALLAHAD III	Teddy	*AJAX*	2
				Rondeau	2
	Hocus Pocus (1928)		Plucky Liege	*SPEARMINT*	1
				Concertina	16
		Hazzaza	Cunard	Goldfinch	4
				Lucania	6
			Inspiration	*AYRSHIRE*	8
				Sister Mary	6
		ORBY	Orme	Ormonde	16
				Angelica	11
	The Boss (1910)		Rhoda B	Hanover	15
				Margerine	26
		Southern Cross	Meteor	St Albans	28
				Deception	3
			Resplendent	Splendor	23
Golden Boss (1920)				Sophietina	24
		Chevele D'Or	*TADCASTER*	Doncaster	5
				Clemence	2
	Golden Hen (1901)		Chevil Grove	Marfiori	6
				Compton Lass	4
		Hazlehen	Hazlehatch	*HERMIT*	11
				Hazledean	11
			Sylvan Lake	Thurio	2
				Leven	19
		ORBY	Orme	Ormonde	16
				Angelica	11
	Diadumenos (1910)		Rhoda B	Hanover	15
Gold Bridge (1929)				Margerine	26
		Donnetta	Donovan	*GALOPIN*	7
				Mowerina	7
			Rinovata	*WENLOCK*	4
				Traviata	2
		Bridge Of Canny	*LOVE WISELY*	Wisdom	7
Flying Diadem (1923)				Lovelorn	11
			Santa Brigida	*ST SIMON*	11
	Flying Bridge (1911)			Bridget	8
		Gadfly	Hampton	Lord Clifden	2
				Lady Langden	10
			Merry Duchess	Speculum	1
				Grand Duchess	22
		John O'Gaunt	*ISINGLASS*	*ISONOMY*	19
				Dead Lock	3
	Swynford (1907)		La Fleche	*ST SIMON*	11
				Quiver	3
		CANTERBURY PILGRIM	Tristan	*HERMIT*	5
Rough Shod (1944)				Thrift	10
			Pilgrimage	The Palmer	5
				Lady Audley	1
		White Eagle	Gallinule	*ISONOMY*	19
				Moorhen	19
BLANDFORD (1919)	Blanche (1912)		Merry Gal	*GALOPIN*	3
				Mary Seaton	5
		Black Cherry	Bendigo	Ben Battle	4
				Hasty Girl	9
			Black Duchess	Galliard	13
				Black Corrie	3
Dalmary (1931)		*ST SIMON*	*GALOPIN*	Vedette	19
				Flying Duchess	3
	Simon Square (1904)		St Angela	King Tom	3
				Adeline	11
		Sweet Marjorie	Kendal	*TADCASTER*	1
				Windermere	16
Simon's Shoes (1914)			St Marguerite	*HERMIT*	5
				Devotion	4
		ISINGLASS	*ISONOMY*	Sterling	12
				Isola Bella	19
GOODY TWO SHOES (1899)			Dead Lock	*WENLOCK*	4
				Malpractice	3
		Sandal	Kisber	Buccaneer	14
				Mineral	4
			Shoestring	Knight Of The Garter	3
				Bowstring	5

Mocassin 1963

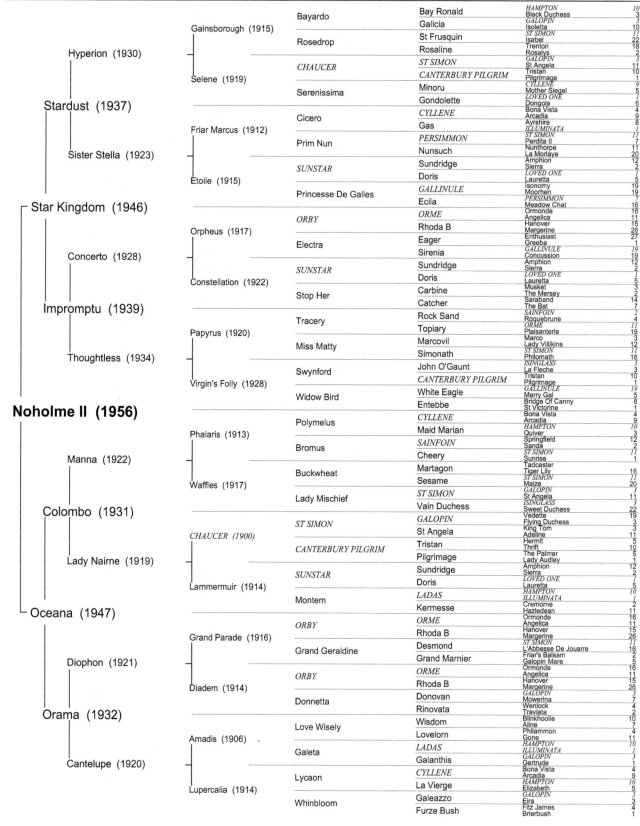

Noholme II (1956)

- **Star Kingdom (1946)**
  - **Stardust (1937)**
    - **Hyperion (1930)**
      - Gainsborough (1915)
        - Bayardo — Bay Ronald — *HAMPTON* 10 / Black Duchess 3
        - Bayardo — Galicia — *GALOPIN* / Isoletta 10
        - Rosedrop — St Frusquin — *ST SIMON* 11 / Isabel 22
        - Rosedrop — Rosaline — Trenton 18 / Rosalys 2
      - Selene (1919)
        - *CHAUCER* — *ST SIMON* — *GALOPIN* 3 / St Angela 11
        - *CHAUCER* — *CANTERBURY PILGRIM* — Tristan 10 / Pilgrimage 1
        - Serenissima — Minoru — *CYLLENE* 9 / Mother Siegel 5
        - Serenissima — Gondolette — *LOVED ONE* 1 / Dongola 6
    - **Sister Stella (1923)**
      - Friar Marcus (1912)
        - Cicero — *CYLLENE* — Bona Vista 4 / Arcadia 9
        - Cicero — Gas — Ayrshire 8 / *ILLUMINATA* 1
        - Prim Nun — *PERSIMMON* — *ST SIMON* 11 / Perdita II 7
        - Prim Nun — Nunsuch — Nunthorpe 11 / La Morlaye 20
      - Etoile (1915)
        - *SUNSTAR* — Sundridge — Amphion 12 / Sierra 2
        - *SUNSTAR* — Doris — *LOVED ONE* 1 / Lauretta 5
        - Princesse De Galles — *GALLINULE* — Isonomy 19 / Moorhen 19
        - Princesse De Galles — Ecila — *PERSIMMON* 7 / Meadow Chat 16
  - **Impromptu (1939)**
    - **Concerto (1928)**
      - Orpheus (1917)
        - *ORBY* — *ORME* — Ormonde 16 / Angelica 11
        - *ORBY* — Rhoda B — Hanover 15 / Margerine 26
        - Electra — Eager — Enthusiast 27 / Greeba 1
        - Electra — Sirenia — *GALLINULE* 19 / Concussion 19
      - Constellation (1922)
        - *SUNSTAR* — Sundridge — Amphion 12 / Sierra 2
        - *SUNSTAR* — Doris — *LOVED ONE* 1 / Lauretta 7
        - Stop Her — Carbine — Musket 5 / The Mersey 3
        - Stop Her — Catcher — Saraband 14 / The Bat 7
    - **Thoughtless (1934)**
      - Papyrus (1920)
        - Tracery — Rock Sand — *SAINFOIN* 2 / Roquebrune 4
        - Tracery — Topiary — *ORME* 11 / Plaisanterie 19
        - Miss Matty — Marcovil — Marco 3 / Lady Villikins 12
        - Miss Matty — Simonath — *ST SIMON* 11 / Philomath 16
      - Virgin's Folly (1928)
        - Swynford — John O'Gaunt — *ISINGLASS* 3 / La Fleche 3
        - Swynford — *CANTERBURY PILGRIM* — Tristan 10 / Pilgrimage 1
        - Widow Bird — White Eagle — *GALLINULE* 19 / Merry Gal 5
        - Widow Bird — Entebbe — Bridge Of Canny 8 / St Victorine 1
- **Oceana (1947)**
  - **Colombo (1931)**
    - **Manna (1922)**
      - Phalaris (1913)
        - Polymelus — *CYLLENE* — Bona Vista 4 / Arcadia 9
        - Polymelus — Maid Marian — *HAMPTON* 10 / Quiver 3
        - Bromus — *SAINFOIN* — Springfield 12 / Sanda 2
        - Bromus — Cheery — *ST SIMON* 11 / Sunrise 1
      - Waffles (1917)
        - Buckwheat — Martagon — Tadcaster 16 / Tiger Lily 16
        - Buckwheat — Sesame — *ST SIMON* 11 / Maize 20
        - Lady Mischief — *ST SIMON* — *GALOPIN* 3 / St Angela 11
        - Lady Mischief — Vain Duchess — *ISINGLASS* 3 / Sweet Duchess 22
    - **Lady Nairne (1919)**
      - *CHAUCER (1900)*
        - *ST SIMON* — *GALOPIN* — Vedette 19 / Flying Duchess 3
        - *ST SIMON* — St Angela — King Tom 3 / Adeline 11
        - *CANTERBURY PILGRIM* — Tristan — Hermit 5 / Thrift 10
        - *CANTERBURY PILGRIM* — Pilgrimage — The Palmer 5 / Lady Audley 1
      - Lammermuir (1914)
        - *SUNSTAR* — Sundridge — Amphion 12 / Sierra 2
        - *SUNSTAR* — Doris — *LOVED ONE* 1 / Lauretta 5
        - Montem — *LADAS* — *HAMPTON* 10 / *ILLUMINATA* 1
        - Montem — Kermesse — Cremorne 2 / Hazledean 11
  - **Orama (1932)**
    - **Diophon (1921)**
      - Grand Parade (1916)
        - *ORBY* — *ORME* — Ormonde 16 / Angelica 11
        - *ORBY* — Rhoda B — Hanover 15 / Margerine 26
        - Grand Geraldine — Desmond — *ST SIMON* 11 / L'Abbesse De Jouarre 16
        - Grand Geraldine — Grand Marnier — Friar's Balsam 2 / Galopin Mare 5
      - Diadem (1914)
        - *ORBY* — *ORME* — Ormonde 16 / Angelica 11
        - *ORBY* — Rhoda B — Hanover 15 / Margerine 26
        - Donnetta — Donovan — *GALOPIN* 3 / Mowerina 7
        - Donnetta — Rinovata — Wenlock 4 / Traviata 2
    - **Cantelupe (1920)**
      - Amadis (1906)
        - Love Wisely — Wisdom — Blinkhoolie 10 / Aline 7
        - Love Wisely — Lovelorn — Philammon 4 / Gone 11
        - Galeta — *LADAS* — *HAMPTON* 10 / *ILLUMINATA* 1
        - Galeta — Galanthis — *GALOPIN* 3 / Gertrude 1
      - Lupercalia (1914)
        - Lycaon — *CYLLENE* — Bona Vista 4 / Arcadia 9
        - Lycaon — La Vierge — *HAMPTON* 10 / Elizabeth 5
        - Whinbloom — Galeazzo — *GALOPIN* 3 / Eira 3
        - Whinbloom — Furze Bush — Fitz James 4 / Brierbush 1

Noholme II 1956

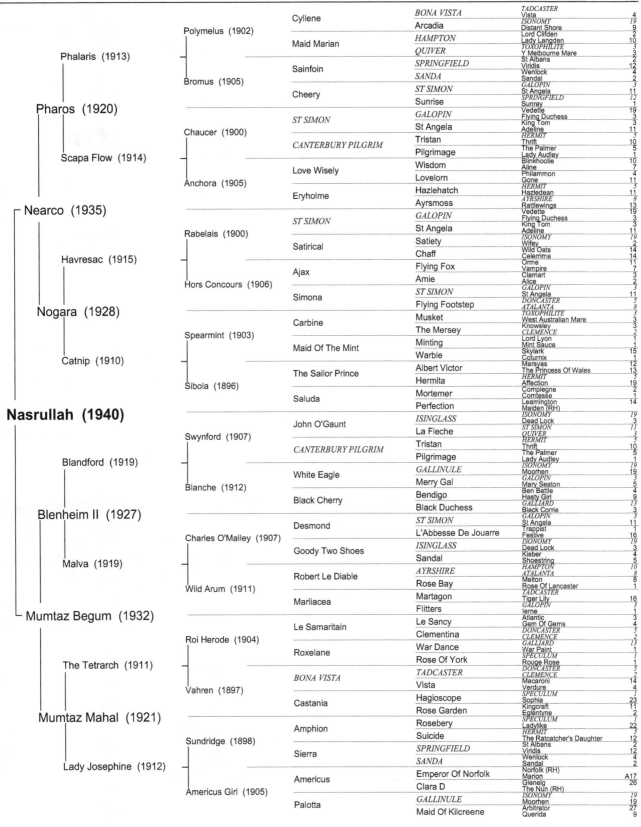

Nasrullah (1940)

- Nearco (1935)
  - Pharos (1920)
    - Phalaris (1913)
    - Scapa Flow (1914)
  - Nogara (1928)
    - Havresac (1915)
    - Catnip (1910)
- Mumtaz Begum (1932)
  - Blenheim II (1927)
    - Blandford (1919)
    - Malva (1919)
  - Mumtaz Mahal (1921)
    - The Tetrarch (1911)
    - Lady Josephine (1912)

Polymelus (1902)

Cyllene	*BONA VISTA*	*TADCASTER* —
		Vista — 4
	Arcadia	*ISONOMY* — 19
		Distant Shore — 9
Maid Marian	*HAMPTON*	Lord Clifden — 2
		Lady Langden — 10
	QUIVER	*TOXOPHILITE* — 3
		Y Melbourne Mare — 3

Bromus (1905)

Sainfoin	*SPRINGFIELD*	St Albans — 2
		Viridis — 12
	SANDA	Wenlock — 4
		Sandal — 2
Cheery	*ST SIMON*	*GALOPIN* — 3
		St Angela — 11
	Sunrise	*SPRINGFIELD* — 12
		Sunray — 1

Chaucer (1900)

ST SIMON	*GALOPIN*	Vedette — 19
		Flying Duchess — 3
	St Angela	King Tom — 3
		Adeline — 11
CANTERBURY PILGRIM	Tristan	*HERMIT* — 5
		Thrift — 10
	Pilgrimage	The Palmer — 5
		Lady Audley — 1

Anchora (1905)

Love Wisely	Wisdom	Blinkhoolie — 10
		Aline — 7
	Lovelorn	Philammon — 4
		Gone — 11
Eryholme	Hazlehatch	*HERMIT* — 5
		Hazledean — 11
	Ayrsmoss	*AYRSHIRE* — 8
		Rattlewings — 13

Rabelais (1900)

ST SIMON	*GALOPIN*	Vedette — 19
		Flying Duchess — 3
	St Angela	King Tom — 3
		Adeline — 11
Satirical	Satiety	*ISONOMY* — 19
		Wifey — 2
	Chaff	Wild Oats — 14
		Celerrima — 14

Hors Concours (1906)

Ajax	Flying Fox	Orme — 11
		Vampire — 7
	Amie	Clamart — 3
		Alice — 2
Simona	*ST SIMON*	*GALOPIN* — 3
		St Angela — 11
	Flying Footstep	*DONCASTER* — 5
		ATALANTA — 8

Spearmint (1903)

Carbine	Musket	*TOXOPHILITE* — 3
		West Australian Mare — 3
	The Mersey	Knowsley — 3
		CLEMENCE — 1
Maid Of The Mint	Minting	Lord Lyon — 1
		Mint Sauce — 15
	Warble	Skylark — 1
		Coturnix — 12

Sibola (1896)

The Sailor Prince	Albert Victor	Marsyas — 13
		The Princess Of Wales —
	Hermita	*HERMIT* — 19
		Affection — 2
Saluda	Mortemer	Compiegne — 1
		Comtesse — 14
	Perfection	Leamington —
		Maiden (RH) —

Swynford (1907)

John O'Gaunt	*ISINGLASS*	*ISONOMY* — 19
		Dead Lock — 3
	La Fleche	*ST SIMON* — 11
		QUIVER — 3
CANTERBURY PILGRIM	Tristan	*HERMIT* — 5
		Thrift — 10
	Pilgrimage	The Palmer — 5
		Lady Audley — 1

Blanche (1912)

White Eagle	*GALLINULE*	*ISONOMY* — 19
		Moorhen — 19
	Merry Gal	*GALOPIN* — 3
		Mary Seaton — 5
Black Cherry	Bendigo	Ben Battle — 4
		Hasty Girl — 9
	Black Duchess	*GALLIARD* — 13
		Black Corrie — 3

Charles O'Malley (1907)

Desmond	*ST SIMON*	*GALOPIN* — 3
		St Angela — 11
	L'Abbesse De Jouarre	Trappist — 1
		Festive — 16
Goody Two Shoes	*ISINGLASS*	*ISONOMY* — 19
		Dead Lock — 3
	Sandal	Kisber — 4
		Shoestring — 3

Wild Arum (1911)

Robert Le Diable	*AYRSHIRE*	*HAMPTON* — 10
		ATALANTA — 8
	Rose Bay	Melton — 8
		Rose Of Lancaster — 1
Marliacea	Martagon	*TADCASTER* — 16
		Tiger Lily —
	Flitters	*GALOPIN* — 3
		Ierne — 3

Roi Herode (1904)

Le Samaritain	Le Sancy	Atlantic — 3
		Gem Of Gems — 4
	Clementina	*DONCASTER* — 5
		CLEMENCE — 2
Roxelane	War Dance	*GALLIARD* — 13
		War Paint — 1
	Rose Of York	*SPECULUM* — 1
		Rouge Rose — 1

Vahren (1897)

BONA VISTA	*TADCASTER*	*DONCASTER* — 5
		CLEMENCE — 2
	Vista	Macaroni — 14
		Verdure — 4
Castania	Hagioscope	*SPECULUM* — 1
		Sophia — 23
	Rose Garden	Kingcraft — 11
		Eglentyne — 2

Sundridge (1898)

Amphion	Rosebery	*SPECULUM* — 1
		Ladylike — 22
	Suicide	*HERMIT* — 5
		The Ratcatcher's Daughter — 12
Sierra	*SPRINGFIELD*	St Albans — 2
		Viridis — 12
	SANDA	Wenlock — 4
		Sandal — 2

Americus Girl (1905)

Americus	Emperor Of Norfolk	Norfolk (RH) —
		Marion — A17
	Clara D	Glenelg — 26
		The Nun (RH) —
Palotta	*GALLINULE*	*ISONOMY* — 19
		Moorhen — 19
	Maid Of Kilcreene	Arbitrator — 27
		Querida — 9

Nasrullah 1940

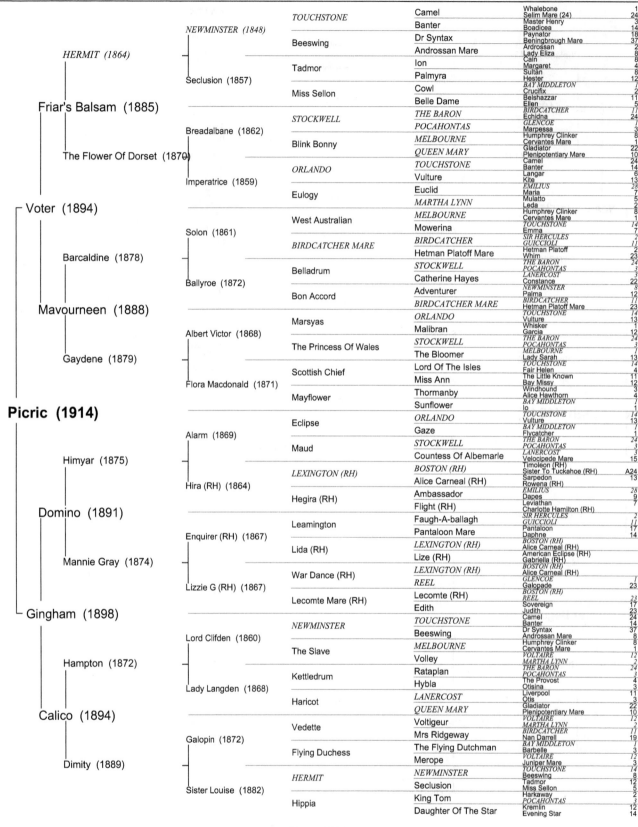

			Whalebone	1
NEWMINSTER (1848)	TOUCHSTONE	Camel	Selim Mare (24)	24
		Banter	Master Henry	3
			Boadicea	14
	Beeswing	Dr Syntax	Paynator	18
HERMIT (1864)			Beningbrough Mare	37
		Androssan Mare	Ardrossan	2
			Lady Eliza	8
	Tadmor	Ion	Cain	8
Seclusion (1857)			Margaret	4
		Palmyra	Sultan	8
			Hester	12
	Miss Sellon	Cowl	BAY MIDDLETON	1
			Crucifix	2
		Belle Dame	Belshazzar	11
			Ellen	5

Friar's Balsam (1885)

			BIRDCATCHER	11
Breadalbane (1862)	STOCKWELL	THE BARON	Echidna	24
		POCAHONTAS	GLENCOE	1
			Marpessa	3
	Blink Bonny	MELBOURNE	Humphrey Clinker	8
			Cervantes Mare	2
		QUEEN MARY	Gladiator	22
			Plenipotentiary Mare	10
	ORLANDO	TOUCHSTONE	Camel	24
Imperatrice (1859)			Banter	14
		Vulture	Langar	6
			Kite	13
	Eulogy	Euclid	EMILIUS	28
			Maria	7
		MARTHA LYNN	Mulatto	5
			Leda	2

The Flower Of Dorset (1870)

Voter (1894)

			Humphrey Clinker	8
Solon (1861)	West Australian	MELBOURNE	Cervantes Mare	1
		Mowerina	TOUCHSTONE	14
			Emma	7
	BIRDCATCHER MARE	BIRDCATCHER	SIR HERCULES	2
			GUICCIOLI	11
		Hetman Platoff Mare	Hetman Platoff	2
			Whim	23

Barcaldine (1878)

			THE BARON	24
Ballyroe (1872)	Belladrum	STOCKWELL	POCAHONTAS	3
		Catherine Hayes	LANERCOST	3
			Constance	22
	Bon Accord	Adventurer	NEWMINSTER	8
			Palma	12
		BIRDCATCHER MARE	BIRDCATCHER	11
			Hetman Platoff Mare	23

Mavourneen (1888)

			TOUCHSTONE	14
Albert Victor (1868)	Marsyas	ORLANDO	Vulture	13
		Malibran	Whisker	1
			Garcia	12
	The Princess Of Wales	STOCKWELL	THE BARON	24
			POCAHONTAS	3
		The Bloomer	MELBOURNE	1
			Lady Sarah	13
Flora Macdonald (1871)	Scottish Chief	Lord Of The Isles	TOUCHSTONE	14
			Fair Helen	4
		Miss Ann	The Little Known	11
			Bay Missy	12
	Mayflower	Thormanby	Windhound	3
			Alice Hawthorn	4
		Sunflower	BAY MIDDLETON	1
			Io	1

Gaydene (1879)

Picric (1914)

			TOUCHSTONE	14
Alarm (1869)	Eclipse	ORLANDO	Vulture	13
		Gaze	BAY MIDDLETON	1
			Flycatcher	1
	Maud	STOCKWELL	THE BARON	24
			POCAHONTAS	3
		Countess Of Albemarle	LANERCOST	3
			Velocipede Mare	15

Himyar (1875)

			Timoleon (RH)	
Hira (RH) (1864)	LEXINGTON (RH)	BOSTON (RH)	Sister To Tuckahoe (RH)	A24
		Alice Carneal (RH)	Sarpedon	13
			Rowena (RH)	
	Hegira (RH)	Ambassador	EMILIUS	28
			Dapes	9
		Flight (RH)	Leviathan	7
			Charlotte Hamilton (RH)	

Domino (1891)

			SIR HERCULES	2
Enquirer (RH) (1867)	Leamington	Faugh-A-ballagh	GUICCIOLI	11
		Pantaloon Mare	Pantaloon	17
			Daphne	14
	Lida (RH)	LEXINGTON (RH)	BOSTON (RH)	
			Alice Carneal (RH)	
		Lize (RH)	American Eclipse (RH)	
			Gabriella (RH)	

Mannie Gray (1874)

			BOSTON (RH)	
Lizzie G (RH) (1867)	War Dance (RH)	LEXINGTON (RH)	Alice Carneal (RH)	
		REEL	GLENCOE	1
			Galopade	23
	Lecomte Mare (RH)	Lecomte (RH)	BOSTON (RH)	
			REEL	23
		Edith	Sovereign	17
			Judith	23

Gingham (1898)

			Camel	24
Lord Clifden (1860)	NEWMINSTER	TOUCHSTONE	Banter	14
		Beeswing	Dr Syntax	37
			Androssan Mare	8
	The Slave	MELBOURNE	Humphrey Clinker	8
			Cervantes Mare	1
		Volley	VOLTAIRE	12
			MARTHA LYNN	2
Lady Langden (1868)	Kettledrum	Rataplan	THE BARON	24
			POCAHONTAS	3
		Hybla	The Provost	4
			Otisina	3
	Haricot	LANERCOST	Liverpool	11
			Otis	3
		QUEEN MARY	Gladiator	22
			Plenipotentiary Mare	10

Hampton (1872)

			VOLTAIRE	12
Galopin (1872)	Vedette	Voltigeur	MARTHA LYNN	2
		Mrs Ridgeway	BIRDCATCHER	11
			Nan Darrell	19
	Flying Duchess	The Flying Dutchman	BAY MIDDLETON	1
			Barbelle	3
		Merope	VOLTAIRE	12
			Juniper Mare	3

Calico (1894)

			TOUCHSTONE	14
Sister Louise (1882)	HERMIT	NEWMINSTER	Beeswing	8
		Seclusion	Tadmor	12
			Miss Sellon	5
	Hippia	King Tom	Harkaway	2
			POCAHONTAS	3
		Daughter Of The Star	Kremlin	12
			Evening Star	14

Dimity (1889)

Picric 1914

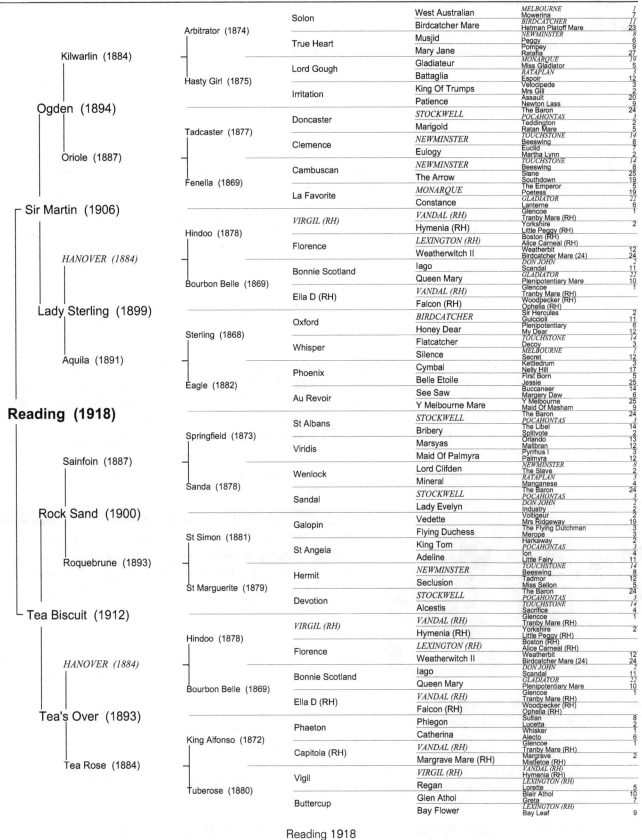

Kilwarlin (1884)	Arbitrator (1874)	Solon	*MELBOURNE* 1
			Mowerina 7
			BIRDCATCHER 11
		Birdcatcher Mare	Hetman Platoff Mare 23
		True Heart	*NEWMINSTER* 8
			Peggy 6
		Musjid	Pompey 9
		Mary Jane	Ratafia 27
Ogden (1894)	Hasty Girl (1875)	Lord Gough	*MONARQUE* 19
		Gladiateur	Miss Gladiator 5
			RATAPLAN 12
		Battaglia	Espoir 3
		Irritation	Velocipede 2
		King Of Trumps	Mrs Gill
			Assault 20
		Patience	Newton Lass 9
Oriole (1887)	Tadcaster (1877)	Doncaster	The Baron 24
		STOCKWELL 3
			POCAHONTAS
		Marigold	Teddington 5
			Ratan Mare
		Clemence	*TOUCHSTONE* 14
		NEWMINSTER	Beeswing 8
			Euclid 7
		Eulogy	Martha Lynn 2
Sir Martin (1906)	Fenella (1869)	Cambuscan	*TOUCHSTONE* 14
		NEWMINSTER	Beeswing 8
			Slane 25
		The Arrow	Southdown 19
		La Favorite	The Emperor 5
		MONARQUE	Poetess 19
			GLADIATOR 22
		Constance	Lanterne 6
HANOVER (1884)	Hindoo (1878)	*VIRGIL (RH)*	Glencoe 1
		VANDAL (RH)	Tranby Mare (RH)
			Yorkshire 2
		Hymenia (RH)	Little Peggy (RH)
		Florence	Boston (RH)
		LEXINGTON (RH)	Alice Carneal (RH)
			Weatherbit 12
		Weatherwitch II	Birdcatcher Mare (24) 24
Lady Sterling (1899)	Bourbon Belle (1869)	Bonnie Scotland	*DON JOHN* 2
		Iago	Scandal 11
			GLADIATOR 22
		Queen Mary	Plenipotentiary Mare 10
		Ella D (RH)	Glencoe 1
		VANDAL (RH)	Tranby Mare (RH)
			Woodpecker (RH)
		Falcon (RH)	Ophelia (RH)
Aquila (1891)	Sterling (1868)	Oxford	Sir Hercules 2
		BIRDCATCHER	Guiccioli 11
			Plenipotentiary 6
		Honey Dear	My Dear 12
		Whisper	*TOUCHSTONE* 14
		Flatcatcher	Decoy 3
			MELBOURNE 1
		Silence	Secret 12
	Eagle (1882)	Phoenix	Kettledrum 3
		Cymbal	Nelly Hill 17
			First Born 5
		Belle Etoile	Jessie 25
		Au Revoir	Buccaneer 14
		See Saw	Margery Daw 6
			Y Melbourne 25
		Y Melbourne Mare	Maid Of Masham 9

Reading (1918)

Sainfoin (1887)	Springfield (1873)	St Albans	The Baron 24
		STOCKWELL 3
			POCAHONTAS
		Bribery	The Libel 14
			Splitvote 2
		Viridis	Orlando 13
		Marsyas	Malibran 12
			Pyrrhus I 3
		Maid Of Palmyra	Palmyra 12
	Sanda (1878)	Wenlock	*NEWMINSTER* 8
		Lord Clifden	The Slave 2
			RATAPLAN 3
		Mineral	Manganese 4
Rock Sand (1900)		Sandal	The Baron 24
		STOCKWELL 3
			POCAHONTAS
		Lady Evelyn	*DON JOHN* 2
			Industry 2
	St Simon (1881)	Galopin	Voltigeur 2
		Vedette	Mrs Ridgeway 19
			The Flying Dutchman 3
		Flying Duchess	Merope 3
Roquebrune (1893)		St Angela	Harkaway 2
		King Tom	*POCAHONTAS* 3
			Ion 4
		Adeline	Little Fairy 11
	St Marguerite (1879)	Hermit	*TOUCHSTONE* 14
		NEWMINSTER	Beeswing 8
			Tadmor 12
		Seclusion	Miss Sellon 5
		Devotion	The Baron 24
		STOCKWELL	*POCAHONTAS* 3
			TOUCHSTONE 14
		Alcestis	Sacrifice 4
HANOVER (1884)	Hindoo (1878)	*VIRGIL (RH)*	Glencoe 1
		VANDAL (RH)	Tranby Mare (RH)
			Yorkshire 2
		Hymenia (RH)	Little Peggy (RH)
		Florence	Boston (RH)
		LEXINGTON (RH)	Alice Carneal (RH)
			Weatherbit 12
		Weatherwitch II	Birdcatcher Mare (24) 24
Tea Biscuit (1912)	Bourbon Belle (1869)	Bonnie Scotland	*DON JOHN* 2
		Iago	Scandal 11
			GLADIATOR 22
		Queen Mary	Plenipotentiary Mare 10
		Ella D (RH)	Glencoe 1
		VANDAL (RH)	Tranby Mare (RH)
			Woodpecker (RH)
		Falcon (RH)	Ophelia (RH)
Tea's Over (1893)	King Alfonso (1872)	Phaeton	Sultan 8
		Phlegon	Lucetta 2
			Whisker 6
		Catherina	Alecto 1
		Capitola (RH)	Glencoe 1
		VANDAL (RH)	Tranby Mare (RH)
			Margrave 2
		Margrave Mare (RH)	Mistletoe (RH)
Tea Rose (1884)	Tuberose (1880)	Vigil	*VANDAL (RH)*
		VIRGIL (RH)	Hymenia (RH)
			LEXINGTON (RH)
		Regan	Lorette
		Buttercup	Blair Athol 5
		Glen Athol	Greta 10
			7
			LEXINGTON (RH)
		Bay Flower	Bay Leaf 9

Reading 1918

Chapter 16

Marcel Boussac and the French Lines

One of the strongest pressures put on the English Jockey Club to repeal the Jersey Act came from the French racing industry. They could not continue to patronize a studbook that excluded their best racehorses.

It all started back in 1910 when the American breeder Herman Duryea, in reaction to the New York blackout in racing, moved his stud operation from Long Island, New York, to France. He brought with him a key broodmare, stallion, and yearling colt that would soon shake things up. The yearling Sweeper II was a son of Broomstick, and when he was three he took the English 2000 Guineas.

> "The Two Thousand Guineas Stakes…the first Classic of the season, was run here today and won by American H.B. Duryea's Sweeper II, ridden by Danny Maher, he was the American jockey…Sweeper II is by Broomstick out of Ravello by Sir Hugo…"(Newmarket, England, May 5,1912).

The mare Frizette turned into one of the greatest broodmares of the twentieth century (*reine-de-course*)—or possibly of all time—she is that good. Bred by James Keene, she was a daughter of the great Hamburg; she was purchased by Duryea and moved with his stock to France. The stallion was the good sire Irish Lad who is linebred 4x5 Touchstone, 4x5 Gladiator (sire of Queen Mary), and 4x5 Lexington RH—he also carries the great four-miler Trifle RH (see Chapters 4 and 5), and Irish Lad became a noted sire of speed horses. When bred to Frizette he became the sire of the important broodmare (*reine*) Banshee. Irish Lad was a large and coarsely built colt, but showed racing class as a two-year-old, and was a handy stakes winning racehorse, having races such as the Brooklyn Handicap and Metropolitan to his credit, but like many large horses he broke down, and it was then he was sent to stud in France.

Irish Lad 1900—what a great image! It looks like he was a handful, an American-bred stakes winner who was brought to France by Herman Duryea and is found in pedigrees everywhere through his granddaughters Durban and Heldifann. —image from *Racing in America*

Herman Duryea not only took Sweeper II to England to train for the races of 1912, but the year after the passing of the Jersey Act his French-bred Durbar II won the Derby. The Jersey Act fell hard on the relocated American-breds and their descendants—overnight, the talented and successful American-bred racers and breeding stock became 'untouchable', because no longer were they allowed status as full Thoroughbred.

But in France an extraordinary breeder was emerging—Marcel Boussac—who was destined to turn the European racing industry upside down with his genius. Some of Boussac's early products such as Sun Briar (originally named Sunday) and his full brother Sunreigh were imported to America and became outstanding sires, and of course there was La Troienne whom he also sold to the US, where she made breeding history (see Chapter 22)—for those three alone Boussac would hold a place in Thoroughbred history—but it turns out he was only warming up.

It was after the death of Herman Duryea that Boussac made his greatest strides. He bought the entire 1919 yearling crop from Mrs. Duryea and did it again in 1921. Among his early purchases were two mares who jump-started his program: Durban (*reine*) and Durzetta, both carriers of those flawed American lines.

KATHLEEN H. KIRSAN

Not daunted by England's rule, Boussac followed his own plans, using race performance as the test for his stock, he culled and purchased and inbred to superior lines. He knew from studying the methods of the most successful breeders, such as France's Edmund Blanc, that the key to success was to increase the lines of important transmitters of performance in his herd. He was an advocate of tight line-breeding and inbreeding; indeed his pedigrees are admired today as illustration of how to do inbreeding correctly. He had his best success with the mares bred by Edmund Blanc and Herman Duryea; he tried others, but ultimately the talent in those two populations won out. He became a world-class breeder, and his products such as Tourbillon and Djebel are now genetic giants in international bloodlines, and they have enriched the modern day racing Thoroughbred everywhere.

Tourbillon 1928—a masterpiece (*chef-de-race*) bred by Marcel Boussac, he has become a top class international line. His dam is the Duryea-bred Durban (*reine*)—Wiki Commons public domain image

It could not have been easy for him—using those 'half-bred' American lines—yet he followed his dream in spite of the official censure of his bloodlines and achieved immortality as one of the greatest breeders of his day. There is a strong lesson in his example.

Here is the genetic trail to his greatest champions: Irish Lad bred to Frizette produced Banshee (winner of 1000 Guineas), who when mated with Durbar II (English Derby winner) produced Durban *reine* (and her full sisters Heldifann *reine* and Sheba), who when mated with the inbred Ksar produced Tourbillon (winner of French Derby); he is now rated a *chef*. Tourbillon's best son Djebel was a stakes winner in England: Middle Park Stakes and the 2000 Guineas in 1940, but the breeders there avoided him because of his American lines—in spite of those prejudgments he still has risen to the status of *chef-de-race*. At home in 1942 he won the Arc de Triomphe. What could he have accomplished if his bloodline was not banned?

[Note the pedigree structure of Tourbillon—through his sire Ksar he is inbred 3x4 to Omnium (whose second dam-sire is Wellingtonia, one of the warehouses for the daughter lines of Pocahontas), and those Omnium lines are daughters, therefore a strong filly factor. Through his dam he is 4x5 St. Simon, and 5x5 Hanover, both lines sex-balanced, which are strong colt factors. This pedigree is the work of a true genius!]

Now Durbar II, who won the English Derby right after the Jersey Act was passed, is panned by Thoroughbred experts as a 'poor' Derby winner—maybe it is just a coincidence that Orby also was panned as such? It is hard to explain this attitude as in hindsight we can see the huge genetic legacy each of these 'poor' Derby winners left. For as a sire Durbar is immortal, because he produced the full sisters Durban, Sheba, and Heldifann, as well as their ¾ sisters Durzetta and Frizelle, and their offspring populate the high-class racer of today (see Chapter 12). These full sisters are 3x4 St Simon and 4x4 Hanover, while the ¾ sisters are 3x3 St Simon and 3x4 Hanover. In ten generations they carry eight lines of Lexington RH (nine of his sire Boston), four lines of Vandal RH, and three of American Eclipse RH (read more about this pedigree in Chapter 36).

Realize that although these lines are further back in the lineage, this is a larger concentration of Lexington RH than found in Domino, and taking in the generation factors, the potency here equals that of Americus, Hamburg, and Domino. All five of these mares are tremendous producers. Galicienne, Asturie, Asteria, Orlanda, Banstar, Diademe, Coronis, Djezima, and of course Tourbillon are some of the commonly found progeny of these sisters. It does not get any better than this—they are the backbone of French breeding. The 'poor' Derby winner Durbar has become a great bloodline, and because of these closely related daughters of his, he is a very valuable target for our line-breeding designs.

Djezima, a daughter of Heldifann, is the dam of the 1941 champion colt and great producer Priam II, and she is also dam of the *chef* Djeddah, a champion stakes winner in both France and England and great sire—he is 3x2 to Durban/Heldifann—this is an extremely valuable line for American breeders. Then there is Djezima's daughter Tourzima by Tourbillon. Tourzima is classified as a *reine-de-course*; she is inbred to the full sisters Durban/Heldifann 2x2. With both a *chef* and a *reine* from inbreeding to Durban/Heldifann, we must recognize that this is an indication of the extreme genet-

The *chef-de-race* Djeddah is a concentrated source of Lexington RH blood.
—photo by Skeet Meadors, courtesy of Keeneland Library

ic power in these lines. Her daughter Corejada became the Champion-Two-Year-Old in both France and England when she won the Goodwood Cup, Chevelery Park Stakes, the 1000 Guineas, and the Irish Oaks. This champion also produced well with many stakes winners including the extremely inbred Apollonia, who is 2x3 Tourbillon, and 3x4x4 Durban/Heldifann. All of these lines are bonanzas for the line-breeder.

Boussac's creations remained top racers and producers for generations, and are today valuable lines in your pedigree designs, most of them potent in those important sources of speed, stamina, and performance: the flawed lines of the Running Horse Lexington and his relatives. A swan song for Boussac may be seen in the great Acamas, who won the Arc de Triomphe and the English Derby in 1978. He is 4x4 to the ¾ siblings Djeddah/Tourzima and is 6x6x6x6 to Durban/Heldifann (that is eighteen lines of Lexington RH).

But there is more to the French connection then this. Herman Duryea was a close friend and business associate of Harry Whitney, a top breeder in his own right—his filly Regret by Broomstick out of a Hamburg daughter won the Kentucky Derby, and together they owned and raced horses in common, especially in England and France. Irish Lad (above) was one of those.

Chicle, bred by Herman Duryea in France. —photo by W. A. Rouch

Whitney fielded great racers in England, such as the Hamburg son Borrow who won the Middle Park Stakes (Chapter 10), and the phenomenal Lady Hamburg—a mare who possessed and transmitted tremendous speed—dam of Dis Donc and Chicle among others. Whitney owned the great sire Broomstick as well.

The American-bred Lady Hamburg when bred to the English sire Spearmint gave birth in France to an important sire: Chicle. He became a stakes winner at two, and later as a three-year-old he won the Dwyer Stakes and others in the US. A stayer, he transmitted this stamina to his offspring, and this can be seen in his racing sons: Enchantment, Cherry Pie, Gadfly, and Rialto. Although he is not mentioned much when the 'big sires' are discussed, he is found continually in the top racers and sport horses. In 1940 he reached #3 as broodmare sire in America. His daughters are fabulous. Incidently, this stayer also founded a top speed line in the racing Quarter Horse: Chicaro, out of a Peter Pan dam (Domino).

Chicle's daughter Mother Goose (*reine*) was a top racer as she won the Futurity Stakes, and she has become the matron of an important female family. She is out of a Broomstick daughter, and her second dam is a Peter Pan daughter (Domino).

You will find her everywhere today, as she is the second-dam of Almahmoud from whom Northern Dancer descends. Mother Goose had a full brother, Whichone, who was an accomplished stakes winner.

Chicle's daughter Frumpery, also out of a Broomstick mare, when bred to the Domino son Dominant gave Whitney the unbeaten two-year-old Dice, who mysteriously bled to death before the season was out.

Switching his formula a little, Whitney bred Chicle to the Fair Play daughter Oval, who then produced another *reine* in Goose Egg—she is the dam of Kentucky Derby and Belmont winner Shut Out.

Chicle's daughter Elf was out of a Peter Pan mare whose second dam carried Broomstick, when she was bred to another of Whitney's great stallions, John P. Grier, she produced the great stakes winner Boojum.

Chicle's daughter the *reine* Chicleight, out of the *reine* Ruddy Light, heads a maternal dynasty. She was a stakes winner as well, and has an unusual line-breeding to the mare Warble 4x4, who is the second-dam of Spearmint and her dam-sire Honeywood, plus she is 4x5 to Hanover and 5x6 to Mannie Gray. Chicleight is the dam of another *reine* Blue Delight, who also a stakes winner and in-turn produced the top mare (*reine*) Real Delight, also a stakes winner and is the second-dam of none other than the *chef* Alydar—obviously this is an awesome reservoir of maternal strength.

Another of the French-breds of note by Whitney was Dis Donc out of Lady Hamburg again, by the French sire Sardana-pale. He too became a significant broodmare sire, as his daughter Fly Swatter by Whisk Broom II, produced First Flight (mentioned above). Perhaps his greatest offspring was Top Flight out of Flyatit—this is the Peter Pan/Broomstick combination again, but who also carries the legend Maggie B. B. RH on her dam-line. An extraordinary race mare, certainly in the league of the modern day Ruffian, she was undefeated at two in seven starts and winning over $200,000. Her three-year-old campaign won her the Champion-Three-Year-Old-Filly title.

Top Flight 1929, a daughter of Dis Donc, who won all seven of her seven starts as a two-year-old setting an earnings record—she is one of the greatest racing fillies of all time. —image from "Thoroughbred Record"

Harry Whitney was a great breeder and sportsman; he bred and owned the magnificent Equipoise as well, another extraordinary racer and good sire. Harry's success was from judicious breeding which intertwined the great American families of Domino/Broomstick/Hanover, with additional success when he added in Spendthrift and Maggie B. B. RH.

I have to admit that I had no idea that France was such a repository of our Lexington RH et al bloodlines, but if I had been paying attention it should have dawned on me to look there. France is a country of extraordinary creative breeding; it is the world leader in stamina sire-lines for instance. But it also has always been the 'savior' of bloodlines that fade in other countries, and somehow the French have excelled in preserving the often missing female strains of important lines. Of course, the clearest case of this is Pocahontas, whose sons Stockwell, Rataplan, and King Tom are everywhere in the Thoroughbred in multiples, but her daughters were mostly absent. France, however, conserved the daughter lines through their good sires. Wellingtonia 1869 is 2x2 to Araucaria and Ayacanora and Chamant out of the Pocahontas daughter Araucaria, and of course there is Ajax 1901 (and his full brother Adam) who carries three Pocahontas daughter lines by adding the very rarely seen Heroine to Lucknow to the other two: Araucaria and Ayacanora, certainly a factor in his son Teddy becoming so successful at stud.

And so it is that in France they have done it again: while the rest of the world was banishing the lines of Lexington RH and his like, the French built their best bloodlines from him, and gave back to us a rich and complex deposit of his power. Tourbillon, Djebel, Djeddah, Chicle, Dis Donc, are all important sire-lines today and are easy to find in international pedigrees. Because of the vision of Herman Duryea who immigrated there and that of Marcel Boussac, the home-bred French pedigree wizard, there are inbred treasure chests of our Heroic Era genes to be found in Durban, Heldifann, Sheba, Djed-dah, Apollina, Tourzima, and Acamas and their descendants; all of these are a sure source of an explosive amount of talent when we combine them with our American designs.

It is interesting that Boussac's successful inbreeding program had a renaissance long after his death when the Aga Khan purchased almost the entire breeding stock from his estate and bred them and their offspring to the sires Never Bend and Mill Reef along with his son Shirley Heights. What was it that the sires Never Bend and Mill Reef provided to the Boussac mares that resulted in such top class? You guessed it—more of the flawed American lines they are based on. The great Darshaan was a high profile result of this design—5x5 to Djeddah/Tourzima, who are themselves inbred to Durban/Heldifann. It doesn't stop there; a new nick has occurred in the European racer when they have crossed Sadlers Wells with daughters of Darshaan, producing consistent high-class stakes winners (see combined pedigree).

Thoroughbred pedigree expert Anne Peters has pointed out that when line-breeding was done back to Boussac's best horses it provided a wealth of top-class racers, especially when it was to the already inbred lines of Djeddah and Tourzima—who are ¾ siblings.

France leads the world in stamina-breds with 34% of the lines; however it is delightful to see that at least 7 of that 34% are bloodlines based on American Heroic Era horses!

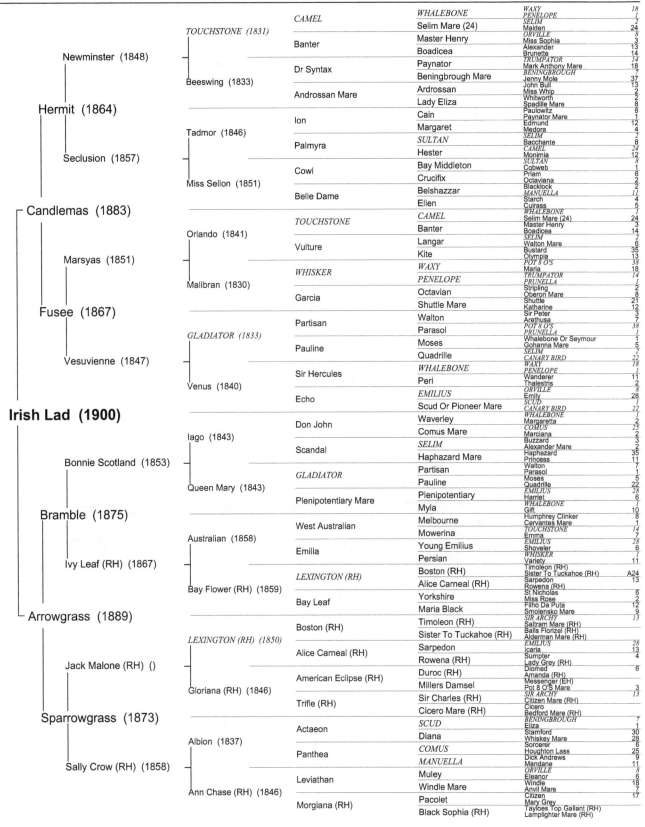

Irish Lad 1900

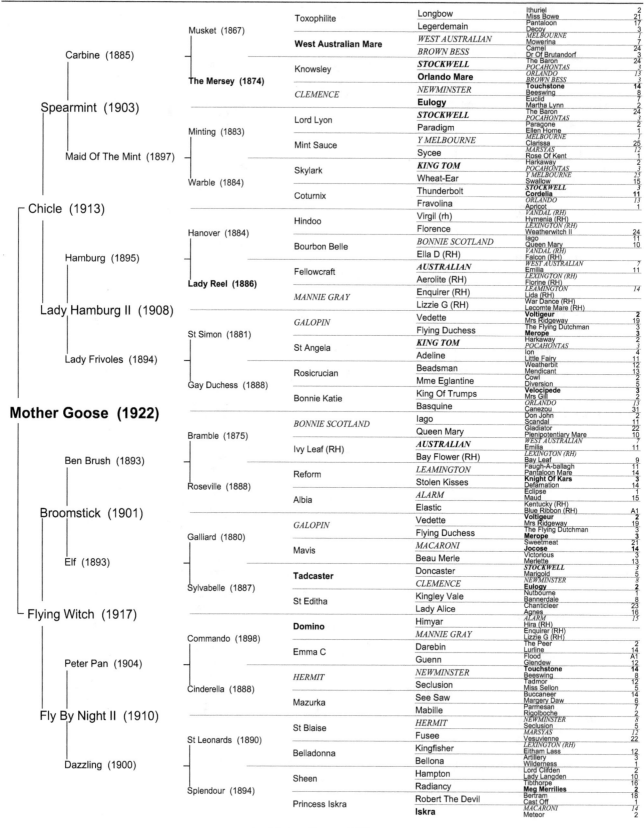

Mother Goose 1922

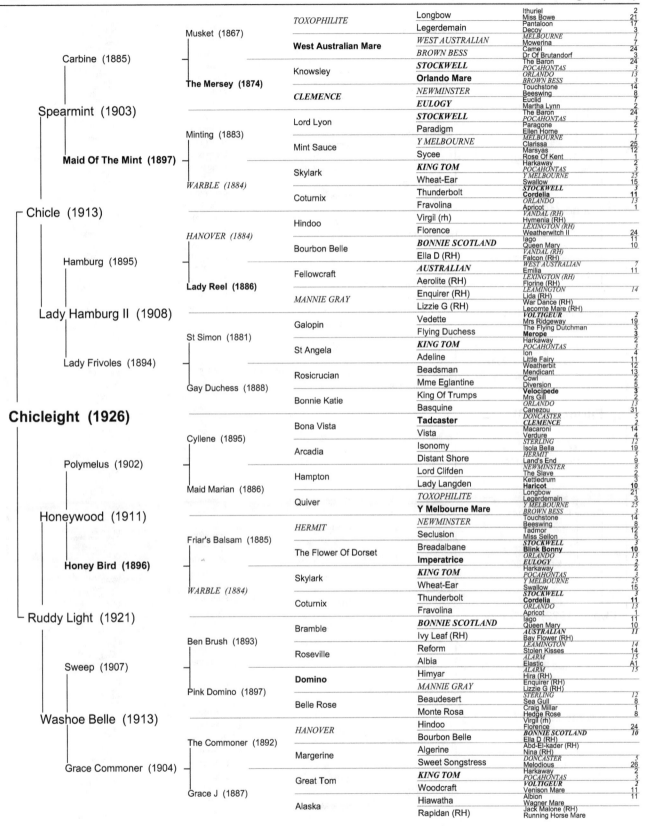

Chicleight 1926

Top Flight (1929)

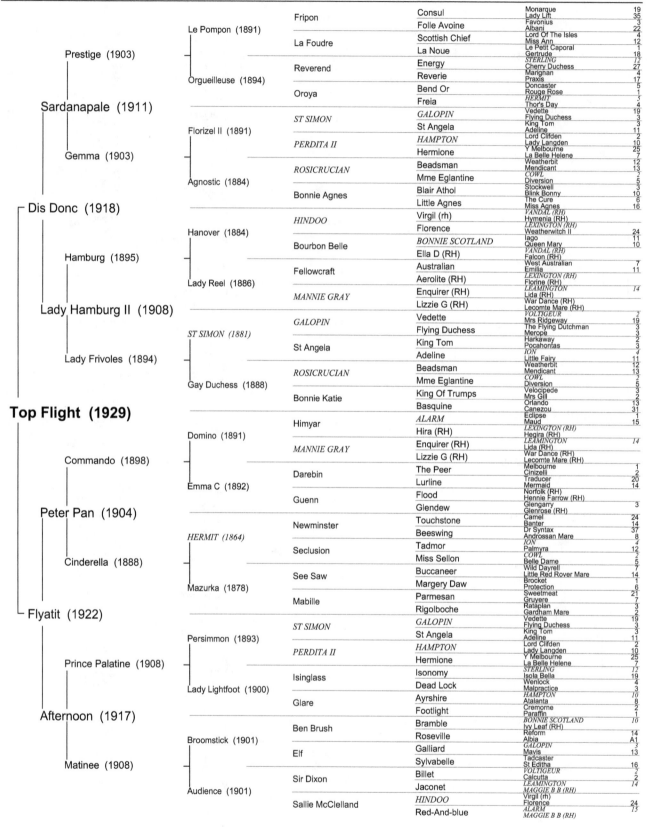

- **Dis Donc (1918)**
  - **Sardanapale (1911)**
    - **Prestige (1903)**
      - Le Pompon (1891)
        - Fripon
          - Consul — Monarque 19 / Lady Lift 35
          - Folle Avoine — Favonius 2 / Albani 22
        - La Foudre
          - Scottish Chief — Lord Of The Isles 4 / Miss Ann 12
          - La Noue — Le Petit Caporal 1 / Gertrude 18
      - Orgueilleuse (1894)
        - Reverend
          - Energy — *STERLING* 12 / Cherry Duchess 27
          - Reverie — Marignan 4 / Praxis 17
        - Oroya
          - Bend Or — Doncaster 5 / Rouge Rose 1
          - Freia — *HERMIT* 5 / Thor's Day 4
    - **Gemma (1903)**
      - Florizel II (1891)
        - *ST SIMON*
          - *GALOPIN* — Vedette 19 / Flying Duchess 3
          - St Angela — King Tom 3 / Adeline 11
        - *PERDITA II*
          - *HAMPTON* — Lord Clifden 2 / Lady Langden 10
          - Hermione — Y Melbourne 25 / La Belle Helene 7
      - Agnostic (1884)
        - *ROSICRUCIAN*
          - Beadsman — Weatherbit 12 / Mendicant 13
          - Mme Eglantine — *COWL* 5 / Diversion 3
        - Bonnie Agnes
          - Blair Athol — Stockwell 10 / Blink Bonny 6
          - Little Agnes — The Cure 6 / Miss Agnes 16
  - **Lady Hamburg II (1908)**
    - **Hamburg (1895)**
      - Hanover (1884)
        - *HINDOO*
          - Virgil (rh) — *VANDAL (RH)* / Hymenia (RH)
          - Florence — *LEXINGTON (RH)* / Weatherwitch II 24
        - Bourbon Belle
          - *BONNIE SCOTLAND* — Iago 11 / Queen Mary 10
          - Ella D (RH) — *VANDAL (RH)* / Falcon (RH)
      - Lady Reel (1886)
        - Fellowcraft
          - Australian — West Australian 7 / Emilia 11
          - Aerolite (RH) — *LEXINGTON (RH)* / Florine (RH)
        - *MANNIE GRAY*
          - Enquirer (RH) — *LEAMINGTON* 14 / Lida (RH)
          - Lizzie G (RH) — War Dance (RH) / Lecomte Mare (RH)
    - **Lady Frivoles (1894)**
      - *ST SIMON (1881)*
        - *GALOPIN*
          - Vedette — *VOLTIGEUR* 2 / Mrs Ridgeway 19
          - Flying Duchess — The Flying Dutchman 3 / Merope 3
        - St Angela
          - King Tom — Harkaway 2 / Pocahontas 3
          - Adeline — *ION* 4 / Little Fairy 11
      - Gay Duchess (1888)
        - *ROSICRUCIAN*
          - Beadsman — Weatherbit 12 / Mendicant 13
          - Mme Eglantine — *COWL* 5 / Diversion 3
        - Bonnie Katie
          - King Of Trumps — Velocipede 3 / Mrs Gill 2
          - Basquine — Orlando 13 / Canezou 31
- **Flyatit (1922)**
  - **Peter Pan (1904)**
    - **Commando (1898)**
      - Domino (1891)
        - Himyar
          - *ALARM* — Eclipse 1 / Maud 15
          - Hira (RH) — *LEXINGTON (RH)* / Hegira (RH)
        - *MANNIE GRAY*
          - Enquirer (RH) — *LEAMINGTON* 14 / Lida (RH)
          - Lizzie G (RH) — War Dance (RH) / Lecomte Mare (RH)
      - Emma C (1892)
        - Darebin
          - The Peer — Melbourne 1 / Cinizelli 2
          - Lurline — Traducer 20 / Mermaid 14
        - Guenn
          - Flood — Norfolk (RH) / Hennie Farrow (RH)
          - Glendew — Glengarry 3 / Glenrose (RH)
    - **Cinderella (1888)**
      - *HERMIT (1864)*
        - Newminster
          - Touchstone — Camel 24 / Banter 14
          - Beeswing — Dr Syntax 37 / Androssan Mare 8
        - Seclusion
          - Tadmor — *ION* 4 / Palmyra 12
          - Miss Sellon — *COWL* / Belle Dame 5
      - Mazurka (1878)
        - See Saw
          - Buccaneer — Wild Dayrell 7 / Little Red Rover Mare 14
          - Margery Daw — Brocket 1 / Protection 6
        - Mabille
          - Parmesan — Sweetmeat 21 / Gruyere 7
          - Rigolboche — Rataplan 3 / Gardham Mare 2
  - **Afternoon (1917)**
    - **Prince Palatine (1908)**
      - Persimmon (1893)
        - *ST SIMON*
          - *GALOPIN* — Vedette 19 / Flying Duchess 3
          - St Angela — King Tom 3 / Adeline 11
        - *PERDITA II*
          - *HAMPTON* — Lord Clifden 2 / Lady Langden 10
          - Hermione — Y Melbourne 25 / La Belle Helene 7
      - Lady Lightfoot (1900)
        - Isinglass
          - Isonomy — *STERLING* 12 / Isola Bella 19
          - Dead Lock — Wenlock 4 / Malpractice 3
        - Glare
          - Ayrshire — *HAMPTON* 10 / Atalanta 8
          - Footlight — Cremorne 6 / Paraffin 2
    - **Matinee (1908)**
      - Broomstick (1901)
        - Ben Brush
          - Bramble — *BONNIE SCOTLAND* 10 / Ivy Leaf (RH)
          - Roseville — Reform 14 / Albia A1
        - Elf
          - Galliard — *GALOPIN* 3 / Mavis 13
          - Sylvabelle — Tadcaster 16 / St Editha
      - Audience (1901)
        - Sir Dixon
          - Billet — *VOLTIGEUR* 2 / Calcutta 2
          - Jaconet — *LEAMINGTON* 14 / *MAGGIE B B (RH)*
        - Sallie McClelland
          - *HINDOO* — Virgil (rh) / Florence 24
          - Red-And-blue — *ALARM* 15 / *MAGGIE B B (RH)*

Top Flight 1929

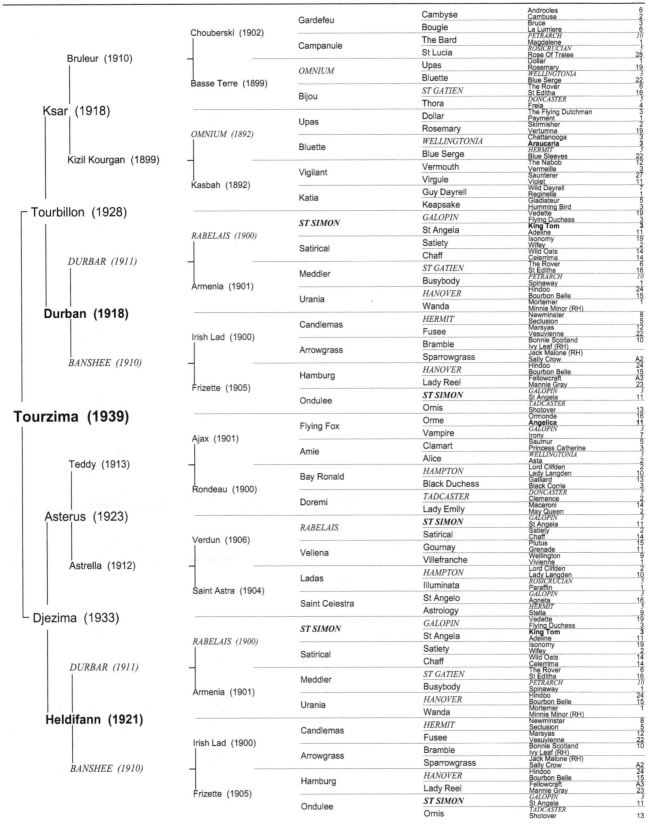

Tourzima (1939)

Ksar (1918)
- Bruleur (1910)
  - Chouberski (1902)
    - Gardefeu
      - Cambyse — Androcles 6 / Cambuse 2
      - Bougie — Bruce 3 / La Lumiere 6
    - Campanule
      - The Bard — PETRARCH 10 / Magdalene 1
      - St Lucia — ROSICRUCIAN 5 / Rose Of Tralee 28
  - Basse Terre (1899)
    - OMNIUM
      - Upas — Dollar 1 / Rosemary 19
      - Bluette — WELLINGTONIA 3 / Blue Serge 22
    - Bijou
      - ST GATIEN — The Rover 6 / St Editha 16
      - Thora — DONCASTER 5 / Freia 4
- Kizil Kourgan (1899)
  - OMNIUM (1892)
    - Upas
      - Dollar — The Flying Dutchman 3 / Payment 1
      - Rosemary — Skirmisher 2 / Vertumna 19
    - Bluette
      - WELLINGTONIA — Chattanooga 3 / Araucaria 3
      - Blue Serge — HERMIT 3 / Blue Sleeves 22
  - Kasbah (1892)
    - Vigilant
      - Vermouth — The Nabob 12 / Vermeille 3
      - Virgule — Saunterer 27 / Violet 11
    - Katia
      - Guy Dayrell — Wild Dayrell 7 / Reginella 1
      - Keapsake — Gladiateur 5 / Humming Bird 3

Tourbillon (1928)

Durban (1918)
- DURBAR (1911)
  - RABELAIS (1900)
    - ST SIMON
      - GALOPIN — Vedette 19 / Flying Duchess 3
      - St Angela — King Tom 3 / Adeline 11
    - Satirical
      - Satiety — Isonomy 19 / Wifey 2
      - Chaff — Wild Oats 14 / Celerrima 14
  - Armenia (1901)
    - Meddler
      - ST GATIEN — The Rover 6 / St Editha 16
      - Busybody — PETRARCH 10 / Spinaway 1
    - Urania
      - HANOVER — Hindoo 24 / Bourbon Belle 15
      - Wanda — Mortemer 1 / Minnie Minor (RH)
- BANSHEE (1910)
  - Irish Lad (1900)
    - Candlemas
      - HERMIT — Newminster 8 / Seclusion 5
      - Fusee — Marsyas 12 / Vesuvienne 22
    - Arrowgrass
      - Bramble — Bonnie Scotland 10 / Ivy Leaf (RH)
      - Sparrowgrass — Jack Malone (RH) / Sally Crow A2
  - Frizette (1905)
    - Hamburg
      - HANOVER — Hindoo 24 / Bourbon Belle 15
      - Lady Reel — Fellowcraft A3 / Mannie Gray 23
    - Ondulee
      - ST SIMON — GALOPIN 3 / St Angela 11
      - Ornis — TADCASTER 13 / Shotover

Asterus (1923)
- Teddy (1913)
  - Ajax (1901)
    - Flying Fox
      - Orme — Ormonde 16 / Angelica 11
      - Vampire — GALOPIN 3 / Irony 7
    - Amie
      - Clamart — Saumur 5 / Princess Catherine 3
      - Alice — WELLINGTONIA 3 / Asta 2
  - Rondeau (1900)
    - Bay Ronald
      - HAMPTON — Lord Clifden 2 / Lady Langden 10
      - Black Duchess — Galliard 13 / Black Corrie 3
    - Doremi
      - TADCASTER — DONCASTER 5 / Clemence 2
      - Lady Emily — Macaroni 14 / May Queen 2
- Astrella (1912)
  - Verdun (1906)
    - RABELAIS
      - ST SIMON — GALOPIN 3 / St Angela 11
      - Satirical — Satiety 2 / Chaff 14
    - Vellena
      - Gournay — Plutus 15 / Grenade 11
      - Villefranche — Wellington 9 / Vivienne
  - Saint Astra (1904)
    - Ladas
      - HAMPTON — Lord Clifden 2 / Lady Langden 10
      - Illuminata — ROSICRUCIAN 5 / Paraffin 1
    - Saint Celestra
      - St Angelo — GALOPIN 3 / Agneta 16
      - Astrology — HERMIT 5 / Stella 9

Djezima (1933)

Heldifann (1921)
- DURBAR (1911)
  - RABELAIS (1900)
    - ST SIMON
      - GALOPIN — Vedette 19 / Flying Duchess 3
      - St Angela — King Tom 3 / Adeline 11
    - Satirical
      - Satiety — Isonomy 19 / Wifey 2
      - Chaff — Wild Oats 14 / Celerrima 14
  - Armenia (1901)
    - Meddler
      - ST GATIEN — The Rover 6 / St Editha 16
      - Busybody — PETRARCH 10 / Spinaway 1
    - Urania
      - HANOVER — Hindoo 24 / Bourbon Belle 15
      - Wanda — Mortemer 1 / Minnie Minor (RH)
- BANSHEE (1910)
  - Irish Lad (1900)
    - Candlemas
      - HERMIT — Newminster 8 / Seclusion 5
      - Fusee — Marsyas 12 / Vesuvienne 22
    - Arrowgrass
      - Bramble — Bonnie Scotland 10 / Ivy Leaf (RH)
      - Sparrowgrass — Jack Malone (RH) / Sally Crow A2
  - Frizette (1905)
    - Hamburg
      - HANOVER — Hindoo 24 / Bourbon Belle 15
      - Lady Reel — Fellowcraft A3 / Mannie Gray 23
    - Ondulee
      - ST SIMON — GALOPIN 3 / St Angela 11
      - Ornis — TADCASTER / Shotover 13

Tourzima 1939

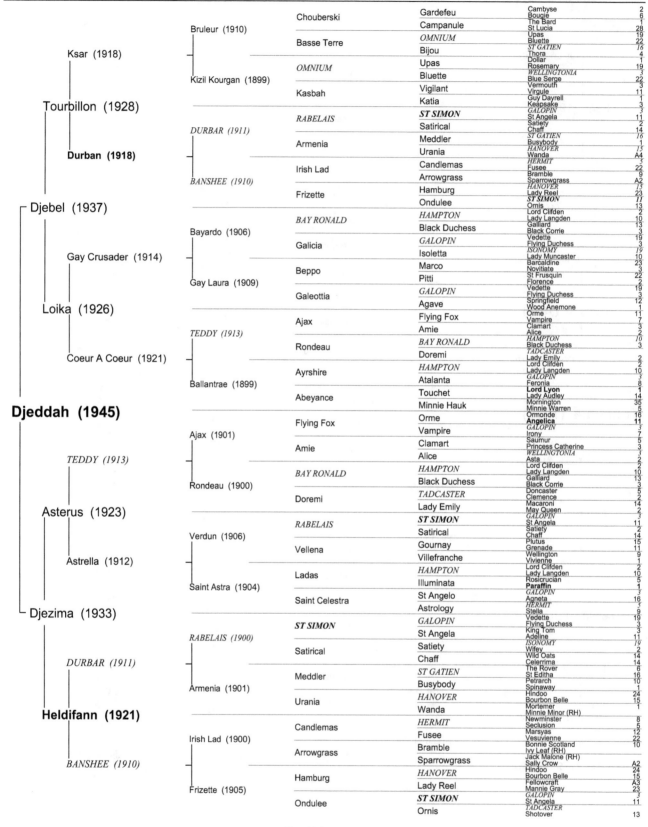

Djeddah 1945

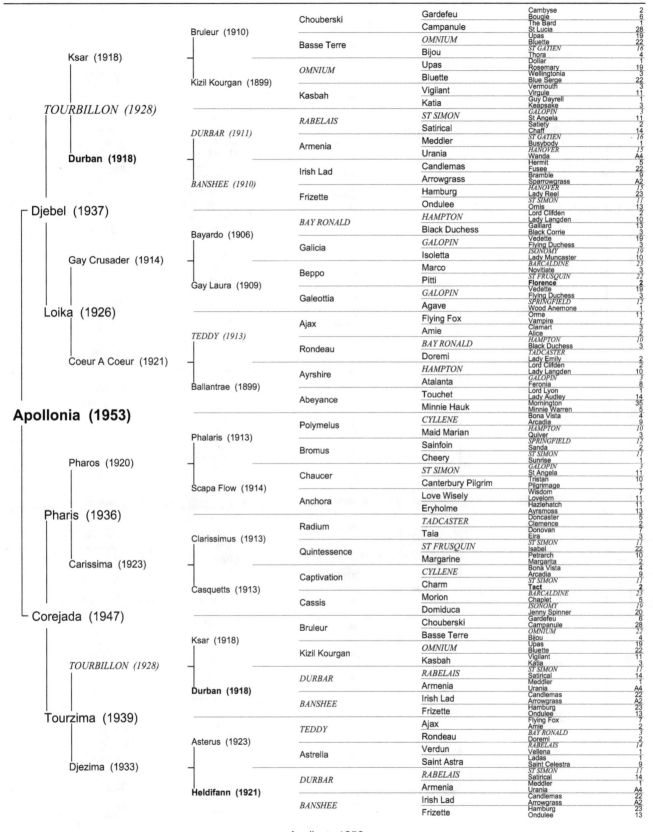

Apollonia 1953

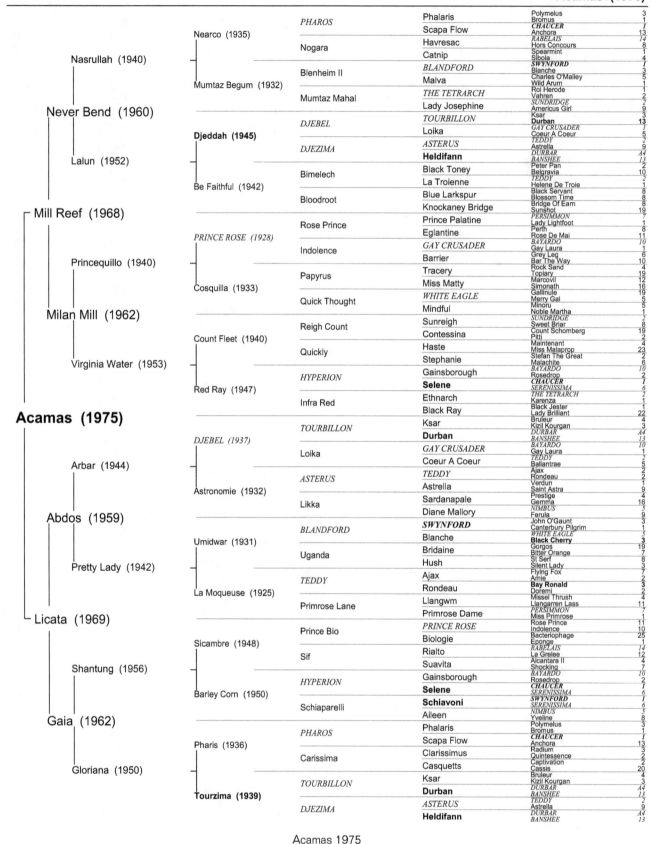

Acamas 1975

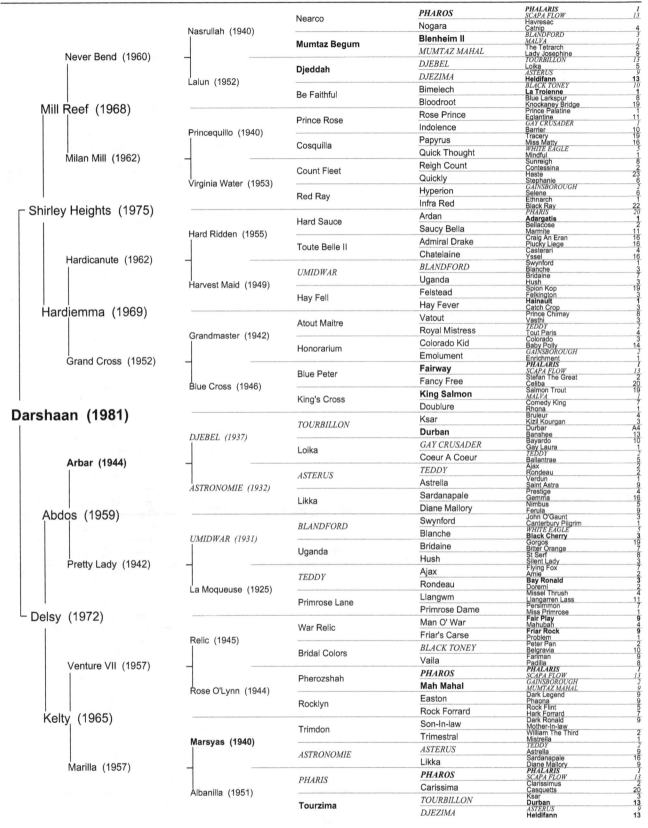

			PHALARIS *1*
	Nearco	**PHAROS**	*SCAPA FLOW* *13*
Nasrullah (1940)		Nogara	Havresac
			Catnip *4*
			BLANDFORD *3*
	Mumtaz Begum	**Blenheim II**	*MALVA* *1*
		MUMTAZ MAHAL	The Tetrarch *2*
			Lady Josephine *9*
		DJEBEL	*TOURBILLON* *13*
	Djeddah		Loika *5*
		DJEZIMA	*ASTERUS* *9*
			Heldifann *13*
		Bimelech	*BLACK TONEY* *10*
	Be Faithful		**La Troienne** *1*
		Bloodroot	Blue Larkspur *8*
			Knockaney Bridge *19*
		Rose Prince	Prince Palatine *1*
	Prince Rose		Eglantine *11*
Princequillo (1940)		Indolence	*GAY CRUSADER* *1*
			Barrier *10*
		Papyrus	Tracery *19*
	Cosquilla		Miss Matty *16*
		Quick Thought	*WHITE EAGLE* *5*
			Mindful *1*
		Reigh Count	Sunreigh *8*
	Count Fleet		Contessina *2*
Virginia Water (1953)		Quickly	Haste *23*
			Stephanie *6*
		Hyperion	*GAINSBOROUGH* *2*
	Red Ray		Selene *6*
		Infra Red	Ethnarch *1*
			Black Ray *22*
		Ardan	*PHARIS* *20*
	Hard Sauce		**Adargatis** *1*
Hard Ridden (1955)		Saucy Bella	Bellacose *11*
			Marmite *16*
		Admiral Drake	Craig An Eran *16*
	Toute Belle II		Plucky Liege *4*
		Chatelaine	Casterari *16*
			Yssel *16*
		BLANDFORD	Swynford *3*
	UMIDWAR		Blanche *7*
Harvest Maid (1949)		Uganda	Bridaine *3*
			Hush *19*
		Felstead	Spion Kop *1*
	Hay Fell		Felkington *3*
		Hay Fever	**Hainault** *8*
			Catch Crop *3*
		Vatout	Prince Chimay *3*
	Atout Maitre		Vasthi *2*
Grandmaster (1942)		Royal Mistress	*TEDDY* *4*
			Tout Paris *3*
		Colorado Kid	Colorado *14*
	Honorarium		Baby Polly *1*
		Emolument	*GAINSBOROUGH* *1*
			Enrichment *13*
		Fairway	*PHALARIS* *2*
	Blue Peter		*SCAPA FLOW* *20*
Blue Cross (1946)		Fancy Free	Stefan The Great *19*
			Celiba *1*
		King Salmon	Salmon Trout *7*
	King's Cross		*MALVA* *1*
		Doublure	Comedy King *3*
			Rhona
		Ksar	Bruleur *3*
	TOURBILLON		Kizil Kourgan *A4*
DJEBEL (1937)		**Durban**	Durbar *13*
			Banshee *10*
		GAY CRUSADER	Bayardo *1*
	Loika		Gay Laura *2*
		Coeur A Coeur	*TEDDY* *5*
			Ballantrae *2*
		TEDDY	Ajax *1*
	ASTERUS		Rondeau *9*
ASTRONOMIE (1932)		Astrella	Verdun *4*
			Saint Astra *5*
		Sardanapale	Prestige *9*
	Likka		Gemma *3*
		Diane Mallory	Nimbus *1*
			Ferula *5*
		Swynford	John O'Gaunt *3*
	BLANDFORD		Canterbury Pilgrim *19*
UMIDWAR (1931)		Blanche	*WHITE EAGLE* *7*
			Black Cherry *8*
		Bridaine	Gorgos *3*
	Uganda		Bitter Orange *7*
		Hush	St Serf *9*
			Silent Lady *3*
		Ajax	Flying Fox *2*
	TEDDY		Amie *4*
La Moqueuse (1925)		Rondeau	**Bay Ronald** *11*
			Doremi *7*
		Llangwm	Missel Thrush *1*
	Primrose Lane		Llangarren Lass *9*
		Primrose Dame	Persimmon *4*
			Miss Primrose *9*
		Man O' War	**Fair Play** *9*
	War Relic		Mahubah *9*
Relic (1945)		Friar's Carse	**Friar Rock** *1*
			Problem *2*
		BLACK TONEY	Peter Pan *10*
	Bridal Colors		Belgravia *9*
		Vaila	Fariman *8*
			Padilla *1*
		PHAROS	*PHALARIS* *13*
	Pherozshah		*SCAPA FLOW* *2*
Rose O'Lynn (1944)		**Mah Mahal**	*GAINSBOROUGH* *9*
			MUMTAZ MAHAL *9*
		Easton	Dark Legend *5*
	Rocklyn		Phaona *7*
		Rock Forrard	Rock Flint *9*
			Hark Forrard
		Son-In-law	Dark Ronald *2*
	Trimdon		Mother-In-law *1*
Marsyas (1940)		Trimestral	William The Third *2*
			Mistrella *16*
		ASTERUS	*TEDDY* *9*
	ASTRONOMIE		Astrella *1*
		Likka	Sardanapale *13*
			Diane Mallory *2*
		PHAROS	*PHALARIS* *20*
	PHARIS		*SCAPA FLOW* *3*
Albanilla (1951)		Carissima	Clarissimus *13*
			Casquetts *9*
		TOURBILLON	Ksar *13*
	Tourzima		**Durban**
		DJEZIMA	*ASTERUS* *13*
			Heldifann

Left column lineage:

- Never Bend (1960)
  - Mill Reef (1968)
    - Milan Mill (1962)
- Shirley Heights (1975)
  - Hardicanute (1962)
    - Hardiemma (1969)
      - Grand Cross (1952)

Darshaan (1981)

- Arbar (1944)
  - Abdos (1959)
    - Pretty Lady (1942)
- Delsy (1972)
  - Venture VII (1957)
    - Kelty (1965)
      - Marilla (1957)

Darshaan 1981

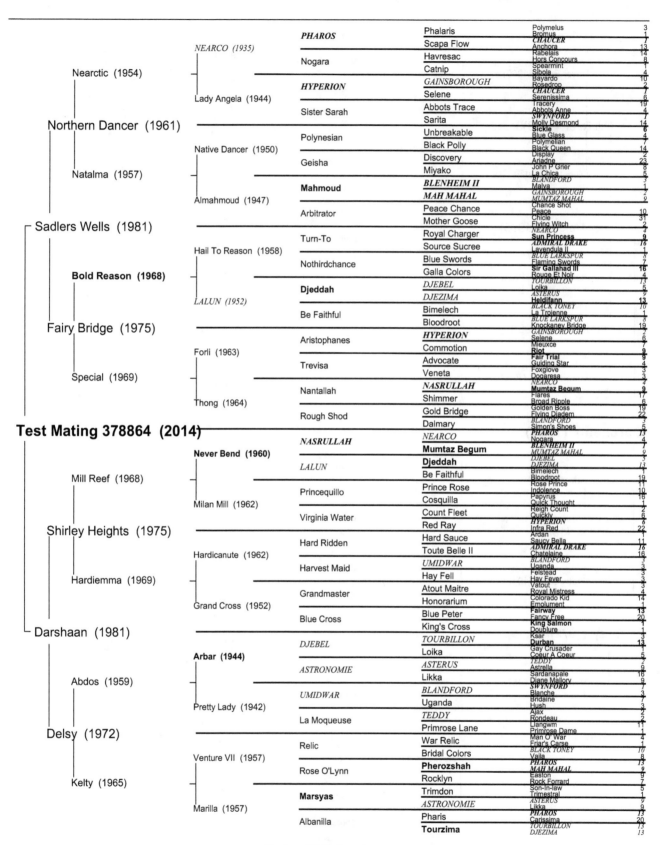

Test Mating 378864 (2014)

Sadlers Wells/Darshaan

Chapter 17

Tesio and the Use of Lexington RH

Sibola 1896—an American-bred mare who made it into the GSB before the Jersey Act—won the 1000 Guineas. —photographer unknown.

Most breeders don't realize that Tesio's first classic winner, Fidia, was out of an American-bred dam, her name was Jiffy II. Fidia was by the important English sire Bay Ronald; however his fourth dam Gladness was 3x3 to Lexington RH. Some pedigree scholars believe that Tesio's racing success with Fidia was instrumental in the later design of Nearco, who also has a Lexington RH daughter on his dam-line—Catnip's fourth-dam is Maiden RH, a Lexington RH daughter whose dam also descends from Blackburns Whip RH (Varola).

Who could have foreseen that the small and slight Catnip would become one of the genetic pillars of international racing (*reine-de-course*)? But Federico Tesio saw something in her and purchased her in 1915 when she was five years old, two years after the Jersey Act had made American lines 'half-bred'. Tesio was not deterred; as always he was looking at her genetic value, and she was a daughter of Spearmint, a stallion with poor front legs who was also undervalued at the time, but Tesio already recognized his genetic worth and it was only later on he was to be recognized by others as one of the greatest sires of his day. But of course, what was worse than having Spearmint as sire was her dam Sibola, an American-bred. Nonetheless, the American-bred Sibola had proven her class by winning the 1000 Guineas in England, and she had already been entered into the GSB—before the Jersey Act. But by this time the axe had fallen on the American-breds, and Tesio was able to purchase Catnip for the paltry sum of seventy-five guineas. The mystery surrounding Catnip is intriguing—for instance, did Tesio realize that her third-dam Perfection was the full sister to the gelding Parole who had come into England and steamrolled the English racing industry, even giving their best Thoroughbred, the invincible undefeated Isonomy, his first defeat? I would guess the answer to this is yes, basing this on what we know about Tesio now; he probably did know as he was a very resourceful researcher, and if he thought a breeding would work he would try it even if the 'power people' of his day disapproved.

Tesio's loyalty to his vision paid off in a large fashion because it was the bargain mare Catnip who Tesio purchased that day who has left his biggest legacy. Catnip however was not a good breeder, and she was barren for five years, but his patience was rewarded, because when she finally produced it was in a spectacular manner. In 1918 she foaled Nera di Bicci, an extraordinary mare who has left an incredible international legacy. Nera di Bicci (*reine*) was by the American TB Tracery (*chef*)—an extremely potent stallion who was 3x3 to St. Simon and his full sister Angelica as well as carrying daughter lines of the taproot mare Pocahontas. Tesio very much wanted to add his genetics to his herd and would have used him more except he was sold to Argentina, so afterward Tesio used Tracery's son Papyrus in his designs. Nera di Bicci lived up to her expectations, as she was a solid racer, winning nine races from fifteen starts.

Nera di Bicci, who has earned *reine* status, has several good daughters: Neroccia, who is by the rarely seen full brother to Swynford: Harry of Hereford (who is found also in War Admiral), plus Nina Pasena and Nuvolona, who was the dam of the good stallion (*chef*) Navarro, who in-turn produced the *reine* Tokamura, who is the dam of greats such as Toulouse Latrec. One of Nera di Bicci's greatest daughters is Nella da Gubbio, also rated a *reine*; she created a dynasty of excellence in Germany (see Chapter 18). She is by Grand Parade—a son of the flawed Orby (also a *chef*)—therefore she carries the Boston RH daughter Nina RH and multiple lines of Lexington RH and Hanover. (Did Tesio realize he was bringing back the American lines in Catnip when mating her daughter to Grand Parade? Once again, I am sure it was part of his design, as Tesio respected performance, and he recognized the talent in the American lines.) But Nera di Bicci may be unknown or go unnoticed by the North American breeder—although she shouldn't as she is made up of ¾ American lines through American TB's Sibola and Tracery. She is in lots

Nella da Gubbio—another *reine* bred by Tesio— is by the Orby son Grand Parade and therefore has reinforcement of her American flawed lines. She created a maternal dynasty of magnitude in the German racehorse and Warmblood. —Wiki Commons public domain image

of European bloodlines, many times through her son Navarro and his daughters Neroccia, Nina Pasana, and Nuvolona.

Nella da Gubbio became a foundation mare of the modern German Thoroughbred and is partially responsible for the elevation of its standings in the international racing world.

When Tesio line-bred to Catnip 4x5 he got the great racer and stallion Toulouse Latrec, a brilliant classic racer remembered for his great courage. Born in 1950, the year Tesio died, he did not have the advantage of Tesio choosing his mates—even so, he produced a great race mare in Marguerite Varnant, who also carries a line of Orby on her dam side.

Catnip's son Nesiotes, by Hurry On, was the Champion National Hunt Sire twice (jumper sires); he is remembered for breeding tough, resilient stock. His son Fante was a stakes winner. The sound Nesiotes was raced successfully for six years and was valued for his 'honesty', but he also is notable for his remarkable display of memory and revenge—for when a groom was assigned to him who had mistreated him in the past, he remembered his cruelty and attacked him savagely, and it required several stable hands to rescue the abusive groom.

But above all, it is Catnip's daughter Nogara who has made her a legend in international breeding (*reine-de-course*), and the excellent bloodline of Nogara has had an enormous impact on the North American breeder of racers and sport horses as well. Catnip would have been considered an important mare for just the previously mentioned progeny, but the offspring of Nogara put Catnip in an altogether different class of broodmare—her legacy is colossal.

Nearco is the 'sire of the century' by Pharos out of Nogara—his dam-line is all American Running Horse. —image courtesy of Wiki Commons public domain images

Like Nera di Bicci, Nogara was a noted race mare before she began her stud career, as she won fourteen of eighteen races and was rated as a brilliant sprinter-miler, plus she is renowned as well for her beautiful movement, which has been described as fluid and exquisite. Her progeny have rewritten the studbooks, dominating racing and non-racing sport ever since. Nogara's fame is extensive through her sons the *chef-de-race* Nearco and the strong sire Niccolo dell' Arca, as they are standard elements in American and international pedigrees. It is much wider than that, though. She did seem to produce mostly stallions; however her only daughter Nervasa is also classified as a *reine* for the excellence of her offspring, and you should look for her when you are trying to double up on this superior mare-line. For example, she is the third-dam of the good sire Fortino II whose son Caro is sire of the great race mare Winning Colors and the wonderful modern sire Cozzene. Caro (*chef-de-race*) also carries the rarey seen line of Black Cherry, his sixth-dam and the full sister to Bay Ronald putting them 6x6 in the dam, this combined with the Nogara double 4x4 in the sire Fortino, is a potent design. Cozzene (pedigree) is a sire whose reputation is growing day by day. His dam adds a double of Princequillo 3x4—building potency generation by generation. Notice his dam brings in not only more lines of Nogara, but also of Black Toney and Man O' War as well as the multiples of Lady Josephine. Check out his dam-line Blue Canoe, who is out of the *reine* Portage from whom also descends the 'mega-*reine*' Fall Aspen, dam of Timber Country. This is a dam-line of immense power, and it goes straight back to Matinee, a daughter of Audience—who is inbred to Maggie B. B. RH. Having Maggie B. B. RH on the dam-line is as close as you can come to a guarantee of excellence. (Matinee is a full sister to Whisk Broom II.)

Nogara's son Nicholas by Solario was a stakes winner and can be found in some lineages. Her son Naucide, who is inbred 3x2 to Nogara's sire Havresac II, was a champion stakes winner and sire. Her son Nakamuro was also a fair producer.

But then we come to Niccolo dell' Arca who has made his mark quite strongly in the classic winners. His best son possibly is Daumier, who coincidently is out of a Mahmoud mare (bringing in more Lexington RH through Lady Josephine).

His daughters will be found quite often, such as Bounamica, Clouette, Scollata, Tiepoletta, and Trevisana from whom the *reine* Valoris descends.

However it is her son Nearco who eclipses all the others—he was retired undefeated, having his wins at the Stakes level, and he is now also called 'sire of the century' by some, with good reason. Nearco was one of those rare horses who excel both at racing and breeding—he is about as good as it ever gets, and his progeny list is gigantic. There are a few combinations that have proved especially strong and are easily found by the sport horse breeder. Of course his son Nasrullah needs no introduction, he is possibly the highest rated sire in sport production—Peter Birdsall rates him as the #1 sport sire. Nasrullah has a full sister Malindi, who is classified a *reine*; she is the dam of the sire Prince Taj among others. It is rare to find full siblings that are equally excellent—usually a breeding is better for a male or a female, but we have it here with Malindi and Nasrullah, both first class producers (see Broomstick for another sire with equally good sons and daughters). Interestingly, they also had another full sister Rivaz, who is not quite in their class, but still is a good producer. Naturally these lines will be desired targets for line-breeding exercises.

Almost up to the super-elite class of Malindi and Nasrullah are the excellent full sisters Netherton Maid (*reine*) and Neasham Belle (pedigree), along with their good sire full brothers Narrator and Nanyuki. These four full siblings are out of Phase (also a *reine*), whose second-dam Orlass is a daughter of Orby (see Chapter 15). Sport horse breeders may find these lines when breeding to Hanoverians for the great dressage performer Weltruhm is out of Navarina, a daughter of Nevado, who is inbred 2x4 to Nearco through daughters. This breeding brings in lines not only of Lexington RH but also of the pacing RH Blackburns Whip who is renowned for transmitting not only speed, but beautiful fluid movement. Bet you never read of Hanoverian experts crediting the movement of their horses to Nearco too often, and I am sure never to Lexington RH or the pacing RH Blackburns Whip, but their presence is there for anyone to see. Before you write off this proposition as far-fetched consider the great Hanoverian dressage typesetter Lauries Crusador (pedigree), who has not only four lines of Nearco, sex-balanced including on his dam-line, but also carries five lines of Lady Juror, a line of Orby, and a line of Tourbillon, therefore is loaded with those same flawed American lines (see Chapter 31 for further discussion of dressage performance).

In America however it will be in Nasrullah combined with Royal Charger (*chef*) and Mahmoud (*chef*) that brings our native lines home in a large way. Royal Charger often preforms the task of providing a sex-balance for the many Nasrullah lines, as he is out of Sun Princess a daughter of Mumtaz Begum—making Sun Princess his (Nasrullah's) ½ sister; together they double up on Mumtaz Begum through a son and a daughter; this a filly factor of immense power. Mahmoud adds to the dynamic, as he is out of a daughter of Mumtaz Mahal (*reine*) therefore a sister to Mumtaz Begum (*reine*): Mah Mahal (*reine*), creating a wonderful maternal strength. All of these mares are descended from Americus, the purveyor of concentrated Lexington RH lines in England, and it all started with a humble mare bought at a bargain price.

[Note: Tesio was not the only Italian breeder who used our flawed lines; another is Razza Oldanigia, who used Americus when he was in Italy, and he is notable for breeding a mare named Araucaria 1921 by Guido Reni who was sold to Germany in 1924—we will find her line there in the next chapter.]

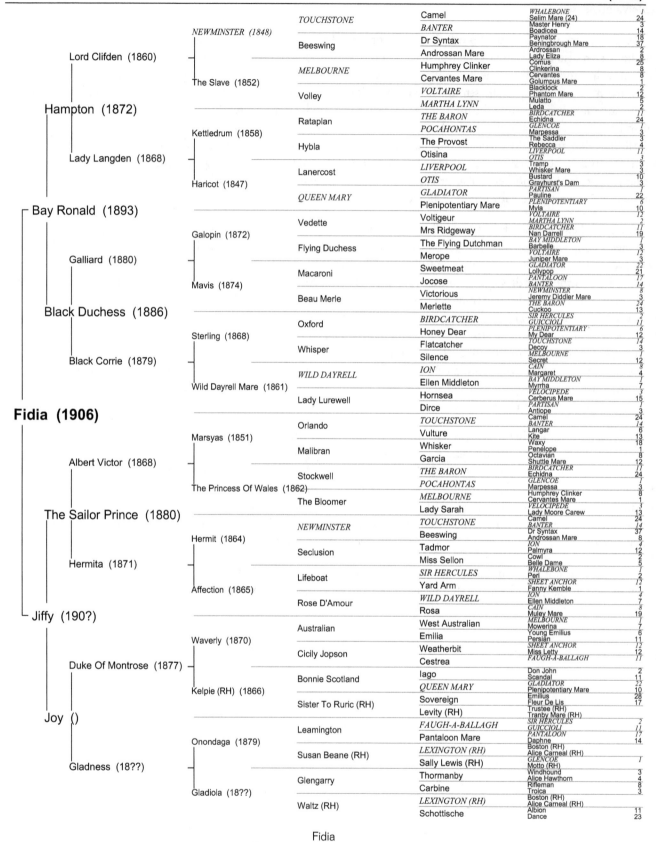

Fidia (1906)

- Bay Ronald (1893)
  - Hampton (1872)
    - Lord Clifden (1860)
      - NEWMINSTER (1848)
        - Touchstone — Camel (*WHALEBONE* 1 / Selim Mare (24) 24); Banter (Master Henry 3 / Boadicea 14)
        - Beeswing — Dr Syntax (Paynator 18 / Beningbrough Mare 37); Androssan Mare (Ardrossan 2 / Lady Eliza 8)
      - The Slave (1852)
        - MELBOURNE — Humphrey Clinker (Comus 25 / Clinkerina 8); Cervantes Mare (Cervantes 8 / Golumpus Mare 1)
        - Volley — *VOLTAIRE* (Blacklock 2 / Phantom Mare 12); *MARTHA LYNN* (Mulatto 5 / Leda 2)
    - Lady Langden (1868)
      - Kettledrum (1858)
        - Rataplan — *THE BARON* (*BIRDCATCHER* 11 / Echidna 24); *POCAHONTAS* (*GLENCOE* 1 / Marpessa 3)
        - Hybla — The Provost (The Saddler 3 / Rebecca 4); Otisina (*LIVERPOOL* 11 / *OTIS* 3)
      - Haricot (1847)
        - Lanercost — *LIVERPOOL* (Tramp 3 / Whisker Mare 3); *OTIS* (Bustard 10 / Grayhurst's Dam 3)
        - QUEEN MARY — *GLADIATOR* (*PARTISAN* 1 / Pauline 22); Plenipotentiary Mare (*PLENIPOTENTIARY* 6 / Myla 10)
  - Black Duchess (1886)
    - Galliard (1880)
      - Galopin (1872)
        - Vedette — Voltigeur (*VOLTAIRE* 12 / *MARTHA LYNN* 2); Mrs Ridgeway (*BIRDCATCHER* 11 / Nan Darrell 19)
        - Flying Duchess — The Flying Dutchman (*BAY MIDDLETON* 3 / Barbelle 3); Merope (*VOLTAIRE* 12 / Juniper Mare 3)
      - Mavis (1874)
        - Macaroni — Sweetmeat (*GLADIATOR* 22 / Lollypop 21); Jocose (*PANTALOON* 17 / *BANTER* 14)
        - Beau Merle — Victorious (*NEWMINSTER* 8 / Jeremy D Diddler Mare 3); Merlette (*THE BARON* 24 / Cuckoo 13)
    - Black Corrie (1879)
      - Sterling (1868)
        - Oxford — *BIRDCATCHER* (*SIR HERCULES* 2 / *GUICCIOLI* 11); Honey Dear (*PLENIPOTENTIARY* 6 / My Dear 12)
        - Whisper — Flatcatcher (*TOUCHSTONE* 14 / Decoy 3); Silence (*MELBOURNE* 1 / Secret 12)
      - Wild Dayrell Mare (1861)
        - *WILD DAYRELL* — *ION* (*CAIN* 8 / Margaret 4); Ellen Middleton (*BAY MIDDLETON* 1 / Myrrha 7)
        - Lady Lurewell — Hornsea (*VELOCIPEDE* 3 / Cerberus Mare 15); Dirce (*PARTISAN* 1 / Antiope 3)
- Jiffy (190?)
  - The Sailor Prince (1880)
    - Albert Victor (1868)
      - Marsyas (1851)
        - Orlando — *TOUCHSTONE* (Camel 24 / *BANTER* 14); Vulture (Langar 6 / Kite 13)
        - Malibran — Whisker (Waxy 18 / Penelope 1); Garcia (Octavian 8 / Shuttle Mare 12)
      - The Princess Of Wales (1862)
        - Stockwell — *THE BARON* (*BIRDCATCHER* 11 / Echidna 24); *POCAHONTAS* (*GLENCOE* 1 / Marpessa 3)
        - The Bloomer — *MELBOURNE* (Humphrey Clinker 8 / Cervantes Mare 1); Lady Sarah (*VELOCIPEDE* 1 / Lady Moore Carew 13)
    - Hermita (1871)
      - Hermit (1864)
        - *NEWMINSTER* — *TOUCHSTONE* (Camel 24 / *BANTER* 14); Beeswing (Dr Syntax 37 / Androssan Mare 8)
        - Seclusion — Tadmor (*ION* 4 / Palmyra 12); Miss Sellon (Cowl 6 / Belle Dame 5)
      - Affection (1865)
        - Lifeboat — *SIR HERCULES* (*WHALEBONE* 1 / Peri 2); Yard Arm (*SHEET ANCHOR* 12 / Fanny Kemble 1)
        - Rose D'Amour — *WILD DAYRELL* (*ION* 4 / Ellen Middleton 7); Rosa (*CAIN* 8 / Muley Mare 19)
  - Joy ()
    - Duke Of Montrose (1877)
      - Waverly (1870)
        - Australian — West Australian (*MELBOURNE* 7 / Mowerina 7); Emilia (Young Emilius 6 / Persian 11)
        - Cicily Jopson — Weatherbit (*SHEET ANCHOR* 12 / Miss Letty 12); Cestrea (*FAUGH-A-BALLAGH* 11)
      - Kelpie (RH) (1866)
        - Bonnie Scotland — Iago (Don John 2 / Scandal 11); *QUEEN MARY* (*GLADIATOR* 22 / Plenipotentiary Mare 10)
        - Sister To Ruric (RH) — Sovereign (Emilius 28 / Fleur De Lis 17); Levity (RH) (Trustee (RH) / Tranby Mare (RH))
    - Gladness (18??)
      - Onondaga (1879)
        - Leamington — *FAUGH-A-BALLAGH* (*SIR HERCULES* 2 / *GUICCIOLI* 11); Pantaloon Mare (*PANTALOON* 17 / Daphne 14)
        - Susan Beane (RH) — *LEXINGTON (RH)* (Boston (RH) / Alice Carneal (RH)); Sally Lewis (RH) (*GLENCOE* 1 / Motto (RH))
      - Gladiola (18??)
        - Glengarry — Thormanby (Windhound 3 / Alice Hawthorn 4); Carbine (Rifleman 8 / Troica 3)
        - Waltz (RH) — *LEXINGTON (RH)* (Boston (RH) / Alice Carneal (RH)); Schottische (Albion 11 / Dance 23)

Fidia

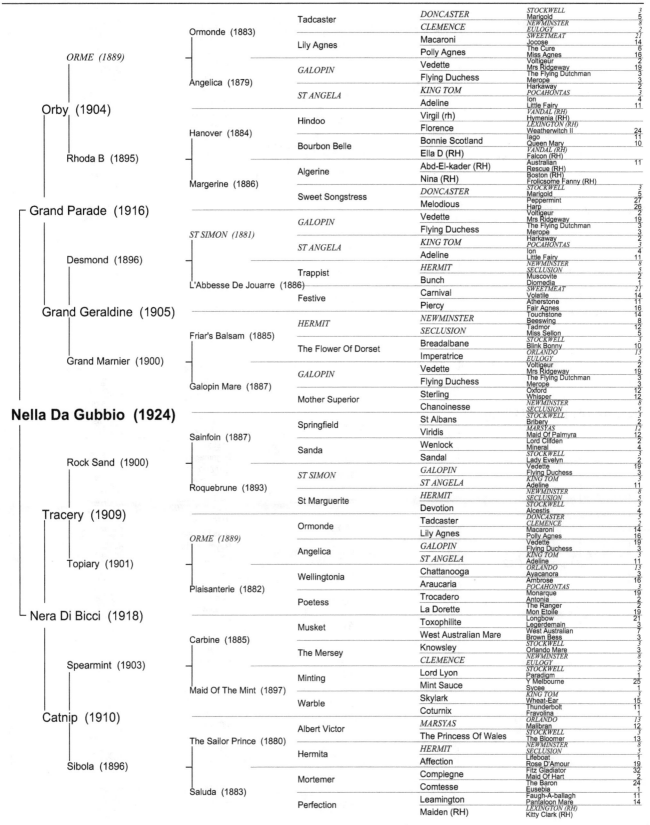

Left-line ancestry (dam/sire line of Nella Da Gubbio):

- ORME (1889)
- Orby (1904)
- Rhoda B (1895)
- Grand Parade (1916)
- Desmond (1896)
- Grand Geraldine (1905)
- Grand Marnier (1900)
- **Nella Da Gubbio (1924)**
- Rock Sand (1900)
- Tracery (1909)
- Topiary (1901)
- Nera Di Bicci (1918)
- Spearmint (1903)
- Catnip (1910)
- Sibola (1896)

Expanded pedigree:

Ormonde (1883)
- Tadcaster
  - DONCASTER — STOCKWELL 3, Marigold 5
  - CLEMENCE — NEWMINSTER 8, EULOGY 2
- Lily Agnes
  - Macaroni — SWEETMEAT 21, Jocose 14
  - Polly Agnes — The Cure 6, Miss Agnes 16

Angelica (1879)
- GALOPIN
  - Vedette — Voltigeur 2, Mrs Ridgeway 19
  - Flying Duchess — The Flying Dutchman 3, Merope 3
- ST ANGELA
  - KING TOM — Harkaway 2, POCAHONTAS 3
  - Adeline — Ion 3, Little Fairy 11

Hanover (1884)
- Hindoo
  - Virgil (rh) — VANDAL (RH), Hymenia (RH)
  - Florence — LEXINGTON (RH), Weatherwitch II 24
- Bourbon Belle
  - Bonnie Scotland — Iago 11, Queen Mary 10
  - Ella D (RH) — VANDAL (RH), Falcon (RH)

Margerine (1886)
- Algerine
  - Abd-El-kader (RH) — Australian, Rescue (RH) 11
  - Nina (RH) — Boston (RH), Frolicsome Fanny (RH)
- Sweet Songstress
  - DONCASTER — STOCKWELL 3, Marigold 5
  - Melodious — Peppermint 27, Harp 26

ST SIMON (1881)
- GALOPIN
  - Vedette — Voltigeur 2, Mrs Ridgeway 19
  - Flying Duchess — The Flying Dutchman 3, Merope 3
- ST ANGELA
  - KING TOM — Harkaway 2, POCAHONTAS 3
  - Adeline — Ion 4, Little Fairy 11

L'Abbesse De Jouarre (1886)
- Trappist
  - HERMIT — NEWMINSTER 8, SECLUSION 5
  - Bunch — Muscovite 2, Diomedia 1
- Festive
  - Carnival — SWEETMEAT 21, Volatile 14
  - Piercy — Atherstone 11, Fair Agnes 16

Friar's Balsam (1885)
- HERMIT
  - NEWMINSTER — Touchstone 14, Beeswing 8
  - SECLUSION — Tadmor 12, Miss Sellon 5
- The Flower Of Dorset
  - Breadalbane — STOCKWELL 3, Blink Bonny 10
  - Imperatrice — ORLANDO 13, EULOGY 2

Galopin Mare (1887)
- GALOPIN
  - Vedette — Voltigeur 2, Mrs Ridgeway 19
  - Flying Duchess — The Flying Dutchman 3, Merope 3
- Mother Superior
  - Sterling — Oxford 12, Whisper 12
  - Chanoinesse — NEWMINSTER 8, SECLUSION 5

Sainfoin (1887)
- Springfield
  - St Albans — STOCKWELL 3, Bribery
  - Viridis — MARSYAS 12, Maid Of Palmyra 12
- Sanda
  - Wenlock — Lord Clifden 2, Mineral 4
  - Sandal — STOCKWELL 3, Lady Evelyn 2

Roquebrune (1893)
- ST SIMON
  - GALOPIN — Vedette 19, Flying Duchess 3
  - ST ANGELA — KING TOM 3, Adeline 11
- St Marguerite
  - HERMIT — NEWMINSTER 8, SECLUSION 5
  - Devotion — STOCKWELL 3, Alcestis 4

ORME (1889)
- Ormonde
  - Tadcaster — DONCASTER 5, CLEMENCE 2
  - Lily Agnes — Macaroni 14, Polly Agnes 16
- Angelica
  - GALOPIN — Vedette 19, Flying Duchess 3
  - ST ANGELA — KING TOM 3, Adeline 11

Plaisanterie (1882)
- Wellingtonia
  - Chattanooga — ORLANDO 13, Ayacanora 3
  - Araucaria — Ambrose 16, POCAHONTAS 3
- Poetess
  - Trocadero — Monarque 19, Antonia 2
  - La Dorette — The Ranger 2, Mon Etoile 19

Carbine (1885)
- Musket
  - Toxophilite — Longbow 21, Legerdemain 3
  - West Australian Mare — West Australian 7, Brown Bess 3
- The Mersey
  - Knowsley — STOCKWELL 3, Orlando Mare 3
  - CLEMENCE — NEWMINSTER 8, EULOGY 2

Maid Of The Mint (1897)
- Minting
  - Lord Lyon — STOCKWELL 3, Paradigm 1
  - Mint Sauce — Y Melbourne 25, Sycee 1
- Warble
  - Skylark — KING TOM 3, Wheat-Ear 15
  - Coturnix — Thunderbolt 11, Fravolina 1

The Sailor Prince (1880)
- Albert Victor
  - MARSYAS — ORLANDO 13, Malibran 12
  - The Princess Of Wales — STOCKWELL 3, The Bloomer 13
- Hermita
  - HERMIT — NEWMINSTER 8, SECLUSION 5
  - Affection — Lifeboat 1, Rose D'Amour 19

Saluda (1883)
- Mortemer
  - Compiegne — Fitz Gladiator 32, Maid Of Hart 2
  - Comtesse — The Baron 24, Eusebia 1
- Perfection
  - Leamington — Faugh-A-ballagh 11, Pantaloon Mare 14
  - Maiden (RH) — LEXINGTON (RH), Kitty Clark (RH)

Nella da Gubbio

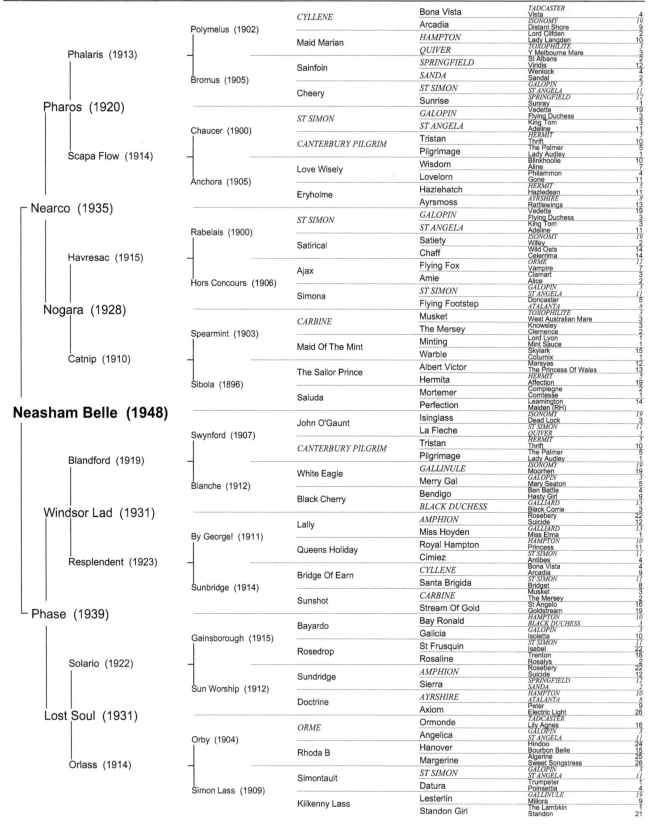

Neasham Belle

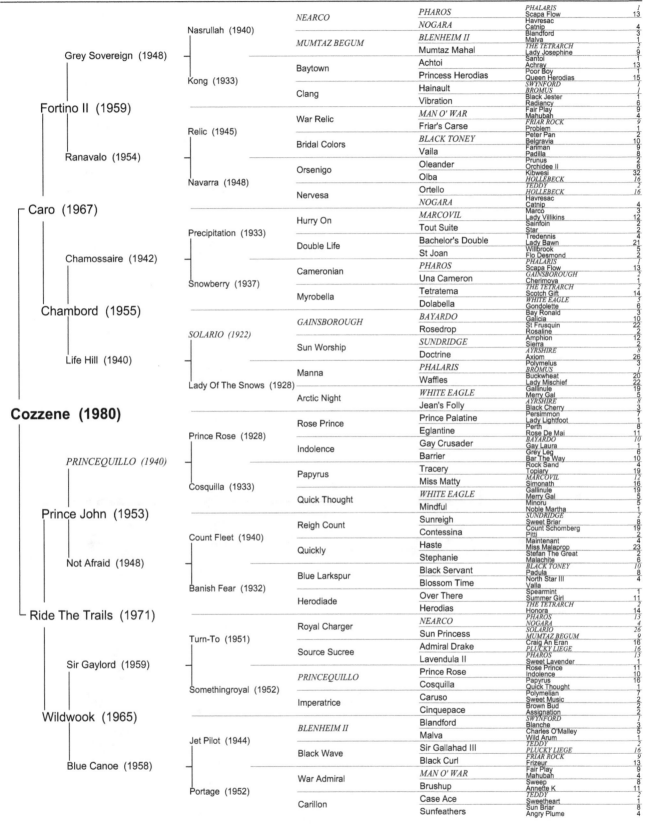

Cozzene 1980

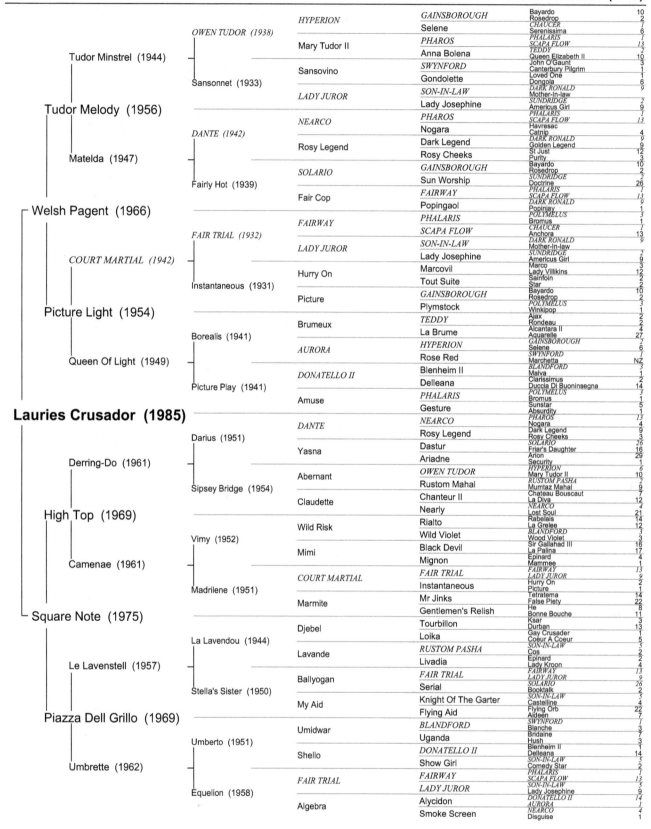

Lauries Crusador 1985

Chapter 18

The Flaw in Germany

This text is written for the North American, and while we love the horses produced by Germany (which is obvious by our whole-hearted participation in their breed societies), we need to clarify the position in sport of our native breeds as well, so this information is provided to dispel several gross misunderstandings regarding the American-bred horse and its valuable sport bloodlines, rather than to pander to the Warmblood industry. No offense is intended, but it is truthfully our turn to speak.

When I was participating in the 'warmblood fad' in this country I would always wonder why there were no American lines in the horses that were held up to us in publications and books, and by the representatives of the Warmblood registries operating in this country. The bloodlines presented to us as those powering the champions in Olympic style sport were all European—or appeared so on the surface (read more on this in Chapters 32 and 34). We already discussed the surprising concentration of American lines in the dressage sensation Weltruhm HA (Chapters 14 & 15)—surely this must be a fluke?

Nordlicht 1941, winner of German Derby, is a son of the Derby-winning mare Nereide and was taken as a prize of war by the US at the close of WWII. His case is tragic, for he was rarely bred to, because not only was he classified as a 'half-bred' for his 'flawed' lines and therefore excluded from GSB registration, but also much of his pedigree was impossible to verify, so therefore he ended up in the Remount, but he produced little because that breeding program had ceased before WWII. After the Jersey Act was rescinded he was flown to France so he would be eligible for their studbook, and finally he was officially registered as a TB—photo taken by US Remount Service.

What I could not comprehend then, but now can see, is that there were several reasons for this apparent lack of American lines in the European horse: the big one is we were being fed our information almost exclusively by Europeans who truly had no knowledge of our sport lines and therefore were unaware of our domestic lines that powered international champions. The second reason was our quality light horse breeds, the racehorses and saddlehorses, which after all are our main contribution to the worldwide sport experience—never even made the trip to England and Europe until the mid and late 1800s, therefore we should not expect to see American lines in the European sport stock before this. Plus our Thoroughbred—the base of our Hunter Horse—once it had made it to Europe and proven its superior genetics, only a short time passed before it was banished from international breeding by the Jersey Act from 1913 until 1949.

Germany as a whole has a long history of state studs standing stallions for the breeders, but the misconception held by most Americans is that those studs were breeding sport warmbloods all along. Instead it is the opposite that is the truth—except for in the eastern (Baltic) provinces, what was being bred was a draft horse—that is a farm horse, which is what we call a 'cold-blood' here. More confusion arises for the American as they called those plow horses 'warmbloods' then and still do. So when you are told the Hanoverian Warmblood was organized in 1735, what they fail to mention or what the typical American fails to note, is that it was a farm horse breed, not a sport horse—indeed the sport Hanoverian did not appear until after WWII.

For example, at a warmblood inspection held in New Hampshire in the 1990s that I took part in, the foreign judge took the time to explain to the participants and the spectators that the Germans had been selectively breeding this **same type** of Holstein for two hundred years, and we were impressed then with their vast experience in sport horse production as we were intended to be. (The century's old designation belongs to their state system of standing stallions for the breeders and their stock inspection system—not their modern sport breeds.) The result of this misconception is that the American breeder of warmbloods assumes that Continental Europe has centuries of experience in producing **sport** warmbloods—not so—the centuries-old history of sport horse breeding, with the exception of the Lipizzaner that specializes in 'high school dressage,' is held by the English, Irish, French, and even the USA and Canada.

Even German racehorse breeding was not organized until the mid-1800s, and it is based on the English Thoroughbred. For example, the great German racehorse and sire Ticino goes tail-male and tail-female right back to exclusively English horses by the 1890s. Germany also bred trotters, but once again their foundation stock came from the French Trotter, the Russian Orloff, and surprisingly the American Standardbred.

Now in eastern Germany, that different 'warmblood' is the Trakehner and East Prussian Horse, which are a dissimilar class of breed, as it is a lighter agricultural and a cavalry-bred since the mid-1800s, based on a utility breed rather than a draft horse and improved for cavalry use mostly by English Thoroughbred with some Arabian added as well. This is more what the American's would recognize as a true warmblood, and it is this breed that was used by most of the German cavalry as mounts (the heavier German breeds were used in pulling artillery), and it is also the breed that was ridden by their cavalry in the early Olympic competitions.

An overlooked point by many sport historians is that the American horses—Thoroughbred, Running Horse, Standardbred and our Hunter Horse—were already true international sport horses from the mid-1800s on, being regularly competed in England and Europe, not just in racing either, but in Hunter sports including the brand new sport of show jumping, and they won consistently.

The amazing race mare Nereide (Derby winner) is a daughter of Nella da Gubbio; she carries almost 30% American lines, and she is dam of the German Derby winner Nordlicht. —public domain image courtesy of Wiki Commons

The American bloodlines that had made an impact in England and then Europe were not then, and are not still today, heralded as American lines. After the ban on our Thoroughbred was lifted and from the 1960s and beyond, we do begin to see familiar lines of our horses appearing here and there in the great European racers and sport horses, such as the Man O' War son War Relic, who shows up repeatedly through his French family of Reliance, Relko, and Match II (Reliance and Relko are not only descended from Fair Play and Black Toney, but they are rated *chef-de-race* in stamina). We also find that the War Relic grandson Pericles 1958 founded a line in the Dutch Warmblood, and American-bred Tracery, who spent his stud career in England and Argentina, is very well represented in bloodlines. But all that changed by the 1970s, as our horses were imported in large numbers—mainly through the Coolmore stud in Ireland (Sangster, Magnier, and O'Brien) —and through their proliferation we find our lines bursting out everywhere. Before this, though, to the casual student of sport horse bloodlines it seems none were involved.

However this is not the case at all. No one was more surprised than I to discover that from those few individual horses who made it into the GSB before the ban and a few others who were sold out of Britain after the ruling came down, that a vast legacy of sport performance flowed from those American lines, not just in the British Isles but in France, Italy, and Germany as well.

I have to admit the German branch has surprised me the most—probably because I listened so attentively to those European experts in the 1990s—and I suspect there is more there than I have uncovered, because I have by no means done an exhaustive search.

For example, I have found that traces of the American Thoroughbred Americus still exist on the Continent. If you remember from Chapter 15; he was sold to Germany and stood there in 1909 and part of 1910 until his death that year. During this time period in Germany there were many Thoroughbreds being imported, especially to the Trakehnen and East Prussian studs, and they were being used to improve their cavalry herds. Germany was intent on having a powerful cavalry, and it was the East Prussian horse that was used far and wide as the cavalry mount.

Fritz Schlike in his comprehensive history of the Trakehner breed said that from 1894 through 1918 the aim was to "…breed a horse closely resembling the English Thoroughbred for use as army remounts with endurance and good performance or, more precisely, sires for such remounts" (*Trakehner Horses – then and now*).

It was in this period that Americus was brought to stand there, and he was bred to Trakehner mares—so his offspring are registered Trakehners. How many of his progeny survived the carnage of both world wars is hard to determine. Here are a few of his Trakehner children: the mare Sadina 1910 was a broodmare from 1913-28; his daughter Rumpelstilzchen 1910 stood from 1913-1924; his daughter Mein Lieb 1910 stood from 1915-19??; his daughter Prophetin 1911 stood from 1914-1917. Some of his Trakehner sons: Pfeffermuenz 1910 stood at Georgenburg stud from 1914-1922; his son Kompass 1910 stood at Zirke in 1914; his son Teufelsdorn 1911 stood at Gudwallen Stud from 1914-1922, and his son Prinz John 1911 stood at Gudwallen 1915-1924.

It was another of his sons, Bachus 1910, who I found a little more information on. It is recorded that he made quite an impression at stud, as he was listed as one of a dozen significant sires of the pre-WWI era, even though he was used only 'lightly;' still his progeny were rated 'very good.' A few examples: his daughter Emmi produced a stallion son Erbherr 1932 who we find, for instance, in the Danish Warmblood sire Lichtenstein 1969, but it is his daughter Sava who has left a huge imprint, as her daughter Saaleck TR 1940 (pedigree) is one of the major mare families in the modern Trakehner Warmblood. With a quick look here on our continent I found one of her descendants who stood in Canada: Schwalbenherbst 1979; she is his fourth-dam. He produced good sport horses, which includes the eventing champion Formal Affair, and the dressage champion Komponist, but it is his son Heart Breaker most will remember here because from 1988 through 1999 he was a champion every year in dressage, starting at first level right up through Prix St. George and then Intermediaire I—an extraordinary career.

Other of Americus's progeny made it to Germany via other routes. The Irish-bred stallion Republic 1905, whose dam even brings in another line of Lexington RH, making him 4x4x3; he did the rounds at the German studs also—standing at Trakehnen 1909 through 1912, then at Rastenberg from 1913 through 1917, at Zirke in 1917, and then at Wardendorf in 1918 (Westphalia).

An Italian-bred mare Araucaria 1921, whose dam-sire is Americus, was sold to Germany in 1924, and she produced among others the mare Aela 1936 by Oleander, who is dam of the stallion Anis 1943 and the mare Albanella 1944.

When Germany lost WWI she was forced to reduce her military and her cavalry—so between 1918 and 1933 the eastern cavalry studs were switched back to agricultural horse production. Meanwhile, in the greater part of Germany, including the studs of Holstein, Hanover, and Oldenburg, there had never been a change from the agricultural focus. In 1933 the Trakehnen/East Prussian studs once again began importing large amounts of Thoroughbreds to produce cavalry remounts, and until after WWII it was still the East Prussian Horse that produced the majority of their Olympic team mounts.

Americus was not the only of our 'flawed' American lines that made it into the German horse. Just in my preliminary exploration I have already found three mares who have made a solid impact in the German sport horse, and I will present them to you as examples: the foundation mare Nella da Gubbio, a Tesio-bred Catnip granddaughter (Lexington RH, Blackburns Whip RH), and the good American-bred mare Grave and Gay (Revenue RH and Lexington RH lines), and the good Irish-bred mare Alabama (Americus and Rhoda B), and all three of them have made their mark quite strongly in the German sport horse, in both their Thoroughbred and in their Warmblood.

I know the least about the mare Alabama, only that she was bred in the British Isles, by Richard Croker no less, and she is by Americus out of Rhoda B. Take a moment to look at her pedigree; she has three lines of Lexington RH plus his close relative Algerine 4x4x5x3, as well as two lines of Vandal RH 5x5 plus multiple other Running Horse lines—this is a concentrated dose of American Running Horse dropped into the German gene pool. This configuration also supplies an immensely powerful filly factor of Alice Carneal RH (dam of Lexington RH). You will come across Alabama's bloodline quite frequently, especially in those descended from her daughter Addi, such as through her granddaughter Uberraschung who produced the great racers Toronado, Formosa, and Apollo (who is 4x5 Orby/Rhoda B on both dam-lines-see pedigree).

Henry of Navarre 1891—a fantastic racehorse and mediocre sire in America; some of his most lasting lines are overseas. —image found in *Racing in America* 1922

Grave and Gay is an American-bred mare who ended up in Germany and left a significant dynasty of excellence. I remembered seeing her in the lineages of warmbloods I was studying years ago, but it never occurred to me at the time that she was an American Thoroughbred—I assumed she was English. American breeder W.C. Whitney maintained a string of racers in England before the Jersey Act in both England and France. Grave and Gay was one of those mares he brought over in 1901, a daughter of the great racehorse Henry of Navarre; she did well racing in England, placing and winning at high levels. She was sold to Englishman Sir John Thursby, and she did fairly well for him also, placing and winning on occasion. Nevertheless she was put up for sale at Newmarket and was picked up by the Weinburg brothers for the stud in Germany. She was sold in foal to Zinfandel, with a weanling colt by Trenton at her side.

Grave and Gay produced very well in Germany, having numerous offspring, many of the highest class. Several of her sons were gelded, and it is interesting that some of those had a career not just as flat racers, but as jumpers as well. Just a side note on the jump aptitude—I keep noticing a correlation between trotting ability or descent with jumpers, and maybe it is just coincidence, but Grave and Gay's great-grandsire Eolus RH was not only a talented four-mile heat racer, but he was a useful trotter as well. Notable also is her grandsire on her dam side, Duke of Magenta, Lexington's great racehorse son, who descends from some of our Quarter Horse foundation stock (up until 1868, when the American Thoroughbred was established, the American TB and the American Quarter Horse were the same breed: Running Horse).

Her greatest German offspring are a pair of full siblings: Graf Ferry and Grolle Nicht, both by Fervor. If you breed warmbloods you already have these lines in your herds—they are everywhere in the German sport horse. Grolle Nicht 1917 heads up a maternal dynasty of performance stars. Her daughter's Grolleja and Grossularia are both great producers. The *reine* Rhea is by a son (Gundomar) of Grossularia for instance.

Graf Ferry 1918 is a son of American-bred Grave and Gay; he was a great racer and sire in Germany—he is 38% American RH! —Wiki Commons image

It is Graf Ferry 1918, the full brother to Grolle Nicht, who stands tallest, and his bloodlines are 38% American Running Horse (both can be targets for line-breeding). A great racehorse, he was rated the top two-year-old in Germany, and he did well for several more years. As a sire he shines; several of his sons were excellent, such as Travertin and Ladro, both good racers and sires. However it is his son Graf Isolani 1926 who proved the best, as he won the German Derby and other prestigious races. He too became an important sire whose offspring are widespread. One of his best performers was the sensational mare Nereide—dam of Nordlicht, who swept all before her including the German Derby. His best producer may well be Nanon, the dam of the great mare Nixe who in-turn produced the German Derby winner Neckar, as well as three of his full siblings: Nostradamus, Nina, and Naxos. Neckar's genetic reach is huge (he led the sire list for five years), and the sport horse breeder may be well familiar with lines of his progeny such as Kronzeuge, Waidsmanndank, and Weisenblute to name a few. Graf Isolani's daughter Naxos produced the superstar Nebos, a son of Caro, who is inbred to Nogara, so he is another strong carrier of the Flaw.

Graf Isolani 1926—best son of Graf Ferry and sire of the fabulous broodmare Nanon. —Wiki Commons image

Perhaps the largest international footprint was left by the Tesio-bred Nella da Gubbio. Another masterpiece by Tesio, she was sold to Germany right before WWII, when he was trying to move and sell off many of his stock before the war reached them.

The *reine-de-course* Nella da Gubbio has Lexington RH twice and his sister Nina RH, plus other close Flawed relatives through her second sire Orby and her second dam Catnip. From her comes a German dynasty of Derby winners through three daughters: Nanon, Nerada, and Nericide. For instance, there is Nerada who is saturated in Lexington RH lines—because her sire brings in the French mare Durban who carries eight lines of Lexington RH plus four of his sister Nina RH. She is the dam of Nadia, Nizam, and Norma. Then we come to Nanon, who through her sire Graf Isolani brings in more American lines such as Henry of Navarre, Orby, and Catnip—as well as a line of the non-flawed American-bred Tracery. She is the dam of the *reine-de-course* Nixe who is the dam of the German Derby winner Neckar, who is the sire of Waidmannsdank and others commonly found in German Warmbloods.

We identified the dressage transmitter Weltruhm HA and Lauries Crusader (Chapters 14 & 15) as carrying significant American lines. It is also interesting that one of the modern lines used in Germany for the production of dressage horses was the Thoroughbred Marcio. His second dam-sire is Graf Ferry, and the dam-sire's third dam is an Orby daughter: Glaze Wheel. Notice how many of the best specimens have RH dam-lines.

Nixe, a *reine-de-course*, is the daughter of the great broodmare Nanon, who is by Graf Isolani out of Nella da Gubbio. Nixe is the dam of German Derby winner and good sire Neckar—Wiki Commons public domain photos.

How many of you realized the Warmblood breeds you revere so steadfastly are laced with both American four-mile heat Running Horses as well as our classic race Thoroughbred stars? It sure gives the American breeder a different perspective, especially those of us who sat under the warmblood registry tutelage in the 1990s, where they discouraged the aspiring American Warmblood breeders from using the American Thoroughbred, because they told us it was too sprint-oriented and not as high quality as those from Europe—like theirs for instance!

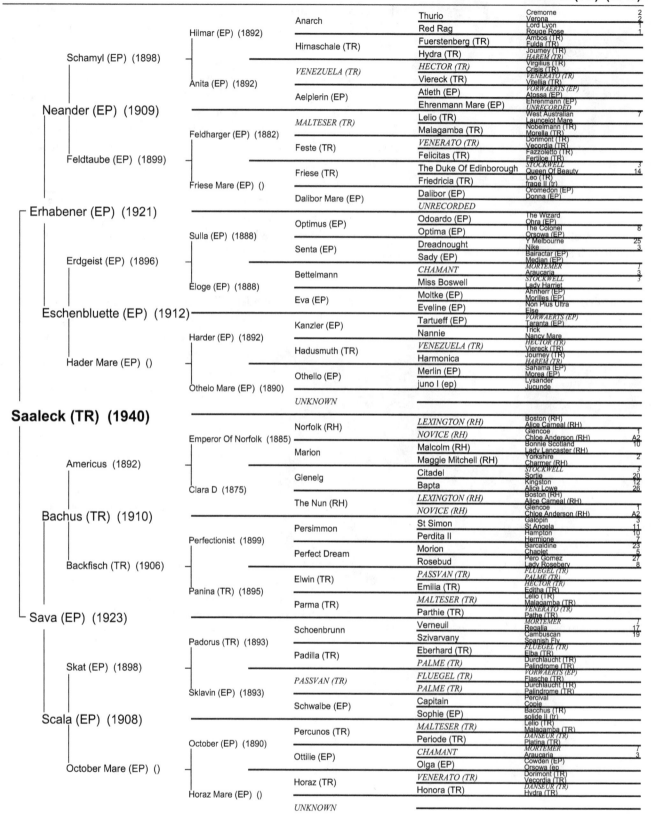

Saaleck TR 1940

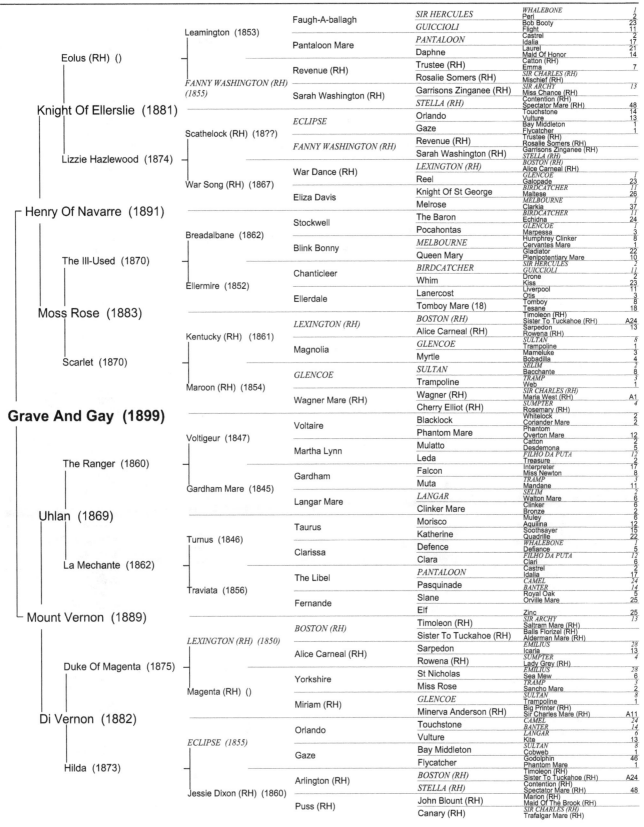

Grave and Gay 1899

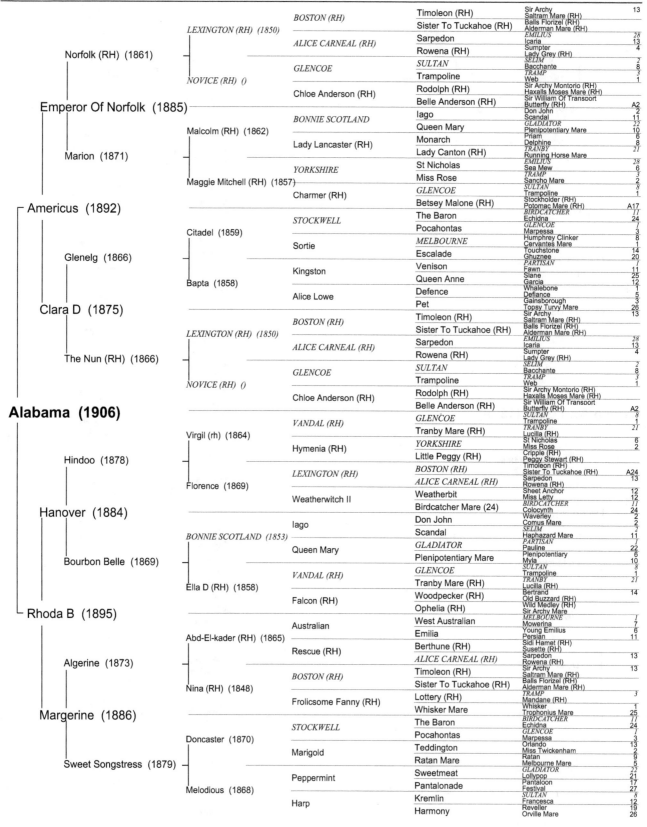

Alabama 1906

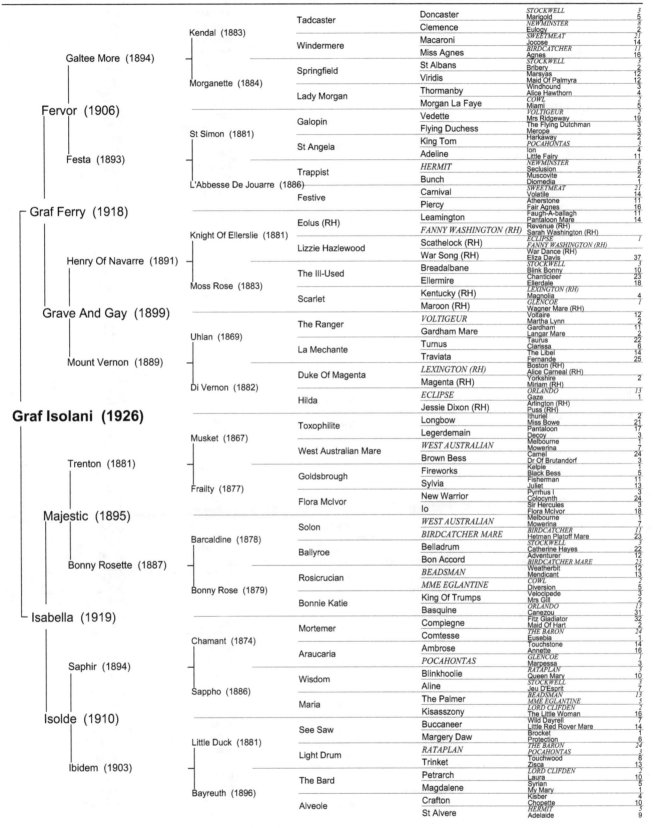

Graf Isolani (1926)

- **Graf Ferry (1918)**
  - **Fervor (1906)**
    - Galtee More (1894)
      - Kendal (1883)
        - Tadcaster
          - Doncaster — *STOCKWELL* 3 / Marigold 5
          - Clemence — *NEWMINSTER* 8 / Eulogy 2
        - Windermere
          - Macaroni — *SWEETMEAT* 21 / Jocose 14
          - Miss Agnes — *BIRDCATCHER* 11 / Agnes 16
      - Morganette (1884)
        - Springfield
          - St Albans — *STOCKWELL* 3 / Bribery
          - Viridis — Marsyas 12 / Maid Of Palmyra 12
        - Lady Morgan
          - Thormanby — Windhound 3 / Alice Hawthorn 4
          - Morgan La Faye — *COWL* 2 / Miami 5
    - Festa (1893)
      - St Simon (1881)
        - Galopin
          - Vedette — *VOLTIGEUR* 2 / Mrs Ridgeway 19
          - Flying Duchess — The Flying Dutchman 3 / Merope 3
        - St Angela
          - King Tom — Harkaway 2 / *POCAHONTAS* 4
          - Adeline — Ion 2 / Little Fairy 11
      - L'Abbesse De Jouarre (1886)
        - Trappist
          - *HERMIT* — *NEWMINSTER* 8 / Seclusion 5
          - Bunch — Muscovite 2 / Diomedia 1
        - Festive
          - Carnival — *SWEETMEAT* 21 / Volatile 14
          - Piercy — Atherstone 11 / Fair Agnes 16
  - **Grave And Gay (1899)**
    - Henry Of Navarre (1891)
      - Knight Of Ellerslie (1881)
        - Eolus (RH)
          - Leamington — Faugh-A-ballagh 11 / Pantaloon Mare 14
          - *FANNY WASHINGTON (RH)* — Revenue 1 / Sarah Washington (RH)
        - Lizzie Hazlewood
          - Scathelock (RH) — *ECLIPSE* / *FANNY WASHINGTON (RH)*
          - War Song (RH) — War Dance (RH) / Eliza Davis 37
      - Moss Rose (1883)
        - The Ill-Used
          - Breadalbane — *STOCKWELL* 3 / Blink Bonny 10
          - Ellermire — Chanticleer 23 / Ellerdale 18
        - Scarlet
          - Kentucky (RH) — *LEXINGTON (RH)* 4 / Magnolia
          - Maroon (RH) — *GLENCOE* 1 / Wagner Mare (RH)
    - Mount Vernon (1889)
      - Uhlan (1869)
        - The Ranger
          - *VOLTIGEUR* — Voltaire 12 / Martha Lynn 11
          - Gardham Mare — Gardham / Langar Mare 22
        - La Mechante
          - Turnus — Taurus 6 / Clarissa
          - Traviata — The Libel 14 / Fernande 25
      - Di Vernon (1882)
        - Duke Of Magenta
          - *LEXINGTON (RH)* — Boston (RH) / Alice Carneal (RH)
          - Magenta (RH) — Yorkshire 2 / Miriam (RH)
        - Hilda
          - *ECLIPSE* — *ORLANDO* 13 / Gaze 1
          - Jessie Dixon (RH) — Arlington (RH) / Puss (RH)
- **Isabella (1919)**
  - **Majestic (1895)**
    - Trenton (1881)
      - Musket (1867)
        - Toxophilite
          - Longbow — Ithuriel 2 / Miss Bowe 21
          - Legerdemain — Pantaloon 17 / Decoy 3
        - West Australian Mare
          - *WEST AUSTRALIAN* — Melbourne 1 / Mowerina 7
          - Brown Bess — Camel 24 / Dr Of Brutandorf 3
      - Frailty (1877)
        - Goldsbrough
          - Fireworks — Kelpie 1 / Black Bess 5
          - Sylvia — Fisherman 11 / Juliet 13
        - Flora McIvor
          - New Warrior — Pyrrhus I 3 / Colocynth 24
          - Io — Sir Hercules 3 / Flora McIvor 18
    - Bonny Rosette (1887)
      - Barcaldine (1878)
        - Solon
          - *WEST AUSTRALIAN* — Melbourne 1 / Mowerina 7
          - *BIRDCATCHER MARE* — *BIRDCATCHER* 11 / Hetman Platoff Mare 23
        - Ballyroe
          - Belladrum — *STOCKWELL* 3 / Catherine Hayes 22
          - Bon Accord — Adventurer 12 / *BIRDCATCHER MARE* 23
      - Bonny Rose (1879)
        - Rosicrucian
          - *BEADSMAN* — Weatherbit 12 / Mendicant 13
          - *MME EGLANTINE* — *COWL* 2 / Diversion 5
        - Bonnie Katie
          - King Of Trumps — Velocipede 3 / Mrs Gill 13
          - Basquine — *ORLANDO* 13 / Canezou 31
  - **Isolde (1910)**
    - Saphir (1894)
      - Chamant (1874)
        - Mortemer
          - Compiegne — Fitz Gladiator 32 / Maid Of Hart 2
          - Comtesse — *THE BARON* 24 / Eusebia 1
        - Araucaria
          - Ambrose — Touchstone 14 / Annette 16
          - *POCAHONTAS* — *GLENCOE* 1 / Marpessa 3
      - Sappho (1886)
        - Wisdom
          - Blinkhoolie — *RATAPLAN* / Queen Mary 10
          - Aline — *STOCKWELL* 3 / Jeu D'Esprit 7
        - Maria
          - The Palmer — *BEADSMAN* 13 / *MME EGLANTINE* 5
          - Kisasszony — *LORD CLIFDEN* 2 / The Little Woman 16
    - Ibidem (1903)
      - Little Duck (1881)
        - See Saw
          - Buccaneer — Wild Dayrell 7 / Little Red Rover Mare 14
          - Margery Daw — Brocket 1 / Protection 6
        - Light Drum
          - *RATAPLAN* — *THE BARON* 24 / *POCAHONTAS* 3
          - Trinket — Touchwood 8 / Zisca 13
      - Bayreuth (1896)
        - The Bard
          - Petrarch — *LORD CLIFDEN* 2 / Laura 10
          - Magdalene — Syrian 5 / My Mary 1
        - Alveole
          - Crafton — Kisber 4 / Chopette 10
          - St Alvere — *HERMIT* 5 / Adelaide 9

Graf Isolani 1926

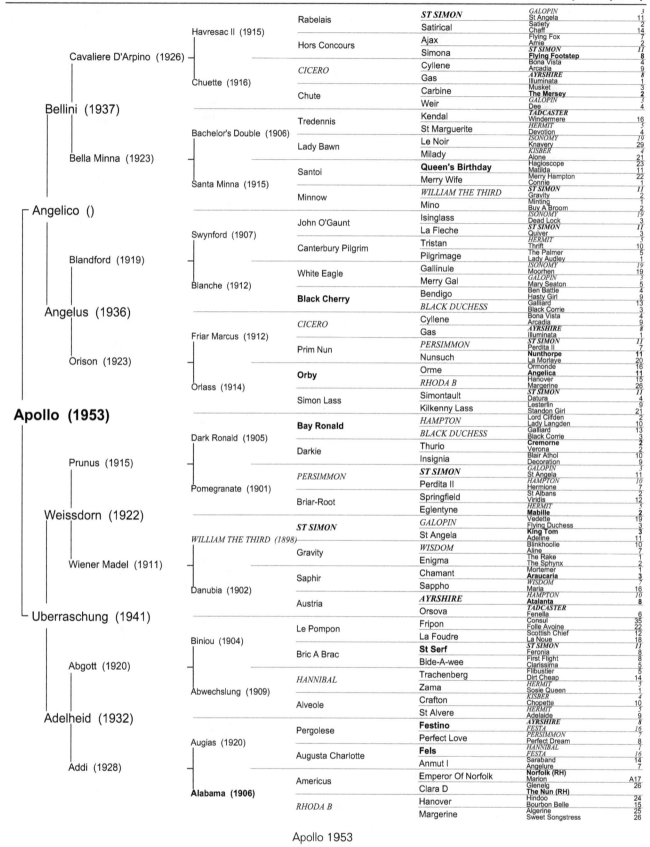

Apollo 1953

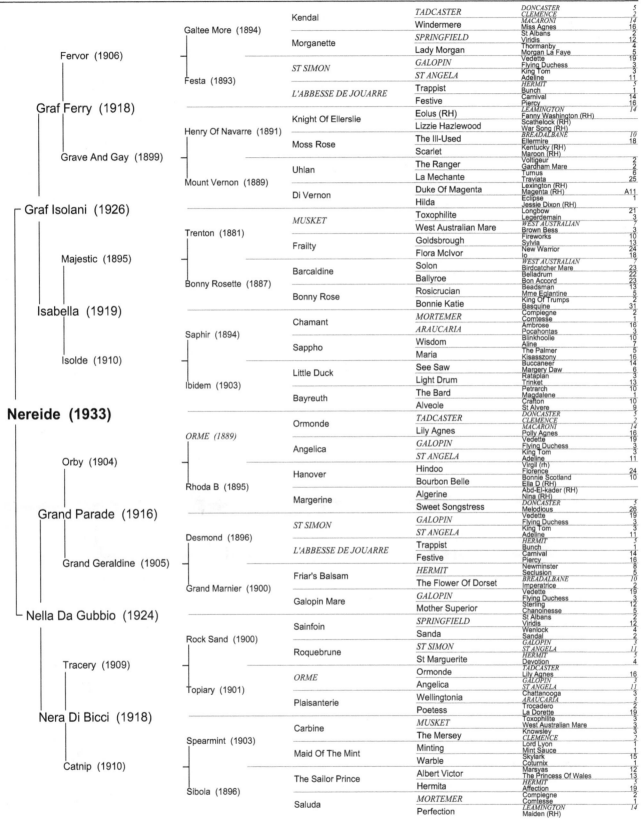

Nereide (1933)

- **Graf Isolani (1926)**
  - **Graf Ferry (1918)**
    - **Fervor (1906)**
      - Galtee More (1894)
        - Kendal
          - *TADCASTER* — DONCASTER 5 / CLEMENCE 2
          - Windermere — MACARONI 14 / Miss Agnes 16
        - Morganette
          - *SPRINGFIELD* — St Albans 2 / Viridis 12
          - Lady Morgan — Thormanby 4 / Morgan La Faye 5
      - Festa (1893)
        - *ST SIMON*
          - *GALOPIN* — Vedette 19 / Flying Duchess 3
          - *ST ANGELA* — King Tom 3 / Adeline 11
        - *L'ABBESSE DE JOUARRE*
          - Trappist — HERMIT 5 / Bunch 1
          - Festive — Carnival 14 / Piercy 16
    - **Grave And Gay (1899)**
      - Henry Of Navarre (1891)
        - Knight Of Ellerslie
          - Eolus (RH) — LEAMINGTON 14 / Fanny Washington (RH)
          - Lizzie Hazlewood — Scathelock (RH) / War Song (RH)
        - Moss Rose
          - The Ill-Used — BREADALBANE 10 / Ellermire 18
          - Scarlet — Kentucky (RH) / Maroon (RH)
      - Mount Vernon (1889)
        - Uhlan
          - The Ranger — Voltigeur 2 / Gardham Mare 2
          - La Mechante — Turnus 6 / Traviata 25
        - Di Vernon
          - Duke Of Magenta — Lexington (RH) / Magenta (RH) A11
          - Hilda — Eclipse 1 / Jessie Dixon (RH)
  - **Isabella (1919)**
    - **Majestic (1895)**
      - Trenton (1881)
        - *MUSKET*
          - Toxophilite — Longbow 21 / Legerdemain 3
          - West Australian Mare — WEST AUSTRALIAN 7 / Brown Bess 3
        - Frailty
          - Goldsbrough — Fireworks 10 / Sylvia 13
          - Flora McIvor — New Warrior 24 / Io 18
      - Bonny Rosette (1887)
        - Barcaldine
          - Solon — WEST AUSTRALIAN 7 / Birdcatcher Mare 23
          - Ballyroe — Belladrum 22 / Bon Accord 23
        - Bonny Rose
          - Rosicrucian — Beadsman 13 / Mme Eglantine 5
          - Bonnie Katie — King Of Trumps 2 / Basquine 31
    - **Isolde (1910)**
      - Saphir (1894)
        - Chamant
          - *MORTEMER* — Compiegne 2 / Comtesse 1
          - *ARAUCARIA* — Ambrose 16 / Pocahontas 3
        - Sappho
          - Wisdom — Blinkhoolie 10 / Aline 7
          - Maria — The Palmer 5 / Kisasszony 16
      - Ibidem (1903)
        - Little Duck
          - See Saw — Buccaneer 14 / Margery Daw 6
          - Light Drum — Rataplan 3 / Trinket 13
        - Bayreuth
          - The Bard — Petrarch 10 / Magdalene 1
          - Alveole — Crafton 10 / St Alvere 9
- **Nella Da Gubbio (1924)**
  - **Grand Parade (1916)**
    - **Orby (1904)**
      - *ORME (1889)*
        - Ormonde
          - *TADCASTER* — DONCASTER 5 / CLEMENCE 2
          - Lily Agnes — MACARONI 14 / Polly Agnes 16
        - Angelica
          - *GALOPIN* — Vedette 19 / Flying Duchess 3
          - *ST ANGELA* — King Tom 3 / Adeline 11
      - Rhoda B (1895)
        - Hanover
          - Hindoo — Virgil (rh) / Florence 24
          - Bourbon Belle — Bonnie Scotland 10 / Ella D (RH)
        - Margerine
          - Algerine — Abd-El-kader (RH) / Nina (RH)
          - Sweet Songstress — DONCASTER 5 / Melodious 26
    - **Grand Geraldine (1905)**
      - Desmond (1896)
        - *ST SIMON*
          - *GALOPIN* — Vedette 19 / Flying Duchess 3
          - *ST ANGELA* — King Tom 3 / Adeline 11
        - *L'ABBESSE DE JOUARRE*
          - Trappist — HERMIT 5 / Bunch 1
          - Festive — Carnival 14 / Piercy 16
      - Grand Marnier (1900)
        - Friar's Balsam
          - *HERMIT* — Newminster 8 / Seclusion 5
          - The Flower Of Dorset — BREADALBANE 10 / Imperatrice 2
        - Galopin Mare
          - *GALOPIN* — Vedette 19 / Flying Duchess 3
          - Mother Superior — Sterling 12 / Chanoinesse 5
  - **Nera Di Bicci (1918)**
    - **Tracery (1909)**
      - Rock Sand (1900)
        - Sainfoin
          - *SPRINGFIELD* — St Albans 2 / Viridis 12
          - Sanda — Wenlock 4 / Sandal 2
        - Roquebrune
          - *ST SIMON* — GALOPIN 3 / ST ANGELA 11
          - St Marguerite — HERMIT 5 / Devotion 4
      - Topiary (1901)
        - *ORME*
          - Ormonde — TADCASTER / Lily Agnes 16
          - Angelica — GALOPIN 3 / ST ANGELA 11
        - Plaisanterie
          - Wellingtonia — Chattanooga 3 / ARAUCARIA 3
          - Poetess — Trocadero 2 / La Dorette 19
    - **Catnip (1910)**
      - Spearmint (1903)
        - Carbine
          - *MUSKET* — Toxophilite 3 / West Australian Mare 3
          - The Mersey — Knowsley 3 / CLEMENCE 2
        - Maid Of The Mint
          - Minting — Lord Lyon 1 / Mint Sauce 1
          - Warble — Skylark 15 / Coturnix 1
      - Sibola (1896)
        - The Sailor Prince
          - Albert Victor — Marsyas 12 / The Princess Of Wales 13
          - Hermita — HERMIT 5 / Affection 19
        - Saluda
          - *MORTEMER* — Compiegne 2 / Comtesse 1
          - Perfection — LEAMINGTON 14 / Maiden (RH)

Nereide 1933

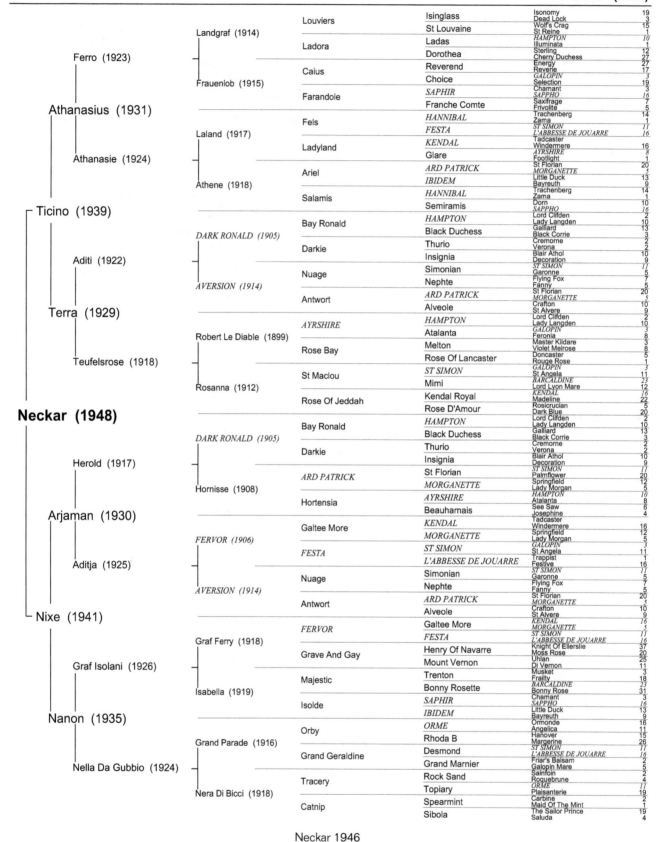

Neckar 1946

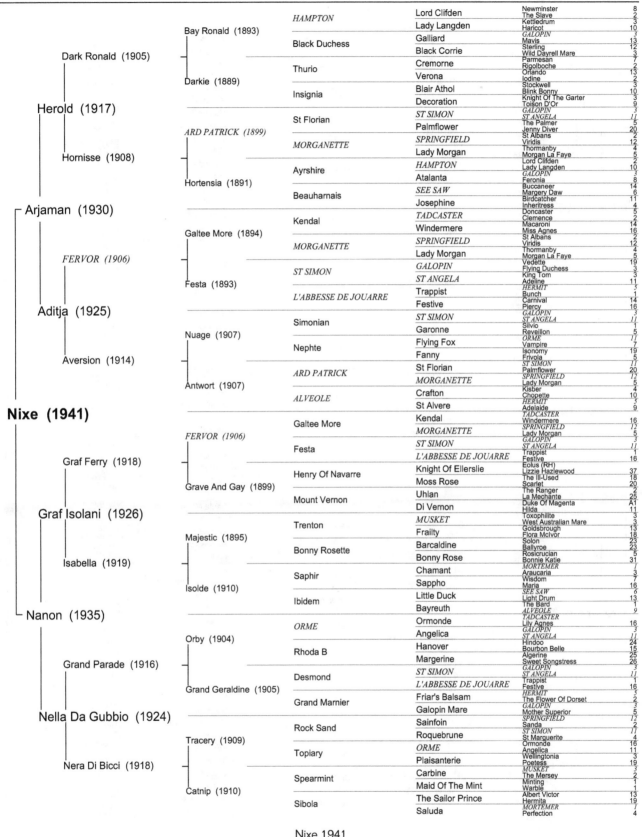

		HAMPTON	Lord Clifden	Newminster	8
				The Slave	2
	Bay Ronald (1893)		Lady Langden	Kettledrum	3
				Haricot	10
		Black Duchess	Galliard	*GALOPIN*	3
				Mavis	13
Dark Ronald (1905)			Black Corrie	Sterling	12
				Wild Dayrell Mare	3
		Thurio	Cremorne	Parmesan	7
				Rigolboche	13
	Darkie (1889)		Verona	Orlando	2
				Iodine	2
		Insignia	Blair Athol	Stockwell	2
				Blink Bonny	10
			Decoration	Knight Of The Garter	3
				Toison D'Or	9
Herold (1917)					
		St Florian	*ST SIMON*	*GALOPIN*	3
				ST ANGELA	11
	ARD PATRICK (1899)		Palmflower	The Palmer	5
				Jenny Diver	20
		MORGANETTE	*SPRINGFIELD*	St Albans	2
				Viridis	12
	Hornisse (1908)		Lady Morgan	Thormanby	4
				Morgan La Faye	5
		Ayrshire	*HAMPTON*	Lord Clifden	2
				Lady Langden	10
	Hortensia (1891)		Atalanta	*GALOPIN*	3
				Feronia	8
		Beauharnais	*SEE SAW*	Buccaneer	14
				Margery Daw	6
			Josephine	Birdcatcher	11
				Inheritress	4
Arjaman (1930)					
		Kendal	*TADCASTER*	Doncaster	5
				Clemence	2
	Galtee More (1894)		Windermere	Macaroni	14
				Miss Agnes	16
		MORGANETTE	*SPRINGFIELD*	St Albans	2
				Viridis	12
			Lady Morgan	Thormanby	4
				Morgan La Faye	5
FERVOR (1906)		*ST SIMON*	*GALOPIN*	Vedette	19
				Flying Duchess	3
	Festa (1893)		*ST ANGELA*	King Tom	3
				Adeline	11
		L'ABBESSE DE JOUARRE	Trappist	*HERMIT*	3
				Bunch	1
			Festive	Carnival	14
				Piercy	16
Aditja (1925)					
		Simonian	*ST SIMON*	*GALOPIN*	3
				ST ANGELA	11
	Nuage (1907)		Garonne	Silvio	1
				Reveillon	5
		Nephte	Flying Fox	*ORME*	11
				Vampire	7
			Fanny	Isonomy	19
				Frivola	5
		ARD PATRICK	St Florian	*ST SIMON*	11
				Palmflower	20
	Antwort (1907)		*MORGANETTE*	*SPRINGFIELD*	12
				Lady Morgan	5
		ALVEOLE	Crafton	Kisber	4
				Chopette	10
			St Alvere	*HERMIT*	3
				Adelaide	9
Aversion (1914)					

		Galtee More	Kendal	*TADCASTER*	16
				Windermere	16
	FERVOR (1906)		*MORGANETTE*	*SPRINGFIELD*	12
				Lady Morgan	5
		Festa	*ST SIMON*	*GALOPIN*	3
				ST ANGELA	11
			L'ABBESSE DE JOUARRE	Trappist	1
				Festive	16
Graf Ferry (1918)					
		Henry Of Navarre	Knight Of Ellerslie	Eolus (RH)	37
				Lizzie Hazlewood	18
	Grave And Gay (1899)		Moss Rose	The Ill-Used	20
				Scarlet	2
		Mount Vernon	Uhlan	The Ranger	25
				La Mechante	A1
			Di Vernon	Duke Of Magenta	11
				Hilda	3
Graf Isolani (1926)					
		Trenton	*MUSKET*	Toxophilite	3
				West Australian Mare	13
	Majestic (1895)		Frailty	Goldsbrough	18
				Flora McIvor	22
		Bonny Rosette	Barcaldine	Solon	23
				Ballyroe	5
			Bonny Rose	Rosicrucian	31
				Bonnie Katie	1
Isabella (1919)					
		Saphir	Chamant	*MORTEMER*	3
				Araucaria	7
	Isolde (1910)		Sappho	Wisdom	16
				Maria	6
		Ibidem	Little Duck	*SEE SAW*	13
				Light Drum	1
			Bayreuth	The Bard	9
				ALVEOLE	
Nanon (1935)					
		ORME	Ormonde	*TADCASTER*	16
				Lily Agnes	3
	Orby (1904)		Angelica	*GALOPIN*	11
				ST ANGELA	24
		Rhoda B	Hanover	Hindoo	15
				Bourbon Belle	25
			Margerine	Algerine	26
				Sweet Songstress	
Grand Parade (1916)					
		Desmond	*ST SIMON*	*GALOPIN*	11
				ST ANGELA	1
	Grand Geraldine (1905)		*L'ABBESSE DE JOUARRE*	Trappist	16
				Festive	2
		Grand Marnier	Friar's Balsam	*HERMIT*	3
				The Flower Of Dorset	5
			Galopin Mare	*GALOPIN*	12
				Mother Superior	1
Nella Da Gubbio (1924)					
		Rock Sand	Sainfoin	*SPRINGFIELD*	1
				Sanda	16
	Tracery (1909)		Roquebrune	*ST SIMON*	4
				St Marguerite	11
		Topiary	*ORME*	Ormonde	19
				Angelica	3
			Plaisanterie	Wellingtonia	2
				Poetess	1
Nera Di Bicci (1918)					
		Spearmint	Carbine	*MUSKET*	13
				The Mersey	19
	Catnip (1910)		Maid Of The Mint	Minting	1
				Warble	7
		Sibola	The Sailor Prince	Albert Victor	4
				Hermita	
			Saluda	*MORTEMER*	
				Perfection	

Nixe 1941

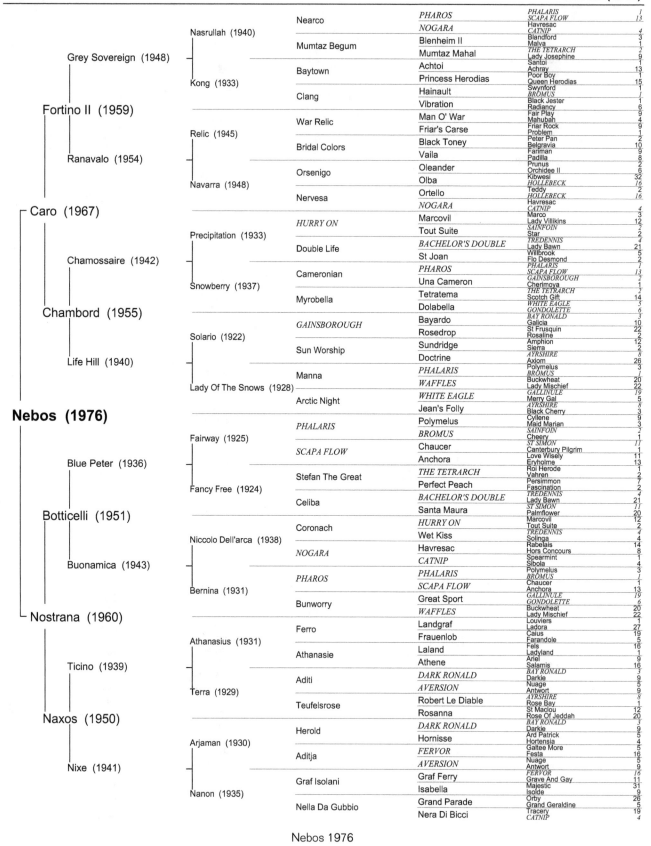

Nebos 1976

Chapter 19

Change of Heart

"Our American cousins wax indignant because certain of their importations to this country who carry a strain of native blood are denied admission to the General Stud-book..." (F. M. Prior 1946).

In 1949 the Jersey Act was repealed by the English Jockey Club, not because of the obvious hypocrisy of it, nor because of the shame of continuing to impose an unfair rule on their loyal allies; rather it was because of the unpleasant result it had brought about in their own experience—they were failing to produce and maintain the measure of horse they desired. Although they could not have realized it at the time, by freezing out American bloodlines they were keeping their own gene pools from receiving the refreshing and rejuvenation they desired, which could come only from the reintroduction of the missing and long separated Hobby/Running Horse bloodlines that were the original source of their speed.

A point for the American breeder to grasp, in viewing the unique American Thoroughbred in comparison to its close relatives, is that all the other Thoroughbred-producing countries were based on the English Thoroughbred product exclusively—but in America ours was built on not only the English Thoroughbred lines, but also the pre-Thoroughbred racehorse: the Hobby and the Running Horse, and we possessed those lines that had been lost in Great Britain during their Civil War, as well as a cache of the foundation Hobby genes from Ireland—which were the original source of the speed. Try to see this, it is why our Thoroughbred is different (and better). Therefore, when they shut us out they lost access to the only lines in the world that could improve their performance and genetic health. This loss showed up pretty quickly as they discovered they were being left behind in racing class. For instance, France and Italy were coming in and beating them fairly regularly with their home-breds that carried American lines. The very bloodlines they were using as an excuse to ban our horses were the very ones that they needed the most. There was no way they could have known this, nor did we, for it is only in our day that the geneticists have discovered the speed factor came from those early broodmare studs.

The above photo is a paddock scene at Santa Anita racetrack in California circa 1945. —*Who's Who in Thoroughbred Racing*

What also appears to play into the change of mind by the English Jockey Club is that they realized they could not exploit the rich American racing industry while they continued banning its best bloodlines. After World War II English racing was in the doldrums, while America was enjoying a vibrant racing industry. The English breeders, along with the French and Irish, were continually complaining of the unfairness of the rule—not the unfairness imposed on the American breeder, but to themselves.

A good example of this attitude was displayed in an article written by F. M. Prior in 1946 for "The Sporting Life" (quotation at the chapter start). By 1946 the British and Irish were certainly feeling the pain and frustration in their industry, as many of their own excellent products were also victims of this stupid act. In this article Prior was discussing the progeny of the superior mare Piersfield Mare and the fact that they were banned from the GSB because the dam was of unknown breeding. The Piersfield Mare had demonstrated she was a producer of the highest racing class, but her descendants were not allowed to breed on. However, the article concludes with a swipe at the Americans, evidently in response to American complaints about the unfairness of the Jersey Act, declaring that the Anglo and Irish breeder were suffering far more in Prior's opinion.

It was a cry of 'what are you American's whining about—we hurt worse than you', and in a sense Prior was right about this. America, after its initial depression in the value of the American Thoroughbred internationally, had proceeded to adjust its industry so that they were a healthy and prosperous entity by this time period, able to stand on its own with no need of outside sales to survive, and America had by then the richest racing purses in the world. Further, American breeders had always brought in foreign outcrosses, so they had no need of fresh blood either. The American racing industry was providing the funds and vehicle for its financial health and prosperity, and it was the envy of the racing world.

You see, at first it seemed that the British had succeeded in vanquishing their competition and cornering the international market for Thoroughbreds with their clever rule. For instance, during just the fifteen years between 1921-1936 the English sold and exported 17,771 of their Thoroughbreds, while their rivals—the American-bred Thoroughbred—were virtually eliminated from the market place, selling only 200 in this same time frame (TRA). But this apparent financial 'coup' achieved by the British was temporary. The problem was that by the 1940s, the effects of the World War they were engaged in, along with the fact that they had noticeably fallen behind in racing class and that the rich purses were now found in the American races, reversed their success, and the racing population of Thoroughbred that they had left for dead in the worldwide market had, after this perceived fatal blow, raised from the ashes to become a resounding success all on its own.

During the Jersey Act the American racing industry reorganized and became a thriving industry. Here's a scene at lovely Hialeh racetrack in Florida. —TRA 1944

During the thirty-six years of the Jersey Act, where the American Thoroughbred was forced out of the international breeding industry by the British Jockey Club, the breeders who survived the squeeze came out of it with a tremendously prepotent type of racehorse. The Jersey Act that was intended to eliminate the American Thoroughbred as competition was initially successful, but by the end it had failed in its mission. The quarantine of our stock from the open market would have been much more effective if it was of average quality to begin with, but it had demonstrated it was the best in the world (Chapter 8), and of course, that was the very reason that it was forced into a confined space in the first place. The English could not tolerate America being better at their game then they were. In the end their strategy backfired as it was a catalyst to the concentration of those same bloodlines they wished to destroy. So when the ban was lifted thirty-six years later, out of the box came once again the greatest racehorse in the world.

In his 1990 work *Thoroughbred Stallions,* Tony Morris says the English racing world was stunned when their classics were won first by Sir Ivor, then Habitat, then Nijinsky, Mill Reef, and Roberto, in consecutive years, winning in such a definitive manner that they far out-classed the best England had, humiliating them because they had assumed they were the best in the world, and it was clear they were not—the American-bred was. Further, the American horse was not just a great runner, it had proven prepotent for it's racing talents as well, clearly demonstrated in the following years in that all five of those American invaders have achieved *chef* status for the excellence of their progeny.

In the introduction to his fine text, in putting the then current stallion situation (1990) in prospective, Tony Morris explains that it harks back to the 1960s, as this was the time of the sea-change in the Thoroughbred world. After the initial invasion of the horses he mentions above, the American-bred horses that followed were brought into their land by their own speculators. This influx came about from the implementation of the great racing scheme of Robert Sangster, John Magnier, and Vincent O'Brien, whose plan was to buy American products, campaign them at home, win the classics with them, and then sell them back to the Americans at a huge profit. They succeeded in this for a season, but only until the Arabs got into the game with their bottomless pockets and outbid them. In the end what they intended as a way to make buckets of money from the Americans, ended by inflating the industry balloon, thereby pricing themselves out of the market, and eventually caused a modern-day international depression in bloodstock sales.

Interesting to our study is not the wholesale run on the American-breds in the mid-twentieth century, as much as the fact that Mr. Morris never mentions how it came to be that the American Thoroughbred was such a rare sight in Europe before this. I have reread his history of this a few times, thinking I must have missed the mention of the Jersey Act. He begins instead with a scenario in the 1920s, when a few American-breds traveled to Europe and won, but as he describes it, they were so few and far between that they were tolerated, and their victories even celebrated, by the generous-spirited English. No mention is made of the fact that they were barred from the GSB and had no real reason to travel to Europe to market or race American horses—he says instead that they did it just for the fun of it; it sounds as if it were just a nice vacation from racing in America. It is curious; however he does say that in the 1960s it never occurred to the English that the American horse would ever be a serious competitor of theirs, especially in their own racing territory (Europe). So maybe they had forgotten; otherwise they would not have been so jolted by the American racing class—after all they had seen it all before. Morris explains that they were truly shocked by the complete supremacy of the American Thoroughbred in the European classics.

American racing at Saratoga during the Jersey Act. —TRA 1944

In their enforced incarceration, the American breeders had consistently imported foreign stallions, very often the English Thoroughbred stallion, for the outcrosses they felt they needed to keep their breeding population from being too inbred. It is notable that in the beginning of this phase those 'purebred' stallions did not leave lasting lines here; they were given every opportunity and were used extensively by the breeders—sires like imported Ogden and Voter for instance—and they received the best mares, and even led the sires lists for a short time; however they failed to breed on here (Thoroughbred Racing Association). Their lines faded and became of little import in the successful racer.

Instead, it was the American 'flawed' lines of Domino, Fair Play, and Ben Brush that remained the consistent producers of the best racehorse. "These three lines have held their own, or actually increased in influence, against a continuing stream of importation of horses from England…but despite those tremendous advantages the imported lines have failed utterly to 'breed on' in competition against the strains which have been 'American' since the Civil War" (Thoroughbred Racing Association 1944).

It was the European importations of the Teddy line (Sir Gallahad/Bull Dog/La Troienne), and those of the Phalaris line, that have over time proven to be significant.

The Teddy line is easy to explain—he is extremely potent in top racing class from his inbreeding to the full siblings St. Simon and his sister Angelica, and a key to his lasting influence is that he also provided the daughter lines of the mare Pocahontas, so he became an essential ingredient in a worldwide breeding population that was overrun by son lines of this important mare.

Phalaris has been discussed by skilled TB researchers everywhere—he is inbred 3x4 to Springfield sex-balanced on his dam side. Springfield is a source of speed, and Phalaris is a modern source of speed. He also carries a line of the rarely found Barnton—a full brother to the Volley/Voltigeur 6x6 et al, which is a strong factor in dominance found in the English TB. So, Phalaris is a potent line and useful as an outcross for the American product; however it is not a sound line and it has brought in potency to produce a large, heavy frame perched on delicate and brittle legs, especially the forelegs (see Chapter 27).

Washington Park circa 1945. —*Who's Who in Thoroughred Racing*

On the Phalaris line, the full brothers Sickle/Pharamond left a lasting legacy here (the good sires Menow and By Jiminy, plus three *reines*: The Squaw, Misty Isle, and Be Like Mom), but it is Nearco and his sons: the ⅞ brothers Royal Charger and Nasrullah who just rocked the entire racing world and influenced the American product strongly as well, especially, their products that were mixed to carriers of the substance of their dam-lines. Remember Nearco's fourth-dam is Perfection, the full sister to Parole (Chapter 8), out of a daughter of Lexington RH and carrying Blackburns Whip RH as well. Then when mated with mares of the Lady Josephine line, who is 4x4 to the American Running Horse full siblings Norfolk RH and The Nun RH and 6x6 to the full brothers Sir Archy Montorio RH and Sir William of Transport RH, (brought in by Mumtaz Mahal and Lady Juror) then another step up in racing class was seen. Catnip (Nearco's second-dam) and Lady Josephine were contemporaries (see combined pedigree) who slipped into the GSB just before the door was slammed shut on American lines—what would the modern European horse have been without them? When combined together they strengthen the very best lines on both sides of the Atlantic: the English horse Stockwell and his full brother Rataplan 6x6x7x6x6x6x6x7x7, and the American Running Horses: the full siblings The Nun RH and Norfolk RH and their ¾ sister Maiden RH are 5x5x5. The American lines dominated both dam-lines—this is notable. Then when these lines were bred to our American broodmares who carried more of the Heroic Era lines, the great performers kept pouring out, but unfortunately many displayed the conformation faults as well.

For example, shortly before the end of the Jersey Act a stallion was imported from England who had a tremendous effect on the American TB—this is Mahmoud, the English Derby winner. His dam is Mah Mahal, a granddaughter of Lady Josephine—therefore she was bringing home to America its own power-line of Americus—inbred to Lexington RH/Glencoe/Sir Archy/Transport RH, which provided a 'nick' of great strength. Americus is one of the close genetic relatives of Domino and Hamburg—all bringing in concentrated elements of Lexington RH, so he was destined to create a nick of immense power when brought together in our lineages (see combined-pedigree). Americus and Domino are inbred, and their inbreeding involves Lexington RH offspring—it is Lexington RH lines that combine the pedigrees. Mahmoud in his revised pedigree (taking the Tadcaster/Bend Or correction into account) shows his most powerful lines are the full siblings Tadcaster/Clementina 6x6x6x6 and the American full siblings The Nun RH and Norfolk RH 7x7 on the dam-line.

Once Mahmoud was mated with the American Thoroughbred, excellence was reached time and again. One of these greats is Almahmoud 1947, who is the dam of Natalma, the dam of Northern Dancer. Almahmoud's dam Arbitrator brought in the strong American lines of Fair Play, Hamburg, Broomstick, and Peter Pan (Domino), creating a nick with Mahmoud's dam-line (see Chapter 20 for more on this nick). More important sires occurred when more of the Flaw was added to the mix in the next generation such as Cohoes 1954 out of a Blue Larkspur dam, and there was The Axe II out of a dam carrying

Mahmoud in his new home in Lexington, KY. One of the many English stallions imported during the Jersey Act, Mahmoud proved not only an immensely potent stallion in his own right, he also provided an automatic nick with American lines as he brought home the power lines of Lexington RH/Novice RH to meet their close relatives. —photo courtesy of Keeneland Library

Equipoise (Domino), Hamburg (Hindoo), Fair Play (Aerolite RH), and Blue Larkspur again. (The Axe is instrumental in the great Holy Bull—Chapter 24).

The ¾ brothers Mahmoud, Nasrullah, and Royal Charger are the bloodlines that melted in with our American strains, and they have dominated racing worldwide till this very day—all three are rated *chef-de-race*. They are now so common in the quality Thoroughbred that they are called a 'standard pattern'.

When the Brits reversed the draconian Jersey Act in 1949, slowly the improved lines began to come back to them. By the 1970s-80s, one hundred years after the original American invasion, they were once again overwhelmed by the racing superiority of the American-bred.

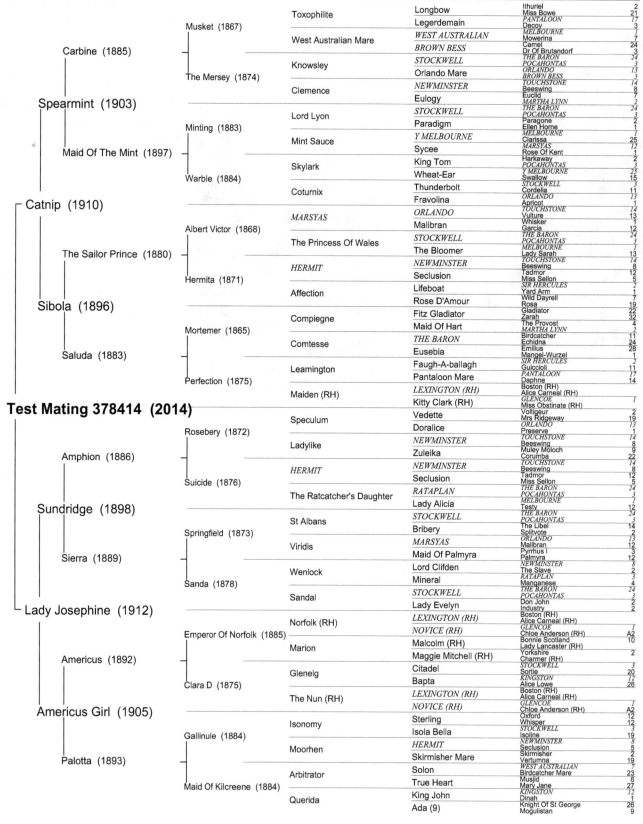

		Toxophilite	Longbow	Ithuriel 2 / Miss Bowe 21
	Musket (1867)		Legerdemain	*PANTALOON* 17 / Decoy 3
		West Australian Mare	*WEST AUSTRALIAN*	*MELBOURNE* 1 / Mowerina 7
Carbine (1885)			*BROWN BESS*	Camel 24 / Dr Of Brutandorf 3
		Knowsley	*STOCKWELL*	*THE BARON* 24 / *POCAHONTAS* 3
	The Mersey (1874)		Orlando Mare	*ORLANDO* 13 / *BROWN BESS* 3
		Clemence	*NEWMINSTER*	*TOUCHSTONE* 14 / Beeswing 8
Spearmint (1903)			Eulogy	Euclid 7 / *MARTHA LYNN* 2
		Lord Lyon	*STOCKWELL*	*THE BARON* 24 / *POCAHONTAS* 3
	Minting (1883)		Paradigm	Paragone 2 / Ellen Horne 1
		Mint Sauce	*Y MELBOURNE*	*MELBOURNE* 1 / Clarissa 25
Maid Of The Mint (1897)			Sycee	*MARSYAS* 12 / Rose Of Kent 1
		Skylark	King Tom	Harkaway 2 / *POCAHONTAS* 3
	Warble (1884)		Wheat-Ear	*Y MELBOURNE* 25 / Swallow 15
		Coturnix	Thunderbolt	*STOCKWELL* 3 / Cordelia 11
Catnip (1910)			Fravolina	*ORLANDO* 13 / Apricot 1
		MARSYAS	*ORLANDO*	*TOUCHSTONE* 14 / Vulture 13
	Albert Victor (1868)		Malibran	Whisker 1 / Garcia 12
		The Princess Of Wales	*STOCKWELL*	*THE BARON* 24 / *POCAHONTAS* 3
The Sailor Prince (1880)			The Bloomer	*MELBOURNE* 1 / Lady Sarah 13
		HERMIT	*NEWMINSTER*	*TOUCHSTONE* 14 / Beeswing 8
	Hermita (1871)		Seclusion	Tadmor 12 / Miss Sellon 5
		Affection	Lifeboat	*SIR HERCULES* 2 / Yard Arm 1
Sibola (1896)			Rose D'Amour	Wild Dayrell 7 / Rosa 19
		Compiegne	Fitz Gladiator	Gladiator 22 / Zarah 32
	Mortemer (1865)		Maid Of Hart	The Provost 4 / *MARTHA LYNN* 2
		Comtesse	*THE BARON*	Birdcatcher 11 / Echidna 24
Saluda (1883)			Eusebia	Emilius 28 / Mangel-Wurzel 1
		Leamington	Faugh-A-ballagh	*SIR HERCULES* 2 / Guiccioli 11
	Perfection (1875)		Pantaloon Mare	*PANTALOON* 17 / Daphne 14
		Maiden (RH)	*LEXINGTON (RH)*	Boston (RH) / Alice Carneal (RH)
			Kitty Clark (RH)	*GLENCOE* 1 / Miss Obstinate (RH)

Test Mating 378414 (2014)

		Speculum	Vedette	Voltigeur 2 / Mrs Ridgeway 19
	Rosebery (1872)		Doralice	*ORLANDO* 13 / Preserve 1
		Ladylike	*NEWMINSTER*	*TOUCHSTONE* 14 / Beeswing 8
Amphion (1886)			Zuleika	Muley Moloch 9 / Corumba 22
		HERMIT	*NEWMINSTER*	*TOUCHSTONE* 14 / Beeswing 8
	Suicide (1876)		Seclusion	Tadmor 12 / Miss Sellon 5
		The Ratcatcher's Daughter	*RATAPLAN*	*THE BARON* 24 / *POCAHONTAS* 3
Sundridge (1898)			Lady Alicia	*MELBOURNE* 1 / Testy 12
		St Albans	*STOCKWELL*	*THE BARON* 24 / *POCAHONTAS* 3
	Springfield (1873)		Bribery	The Libel 14 / Splitvote 2
		Viridis	*MARSYAS*	*ORLANDO* 13 / Malibran 12
Sierra (1889)			Maid Of Palmyra	Pyrrhus I 3 / Palmyra 12
		Wenlock	Lord Clifden	*NEWMINSTER* 8 / The Slave 2
	Sanda (1878)		Mineral	*RATAPLAN* 3 / Manganese 4
		Sandal	*STOCKWELL*	*THE BARON* 24 / *POCAHONTAS* 3
Lady Josephine (1912)			Lady Evelyn	Don John 2 / Industry 2
		Norfolk (RH)	*LEXINGTON (RH)*	Boston (RH) / Alice Carneal (RH)
	Emperor Of Norfolk (1885)		*NOVICE (RH)*	*GLENCOE* 1 / Chloe Anderson (RH) A2
		Marion	Malcolm (RH)	Bonnie Scotland 10 / Lady Lancaster (RH)
Americus (1892)			Maggie Mitchell (RH)	Yorkshire 2 / Charmer (RH)
		Glenelg	Citadel	*STOCKWELL* 3 / Sortie 20
	Clara D (1875)		Bapta	*KINGSTON* 12 / Alice Lowe 26
		The Nun (RH)	*LEXINGTON (RH)*	Boston (RH) / Alice Carneal (RH)
Americus Girl (1905)			*NOVICE (RH)*	*GLENCOE* 1 / Chloe Anderson (RH) A2
		Isonomy	Sterling	Oxford 12 / Whisper 12
	Gallinule (1884)		Isola Bella	*STOCKWELL* 3 / Isoline 19
		Moorhen	*HERMIT*	*NEWMINSTER* 8 / Seclusion 5
Palotta (1893)			Skirmisher Mare	Skirmisher 2 / Verturnna 19
		Arbitrator	Solon	*WEST AUSTRALIAN* 1 / Birdcatcher Mare 23
	Maid Of Kilcreene (1884)		True Heart	Musjid 6 / Mary Jane 27
		Querida	King John	*KINGSTON* 12 / Dinah 1
			Ada (9)	Knight Of St George 26 / Mogulistan 9

Catnip/Lady Josephine

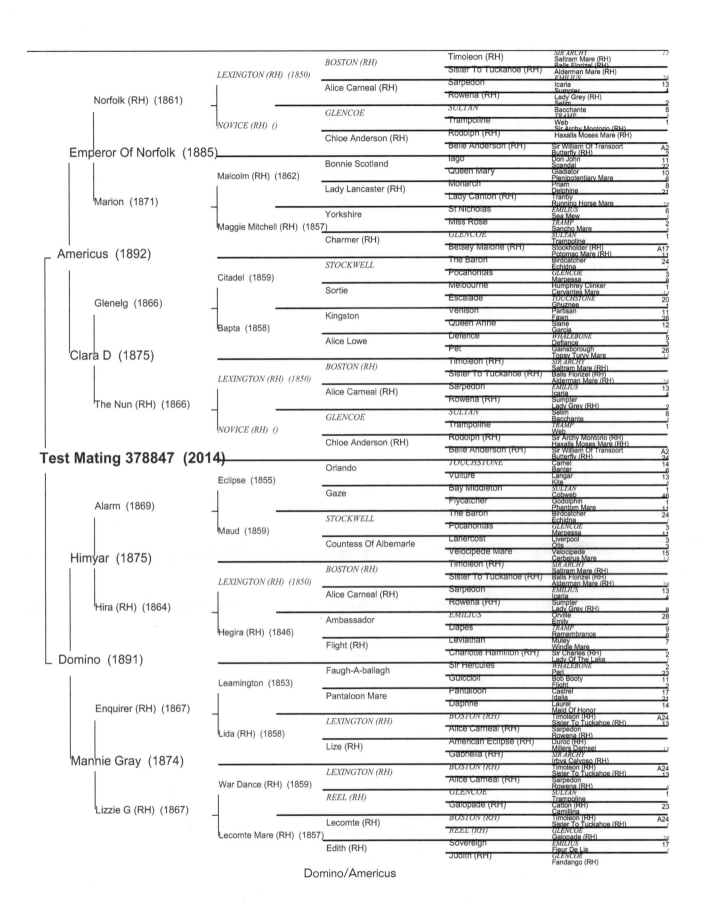

Test Mating 378847 (2014)

Emperor Of Norfolk (1885)

Norfolk (RH) (1861)

LEXINGTON (RH) (1850)

BOSTON (RH)

Timoleon (RH)
SIR ARCHY
Saltram Mare (RH)
Balls Florizel (RH)

Sister To Tuckahoe (RH)
Alderman Mare (RH)

Alice Carneal (RH)

Sarpedon
EMILIUS
Icaria

Rowena (RH)
Sumpter
Lady Grey (RH)

NOVICE (RH) ()

GLENCOE

SULTAN
Selim
Bacchante

Trampoline
TRAMP
Web

Chloe Anderson (RH)

Rodolph (RH)
Sir Archy Montorio (RH)
Haxalls Moses Mare (RH)

Belle Anderson (RH)
Sir William Of Transport
Butterfly (RH)

Marion (1871)

Malcolm (RH) (1862)

Bonnie Scotland

Iago
Don John
Scandal

Queen Mary
Gladiator
Plenipotentiary Mare

Lady Lancaster (RH)

Monarch
Priam
Delphine

Lady Canton (RH)
Tranby
Running Horse Mare

Maggie Mitchell (RH) (1857)

Yorkshire

St Nicholas
EMILIUS
Sea Mew

Miss Rose
TRAMP
Sancho Mare

Charmer (RH)

GLENCOE
SULTAN
Trampoline

Betsey Malone (RH)
Stockholder (RH)
Potomac Mare (RH)

Americus (1892)

Glenelg (1866)

Citadel (1859)

STOCKWELL

The Baron
Birdcatcher
Echidna

Pocahontas
GLENCOE
Marpessa

Sortie

Melbourne
Humphrey Clinker
Cervantes Mare

Escalade
TOUCHSTONE
Ghuznee

Bapta (1858)

Kingston

Venison
Partisan
Fawn

Queen Anne
Slane
Garcia

Alice Lowe

Defence
WHALEBONE
Defiance

Pet
Gainsborough
Topsy Turvy Mare

Clara D (1875)

The Nun (RH) (1866)

LEXINGTON (RH) (1850)

BOSTON (RH)

Timoleon (RH)
SIR ARCHY
Saltram Mare (RH)
Balls Florizel (RH)

Sister To Tuckahoe (RH)
Alderman Mare (RH)

Alice Carneal (RH)

Sarpedon
EMILIUS
Icaria

Rowena (RH)
Sumpter
Lady Grey (RH)

NOVICE (RH) ()

GLENCOE

SULTAN
Selim
Bacchante

Trampoline
TRAMP
Web

Chloe Anderson (RH)

Rodolph (RH)
Sir Archy Montorio (RH)
Haxalls Moses Mare (RH)

Belle Anderson (RH)
Sir William Of Transport
Butterfly (RH)

Domino (1891)

Himyar (1875)

Alarm (1869)

Eclipse (1855)

Orlando

TOUCHSTONE
Camel
Banter

Vulture
Langar
Kite

Gaze

Bay Middleton
SULTAN
Cobweb

Flycatcher
Godolphin
Phantom Mare

Maud (1859)

STOCKWELL

The Baron
Birdcatcher
Echidna

Pocahontas
GLENCOE
Marpessa

Countess Of Albemarle

Lanercost
Liverpool
Otis

Velocipede Mare
Velocipede
Cerberus Mare

Hira (RH) (1864)

LEXINGTON (RH) (1850)

BOSTON (RH)

Timoleon (RH)
SIR ARCHY
Saltram Mare (RH)
Balls Florizel (RH)

Sister To Tuckahoe (RH)
Alderman Mare (RH)

Alice Carneal (RH)

Sarpedon
EMILIUS
Icaria

Rowena (RH)
Sumpter
Lady Grey (RH)

Hegira (RH) (1846)

Ambassador

EMILIUS
Orville
Emily

Dapes
TRAMP
Remembrance

Flight (RH)

Leviathan
Muley
Windle Mare

Charlotte Hamilton (RH)
Sir Charles (RH)
Lady Of The Lake

Mannie Gray (1874)

Enquirer (RH) (1867)

Leamington (1853)

Faugh-A-ballagh

Sir Hercules
WHALEBONE
Peri

Guiccioli
Bob Booty
Flight

Pantaloon Mare

Pantaloon
Castrel
Idalia

Daphne
Laurel
Maid Of Honor

Lida (RH) (1858)

LEXINGTON (RH)

BOSTON (RH)
Timoleon (RH)
Sister To Tuckahoe (RH)

Alice Carneal (RH)
Sarpedon
Rowena (RH)

Lize (RH)

American Eclipse (RH)
Duroc (RH)
Millers Damsel

Gabriella (RH)
SIR ARCHY
Irbys Calypso (RH)

Lizzie G (RH) (1867)

War Dance (RH) (1859)

LEXINGTON (RH)

BOSTON (RH)
Timoleon (RH)
Sister To Tuckahoe (RH)

Alice Carneal (RH)
Sarpedon
Rowena (RH)

REEL (RH)

GLENCOE
SULTAN
Trampoline

Galopade (RH)
Catton (RH)
Camillina

Lecomte Mare (RH) (1857)

Lecomte (RH)

BOSTON (RH)
Timoleon (RH)
Sister To Tuckahoe (RH)

REEL (RH)
GLENCOE
Galopade (RH)

Edith (RH)

Sovereign
EMILIUS
Fleur De Lis

Judith (RH)
GLENCOE
Fandango (RH)

Domino/Americus

Part III

The Shoe on the Other Foot

Chapter 20

After the Thaw—Stateside

"The main thing to keep in mind is that American pedigrees are not the same as pedigrees in Europe, South America, Japan or Australia. While Thoroughbreds stateside and abroad may have many English and French ancestors in common, the concentration of certain ancestors that are uniquely American can make the difference between victory and defeat…." —Ken McLean

The Jersey Act ended in 1949; it went out with a whimper. On June 16, 1949, the General Stud Book decided to "enlarge to include strains which have hitherto been banned…"(See Appendix A for more on the Jersey Act). That was that; there was a short announcement in Thoroughbred Record, which said that it was received with gladness all around, but other than that reaction, there doesn't seem to be much press about it.

It appears that no one here really gave it much thought, because it seems the Jersey Act was no longer a matter of much consequence to the American racing industry. It had been only a few years before that the American Breeders had appealed once again to the British Jockey Club (see Appendix A - Welch article 1946) for its repeal—and again were rebuffed rudely by the British, but just a few years later it didn't seem to concern the American industry one way or another. Nor does there seem to be a rush to expand overseas or enter the foreign markets again. Instead there was plenty of market in our own country, and it was the foreign buyers that came here instead.

A scene at Belmont Park in 1946, the American racing industry had recovered from the effects of the Jersey Act and was prosperous, with the largest purses in the world, and the healthiest industry. —image from *Who's Who in Thoroughbred Racing*

Naturally, the worldwide Thoroughbred industry as a whole was in a slump during WWII. In Europe it was almost destroyed by the rampaging Nazis seizing whatever good stock they could find in the countries they conquered, and many important horses were lost during this time. For an example of what it was like, we have a first-hand witness in the former American jockey, Jimmy Winkfield, who had been a trainer in France at the time that the war broke out; he had to dissolve his operation and leave France. On his return here he was interviewed by the Thoroughbred Record about his experience. He recounted how when the war first began his facility was taken over by the French Government to house its military and that they behaved with courtesy toward him and his property, but it was only a short time after that the Germans overran France, and then it was the Nazis who grabbed his stable for their own army and they confiscated everything he had left there. The Nazis stripped France of all their valuable Thoroughbred stock; Jimmy said they virtually took all that France had—stallions, mares, foals—and that they shipped it all to Germany. And that was the end of racing and breeding in France for the duration. This scene was repeated in all the areas subjected by Germany.

After such a devastating conquest, with all their important stock looted, the post-war racing recovery in Europe was slow and sporadic. However, here in the States, we began experiencing a boom in everything almost immediately, and the racing industry was part of this. During the time of the Jersey Act the American industry was forced to rely solely on itself for its survival and expansion, and it learned how to function so that it was prosperous overall. It was the largest spectator sport in that era, which is a hard thing in our day to understand with the current huge football, baseball, basketball, and soccer events, but back then it was racing that drew the crowds. Besides, it provided a legal way to gamble, which increased attendance also. There were ups and downs of course, but ultimately the purses increased, attendance increased, and the breeders could rely on a return for a good product. So when the British lifted the ban, the American attitude was 'so what'? It made little difference to the majority of American breeders and owners. The big purses were here at home—not in Europe—plus we had always imported whatever foreign stock we wanted, and more important, our horses were in the least case an equal to anything England or Europe could produce, but truly in most instances they were a far better horse than any other country could boast of, and we knew it, having tested the foreign stock we imported over the years.

And so it was that the average American Thoroughbred breeder and owner was not tempted to engage in the sport outside our own country. America was where the action was, not Europe. Plus many Americans were justly weary of the European scene, after spending American lives and resources for the second time in its defense. It followed then that there was little international interaction except for when the foreign sportsmen came here to participate in our races—hoping to win the big purses, but not so much the other way around.

For the next fifteen years or so with all the countries impacted by WWII attempting to recover, we find that racing was pretty quiet internationally. Our horse was changing, too, and not all of it was positive. Since 1930 certain imported sires had brought in unsoundness, along with a delicateness that had not been part of our equine base. There were imported stallions who were great purveyors of speed, such as Sir Gallahad and his brother Bull Dog, Challedon, North Star III, St. Germans, Heliopolis, Ambroix, Mahmoud, Sickle, Pharamond, Royal Charger, and Nasrullah, but they also brought problems with them, especially those from the Phalaris line which combined hugely-muscled frames with fragility in their limbs—a design that tempts disaster.

Before this, Domino was our prime domestic transmitter of tremendous concentrated speed, but he too was not the soundest of lines. Previous to this era Domino's faults had been tempered by the tough and stout lines of Fair Play and Ben Brush that he was bred to, so the flaws were rarely manifested in our racer.

Then, over the years, more of the Phalaris line entered our gene pool, such as through the great sire Sickle, his full brother Pharamond, and the potent Turn-To, bringing brilliance but also more of the softness with short, upright pasterns, fragile bones and tendons, and small underpinnings combined with the great bulk. In addition, over time the international Thoroughbred had become massive; a large horse a hundred years before had been 16 hands and 1000 lbs, but in the 1950s and beyond 17-hand or even taller horses weighing in at 1200 lbs were not uncommon, and these 'super-sized' versions brought with them less density of bone in relation to their size as well as the other problems. In our Heroic Era, this size horse was a rarity, and most of those who were very large broke down in racing, or they would have been culled before they were ever seen in a heat race—there were some exceptions like Preakness RH and Longstreet, but they were oddities. Generally, this type of conformation cannot stand up to long-distance racing or is not able to stay sound to race for a decade or more. But with the change that began since the adoption of the classic race standard in 1868, a noticeable downward slide in stamina, soundness, and resiliency became much more evident. This shorter, easier test was run by two- and three-year-olds—horses who had not even finished growing, and most were retired before they were five. Therefore it followed then, that many of these problems would not show up for a while—hidden by youth—when they did show, the horse was quickly retired to stud.

The overall result of this change in our performance standard and the continued breeding in of the English classic race specialist was weaker strains entering our gene pools, and they found an affinity here as they also all carried strains of Running Horse, which resulted in additional performance brilliance. So these new hybrid Anglo-American horses produced spectacular racers in the short term, although they also brought in unsoundness with them as well.

The 1950s were bonanza years, prosperity everywhere in the US and in racing the focus was on the brilliant racer, so the soundness issues increased but were ignored because the show they were providing was spectacular. As the decade dawned the incomparable Native Dancer was born (*chef-de-race*) and became the first televised racing hero—the 'Grey Ghost'—he was a media treat. Native Dancer was not just a racing machine; he was destined to be the leading bloodline worldwide in the early twenty-first century. He possessed potency in speed, but also became noted for carrying a recessive in conformation faults, especially the ankles and feet. The great Bold Ruler was a show stealer in the later 1950s, and the brilliant and unsound Bold Ruler (ankles, feet also) was leading sire with a post-war record of eight times (*chef-de-race*) (See Chapter 27 for a continued discussion on soundness).

The racing machine Native Dancer. —photo by Bert Morgan, courtesy of Keeneland Library collection

In the 1960s our prosperous racing industry and our superior product had not gone unnoticed in Europe. For it was in 1967 that Raymond Guest brought over Sir Ivor to race in Europe, and his performance was such a class act it earned him the Champion-Two-Year-Old title in Europe and English Horse-of-the-Year in 1968. He won in England, Ireland, and France as well as in the USA. His wins included the English Derby and 2000 Guineas, the Champion Stakes, Grand Criterium, and National Stakes. He also came in second in the Prix l'Arc de Triomphe. This was the beginning of the change to American dominance in international racing, and while Sir Ivor was cleaning up in Europe, a small colt was born in Canada named Northern Dancer, and this little guy was destined to change the entire fabric of the modern international Thoroughbred. Sir Ivor carried eighteen lines of Lexington RH, and also proved to be a great sire, earning the prestigious *chef* status.

Little by little, more American-breds were crossing the Atlantic. For instance, American sportsman Charles Englehardt brought over Habitat to race, and at three he took the Prix du Moulin de Longchampe, Prix Quincey, Lockinge Stakes, and Wills Mile. Bred by the Nicholas Brothers in America, he later became a top sire in England. Habitat has also earned the envied *chef-de-race* status, and he carries thirty-two lines of Lexington RH.

But it was Nijinsky, a son of Northern Dancer, who completely turned over the apple cart; bred by E. P. Taylor in Canada, he too was brought over by Englehardt. He raced at two and three, in England, Ireland, and France where he swept all before him—winning the Derby Stakes, 2000 Guineas, St. Leger, Irish Sweeps Derby, and others. Nijinksy returned to America to stud and went on to be one of the greatest sires of modern times (*chef*). He carries a whopping seventy-nine lines of Lexington RH.

Born the same year was Mill Reef, bred by Paul Mellon; he too raced in Europe and stayed there to breed. A phenomenal racehorse, he won twelve major races in England and France, including the Derby Stakes, Coronation Cup, and the Prix de l'Arc de Triomphe. He remained there, standing at the National Stud, and at one time he was proclaimed the best stallion in England—a *chef-de-race*. His legacy grew even wider when later his bloodlines were crossed with those created by Boussac, bringing in a modern day harvest of top racers (see Chapter 16). He is now rated one of the most significant sires in Europe this century. He carries forty-one lines of Lexington RH.

Roberto was not as consistent an American invader as some of the others but still managed to win the Derby Stakes, Benson & Hedges Gold Cup, and the Coronation Cup, and at home he became a wonderful sire also, and in our day a very valued bloodline—he too has earned *chef* status. He carries forty lines of Lexington RH.

These envoys of the American product were like cold water in the face of the European racing industry who had never imagined that the American horse could best theirs. It was painfully apparent that they could not only race exceptionally well, but they became the best sires of their time also. Sportsman that our cousins are, they were not about to take this challenge sitting down, and so began the raid on the Keeneland yearlings sales. A small amount of enterprising breeders came at first, but then it wasn't that long before a carefully thought-out assault was designed by the partnership of Robert Sangster, Vincent O'Brien, and John Magnier—named 'the Brethren' by the press. Their plan was simply to buy the best of the

KATHLEEN H. KIRSAN

yearling crop at the Keeneland sales, especially the progeny of Northern Dancer, to bring them home, train them, and then race them in the European classics, and once they had won a few, they could then sell them back to American buyers or syndicate their stallion shares at enormous profits. And they were successful with this scheme for a time, making huge amounts of cash, with which they bought more of the best—for instance, they paid $200,000 for The Minstrel who went on to win the English Derby, and they sold him back to America for $9 million. They also bought Alleged as a two-year-old for $175,000 and sold him back to America as a three-year-old for $16 million. With their vast profits they established Coolmore Stud in Ireland and then stood other of their purchased stars there, starting with Be My Guest at tremendous stud fees. Their $800,000 purchase of Carleon (pedigree) reaped over 17 million in pounds at stud! Caerleon carried over eighty lines of Lexington RH. Fabulous success followed them, the height being the magnificent Sadlers Wells. The genetic impact of this horse is enormous. When Sadlers died in 2011, the manager at Coolmore stated that he was **the best sire who had ever stood in Great Britain**.

[Note: Sadlers Wells is sometimes reported as having been foaled at Sangster's own stud in Ireland and therefore an Irish-bred, this is not accurate. The partnership had bought his dam Fairy Bridge at the Keeneland Sales as a yearling and moved her to Ireland, but she was brought back to Claiborne Farm in Kentucky for her stud career where she was bred to Northern Dancer and his sons Danzig and Nijinsky. There is no AI (artificial insemination) allowed in Thoroughbred breeding, and Northern Dancer never stood in Ireland; therefore, not only is Sadlers Wells of strictly North American parentage, he was born here in the USA also, and with over one hundred lines of the Running Horse Lexington in his lineage, he is about as American as it gets. He has four full siblings: Fairy King, Tate Gallery, Fairy Gold, and Puppet Dance (all born and bred in the USA) who can be line-breeding targets for those who want to keep his type potent—see Chapter 23.]

The Brethern also succeeded in something they had not envisioned in that they changed the way the industry functioned; their purchasing practices inflated the price of yearlings and then also the stallion market beyond what many breeders could afford. Syndications of stallions became more commonplace. Then the Arabs got into the game, and it changed the fortunes of the partnership. The difference was that the Maktoum brothers did not have to restrain their spending at all. The Brethern had to rely on the resale of the stock and huge stud fees to finance their expansion; the Arabs had no such need—their oil money purses were bottomless. Also bidding wars developed, resulting in Snaafi Dancer selling for $10.2 million and Seattle Dancer for $13.1 million. This state of affairs could not last—it was destroying the industry. Many owners and breeders dropped out of the business; some went belly up. The bubble finally burst in 1987 with a resulting rapid decline in stud fees and some semblance of sanity arriving, but with many investors losing enormously.

Curious Thoroughbred yearlings as depicted by American artist C. W. Anderson in a sketch for *Who's Who in Thoroughbred Racing*.

Through the 1990s the industry was attempting to recover, and gradually corrections in practices were made, so by the late 1990s the price of yearlings were climbing again but at a much slower, saner rate than seen in the boom years of the 1980s. Also, the soundness issues and uncertainty with yearlings had turned the focus to the two-year-old market instead of the yearlings—the thought being to lessen the risks, wagering that at least those youngsters were already in training, and hopefully soundness indications would be revealed by then.

This string of events leaves us with a breed population today that while certainly possessing speed; it is far less sound and lacks the bottom that was commonplace a hundred years ago (see Chapter 27). What a contrast to our pre-Civil War racehorse, which was long in stamina, soundness, and speed—many able to win at a sprint as easily as a four-mile heat race and so durable that many were racing at twelve and beyond.

It is clear that the breed selection standard of 'dash' form, adopted in 1776 in England and 1868 here, resulted in a horse with less stamina and overall produced a weaker, less sound population. The predictions made by the four-mile heat breeders that switching to the dash standard would encourage and reward the breeding of unsoundness and those lacking bottom has been fulfilled (Chapter 4). The bad news is that an industry market driven for quick return was headed to oblivion, and without an incentive to change course nothing much would improve. It took the industry crashing before it altered its direction, and some corrective movements are in place now since the 1980s, with some longer distance races and appropriate purses for them, but we are a long way from the finish line with this reform.

On the other hand, the forecast is not all gloomy, because there is some good news for the breeders, which is: the genetic fabric of the American racehorse forged in the Heroic Era is not lost; those supreme athletes of one hundred seventy years ago are still providing those strong traits unchanged, because genes travel down unchanged through the generations (Bowling, *Horse Genetics*). We have the tools (see Appendix B) available to increase the percentage of those supreme foundation genes in our stock until they manifest in our product—however the question now is, "do we have the will to do what it takes?"

In the meantime, the sport horse breeders can take our knowledge on pedigree design and make our selections to increase the carriers from our Heroic Era in the background, and provide the necessary refocusing of the genes closer up to bring these supreme athletes to the fore. Will there be problems? Of course there will be. One I can see right away is our premier bloodline saturated in Lexington RH is Domino, which also carries some weakness especially with the front hooves. Further, the English branch of concentrated Lexington RH flows through Americus to the Lady Josephine family, and Lady Josephine is usually harnessed with other bloodlines that bring in more faults. This then will be the challenge—to recapture the goodness and eliminate the weakness.

Sport horse breeders have the advantage in this as their product is seldom a purebred racehorse, and a substance or specialized talent provider in our recipes can temper some of the weakness. That is, if they are well chosen, for all other breeds are loaded with faults themselves. To waste the genetic gold we have in the background of our native race and sport horse would be foolish—what other country's native breeds carry such treasure? We have the genetics of the greatest sport horse the world has ever seen—it is right here in our domestic stock, waiting to be recognized and utilized.

How do we begin? First we need to become familiar with the bloodlines available to us that carry a strong potency in our target lines—Lexington RH et al. Then we pick the individuals from those that demonstrate less of the faults overall but with the talent we desire. We will be focusing on the American bloodlines or those from Europe that carry them. Keep in mind most American-bred Thoroughbreds have multiple background lines of Lexington RH; however, not all have critical mass in them, and the ones that do are producing far and above over what was expected of them. We will illustrate this for you in this section with examples that have critical mass in Heroic Era genes, but keep in mind, this not a comprehensive coverage of those carriers, and your own investigations can uncover more of them.

Caerleon (1980)

Nijinsky II (1967)

- **Northern Dancer (1961)**
  - **Nearctic (1954)**
    - *NEARCO (1935)*
      - *PHAROS*
        - *PHALARIS* — Polymelus 3, Bromus 1
        - Scapa Flow — *CHAUCER* 7, Anchora 13
      - Nogara
        - Havresac — Rabelais 14, Hors Concours 8
        - Catnip — *SPEARMINT* 7, Sibola 4
    - **Lady Angela (1944)**
      - Hyperion
        - *GAINSBOROUGH* — *BAYARDO* 10, Rosedrop 2
        - *SELENE* — *CHAUCER* 7, Serenissima 6
      - Sister Sarah
        - Abbots Trace — *TRACERY* 19, Abbots Anne 4
        - Sarita — Swynford 1, Molly Desmond 14
  - **Natalma (1957)**
    - **Native Dancer (1950)**
      - Polynesian
        - Unbreakable — Sickle 6, Blue Glass 4
        - Black Polly — Polymelian 7, Black Queen 14
      - Geisha
        - Discovery — Display 7, Ariadne 23
        - Miyako — John P Grier 8, La Chica 5
    - **Almahmoud (1947)**
      - Mahmoud
        - Blenheim II — Blandford 3, Malva 1
        - Mah Mahal — *GAINSBOROUGH* 2, Mumtaz Mahal 9
      - Arbitrator
        - Peace Chance — Chance Shot 10, Peace 31
        - Mother Goose — Chicle 2, Flying Witch 1

Bull Page (1947)

- **Bull Lea (1935)**
  - Bull Dog
    - *TEDDY* — Ajax 2, Rondeau 7
    - *PLUCKY LIEGE* — *SPEARMINT* 1, Concertina 16
  - Rose Leaves
    - Ballot — Voter 14, Cerito 18
    - Colonial — Trenton 9, Thankful Blossom
- **Our Page (1940)**
  - *BLUE LARKSPUR*
    - Black Servant — *BLACK TONEY* 10, Padula 8
    - Blossom Time — North Star III 4, Valla
  - Occult
    - Dis Donc — Sardanapale 16, Lady Hamburg II 31
    - Bonnie Witch — Broomstick 16, Bonnie Star 4

Flaming Page (1959) / Flaring Top (1947)

- **Menow (1935)**
  - *PHARAMOND II*
    - *PHALARIS* — Polymelus 3, Bromus 1
    - *SELENE* — *CHAUCER* 7, Serenissima 6
  - Alcibiades
    - Supremus — *ULTIMUS* 14, Mandy Hamilton 32
    - Regal Roman — Roi Herode 8, Lady Cicero
- **Flaming Top (1941)**
  - Omaha
    - Gallant Fox — *SIR GALLAHAD III* 16, Marguerite 4
    - Flambino — Wrack 1, Flambette 17
  - Firetop
    - *MAN O' WAR* — Fair Play 9, Mahubah 4
    - Summit — *ULTIMUS* 14, Torpenhow 8

Foreseer (1969)

- **Round Table (1954)**
  - **Princequillo (1940)**
    - **Prince Rose (1928)**
      - Rose Prince
        - Prince Palatine — *PERSIMMON* 7, Lady Lightfoot 7
        - Eglantine — Perth 8, Rose De Mai 11
      - Indolence
        - Gay Crusader — *BAYARDO* 10, Gay Laura 1
        - Barrier — Grey Leg 6, Bar The Way 10
    - **Cosquilla (1933)**
      - Papyrus
        - *TRACERY* — Rock Sand 19, Topiary 12
        - Miss Matty — Marcovil 16, Simonath
      - Quick Thought
        - White Eagle — *GALLINULE* 19, Merry Gal 5
        - Mindful — Minoru 5, Noble Martha
  - **Knight's Daughter (1941)**
    - **Sir Cosmo (1926)**
      - The Boss
        - Orby — Orme 11, Rhoda B 26
        - Southern Cross — Meteor 24, Resplendent 11
      - Ayn Hali
        - Desmond — St Simon 16, L'Abbesse De Jouarre 7
        - Lalla Rookh — Hackler 6, Lady Gough 9
    - **Feola (1933)**
      - Friar Marcus
        - Cicero — Cyllene 1, Gas 7
        - Prim Nun — *PERSIMMON* 20, Nunsuch 9
      - Aloe
        - Son-In-Law — Dark Ronald 19, Mother-In-Law 2
        - Alope — *GALLINULE* 13, Altoviscar

Hail To Reason (1958)

- **Turn-To (1951)**
  - Royal Charger
    - *NEARCO* — *PHAROS* 26, Nogara 9
    - Sun Princess — Solario 16, Mumtaz Begum 16
  - Source Sucree
    - Admiral Drake — Craig An Eran 13, *PLUCKY LIEGE* 1
    - Lavendula II — *PHAROS* 8, Sweet Lavender 8
- **Nothirdchance (1948)**
  - Blue Swords
    - *BLUE LARKSPUR* — Black Servant 7, Blossom Time 2
    - Flaming Swords — *MAN O' WAR* 16, Exalted 4
  - Galla Colors
    - *SIR GALLAHAD III* — *TEDDY* 8, *PLUCKY LIEGE* 5
    - Rouge Et Noir — St Germans 4, Baton Rouge

Regal Gleam (1964)

- **Stymie (1941)**
  - Equestrian
    - Equipoise — Pennant 4, Swinging A1
    - Frilette — *MAN O' WAR* 19, Frillery 4
  - Stop Watch
    - On Watch — Colin 1, Rubia Granda
    - Sunset Gun — *MAN O' WAR*, Eventide 6
- **Miz Carol (1953)**
  - **No Fiddling (1945)**
    - King Cole
      - *PHARAMOND II* — *PHALARIS* 5, *SELENE* 8
      - Golden Melody — Mont D'Or II 2, Ormonda 10
    - Big Hurry
      - *BLACK TONEY* — Peter Pan 2, Belgravia 1
      - La Troienne — *TEDDY*, Helene De Troie 1

Caerleon 1980

Chapter 21

Selected Mares Who Passed on the Heroic Era Genes

W hen discussing what makes a successful breeder, Ken McLean emphasizes the best breeders recognize the importance of building up the broodmare. "Their aim is to upgrade each foal from an individual mare and to do this they choose the very best genetic material to send to the mare. Successful breeders do not generalize, they select according to specifics. After all, it only takes one mare to breed a champion racehorse or classic winner" (*Quest for a Classic Winner*).

Sketch of a newborn Thoroughbred by C. W. Anderson for *Who's Who in Thoroughbred Racing*.

Our specifics are to increase the percentage of our Heroic Era talent in our herds. To that end we will seek out mares who carried those elements in multiples and have proven it by their performance in racing or at stud. We already discussed foreign mares of significance such as Lady Josephine, Catnip, Frizette (French branch), Nella da Gubbio, and the French sisters Durban/Heldifann, so now we will see what is cooking in our American mares. This study will not be exhaustive, but through selecting a few important maternal conduits of those qualities we want to make dominant in our herds again, we hope to demonstrate a way to achieve our overall goal of top sport performance.

Frizette

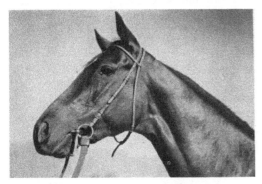

Jet Pilot—an important bloodline as he is a grandson of Black Curl. —image from *Who's Who in Thoroughbred Racing*

An important taproot mare that reflects not only the highest racing class but tremendous heart as well and the ability to pass it on is Frizette (see Chapter 16). Whatever avenue you follow in building up her lines—the French or the American branch—you will have elevated your sport product; Frizette is that good. She is a super-star. A daughter of Hamburg, when Frizette was bred to sires who connected to her pedigree strengths, her descendants that followed excelled. Her French daughters Durban and Heldifann are important lines in France and now in international breeding and are one of the top concentrations of Lexington RH in our modern day. Her daughter Frizeur 1910 is rated a *reine-de-course*; she was by Sweeper II, a son of Broomstick. Frizeur's daughter Black Curl by Friar Rock is the second dam of the good sire Jet Pilot; Black Curl is also a desired line for her sire Friar Rock's (¾ genetic brother to Man O' War) dam is the very genetically valuable Friars Carse, who should be a target line for us also. In addition, Black Curl is a line that adds complexity to Frizette's other daughter of significance in the USA who is found much more often; this is Myrtlewood 1932 by Blue Larkspur, who has left a very deep footprint in the American Thoroughbred. Naturally, combining this American branch with the French lines of Frizette is recipe for success.

Myrtlewood 1932

Myrtlewood—a mare of outstanding performance in both racing and breeding. —image courtesy of Wiki Commons

Myrtlewood is exactly the type of filly we would want to produce, as she was both a great racer and an over-the-top producer—she has created a maternal dynasty of immense power and reach; she is a *reine*. She raced from two to four years old and ran a total of twenty-two races, won fifteen of them, and was out of the money only once. She earned the titles of Champion-Handicap-Mare and Champion-Sprinter. Bought by Mr. Leslie Combs who had seen her grandmother Frizette in France years before and never forgot her quality, he set Myrtlewood at his Spendthrift farm, and she became a cornerstone of his success. As a broodmare she was equally brilliant—out of eleven foals, eight raced, and six were winners; two of those were stakes winners. It is her daughters who have proven to be the most consistent source of class. She carries thirteen lines of Lexington RH.

Her offspring:

Spring Beauty produced several good horses here and abroad: Tres Jolie—winner in Venezuela, Al Mundher in Germany, and Silent Beauty here in the US.

Myrtlewood's daughter Durazna was like her mom in that she was a stakes winner: nine wins out of nineteen starts, earning the Champion-Two-Year-Old Filly title. Then she went on to earn *reine* status as a broodmare as well: out of five foals, four were stakes winners.

Durazna's full sister Miss Dogwood repeated the pattern, winning fourteen of twenty-one starts and retiring to stud; she had nine foals, and seven of them were winners, earning her *reine* status as well. From one of her daughters descends Mr. Prospector. Durazna and Miss Dogwood are by Bull Lea.

Then there is her daughter Crepe Myrtle, another *reine*, dam of Myrtle's Jet from whom Seattle Slew descends. Obviously there is something worthwhile being transmitted via mtDNA and the X chromosome here, as regardless of sire Myrtlewood continues to send down excellence, so to find her on your dam-line is an invitation to greatness. It is notable that Seattle Slew (whom we will be discussing in length later on) carries Frizeur doubled through daughters in the bottom quadrant of his lineage through Myrtlewood and her ½ sister Black Curl 5x6—from this design we can see Frizeur is reinforced on the X chromosome. Designs like this, which tap back to potent ancestors, are proven avenues to success.

Ellen Parker, who we are indebted for the creation and editing of the *reines-de-course* list, alerts us to the fact that **five stakes winners bred by Seattle Slew were inbred to Myrtlewood.**

All those aside, ask yourself, where does the original excellence spring from? And what was it built on? Entire libraries could be built to house the literature produced on the English Thoroughbred and its bloodlines; they have been examined and explained and proclaimed to the point that the casual breeder or enthusiast could easily assume that the only lines that matter are those that trace back to those proper English sources. And Frizette, the wellspring of this power, is out of a mare by the English icon St. Simon out of a dam by Tadcaster (corrected pedigree—see Appendix C). These two are genetic giants of the English Thoroughbred and always are a source of excellence. So it would seem right to attribute the massive genetic reach of Frizette to those two, but Frizette's genetic supremacy appears strongest through her daughters—an indication that powerful sex-linked genes are being transmitted. Frizette possessed two X chromosomes, and those English heroes rule only one of them. The second one is from her sire Hamburg.

Hamburg is a **genetic giant** in his own right—every bit the equal or possibly the better of those two mentioned above. Plus he is an undiluted source of the best of our four-mile racer genes. He is loaded with the very best: Lexington RH (and Lecomte RH) 4x4x5x5x5, plus the great Vandal RH 4x4, all funneled through Mannie Gray, Fellowcraft, and Hanover—the best of their eras and possibly of any era. For our purposes it is the descendants of this line who built on what Hamburg brought to the gene pool that we want to target (Chapters 9 and 10).

This instance is not just an isolated transmission of this power, for the great modern sires: Damascus, Icecapade, Dr. Fager, In Reality, Shut Out, and others all carry Hamburg daughters on their dam sides. For example, the great taproot mare Rosie O'Grady is by Hamburg out of a Peter Pan mare (Domino line), and she is found in modern greats such as Fusaichi Pegasus, Holy Bull, and Intentionally. The wonderful weight carrier Discovery, one of the most influential broodmare sires of modern times (Native Dancer, Bold Ruler etc.), has a dam-line that also goes straight back to Hamburg.

What we should be asking then is what makes Hamburg's sex-linked genes so powerful? His dam Lady Reel is a daughter of Fellowcraft (full brother to Spendthrift from whom Fair Play, Man O' War, and Discovery descend) whose own dam is Aerolite RH, a daughter of Lexington RH—so that is one of her X chromosomes. Lady Reel's dam is none other than Mannie Gray, dam of Domino et al—ruling the other X chromosome. These individuals are the bedrock of American performance, the lines that make the American Thoroughbred uniquely 'American'. Naturally, combining strains of Hamburg with both Aerolite RH (Spendthrift et al) and Domino (et al) is a recipe for success we should be looking to copy and multiply in our lineages.

Beaming Beauty 1917

Another broodmare that is a concentrated carrier of the four-mile genes is Beaming Beauty 1917—who with relatively few offspring was able to shape our modern Thoroughbred. By the great broodmare sire and large heart transmitter Sweep, a son of Ben Brush, she is out of Bellisario, who is a daughter of the inbred Hippodrome (Domino 2x2) out of the Hamburg daughter Biturica—this makes her an important source of the genes we want to target. She carries fifteen lines of Lexington RH/Lecomte RH and two of Vandal RH. Beaming Beauty is 3x4x4x4 to Domino/Lady Reel.

In our quest to increase the Heroic Era genes we will repeatedly run in to the problem of dilution. Over the years these lines were crossed and recrossed with foreign—usually English—bloodlines. Therefore the power of the four-mile heat racer becomes dissipated. We will want then to find those conduits that either have remained strong in these genes or have been refocused strongly in later generations to bring back the soundness, resiliency, speed, and stamina of those horses, for they are the pinnacle worldwide of top sport performance.

Unfortunately, only once was Beaming Beauty bred to another carrier of the four-milers—this is typical of what we have to deal with in our quest. The filly Bar Nothing who is by Blue Larkspur (a *chef* with seven lines of Lexington RH) is the only one to be bred back to our targets—the others are valuable of course, but are more diluted. Bar Nothing produced a daughter of significance in Blade of Time who in-turn produced several stakes winners, such as Blue Bonder, Bymeabond, Ruddy, and Guillotine. Her daughter Blonde Belle is the dam of the broodmare Peroxide, who in turn is second dam of the stakes winner Native Charger. But it is her daughter Kerala who is the superstar, a *reine* who produced the incomparable Damascus—a racing machine and a genetic giant of modern times. Kerala builds on the Heroic Era genes as she has thirty-four lines of Lexington RH. It is interesting that Damascus also carries the ¾ brother to Bar Nothing: By Jiminy, making them 3x3—therefore his genetic fabric built on and reinforced those genetics. We would have to be brain-dead not to see the correlation here between reinforcing the Heroic Era bloodlines and the best performers of our time. Damascus has forty-eight lines of Lexington RH. Damascus has a full sister, Arlene Francis 1970.

Kerala produced an interesting daughter in Mavala 1965, as she is by the Eight Thirty son Bolero, who adds an additional twenty-two lines of Lexington RH to her thirty-four, giving us fifty six total lines. This line is easily found in the New Zealand and Australian Thoroughbred.

Bubbling Over 1923—son of the foundation mare Beaming Beauty, his daughters are genetic gold. —image courtesy of Keeneland Library

All that aside, it is Beaming Beauty's stallion son Bubbling Over 1923, by imported North Star III, who casts the longest shadow. A top racehorse, he was the winner of the 1926 Kentucky Derby and was never out of the money in his career with ten wins, two seconds, and one third in thirteen starts. Bubbling Over's sire North Star III unfortunately was one of those imports who transmitted unsoundness, and Colonel Bradley stood him at his stud where his weakness was imparted widely to his stock. Bubbling Over himself was one of those North Star sons who were never completely sound, and his race record is a testament to his heart and class. However, in spite of this weakness his genetic legacy is huge, and he is sire of the Kentucky Derby and Preakness winner Burgoo King.

Nonetheless, we can see it is usually his sex-linked genes that are in play here making his record as a top sire, as it is his daughters who have left a large genetic impression—here are a few of them:

Baby League is a *reine* out of the formidable mare La Troienne, who of course, is usually given the lion's share of credit for the broodmare success of her daughter, but we find it was when Baby League was bred to War Admiral that she produced her best offspring, a triplicate of supreme class and potency: Busher, Striking and Mr. Busher (twenty-three lines of Lexington RH). It is interesting that the leading dominance in these three is not the English/European lines represented in La Troienne, but the American line of Sweep who is 3x4 through Beaming Beauty and her sister Brush Up. Busher was Horse-of-the-Year; Striking was Broodmare-of-the-Year (*reine*), and Mr. Busher was a great racer and good sire in his own right (see Chapter 22). They are found in the champions Jet Action, Poker, Woodman, and Private Account among others. Seattle Slew is 4x4 to Striking/Busher. It does not get much better than this. Seattle Slew received critical mass from both his parents, seventy-one lines of Lexington RH from his dam and sixty-nine lines from his sire—making one hundred forty lines of Lexington RH in Seattle Slew. Do you think this buildup of Lexington RH might be a significant element in his success?

Busher 1942—Horse-of-the-Year and good broodmare—this is as good as it gets. —image by Bert Morgan, *Who's Who in Thoroughbred Racing*

Liz F, also a *reine*, is loaded with the four-milers and their transmitters: 4x4 Ben Brush, 3x5 Hamburg, 5x5x7 Hindoo, 5x5 Commando (Domino), 5x7x7x7x7 Mannie Gray, and even 6x6 Maggie B. B. RH—Liz has twenty-nine lines of Lexington RH. Her daughters produced well, Harriet's Kid is grandma to Princess Taj for instance, but it is her son Intent who is found continually in the best pedigrees. He is by the intensely-inbred War Relic—2x2 to the ¾ brothers Man O' War/Friar Rock, with a dam-line that adds more Commando but also pulls in a sister to Domino: Quesal, making them 4x5 and has a Lexington RH daughter on both his sire-line (Aerolite RH) and his dam-line (Hira RH). This concentration of Heroic Era genes connects to the intensely bred Liz F's multiple lines of Domino—Mannie Gray and all the background Lexington RH (thirty-seven lines). Intent was a great racer and a significant sire. His daughter Intent One (fifty-two lines of Lexington RH) is the second-dam of the world-beater John Henry (gelding), and others of his daughters will be easily found.

However, it is his son Intentionally that has become a key modern-day sire (forty-nine Lexington RH lines). Champion 1959 Sprinter, he was so very fast that he became celebrated as the 'Black Bullet'. His progeny are widespread, and all are valuable, but three especially are exceptional:

Tentam, a stakes winner who also a good sire of winners (seventy-three Lexington RH lines). His dam brought in more of Sweep, Domino, Chicle, and Lady Josephine (Americus).

Ta Wee, a *reine*, plus a great racer (ninety-five lines of Lexington RH). Her dam Aspidistra is also a *reine* who will be discussed below. Ta Wee is the dam of Great Above, the sire of Holy Bull (see Chapter 24).

In Reality, a modern sire of immense influence siring 15% stakes winners (with one hundred one lines of Lexington RH). He is inbred to War Relic 3x3, Whisk Broom II 5x6x6, Fair Play 5x5x5, and Hamburg 6x7x7. Some of his most notable sons are Known Fact, Relaunch, Valid Appeal, and Believe It. His daughters Desert Vixen and Moon Glitter are good producers also. In Reality is found in such greats as Bold Fact (Ireland), Arromanches, Skywalker, Betrando, Real Quiet, and Real Shadai, a top sire in Japan.

Hildene 1938 is also a *reine* and a titan among mares (twenty-seven lines of Lexington RH) but also has notable English strengths: a filly factor in four daughters of the obscure Scottish Chief 8x7x7x6, refocused in the filly factor of the offspring of his daughter Violet Melrose: the full siblings Editha/Melton 6x5—this is genetic power. She is especially known for her sons; Hill Prince, a champion at two, then earned Champion-Three-Year-Old and Horse-of-the-Year as well. A top sire, he has produced twenty stakes winners and is best as a broodmare sire with such daughters as Bayou and Levee, who are both *reines*. Prince Hill, his full brother, was also a good racer. Hildene's son Third Brother was a stakes winner, and her son First Landing by Turn-To (source of unsoundness) was a fantastic racer voted Champion Two-Year-Old; he is the sire of Kentucky Derby winner Riva Ridge, who in-turn is a good broodmare sire. Hildene's daughters: Satusuma, dam of champion racer Cicada and her full sister Sabana, a top producer; First Flush is herself a *reine*, a poor racer but great producer with many stakes winning progeny.

Aspidistra 1954

The next mare for us to consider is Aspidistra, whose success as a broodmare seems to have puzzled many, especially those who look only at the tail-female line as an indication of maternal success. The mares on her direct tail-female line produced little in racing class through the generations, and yes the tail-female line is the source of the mtDNA, so it is an important consideration in mares, but it is obviously not the sole component that makes an exceptional broodmare.

If we expand our examination to those ancestors who could contribute to her X chromosomes (sex-linked material), we get a different picture. First, we find that the taproot mare Frizette is present strongly through her rarely-found son Frizzle, who is here by a daughter and therefore able to bring Frizette's gifts to the granddaughter Fricassee. Plus the 3rd dam Teak receives an X from her sire Tea Caddy's dam: Tea's Over, a Hamburg daughter. Here is reinforcement value, as Tea Caddy is the full brother to Tea Biscuit, the dam of Hard Tack, who is the sire of Seabiscuit, plus he is also the full brother to the *reine* Toggery whose daughters Cri De Coeur and Mademoiselle Dazie produced the good sires The Doge and Jamestown—a tough and sound line. Aspidistra is providing the racing population with the rarely seen male lines of Frizette and Toggery found in Frizzle and Tea Caddy. Obviously this is a producing family and is notable for containing the rarely seen sex-balance for the lines of Frizette, Tea Biscuit, and Toggery. Her second dam Tilly Rose receives one of her Xs from the Hamburg daughter Parkview, and Aspidistra's sire Better Self gives her an X from Bee Mac—a War Admiral daughter. Further, Aspidistra is an example of critical mass, as she has forty-six lines of Lexington RH in her background, a huge amount for a mare born in 1954.

Aspidistra, however, while she did display speed and courage, was not the best racer, because her knees were weak, yet she still won two out of fourteen starts. In spite of this she proved to be a top broodmare—a *reine*—and dam of two super stars: Dr. Fager and Ta Wee, both exceptionally sound and talented racers and producers. She is inbred 3x5 Black Toney, 3x5 Sweep, 4x6x6 Peter Pan, 5x6x6x6 Ben Brush—plus 6x5 Rock Sand and 4x4 Teddy—clearly refocusing the genetic power in her background.

Better Self—broodmare sire of Aspidstria and Lady Be Good. —image by Skeet Meadors, courtesy of Keeneland Library.

Her sire Better Self won sixteen of fifty starts at distances of six furlongs to 1⅝ miles, plus he was a good broodmare sire in spite of being sub-fertile. He produced another important daughter in Lady Be Good, who is out of an Eight Thirty dam and is 4x4x5 to the ¾ brothers Friar Rock/Man O' War and has the Spearmint daughter Bathing Girl 5x6. What's interesting is that since the discovery that Bend Or is really another stallion named Tadcaster (see Appendix C), who have the same sire Doncaster but different dams, our pedigrees appear to be making more genetic sense. Lady Be Good is a study (pedigree) in this—as Tadcaster's dam Clemence is also the second-dam of Carbine, which helps explains Carbine's success as a sire and why he nicks automatically with the many Tadcaster (Bend Or) lines in the TB, and here in Lady Be Good we find Tadcaster and his ½ sister The Mersey are 7x8x7x7x6x8x6x6, which is a tremendous background buildup of this superior mare. Lady Be Good also has a powerful Ben Brush sex balance 4x5x6. Lady Be Good is a *reine* who produced two *reines*, Bold Example and Discipline—this is a powerful maternal family.

Prayer Bell is the ¾ sister to Lady Be Good, and she is also a *reine,* as she too is out of a Eight Thirty dam with much the same inbreeding pattern: Man O' War/Friar Rock 4x4x5, and Bathing Girl 5x6; however her dam-line is not ruled by Clemence (dam of Tadcaster), rather it is from Ben Brush/Domino line mares. Lady Be Good had top mares while Prayer Bell's best was the good stallion: Silent Screen.

Aspidistra had decent racers such as A Deck and Chinatowner, who was a good turf horse who died before he could go to stud. She had a good broodmare daughter in Quit Me Not; even better however was Magic by Buckpasser (broodmare sire), as she is the third-dam of Unbridled, a great stallion who is 4x4 to Aspidistra.

But her greatest daughter is Ta Wee (mentioned above); she was a wonderful, stakes-winning racer who won the Champion Sprinter title two years in a row (1969-70). She was also a tremendous weight carrier, and the Thoroughbred expert Avalyn Hunter reminds us that Ta Wee is a contender for top female weight carrier ever (*Classic Pedigrees*).

Ta Wee is a top broodmare as well; her good son Entropy by What a Pleasure, her daughter Thill by Iron Ruler, and Tweak by Secretariat—all good producers. Her greatest fame rests on her stallion son Great Above, a good sire who gave us the modern-day sensation Holy Bull, a top stakes winner and great sire. Giacomo and Macho Uno are a few of his exceptional offspring (Holy Bull carries one hundred eighty-eight lines of Lexington RH—see Chapter 24).

Ta Wee is hard to top, but perhaps Aspidisra's son Dr. Fager can do that (see Chapter 24). A setter of a speed record that stood for twenty-nine years, he has been described as 'raw speed personified,' and he could win at both sprint and classic distances up to 1¼ miles, but he was difficult to ride because he refused to be rated and sometimes would spend his energy too soon. Dr. Fager died young at twelve years but has managed to leave a lasting legacy, leading the sire list in 1977, and he was a fabulous broodmare sire as well. Dr. Fager's daughter Killaloe is inbred 4x5x5 to full siblings Bull Dog/Marguerite De Valois. Her fourth-dam Hostility is by Man O' War and is a *reine*, an example of extreme maternal strength. Killaloe produced the mega-sire Fappiano, who is said to resemble Dr. Fager, but clearly his dominance is in English lines with another line of Bull Dog adding to the full sibling strength 5x5x6x6, and also the ¾ siblings Mahmoud/Mumtaz Begum 5x5 (conduits of Americus). Fappiano is a truly great sire with stallion sons like Cahill Road and Rubiano, but then a few of his other sons have gone beyond good and have proven to be dominant influences in our day: Cryptoclearance, Quiet American, and Unbridled—who is 4x4 to Aspidistra.

Grey Flight 1946

Next we will look at the modern-day wonder mare Grey Flight, as she has become a prime line-breeding target for the racehorse breeder. Her second-dam is La Chica, a Sweep daughter who is also the third-dam of Native Dancer; therefore bringing together Native Dancer and Grey Flight in your pedigrees will create a powerful maternal influence of La Chica. Having top broodmare sires (War Admiral, Buckpasser, Discovery, etc.) in our dam quadrants are always an indication of potency, and any daughter of Sweep is a valuable line to have. Sweep is a **genetic giant**—a son of Ben Brush out of a Domino dam—and he reliably transfers soundness, speed, class, and even the large heart gene.

Grey Flight. —photo by Skeet Meadors, courtesy of Keeneland Library.

Grey Flight's dam is Planetoid, who is by the interesting sire Ariel. Not exactly a household name, yet he is a very significant sire who is found doubled in the modern stars Curlin and Louis Quatorze (and is seen here in the pedigree Bold Lad). Ariel also brings extra genetic bonuses with him, as he carries the rarely seen sex balance or full sibling for several important lines: Adam, full brother to Ajax (sire of Teddy); Mannie Himyar, full sister to Domino, and his sire Eternal is a Sweep son. All of these elements were instrumental in Grey Flight's broodmare success. Planetoid had another successful broodmare daughter Just-a-Minute. Note her pedigree pattern: she carries seven lines of the full siblings Domino/Correction/Mannie Himyar 6x6x6x6x6x4x5.

When Planetoid was mated with Mahmoud—also a great broodmare sire—they produced Grey Flight. We can see what occurs when close relatives meet up in pedigrees; here the many lines of Domino/Mannie Himyar 5x3x4 meet up with their close relative Americus through the Lady Josephine lines. Americus, dam-sire of Lady Josephine, is 3x3 to Lexington RH, sex-balanced full siblings (see Chapter 15). Domino et al is 3x4x4 to Lexington RH—also sex-balanced, which makes both these bloodlines equal in potency of Lexington RH. Try to see the significance of building up lines of important ancestors, sex-balancing them and adding close relatives—it is one of the keys to the massive international success of the modern American Thoroughbred. The imported stallion ¾ brothers Mahmoud/Nasrullah/Royal Charger all have Lady Josephine (Americus) on their dam-line.

Bold Ruler—a *chef-de-race*, he nicked particularly well with Grey Flight and her daughters. — photo by Skeet Meadors, courtesy of Keeneland Library.

Grey Flight is the dam of nine stakes winners and was remarkable for her ability to nick extremely well with Bold Ruler, resulting in her great daughters' stakes winners Bold Princess, Pleasant Flight, and the *reine* Clear Ceiling, who is dam of stakes winners Quick as Lightening, Stratospheric, and Infinite, as well as Pure Profit—the dam of stakes winners. Grey Flight's best son was by Bold Ruler also: What a Pleasure; he became leading sire twice with offspring such as Kentucky Derby winner Foolish Pleasure, himself a sire of forty-three stakes winners.

Grey Flight had another daughter who achieved *reine* status: Misty Morn. Twice a champion racer, she was also 1963 Broodmare-of-the-Year. A daughter of the great broodmare sire Princequillo, Misty Morn's best offspring was the good sire Bold Lad 1962 (a son of Bold Ruler), himself sire of two *reines* as well as the good sons On to Glory and Twice Bold.

This combination of Grey Flight and Bold Ruler is worthy of our study, because of its vast influence. Bold Ruler builds on Grey Flight's pedigree dominances—together there are twenty-one lines of Lexington RH—but it is not enough to have strong background strength, and many American pedigrees by her day have this many or more lines of Lexington RH in the background. What we have learned is there must be a refocusing of the important lines closer up, or their influences scatter resulting in little manifesting in the foals (see Appendix B). But here we have the concentrated conduits of Lexington RH (Domino et al/ Americus) in multiples. There are six lines of them 7x8x7x7x5x6; also notable in dominance are the three lines of the good French sire Roi Herode 4x5x5 (Clemence lines). All of these are then reconcentrated through the Sweep sons and daughters 5x4x3 and the ¾ siblings Mahmoud and Mumtaz Begum 3x2. This type of pedigree design has insured the potency in the background comes through in force to the foals (see these two combined in the Bold Lad pedigree).

I have to keep reminding myself that the focus here is not just carriers of the flaw, which all of our native bred horses carry, but those individuals who have a higher proportion of those genes, as our ultimate goal is to build them up in our backgrounds until we reach critical mass.

So I will just give the great broodmare Two Bob a passing mention, as she has Sweep and Chicle in the second generation, but is disappointing in the overall buildup of the four-milers in the background as compared to some of the others we will highlight here, as she has only thirteen lines of Lexington RH and an additional two of the Running Horse mare Rosalie Somers. She had three full sister daughters, all by Bull Lea, but he did not bring in any of our target lines, so the four-miler influence is dissipated somewhat. These are Twosy, Two Lea, and Miz Clemintine. Twosy and Two Lea were good racers; Miz Clementine was a stakes winner. Twosy is ancestress of greats such as Chris Evert and Winning Colors. Two Lea is dam of Kentucky Derby winner Tim Tam, and stakes winner and good sire On and On. Miz Clementine through her daughter Sweet Clementine produced Best Turn. American breeders always could produce winners of largely British lines—such as these here—and while I am sure the Lexington RH in the background delivered speed to this family it is not concentrated enough for us to study.

Almahmoud 1947

On the other hand, however, is Almahmoud, one of the greatest broodmares of modern times, and certainly a target in international breeding for duplications—a practice that has proven highly successful. By the imported stallion Mahmoud who carries Americus on his dam-line, she is a queen in pedigrees, and so too are two of her daughters. She was a fair racer, winning four out of eleven starts, plus she had fertility problems, but still she ended up with six foals, two of them stakes winners (Cosmah, Folk Dancer). In spite of her shortcomings, some of the most influential stallions of our time descend

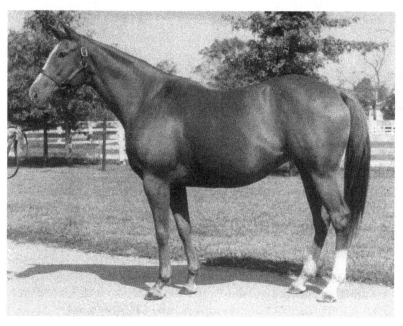

Almahmoud—one of the greatest broodmares of modern times.
—photo by Skeet Meadors, courtesy of Keeneland Library

from her: Halo, Arctic Tern, Danehill, Ashado, Rahy, Machiavellian (who is 4x4 Almahmoud), and of course Northern Dancer—she is a genetic giant. She naturally has become a target internationally of line-breeders with great results such as Giant's Causeway, who is 4x5 to Almahmoud.

Her sons were either gelded (Armistice, Folk Dancer) or a disappointment (Ramaden). It is her daughters who have made her name so great—Cosmah, Natalma, and Bubbling Beauty—therefore we can surmise that her power is largely sex-linked.

First let's look at her pedigree. She has a leading dominance in The Tetrarch with a son and daughter 3x4. The Tetrarch is a key line in the modern sport horse, a son of the good Irish-bred Roi Herode, but he had leg problems that caused his early retirement, and he was sub-fertile as well. Nonetheless, he has become an important line in our modern TB and in sport horses, and his presence should be welcomed in your pedigrees. This lasting influence may have a lot to do with his leading dominance being the full siblings 3x3 Tadcaster/Clementina, by Doncaster out of the taproot mare Clemence, who is also the second-dam of the key sire Carbine and is found in our American line of Fair Play. Clemence will be found in multiples in many top horses, and she is 8x8x7x7 in Almahmoud (See the sport power of Clemence displayed in the top international jumper Sinjon in Chapter 34).

Almahmoud's second-dam is the *reine* Mother Goose, daughter of the important sire Chicle (bred by an American, conceived in England, born in France), a son of Spearmint, but his dam is Lady Hamburg, a Hamburg daughter. Wherever you find Hamburg realize his dam-sire is Fellowcraft, the full brother to Spendthrift who is the grandsire of Fair Play, and both are found here 6x7 sex-balanced, plus Hamburg is out of a Mannie Gray mare, so she is a sister to Domino. Hamburg is a key sire for our mission as he carries Lexington RH/Boston RH 4x4x5x5x5 and Vandal RH 4x4.

Mother Goose's dam is a daughter of Broomstick out of a Peter Pan dam. This puts seventeen Lexington RH/Boston RH lines in the background, along with three of American Eclipse—another Running Horse sire from our four-mile era, in Arbitrator. The majority of the Lexington RH/Boston RH (fourteen) arrives with Mother Goose. When Arbitrator was mated with Mahmoud two more were added—once again on the dam-line, along with four of the Running Horse mare Transport. Do you think this might be significant in her success? The only way to see if that is so is if her successful offspring add to this total.

Almahmoud's daughter Cosmah was her first foal, and she is a *reine*, a tremendous producer as well as a minor stakes winner herself. Four of her offspring are stakes winners. By Cosmic Bomb, a son of Pharamond, a purveyor of speed and unsoundness, his dam however brings in another line of the The Tetrarch making him 5x5x6 plus Blue Larkspur—a genetic giant who is inbred to the ½ sisters Padilla/Padua—but for our study it is his grandsire Black Toney who carries the gold, as he brings in seven additional lines of Lexington RH/Boston RH through Commando and Ben Brush, which is a total in Cosmah of twenty-five lines—not a huge amount but good.

Her daughter Tosmah was one of her talented racers; however still Cosmah is rated a disappointment at stud by some experts— (although how that can be said when she is the dam of Halo may be hard to understand), because she has now reached *reine* status. Her son Halo is a superstar, a stakes winner and an influential sire—he is the father of two Kentucky Derby winners: Sunny's Halo and Sunday Silence, which makes him one of the greatest modern-day sires. Other important offspring are Devil's Bag, Rainbow Connection, and Glorious Song. Halo led the sires list in 1983 and is a great broodmare sire. Not too bad for a poor broodmare—I'll take her any day.

Let's take a minute and see what was built on to produce this star. Halo is a son of Hail to Reason, a modern *chef-de-race* by the brilliant but unsound Turn-To, who was definitely a transmitter of speed, but also of fragility—he is 3x3 to Pharos plus carries the unsound Swynford as his third-dam-sire. Hail to Reason got plenty of substance from his dam Nothird-chance, who is inbred to Man O' War 3x4. Combined together in Hail to Reason we get Plucky Liege 4x4, plus Swynford 5x5, Maid of the Mist 5x6—but we also get an additional twenty-seven lines of Lexington RH/Boston RH for a total in Halo of fifty-two background lines of Lexington RH/Boston RH. We should notice that over time our American racer has become infected with multiple lines of weakness, to the point that a significant amount of the offspring will break down—this is our challenge in the years to come: to stop the downward slide and beef up out stock with fast but sound lines (more on Halo and his progeny in Chapter 27).

Cosmah had other good racers such as Fathers Image by Swaps and Maribeau by Ribot. Some of her daughters have bred on exceptionally well, such as Queen Sucree by Ribot, who produced the full brothers Cannonade—a major sire—and Circle Home.

Almahmoud's daughter Natalma 1957, who is by Native Dancer, is also classified a *reine*. She is dam of the stakes winners Native Victor, Regal Dancer, Born a Lady, and Northern Dancer—possibly the most influential sire of the last fifty years. She also produced the full sister to Northern Dancer: Arctic Dancer, who was a good broodmare, plus Spring Adieu, Raise the Standard, and Native Era. The great modern broodmare sire Danehill is 3x3 to Natalma.

Natalma carries forty lines of Lexington RH/Boston RH as well as seven of the important Enquirer RH. She has five lines of Domino, four of Ben Brush, two of Broomstick, three of Hindoo, and two of Fair Play—this is a step up in American lines. Natalma is by Native Dancer, a fantastic sire and racehorse that has become known for occasionally transferring bad ankles; this is something that has come down the genetic trail from his sire Polynesian, who was sound himself but evidently was a carrier (See Chapter 27 for an expanded discussion of unsoundness in some modern bloodlines.)

Then there is the good producer Bubbling Beauty 1961 by Hasty Road (out of a Discovery mare) out of Almahmoud, she carries forty-five lines of Lexington RH/Boston RH. Although she has not earned *reine* status, she has proven a good producer, as her son Arctic Tern is a G1 stakes winner and exceptional sire, and her daughters Champagne Cocktail and Simple Beauty are good broodmares also. She has Broomstick 4x5, Fair Play 5x5, and Hamburg 7x6.

Rare Treat 1952

Topping both Natalma and Aspidistria in Lexington RH buildup is a mare named Rare Treat 1952. By the champion Stymie out of the *reine* Rare Perfume, she is definitely an example of critical mass, as she carries fifty-two lines of Lexington RH in her background. There is a tremendously powerful pedigree pattern here—the full siblings Pennant/Cherokee Rose 4x5 on the dam and sire-line, then focused even closer, as their offspring are ¾ siblings Equipoise/Rowes Bud, and there is another ¾ sibling formation of Noontide/High Time 5x4—these all pull Lexington RH to the front. A durable racer, she started one hundred times and won sixteen of those, racing through her seventh year, so we are looking at great soundness here also.

She is a notable dam of good mares; What a Treat by the great Tudor Minstrel is perhaps the best, as she is the dam of the champion mid-distance runner Be My Guest, who was the first big stallion to stand at Coolmore Stud in Ireland. He in turn produced stakes winners including Go and Go who won the Belmont, and the champion Assert—winner of both the French and Irish Derbies—his line is often found in jumpers as well. She had a significant daughter in Bendara who is dam to three stakes winners: Ida Delia, Niskashka, and Esperanto, and the good mare Ida's Image.

Her daughter Exotic Treat by Vaguely Noble was unraced but produced the Epsom Derby winner Golden Fleece, who was bought by Coolmore partners for $775,000. He sired some good racers but died at age five. She also produced the noted mare Office Wife, a Secretariat daughter.

Another Treat by Cornish Prince is also one of her daughters. Her daughter Rare Mint produced five stakes winners.

Rare Treat, although a great mare, has been bred-down by her mates, and it is time to use her in line-breeding with other great Lexington RH gene pools to bring back the tough, sound speed she possessed.

Sex Appeal 1970

Another mare worthy of our notice is the great Buckpasser daughter Sex Appeal; she too has a healthy buildup of Lexington RH with thirty-seven lines in the background—made more powerful as it is reinforced through the ¾ siblings Busanda/Mr. Busher 2x3. Her dam Best in Show was Broodmare-of-the-Year in 1982, and Sex Appeal has a full brother named Perferred Position, who was only a fair racer and sire of ninety-five foals—no great shakes but may be valuable down the road for line-breeding. Sex Appeal was not raced, but out of sixteen foals she had ten who raced, and seven of those were winners. Sex Appeal is clearly the best of her siblings as a producer, as she is the dam of the important sires and full brothers El Gran Senor and Try My Best.

El Gran Senor 1981 by Northern Dancer was the champion Two-Year-Old in both England and France in 1983. He won the 2000 Guineas and came in second in the Derby. A top miler, he was also the top Three-Year-Old in England. He had fertility problems but still managed to sire forty stakes winners.

His full brother Try My Best 1975 was the champion Two-Year-Old in England and Ireland in 1977 and the champion Three-Year-Old miler in Ireland in 1978—obviously this combination was very worthwhile. What exactly did Northern Dancer bring to the match that produced these good racers and sires? He brought Natalma with forty-five lines of Lexington RH/Boston RH added to the thirty-seven of Lexington RH that Sex Appeal had, which equals ninety-two lines of Lexington RH/Boston RH—once again critical mass. Try My Best was shipped to Japan for stud duty and is sire of thirty stakes winners. Perhaps his best son is Last Tycoon who is out of a Mill Reef dam—which brought in more Lexington RH lines.

There is another full brother, Compliance, who is also a notable sire producing many stakes winners including Fourstar All-star and Fourstar Dancer; both have won over $1 million.

Future breeding strategies for us may be to include those mares such as Hildene, Frizette, Aspidistra, Rare Treat, Natalma, and Sex Appeal in multiples in our designs, as they are concentrated carriers of Lexington RH. Clearly continual out-crossing causes loss of class. We will need to find the most concentrated conduits of Lexington RH in our gene pools and inbreed to them or add to them with other strong carriers of Lexington RH, so we continue to produce those exceptional racers and sport horses with soundness, toughness, and stamina combined with speed. These mares I covered briefly here are just a few examples of the riches in our gene pool. The following two chapters will cover other maternal dynasties of note (Chapters 22 and 23).

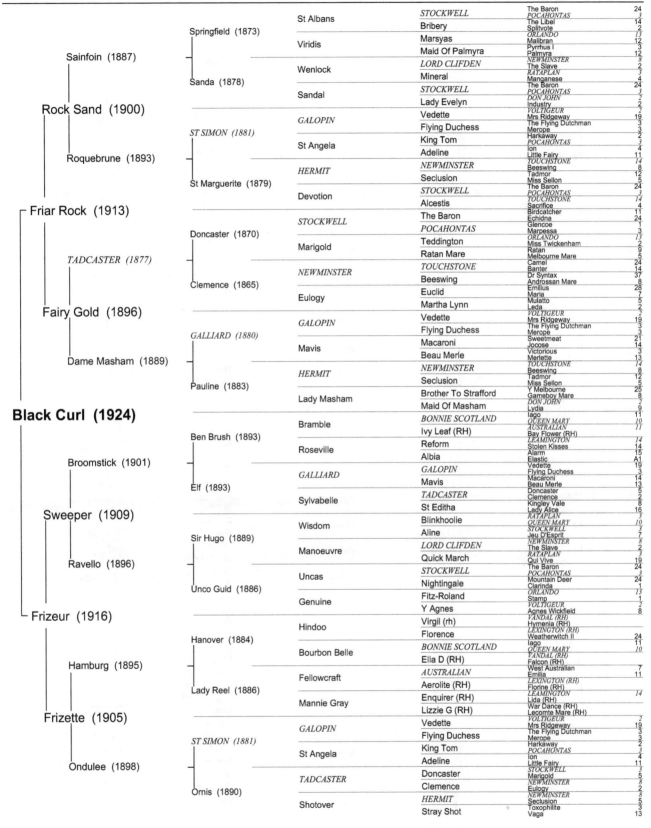

Black Curl 1924

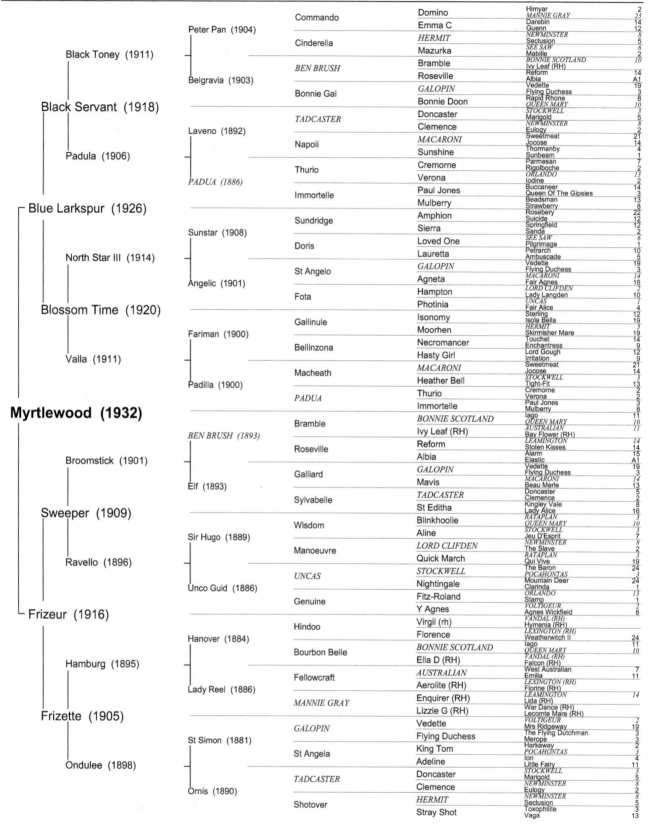

Myrtlewood 1932

Beaming Beauty (1917)

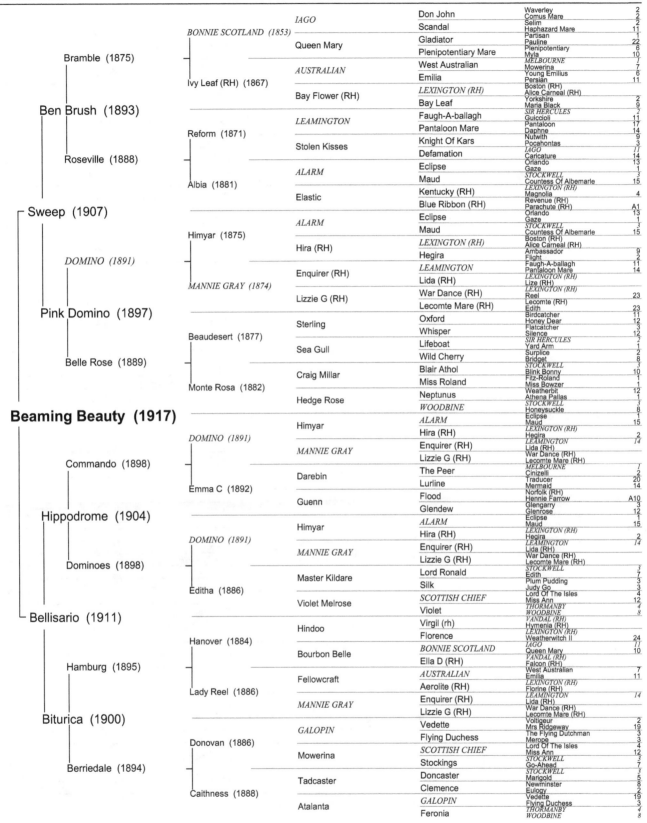

		IAGO	Don John	Waverley	2
				Comus Mare	2
	BONNIE SCOTLAND (1853)		Scandal	Selim	2
				Haphazard Mare	11
Bramble (1875)		Queen Mary	Gladiator	Partisan	1
				Pauline	22
			Plenipotentiary Mare	Plenipotentiary	6
				Myla	10
		AUSTRALIAN	West Australian	MELBOURNE	7
				Mowerina	7
	Ivy Leaf (RH) (1867)		Emilia	Young Emilius	6
				Persian	11
Ben Brush (1893)		Bay Flower (RH)	LEXINGTON (RH)	Boston (RH)	
				Alice Carneal (RH)	
			Bay Leaf	Yorkshire	2
				Maria Black	9
		LEAMINGTON	Faugh-A-ballagh	SIR HERCULES	2
				Guiccioli	11
	Reform (1871)		Pantaloon Mare	Pantaloon	17
				Daphne	14
		Stolen Kisses	Knight Of Kars	Nutwith	9
Roseville (1888)				Pocahontas	3
			Defamation	IAGO	11
				Caricature	14
		ALARM	Eclipse	Orlando	13
				Gaze	1
	Albia (1881)		Maud	STOCKWELL	3
				Countess Of Albemarle	15
		Elastic	Kentucky (RH)	LEXINGTON (RH)	
				Magnolia	4
			Blue Ribbon (RH)	Revenue (RH)	
				Parachute (RH)	A1
Sweep (1907)		ALARM	Eclipse	Orlando	13
				Gaze	1
	Himyar (1875)		Maud	STOCKWELL	3
				Countess Of Albemarle	15
		Hira (RH)	LEXINGTON (RH)	Boston (RH)	
				Alice Carneal (RH)	
			Hegira	Ambassador	9
				Flight	2
DOMINO (1891)		Enquirer (RH)	LEAMINGTON	Faugh-A-ballagh	11
				Pantaloon Mare	14
	MANNIE GRAY (1874)		Lida (RH)	LEXINGTON (RH)	
				Lize (RH)	
		Lizzie G (RH)	War Dance (RH)	LEXINGTON (RH)	
				Reel	23
Pink Domino (1897)			Lecomte Mare (RH)	Lecomte (RH)	
				Edith	23
		Sterling	Oxford	Birdcatcher	11
				Honey Dear	12
	Beaudesert (1877)		Whisper	Flatcatcher	3
				Silence	12
		Sea Gull	Lifeboat	SIR HERCULES	2
				Yard Arm	1
Belle Rose (1889)			Wild Cherry	Surplice	2
				Bridget	8
		Craig Millar	Blair Athol	STOCKWELL	3
				Blink Bonny	10
	Monte Rosa (1882)		Miss Roland	Fitz-Roland	1
				Miss Bowzer	1
		Hedge Rose	Neptunus	Weatherbit	12
				Athena Pallas	1
			WOODBINE	STOCKWELL	3
				Honeysuckle	8

Beaming Beauty (1917)

		Himyar	ALARM	Eclipse	1
				Maud	15
	DOMINO (1891)		Hira (RH)	LEXINGTON (RH)	
				Hegira	2
		MANNIE GRAY	Enquirer (RH)	LEAMINGTON	14
				Lida (RH)	
Commando (1898)			Lizzie G (RH)	War Dance (RH)	
				Lecomte Mare (RH)	
		Darebin	The Peer	MELBOURNE	1
				Cinizelli	2
	Emma C (1892)		Lurline	Traducer	20
				Mermaid	14
		Guenn	Flood	Norfolk (RH)	
				Hennie Farrow	A10
			Glendew	Glengarry	3
				Glenrose	12
Hippodrome (1904)		Himyar	ALARM	Eclipse	1
				Maud	15
	DOMINO (1891)		Hira (RH)	LEXINGTON (RH)	
				Hegira	2
		MANNIE GRAY	Enquirer (RH)	LEAMINGTON	14
				Lida (RH)	
			Lizzie G (RH)	War Dance (RH)	
				Lecomte Mare (RH)	
Dominoes (1898)		Master Kildare	Lord Ronald	STOCKWELL	3
				Edith	7
	Editha (1886)		Silk	Plum Pudding	3
				Judy Go	3
		Violet Melrose	SCOTTISH CHIEF	Lord Of The Isles	4
				Miss Ann	12
			Violet	THORMANBY	4
				WOODBINE	8
Bellisario (1911)		Hindoo	Virgil (rh)	VANDAL (RH)	
				Hymenia (RH)	
	Hanover (1884)		Florence	LEXINGTON (RH)	
				Weatherwitch II	24
		Bourbon Belle	BONNIE SCOTLAND	IAGO	11
				Queen Mary	10
			Ella D (RH)	VANDAL (RH)	
				Falcon (RH)	
Hamburg (1895)		Fellowcraft	AUSTRALIAN	West Australian	7
				Emilia	11
	Lady Reel (1886)		Aerolite (RH)	LEXINGTON (RH)	
				Florine (RH)	
		MANNIE GRAY	Enquirer (RH)	LEAMINGTON	14
				Lida (RH)	
			Lizzie G (RH)	War Dance (RH)	
				Lecomte Mare (RH)	
Biturica (1900)		Vedette	Voltigeur	2
		GALOPIN		Mrs Ridgeway	19
			Flying Duchess	The Flying Dutchman	3
	Donovan (1886)			Merope	3
		Mowerina	SCOTTISH CHIEF	Lord Of The Isles	4
				Miss Ann	12
			Stockings	STOCKWELL	3
				Go-Ahead	7
Berriedale (1894)		Tadcaster	Doncaster	STOCKWELL	3
				Marigold	5
	Caithness (1888)		Clemence	Newminster	8
				Eulogy	2
		Atalanta	GALOPIN	Vedette	19
				Flying Duchess	3
			Feronia	THORMANBY	4
				WOODBINE	8

Beaming Beauty 1917

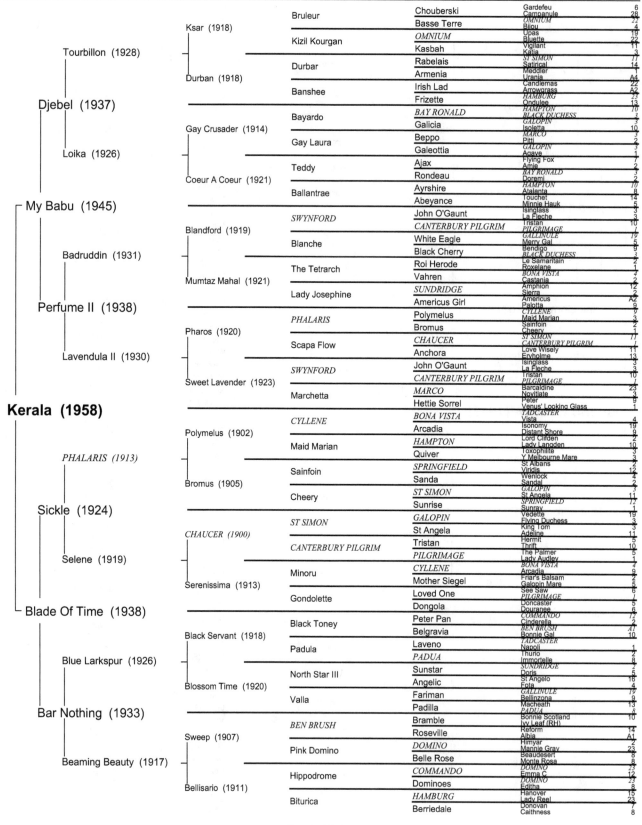

Kerala 1958

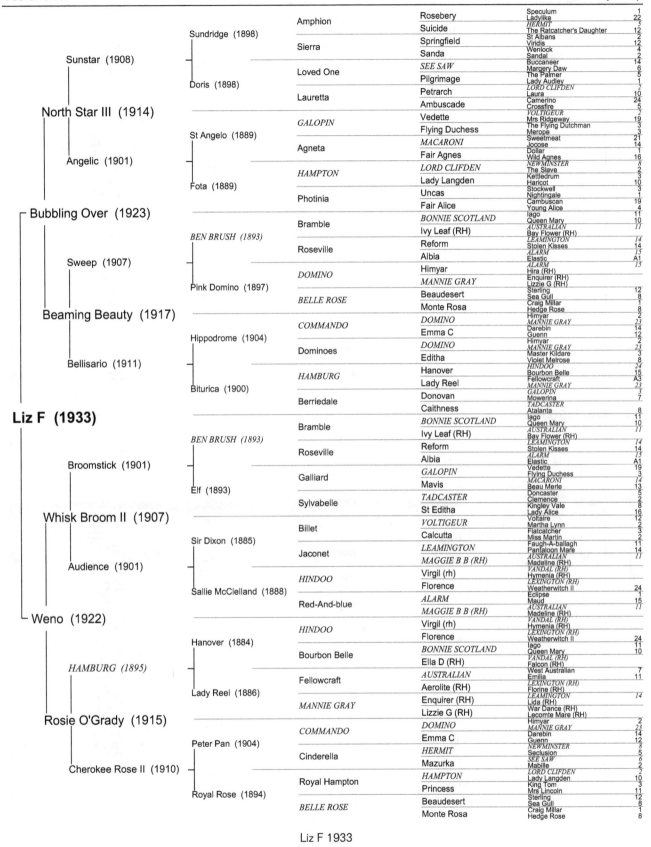

Liz F 1933

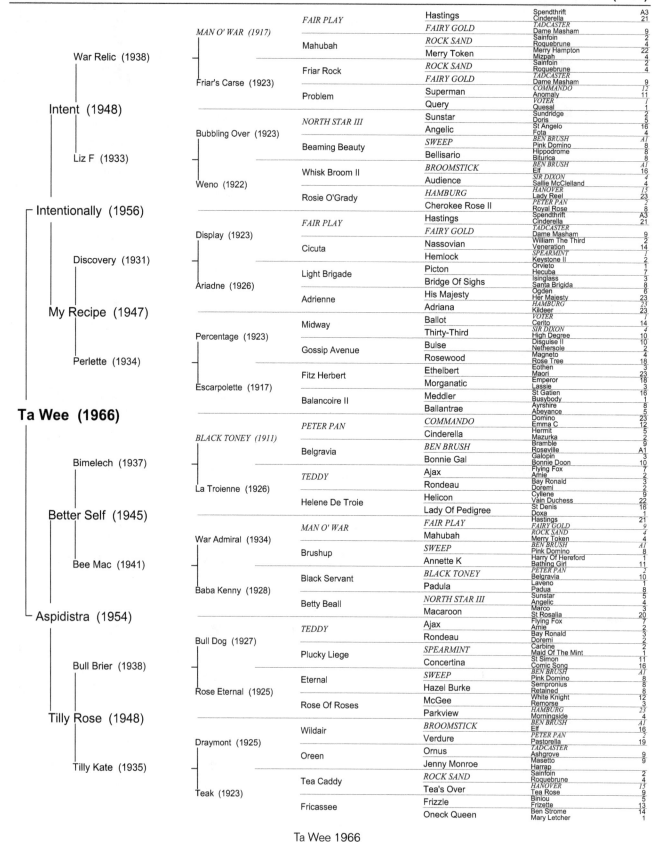

			Hastings	Spendthrift	A3
		FAIR PLAY		Cinderella	21
	MAN O' WAR (1917)		FAIRY GOLD	TADCASTER	9
				Dame Masham	2
War Relic (1938)			ROCK SAND	Sainfoin	4
		Mahubah		Roquebrune	22
			Merry Token	Merry Hampton	4
				Mizpah	2
Intent (1948)			Friar Rock	ROCK SAND	Sainfoin	4
	Friar's Carse (1923)			Roquebrune	4
			FAIRY GOLD	TADCASTER	9
				Dame Masham	12
		Problem	Superman	COMMANDO	1
				Anomaly	11
Liz F (1933)			Query	VOTER	1
				Quesal	1
			Sunstar	Sundridge	2
		NORTH STAR III		Doris	5
	Bubbling Over (1923)		Angelic	St Angelo	16
				Fota	4
Intentionally (1956)			SWEEP	BEN BRUSH	A1
		Beaming Beauty		Pink Domino	8
			Bellisario	Hippodrome	8
				Biturica	8
	Weno (1922)		Whisk Broom II	BROOMSTICK	BEN BRUSH	A1
				Elf	16
			Audience	SIR DIXON	4
				Sallie McClelland	4
Discovery (1931)		Rosie O'Grady	HAMBURG	HANOVER	15
				Lady Reel	23
			Cherokee Rose II	PETER PAN	2
				Royal Rose	2
			Hastings	Spendthrift	A3
		FAIR PLAY		Cinderella	21
	Display (1923)		FAIRY GOLD	TADCASTER	9
My Recipe (1947)				Dame Masham	2
		Cicuta	Nassovian	William The Third	14
				Veneration	1
			Hemlock	SPEARMINT	2
				Keystone II	1
	Ariadne (1926)		Picton	Orvieto	7
		Light Brigade		Hecuba	3
			Bridge Of Sighs	Isinglass	8
Perlette (1934)				Santa Brigida	6
			His Majesty	Ogden	23
		Adrienne		Her Majesty	23
			Adriana	HAMBURG	23
				Kildeer	1
			Ballot	VOTER	14
		Midway		Cerito	4
	Percentage (1923)		Thirty-Third	SIR DIXON	10
				High Degree	2
		Gossip Avenue	Bulse	Disguise II	4
				Nethersole	18
Ta Wee (1966)			Rosewood	Magneto	3
				Rose Tree	23
	Escarpolette (1917)		Ethelbert	Eothen	18
		Fitz Herbert		Maori	3
			Morganatic	Emperor	16
				Lassie	1
		Balancoire II	Meddler	St Gatien	8
				Busybody	5
			Ballantrae	Ayrshire	23
				Abeyance	12
Bimelech (1937)			COMMANDO	Domino	5
		PETER PAN		Emma C	2
	BLACK TONEY (1911)		Cinderella	Hermit	9
				Mazurka	A1
		Belgravia	BEN BRUSH	Bramble	3
				Roseville	10
			Bonnie Gal	Galopin	7
				Bonnie Doon	2
Better Self (1945)			Ajax	Flying Fox	3
		TEDDY		Amie	2
	La Troienne (1926)		Rondeau	Bay Ronald	9
				Doremi	22
		Helene De Troie	Helicon	Cyllene	16
				Vain Duchess	1
Bee Mac (1941)			Lady Of Pedigree	St Denis	21
				Doxa	9
			FAIR PLAY	Hastings	4
		MAN O' WAR		FAIRY GOLD	A1
	War Admiral (1934)		Mahubah	ROCK SAND	4
				Merry Token	8
		Brushup	SWEEP	BEN BRUSH	1
				Pink Domino	11
			Annette K	Harry Of Hereford	2
				Bathing Girl	10
Aspidistra (1954)			BLACK TONEY	PETER PAN	1
		Black Servant		Belgravia	8
	Baba Kenny (1928)		Padula	Laveno	5
				Padua	4
		Betty Beall	NORTH STAR III	Sunstar	3
				Angelic	20
			Macaroon	Marco	7
				St Rosalia	3
			Ajax	Flying Fox	2
		TEDDY		Amie	2
	Bull Dog (1927)		Rondeau	Bay Ronald	1
Bull Brier (1938)				Doremi	16
		Plucky Liege	SPEARMINT	Carbine	A1
				Maid Of The Mint	8
			Concertina	St Simon	8
				Comic Song	12
	Rose Eternal (1925)		SWEEP	BEN BRUSH	3
		Eternal		Pink Domino	23
			Hazel Burke	Sempronius	A1
				Retained	16
		Rose Of Roses	McGee	White Knight	2
Tilly Rose (1948)				Remorse	19
			Parkview	HAMBURG	9
				Morningside	9
			BROOMSTICK	BEN BRUSH	2
		Wildair		Elf	4
	Draymont (1925)		Verdure	PETER PAN	15
				Pastorella	9
		Oreen	Ornus	TADCASTER	5
				Ashgrove	13
Tilly Kate (1935)			Jenny Monroe	Masetto	14
				Harrap	1
		Tea Caddy	ROCK SAND	Sainfoin	
	Teak (1923)			Roquebrune	
			Tea's Over	HANOVER	
				Tea Rose	
		Fricassee	Frizzle	Biniou	
				Frizette	
			Oneck Queen	Ben Strome	
				Mary Letcher	

Ta Wee 1966

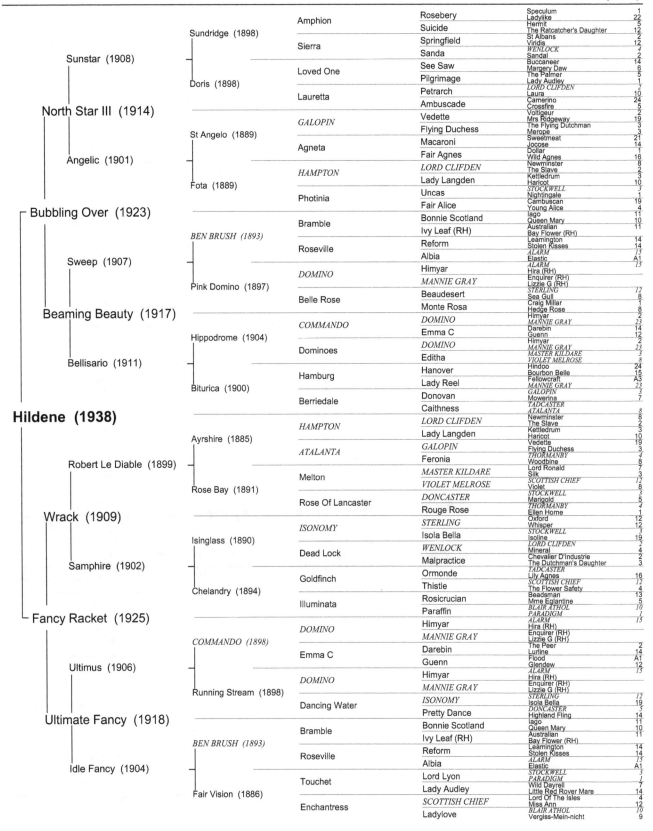

Hildene 1938

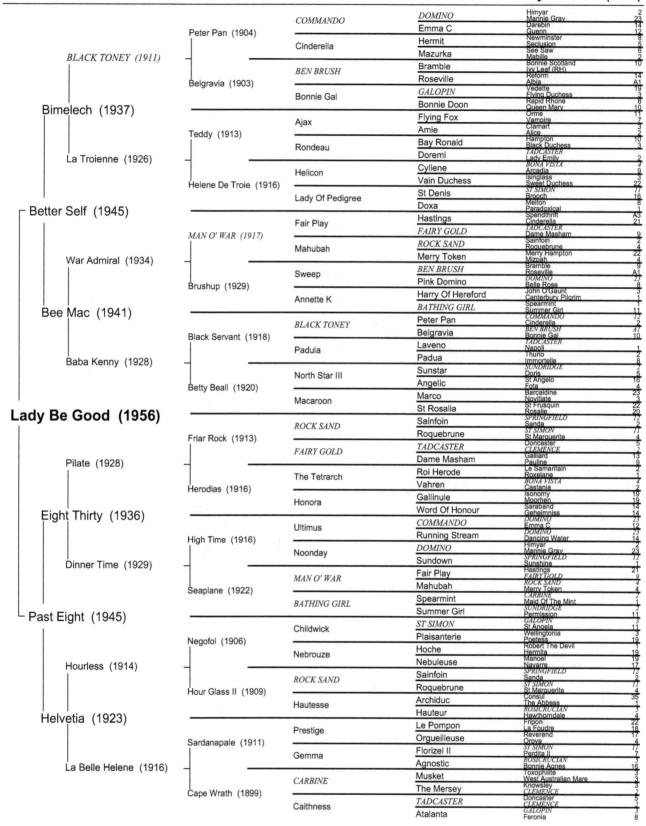

BLACK TONEY (1911)

Bimelech (1937)

La Troienne (1926)

Better Self (1945)

War Admiral (1934)

Bee Mac (1941)

Baba Kenny (1928)

Lady Be Good (1956)

Pilate (1928)

Eight Thirty (1936)

Dinner Time (1929)

Past Eight (1945)

Hourless (1914)

Helvetia (1923)

La Belle Helene (1916)

Peter Pan (1904)	COMMANDO	DOMINO	Himyar 2 / Mannie Gray 23
		Emma C	Darebin 14 / Guenn 12
	Cinderella	Hermit	Newminster 8 / Seclusion 5
		Mazurka	See Saw 6 / Mabille 2
Belgravia (1903)	BEN BRUSH	Bramble	Bonnie Scotland 10 / Ivy Leaf (RH)
		Roseville	Reform 14 / Albia A1
	Bonnie Gal	GALOPIN	Vedette 19 / Flying Duchess 3
		Bonnie Doon	Rapid Rhone 8 / Queen Mary 10
Teddy (1913)	Ajax	Flying Fox	Orme 11 / Vampire 7
		Amie	Clamart 3 / Alice 2
	Rondeau	Bay Ronald	Hampton 10 / Black Duchess 3
		Doremi	TADCASTER / Lady Emily 2
Helene De Troie (1916)	Helicon	Cyllene	BONA VISTA 4 / Arcadia 9
		Vain Duchess	Isinglass 3 / Sweet Duchess 22
	Lady Of Pedigree	St Denis	ST SIMON 11 / Brooch 16
		Doxa	Melton 8 / Paradoxical
MAN O' WAR (1917)	Fair Play	Hastings	Spendthrift A3 / Cinderella 21
		FAIRY GOLD	TADCASTER / Dame Masham 9
	Mahubah	ROCK SAND	Sainfoin 2 / Roquebrune 4
		Merry Token	Merry Hampton 22 / Mizpah 4
Brushup (1929)	Sweep	BEN BRUSH	Bramble 9 / Roseville A1
		Pink Domino	DOMINO 23 / Belle Rose 8
	Annette K	Harry Of Hereford	John O'Gaunt 1 / Canterbury Pilgrim 1
		BATHING GIRL	Spearmint 1 / Summer Girl 11
Black Servant (1918)	BLACK TONEY	Peter Pan	COMMANDO 12 / Cinderella
		Belgravia	BEN BRUSH A1 / Bonnie Gal 10
	Padula	Laveno	TADCASTER / Napoli 1
		Padua	Thurio 2 / Immortelle 8
Betty Beall (1920)	North Star III	Sunstar	SUNDRIDGE 2 / Doris 5
		Angelic	St Angelo 16 / Fota 4
	Macaroon	Marco	Barcaldine 23 / Novitiate 3
		St Rosalia	St Frusquin 22 / Rosalie 20
Friar Rock (1913)	ROCK SAND	Sainfoin	SPRINGFIELD 12 / Sanda
		Roquebrune	ST SIMON 11 / St Marguerite 4
	FAIRY GOLD	TADCASTER	Doncaster 5 / CLEMENCE
		Dame Masham	Galliard 13 / Pauline 9
Herodias (1916)	The Tetrarch	Roi Herode	Le Samaritain 2 / Roxelane 1
		Vahren	BONA VISTA 4 / Castania 2
	Honora	Gallinule	Isonomy 19 / Moorhen 19
		Word Of Honour	Saraband 14 / Geheimniss 14
High Time (1916)	Ultimus	COMMANDO	DOMINO 23 / Emma C 12
		Running Stream	DOMINO 23 / Dancing Water 14
	Noonday	DOMINO	Himyar 2 / Mannie Gray 23
		Sundown	SPRINGFIELD 12 / Sunshine
Seaplane (1922)	MAN O' WAR	Fair Play	Hastings 21 / FAIRY GOLD 9
		Mahubah	ROCK SAND 4 / Merry Token 4
	BATHING GIRL	Spearmint	CARBINE 2 / Maid Of The Mint 1
		Summer Girl	SUNDRIDGE 2 / Permission 11
Negofol (1906)	Childwick	ST SIMON	GALOPIN / St Angela 11
		Plaisanterie	Wellingtonia 3 / Poetess 19
	Nebrouze	Hoche	Robert The Devil 19 / Hermita 19
		Nebuleuse	Manoel 17 / Navarre 17
Hour Glass II (1909)	ROCK SAND	Sainfoin	SPRINGFIELD 12 / Sanda
		Roquebrune	ST SIMON 11 / St Marguerite 4
	Hautesse	Archiduc	Consul 35 / The Abbess
		Hauteur	ROSICRUCIAN 3 / Hawthorndale 4
Sardanapale (1911)	Prestige	Le Pompon	Fripon 22 / La Foudre 18
		Orgueilleuse	Reverend 17 / Oroya 4
	Gemma	Florizel II	ST SIMON 11 / Perdita II 7
		Agnostic	ROSICRUCIAN 3 / Bonnie Agnes 16
Cape Wrath (1899)	CARBINE	Musket	Toxophilite 3 / West Australian Mare 3
		The Mersey	Knowsley 3 / CLEMENCE 2
	Caithness	TADCASTER	Doncaster 5 / CLEMENCE 2
		Atalanta	GALOPIN / Feronia 8

Lady Be Good 1956

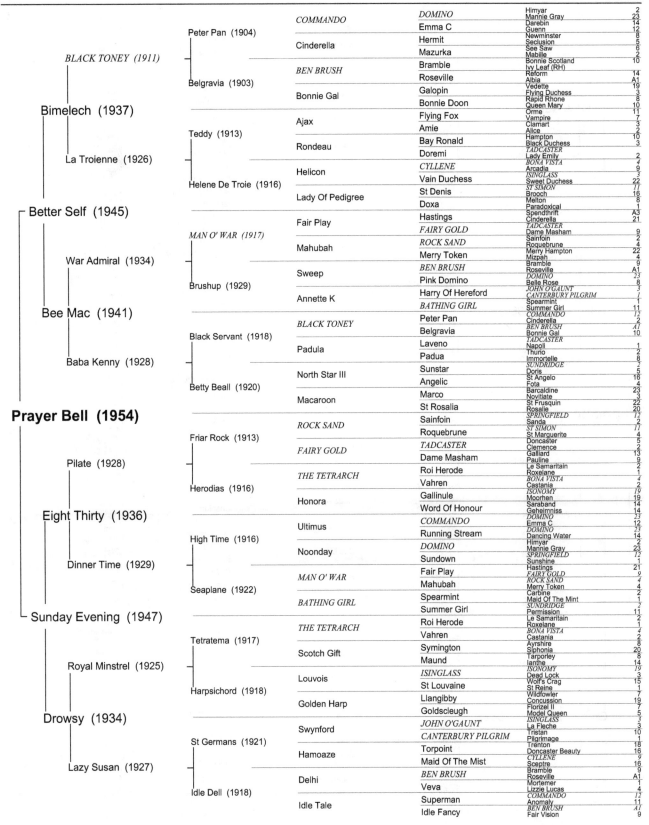

Prayer Bell (1954)

- Better Self (1945)
  - Bimelech (1937)
    - BLACK TONEY (1911)
    - La Troienne (1926)
  - Bee Mac (1941)
    - War Admiral (1934)
    - Baba Kenny (1928)
- Sunday Evening (1947)
  - Eight Thirty (1936)
    - Pilate (1928)
    - Dinner Time (1929)
  - Drowsy (1934)
    - Royal Minstrel (1925)
    - Lazy Susan (1927)

Peter Pan (1904)	COMMANDO	DOMINO	Himyar 2 / Mannie Gray 23
		Emma C	Darebin 14 / Guenn 12
	Cinderella	Hermit	Newminster 8 / Seclusion 5
		Mazurka	See Saw 6 / Mabille 2
Belgravia (1903)	BEN BRUSH	Bramble	Bonnie Scotland 10 / Ivy Leaf (RH)
		Roseville	Reform 14 / Albia A1
	Bonnie Gal	Galopin	Vedette 19 / Flying Duchess 3
		Bonnie Doon	Rapid Rhone 8 / Queen Mary 10
Teddy (1913)	Ajax	Flying Fox	Orme 11 / Vampire 7
		Amie	Clamart 3 / Alice 2
	Rondeau	Bay Ronald	Hampton 10 / Black Duchess 3
		Doremi	TADCASTER / Lady Emily 4
Helene De Troie (1916)	Helicon	CYLLENE	BONA VISTA 4 / Arcadia 9
		Vain Duchess	ISINGLASS 3 / Sweet Duchess 22
	Lady Of Pedigree	St Denis	ST SIMON 11 / Brooch 16
		Doxa	Melton 8 / Paradoxical
MAN O' WAR (1917)	Fair Play	Hastings	Spendthrift A3 / Cinderella 21
		FAIRY GOLD	TADCASTER / Dame Masham 9
	Mahubah	ROCK SAND	Sainfoin 2 / Roquebrune 4
		Merry Token	Merry Hampton 22 / Mizpah 4
Brushup (1929)	Sweep	BEN BRUSH	Bramble 9 / Roseville A1
		Pink Domino	DOMINO 23 / Belle Rose 8
	Annette K	Harry Of Hereford	JOHN O'GAUNT 3 / CANTERBURY PILGRIM
		BATHING GIRL	Spearmint 1 / Summer Girl 11
Black Servant (1918)	BLACK TONEY	Peter Pan	COMMANDO 12 / Cinderella 2
		Belgravia	BEN BRUSH A1 / Bonnie Gal 10
	Padula	Laveno	TADCASTER / Napoli 1
		Padua	Thurio 2 / Immortelle 8
Betty Beall (1920)	North Star III	Sunstar	SUNDRIDGE 2 / Doris 5
		Angelic	St Angelo 16 / Fota 4
	Macaroon	Marco	Barcaldine 23 / Novitiate 3
		St Rosalia	St Frusquin 22 / Rosalie 20
Friar Rock (1913)	ROCK SAND	Sainfoin	SPRINGFIELD 12 / Sanda 11
		Roquebrune	ST SIMON / St Marguerite 4
	FAIRY GOLD	TADCASTER	Doncaster 5 / Clemence 2
		Dame Masham	Galliard 13 / Pauline 9
Herodias (1916)	THE TETRARCH	Roi Herode	Le Samaritain 2 / Roxelane 1
		Vahren	BONA VISTA 4 / Castania 2
	Honora	Gallinule	ISONOMY 19 / Moorhen 19
		Word Of Honour	Saraband 14 / Geheimniss 14
High Time (1916)	Ultimus	COMMANDO	DOMINO 23 / Emma C 12
		Running Stream	DOMINO 23 / Dancing Water 14
	Noonday	DOMINO	Himyar 2 / Mannie Gray 23
		Sundown	SPRINGFIELD 12 / Sunshine
Seaplane (1922)	MAN O' WAR	Fair Play	Hastings 21 / FAIRY GOLD 9
		Mahubah	ROCK SAND 4 / Merry Token 4
	BATHING GIRL	Spearmint	Carbine 2 / Maid Of The Mint 1
		Summer Girl	SUNDRIDGE / Permission 11
Tetratema (1917)	THE TETRARCH	Roi Herode	Le Samaritain 2 / Roxelane 1
		Vahren	BONA VISTA 4 / Castania 2
	Scotch Gift	Symington	Ayrshire 8 / Siphonia 20
		Maund	Tarporley 8 / Ianthe 14
Harpsichord (1918)	Louvois	ISINGLASS	ISONOMY 19 / Dead Lock 3
		St Louvaine	Wolf's Crag 15 / St Reine 1
	Golden Harp	Llangibby	Wildfowler 7 / Concussion 19
		Goldscleugh	Florizel II 7 / Model Queen 5
St Germans (1921)	Swynford	JOHN O'GAUNT	ISINGLASS 3 / La Fleche 3
		CANTERBURY PILGRIM	Tristan 10 / Pilgrimage 1
	Hamoaze	Torpoint	Trenton 18 / Doncaster Beauty 16
		Maid Of The Mist	CYLLENE 9 / Sceptre 16
Idle Dell (1918)	Delhi	BEN BRUSH	Bramble 9 / Roseville A1
		Veva	Mortemer 1 / Lizzie Lucas 4
	Idle Tale	Superman	COMMANDO 12 / Anomaly 11
		Idle Fancy	BEN BRUSH A1 / Fair Vision 9

Intermediate generations (left-to-right):

Bimelech (1937): BLACK TONEY (1911) — Peter Pan (1904), Belgravia (1903); La Troienne (1926) — Teddy (1913), Helene De Troie (1916)

Bee Mac (1941): War Admiral (1934) — MAN O' WAR (1917), Brushup (1929); Baba Kenny (1928) — Black Servant (1918), Betty Beall (1920)

Eight Thirty (1936): Pilate (1928) — Friar Rock (1913), Herodias (1916); Dinner Time (1929) — High Time (1916), Seaplane (1922)

Drowsy (1934): Royal Minstrel (1925) — Tetratema (1917), Harpsichord (1918); Lazy Susan (1927) — St Germans (1921), Idle Dell (1918)

Prayer Bell 1954

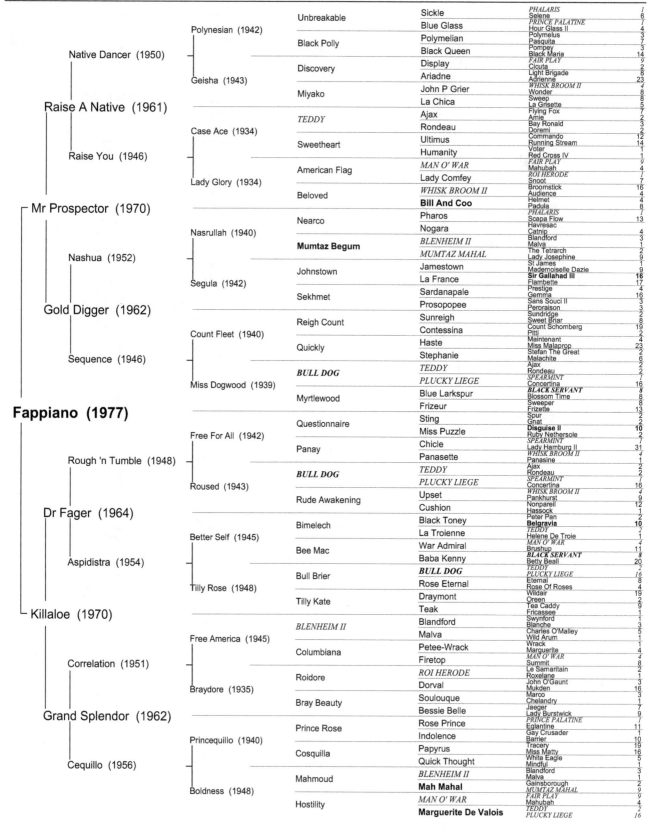

		Unbreakable	Sickle	*PHALARIS* 1 / Selene 6
	Polynesian (1942)		Blue Glass	*PRINCE PALATINE* 1 / Hour Glass II 4
Native Dancer (1950)		Black Polly	Polymelian	Polymelus 3 / Pasquita 7
			Black Queen	Pompey 3 / Black Maria 14
	Geisha (1943)	Discovery	Display	*FAIR PLAY* 9 / Cicuta 2
			Ariadne	Light Brigade 8 / Adrienne 23
Raise A Native (1961)		Miyako	John P Grier	*WHISK BROOM II* 4 / Wonder 8
			La Chica	Sweep 5 / La Grisette 5
		TEDDY	Ajax	Flying Fox 7 / Amie 2
	Case Ace (1934)		Rondeau	Bay Ronald 3 / Doremi 2
Raise You (1946)		Sweetheart	Ultimus	Commando 12 / Running Stream 14
			Humanity	Voter 1 / Red Cross IV 1
	Lady Glory (1934)	American Flag	*MAN O' WAR*	*FAIR PLAY* 9 / Mahubah 4
			Lady Comfey	*ROI HERODE* 1 / Snoot 7
		Beloved	*WHISK BROOM II*	Broomstick 16 / Audience 4
			Bill And Coo	Helmet 4 / Padula 8
Mr Prospector (1970)		Nearco	Pharos	*PHALARIS* 1 / Scapa Flow 13
	Nasrullah (1940)		Nogara	Havresac 4 / Catnip 4
		Mumtaz Begum	*BLENHEIM II*	Blandford 3 / Malva 1
			MUMTAZ MAHAL	The Tetrarch 2 / Lady Josephine 9
Nashua (1952)		Johnstown	Jamestown	St James 1 / Mademoiselle Dazie 9
	Segula (1942)		La France	**Sir Gallahad III** 16 / Flambette 17
		Sekhmet	Sardanapale	Prestige 4 / Gemma 16
			Prosopopee	Sans Souci II 3 / Peroraison 3
		Reigh Count	Sunreigh	Sundridge 2 / Sweet Briar 8
	Count Fleet (1940)		Contessina	Count Schomberg 19 / Pitti 2
Gold Digger (1962)		Quickly	Haste	Maintenant 4 / Miss Malaprop 23
			Stephanie	Stefan The Great 2 / Malachite 6
	Miss Dogwood (1939)	*BULL DOG*	*TEDDY*	Ajax 2 / Rondeau 2
			PLUCKY LIEGE	*SPEARMINT* 1 / Concertina 16
Sequence (1946)		Myrtlewood	Blue Larkspur	*BLACK SERVANT* 8 / Blossom Time 8
			Frizeur	Sweeper 8 / Frizette 13
		Questionnaire	Sting	Spur 2 / Gnat 2
	Free For All (1942)		Miss Puzzle	**Disguise II** 10 / Ruby Nethersole 2
Rough 'n Tumble (1948)		Panay	Chicle	*SPEARMINT* 1 / Lady Hamburg II 31
			Panasette	*WHISK BROOM II* 4 / Panasine 1
	Roused (1943)	*BULL DOG*	*TEDDY*	Ajax 2 / Rondeau 2
			PLUCKY LIEGE	*SPEARMINT* 1 / Concertina 16
		Rude Awakening	Upset	*WHISK BROOM II* 4 / Pankhurst 9
			Cushion	Nonpareil 12 / Hassock 1
Dr Fager (1964)		Bimelech	Black Toney	Peter Pan 2 / **Belgravia** 10
	Better Self (1945)		La Troienne	*TEDDY* 2 / Helene De Troie 1
		Bee Mac	War Admiral	*MAN O' WAR* 4 / Brushup 11
			Baba Kenny	*BLACK SERVANT* 8 / Betty Beall 20
Aspidistra (1954)		Bull Brier	*BULL DOG*	*TEDDY* 2 / *PLUCKY LIEGE* 16
	Tilly Rose (1948)		Rose Eternal	Eternal 8 / Rose Of Roses 4
		Tilly Kate	Draymont	Wildair 19 / Oreen 2
			Teak	Tea Caddy 9 / Fricassee 1
Fappiano (1977)				
		BLENHEIM II	Blandford	Swynford 1 / Blanche 3
	Free America (1945)		Malva	Charles O'Malley 5 / Wild Arum 1
Killaloe (1970)		Columbiana	Petee-Wrack	Wrack 1 / Marguerite 4
			Firetop	*MAN O' WAR* 4 / Summit 8
	Braydore (1935)	Roidore	*ROI HERODE*	Le Samaritain 2 / Roxelane 1
			Dorval	John O'Gaunt 3 / Mukden 16
Correlation (1951)		Bray Beauty	Soulouque	Marco 3 / Chelandry 3
			Bessie Belle	Jaeger 7 / Lady Burstwick 9
		Prince Rose	Rose Prince	*PRINCE PALATINE* 1 / Eglantine 11
	Princequillo (1940)		Indolence	Gay Crusader 1 / Barrier 10
Grand Splendor (1962)		Cosquilla	Papyrus	Tracery 19 / Miss Matty 16
			Quick Thought	White Eagle 5 / Mindful 1
	Boldness (1948)	Mahmoud	*BLENHEIM II*	Blandford 3 / Malva 1
Cequillo (1956)			**Mah Mahal**	Gainsborough 2 / *MUMTAZ MAHAL* 9
		Hostility	*MAN O' WAR*	*FAIR PLAY* 9 / Mahubah 4
			Marguerite De Valois	*TEDDY* 2 / *PLUCKY LIEGE* 16

Fappiano 1977

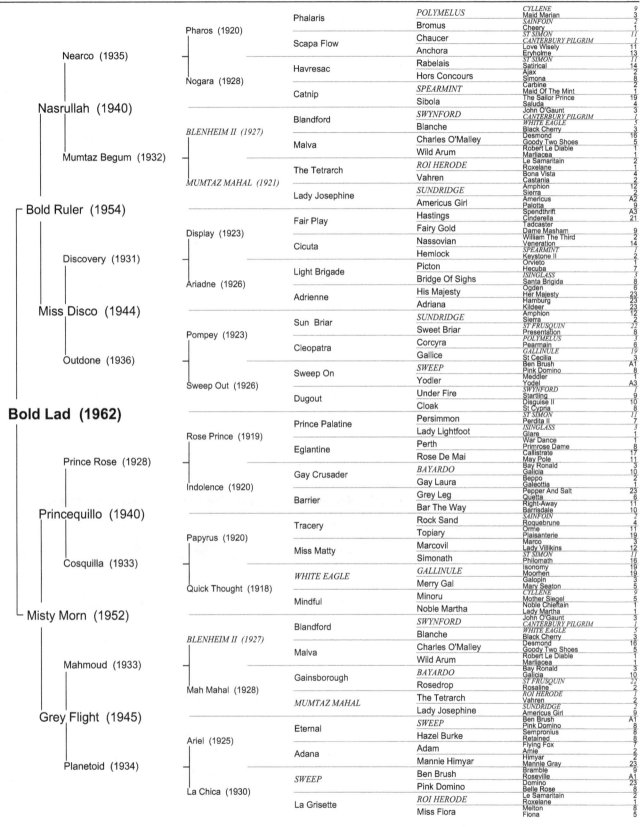

Bold Lad (1962)

Bold Ruler (1954)

- Nasrullah (1940)
  - Nearco (1935)
    - Pharos (1920)
      - Phalaris
        - POLYMELUS — *CYLLENE* 9 / Maid Marian 3
        - Bromus — *SAINFOIN* 2 / Cheery 1
      - Scapa Flow
        - Chaucer — *ST SIMON* 11 / *CANTERBURY PILGRIM* 1
        - Anchora — Love Wisely 11 / Eryholme 13
    - Nogara (1928)
      - Havresac
        - Rabelais — *ST SIMON* 11 / Satirical 14
        - Hors Concours — Ajax 2 / Simona 8
      - Catnip
        - *SPEARMINT* — Carbine 2 / Maid Of The Mint 1
        - Sibola — The Sailor Prince 19 / Saluda 4
  - Mumtaz Begum (1932)
    - BLENHEIM II (1927)
      - Blandford
        - *SWYNFORD* — John O'Gaunt 3 / *CANTERBURY PILGRIM* 1
        - Blanche — *WHITE EAGLE* 5 / Black Cherry 3
      - Malva
        - Charles O'Malley — Desmond 16 / Goody Two Shoes 5
        - Wild Arum — Robert Le Diable 1 / Marliacea 1
    - MUMTAZ MAHAL (1921)
      - The Tetrarch
        - *ROI HERODE* — Le Samaritain 2 / Roxelane 1
        - Vahren — Bona Vista 4 / Castania 2
      - Lady Josephine
        - *SUNDRIDGE* — Amphion 12 / Sierra 2
        - Americus Girl — Americus A2 / Palotta 9

Discovery (1931)

- Miss Disco (1944)
  - Discovery (1931)
    - Display (1923)
      - Fair Play
        - Hastings — Spendthrift A3 / Cinderella 21
        - Fairy Gold — Tadcaster / Dame Masham 9
      - Cicuta
        - Nassovian — William The Third 2 / Veneration 14
        - Hemlock — *SPEARMINT* 1 / Keystone II 2
    - Ariadne (1926)
      - Light Brigade
        - Picton — Orvieto 1 / Hecuba 7
        - Bridge Of Sighs — *ISINGLASS* 3 / Santa Brigida 8
      - Adrienne
        - His Majesty — Ogden 6 / Her Majesty 23
        - Adriana — Hamburg 23 / Kildeer 23
  - Outdone (1936)
    - Pompey (1923)
      - Sun Briar
        - *SUNDRIDGE* — Amphion 12 / Sierra 2
        - Sweet Briar — *ST FRUSQUIN* 22 / Presentation 8
      - Cleopatra
        - Corcyra — *POLYMELUS* 3 / Pearmain 6
        - Gallice — *GALLINULE* 19 / St Cecilia 3
    - Sweep Out (1926)
      - Sweep On
        - *SWEEP* — Ben Brush A1 / Pink Domino 8
        - Yodler — Meddler 1 / Yodel A3
      - Dugout
        - Under Fire — *SWYNFORD* 1 / Startling 9
        - Cloak — Disguise II 10 / St Cypria 8

Princequillo (1940)

- Prince Rose (1928)
  - Rose Prince (1919)
    - Prince Palatine
      - Persimmon — *ST SIMON* 11 / Perdita II 7
      - Lady Lightfoot — *ISINGLASS* 3 / Glare 1
    - Eglantine
      - Perth — War Dance 1 / Primrose Dame 8
      - Rose De Mai — Callistrate 17 / May Pole 11
  - Indolence (1920)
    - Gay Crusader
      - *BAYARDO* — Bay Ronald 3 / Galicia 10
      - Gay Laura — Beppo 2 / Galeottia 1
    - Barrier
      - Grey Leg — Pepper And Salt 23 / Quetta 6
      - Bar The Way — Right-Away 11 / Barrisdale 10
- Cosquilla (1933)
  - Papyrus (1920)
    - Tracery
      - Rock Sand — *SAINFOIN* 2 / Roquebrune 4
      - Topiary — Orme 11 / Plaisanterie 19
    - Miss Matty
      - Marcovil — Marco 3 / Lady Villikins 12
      - Simonath — *ST SIMON* 11 / Philomath 16
  - Quick Thought (1918)
    - WHITE EAGLE
      - *GALLINULE* — Isonomy 19 / Moorhen 19
      - Merry Gal — Galopin 3 / Mary Seaton 5
    - Mindful
      - Minoru — *CYLLENE* 9 / Mother Siegel 5
      - Noble Martha — Noble Chieftain 1 / Lady Martha 1

Bold Lad (1962)

- Misty Morn (1952)
  - Princequillo (1940) *(see above)*
  - Grey Flight (1945)
    - Mahmoud (1933)
      - BLENHEIM II (1927)
        - Blandford
          - *SWYNFORD* — John O'Gaunt 3 / *CANTERBURY PILGRIM* 1
          - Blanche — *WHITE EAGLE* 5 / Black Cherry 3
        - Malva
          - Charles O'Malley — Desmond 16 / Goody Two Shoes 5
          - Wild Arum — Robert Le Diable 1 / Marliacea 1
      - Mah Mahal (1928)
        - Gainsborough
          - *BAYARDO* — Bay Ronald 3 / Galicia 10
          - Rosedrop — *ST FRUSQUIN* 22 / Rosaline 2
        - MUMTAZ MAHAL
          - The Tetrarch — *ROI HERODE* 1 / Vahren 2
          - Lady Josephine — *SUNDRIDGE* 2 / Americus Girl 2
    - Planetoid (1934)
      - Ariel (1925)
        - Eternal
          - *SWEEP* — Ben Brush A1 / Pink Domino 8
          - Hazel Burke — Sempronius 8 / Retained 8
        - Adana
          - Adam — Flying Fox 7 / Amie 2
          - Mannie Himyar — Himyar 2 / Mannie Gray 23
      - La Chica (1930)
        - SWEEP
          - Ben Brush — Bramble 9 / Roseville A1
          - Pink Domino — Domino 23 / Belle Rose 8
        - La Grisette
          - *ROI HERODE* — Le Samaritain 2 / Roxelane 1
          - Miss Fiora — Melton 8 / Fiona 5

Bold Lad 1963

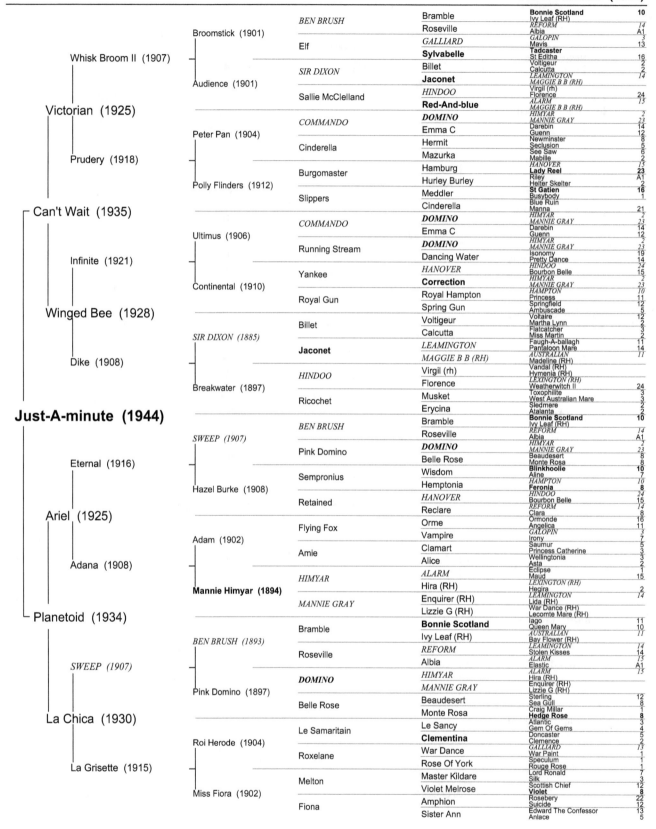

Left-hand lineage tree

- Victorian (1925)
  - Whisk Broom II (1907)
  - Prudery (1918)
- Can't Wait (1935)
  - Infinite (1921)
  - Winged Bee (1928)
  - Dike (1908)
- **Just-A-minute (1944)**
- Ariel (1925)
  - Eternal (1916)
  - Adana (1908)
- Planetoid (1934)
  - *SWEEP (1907)*
  - La Chica (1930)
  - La Grisette (1915)

Detailed pedigree

Broomstick (1901)
- BEN BRUSH
  - Bramble — **Bonnie Scotland** 10 / Ivy Leaf (RH)
  - Roseville — *REFORM* 14 / Albia A1
- Elf
  - *GALLIARD* — *GALOPIN* 3 / Mavis 13
  - **Sylvabelle** — Tadcaster 16 / St Editha

Audience (1901)
- SIR DIXON
  - Billet — Voltigeur 2 / Calcutta 2
  - **Jaconet** — *LEAMINGTON* 14 / *MAGGIE B B (RH)*
- Sallie McClelland
  - *HINDOO* — Virgil (rh) / Florence 24
  - **Red-And-blue** — *ALARM* 15 / *MAGGIE B B (RH)*

Peter Pan (1904)
- *COMMANDO*
  - **DOMINO** — *HIMYAR* 2 / *MANNIE GRAY* 23
  - Emma C — Darebin 14 / Guenn 12
- Cinderella
  - Hermit — Newminster 8 / Seclusion 5
  - Mazurka — See Saw 6 / Mabille

Polly Flinders (1912)
- Burgomaster
  - Hamburg — *HANOVER* 15 / **Lady Reel** 23
  - Hurley Burley — Riley A1 / Helter Skelter 2
- Slippers
  - Meddler — **St Gatien** 16 / Busybody 1
  - Cinderella — Blue Ruin / Manna 21

Ultimus (1906)
- *COMMANDO*
  - **DOMINO** — *HIMYAR* 2 / *MANNIE GRAY* 23
  - Emma C — Darebin 14 / Guenn 12
- Running Stream
  - **DOMINO** — *HIMYAR* 2 / *MANNIE GRAY* 23
  - Dancing Water — Isonomy 19 / Pretty Dance 14

Continental (1910)
- Yankee
  - *HANOVER* — *HINDOO* 24 / Bourbon Belle 15
  - **Correction** — *HIMYAR* 2 / *MANNIE GRAY* 23
- Royal Gun
  - Royal Hampton — *HAMPTON* 10 / Princess 11
  - Spring Gun — Springfield 12 / Ambuscade 5

SIR DIXON (1885)
- Billet
  - Voltigeur — Voltaire 12 / Martha Lynn 2
  - Calcutta — Flatcatcher 3 / Miss Martin 2
- **Jaconet**
  - *LEAMINGTON* — Faugh-A-ballagh 11 / Pantaloon Mare 14
  - *MAGGIE B B (RH)* — *AUSTRALIAN* 11 / Madeline (RH)

Breakwater (1897)
- *HINDOO*
  - Virgil (rh) — Vandal (RH) / Hymenia (RH)
  - Florence — *LEXINGTON (RH)* / Weatherwitch II 24
- Ricochet
  - Musket — Toxophilite 3 / West Australian Mare 3
  - Erycina — Sledmere 2 / Atalanta

SWEEP (1907)
- BEN BRUSH
  - Bramble — **Bonnie Scotland** 10 / Ivy Leaf (RH)
  - Roseville — *REFORM* 14 / Albia A1
- Pink Domino
  - **DOMINO** — *HIMYAR* 2 / *MANNIE GRAY* 23
  - Belle Rose — Beaudesert 8 / Monte Rosa 8

Hazel Burke (1908)
- Sempronius
  - Wisdom — **Blinkhoolie** 10 / Aline 7
  - Hemptonia — *HAMPTON* 10 / **Feronia** 8
- Retained
  - *HANOVER* — *HINDOO* 24 / Bourbon Belle 15
  - Reclare — *REFORM* 14 / Clara 8

Adam (1902)
- Flying Fox
  - Orme — Ormonde 16 / Angelica 11
  - Vampire — *GALOPIN* 3 / Irony 7
- Amie
  - Clamart — Saumur 5 / Princess Catherine 3
  - Alice — Wellingtonia 2 / Asta 1

Mannie Himyar (1894)
- *HIMYAR*
  - *ALARM* — Eclipse 1 / Maud 15
  - Hira (RH) — *LEXINGTON (RH)* / Hegira 14
- *MANNIE GRAY*
  - Enquirer (RH) — *LEAMINGTON* / Lida (RH)
  - Lizzie G (RH) — War Dance (RH) / Lecomte Mare (RH)

BEN BRUSH (1893)
- Bramble
  - **Bonnie Scotland** — Iago 11 / Queen Mary 10
  - Ivy Leaf (RH) — *AUSTRALIAN* 11 / Bay Flower (RH)
- Roseville
  - *REFORM* — *LEAMINGTON* 14 / Stolen Kisses 14
  - Albia — *ALARM* 15 / Elastic A1

Pink Domino (1897)
- **DOMINO**
  - *HIMYAR* — Hira (RH)
  - *MANNIE GRAY* — Enquirer (RH) / Lizzie G (RH)
- Belle Rose
  - Beaudesert — Sterling 12 / Sea Gull 8
  - Monte Rosa — Craig Millar 1 / **Hedge Rose** 8

Roi Herode (1904)
- Le Samaritain
  - Le Sancy — Atlantic 3 / Gem Of Gems 4
  - **Clementina** — Doncaster 5 / Clemence 2
- Roxelane
  - War Dance — *GALLIARD* 13 / War Paint 1
  - Rose Of York — Speculum 1 / Rouge Rose 7

Miss Fiora (1902)
- Melton
  - Master Kildare — Lord Ronald 3 / Silk 12
  - Violet Melrose — Scottish Chief 12 / **Violet** 8
- Fiona
  - Amphion — Rosebery 22 / Suicide 12
  - Sister Ann — Edward The Confessor 13 / Anlace 5

Just-A-Minute 1944

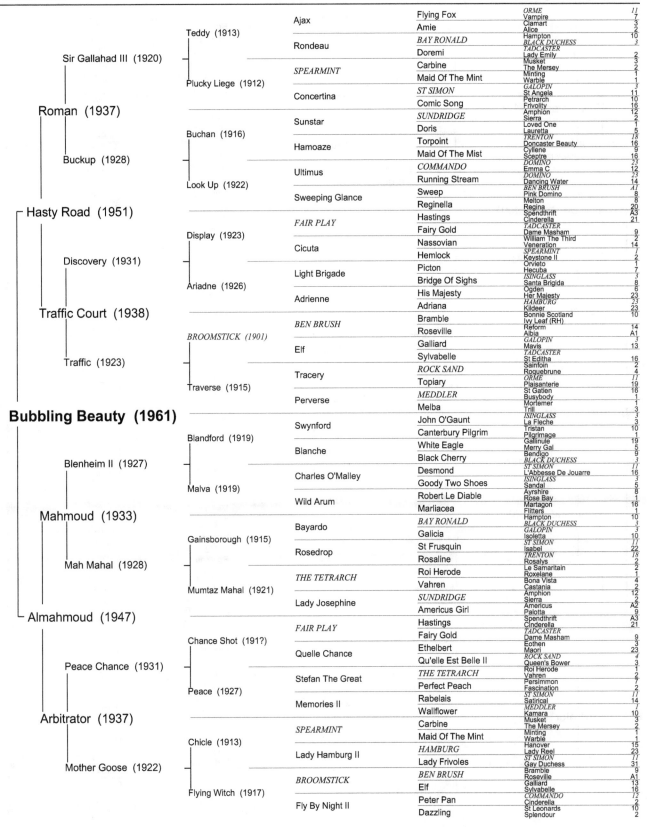

Roman (1937)
— Sir Gallahad III (1920)
— Buckup (1928)

Hasty Road (1951)
— Discovery (1931)
— Traffic Court (1938)
— Traffic (1923)

Bubbling Beauty (1961)
— Blenheim II (1927)
— Mahmoud (1933)
— Mah Mahal (1928)
— Almahmoud (1947)
— Peace Chance (1931)
— Arbitrator (1937)
— Mother Goose (1922)

Teddy (1913)	Ajax	Flying Fox	*ORME* 11 / Vampire 7
		Amie	Clamart 3 / Alice 2
	Rondeau	*BAY RONALD*	Hampton 10 / *BLACK DUCHESS* 3
		Doremi	*TADCASTER* / Lady Emily 2
Plucky Liege (1912)	*SPEARMINT*	Carbine	Musket 3 / The Mersey 2
		Maid Of The Mint	Minting 1 / Warble 1
	Concertina	*ST SIMON*	*GALOPIN* 3 / St Angela 11
		Comic Song	Petrarch 10 / Frivolity 16
Buchan (1916)	Sunstar	*SUNDRIDGE*	Amphion 12 / Sierra 2
		Doris	Loved One 1 / Lauretta 5
	Hamoaze	Torpoint	*TRENTON* 18 / Doncaster Beauty 16
		Maid Of The Mist	Cyllene 9 / Sceptre 16
Look Up (1922)	Ultimus	*COMMANDO*	*DOMINO* 23 / Emma C 12
		Running Stream	*DOMINO* 23 / Dancing Water 14
	Sweeping Glance	Sweep	*BEN BRUSH* A1 / Pink Domino 8
		Reginella	Melton 8 / Regina 20
Display (1923)	*FAIR PLAY*	Hastings	Spendthrift A3 / Cinderella 21
		Fairy Gold	*TADCASTER* / Dame Masham 9
	Cicuta	Nassovian	William The Third 2 / Veneration 14
		Hemlock	*SPEARMINT* 1 / Keystone II 2
Ariadne (1926)	Light Brigade	Picton	Orvieto 1 / Hecuba 7
		Bridge Of Sighs	*ISINGLASS* 3 / Santa Brigida 8
	Adrienne	His Majesty	Ogden 6 / Her Majesty 23
		Adriana	*HAMBURG* 23 / Kildeer 23
BROOMSTICK (1901)	*BEN BRUSH*	Bramble	Bonnie Scotland 10 / Ivy Leaf (RH)
		Roseville	Reform 14 / Albia A1
	Elf	Galliard	*GALOPIN* 3 / Mavis 13
		Sylvabelle	*TADCASTER* / St Editha 16
Traverse (1915)	Tracery	*ROCK SAND*	Sainfoin 2 / Roquebrune 4
		Topiary	*ORME* 11 / Plaisanterie 19
	Perverse	*MEDDLER*	St Gatien 16 / Busybody 1
		Melba	Mortemer 1 / Trill 3
Blandford (1919)	Swynford	John O'Gaunt	*ISINGLASS* 3 / La Fleche 3
		Canterbury Pilgrim	Tristan 10 / Pilgrimage 1
	Blanche	White Eagle	Gallinule 19 / Merry Gal 5
		Black Cherry	Bendigo 9 / *BLACK DUCHESS* 3
Malva (1919)	Charles O'Malley	Desmond	*ST SIMON* 11 / L'Abbesse De Jouarre 16
		Goody Two Shoes	*ISINGLASS* 3 / Sandal 5
	Wild Arum	Robert Le Diable	Ayrshire 8 / Rose Bay 1
		Marliacea	Martagon 16 / Flitters 1
Gainsborough (1915)	Bayardo	*BAY RONALD*	Hampton 10 / *BLACK DUCHESS* 3
		Galicia	*GALOPIN* 3 / Isoletta 10
	Rosedrop	St Frusquin	*ST SIMON* 11 / Isabel 22
		Rosaline	*TRENTON* 18 / Rosalys 2
Mumtaz Mahal (1921)	*THE TETRARCH*	Roi Herode	Le Samaritain 2 / Roxelane 1
		Vahren	Bona Vista 4 / Castania 2
	Lady Josephine	*SUNDRIDGE*	Amphion 12 / Sierra 2
		Americus Girl	Americus A2 / Palotta 9
Chance Shot (191?)	*FAIR PLAY*	Hastings	Spendthrift A3 / Cinderella 21
		Fairy Gold	*TADCASTER* / Dame Masham 9
	Quelle Chance	Ethelbert	Eothen 3 / Maori 23
		Qu'elle Est Belle II	*ROCK SAND* 4 / Queen's Bower 3
Peace (1927)	Stefan The Great	*THE TETRARCH*	Roi Herode 1 / Vahren 2
		Perfect Peach	Persimmon 7 / Fascination 2
	Memories II	Rabelais	*ST SIMON* 11 / Satirical 14
		Wallflower	*MEDDLER* 1 / Kamara 10
Chicle (1913)	*SPEARMINT*	Carbine	Musket 3 / The Mersey 2
		Maid Of The Mint	Minting 1 / Warble 1
	Lady Hamburg II	*HAMBURG*	Hanover 15 / Lady Reel 23
		Lady Frivoles	*ST SIMON* 11 / Gay Duchess 31
Flying Witch (1917)	*BROOMSTICK*	*BEN BRUSH*	Bramble 9 / Roseville A1
		Elf	Galliard 13 / Sylvabelle 16
	Fly By Night II	Peter Pan	*COMMANDO* 12 / Cinderella 2
		Dazzling	St Leonards 10 / Splendour 2

Bubbling Beauty 1961

Natalma (1957)

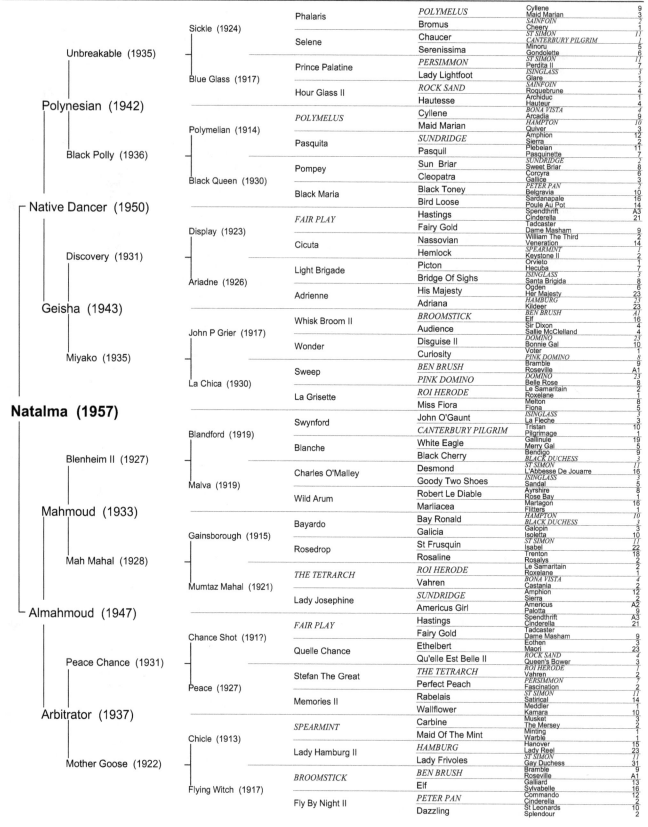

Native Dancer (1950)
- Polynesian (1942)
  - Unbreakable (1935)
  - Black Polly (1936)
- Geisha (1943)
  - Discovery (1931)
  - Miyako (1935)

Almahmoud (1947)
- Mahmoud (1933)
  - Blenheim II (1927)
  - Mah Mahal (1928)
- Arbitrator (1937)
  - Peace Chance (1931)
  - Mother Goose (1922)

Sickle (1924)			
	Phalaris	POLYMELUS	Cyllene 9 / Maid Marian 3
		Bromus	SAINFOIN 2 / Cheery 1
	Selene	Chaucer	ST SIMON 11 / CANTERBURY PILGRIM 1
		Serenissima	Minoru 5 / Gondolette 6
Blue Glass (1917)			
	Prince Palatine	PERSIMMON	ST SIMON 11 / Perdita II 7
		Lady Lightfoot	ISINGLASS 3 / Glare 1
	Hour Glass II	ROCK SAND	SAINFOIN 2 / Roquebrune 4
		Hautesse	Archiduc 1 / Hauteur 4
Polymelian (1914)			
	POLYMELUS	Cyllene	BONA VISTA 4 / Arcadia 9
		Maid Marian	HAMPTON 10 / Quiver 3
	Pasquita	SUNDRIDGE	Amphion 12 / Sierra 1
		Pasquil	Plebeian 11 / Pasquinette 7
Black Queen (1930)			
	Pompey	Sun Briar	SUNDRIDGE 2 / Sweet Briar 8
		Cleopatra	Corcyra 6 / Gallice 3
	Black Maria	Black Toney	PETER PAN 2 / Belgravia 10
		Bird Loose	Sardanapale 16 / Poule Au Pot 14
Display (1923)			
	FAIR PLAY	Hastings	Spendthrift A3 / Cinderella 21
		Fairy Gold	Tadcaster / Dame Masham 9
	Cicuta	Nassovian	William The Third 2 / Veneration 14
		Hemlock	SPEARMINT 1 / Keystone II 2
Ariadne (1926)			
	Light Brigade	Picton	Orvieto 1 / Hecuba 7
		Bridge Of Sighs	ISINGLASS 3 / Santa Brigida 8
	Adrienne	His Majesty	Ogden 6 / Her Majesty 23
		Adriana	HAMBURG 23 / Kildeer 23
John P Grier (1917)			
	Whisk Broom II	BROOMSTICK	BEN BRUSH A1 / Elf 16
		Audience	Sir Dixon 4 / Sallie McClelland 4
	Wonder	Disguise II	DOMINO 23 / Bonnie Gal 10
		Curiosity	Voter 1 / PINK DOMINO 8
La Chica (1930)			
	Sweep	BEN BRUSH	Bramble 9 / Roseville A1
		PINK DOMINO	DOMINO 23 / Belle Rose 8
	La Grisette	ROI HERODE	Le Samaritain 2 / Roxelane 1
		Miss Fiora	Melton 8 / Fiona 5
Blandford (1919)			
	Swynford	John O'Gaunt	ISINGLASS 3 / La Fleche 3
		CANTERBURY PILGRIM	Tristan 10 / Pilgrimage 1
	Blanche	White Eagle	Gallinule 19 / Merry Gal 5
		Black Cherry	Bendigo 9 / BLACK DUCHESS 3
Malva (1919)			
	Charles O'Malley	Desmond	ST SIMON 11 / L'Abbesse De Jouarre 16
		Goody Two Shoes	ISINGLASS 3 / Sandal 5
	Wild Arum	Robert Le Diable	Ayrshire 8 / Rose Bay 1
		Marliacea	Martagon 16 / Flitters 1
Gainsborough (1915)			
	Bayardo	Bay Ronald	HAMPTON 10 / BLACK DUCHESS 3
		Galicia	Galopin 3 / Isoletta 10
	Rosedrop	St Frusquin	ST SIMON 11 / Isabel 22
		Rosaline	Trenton 18 / Rosalys 2
Mumtaz Mahal (1921)			
	THE TETRARCH	ROI HERODE	Le Samaritain 2 / Roxelane 1
		Vahren	BONA VISTA 4 / Castania 2
	Lady Josephine	SUNDRIDGE	Amphion 12 / Sierra 1
		Americus Girl	Americus A2 / Palotta 9
Chance Shot (191?)			
	FAIR PLAY	Hastings	Spendthrift A3 / Cinderella 21
		Fairy Gold	Tadcaster / Dame Masham 9
	Quelle Chance	Ethelbert	Eothen 3 / Maori 23
		Qu'elle Est Belle II	ROCK SAND 4 / Queen's Bower 3
Peace (1927)			
	Stefan The Great	THE TETRARCH	ROI HERODE 1 / Vahren 2
		Perfect Peach	PERSIMMON 2 / Fascination 2
	Memories II	Rabelais	ST SIMON 11 / Satirical 14
		Wallflower	Meddler 1 / Kamara 10
Chicle (1913)			
	SPEARMINT	Carbine	Musket 3 / The Mersey 2
		Maid Of The Mint	Minting 1 / Warble 1
	Lady Hamburg II	HAMBURG	Hanover 15 / Lady Reel 23
		Lady Frivoles	ST SIMON 11 / Gay Duchess 31
Flying Witch (1917)			
	BROOMSTICK	BEN BRUSH	Bramble 9 / Roseville A1
		Elf	Galliard 13 / Sylvabelle 16
	Fly By Night II	PETER PAN	Commando 12 / Cinderella 2
		Dazzling	St Leonards 10 / Splendour 2

Natalma 1987

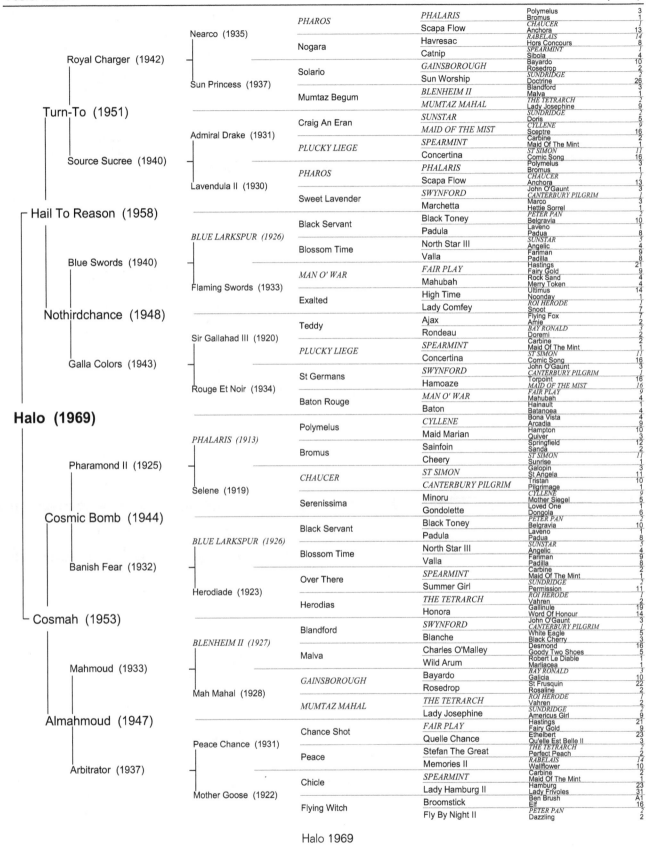

Halo (1969)

- **Hail To Reason (1958)**
  - **Turn-To (1951)**
    - **Royal Charger (1942)**
      - Nearco (1935)
        - *PHAROS* — *PHALARIS* (Polymelus 3, Bromus 1); Scapa Flow (*CHAUCER* 1, Anchora 13)
        - Nogara — Havresac (*RABELAIS* 14, Hors Concours 8); Catnip (*SPEARMINT* 1, Sibola 4)
      - Sun Princess (1937)
        - Solario — *GAINSBOROUGH* (Bayardo 10, Rosedrop 2); Sun Worship (*SUNDRIDGE* 1, Doctrine 26)
        - Mumtaz Begum — *BLENHEIM II* (Blandford 3, Malva 1); *MUMTAZ MAHAL* (*THE TETRARCH* 1, Lady Josephine 9)
    - **Source Sucree (1940)**
      - Admiral Drake (1931)
        - Craig An Eran — *SUNSTAR* (*SUNDRIDGE* 2, Doris 5); *MAID OF THE MIST* (*CYLLENE* 9, Sceptre 16)
        - *PLUCKY LIEGE* — *SPEARMINT* (Carbine 2, Maid Of The Mint 1); Concertina (*ST SIMON* 11, Comic Song 16)
      - Lavendula II (1930)
        - *PHAROS* — *PHALARIS* (Polymelus 3, Bromus 1); Scapa Flow (*CHAUCER* 1, Anchora 13)
        - Sweet Lavender — *SWYNFORD* (John O'Gaunt 3, *CANTERBURY PILGRIM* 1); Marchetta (Marco 3, Hettie Sorrel 1)
  - **Nothirdchance (1948)**
    - **Blue Swords (1940)**
      - *BLUE LARKSPUR* (1926)
        - Black Servant — Black Toney (*PETER PAN* 2, Belgravia 10); Padula (Laveno 1, Padua 8)
        - Blossom Time — North Star III (*SUNSTAR* 3, Angelic 4); Valla (Fariman 9, Padilla 8)
      - Flaming Swords (1933)
        - *MAN O' WAR* — *FAIR PLAY* (Hastings 21, Fairy Gold 9); Mahubah (Rock Sand 4, Merry Token 1)
        - Exalted — High Time (Ultimus 14, Noonday 1); Lady Comfey (*ROI HERODE* 1, Snoot 7)
    - **Galla Colors (1943)**
      - Sir Gallahad III (1920)
        - Teddy — Ajax (Flying Fox 7, Amie 2); Rondeau (*BAY RONALD* 3, Doremi 2)
        - *PLUCKY LIEGE* — *SPEARMINT* (Carbine 2, Maid Of The Mint 1); Concertina (*ST SIMON* 11, Comic Song 16)
      - Rouge Et Noir (1934)
        - St Germans — *SWYNFORD* (John O'Gaunt 3, *CANTERBURY PILGRIM* 1); Hamoaze (Torpoint 16, *MAID OF THE MIST* 16)
        - Baton Rouge — *MAN O' WAR* (*FAIR PLAY*, Mahubah 4); Baton (Hainault 1, Batanoea 4)

- **Cosmah (1953)**
  - **Cosmic Bomb (1944)**
    - **Pharamond II (1925)**
      - *PHALARIS* (1913)
        - Polymelus — *CYLLENE* (Bona Vista 4, Arcadia 9); Maid Marian (Hampton 10, Quiver 3)
        - Bromus — Sainfoin (Springfield 12, Sanda 2); Cheery (*ST SIMON* 11, Sunrise 1)
      - Selene (1919)
        - *CHAUCER* — *ST SIMON* (Galopin 3, St Angela 11); *CANTERBURY PILGRIM* (Tristan 10, Pilgrimage 1)
        - Serenissima — Minoru (*CYLLENE* 9, Mother Siegel 5); Gondolette (Loved One 1, Dongola 6)
    - **Banish Fear (1932)**
      - *BLUE LARKSPUR* (1926)
        - Black Servant — Black Toney (*PETER PAN* 2, Belgravia 10); Padula (Laveno 1, Padua 8)
        - Blossom Time — North Star III (*SUNSTAR* 3, Angelic 4); Valla (Fariman 9, Padilla 8)
      - Herodiade (1923)
        - Over There — *SPEARMINT* (Carbine 2, Maid Of The Mint 1); Summer Girl (*SUNDRIDGE* 2, Permission 11)
        - Herodias — *THE TETRARCH* (*ROI HERODE* 1, Vahren 19); Honora (Gallinule 14, Word Of Honour 3)
  - **Almahmoud (1947)**
    - **Mahmoud (1933)**
      - *BLENHEIM II* (1927)
        - Blandford — *SWYNFORD* (John O'Gaunt 3, *CANTERBURY PILGRIM* 1); Blanche (White Eagle 5, Black Cherry 3)
        - Malva — Charles O'Malley (Desmond 16, Goody Two Shoes 5); Wild Arum (Robert Le Diable 1, Marliacea)
      - Mah Mahal (1928)
        - *GAINSBOROUGH* — Bayardo (*BAY RONALD* 10, Galicia 22); Rosedrop (St Frusquin 2, Rosaline)
        - *MUMTAZ MAHAL* — *THE TETRARCH* (*ROI HERODE* 1, Vahren 2); Lady Josephine (*SUNDRIDGE* 9, Americus Girl 21)
    - **Arbitrator (1937)**
      - Peace Chance (1931)
        - Chance Shot — *FAIR PLAY* (Hastings 21, Fairy Gold 9); Quelle Chance (Ethelbert 23, Qu'elle Est Belle II 3)
        - Peace — Stefan The Great (*THE TETRARCH* 2, Perfect Peach 2); Memories II (*RABELAIS* 14, Wallflower 10)
      - Mother Goose (1922)
        - Chicle — *SPEARMINT* (Carbine 2, Maid Of The Mint 1); Lady Hamburg II (Hamburg 23, Lady Frivoles 31)
        - Flying Witch — Broomstick (Ben Brush A1, Elf 16); Fly By Night II (*PETER PAN* 2, Dazzling 2)

Halo 1969

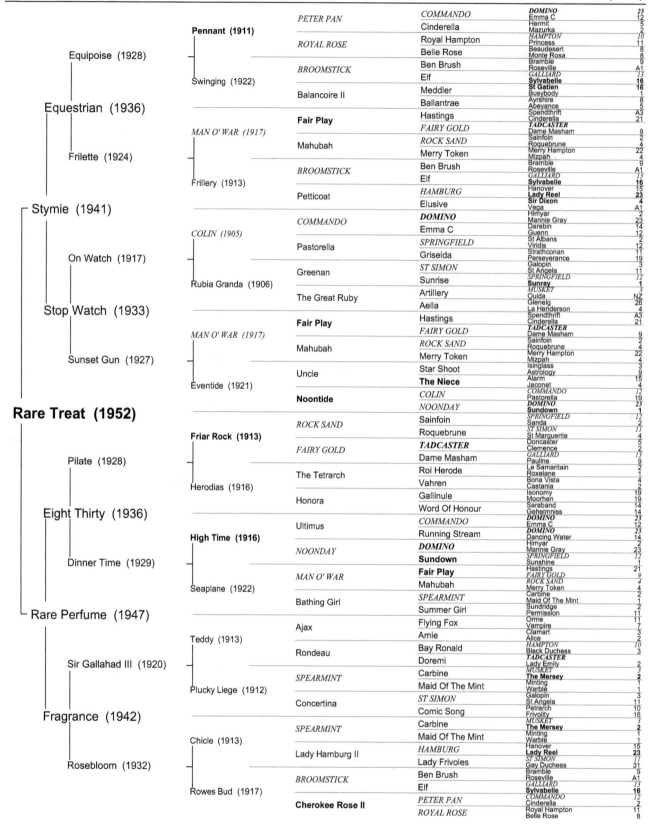

Rare Treat 1952

Sex Appeal (1970)

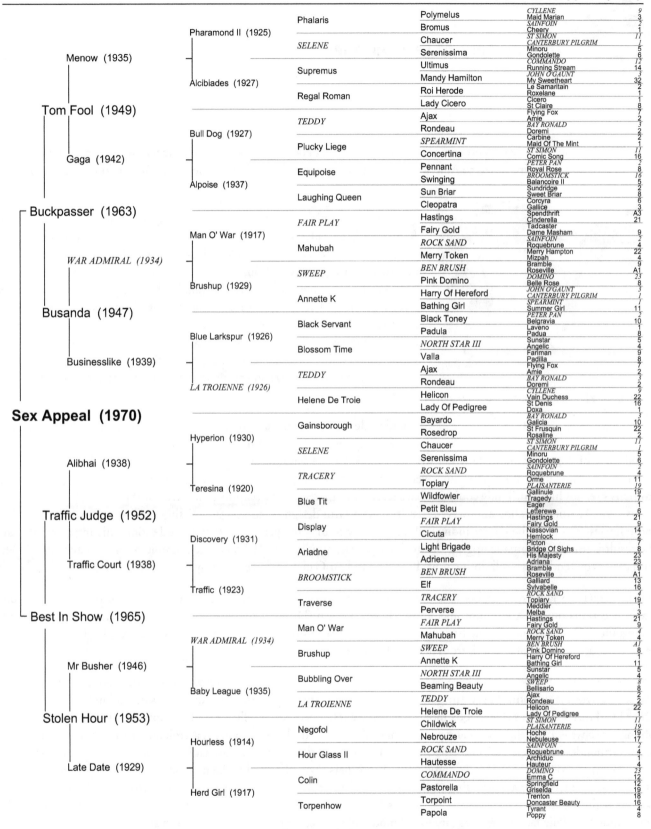

Sex Appeal 1970

Chapter 22

The Mystery of La Troienne

"La Troienne is easily the best source of a steady stream of good stakes winners, classic winners, champions and foundation mares imported to America in this century" (Les Brinsfield "La Troienne: a Distaff Fountainhead").

The modest-looking genetic powerhouse La Troienne, she has a tremendous background power of Young Giantess. —image courtesy of Wiki Commons

I never quite understood the 'La Troienne thing'—not until recently anyway. She has been called the "broodmare of the century," and her advent here in America is revered as almost a blessed event. How lucky we were to have imported such a great mare! It just never sat right with me, though the evidence of the excellence of her offspring is undeniable; they are genetic treasures in our modern horse and should be a target for increase in our stock. But I never understood what it was about this mediocre racer—although with a very good pedigree that has some solid potency—I always felt the pedigree strength, while wonderful, certainly was not dynamic enough to account for her astounding **maternal dynasty**. So I was on the lookout for an explanation that made sense to me.

I could understand why her sire Teddy was so influential a bloodline, as he carried not only the ¾ siblings Ormonde/Doremi 4x2 (by Tadcaster), but he possessed three of the rarely found daughter strains of the key mare Pocahontas through his sire Ajax, and she was most often found by multiple lines of her sons Stockwell, Rataplan, and King Tom in most pedigrees. However, coming as they did from his sire, not his dam, Teddy could not have received or passed on the sex-linked material or the mtDNA of Pocahontas to his tribe. History has shown, however, that it is a powerful design to possess the missing sex lines of an ancestor; when those horses who have these rarer individuals are bred back into the gene pool they provide some missing elements, and the result is usually a dramatic upgrade in stock (Aspidistra in Chapter 21 is another example of this enhancement). The stud careers of Teddy's two full sibling sons, Bull Dog and Sir Gallahad, have certainly demonstrated that fact in the States.

But La Troienne's fame rests on her career as a broodmare. For a broodmare to be great she needs to be a carrier of good sex-linked traits on her X chromosome, and/or have strong mtDNA. After all that is what the entire clamor about the importance of superior tail-female lines and filly factors arises from isn't it? However, as we can see, La Troienne did not receive her great maternal strength from her Pocahontas lines.

Let's take a look at her pedigree. I have had to reassess it because of the Bend Or discovery, to enter Tadcaster in his proper place. This effort is tiresome, but we are going to have to rewrite many pedigrees because of this deception (see Appendix C). Once I had this done I was able to look more closely at what her pedigree is telling us—I am hopeful it is all correct now. Full siblings are always a key element in any pedigree and often point to the dominance. La Troienne has two important full siblings: Ormonde/Ornament 5x5 and Angelica/St. Simon 5x4—these are very powerful placements, but they become even more concentrated as they are focused through the ¾ brothers Flying Fox and St. Denis who are 3x3. This pedigree is strongly inbred—wonderful for any breeding stock, but better for a male as this forms a strong colt factor. Now La Troienne has a two good filly factors in her dam: the ¾ siblings Distant Shore/Timothy through daughters 5x5 and the ¾ sisters Violet/Verdure 6x6. Filly factors are necessary for a broodmares success and are also important in stallions.

La Troienne's pedigree is a very good and powerful one, but certainly is not strong enough in female factors to account for her maternal dynasty, especially when they are weighed against the overpowering male configuration of St. Denis and Flying Fox in the front of the pedigree. If I was looking at this lineage and did not know her breeding history, I would say she was an exceptionally good broodmare, but her sons would be generally better than her daughters. Yet, I could see the almost immeasurable greatness of her daughters and granddaughters—outstanding racers and broodmares—who far outshine her sons. Where is this level of talent coming from? Then I stumbled upon the writings of Les Brinsfield, and he had the answer! Thank you Les, this has bothered me for a long time. I refer you to his work "Domino—the Pedigree" and "La Troienne: A Distaff Fountainhead" (Both articles are found on www.pedigreepost.net in the archives).

It turns out her secret genetic strength is all about Diomed! Hold on, I know it sounds crazy, but I believe Les has hit upon the solution of the mystery of La Troienne.

If you did not notice this when you read Chapter 1, I suggest you turn back to Lexington's pedigree (at chapter end), and you will see he is inbred 3x3x4 to Diomed sons. The statistics have shown that repeated lines of a sire through sons only—no daughters—causes some loss of power in genetic transmission (the theory being there needs to be the X chromosome material contributed by the female line—see Appendix B). This rule has proved more crucial in stallions than performance colts. Here in the USA it is very often the sons of Diomed who bred on—his son Sir Archy for instance was inbred to on a regular basis, so we seldom see Diomed daughters. Diomed is a key bloodline (Chapter 6) in our four-mile heat racer and is one of the very few of the imported English Thoroughbreds of his time who improved our racehorse base. Lexington RH of course has some strong female influences that balance out this male-leaning design (Cypron, Papillon, Wildair Mare, Lady Grey), proving powerful enough to make him a top broodmare sire.

Busanda, by War Admiral out of Businesslike, is the dam of *chef-de-race* Buckpasser. —photo by Skeet Meadors, courtesy of Keeneland Library

Diomed was a key typesetter for the future American Thoroughbred. He was born at the close of the four-mile heat race selection criteria for the English Thoroughbred; therefore he possessed the height of their program's genes: great stamina, soundness, and speed. He raced in a few four-mile heat races, but as they were being abandoned in England he also ran in the new classic distance performance standards. He is the first winner of the Epsom Derby.

Diomed carried key full sibling groupings: the full brothers Flying Childers/Bartletts Childers 5x6x7x7x6x5x4, and their second dam Cream Cheeks finds her full sister Betty Percival on his dam-line—his sixth dam, so they are 7x8x9x9x7x7x6x6. Also important to American pedigrees is the full siblings Bald Galloway/Points as they hark back to the old Hobby genes (the great Janus carried both also). Cream Cheeks and Betty Percival were out of the Spanker Mare who is inbred 2x1 to an Old Morrocco mare (aka Bald Peg) who is the dam of Spanker (first TB) and is out of a Hobby dam (see Chapters 1 and 2).

With our American Running Horse mare base, which was descended from Hobby roots, Diomed was on a level with Janus twenty years before him. His contemporary English imports were disappointing and actually were downgrading our racehorse population, but not Diomed, he was a genetic sensation (see Chapters 1, 2, and 6). He is everywhere in the American Thoroughbred, found mostly however through his immensely successful stallion sons: Duroc RH, Balls Florizel RH, and the incomparable Sir Archy—the foundation sire of our Thoroughbred.

Our greatest sire of the 1800s (or anytime—his record as a stallion has never been bettered), Lexington RH is inbred to Diomed 3x3x4 through Sir Archy and Balls Florizel RH—there are no daughter strains in him. Domino, possibly the most prolific sire-line of the 1900s is 3x4x4 to Lexington RH, plus carries his half-brother Lecomte RH in the fourth; this equals eleven male lines of Diomed—no daughter lines. Obviously this is a huge concentration of male Diomed lines.

Now in English and European breeding, Diomed left his share of offspring, but generally it is his daughter Young Giantess who bred on significantly as she has created a maternal dynasty of great power. He produced a very good son there, Grey Diomed, but he was shortly sent to Russia. Here is the answer to the mystery—La Troienne 1926 has forty-nine lines of Young Giantess in twelve generations and no other Diomed lines. Young Giantess is represented by both sons and daughters in La Troienne, so it is a massive background filly factor in its own right, but this very large concentration of Diomed is by a single daughter only (it would be better if there was another daughter as well), so there is a huge sex-imbalance that robs her of the full power of the great Diomed. La Troienne was no great shakes as a racer, but she is off the charts as a broodmare, an outcome that demands a strong maternal presence, and she did not receive the sex-linked benefits from the Pocahontas lines she carries either. Her dam has multiple lines of Pocahontas sons, but none of them could provide an open path to any of her X chromosomes. Instead her amazing career as a broodmare rests on two elements—the massive background filly factor of Young Giantess refocused through her dam's two filly factors, and secondly on the genetics of her mates.

Here is the key provided by Les Brinsfield, "She was never bred to anything except a Domino line horse with the exception of their homebred Kentucky Derby winner, Bubbling Over, and his dam was tripled to Domino…" Therefore, La Troienne's entire stud career was made up of offspring out of stallions who were strong carriers of Domino and therefore warehouses of Lexington RH and the male Diomed lines. La Troienne was bred to Black Toney (seven Lexington RH/one Lecomte RH) and to Blue Larkspur (seven Lexington RH/ one Lecomte RH); each of these lines is inbred to Diomed by sons only (twenty-three lines). So when her forty-nine lines of Young Giantess met the carriers of enormous concentration of male Diomed lines present in Lexington RH and reconcentrated through Domino, there was a release of Diomed's gifts in immense genetic power and depth. This was a seismic genetic event of massive magnitude—this explains her unmatched record!

So here is a tremendous lesson for us breeders. Do we have breeding stock that carries a large buildup of a superior ancestor but by one sex only? For this can work both ways. Because then for us to find a mate with a large collection of the same line but in the multiples of the opposite sex—even if it is deep in the background—then we can reap an incredible genetic harvest (See Aspidistra for another example of this in Chapter 21).

In the meantime—we can be sure that we will build up the superb sport genetics by including multiples of her progeny and descendants. La Troienne had a ¾ sister Adaragatis, and she is a valuable addition for your line-breeding exercises.

The Legacy of La Troienne

Her fourteen offspring are listed with the producers in bold type—notice how many of her daughters and granddaughters have reached *reine-de-course* status—once again I feel I must remind you that *reines* are not common; the number here is an indication of the tremendous level of genetic superiority in this family:

Sketch of Bimelech by C.W. Anderson for
Who's Who in Thoroughbred Racing.

1932 **Black Helen** by Black Toney (*reine*)

1934 Biologist by Bubbling Over (gelding)

1935 **Baby League** by Bubbling Over (*reine*)

1936 **Big Hurry** by Black Toney (*reine*)

1937 **Bimelech** by Black Toney (stallion and Hall of Fame inductee)

1938 **Big Event** by Blue Larkspur (*reine*)

1939 **Businesslike** by Blue Larkspur (dam of Busanda)

1940 **Besieged** by Balladier (mare)

1941 **Broke Even** by Blue Larkspur (stallion—sixty-nine foals)

1942 Back Yard by Balladier (gelding)

1944 **Bee Ann Mac** by Blue Larkspur (mare—dam of Better Self)

1945 **Belle Histoire** by Blue Larkspur (*reine*)

1947 **Belle of Troy** by Blue Larkspur (*reine*—dam of Cohoes)

1948 Trojan War by Shut Out (gelding)

Of these offspring Black Helen/Big Hurry/Bimelech are full siblings, as are Big Event/Businesslike/Belle of Troy/Broke Even, and these groups are ¾ siblings to each other, giving the line-breeder an easy way to create critical mass and to refocus it. As you can see Bimelech, who was a great racehorse and sire, was not the only stallion son of La Troienne, as there is the seldom-seen Broke Even, who was a solid racer winning eleven of forty-four, and while he is not easy to find in modern lineages, he is still out there.

War Admiral. —a public domain image courtesy of Wiki Commons

But the whole bonanza for American breeders actually gets better than this, as many of her daughters were then bred to **War Admiral**, another concentrated carrier of Lexington RH (six lines—therefore eighteen more male lines of Diomed, which puts the total of male Diomed lines at forty-one, basically an equal to La Troienne's female Diomed lines). This fortunate mating almost didn't happen because Col Bradley hated the Fair Play line (War Admiral's grandsire), because he felt many were temperamental and could lose races because of it, and they were late maturing stamina horses, while Bradley liked a quick-maturing speed horse, and further, some of the Man O' Wars were large, and Bradley preferred a smaller racer. All those issues aside, the Fair Play line had soundness, stamina, and resiliency going for it, and this is something Bradley's herd needed desperately. As mentioned above, Bradley had stood the imported North Star II at his stud, and most of his mares carried him close-up, but North Star had imparted delicacy and weakness into the herd, plus the Domino line which his stud was based on occasionally threw in some hoof issues. Therefore Bradley needed a stout input, but not one that would slow him down. War Admiral was the answer, as he had the soundness, the speed, the stamina, and toughness, and of those progeny the daughters are generally the best—several of them may even be called masterpieces (Busher/Striking/Searching).

Image of Busher and her foal by American artist C. W. Anderson. Mr. Anderson declared that Busher's head was near perfection.

Progeny results of those La Troienne daughters listed above who were bred by War Admiral:

1942 **Busher** out of Baby League (Horse-of-the-Year—she is the dam of Jet Action)

1944 **Blue Eyed Momo** out of Big Event (dam of Francis S)

1946 **Mr. Busher** out of Baby League (stallion)

1947 **Busanda** out of Businesslike (dam of Buckpasser)

1947 **Striking** out of Baby League (*reine*—dam of Glamour)

1948 **The Battler** out of Baby League (stallion)

1949 **Great Captain** out of Big Hurry (stallion)

1950 **Bushleaguer** out of Baby League (mare)

1951 **Activate** out of Big Hurry (mare)

1952 **Searching** out of Big Hurry (*reine*—Admiring, Affectionately, Priceless Gem)

Of these, Busher/Mr Busher/Striking/The Battler/Bushleaguer are full siblings, as well as another full sibling group of Great Captain/Activate/Searching—they are all ¾ siblings to each other.

Plus, between these two groups of Blue Larkspur and War Admiral offspring there are multiple ¾ siblings also, and combining groups of them in pedigrees refocuses the power, which makes them deliver even more dominance. What an opportunity we have with this family! You could spend your entire breeding years just building on these top-rate lines and succeed year after year. It gets no better than this.

The *reine-de-course* Searching by War Admiral out of Big Hurry. —photo by Skeet Meadors, courtesy of Keeneland Library

Examples:

Look at what happened when a pedigree was constructed with the full sisters Striking and Busher 3x3; the result was the *reine* My Charmer, a broodmare of legendary status. Notice also the double of Frizeur and the ¾ siblings Colin/Verdure. With forty-five lines of Lexington RH, this mare is a serious transmitter of our Heroic Era genes. She was just a mediocre racer, but as a broodmare she excelled. Bred to Bold Reasoning she produced the Triple Crown winner Seattle Slew (one hundred forty lines of Lexington RH). Bred to Northern Dancer she gave us the good racer and sire Lomond (seventy lines of Lexington RH); he won the 2000 Guineas in England. Bred to Nijinsky she produced the yearling that sold for more than any other: $13 million! This is Seattle Dancer (one hundred eleven lines of Lexington RH).

Another good example is the *reine* Relaxing; she is 3x3 to the ¾ sisters Businesslike and Big Hurry (she also has seventy-nine lines of Lexington RH). Her pedigree is powerful, with other strong full sibling groups: Sickle/Pharamond 4x5, Sun Briar/Sunreigh 6x6—both sex-balanced—and another ¾ group closer to the front of War Admiral/Frilette 3x5—this is potency of the highest order. This mare was a super racer, a stakes winner, beating colts regularly and winning $600,000. She was voted Champion-Older-Female 1981, and she also was a top producer and was voted Kentucky Broodmare-of-the-Year in 1989. She had twelve foals, and nine of them were runners; three of those are stakes winners: the mares Cadillacing and Easy Now, and the superstar Easy Goer (see Chapter 26) who was Champion Two-Year-Old, and at three he won the Belmont and totaled $4.8 million in earnings. Her best offspring were by Alydar (with forty-four more lines of Lexington RH): full siblings Easy Goer and Cadillacing—that's one hundred twenty-three lines of Lexington RH in them. She also had a nice filly by Seattle Slew: Comfy.

2014 update: The magnificent California Chrome, who took both the Kentucky Derby and Preakness in fine form this year, is a modern day example of this mare power in action. His dam is 3x3 to Numbered Account, a top broodmare whose genetics are concentrated elements of this same family, and he demonstrates a pedigree pattern that is almost identical to that of Seattle Slew and Easy Goer, horses born more than forty years before him—read more of this in Chapter 26.

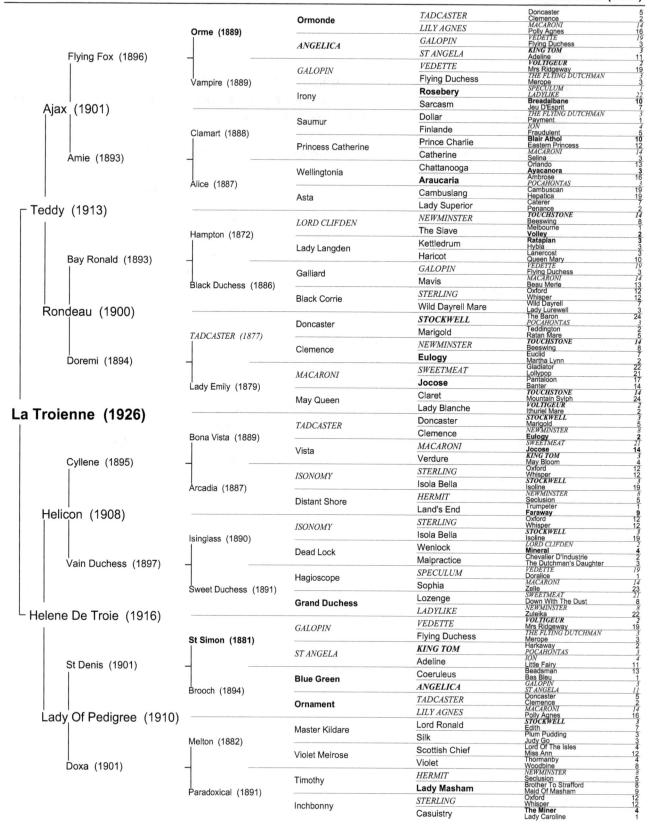

La Troienne 1926

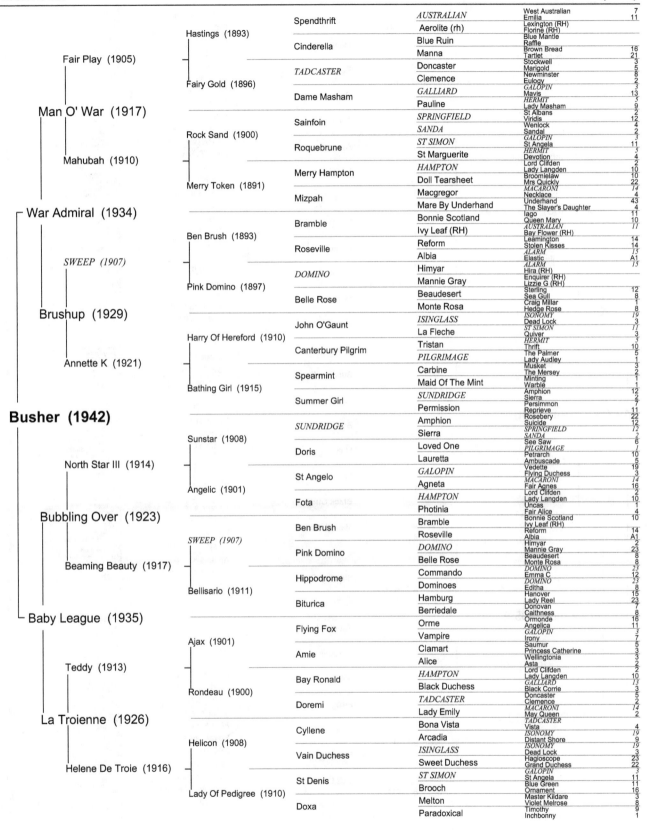

Busher 1942

My Charmer (1969)

Round Table (1954)

Princequillo (1940)
- Prince Rose (1928)
  - Rose Prince
    - Prince Palatine — *PERSIMMON* 7 / Lady Lightfoot 1
    - Eglantine — Perth 8 / Rose De Mai 11
  - Indolence
    - Gay Crusader — Bayardo 10 / Gay Laura 1
    - Barrier — Grey Leg 6 / Bar The Way 10
- Cosquilla (1933)
  - Papyrus
    - Tracery — *ROCK SAND* 4 / Topiary 19
    - Miss Matty — Marcovil 12 / Simonath 16
  - Quick Thought
    - *WHITE EAGLE* — *GALLINULE* 19 / Merry Gal 5
    - Mindful — Minoru 5 / Noble Martha 1

Knight's Daughter (1941)
- Sir Cosmo (1926)
  - The Boss
    - Orby — Orme 11 / Rhoda B 26
    - Southern Cross — Meteor 1 / Resplendent 24
  - Ayn Hali
    - *DESMOND* — *ST SIMON* 11 / L'Abbesse De Jouarre 16
    - Lalla Rookh — Hackler 7 / Lady Gough 6
- Feola (1933)
  - Friar Marcus
    - Cicero — Cyllene 9 / Gas 1
    - Prim Nun — *PERSIMMON* 7 / Nunsuch 20
  - Aloe
    - Son-In-law — Dark Ronald 9 / Mother-In-law
    - Alope — *GALLINULE* 19 / Altoviscar 2

Poker (1963)

Nasrullah (1940)
- Nearco (1935)
  - Pharos
    - Phalaris — Polymelus 3 / Bromus 1
    - Scapa Flow — **Chaucer** 1 / Anchora 13
  - Nogara
    - Havresac — Rabelais 14 / Hors Concours 8
    - Catnip — *SPEARMINT* 1 / Sibola 4
- Mumtaz Begum (1932)
  - *BLENHEIM II*
    - Blandford — **Swynford** 1 / Blanche 3
    - Malva — Charles O'Malley 5 / Wild Arum 1
  - Mumtaz Mahal
    - The Tetrarch — Roi Herode 1 / Vahren 2
    - Lady Josephine — Sundridge 2 / Americus Girl 9

Glamour (1953)

Striking (1947)
- *WAR ADMIRAL (1934)*
  - Man O' War
    - *FAIR PLAY* — Hastings 21 / *FAIRY GOLD* 9
    - Mahubah — *ROCK SAND* 4 / Merry Token 4
  - Brushup
    - *SWEEP* — *BEN BRUSH* A1 / **Pink Domino** 8
    - Annette K — **Harry Of Hereford** 1 / Bathing Girl 11
- *BABY LEAGUE (1935)*
  - Bubbling Over
    - *NORTH STAR III* — Sunstar 5 / Angelic 4
    - Beaming Beauty — *SWEEP* 8 / Bellisario 8
  - La Troienne
    - *TEDDY* — Ajax 2 / Rondeau 2
    - Helene De Troie — Helicon 22 / Lady Of Pedigree 1

My Charmer (1969)

Jet Pilot (1944)
- *BLENHEIM II (1927)*
  - Blandford
    - **Swynford** — John O'Gaunt 3 / Canterbury Pilgrim 1
    - Blanche — *WHITE EAGLE* 5 / Black Cherry 3
  - Malva
    - Charles O'Malley — *DESMOND* 16 / Goody Two Shoes 5
    - Wild Arum — Robert Le Diable 1 / Marliacea 1
- Black Wave (1935)
  - Sir Gallahad III
    - *TEDDY* — Ajax 2 / Rondeau 2
    - Plucky Liege — *SPEARMINT* 2 / Concertina 16
  - **Black Curl**
    - **Friar Rock** — *ROCK SAND* 4 / *FAIRY GOLD* 9
    - *FRIZEUR* — Sweeper 8 / Frizette 13

Jet Action (1951)

Busher (1942)
- *WAR ADMIRAL (1934)*
  - Man O' War
    - *FAIR PLAY* — Hastings 21 / *FAIRY GOLD* 9
    - Mahubah — *ROCK SAND* 4 / Merry Token 4
  - Brushup
    - *SWEEP* — *BEN BRUSH* A1 / **Pink Domino** 8
    - Annette K — **Harry Of Hereford** 1 / Bathing Girl 11
- *BABY LEAGUE (1935)*
  - Bubbling Over
    - *NORTH STAR III* — Sunstar 5 / Angelic 4
    - Beaming Beauty — *SWEEP* 8 / Bellisario 8
  - La Troienne
    - *TEDDY* — Ajax 2 / Rondeau 2
    - Helene De Troie — Helicon 22 / Lady Of Pedigree 1

Fair Charmer (1959)

Alsab (1939)
- Good Goods (1931)
  - Neddie
    - **Colin** — *COMMANDO* 12 / *PASTORELLA* 19
    - Black Flag — Light Brigade 8 / Misplay 6
  - Brocatelle
    - Radium — Tadcaster / Taia 3
    - Pietra — Pietermaritzburg 2 / Briar-Root 2
- Winds Chant (1931)
  - Wildair
    - *BROOMSTICK* — *BEN BRUSH* A1 / Elf 16
    - **Verdure** — *PETER PAN* 2 / *PASTORELLA* 19
  - Eulogy
    - *FAIR PLAY* — Hastings 21 / *FAIRY GOLD* 9
    - St Eudora — *ST SIMON* 11 / Dorothea 27

Myrtle Charm (1946)

Crepe Myrtle (1938)
- Equipoise (1928)
  - Pennant
    - *PETER PAN* — *COMMANDO* 12 / Cinderella 11
    - **Royal Rose** — Royal Hampton 1 / Belle Rose 8
  - Swinging
    - *BROOMSTICK* — *BEN BRUSH* A1 / Elf 16
    - Balancoire II — Meddler 1 / Ballantrae 5
- **Myrtlewood (1932)**
  - Blue Larkspur
    - Black Servant — Black Toney 10 / Padula 8
    - Blossom Time — *NORTH STAR III* 4 / Valla
  - *FRIZEUR*
    - Sweeper — *BROOMSTICK* 16 / Ravello 8
    - Frizette — Hamburg 23 / Ondulee 13

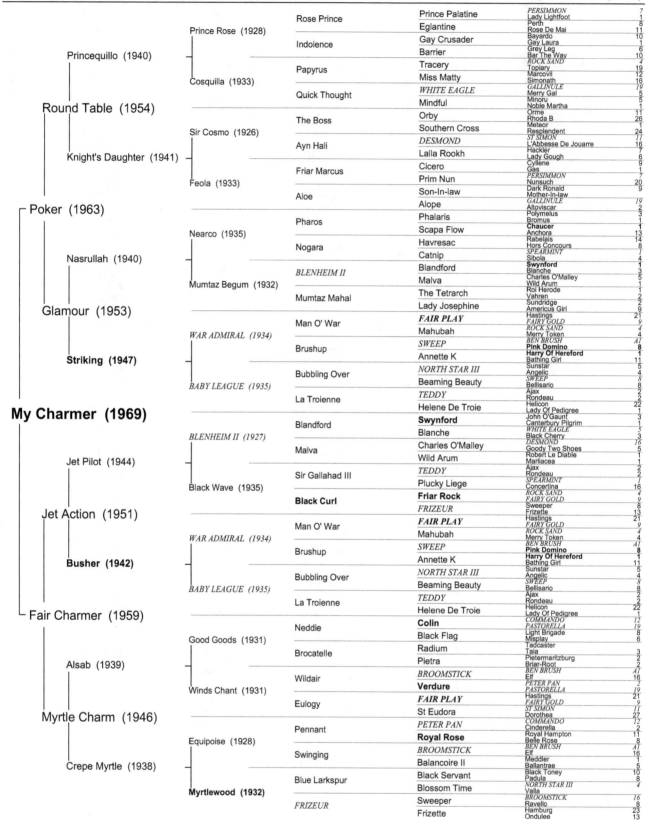

My Charmer 1969

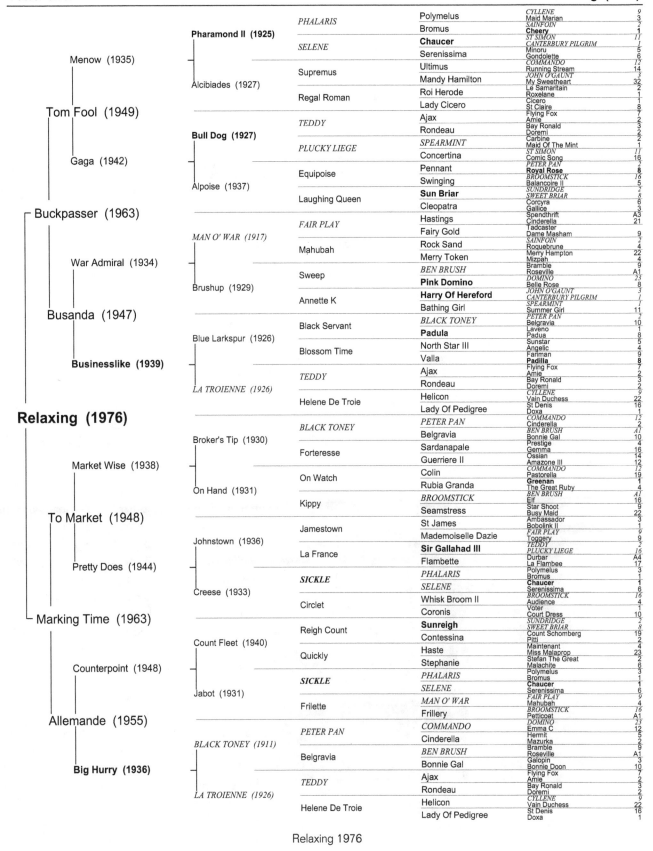

Relaxing (1976)

Left-hand generations:

- Tom Fool (1949)
  - Menow (1935)
  - Gaga (1942)
- Buckpasser (1963)
  - War Admiral (1934)
  - Busanda (1947)
    - Businesslike (1939)
- Relaxing (1976)
  - Market Wise (1938)
  - To Market (1948)
  - Pretty Does (1944)
- Marking Time (1963)
  - Counterpoint (1948)
  - Allemande (1955)
  - Big Hurry (1936)

Pharamond II (1925)
- PHALARIS
  - Polymelus — CYLLENE 9 / Maid Marian 3
  - Bromus — SAINFOIN 2 / Cheery 1
- SELENE
  - Chaucer — ST SIMON 11 / CANTERBURY PILGRIM 1
  - Serenissima — Minoru 5 / Gondolette 6

Alcibiades (1927)
- Supremus
  - Ultimus — COMMANDO 12 / Running Stream 14
  - Mandy Hamilton — JOHN O'GAUNT 3 / My Sweetheart 32
- Regal Roman
  - Roi Herode — Le Samaritain 2 / Roxelane 1
  - Lady Cicero — Cicero 1 / St Claire 8

Bull Dog (1927)
- TEDDY
  - Ajax — Flying Fox 7 / Amie 2
  - Rondeau — Bay Ronald 3 / Doremi 2
- PLUCKY LIEGE
  - SPEARMINT — Carbine 2 / Maid Of The Mint 1
  - Concertina — ST SIMON 11 / Comic Song 16

Alpoise (1937)
- Equipoise
  - Pennant — PETER PAN 2 / Royal Rose 8
  - Swinging — BROOMSTICK 16 / Balancoire II 5
- Laughing Queen
  - Sun Briar — SUNDRIDGE 2 / SWEET BRIAR 8
  - Cleopatra — Corcyra 6 / Gallice 3

MAN O' WAR (1917)
- FAIR PLAY
  - Hastings — Spendthrift A3 / Cinderella 21
  - Fairy Gold — Tadcaster / Dame Masham 9
- Mahubah
  - Rock Sand — SAINFOIN 2 / Roquebrune 4
  - Merry Token — Merry Hampton 22 / Mizpah 4

Brushup (1929)
- Sweep
  - BEN BRUSH — Bramble 9 / Roseville A1
  - Pink Domino — DOMINO 23 / Belle Rose 8
- Annette K
  - Harry Of Hereford — JOHN O'GAUNT 3 / CANTERBURY PILGRIM 1
  - Bathing Girl — SPEARMINT 1 / Summer Girl 11

Blue Larkspur (1926)
- Black Servant
  - BLACK TONEY — PETER PAN 2 / Belgravia 10
  - Padula — Laveno 1 / Padua 8
- Blossom Time
  - North Star III — Sunstar 5 / Angelic 4
  - Valla — Fariman 9 / Padilla 8

LA TROIENNE (1926)
- TEDDY
  - Ajax — Flying Fox 7 / Amie 2
  - Rondeau — Bay Ronald 3 / Doremi 2
- Helene De Troie
  - Helicon — CYLLENE 9 / Vain Duchess 22
  - Lady Of Pedigree — St Denis 16 / Doxa 1

Broker's Tip (1930)
- BLACK TONEY
  - PETER PAN — COMMANDO 12 / Cinderella 2
  - Belgravia — BEN BRUSH A1 / Bonnie Gal 10
- Forteresse
  - Sardanapale — Prestige 4 / Gemma 16
  - Guerriere II — Ossian 14 / Amazone III 12

On Hand (1931)
- On Watch
  - Colin — COMMANDO 12 / Pastorella 19
  - Rubia Granda — Greenan 1 / The Great Ruby 4
- Kippy
  - BROOMSTICK — BEN BRUSH A1 / Elf 16
  - Seamstress — Star Shoot 9 / Busy Maid 22

Johnstown (1936)
- Jamestown
  - St James — Ambassador 3 / Bobolink II 1
  - Mademoiselle Dazie — FAIR PLAY 9 / Toggery 9
- La France
  - Sir Gallahad III — TEDDY 7 / PLUCKY LIEGE 16
  - Flambette — Durbar A4 / La Flambee 17

Creese (1933)
- SICKLE
  - PHALARIS — Polymelus 3 / Bromus 1
  - SELENE — Chaucer 1 / Serenissima 6
- Circlet
  - Whisk Broom II — BROOMSTICK 16 / Audience 4
  - Coronis — Voter 1 / Court Dress 10

Count Fleet (1940)
- Reigh Count
  - Sunreigh — SUNDRIDGE 2 / SWEET BRIAR 8
  - Contessina — Count Schomberg 19 / Pitti 2
- Quickly
  - Haste — Maintenant 4 / Miss Malaprop 23
  - Stephanie — Stefan The Great 2 / Malachite 6

Jabot (1931)
- SICKLE
  - PHALARIS — Polymelus 3 / Bromus 1
  - SELENE — Chaucer 1 / Serenissima 6
- Frilette
  - MAN O' WAR — FAIR PLAY 9 / Mahubah 16
  - Frillery — BROOMSTICK 16 / Petticoat A1

BLACK TONEY (1911)
- PETER PAN
  - COMMANDO — DOMINO 23 / Emma C 12
  - Cinderella — Hermit 5 / Mazurka 2
- Belgravia
  - BEN BRUSH — Bramble A1 / Roseville A1
  - Bonnie Gal — Galopin 3 / Bonnie Doon 10

LA TROIENNE (1926)
- TEDDY
  - Ajax — Flying Fox 7 / Amie 2
  - Rondeau — Bay Ronald 3 / Doremi 2
- Helene De Troie
  - Helicon — CYLLENE 9 / Vain Duchess 22
  - Lady Of Pedigree — St Denis 16 / Doxa 1

Relaxing 1976

Chapter 23

Sweet Revenge: Fairy Bridge

Who could have predicted one hundred years after the ban of Lexington's blood that the progeny of a mare who carries **eighty-three lines** of him (plus eleven lines of his ½ brother Lecomte RH) would be dominating the European population of Thoroughbreds? This mare was American-bred, born at Claiborne Farm in Kentucky in 1975, by Bold Reason out of Special; she was moved to Ireland in 1976. She was trained there, and at two years old she raced twice and won twice, and then in 1978 she was returned to the USA to stand at stud—her name is Fairy Bridge.

Fairy Bridge had ten registered foals of which seven were raced—of those racers six were winners, three were graded stakes winners, and one was a champion. Not a bad start.

She was bred to Northern Dancer (five foals) and his sons: Nijinksy II (one foal) and Danzig (two foals), as well as Storm Bird (two foals). Her stakes winners were all by Northern Dancer, whose dam Natalma carries an additional forty-five lines of Lexington RH/Boston RH—plus the one contributed by Nearco, which equals **one hundred fifty** lines (!) of Lexington RH/Boston RH in those foals.

But that was just the beginning because it is the legacy of those offspring at stud (a record that is still being written as several are still producing) that has already has turned the international Thoroughbred world upside down—most of those stallions stood in Europe. It is rich indeed that the horse the English Jockey Club banned came back and took it all through his descendants.

Banned in England, banished from the worldwide gene pool, Lexington RH returns in the twentieth century and conquers all before him—with Sadlers Wells, the greatest sire who has ever stood in Europe has one hundred fifty lines of Lexington RH. —image of Lexington from a painting by Henry Stull, courtesy of Encore Editions

She need only have bred one foal to achieve her renowned position, as her first live foal, born in 1981, was a son who reached a status as a sire that few horses come near, and he—Sadlers Wells—is the only horse in modern time who has come close to Lexington's own record at stud. He has led the sires list in Europe for fourteen years. At his death in 2011 the management of Coolmore stud declared that he was **the greatest stallion that has ever stood in Europe**—what a sweet revenge!

Fairy Bridge is an example of the principle of critical mass and of the importance of close siblings to refocus the background genetic power. She carries eighty-three lines of Lexington RH with additional bloodlines of his ½ sisters and brothers present—there are eleven lines of his half-brother Lecomte RH for instance, which easily brings the lines of the American Running Horse Boston to the century mark. This isn't something you would expect at the first glance of her pedigree, as she appears to be strongest in the European lines found up front: Nearco, Djebel, Hyperion, Fair Trial, Gold Bridge, and Blandford. However, many of those lines and their progeny were the Trojan horses for Lexington RH blood in Europe. It is retribution of sorts, in that the greatest 'European' stallion of modern times is not only an American-bred, but delivers the genetics of the banned Lexington RH in concentration.

It is also extraordinary to find an individual American-bred mare who carries so many conduits of Lexington RH that were developed on foreign soil—but that is the case. Nearco of course has an American dam-line that brings in Lexington RH and Blackburns Whip RH, and he is here twice through his most prolific sons: Nasrullah and Royal Charger 4x4, both of whom have the Lady Josephine's daughter Mumtaz Mahal as third or fourth dam—therefore bringing in a concentrated element of inbreeding to Lexington RH from Americus as well. Traveling down the pedigree we also find traditional Domino doses of Lexington RH/Boston RH coming from High Time (eleven), Ultimus (eight), Supremus (eight), and others, but they are not the focal points in the engine room area (four to six generations). It is the European lines of Lexington RH that refocus to the front all that background power. The great American-bred mare Lalun (dam of her sire) is inbred to the French-bred full sisters Heldifann/Durban (5x6 in Fairy Bridge), and each carry eight lines of Lexington RH (nine of Boston RH) plus two of Blackburns Whip RH, three of American Eclipse RH, and four of Vandal RH—a smorgasbord of American Running Horse lines, and being full sisters this is an extremely powerful typesetting design. Then there is the powerful ⅞ siblings Riot/Fair Trial 5x5 whose second dam is Lady Josephine—carrier of inbreeding to Lexington RH and Transport RH. Of course there is a double of Orby (7x7), out of Rhoda B, the imported American mare that produced two classic winners in England: Orby and Rhodora, who carries Lexington RH and his ½ siblings Nina RH and Rescue RH 4x4x3, plus Vandal RH 4x4. Plus Rescue RH is a daughter of Lexington's dam Alice Carneal RH—combined with the Lexington RH lines this provides a powerful filly factor of the very best in sport performance. These carriers of Lexington RH, his sire Boston RH and his dam Alice Carneal act as genetic arteries bringing forward to the heart of the lineage their own, plus all the rest of the background conglomeration of Lexington RH and the other four-milers, from the traditional American sources, right to the front of the pedigree.

Fairy Bridge's offspring, like those of La Troienne, offer multiple opportunities for full sibling line-breeding and are sure to be major players for the next fifty years in the international Thoroughbred. Indeed, it may be possible in later years that the progeny of Fairy Bridge elevate her to the status of the new 'Pocahontas,' as her son Sadlers Wells already exceeds Pocahontas's 'emperor of stallions' son Stockwell, and Sadlers Wells has his full brothers Tate Gallery, Fairy King, and two full sisters Puppet Dance and Fairy Gold to help pull this feat off. I think they will easily do it.

Fairy Bridge Offspring:

Sadlers Wells 1981 by Northern Dancer—born in the USA, a stallion, he was sent to Ireland in 1981 when weaned. Trained there, he started eleven times, won five and was second three times. He raced in England, France, and Ireland. He was the champion miler in France in 1984. A wonderful racer, but it is rather his career as a sire that has made him a superstar. His stallion titles:

England: Leading sire 1990, 1992, 1993, 1995, 1998, 1999, 2000, 2001, 2002, 2003, 2004

Leading broodmare sire: 2006, 2007, 2008, 2009, 2011

France: Leading sire 1990, 1993, 1994, 1999

Leading broodmare sire: 2001, 2004, 2005, 2007, 2009, 2010

Ireland: Leading sire: 1992, 1993, 1997, 2001, 2002, 2003, 2004

Leading broodmare sire: 2005, 2006, 2007, 2008, 2010, 2011

Fairy King 1982 by Northern Dancer—a stallion who stood in his brother's shadow at Coolmore Stud. He was sent to Ireland in 1982 from the US, and while he was unremarkable as a racer, he was listed as a good sire in 1991; he died in 1999. Read about his daughter Fairy Heights below.

Tate Gallery 1983 also by Northern Dancer—a stallion, he was sent from the US to Ireland in 1983. He was a stakes winner, and he won two out of five starts. In 1989 he was sent to Australia to stand stud.

Fairy Dancer 1984 by Nijinsky—a mare, she was sent from the US to Ireland in 1984. A good racer with one win and one third out of two starts, she was sent back to the US for stud duty in 1991. She is dam of stallion son Mellifont who stands in NZ. This puts the ¾ siblings Fairy Dancer/Tate Gallery in a location to provide a powerful inbreeding or line-breeding opportunity for the southern hemisphere.

Fairy Gold 1985 by Northern Dancer—a mare, she was shipped from the US to Ireland in 1985, where she raced admirably five times, winning twice and receiving second twice and third once—she is a stakes winner. She was returned to the US for stud duty in 1990.

Puppet Dance 1986 by Northern Dancer—a mare, she was shipped from the US to France where she raced at age two and three, starting eleven times, winning two, placing third three—she too is a stakes winner. She was shipped back to the US in 1989 for stud duty; she is the dam of the stallion Velasquez (by Gulch).

Classic Music 1987 by Northern Dancer—a stallion, he was shipped from the US to Ireland in 1987, then returned in 1990, and reshipped from there back to Ireland in 1991 where he stands. He is unraced.

Hermitage 1988 by Storm Bird—a stallion, he is unraced. He was sent from the US to Ireland in 1988, and then shipped back in 1992, and then he was shipped from there to South Africa in 1999.

Unnamed colt by Storm Bird 1989, he was sent from the US to Ireland in 1989; he is unraced.

Perugino 1991 by Danzig—a stallion, he was sent from the US to Ireland in 1992. He raced there as a two-year-old, winning his only start. He stands as a stallion in Ireland.

Most of these offspring will be valued line-breeding targets in future generations.

Rough Shod II is important broodmare of the twentieth century. —photo by Skeet Meadors, courtesy of Keeneland Library collection

Fairy Bridge's second dam was the *reine* Rough Shod II, her full sibling offspring Ridan, Thong, Lt Stevens, and Mocassin are valued line-breeding targets now. Rough Shod is by the inbred Gold Bridge, who is 3x3 to Orby (the Rhoda B son who carries not only a line of Lexington RH but two lines of his ½ siblings Nina RH and Rescue RH as well as a double of Vandal RH). Although Orby provides complexity in building Lexington RH lines, he also carries the key filly factor of Alice Carneal RH x3. In addition, Rough Shod's dam Dalmary is a vital line for sex-balancing in modern pedigrees, as she is the ⅞ sister of Blenheim. It is interesting to us that Rough Shod's best offspring are out of concentrated carriers of Lexington RH. The four full siblings mentioned above are out of the Nasrullah son Nantallah, who brings in an additional twenty-four lines of Lexington RH. The other good producer is Gambetta by My Babu, who brings in ten more lines of Lexington RH.

All that greatness aside, I also want to draw attention now to her sire's dam Lalun, who is a more concentrated source of Lexington RH blood than Rough Shod II. She had several offspring, including two major sires: Never Bend (*chef*) and Bold Reason (sire of Fairy Bridge).

A daughter of Djeddah, Lalun is line-bred to the full sisters Heldifann/Durban through him 4x5, plus her dam, the stakes winner Be Faithful, brings in Black Toney twice 3x5, building on the Lexington RH lines, as eight each coming from the

Never Bend—a son of the wonderful mare Lalun, he proved to be one of the most significant sires to stand in Europe in the twentieth century; he is a potent source of Lexington RH blood. —photo by Skeet Meadors, courtesy of Keeneland Library

full sisters and seven each from the Black Toney lines—giving Lalun thirty lines in ten generations. Lalun also has two ¾ siblings out of Be Faithful by Ambiorix. She is a Lexington RH powerhouse.

Her son Never Bend is a great stallion, achieving the coveted *chef-de-race* status; he, who has impacted European breeding like few others, will be found continually in international pedigrees because he is the sire of Mill Reef and to a lesser degree because of his son J O Tobin. His daughter Courtly Dee is a *reine* with her daughter, Princess Oola, and sons such as Press Card and Twining.

Naturally line-breeding to Lalun has been occurring with wonderful results, such as the G1 stakes winner Fairy Heights, a daughter of Fairy King (full brother to Sadlers Wells), out of a mare descended from Mill Reef—she is 4x5 to Lalun. Another good mare is the Epsom Oaks winner Moonshell by Sadlers Wells, whose second dam is a Mill Reef daughter making Lalun 4x5. Great champions have shown up in Carnegie, the Arc de Triomphe winner and French champion—he is 4x4 to Lalun. In the Wings—4x5 Lalun—is also a French champion who has won stakes races in the US and England as well. He was champion sire in 1996 and has an exciting son in Singspiel (one hundred ninety-six lines of Lexington RH) who won the Dubai World Cup. Singspiel is 5x6 Lalun, but is also 4x5 Almahmoud and 6x8x8x6x6x6 to the full siblings Mirza II/Mah Mahal, bringing the inbreeding of Americus in multiples.

Of the four grandparents of Fairy Bridge, Lalun is the most concentrated carrier of Lexington RH, although Hail to Reason (twenty-three) and Special (twenty-six) are close to her thirty. There has been a lot of discussion on the Sadlers Wells/Mill Reef nick—some say it is because of the double of Lalun that occurs, while others say it has more to do with the buildup of Lady Josephine. I believe they are not looking far enough back, and that this nick has more to do with the critical mass that is achieved in Lexington RH, as both influences build up enormous pools of his genes and then reinforce them to the front.

We can look at the pedigree of the good racer and sire Singspiel, as he is the next step in this buildup—adding a double of Almahmoud through Cosmah (twenty-five lines) and Natalma (forty) this brings the tally to another sixty-five lines, plus there is four more lines of Lady Josephine, another Hail to Reason (twenty-three), and three more lines of Blue Larkspur (twenty-one)—with a total of one hundred ninety-six lines. Plus there is the La Troienne factor (discussed in Chapter 22)—truly critical mass continued.

Through all this I feel as if the great Clive Harper is speaking in my ear, as one of the last points he made about pedigree construction before he passed on was that the background buildup of significant lines is even more important than the sex-balance factor. His last book *Pattern of Patterns* was an exercise in demonstrating this, although he did emphasize the female element in this power.

Lexington RH obviously is not a female and has inbreeding to Diomed by sons only. However he is a conduit of significant concentrations of the key taproot mares: Cypron, Kitty Fisher, Lady Grey RH, Papillon, Calista ERH, and Wildair Mare RH, and his record as a broodmare sire is colossal. His longest reach today is through his amazing daughters who provided the speed and racing class for Enquirer RH, Mannie Gray, Hanover, Hamburg, Domino, Ben Brush—Sweep and Broomstick, Fair Play, Himyar, Black Toney, Americus, Durban/Heldifann, and Catnip—this is a legacy that is matched by few or any other stallion in the history of the racehorse.

Never Bend is of a type very reminiscent of that of his sire Nasrullah, as his temperament and energy level got in the way of his best performances. Like a flame he was flickering with light and fire, difficult to train and ride, and although he won several good races, he also lost many because of his inability to contain himself. He could not be rated and would just run his heart out at full speed, with his wild and untamable power.

Also like his sire he has become a great stallion, and his progeny are everywhere in the modern racer. His pedigree has two sets of full siblings, one from the sire and one from the dam. His sire Nasrullah brings in Sainfoin/Sierra 6x6, and his dam brings in Durban/Heldifann 5x4. This pedigree pattern—inbreeding or strong line-breeding from both parents in different lines—is a hugely successful design.

His son Mill Reef has become one of the top sires in Europe, whose best son is the stellar stallion Shirley Heights—this is an unusually potent sire-line. His dam Milan Mill, a daughter of Princequillo, brought in some reinforcement of the Heroic Era lines, but really built on the English lines more (she brought in Hindoo 2x and Maggie B. B. RH x2). Mill Reef was a finely drawn and balanced horse—almost delicate—and he tends to throw a type that can lack substance, showing his dominance in the finer English type. What happened when he was returned to a mate that carried a dominance of Heroic Era genes? It was then he produced his two toughest racers, the full brothers Glint of Gold and Diamond Shoal. I am bringing this up for a reason. We are lamenting the loss of substance and toughness in our TB—here is an illustration of what is possible to do with our extremely talented but fragile lines. These two's dam Crown Treasure, a daughter of Graustark—mostly Italian and English lines, but her dam is Treasure Chest, a daughter of Rough n' Tumble out of the War Relic daughter Iltis—carriers of multiples of our tough four-miler genes from Fair Play, Whisk Broom II, Ben Brush, and Domino (see Chapter 27 for a discussion on soundness in the modern racer).

One of Mill Reef's other great sons is Reference Point. His dam brings in more Princequillo, Nasrullah, etc, but she also has Tourbillon, who brings back another line of Durban—connecting right back into the strength of Never Bend. All these horses are standing in the British Isles or Europe, so they have fewer opportunities to build up in the good tough American lines, but when they are able to something notable occurs.

In America, one of Never Bend's great stallion sons was Riverman, and while he raced and won in England and France, he then returned to the US and became a sire of note—earning the *chef-de-race* title. Naturally here in the States he has more access to mares who are rich in our American lines. Note Riverman's pedigree structure: he has two full sibling configurations, one in the sire and another in the dam: Heldifann/Durban 6x5 and Sunreigh/Sun Briar 6x6—each sex-balanced—which equals genetic power. His dam is loaded with additional lines of Domino/Broomstick/Fair Play that empower those in the sire.

The Fairy Bridge legacy will continue to expand for generations. As the American comedian Jackie Gleason would say, "How sweet it is!"

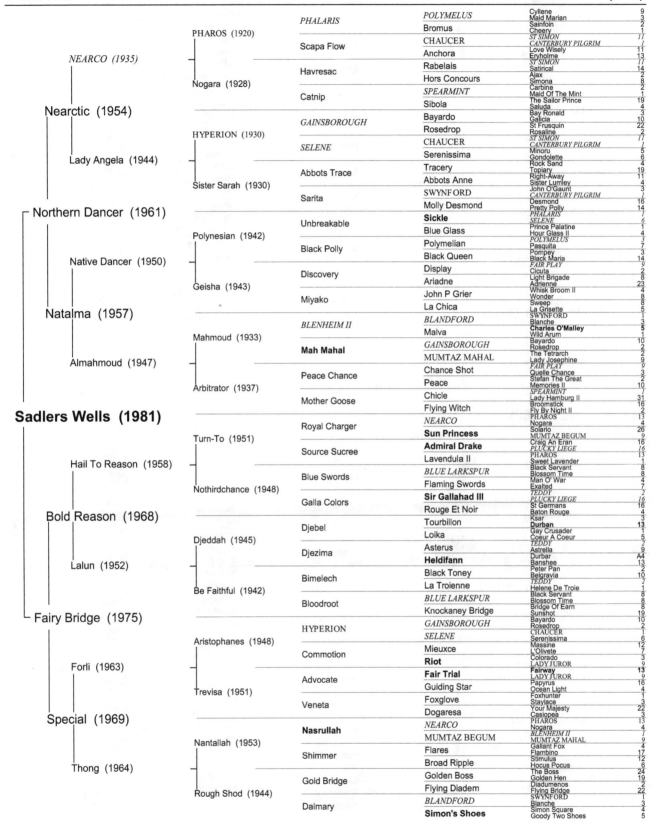

			PHALARIS	*POLYMELUS*	Cyllene / 9
					Maid Marian / 3
				Bromus	Sainfoin / 2
		PHAROS (1920)			Cheery / 1
			Scapa Flow	CHAUCER	*ST SIMON* / 11
					CANTERBURY PILGRIM / 1
	NEARCO (1935)			Anchora	Love Wisely / 11
					Eryholme / 13
			Havresac	Rabelais	*ST SIMON* / 11
		Nogara (1928)			Satirical / 14
				Hors Concours	Ajax / 2
					Simona / 8
Nearctic (1954)			Catnip	*SPEARMINT*	Carbine / 2
					Maid Of The Mint / 1
				Sibola	The Sailor Prince / 19
					Saluda / 4
			GAINSBOROUGH	Bayardo	Bay Ronald / 3
					Galicia / 10
		HYPERION (1930)		Rosedrop	St Frusquin / 22
					Rosaline / 2
	Lady Angela (1944)		*SELENE*	CHAUCER	*ST SIMON* / 11
					CANTERBURY PILGRIM / 1
				Serenissima	Minoru / 5
		Sister Sarah (1930)			Gondolette / 6
			Abbots Trace	Tracery	Rock Sand / 4
					Topiary / 19
				Abbots Anne	Right-Away / 11
					Sister Lumley / 4
			Sarita	SWYNFORD	John O'Gaunt / 3
					CANTERBURY PILGRIM / 1
				Molly Desmond	Desmond / 16
					Pretty Polly / 14
Northern Dancer (1961)			Unbreakable	**Sickle**	*PHALARIS* / 1
					SELENE / 6
		Polynesian (1942)		Blue Glass	Prince Palatine / 1
					Hour Glass II / 4
			Black Polly	Polymelian	*POLYMELUS* / 3
					Pasquita / 7
	Native Dancer (1950)			Black Queen	Pompey / 3
					Black Maria / 14
			Discovery	Display	*FAIR PLAY* / 9
					Cicuta / 2
		Geisha (1943)		Ariadne	Light Brigade / 8
					Adrienne / 23
			Miyako	John P Grier	Whisk Broom II / 4
					Wonder / 8
Natalma (1957)				La Chica	Sweep / 8
					La Grisette / 5
			BLENHEIM II	*BLANDFORD*	SWYNFORD / 1
					Blanche / 3
		Mahmoud (1933)		Malva	**Charles O'Malley** / 5
					Wild Arum /
			Mah Mahal	*GAINSBOROUGH*	Bayardo / 10
					Rosedrop / 2
	Almahmoud (1947)			MUMTAZ MAHAL	The Tetrarch / 2
					Lady Josephine / 9
			Peace Chance	Chance Shot	*FAIR PLAY* / 9
					Quelle Chance / 3
		Arbitrator (1937)		Peace	Stefan The Great / 2
					Memories II / 10
			Mother Goose	Chicle	*SPEARMINT* / 1
					Lady Hamburg II / 31
Sadlers Wells (1981)				Flying Witch	Broomstick / 16
					Fly By Night II / 2
			Royal Charger	*NEARCO*	PHAROS / 13
					Nogara / 4
		Turn-To (1951)		**Sun Princess**	Solario / 26
					MUMTAZ BEGUM / 9
			Source Sucree	**Admiral Drake**	Craig An Eran / 16
					PLUCKY LIEGE / 16
Hail To Reason (1958)				Lavendula II	PHAROS / 13
					Sweet Lavender / 1
			Blue Swords	*BLUE LARKSPUR*	Black Servant / 8
					Blossom Time / 8
		Nothirdchance (1948)		Flaming Swords	Man O' War / 4
					Exalted / 7
			Galla Colors	**Sir Gallahad III**	*TEDDY* / 2
					PLUCKY LIEGE / 16
				Rouge Et Noir	St Germans / 16
					Baton Rouge / 4
Bold Reason (1968)			Djebel	Tourbillon	Ksar / 3
					Durban / 13
		Djeddah (1945)		Loika	Gay Crusader / 1
					Coeur A Coeur / 5
			Djezima	Asterus	*TEDDY* / 2
					Astrella / 9
	Lalun (1952)		**Heldifann**	Durbar / A4
					Banshee / 13
			Bimelech	Black Toney	Peter Pan / 2
					Belgravia / 10
		Be Faithful (1942)		La Troienne	*TEDDY* / 2
					Helene De Troie / 1
			Bloodroot	*BLUE LARKSPUR*	Black Servant / 8
					Blossom Time / 8
Fairy Bridge (1975)				Knockaney Bridge	Bridge Of Earn / 2
					Sunshot / 19
			HYPERION	*GAINSBOROUGH*	Bayardo / 10
					Rosedrop / 2
		Aristophanes (1948)		*SELENE*	CHAUCER / 1
					Serenissima / 6
			Commotion	Mieuxce	Massine / 12
					L'Olivete / 7
	Forli (1963)		**Riot**	Colorado / 3
					LADY JUROR / 9
			Advocate	**Fair Trial**	Fairway / 13
					LADY JUROR / 9
		Trevisa (1951)		Guiding Star	Papyrus / 16
					Ocean Light / 4
			Veneta	Foxglove	Foxhunter / 1
					Staylace / 3
				Dogaresa	Your Majesty / 22
					Casiopea / 3
Special (1969)			**Nasrullah**	*NEARCO*	PHAROS / 13
					Nogara / 4
		Nantallah (1953)		MUMTAZ BEGUM	*BLENHEIM II* / 1
					MUMTAZ MAHAL / 9
			Shimmer	Flares	Gallant Fox / 4
					Flambino / 17
				Broad Ripple	Stimulus / 12
					Hocus Pocus / 6
Thong (1964)			Gold Bridge	Golden Boss	The Boss / 24
					Golden Hen / 19
		Rough Shod (1944)		Flying Diadem	Diadumenos / 2
					Flying Bridge / 22
			Dalmary	*BLANDFORD*	SWYNFORD / 1
					Blanche / 3
				Simon's Shoes	Simon Square / 4
					Goody Two Shoes / 5

Sadlers Wells 1981

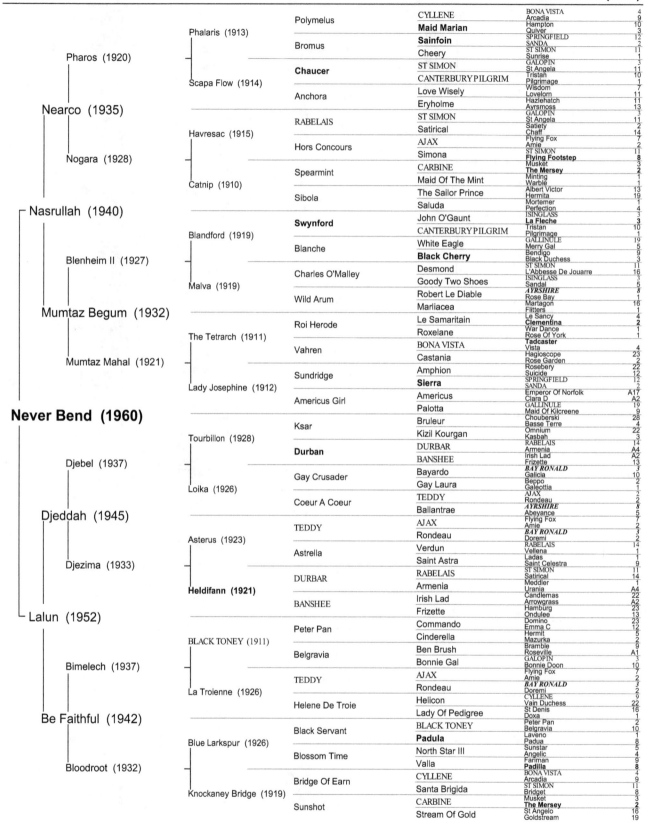

		Polymelus	CYLLENE	BONA VISTA 4 / Arcadia 9
	Phalaris (1913)		Maid Marian	Hampton 10 / Quiver 3
		Bromus	**Sainfoin**	SPRINGFIELD 12 / SANDA 2
Pharos (1920)			Cheery	ST SIMON 11 / Sunrise 1
	Scapa Flow (1914)	**Chaucer**	ST SIMON	GALOPIN 3 / St Angela 11
			CANTERBURY PILGRIM	Tristan 10 / Pilgrimage 1
Nearco (1935)		Anchora	Love Wisely	Wisdom 7 / Lovelorn 11
			Eryholme	Hazlehatch 11 / Ayrsmoss 13
		RABELAIS	ST SIMON	GALOPIN 3 / St Angela 11
	Havresac (1915)		Satirical	Satiety 2 / Chaff 14
		Hors Concours	AJAX	Flying Fox 7 / Amie 2
Nogara (1928)			Simona	ST SIMON 11 / Flying Footstep 8
	Catnip (1910)	Spearmint	CARBINE	Musket 3 / The Mersey 2
			Maid Of The Mint	Minting 1 / Warble 1
		Sibola	The Sailor Prince	Albert Victor 13 / Hermita 19
			Saluda	Mortemer 1 / Perfection 4

		Swynford	John O'Gaunt	ISINGLASS 3 / La Fleche 3
	Blandford (1919)		CANTERBURY PILGRIM	Tristan 10 / Pilgrimage 1
		Blanche	White Eagle	GALLINULE 19 / Merry Gal 5
Nasrullah (1940)			**Black Cherry**	Bendigo 9 / Black Duchess 3
	Malva (1919)	Charles O'Malley	Desmond	ST SIMON 11 / L'Abbesse De Jouarre 16
			Goody Two Shoes	ISINGLASS 3 / Sandal 5
Blenheim II (1927)		Wild Arum	Robert Le Diable	*AYRSHIRE* 8 / Rose Bay 1
			Marliacea	Martagon 16 / Flitters 1
		Roi Herode	Le Samaritain	Le Sancy 4 / **Clementina** 2
	The Tetrarch (1911)		Roxelane	War Dance 1 / Rose Of York 1
		Vahren	BONA VISTA	**Tadcaster** 3 / Vista 4
Mumtaz Begum (1932)			Castania	Hagioscope 23 / Rose Garden 2
	Lady Josephine (1912)	Sundridge	Amphion	Rosebery 22 / Suicide 12
			Sierra	SPRINGFIELD 12 / SANDA 2
		Americus Girl	Americus	Emperor Of Norfolk A17 / Clara D A2
Mumtaz Mahal (1921)			Palotta	GALLINULE 19 / Maid Of Kilcreene 1

Never Bend (1960)

		Ksar	Bruleur	Chouberski 28 / Basse Terre 4
	Tourbillon (1928)		Kizil Kourgan	Omnium 22 / Kasbah 3
		Durban	DURBAR	RABELAIS 14 / Armenia A4
Djebel (1937)			BANSHEE	Irish Lad A2 / Frizette 13
	Loika (1926)	Gay Crusader	Bayardo	*BAY RONALD* 3 / Galicia 10
			Gay Laura	Beppo 2 / Galeottia 1
Djeddah (1945)		Coeur A Coeur	TEDDY	AJAX 2 / Rondeau 2
			Ballantrae	*AYRSHIRE* 8 / Abeyance 5
		TEDDY	AJAX	Flying Fox 7 / Amie 2
	Asterus (1923)		Rondeau	*BAY RONALD* 3 / Doremi 2
		Astrella	Verdun	RABELAIS 14 / Vellena 1
Djezima (1933)			Saint Astra	Ladas 1 / Saint Celestra 9
	Heldifann (1921)	DURBAR	RABELAIS	ST SIMON 11 / Satirical 14
			Armenia	Meddler 1 / Urania A4
		BANSHEE	Irish Lad	Candlemas 22 / Arrowgrass A2
			Frizette	Hamburg 23 / Ondulee 13

		Peter Pan	Commando	Domino 23 / Emma C 12
	BLACK TONEY (1911)		Cinderella	Hermit 5 / Mazurka 2
		Belgravia	Ben Brush	Bramble 9 / Roseville A1
Lalun (1952)			Bonnie Gal	GALOPIN 3 / Bonnie Doon 10
	La Troienne (1926)	TEDDY	AJAX	Flying Fox 7 / Amie 2
			Rondeau	*BAY RONALD* 3 / Doremi 2
Bimelech (1937)		Helene De Troie	Helicon	CYLLENE 9 / Vain Duchess 22
			Lady Of Pedigree	St Denis 16 / Doxa 1
		Black Servant	BLACK TONEY	Peter Pan 2 / Belgravia 10
	Blue Larkspur (1926)		**Padula**	Laveno 1 / Padua 8
Be Faithful (1942)		Blossom Time	North Star III	Sunstar 5 / Angelic 4
			Valla	Fariman 9 / **Padilla** 8
	Knockaney Bridge (1919)	Bridge Of Earn	CYLLENE	BONA VISTA 4 / Arcadia 9
Bloodroot (1932)			Santa Brigida	ST SIMON 11 / Bridget 8
		Sunshot	CARBINE	Musket 3 / **The Mersey** 2
			Stream Of Gold	St Angelo 16 / Goldstream 19

Never Bend 1960

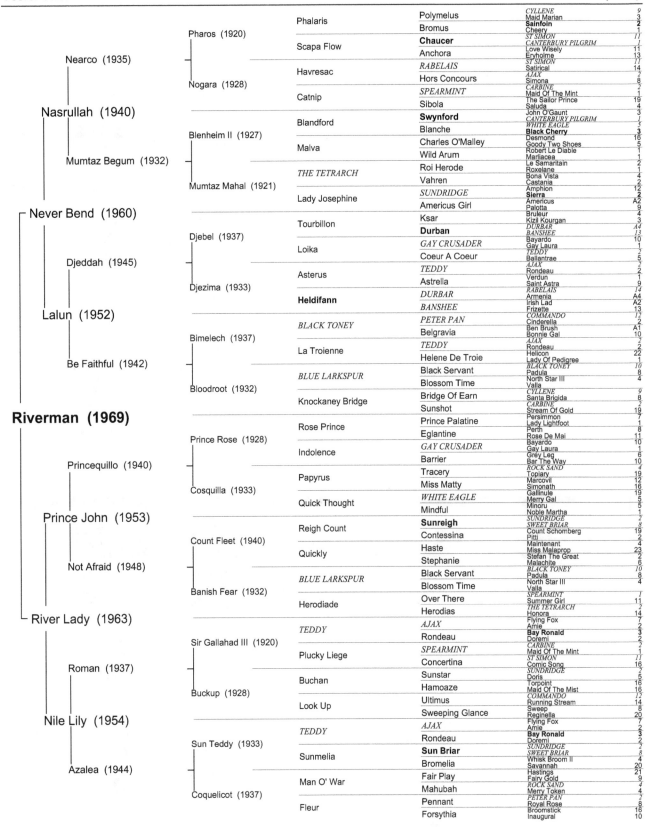

			Phalaris	Polymelus	*CYLLENE* 9 / Maid Marian 3
		Pharos (1920)		Bromus	**Sainfoin** 2 / Cheery 1
			Scapa Flow	**Chaucer**	*ST SIMON* 11 / *CANTERBURY PILGRIM* 1
	Nearco (1935)			Anchora	Love Wisely 11 / Eryholme 13
			Havresac	*RABELAIS*	*ST SIMON* 11 / Satirical 14
		Nogara (1928)		Hors Concours	*AJAX* 8 / Simona 2
			Catnip	*SPEARMINT*	*CARBINE* 2 / Maid Of The Mint 1
Nasrullah (1940)				Sibola	The Sailor Prince 19 / Saluda 4
			Blandford	**Swynford**	John O'Gaunt 3 / *CANTERBURY PILGRIM* 1
		Blenheim II (1927)		Blanche	*WHITE EAGLE* 3 / **Black Cherry** 3
			Malva	Charles O'Malley	Desmond 16 / Goody Two Shoes 5
	Mumtaz Begum (1932)			Wild Arum	Robert Le Diable 1 / Marliacea 2
			THE TETRARCH	Roi Herode	Le Samaritain 1 / Roxelane 4
		Mumtaz Mahal (1921)		Vahren	Bona Vista 2 / Castania 12
			Lady Josephine	*SUNDRIDGE*	Amphion 2 / **Sierra** A2
				Americus Girl	Americus 9 / Palotta 4
Never Bend (1960)			Tourbillon	Ksar	Bruleur 3 / Kizil Kourgan A4
		Djebel (1937)		**Durban**	*DURBAR* 13 / *BANSHEE* 10
			Loika	*GAY CRUSADER*	Bayardo 1 / Gay Laura 2
	Djeddah (1945)			Coeur A Coeur	*TEDDY* 5 / Ballantrae 2
			Asterus	*TEDDY*	*AJAX* 1 / Rondeau 9
		Djezima (1933)		Astrella	Verdun 14 / Saint Astra A4
			Heldifann	*DURBAR*	*RABELAIS* A2 / Armenia 13
				BANSHEE	Irish Lad 12 / Frizette 2
Lalun (1952)			*BLACK TONEY*	PETER PAN	*COMMANDO* A1 / Cinderella 10
		Bimelech (1937)		Belgravia	Ben Brush 2 / Bonnie Gal 22
			La Troienne	*TEDDY*	*AJAX* 1 / Rondeau 10
				Helene De Troie	Helicon 8 / Lady Of Pedigree 4
	Be Faithful (1942)		*BLUE LARKSPUR*	Black Servant	*BLACK TONEY* 9 / Padula 8
		Bloodroot (1932)		Blossom Time	North Star III 2 / Valla 19
			Knockaney Bridge	Bridge Of Earn	*CYLLENE* 7 / Santa Brigida 1
				Sunshot	*CARBINE* 8 / Stream Of Gold 10
Riverman (1969)			Rose Prince	Prince Palatine	Persimmon 1 / Lady Lightfoot 6
		Prince Rose (1928)		Eglantine	Perth 10 / Rose De Mai 4
			Indolence	*GAY CRUSADER*	Bayardo 19 / Gay Laura 12
	Princequillo (1940)			Barrier	Grey Leg 16 / Bar The Way 19
			Papyrus	Tracery	*ROCK SAND* 5 / Topiary 5
		Cosquilla (1933)		Miss Matty	Marcovil 2 / Simonath 8
			Quick Thought	*WHITE EAGLE*	Gallinule 4 / Merry Gal 2
Prince John (1953)				Mindful	Minoru 19 / Noble Martha 23
			Reigh Count	**Sunreigh**	*SUNDRIDGE* 4 / *SWEET BRIAR* 2
		Count Fleet (1940)		Contessina	Count Schomberg 6 / Pitti 10
			Quickly	Haste	Maintenant 8 / Miss Malaprop 4
	Not Afraid (1948)			Stephanie	Stefan The Great 2 / Malachite 3
			BLUE LARKSPUR	Black Servant	*BLACK TONEY* 1 / Padula 11
		Banish Fear (1932)		Blossom Time	North Star III 14 / Valla 7
			Herodiade	Over There	*SPEARMINT* 2 / Summer Girl 3
River Lady (1963)				Herodias	*THE TETRARCH* 2 / Honora 1
			TEDDY	*AJAX*	Flying Fox 16 / Amie 5
		Sir Gallahad III (1920)		Rondeau	**Bay Ronald** 5 / Doremi 16
			Plucky Liege	*SPEARMINT*	*CARBINE* 16 / Maid Of The Mint 12
	Roman (1937)			Concertina	*ST SIMON* 14 / Comic Song 2
			Buchan	Sunstar	*SUNDRIDGE* 4 / Doris 20
		Buckup (1928)		Hamoaze	Torpoint 7 / Maid Of The Mist 2
			Look Up	Ultimus	*COMMANDO* 8 / Running Stream 7
				Sweeping Glance	Sweep 3 / Reginella 2
Nile Lily (1954)			*TEDDY*	*AJAX*	Flying Fox 2 / Amie 8
		Sun Teddy (1933)		Rondeau	**Bay Ronald** 4 / Doremi 20
			Sunmelia	**Sun Briar**	*SUNDRIDGE* 21 / *SWEET BRIAR* 9
	Azalea (1944)			Bromelia	Whisk Broom II 4 / Savannah 4
			Man O' War	Fair Play	Hastings 2 / Fairy Gold 8
		Coquelicot (1937)		Mahubah	*ROCK SAND* 16 / Merry Token 10
			Fleur	Pennant	*PETER PAN* / Royal Rose
				Forsythia	Broomstick / Inaugural

Riverman 1969

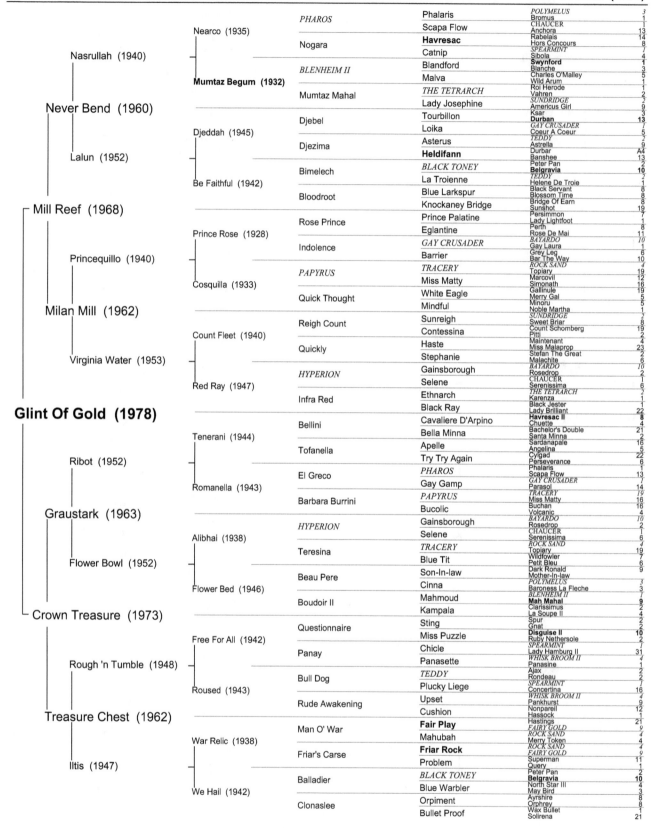

Nasrullah (1940)	Nearco (1935)	*PHAROS*	Phalaris	*POLYMELUS* 3 / Bromus 1
			Scapa Flow	*CHAUCER* 13 / Anchora 1
		Nogara	**Havresac**	Rabelais 14 / Hors Concours 8
			Catnip	*SPEARMINT* 1 / Sibola 4
	Mumtaz Begum (1932)	*BLENHEIM II*	Blandford	**Swynford** 1 / Blanche 3
			Malva	Charles O'Malley 5 / Wild Arum 1
		Mumtaz Mahal	*THE TETRARCH*	Roi Herode 1 / Vahren 2
			Lady Josephine	*SUNDRIDGE* 2 / Americus Girl 9
Never Bend (1960)	Djeddah (1945)	Djebel	Tourbillon	Ksar 3 / **Durban** 13
			Loika	*GAY CRUSADER* 1 / Coeur A Coeur 5
		Djezima	Asterus	*TEDDY* 1 / Astrella 9
			Heldifann	Durbar 4 / Banshee 13
Lalun (1952)	Be Faithful (1942)	Bimelech	*BLACK TONEY*	Peter Pan 2 / **Belgravia** 10
			La Troienne	*TEDDY* 2 / Helene De Troie 1
		Bloodroot	Blue Larkspur	Black Servant 8 / Blossom Time 8
			Knockaney Bridge	Bridge Of Earn 8 / Sunshot 19
Mill Reef (1968)	Prince Rose (1928)	Rose Prince	Prince Palatine	Persimmon 7 / Lady Lightfoot 1
			Eglantine	Perth 8 / Rose De Mai 11
		Indolence	*GAY CRUSADER*	*BAYARDO* 10 / Gay Laura 1
			Barrier	Grey Leg 6 / Bar The Way 10
Princequillo (1940)	Cosquilla (1933)	*PAPYRUS*	*TRACERY*	*ROCK SAND* 4 / Topiary 19
			Miss Matty	Marcovil 12 / Simonath 16
		Quick Thought	White Eagle	Gallinule 19 / Merry Gal 5
			Mindful	Minoru 5 / Noble Martha 1
Milan Mill (1962)	Count Fleet (1940)	Reigh Count	Sunreigh	*SUNDRIDGE* 2 / Sweet Briar 8
			Contessina	Count Schomberg 19 / Pitti 2
		Quickly	Haste	Maintenant 4 / Miss Malaprop 23
			Stephanie	Stefan The Great 2 / Malachite 6
Virginia Water (1953)	Red Ray (1947)	*HYPERION*	Gainsborough	*BAYARDO* 10 / Rosedrop 2
			Selene	*CHAUCER* 1 / Serenissima 6
		Infra Red	Ethnarch	*THE TETRARCH* 2 / Karenza 1
			Black Ray	Black Jester 1 / Lady Brilliant 22
Glint Of Gold (1978)	Tenerani (1944)	Bellini	Cavaliere D'Arpino	**Havresac II** 8 / Chuette 4
			Bella Minna	Bachelor's Double 21 / Santa Minna 2
		Tofanella	Apelle	Sardanapale 16 / Angelina 5
			Try Try Again	Cylgad 22 / Perseverance 6
Ribot (1952)	Romanella (1943)	El Greco	*PHAROS*	Phalaris 1 / Scapa Flow 13
			Gay Gamp	*GAY CRUSADER* 1 / Parasol 14
		Barbara Burrini	*PAPYRUS*	*TRACERY* 19 / Miss Matty 16
			Bucolic	Buchan 16 / Volcanic 4
Graustark (1963)	Alibhai (1938)	*HYPERION*	Gainsborough	*BAYARDO* 10 / Rosedrop 2
			Selene	*CHAUCER* 1 / Serenissima 6
		Teresina	*TRACERY*	*ROCK SAND* 4 / Topiary 19
			Blue Tit	Wildfowler 7 / Petit Bleu 6
Flower Bowl (1952)	Flower Bed (1946)	Beau Pere	Son-In-law	Dark Ronald 9 / Mother-In-law
			Cinna	*POLYMELUS* 3 / Baroness La Fleche 3
		Boudoir II	Mahmoud	*BLENHEIM II* 1 / **Mah Mahal** 9
			Kampala	Clarissimus 2 / La Soupe II 2
Crown Treasure (1973)	Free For All (1942)	Questionnaire	Sting	Spur 2 / Gnat 2
			Miss Puzzle	**Disguise II** 10 / Ruby Nethersole 2
		Panay	Chicle	*SPEARMINT* 1 / Lady Hamburg II 31
			Panasette	*WHISK BROOM II* 4 / Panasine 1
Rough 'n Tumble (1948)	Roused (1943)	Bull Dog	*TEDDY* 2 / Rondeau 2
			Plucky Liege	*SPEARMINT* 2 / Concertina 16
		Rude Awakening	Upset	*WHISK BROOM II* 4 / Pankhurst 9
			Cushion	Nonpareil 12 / Hassock 1
Treasure Chest (1962)	War Relic (1938)	Man O' War	**Fair Play**	Hastings 21 / *FAIRY GOLD* 9
			Mahubah	*ROCK SAND* 4 / Merry Token 4
		Friar's Carse	**Friar Rock**	*ROCK SAND* 4 / *FAIRY GOLD* 4
			Problem	Superman 11 / Query 1
Iltis (1947)	We Hail (1942)	Balladier	*BLACK TONEY*	Peter Pan 2 / **Belgravia** 10
			Blue Warbler	North Star III 4 / May Bird 3
		Clonaslee	Orpiment	Ayrshire 8 / Orphrey 8
			Bullet Proof	Wax Bullet / Solirena 21

Glint of Gold 1978

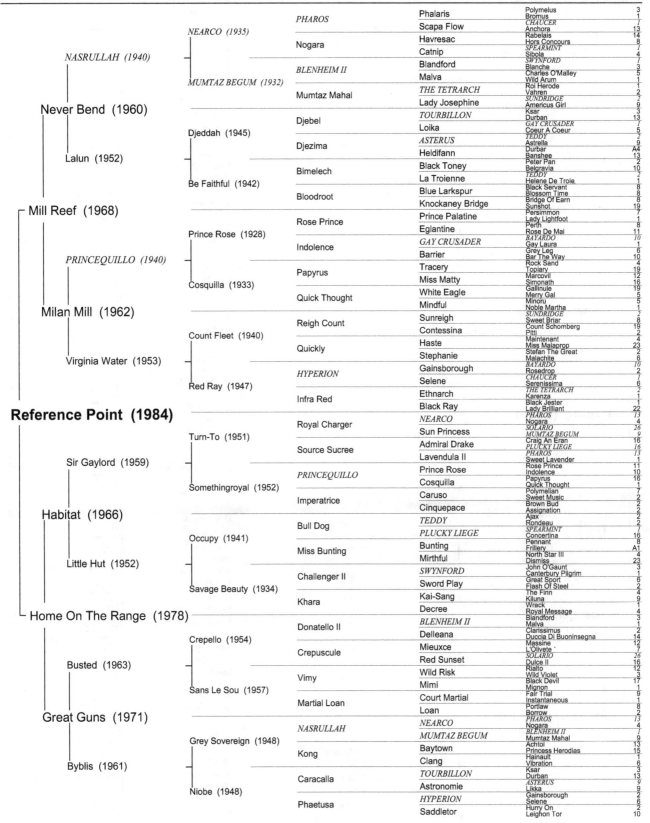

Pedigree of **Reference Point (1984)**

- **Mill Reef (1968)**
  - **Never Bend (1960)**
    - *NASRULLAH (1940)*
      - *NEARCO (1935)*
        - *PHAROS*
          - Phalaris — Polymelus 3 / Bromus 1
          - Scapa Flow — *CHAUCER* 1 / Anchora 13
        - Nogara
          - Havresac — Rabelais 14 / Hors Concours 8
          - Catnip — *SPEARMINT* 1 / Sibola 4
      - *MUMTAZ BEGUM (1932)*
        - *BLENHEIM II*
          - Blandford — *SWYNFORD* 1 / Blanche 3
          - Malva — Charles O'Malley 5 / Wild Arum 1
        - Mumtaz Mahal
          - *THE TETRARCH* — Roi Herode 1 / Vahren 2
          - Lady Josephine — *SUNDRIDGE* 2 / Americus Girl 9
    - **Lalun (1952)**
      - Djeddah (1945)
        - Djebel
          - *TOURBILLON* — Ksar 3 / Durban 13
          - Loika — *GAY CRUSADER* 1 / Coeur A Coeur 5
        - Djezima
          - *ASTERUS* — *TEDDY* 2 / Astrella 1
          - Heldifann — Durbar A4 / Banshee 13
      - Be Faithful (1942)
        - Bimelech
          - Black Toney — Peter Pan 2 / Belgravia 10
          - La Troienne — *TEDDY* 1 / Helene De Troie 2
        - Bloodroot
          - Blue Larkspur — Black Servant 8 / Blossom Time 8
          - Knockaney Bridge — Bridge Of Earn 8 / Sunshot 19
  - **Milan Mill (1962)**
    - *PRINCEQUILLO (1940)*
      - Prince Rose (1928)
        - Rose Prince
          - Prince Palatine — Persimmon 7 / Lady Lightfoot 1
          - Eglantine — Perth 8 / Rose De Mai 11
        - Indolence
          - *GAY CRUSADER* — *BAYARDO* 10 / Gay Laura 1
          - Barrier — Grey Leg 6 / Bar The Way 10
      - Cosquilla (1933)
        - Papyrus
          - Tracery — Rock Sand 4 / Topiary 19
          - Miss Matty — Marcovil 12 / Simonath 16
        - Quick Thought
          - White Eagle — Gallinule 19 / Merry Gal 5
          - Mindful — Minoru 5 / Noble Martha 1
    - **Virginia Water (1953)**
      - Count Fleet (1940)
        - Reigh Count
          - Sunreigh — *SUNDRIDGE* 2 / Sweet Briar 8
          - Contessina — Count Schomberg 19 / Pitti 2
        - Quickly
          - Haste — Maintenant 2 / Miss Malaprop 23
          - Stephanie — Stefan The Great 2 / Malachite 6
      - Red Ray (1947)
        - *HYPERION*
          - Gainsborough — *BAYARDO* 10 / Rosedrop 2
          - Selene — *CHAUCER* 1 / Serenissima 6
        - Infra Red
          - Ethnarch — *THE TETRARCH* 2 / Karenza 1
          - Black Ray — Black Jester 1 / Lady Brilliant 22

- **Home On The Range (1978)**
  - **Habitat (1966)**
    - Sir Gaylord (1959)
      - Turn-To (1951)
        - Royal Charger
          - *NEARCO* — *PHAROS* 13 / Nogara 4
          - Sun Princess — *SOLARIO* 26 / *MUMTAZ BEGUM* 9
        - Source Sucree
          - Admiral Drake — Craig An Eran 16 / *PLUCKY LIEGE* 16
          - Lavendula II — *PHAROS* 13 / Sweet Lavender 1
      - Somethingroyal (1952)
        - *PRINCEQUILLO*
          - Prince Rose — Rose Prince 11 / Indolence 10
          - Cosquilla — Papyrus 16 / Quick Thought 1
        - Imperatrice
          - Caruso — Polymelian 7 / Sweet Music 2
          - Cinquepace — Brown Bud 2 / Assignation 2
    - Little Hut (1952)
      - Occupy (1941)
        - Bull Dog
          - *TEDDY* — Ajax 2 / Rondeau 2
          - *PLUCKY LIEGE* — *SPEARMINT* 1 / Concertina 16
        - Miss Bunting
          - Bunting — Pennant 8 / Frillery A1
          - Mirthful — North Star III 4 / Dismiss 23
      - Savage Beauty (1934)
        - Challenger II
          - *SWYNFORD* — John O'Gaunt 3 / Canterbury Pilgrim 1
          - Sword Play — Great Sport 6 / Flash Of Steel 2
        - Khara
          - Kai-Sang — The Finn 4 / Kiluna 9
          - Decree — Wrack 1 / Royal Message 4
  - **Great Guns (1971)**
    - Busted (1963)
      - Crepello (1954)
        - Donatello II
          - *BLENHEIM II* — Blandford 3 / Malva 1
          - Delleana — Clarissimus 2 / Duccia Di Buoninsegna 14
        - Crepuscule
          - Mieuxce — Massine 12 / L'Olivete 7
          - Red Sunset — *SOLARIO* 26 / Dulce II 16
      - Sans Le Sou (1957)
        - Vimy
          - Wild Risk — Rialto 12 / Wild Violet 12
          - Mimi — Black Devil 17 / Mignon 1
        - Martial Loan
          - Court Martial — Fair Trial 9 / Instantaneous 1
          - Loan — Portlaw 8 / Borrow 2
    - Byblis (1961)
      - Grey Sovereign (1948)
        - *NASRULLAH*
          - *NEARCO* — *PHAROS* 13 / Nogara 4
          - *MUMTAZ BEGUM* — *BLENHEIM II* 7 / Mumtaz Mahal 9
        - Kong
          - Baytown — Achtoi 13 / Princess Herodias 15
          - Clang — Hainault 1 / Vibration 6
      - Niobe (1948)
        - Caracalla
          - *TOURBILLON* — Ksar 3 / Durban 13
          - Astronomie — *ASTERUS* 9 / Likka 9
        - Phaetusa
          - *HYPERION* — Gainsborough 2 / Selene 6
          - Saddletor — Hurry On 2 / Leighon Tor 10

Reference Point 1984

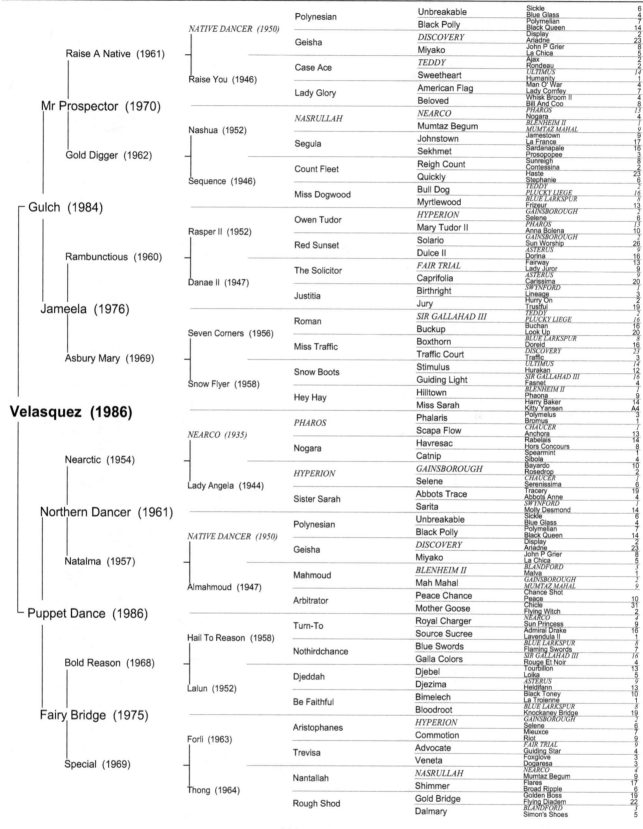

		Polynesian	Unbreakable	Sickle 6 / Blue Glass 4
	NATIVE DANCER (1950)		Black Polly	Polymelian 7 / Black Queen 14
		Geisha	*DISCOVERY*	Display 2 / Ariadne 23
Raise A Native (1961)			Miyako	John P Grier 8 / La Chica 5
		Case Ace	*TEDDY*	Ajax 2 / Rondeau 14
	Raise You (1946)		Sweetheart	*ULTIMUS* 1 / Humanity
		Lady Glory	American Flag	Man O' War 4 / Lady Comfey 7
Mr Prospector (1970)			Beloved	Whisk Broom II 4 / Bill And Coo 8
		NASRULLAH	*NEARCO*	*PHAROS* 13 / Nogara 4
	Nashua (1952)		Mumtaz Begum	*BLENHEIM II* 1 / *MUMTAZ MAHAL*
		Segula	Johnstown	Jamestown 9 / La France 17
Gold Digger (1962)			Sekhmet	Sardanapale 16 / Prosopopee 3
		Count Fleet	Reigh Count	Sunreigh 8 / Contessina 2
	Sequence (1946)		Quickly	Haste 23 / Stephanie 6
		Miss Dogwood	Bull Dog	*TEDDY* 2 / *PLUCKY LIEGE* 16
Gulch (1984)			Myrtlewood	*BLUE LARKSPUR* 8 / Frizeur 13
		Owen Tudor	*HYPERION*	*GAINSBOROUGH* 3 / Selene 6
	Rasper II (1952)		Mary Tudor II	*PHAROS* 13 / Anna Bolena 10
		Red Sunset	Solario	*GAINSBOROUGH* 3 / Sun Worship 26
Rambunctious (1960)			Dulce II	*ASTERUS* 9 / Dorina 16
		The Solicitor	*FAIR TRIAL*	Fairway 13 / Lady Juror 9
	Danae II (1947)		Caprifolia	*ASTERUS* 9 / Carissima 20
		Justitia	Birthright	*SWYNFORD* 1 / Lineage 3
Jameela (1976)			Jury	Hurry On 2 / Trustful 19
		Roman	*SIR GALLAHAD III*	*TEDDY* 2 / *PLUCKY LIEGE* 16
	Seven Corners (1956)		Buckup	Buchan 16 / Look Up 20
		Miss Traffic	Boxthorn	*BLUE LARKSPUR* 8 / Doreid 16
Asbury Mary (1969)			Traffic Court	*DISCOVERY* 23 / Traffic 3
		Snow Boots	Stimulus	*ULTIMUS* 14 / Hurakan 12
	Snow Flyer (1958)		Guiding Light	*SIR GALLAHAD III* 16 / Fasnet 4
		Hey Hay	Hilltown	*BLENHEIM II* 1 / Phaona 9
Velasquez (1986)			Miss Sarah	Harry Baker 14 / Kitty Yansen A4
		PHAROS	Phalaris	Polymelus 3 / Bromus 1
	NEARCO (1935)		Scapa Flow	*CHAUCER* 1 / Anchora 13
		Nogara	Havresac	Rabelais 14 / Hors Concours 8
Nearctic (1954)			Catnip	Spearmint 1 / Sibola 4
		HYPERION	*GAINSBOROUGH*	Bayardo 10 / Rosedrop 2
	Lady Angela (1944)		Selene	*CHAUCER* 1 / Serenissima 6
		Sister Sarah	Abbots Trace	Tracery 19 / Abbots Anne 4
Northern Dancer (1961)			Sarita	*SWYNFORD* 1 / Molly Desmond 14
		Polynesian	Unbreakable	Sickle 6 / Blue Glass 4
	NATIVE DANCER (1950)		Black Polly	Polymelian 7 / Black Queen 14
		Geisha	*DISCOVERY*	Display 2 / Ariadne 23
Natalma (1957)			Miyako	John P Grier 8 / La Chica 5
		Mahmoud	*BLENHEIM II*	*BLANDFORD* 3 / Malva 1
	Almahmoud (1947)		Mah Mahal	*GAINSBOROUGH* 2 / *MUMTAZ MAHAL* 9
		Arbitrator	Peace Chance	Chance Shot 10 / Peace 31
Puppet Dance (1986)			Mother Goose	Chicle 2 / Flying Witch
		Turn-To	Royal Charger	*NEARCO* 4 / Sun Princess 9
	Hail To Reason (1958)		Source Sucree	Admiral Drake 16 / Lavendula II 1
		Nothirdchance	Blue Swords	*BLUE LARKSPUR* 8 / Flaming Swords 7
Bold Reason (1968)			Galla Colors	*SIR GALLAHAD III* 16 / Rouge Et Noir 4
		Djeddah	Djebel	Tourbillon 13 / Loika 5
	Lalun (1952)		Djezima	*ASTERUS* 9 / Heldifann 13
		Be Faithful	Bimelech	Black Toney 10 / La Troienne 1
Fairy Bridge (1975)			Bloodroot	*BLUE LARKSPUR* 8 / Knockaney Bridge 19
		Aristophanes	*HYPERION*	*GAINSBOROUGH* 2 / Selene 6
	Forli (1963)		Commotion	Mieuxce 7 / Riot 9
		Trevisa	Advocate	*FAIR TRIAL* 9 / Guiding Star 4
Special (1969)			Veneta	Foxglove 3 / Dogaresa 3
		Nantallah	*NASRULLAH*	*NEARCO* 4 / Mumtaz Begum 9
	Thong (1964)		Shimmer	Flares 17 / Broad Ripple 6
		Rough Shod	Gold Bridge	Golden Boss 19 / Flying Diadem 22
			Dalmary	*BLANDFORD* 3 / Simon's Shoes 5

Velaquez 1986

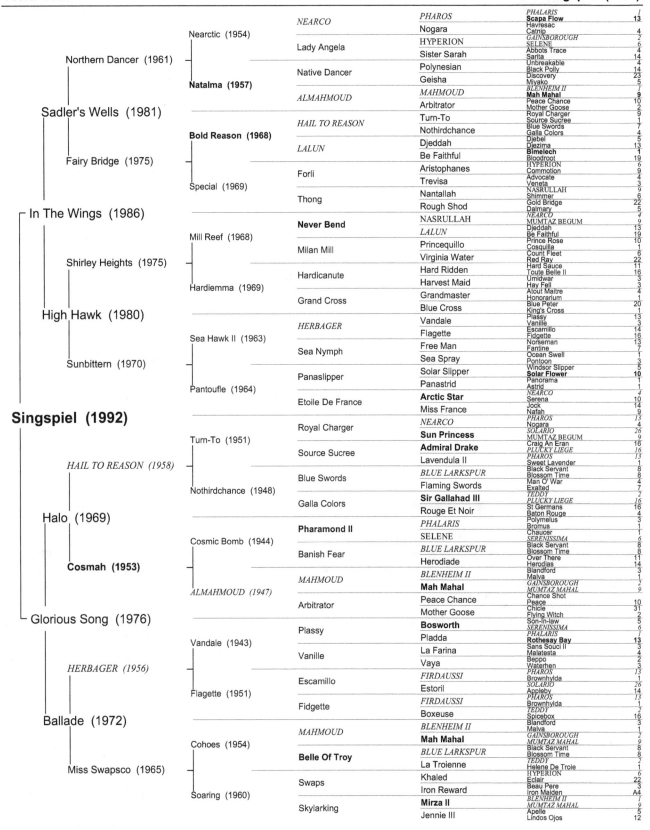

Singspiel 1992

Chapter 24

The Plaid Lads and a Grey Pelican

Maybe it is the citrus, or perhaps it is the water—but something good keeps happening in the Sunshine State. Florida: visions of oranges and tropical birds and alligators, deep sea fishing, beautiful beaches, the vast preserve of the Everglades—but top Thoroughbreds?

The products of the Tartan Stud in Florida surprised most everyone. Florida was considered a backwater of Thoroughbred breeding, but then in 1964 two colts were born that changed all that. Both bred by William McKnight and his stud manager John Nerud out of unfashionable stock; they would have been ignored except they could not because they were the best of their time, and both later earned the elusive Horse-of-the-Year title. In the succeeding years they have proven they are also highly significant sires, and extremely valuable to the reviving of the American Thoroughbred.

My interest is what they carry in their genes: concentrated elements from our Heroic Era. How else could two 'long shots' come against the formidable products of the Bluegrass and win? It is only because they are the outcome of critical mass as well as good pedigree design (see another 'long-shot' in Chapter 27). One of our most important lessons from our study that we can apply to our projects is to stack the background of our pedigree designs with multitudes of excellent horses and their close relations—this is what Clive Harper stressed, a factor in success he felt outranked in importance even the sex-balancing power closer up (see Appendix B).

Dr. Fager 1964

Dr. Fager started his race career late in the two-year-old season because he needed more time to mature; his knees were considered delicate because his dam demonstrated this weakness. But once he got out there he won three out of four starts. He had straight, correct front legs; although he is believed to be recessive for offset knees and pigeon toes, a trait which travels down from his grandsire Free for All who broke down as a three-year-old. His sire Rough n' Tumble also broke down with a sprung splint at age three, and his conformation was a little rough: cresty neck, upright pasterns, and long, level back and slight sickle hocks. So then people had questions about Dr. Fager, a son of Rough n' Tumble, plus his dam Aspidistra was not appreciated at the time either, so he was definitely underrated at the start of his career. However his hindquarter was massive, and he had a wonderful long and free-action in his stride, which is believed to be transmitted from the mare Tilly Rose (McLean)—she is descended from Hanover and Frilette. He was 16.2 hands with a long shoulder and level back, and when he was finished growing he was powerful—an impressive physical specimen. So it was then that his appearance and his apparent soundness was a surprise to all. He was very agile, and of course fast; he liked to run in front and was very hard to hold back. His losses were usually the result of a tag-team affair, when a pace setter wore him out before the come-from-behind racer could best him. His racing class is undeniable—he raced twenty-two times and was first eighteen of them, second in two, and third once, earning a total of $1 million.

Dr. Fager is a bloodline for us to treasure. He was a fantastic racer, racing against contemporaries In Reality and Damascus and winning more often than he lost; his victories in the Gotham, Withers, Jersey Derby, and Rockingham Special are well remembered. He set a track record for 1¼ miles at the NH Sweepstakes. He was named Three-Year-Old-Champion-Sprinter. He also set a world record for a mile of 1:32.2, and he won on turf also. He was named Horse-of-the-Year and has been entered into the Hall of Fame.

His dam Aspidistra was discussed in Chapter 21, a concentrated carrier of Lexington RH herself and a top producer. What did he receive from his sire that built on her genetics to produce such a great horse? Rough n' Tumble was a stakes winner, including the Santa Anita Derby at three before he was retired. His pedigree is intriguing, not the usual suspects at all. His sire-line descends from Plaudit—that other Himyar son—a great racer and good sire, but he pales beside his ½ brother Domino. Domino himself, along with his full sister Correction and his ½ sister Lady Reel, are 6x4x5x6x5x5 in Dr. Fager, but Himyar also appears again with a rarely seen daughter Annul on the dam-line—this surely is significant, as besides Domino's full sister Correction, Himyar daughters are hard to find in modern pedigrees. In spite of his weaknesses Rough n' Tumble has become a formidable sire-line with other notable sons such as Flag Raiser and Minnesota Mac—from whom Holy Bull descends, as well as the *reine* daughter My Dear Girl, the dam of Dr. Fager's contemporary In Reality. This unfashionable sire who is powerfully found in three important modern sires: Dr. Fager, Holy Bull and In Reality, came literally out of the backwaters of Florida and has produced an impressive 14% stakes winners—and he did it the hard way, being bred to less than first-cut mares.

Rough n' Tumble—a surprisingly strategic sire of the twentieth century and a descendant of Plaudit. —photo by Skeet Meadors, courtesy of Keeneland Library

Why is this plebian sire so powerful? Over the years, the Plaudit sire-line has been definitely second-rate to the Hastings branch, although Plaudit was a good racer and sire, but the line declined in quality after his good son King James, then followed the grandson Spur and then the great-grandson Sting, who marks the nadir of class in this line of sires; the bloodline just wasn't rated of high class anymore, but then there was Questionnaire, who began the climb back upward, as he was a good sire. Questionnaire is 4x5x5 to Domino—surely a factor in his success. Then his son Free for All won six of seven starts as a two-year-old, a brilliant racer who was on the fast track for the Kentucky Derby, but at three he broke down in Derby Trial Stakes and was retired to stud—so there is unsoundness here as well as speed. His early speed and class might be credited to the buildup of significant mare-lines: Mannie Gray 6x4x5, Cinderella 5x6, Clemence 6x6, and Sandiway 6x6—this is an unusual concentration of mare-lines. Free For All's son Rough n' Tumble is far and away his best offspring—a surprise to all. He carries an upfront design of Whisk Broom II 4x4 sex-balanced, plus Spearmint 4x4 sex-balanced also, and then the ¾ brothers Hamburg/Yankee are 6x6. All these strong pedigree elements are then funneled forward through the ¾ brother and sister Panasette/Upset—a potent pedigree, and in lines not that common. Rough n' Tumble produced twenty-four stakes winners.

When a horse surprises us with its class, seemingly far out-racing its pedigree strengths, it usually means we are missing something in our pedigree evaluation. In La Troienne's case it was the massive filly factor of a Diomed daughter in her background (Chapter 22). Here with Dr. Fager and his sire Rough n' Tumble it is the huge build-up of Heroic Era genes that burst forth—overtaking the lesser-performed lines and the physical weaknesses that were manifest in the line; this is critical mass. The fact that this is possible is the best news for any breeder; it gives us all hope that we can succeed in our mission of bringing back the talent and soundness of our bygone era.

Then the phenomenon Dr. Fager arrived—and he is off the charts as a racer and sire. He won over $1 million and was unanimously voted Horse-of-the-Year. What he added to the above strong lineage was a double of Bull Dog 3x4, Black Toney 4x6, and he also presents a now colossal strength in background lines of Domino/Correction/Lady Reel 8x6x7x8x7x7x7x9x8x9. I hope you have noted by now the class and upgrading that consistently arises when the line of Domino, his dam Mannie Gray, and his sire Himyar are built up (also demonstrated clearly in the next chapter).

It appears Rough n' Tumble's background is well stocked in Heroic Era genes with its thirty-seven lines of Lexington RH. What is notable and unusual is that there is an additional ten lines of his sire Boston RH, plus seven of American Eclipse RH, and five of Blackburns Whip RH—a rich and complex genetic fabric. This background gives Dr. Fager at least ninety-two lines of Lexington RH/Boston RH, definitely at a critical mass level. Dr Fager's best results seem to be as a broodmare sire, as a daughter produced Fappiano (in his pedigree note the full siblings Bull Dog/Marquerit de Valois 5x5x6x6) the sire of both Cryptoclearance (whose dam adds two lines of the full brother Sir Gallahad 5x6) and Unbridled, and then there is the good sire Cure the Blues from another of his daughters. Inbreeding to Dr. Fager has worked very well also, as seen in Quiet American who is tremendously inbred—2x1 to the ¾ sisters Killaloe/Demure, both by Dr. Fager out of a Cequillo mare. Inbreeding to his dam Aspidistra and his sire Rough n' Tumble have both proven their worth as well. He was syndicated as a stallion with thirty-two shares of $100k each, but stood only eight years before he died of colic.

"And, in the end, it seems that concentrating the influence of Rough n' Tumble and Aspidistra through inbreeding has been key to success when using their descendants in pedigrees. It's a pattern that has been repeated time and time again with success" (Edwin Anthony *The American Thoroughbred*).

It has also become noticeable that the best results in breeding to Dr. Fager—perhaps it could be called a 'nick'—is with the lines of Intent and his son Intentionally, which lead us to his contemporary, his Tartan Farm stable mate and competitor: In Reality.

In Reality 1964

In Reality was rated third best racer of his season. Like his ancestor Fair Play who raced against Colin and Celt, In Reality raced against Dr. Fager and Damascus, although he still ended up winning twenty-five of twenty-seven starts—he was a very high-class racer. Born the same year at Tartan Stud, In Reality stands above Dr. Fager as a sire, as he achieved 16% stakes winners and is listed as a *chef-de-race* in both brilliant and classic columns. These boys in plaid were exceptional both as racers and breeders.

In Reality carries one hundred lines of Lexington RH—this is colossal for a horse born in 1964—thirty-seven lines from Rough n' Tumble, and thirty-seven lines from Intent, plus the twenty-six from other sources. Intent and his descendants have also nicked well with both Rough n' Tumble and Aspidistra—the parents of Dr. Fager; Aspidistra has forty-six lines of Lexington RH—the buildup continues. Notable offspring of In Reality crossed on Dr. Fager are Banshee Breeze, Folklore, Real Quiet, Unbridled, Cahill Road, Discreet Cat, Empire Maker and Great Above—a virtual who's who of significant modern horses.

In Reality is often noted as being the surviving sire-line of Man O' War/Fair Play, and he is inbred 3x3 to War Relic, who in turn is 2x2 to the ¾ brothers Man O' War/Friar Rock—this then is an accurate statement of dominance, for not only is he of sire-line descent from Man O' War, but it is reinforced with a sex-balanced double of his son War Relic. His grandsire Intent, a wonderful stayer, is out of the important mare Liz F; this *reine* is a daughter of Bubbling Over out of a Whisk Broom II dam, out of a Hamburg dam, and she even has Maggie B. B. RH on her distaff side—providing huge maternal power in Heroic Era genes (see Chapter 21). Also notable in the lineage is the ¾ siblings Bulse/Miss Puzzle 6x5 connecting the pedigree halves. In Reality's son Intentionally is line-bred 4x4 to Fair Play through sons; he's a performance setter, and he was a champion at a mile or under, one of the best ever. We have seen this increase of speed and loss of stamina when stamina lines are doubled up in the front of the pedigree—Domino is the best example as he is 3x4x4 to Lexington RH, and he is pure speed at a mile also. The War Relic line that comes from My Dear Girl carries Ben Brush and Domino as does the male line in the sire. There is also a notable buildup of Whisk Broom II lines 5x6x6, all in all a very powerful and focused pedigree—definitely an 'American' dominance horse, and with his one hundred lines of Lexington RH he is one for us to treasure in our exercises to build up the dominance in four-miler genes.

His son Valid Appeal is an important broodmare sire, although he did have a significant son in Valid Expectations. His dam, Desert Trial, has a very American second dam in Scotch Verdict, which brings in an additional thirty-one lines of

Whisk Broom II—both Dr. Fager and In Reality have significant buildups of this racing paragon and warehouse for Broomstick and Maggie B. B. RH bloodlines. —photo by W.A. Rouch found in *Thoroughbred Types*

Lexington RH—making one hundred thirty in Valid Appeal. She carries the ¾ siblings Colin/Verdire 6x6, but most significant and indicative of his success as a filly sire is the strong filly factor she creates when she adds another Bubbling Over daughter making them 4x5. An interesting fact is that he had a full sister who is rated very high as well: Desert Vixen, plus three full brothers: Classic Trial Court Trial, and Defense Verdict—certainly these will be interesting individuals for future line-breeding exercises.

In Reality's son Known Fact was a top racer, who won the English 2000 Guineas and the Middle Park Stakes, and was a fair sire in England, producing among others the good sire Warning who is out of a Roberto dam—adding more Lexington RH.

Believe It is another of his good sons, out of a Buckpasser mare; he is dam-sire of the Preakness winner Real Quiet and second dam-sire of Discreet Cat.

However, his best son is probably Relaunch (one hundred forty lines of Lexington RH) out of Foggy Note by The Axe II; he has an interesting double of Balladier 5x5, plus Chicle daughters 5x5, and he carries the French sire Djeddah who is inbred to Heldifann/Durban 3x2—those French sisters carry an amazing eight lines of Lexington RH each. This makes Djeddah one of the most concentrated sources of Lexington RH blood—surely coming close to the Domino clan, and a far better source for us than Lady Josephine's family. His dam also carries the Man O' War daughter Spotted Beauty as her fifth-dam, sex-balancing the inbred War Relic lines—this stallion pedigree is powerful and one we want to target.

Relaunch's record at stud is excellent; sire of Cee's Tizzy, the grandsire in-turn of Tiznow, the only horse to win the Breeder's Cup Classic twice—an indication of soundness combined with class. Tiznow's dam-sire brings in Seattle Slew, Blue

Larkspur and Man O'War. Another son of his Arromanches is making quite a name currently, as his son Caixa Eletronica is a handicap champion. Another wonderful son is Skywalker, who also won the Breeder's Cup and the Santa Anita Derby, and has become a solid sire, producing among others the champion Bertrando. Another son of interest is Honour and Glory—who by the way carries one hundred sixty-six lines of Lexington RH—more Man O' War buildup plus another Man O' War daughter is his sixth dam: Hostility. Mahmoud is 4x6 sex-balanced. Also the La Troienne daughter Big Event is here with her daughter Blue Eyed Momo and son Blackball; they are 4x4, a filly factor of immense power. Relaunch appears to be best as a sire of sires; however, he is second dam-sire of the champion Point Given.

Another good son is Waquoit, a great racer who won over $2.2 million! We, as line-breeders, can target these lines in our engine rooms for success in sport.

Holy Bull 1991

Lightening has indeed appeared to have struck twice for the Florida breeders, as almost thirty years after the Tartan duo there is yet another superstar that has been bred and born there. This is Holy Bull, and like the plaid boys this Pelican Stable product is a reservoir of lines that are not so common, yet are very important for our national product. There is definitely a parallel apparent between the relationship of the Florida racehorse to Kentucky's, that resembles that of France's racehorse to Britain's. Those lines that were ignored, rejected, and forgotten in the Kentucky industry until they have become obscure, have been cherished and nurtured among the Orange groves, and finally emerge as a vital part of the rejuvenation of the tired and overused blood in Kentucky. It is wonderful.

Holy Bull was bred by Rachel Carpenter; he is by the Tartan Farm stallion Great Above (Minnesota Mac out of Ta Wee) by the Pelican Stables own home-bred Sharon Brown. Upon Rachel Carpenter's death Holy Bull was deeded to his trainer, Warren A. Croll. This is not your typical pedigree—Sharon Brown was not considered a valuable mare, and she was sold as a cull before Holy Bull proved himself. She was by the moderate sire Al Hattab, a son of the important sire The Axe II, and her dam Agathea's Dawn was unremarkable (Note that The Axe is also prominent in Relaunch.)

So what happened to produce one of the greatest racers and sires of modern times? This is when we really learn something, for many of us are small breeders with nice but not great bloodstock, and to see how this superhero horse was made can illustrate to us how to bring our own programs into the stratosphere. Obviously a critical mass was created here as he is a very consistent sire of high-class stock, and talent does not drop from the sky—in spite of the lack luster front ancestors something big was cooking in the background of this lineage that reached a level that it produced not just the star racer but provided enough potency for him to be a legendary sire. This is something you and I want to get a good look at.

Here is Plaudit, the rarely seen son of Himyar (Domino is his commonly found son); he is also a very close relative to Hastings, the sire of Fair Play. —image found in *Racing in America* 1922

What makes Holy Bull's pedigree different from the usual respected sires? First he is over the top in Lexington RH lines: one hundred eighty-eight! But he is also strong, far stronger than most others, in the lesser seen Heroic Era lines as he carries nine of Maggie B. B. RH, and fifteen lines of Hindoo, but what staggered me was he has thirty-two lines of Himyar—no one has that many, and besides they were not all from Domino; there were his daughters Annul and Correction found there and his other son Plaudit—who is out of that nasty Cinderella who is also Hastings dam. Further there is a significant buildup of Hasting lines, of course Fair Play, but also a rarely seen daughter Octoroon who is Holy Bull's 8th dam.

See how closely related Hastings and Plaudit are (combined pedigree); the dam of both is imported Cinderella who was a source of racing class, but she was a serious bad temperament transmitter—she was wild and mean. Hastings got some of her gifts that way, Plaudit not as much. But here is why I am going over this, Holy Bull is one of the best of the century, and his dam was poorly regarded—the common Sharon Brown. But this mare combined with his sire Great Above made dominance in those bedrock lines of Hastings (out of Cinderella) and Domino (by Himyar). Plaudit is the 'genetic glue' between these two lines that are here in mass. But there is more, look at Holy Bull's dam-line—see his seventh dam Oktibbena; she is a ¾ sister to Man O' War and his full brother My Play—which means the fifth-dam Xanthina is inbred to My Play/Oktibbena 1x2—do you think that is consolidation of type? Yes of course it is—in a big way—and Great Above brings in two more lines of Man O' War. No wonder he was so tough, and like all Fair Play's he got better with time. (Hastings/Plaudit/Fair Play/Himyar all transfer jumping talent—therefore Holy Bull can be a modern source of jump also).

Holy Bull has several close sibling conduits of power: the full brothers Bull Dog and Sir Gallahad are 5x6x6, and there is more of Teddy through his daughter La Troienne. The full brothers Man O' War and My Play are 6x7x8x6, and their ¾ sisters Oval and Oktibbena are in the seventh. War Relic is also a ¾ brother to My Play. The ¾ siblings Big Event/Bimelech focus the Black Toney/Teddy lines again. Not quite as potent but still of import is the sex-balanced Questionnaire double, the Mahmoud double, and the five lines of Lady Josephine.

Truly it is that rare Himyar/Cinderella concentration focused through the Fair Play, Domino, and Plaudit lines that are unique in their strength (See Chapter 30 for another superstar that has a surprising concentration on the dam-line that powers him.)

Holy Bull has had many offspring; his two most prominent are Giacomo and Macho Uno, winners of so much money they will need an armored car to take it away.

Florida has continued to produce remarkable racers such as Monarchos, Real Quiet, and Silver Charm.

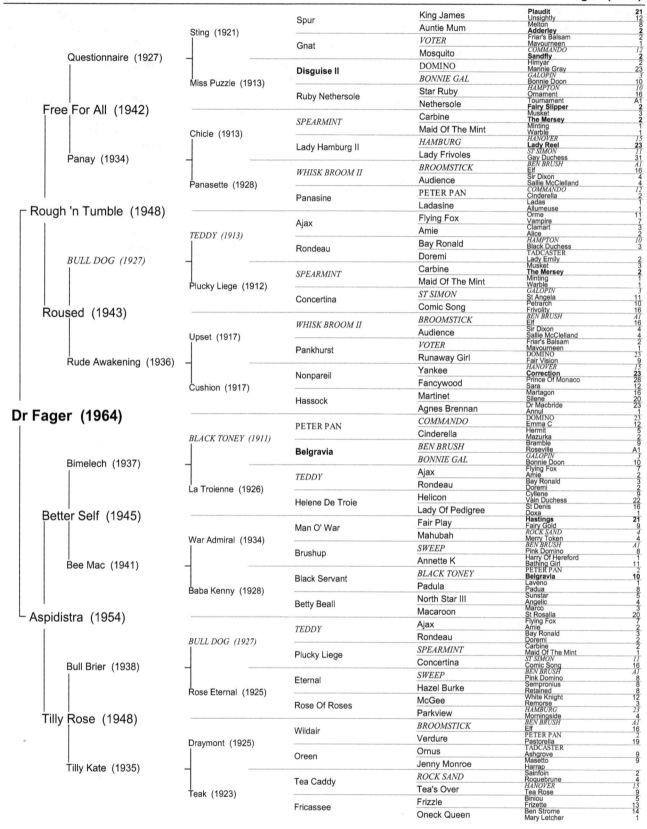

		Spur	King James	**Plaudit** 21 / Unsightly 12
	Sting (1921)		Auntie Mum	Melton 8 / **Adderley** 2
		Gnat	*VOTER*	Friar's Balsam 2 / Mavourneen 1
Questionnaire (1927)			Mosquito	*COMMANDO* 12 / **Sandfly** 2
		Disguise II	DOMINO	Himyar 2 / Mannie Gray 23
	Miss Puzzle (1913)		*BONNIE GAL*	*GALOPIN* 3 / Bonnie Doon 10
		Ruby Nethersole	Star Ruby	*HAMPTON* 10 / Ornament 16
Free For All (1942)			Nethersole	Tournament A1 / **Fairy Slipper** 2
		SPEARMINT	Carbine	Musket 3 / **The Mersey** 2
	Chicle (1913)		Maid Of The Mint	Minting 1 / Warble 1
		Lady Hamburg II	*HAMBURG*	*HANOVER* 15 / **Lady Reel** 23
Panay (1934)			Lady Frivoles	*ST SIMON* 11 / Gay Duchess 31
		WHISK BROOM II	*BROOMSTICK*	*BEN BRUSH* A1 / Elf 16
	Panasette (1928)		Audience	Sir Dixon 4 / Sallie McClelland 4
		Panasine	PETER PAN	*COMMANDO* 12 / Cinderella 2
			Ladasine	Ladas 1 / Allumeuse 1

Rough 'n Tumble (1948)

		Ajax	Flying Fox	Orme 11 / Vampire 7
	TEDDY (1913)		Amie	Clamart 3 / Alice 2
		Rondeau	Bay Ronald	*HAMPTON* 10 / Black Duchess 3
BULL DOG (1927)			Doremi	*TADCASTER* / Lady Emily
		SPEARMINT	Carbine	Musket 3 / **The Mersey** 2
	Plucky Liege (1912)		Maid Of The Mint	Minting 1 / Warble 1
		Concertina	*ST SIMON*	*GALOPIN* 3 / St Angela 11
Roused (1943)			Comic Song	Petrarch 10 / Frivolity 16
		WHISK BROOM II	*BROOMSTICK*	*BEN BRUSH* A1 / Elf 16
	Upset (1917)		Audience	Sir Dixon 4 / Sallie McClelland 4
		Pankhurst	*VOTER*	Friar's Balsam 2 / Mavourneen 1
Rude Awakening (1936)			Runaway Girl	DOMINO 23 / Fair Vision 9
		Nonpareil	Yankee	*HANOVER* 15 / **Correction** 23
	Cushion (1917)		Fancywood	Prince Of Monaco 28 / Sara 12
		Hassock	Martinet	Martagon 16 / Silene 20
			Agnes Brennan	Dr Macbride 23 / Annul 1

Dr Fager (1964)

		PETER PAN	*COMMANDO*	DOMINO 23 / Emma C 12
	BLACK TONEY (1911)		Cinderella	Hermit 5 / Mazurka 2
		Belgravia	*BEN BRUSH*	Bramble 9 / Roseville A1
Bimelech (1937)			*BONNIE GAL*	*GALOPIN* 3 / Bonnie Doon 10
		TEDDY	Ajax	Flying Fox 7 / Amie 3
	La Troienne (1926)		Rondeau	Bay Ronald 2 / Doremi 2
		Helene De Troie	Helicon	Cyllene 9 / Vain Duchess 22
			Lady Of Pedigree	St Denis 16 / Doxa 1

Better Self (1945)

		Man O' War	Fair Play	**Hastings** 21 / Fairy Gold 9
	War Admiral (1934)		Mahubah	*ROCK SAND* 4 / Merry Token 4
		Brushup	*SWEEP*	*BEN BRUSH* A1 / Pink Domino 8
Bee Mac (1941)			Annette K	Harry Of Hereford 1 / Bathing Girl 11
		Black Servant	*BLACK TONEY*	PETER PAN 2 / **Belgravia** 10
	Baba Kenny (1928)		Padula	Laveno 1 / Padua 8
		Betty Beall	North Star III	Sunstar 5 / Angelic 4
			Macaroon	Marco 2 / St Rosalia 20

Aspidistra (1954)

		TEDDY	Ajax	Flying Fox 7 / Amie 3
	BULL DOG (1927)		Rondeau	Bay Ronald 2 / Doremi 2
		Plucky Liege	*SPEARMINT*	Carbine 2 / Maid Of The Mint 1
Bull Brier (1938)			Concertina	*ST SIMON* 11 / Comic Song 16
		Eternal	*SWEEP*	*BEN BRUSH* A1 / Pink Domino 8
	Rose Eternal (1925)		Hazel Burke	Sempronius 8 / Retained 8
		Rose Of Roses	McGee	White Knight 12 / Remorse 3
			Parkview	*HAMBURG* 23 / Morningside 4
		Wildair	*BROOMSTICK*	*BEN BRUSH* A1 / Elf 16
	Draymont (1925)		Verdure	PETER PAN 2 / Pastorella 19
		Oreen	Ornus	*TADCASTER* / Ashgrove 9
Tilly Rose (1948)			Jenny Monroe	Masetto 9 / Harrap
		Tea Caddy	*ROCK SAND*	Sainfoin 2 / Roquebrune 4
	Teak (1923)		Tea's Over	*HANOVER* 15 / Tea Rose 9
		Fricassee	Frizzle	Biniou 5 / Frizette 13
Tilly Kate (1935)			Oneck Queen	Ben Strome 14 / Mary Letcher 1

Dr. Fager 1964

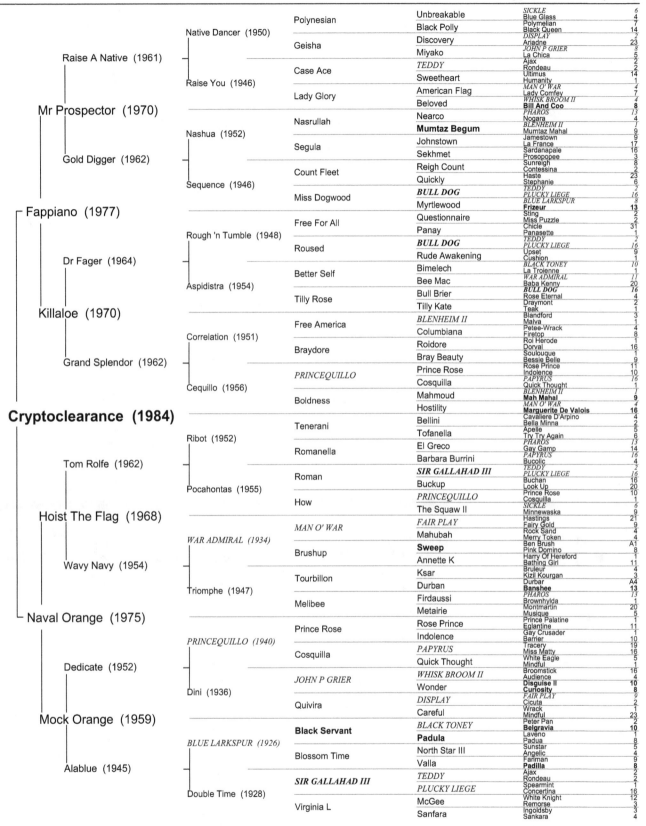

Cryptoclearance 1984

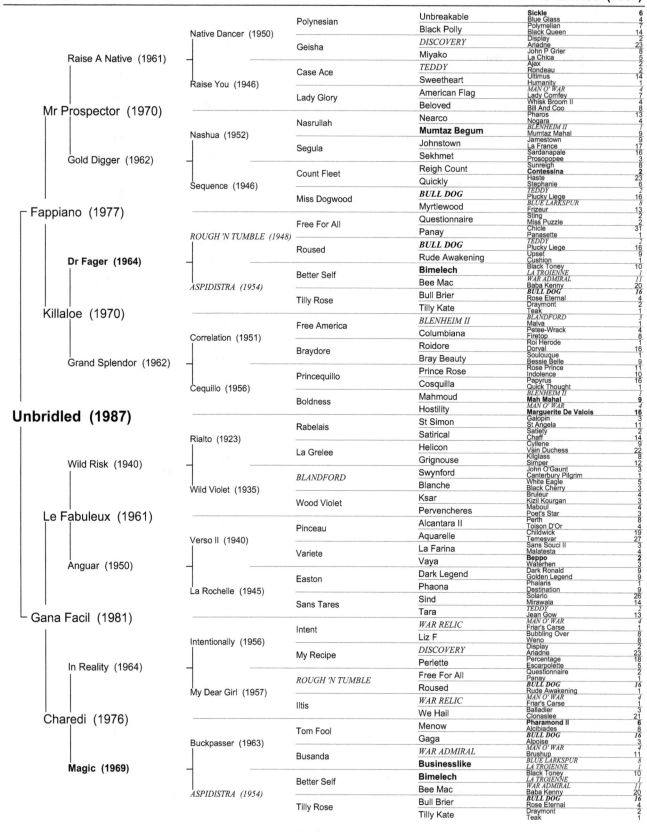

Left-hand pedigree tree:

- Mr Prospector (1970)
  - Raise A Native (1961)
  - Gold Digger (1962)
- Fappiano (1977)
  - Dr Fager (1964)
  - Killaloe (1970)
    - Grand Splendor (1962)
- **Unbridled (1987)**
  - Wild Risk (1940)
  - Le Fabuleux (1961)
  - Anguar (1950)
  - Gana Facil (1981)
    - In Reality (1964)
    - Charedi (1976)
      - **Magic (1969)**

Extended pedigree:

Native Dancer (1950)	Polynesian	Unbreakable	**Sickle** 6 / Blue Glass 4	
		Black Polly	Polymelian 7 / Black Queen 14	
	Geisha	*DISCOVERY*	Display 2 / Ariadne 23	
		Miyako	John P Grier 8 / La Chica 5	
Raise You (1946)	Case Ace	*TEDDY*	Ajax 2 / Rondeau 14	
		Sweetheart	Ultimus 14 / Humanity 1	
	Lady Glory	American Flag	*MAN O' WAR* 4 / Lady Comfey 7	
		Beloved	Whisk Broom II 4 / Bill And Coo 8	
Nashua (1952)	Nasrullah	Nearco	Pharos 13 / Nogara 4	
		Mumtaz Begum	*BLENHEIM II* 7 / Mumtaz Mahal 9	
	Segula	Johnstown	Jamestown 17 / La France 4	
		Sekhmet	Sardanapale 16 / Prosopopee 3	
Sequence (1946)	Count Fleet	Reigh Count	Sunreigh 8 / **Contessina** 2	
		Quickly	Haste 23 / Stephanie 6	
	Miss Dogwood	**BULL DOG**	*TEDDY* 2 / Plucky Liege 16	
		Myrtlewood	*BLUE LARKSPUR* 8 / Frizeur 13	
ROUGH 'N TUMBLE (1948)	Free For All	Questionnaire	Sting 2 / Miss Puzzle 2	
		Panay	Chicle 31 / Panasette 1	
	Roused	**BULL DOG**	*TEDDY* 2 / Plucky Liege 16	
		Rude Awakening	Upset 9 / Cushion 1	
ASPIDISTRA (1954)	Better Self	**Bimelech**	Black Toney 10 / *LA TROIENNE* 1	
		Bee Mac	*WAR ADMIRAL* 11 / Baba Kenny 20	
	Tilly Rose	Bull Brier	*BULL DOG* 16 / Rose Eternal 4	
		Tilly Kate	Draymont 2 / Teak 1	
Correlation (1951)	Free America	*BLENHEIM II*	*BLANDFORD* 3 / Malva 1	
		Columbiana	Petee-Wrack 4 / Firetop 8	
	Braydore	Roidore	Roi Herode 16 / Dorval 1	
		Bray Beauty	Soulouque 1 / Bessie Belle 9	
Cequillo (1956)	Princequillo	Prince Rose	Rose Prince 11 / Indolence 10	
		Cosquilla	Papyrus 16 / Quick Thought 1	
	Boldness	Mahmoud	*BLENHEIM II* 7 / **Mah Mahal** 9	
		Hostility	*MAN O' WAR* 4 / **Marguerite De Valois** 16	
Rialto (1923)	Rabelais	St Simon	Galopin 3 / St Angela 11	
		Satirical	Satiety 2 / Chaff 14	
	La Grelee	Helicon	Cyllene 9 / Vain Duchess 22	
		Grignouse	Kilglass 8 / Simper 12	
Wild Violet (1935)	*BLANDFORD*	Swynford	John O'Gaunt 3 / Canterbury Pilgrim 1	
		Blanche	White Eagle 5 / Black Cherry 3	
	Wood Violet	Ksar	Bruleur 4 / Kizil Kourgan 3	
		Pervencheres	Maboul 4 / Poet's Star 3	
Verso II (1940)	Pinceau	Alcantara II	Perth 8 / Toison D'Or 4	
		Aquarelle	Childwick 19 / Temesvar 27	
	Variete	La Farina	Sans Souci II 3 / Malatesta 4	
		Vaya	**Beppo** 2 / Waterhen 3	
La Rochelle (1945)	Easton	Dark Legend	Dark Ronald 9 / Golden Legend 9	
		Phaona	Phalaris 1 / Destination 4	
	Sans Tares	Sind	Solario 26 / Mirawala 14	
		Tara	*TEDDY* 2 / Jean Gow 13	
Intentionally (1956)	Intent	*WAR RELIC*	*MAN O' WAR* 4 / Friar's Carse 1	
		Liz F	Bubbling Over 8 / Weno 8	
	My Recipe	*DISCOVERY*	Display 2 / Ariadne 23	
		Perlette	Percentage 18 / Escarpolette 5	
My Dear Girl (1957)	*ROUGH 'N TUMBLE*	Free For All	Questionnaire 2 / Panay 1	
		Roused	*BULL DOG* 16 / Rude Awakening 1	
	Iltis	*WAR RELIC*	*MAN O' WAR* 4 / Friar's Carse 1	
		We Hail	Balladier 3 / Clonaslee 21	
Buckpasser (1963)	Tom Fool	Menow	**Pharamond II** 6 / Alcibiades 8	
		Gaga	*BULL DOG* 16 / Alpoise 3	
	Busanda	*WAR ADMIRAL*	*MAN O' WAR* 4 / Brushup 11	
		Businesslike	*BLUE LARKSPUR* 8 / *LA TROIENNE* 1	
ASPIDISTRA (1954)	Better Self	**Bimelech**	Black Toney 10 / *LA TROIENNE* 1	
		Bee Mac	*WAR ADMIRAL* 11 / Baba Kenny 20	
	Tilly Rose	Bull Brier	*BULL DOG* 16 / Rose Eternal 4	
		Tilly Kate	Draymont 2 / Teak 1	

Unbridled 1987

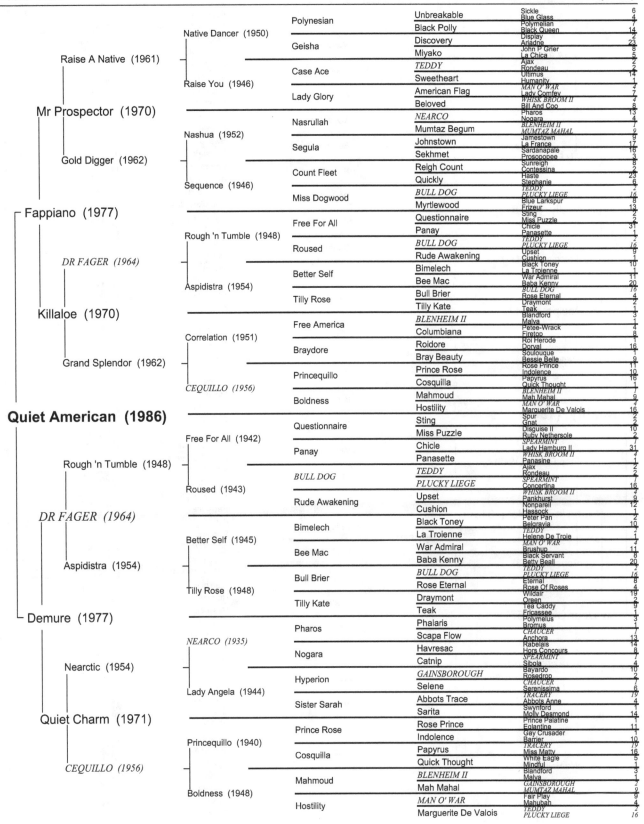

Quiet American 1986

Quiet American (1986)

- Fappiano (1977)
  - Mr Prospector (1970)
    - Raise A Native (1961)
      - Native Dancer (1950)
        - Polynesian
          - Unbreakable — Sickle 6 / Blue Glass 4
          - Black Polly — Polymelian 7 / Black Queen 14
        - Geisha
          - Discovery — Display 2 / Ariadne 23
          - Miyako — John P Grier 8 / La Chica 5
      - Raise You (1946)
        - Case Ace
          - TEDDY — Ajax 2 / Rondeau 2
          - Sweetheart — Ultimus 14 / Humanity 1
        - Lady Glory
          - American Flag — MAN O' WAR 7 / Lady Comfey 7
          - Beloved — WHISK BROOM II 4 / Bill And Coo 8
    - Gold Digger (1962)
      - Nashua (1952)
        - Nasrullah
          - NEARCO — Pharos 13 / Nogara 4
          - Mumtaz Begum — BLENHEIM II 1 / MUMTAZ MAHAL 9
        - Segula
          - Johnstown — Jamestown 9 / La France 17
          - Sekhmet — Sardanapale 16 / Prosopopee 3
      - Sequence (1946)
        - Count Fleet
          - Reigh Count — Sunreigh 8 / Contessina 2
          - Quickly — Haste 23 / Stephanie 6
        - Miss Dogwood
          - BULL DOG — TEDDY 2 / PLUCKY LIEGE 16
          - Myrtlewood — Blue Larkspur 8 / Frizeur 13
  - Killaloe (1970)
    - DR FAGER (1964)
      - Rough 'n Tumble (1948)
        - Free For All
          - Questionnaire — Sting 2 / Miss Puzzle 2
          - Panay — Chicle 31 / Panasette 1
        - Roused
          - BULL DOG — TEDDY 2 / PLUCKY LIEGE 16
          - Rude Awakening — Upset 9 / Cushion 1
      - Aspidistra (1954)
        - Better Self
          - Bimelech — Black Toney 10 / La Troienne 1
          - Bee Mac — War Admiral 11 / Baba Kenny 20
        - Tilly Rose
          - Bull Brier — BULL DOG 16 / Rose Eternal 4
          - Tilly Kate — Draymont 2 / Teak
    - Grand Splendor (1962)
      - Correlation (1951)
        - Free America
          - BLENHEIM II — Blandford 3 / Malva 4
          - Columbiana — Petee-Wrack 8 / Firetop 1
        - Braydore
          - Roidore — Rol Herode 16 / Dorval
          - Bray Beauty — Souleouque 9 / Bessie Belle
      - CEQUILLO (1956)
        - Princequillo
          - Prince Rose — Rose Prince 11 / Indolence 10
          - Cosquilla — Papyrus 16 / Quick Thought 1
        - Boldness
          - Mahmoud — BLENHEIM II 7 / Mah Mahal 9
          - Hostility — MAN O' WAR 4 / Marguerite De Valois 16
- Demure (1977)
  - DR FAGER (1964)
    - Rough 'n Tumble (1948)
      - Free For All (1942)
        - Questionnaire
          - Sting — Spur 2 / Gnat
          - Miss Puzzle — Disguise II 10 / Ruby Nethersole 2
        - Panay
          - Chicle — SPEARMINT 7 / Lady Hamburg II 31
          - Panasette — WHISK BROOM II 4 / Panasine 1
      - Roused (1943)
        - BULL DOG
          - TEDDY — Ajax 2 / Rondeau 2
          - PLUCKY LIEGE — SPEARMINT 7 / Concertina 16
        - Rude Awakening
          - Upset — WHISK BROOM II 4 / Pankhurst 9
          - Cushion — Nonpareil 12 / Hassock 1
    - Aspidistra (1954)
      - Better Self (1945)
        - Bimelech
          - Black Toney — Peter Pan 2 / Belgravia 10
          - La Troienne — TEDDY 1 / Helene De Troie 1
        - Bee Mac
          - War Admiral — MAN O' WAR 11 / Brushup
          - Baba Kenny — Black Servant 8 / Betty Beall
      - Tilly Rose (1948)
        - Bull Brier
          - BULL DOG — TEDDY 2 / PLUCKY LIEGE 16
          - Rose Eternal — Eternal 8 / Rose Of Roses 4
        - Tilly Kate
          - Draymont — Wildair 19 / Oreen 2
          - Teak — Tea Caddy 9 / Fricassee 1
  - Quiet Charm (1971)
    - Nearctic (1954)
      - NEARCO (1935)
        - Pharos
          - Phalaris — Polymelus 3 / Bromus 1
          - Scapa Flow — CHAUCER 7 / Anchora 13
        - Nogara
          - Havresac — Rabelais 14 / Hors Concours 8
          - Catnip — SPEARMINT 7 / Sibola 4
      - Lady Angela (1944)
        - Hyperion
          - GAINSBOROUGH — Bayardo 10 / Rosedrop 7
          - Selene — CHAUCER 7 / Serenissima 6
        - Sister Sarah
          - Abbots Trace — TRACERY 19 / Abbots Anne 4
          - Sarita — Swynford 1 / Molly Desmond 14
    - CEQUILLO (1956)
      - Princequillo (1940)
        - Prince Rose
          - Rose Prince — Prince Palatine 1 / Eglantine 11
          - Indolence — Gay Crusader 10 / Barrier
        - Cosquilla
          - Papyrus — TRACERY 19 / Miss Matty 16
          - Quick Thought — White Eagle 5 / Mindful 1
      - Boldness (1948)
        - Mahmoud
          - BLENHEIM II — Blandford 3 / Malva 1
          - Mah Mahal — GAINSBOROUGH 7 / MUMTAZ MAHAL 9
        - Hostility
          - MAN O' WAR — Fair Play 9 / Mahubah 4
          - Marguerite De Valois — TEDDY 2 / PLUCKY LIEGE 16

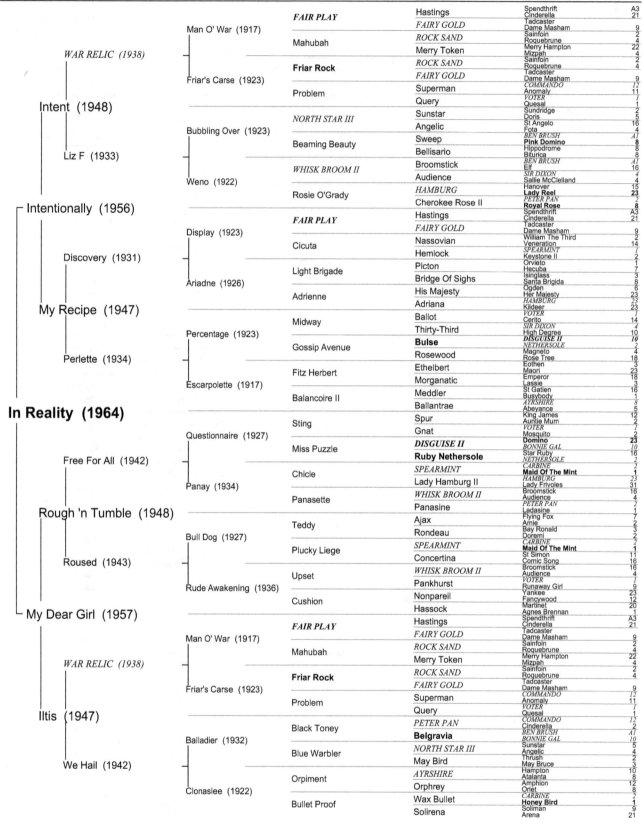

Left-line ancestry:

- *WAR RELIC (1938)*
  - **Intent (1948)**
  - Liz F (1933)
    - Intentionally (1956)
    - Discovery (1931)
      - My Recipe (1947)
      - Perlette (1934)

In Reality (1964)

- Free For All (1942)
  - Rough 'n Tumble (1948)
  - Roused (1943)
    - My Dear Girl (1957)
- *WAR RELIC (1938)*
  - Iltis (1947)
  - We Hail (1942)

Gen 1	Gen 2	Gen 3	Gen 4	Gen 5	No.
Man O' War (1917)	*FAIR PLAY*	Hastings	Spendthrift		A3
			Cinderella		21
		FAIRY GOLD	Tadcaster		
			Dame Masham		9
	Mahubah	*ROCK SAND*	Sainfoin		2
			Roquebrune		4
		Merry Token	Merry Hampton		22
			Mizpah		4
Friar's Carse (1923)	**Friar Rock**	*ROCK SAND*	Sainfoin		2
			Roquebrune		4
		FAIRY GOLD	Tadcaster		
			Dame Masham		9
	Problem	Superman	*COMMANDO*		12
			Anomaly		11
		Query	*VOTER*		1
			Quesal		1
Bubbling Over (1923)	*NORTH STAR III*	Sunstar	Sundridge		2
			Doris		5
		Angelic	St Angelo		16
			Fota		4
	Beaming Beauty	Sweep	*BEN BRUSH*		A1
			Pink Domino		8
		Bellisario	Hippodrome		8
			Biturica		8
Weno (1922)	*WHISK BROOM II*	Broomstick	*BEN BRUSH*		A1
			Elf		16
		Audience	*SIR DIXON*		4
			Sallie McClelland		4
	Rosie O'Grady	*HAMBURG*	Hanover		15
			Lady Reel		23
		Cherokee Rose II	*PETER PAN*		2
			Royal Rose		8
Display (1923)	*FAIR PLAY*	Hastings	Spendthrift		A3
			Cinderella		21
		FAIRY GOLD	Tadcaster		
			Dame Masham		9
	Cicuta	Nassovian	William The Third		2
			Veneration		14
		Hemlock	*SPEARMINT*		1
			Keystone II		2
Ariadne (1926)	Light Brigade	Picton	Orvieto		1
			Hecuba		7
		Bridge Of Sighs	Isinglass		3
			Santa Brigida		8
	Adrienne	His Majesty	Ogden		6
			Her Majesty		23
		Adriana	*HAMBURG*		23
			Kildeer		23
Percentage (1923)	Midway	Ballot	*VOTER*		1
			Cerito		14
		Thirty-Third	*SIR DIXON*		4
			High Degree		10
	Gossip Avenue	**Bulse**	*DISGUISE II*		10
			NETHERSOLE		2
		Rosewood	Magneto		
			Rose Tree		18
Escarpolette (1917)	Fitz Herbert	Ethelbert	Eothen		3
			Maori		23
		Morganatic	Emperor		18
			Lassie		3
	Balancoire II	Meddler	St Gatien		16
			Busybody		1
		Ballantrae	*AYRSHIRE*		8
			Abeyance		5
Questionnaire (1927)	Sting	Spur	King James		12
			Auntie Mum		1
		Gnat	*VOTER*		1
			Mosquito		2
	Miss Puzzle	*DISGUISE II*	**Domino**		23
			BONNIE GAL		10
		Ruby Nethersole	Star Ruby		16
			NETHERSOLE		2
Panay (1934)	Chicle	*SPEARMINT*	*CARBINE*		2
			Maid Of The Mint		1
		Lady Hamburg II	*HAMBURG*		23
			Lady Frivoles		31
	Panasette	*WHISK BROOM II*	Broomstick		16
			Audience		4
		Panasine	*PETER PAN*		2
			Ladasine		1
Bull Dog (1927)	Teddy	Ajax	Flying Fox		7
			Amie		2
		Rondeau	Bay Ronald		3
			Doremi		2
	Plucky Liege	*SPEARMINT*	*CARBINE*		2
			Maid Of The Mint		1
		Concertina	St Simon		11
			Comic Song		16
Rude Awakening (1936)	Upset	*WHISK BROOM II*	Broomstick		16
			Audience		4
		Pankhurst	*VOTER*		1
			Runaway Girl		9
	Cushion	Nonpareil	Yankee		23
			Fancywood		12
		Hassock	Martinet		20
			Agnes Brennan		1
Man O' War (1917)	*FAIR PLAY*	Hastings	Spendthrift		A3
			Cinderella		21
		FAIRY GOLD	Tadcaster		
			Dame Masham		9
	Mahubah	*ROCK SAND*	Sainfoin		2
			Roquebrune		4
		Merry Token	Merry Hampton		22
			Mizpah		4
Friar's Carse (1923)	**Friar Rock**	*ROCK SAND*	Sainfoin		2
			Roquebrune		4
		FAIRY GOLD	Tadcaster		
			Dame Masham		9
	Problem	Superman	*COMMANDO*		12
			Anomaly		11
		Query	*VOTER*		1
			Quesal		1
Balladier (1932)	Black Toney	*PETER PAN*	*COMMANDO*		12
			Cinderella		A1
		Belgravia	*BEN BRUSH*		A1
			BONNIE GAL		10
	Blue Warbler	*NORTH STAR III*	Sunstar		5
			Angelic		4
		May Bird	Thrush		2
			May Bruce		3
Clonaslee (1922)	Orpiment	*AYRSHIRE*	Hampton		10
			Atalanta		8
		Orphrey	Amphion		12
			Orlet		8
	Bullet Proof	Wax Bullet	*CARBINE*		2
			Honey Bird		1
		Solirena	Soliman		
			Arena		21

In Reality 1964

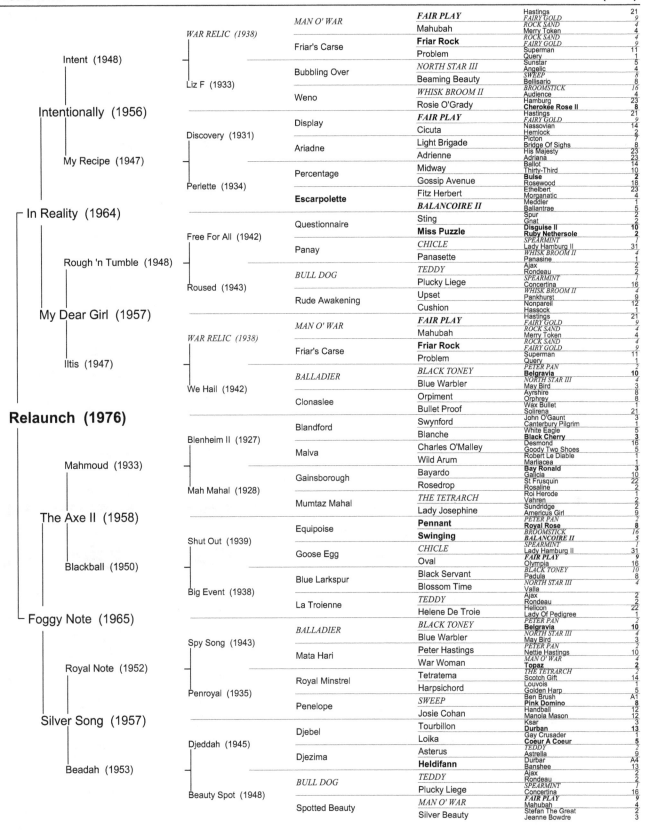

Relaunch 1976

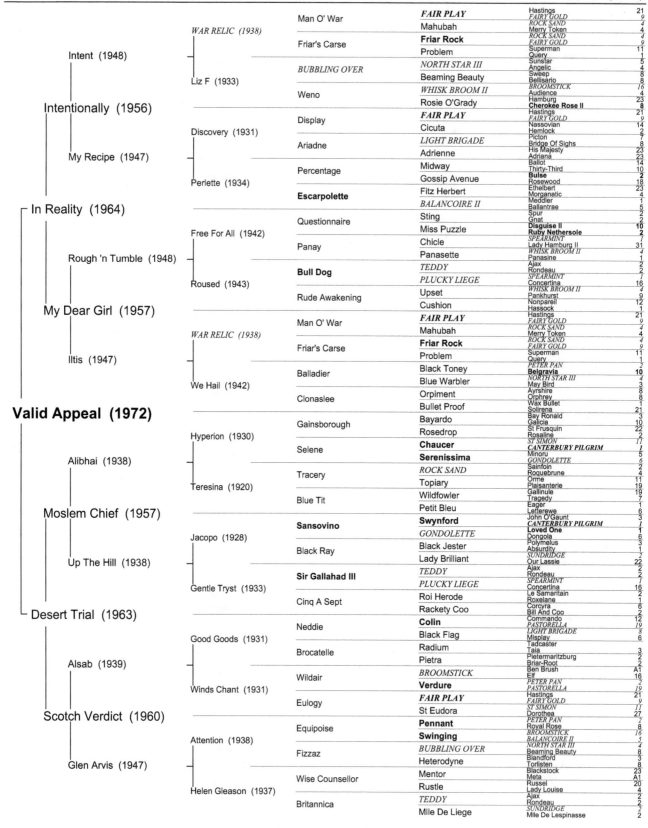

		Man O' War	*FAIR PLAY*	Hastings 21
				FAIRY GOLD 9
	WAR RELIC (1938)		Mahubah	*ROCK SAND* 4
				Merry Token 4
		Friar's Carse	**Friar Rock**	*ROCK SAND* 4
Intent (1948)				*FAIRY GOLD* 9
			Problem	Superman 11
				Query 1
		BUBBLING OVER	*NORTH STAR III*	Sunstar 5
	Liz F (1933)			Angelic 4
		Beaming Beauty	Sweep 8
Intentionally (1956)				Bellisario 8
		Weno	*WHISK BROOM II*	*BROOMSTICK* 16
				Audience 4
			Rosie O'Grady	Hamburg 23
				Cherokee Rose II 8
		Display	*FAIR PLAY*	Hastings 21
				FAIRY GOLD 9
My Recipe (1947)	Discovery (1931)		Cicuta	Nassovian 14
				Hemlock 2
		Ariadne	**LIGHT BRIGADE**	Picton 7
				Bridge Of Sighs 8
			Adrienne	His Majesty 23
				Adriana 23
		Percentage	Midway	Ballot 14
	Perlette (1934)			Thirty-Third 10
			Gossip Avenue	**Bulse** 2
				Rosewood 18
		Escarpolette	Fitz Herbert	Ethelbert 23
				Morganatic 4
In Reality (1964)			*BALANCOIRE II*	Meddler 1
				Ballantrae 5
		Questionnaire	Sting	Spur 2
				Disguise II 10
			Miss Puzzle	**Ruby Nethersole** 2
	Free For All (1942)			*SPEARMINT* 1
		Panay	Chicle	Lady Hamburg II 31
				WHISK BROOM II 4
			Panasette	Panasine 1
Rough 'n Tumble (1948)		**Bull Dog**	*TEDDY*	Ajax 2
				Rondeau 2
			PLUCKY LIEGE	*SPEARMINT* 1
	Roused (1943)			Concertina 16
		Rude Awakening	Upset	*WHISK BROOM II* 4
				Pankhurst 9
			Cushion	Nonpareil 12
				Hassock 1
		Man O' War	*FAIR PLAY*	Hastings 21
				FAIRY GOLD 9
	WAR RELIC (1938)		Mahubah	*ROCK SAND* 4
				Merry Token 4
		Friar's Carse	**Friar Rock**	*ROCK SAND* 4
My Dear Girl (1957)				*FAIRY GOLD* 9
			Problem	Superman 11
				Query 1
		Balladier	Black Toney	*PETER PAN* 1
	We Hail (1942)			**Belgravia** 10
			Blue Warbler	*NORTH STAR III* 4
				May Bird 3
		Clonaslee	Orpiment	Ayrshire 8
				Orphrey 8
			Bullet Proof	Wax Bullet 1
				Solirena 21
		Gainsborough	Bayardo	Bay Ronald 3
				Galicia 10
Iltis (1947)	Hyperion (1930)		Rosedrop	St Frusquin 22
				Rosaline 9
		Selene	**Chaucer**	*ST SIMON* 11
				CANTERBURY PILGRIM 1
			Serenissima	Minoru 5
				GONDOLETTE 6
		Tracery	*ROCK SAND*	Sainfoin 2
	Teresina (1920)			Roquebrune 4
			Topiary	Orme 11
				Plaisanterie 19
Valid Appeal (1972)		Blue Tit	Wildfowler	Gallinule 19
				Tragedy 7
			Petit Bleu	Eager 1
				Letterewe 6
		Sansovino	**Swynford**	John O'Gaunt 3
				CANTERBURY PILGRIM 1
	Jacopo (1928)		*GONDOLETTE*	**Loved One** 1
				Dongola 6
		Black Ray	Black Jester	Polymelus 3
				Absurdity 1
Alibhai (1938)			Lady Brilliant	*SUNDRIDGE* 1
				Our Lassie 22
		Sir Gallahad III	*TEDDY*	Ajax 2
				Rondeau 2
	Gentle Tryst (1933)		*PLUCKY LIEGE*	*SPEARMINT* 1
				Concertina 16
		Cinq A Sept	Roi Herode	Le Samaritain 2
				Roxelane 1
			Rackety Coo	Corcyra 6
Moslem Chief (1957)				Bill And Coo 2
		Neddie	**Colin**	Commando 12
				PASTORELLA 19
	Good Goods (1931)		Black Flag	**LIGHT BRIGADE** 8
				Misplay 6
		Brocatelle	Radium	Tadcaster 2
				Taia 3
			Pietra	Pietermaritzburg 2
Up The Hill (1938)				Briar-Root 2
		Wildair	*BROOMSTICK*	Ben Brush A1
				Elf 16
	Winds Chant (1931)		**Verdure**	*PETER PAN* 1
				PASTORELLA 19
		Eulogy	*FAIR PLAY*	Hastings 21
				FAIRY GOLD 9
			St Eudora	*ST SIMON* 11
				Dorothea 27
Desert Trial (1963)		Equipoise	**Pennant**	*PETER PAN* 2
				Royal Rose 8
			Swinging	*BROOMSTICK* 16
				BALANCOIRE II 5
	Attention (1938)	Fizzaz	*BUBBLING OVER*	*NORTH STAR III* 4
				Beaming Beauty 8
			Heterodyne	Blandford 8
				Torlisten 3
Alsab (1939)		Wise Counsellor	Mentor	Blackstock 23
				Meta A1
			Rustle	Russel 20
	Helen Gleason (1937)			Lady Louise 4
		Britannica	*TEDDY*	Ajax 2
				Rondeau 2
Scotch Verdict (1960)			Mlle De Liege	*SUNDRIDGE* 2
				Mlle De Lespinasse 2
Glen Arvis (1947)				

Valid Appeal 1972

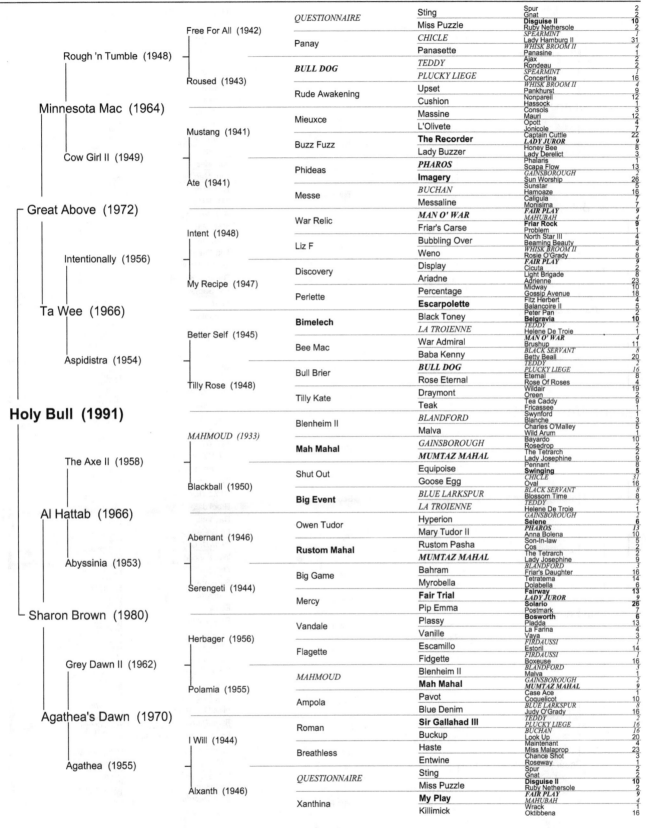

		Sting	Spur 2
	QUESTIONNAIRE		Gnat 2
		Miss Puzzle	**Disguise II** 10
Free For All (1942)			Ruby Nethersole 2
		CHICLE	*SPEARMINT* 1
	Panay		Lady Hamburg II 31
		Panasette	*WHISK BROOM II* 4
Rough 'n Tumble (1948)			Panasine 1
		TEDDY	Ajax 2
	BULL DOG		Rondeau 2
		PLUCKY LIEGE	*SPEARMINT* 1
Roused (1943)			Concertina 16
		Upset	*WHISK BROOM II* 4
	Rude Awakening		Pankhurst 9
		Cushion	Nonpareil 12
			Hassock 1
		Massine	Consols 3
	Mieuxce		Mauri 12
		L'Olivete	Opott 4
Mustang (1941)			Jonicole 1
		The Recorder	Captain Cuttle 22
	Buzz Fuzz		*LADY JUROR* 9
		Lady Buzzer	Honey Bee 8
Minnesota Mac (1964)			Lady Derelict 3
		PHAROS	Phalaris 1
	Phideas		Scapa Flow 13
		Imagery	*GAINSBOROUGH* 2
Ate (1941)			Sun Worship 26
		BUCHAN	Sunstar 5
	Messe		Hamoaze 16
		Messaline	Caligula 7
Cow Girl II (1949)			Monisima 7
		MAN O' WAR	*FAIR PLAY* 9
	War Relic		*MAHUBAH* 4
		Friar's Carse	**Friar Rock** 9
Intent (1948)			Problem 1
		Bubbling Over	North Star III 4
	Liz F		Beaming Beauty 8
		Weno	*WHISK BROOM II* 4
Great Above (1972)			Rosie O'Grady 8
		Display	*FAIR PLAY* 9
	Discovery		Cicuta 2
		Ariadne	Light Brigade 8
My Recipe (1947)			Adrienne 23
		Percentage	Midway 10
	Perlette		Gossip Avenue 18
		Escarpolette	Fitz Herbert 4
Intentionally (1956)			Balancoire II 5
		Black Toney	Peter Pan 2
	Bimelech		**Belgravia** 10
		LA TROIENNE	*TEDDY* 2
Better Self (1945)			Helene De Troie 1
		War Admiral	*MAN O' WAR* 4
	Bee Mac		Brushup 11
		Baba Kenny	*BLACK SERVANT* 8
Ta Wee (1966)			Betty Beall 20
		BULL DOG	*TEDDY* 2
	Bull Brier		*PLUCKY LIEGE* 16
		Rose Eternal	Eternal 8
Tilly Rose (1948)			Rose Of Roses 4
		Draymont	Wildair 19
	Tilly Kate		Oreen 2
Aspidistra (1954)			Tea Caddy 9
		Teak	Fricassee 1
		BLANDFORD	Swynford 1
	Blenheim II		Blanche 3
		Malva	Charles O'Malley 5
MAHMOUD (1933)			Wild Arum 1
		GAINSBOROUGH	Bayardo 10
	Mah Mahal		Rosedrop 2
		MUMTAZ MAHAL	The Tetrarch 2
Blackball (1950)			Lady Josephine 9
Holy Bull (1991)		Equipoise	Pennant 8
	Shut Out		**Swinging** 5
		Goose Egg	*CHICLE* 31
			Oval 16
		BLUE LARKSPUR	*BLACK SERVANT* 8
The Axe II (1958)	**Big Event**		Blossom Time 8
		LA TROIENNE	*TEDDY* 2
			Helene De Troie 1
		Hyperion	*GAINSBOROUGH* 2
	Owen Tudor		**Selene** 6
		Mary Tudor II	*PHAROS* 13
Abernant (1946)			Anna Bolena 10
		Rustom Pasha	Son-In-law 5
	Rustom Mahal		Cos 2
		MUMTAZ MAHAL	The Tetrarch 2
Al Hattab (1966)			Lady Josephine 9
		Bahram	*BLANDFORD* 3
	Big Game		Friar's Daughter 16
		Myrobella	Tetratema 14
Serengeti (1944)			Dolabella 6
		Fair Trial	Fairway 13
	Mercy		*LADY JUROR* 9
		Pip Emma	Solario 26
Abyssinia (1953)			Postmark 7
		Plassy	**Bosworth** 6
	Vandale		Pladda 13
		Vanille	La Farina 4
Herbager (1956)			Vaya 3
		Escamillo	*FIRDAUSSI* 1
	Flagette		Estoril 14
		Fidgette	*FIRDAUSSI* 1
Polamia (1955)			Boxeuse 16
		Blenheim II	*BLANDFORD* 3
	MAHMOUD		Malva 1
		Mah Mahal	*GAINSBOROUGH* 2
Sharon Brown (1980)			*MUMTAZ MAHAL* 9
		Pavot	Case Ace 1
	Ampola		Coquelicot 10
		Blue Denim	*BLUE LARKSPUR* 8
Grey Dawn II (1962)			Judy O'Grady 16
		Sir Gallahad III	*TEDDY* 2
	Roman		*PLUCKY LIEGE* 16
		Buckup	*BUCHAN* 16
I Will (1944)			Look Up 20
		Haste	Maintenant 4
	Breathless		Miss Malaprop 23
		Entwine	Chance Shot 3
Agathea's Dawn (1970)			Roseway 1
		Sting	Spur 2
	QUESTIONNAIRE		Gnat 2
		Miss Puzzle	**Disguise II** 10
Alxanth (1946)			Ruby Nethersole 2
		My Play	*FAIR PLAY* 9
Agathea (1955)	Xanthina		*MAHUBAH* 4
		Killimick	Wrack 2
			Oktibbena 16

Holy Bull 1991

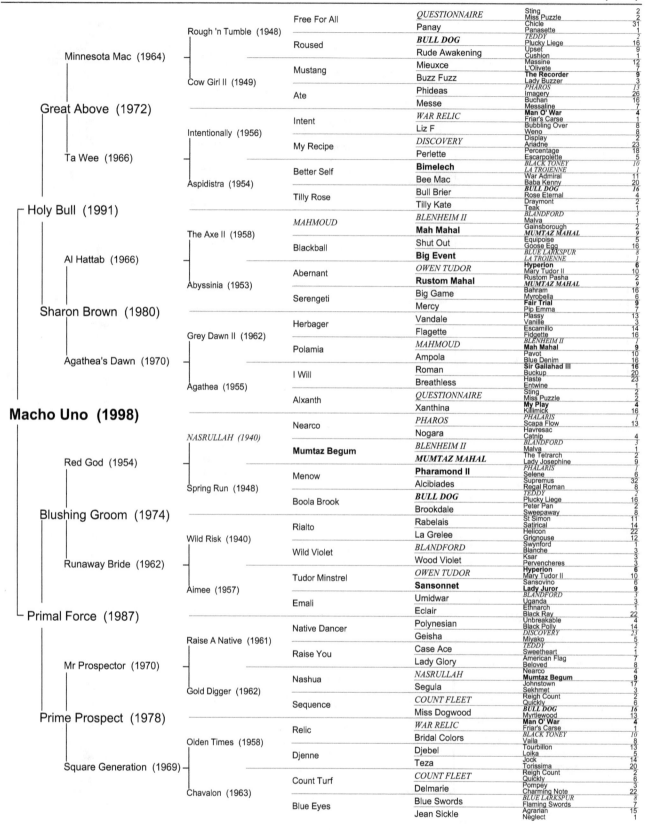

Macho Uno 1998

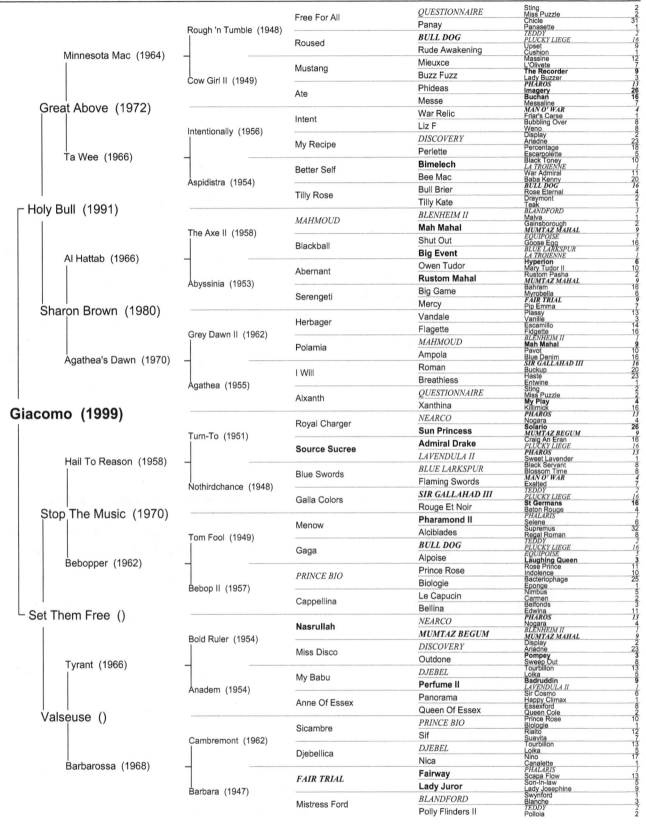

Giacomo (1999)

- **Holy Bull (1991)**
  - Great Above (1972)
    - Minnesota Mac (1964)
      - Rough 'n Tumble (1948)
        - Free For All
          - *QUESTIONNAIRE* — Sting 2, Miss Puzzle 2
          - Panay — Chicle 31, Panasette 1
        - Roused
          - **BULL DOG** — *TEDDY* 2, *PLUCKY LIEGE* 16
          - Rude Awakening — Upset 9, Cushion 12
      - Cow Girl II (1949)
        - Mustang
          - Mieuxce — Massine 7, L'Olivete 7
          - Buzz Fuzz — **The Recorder** 9, Lady Buzzer 3
        - Ate
          - Phideas — *PHAROS* 13, Imagery 26
          - Messe — Buchan 16, Messaline 7
    - Ta Wee (1966)
      - Intentionally (1956)
        - Intent
          - War Relic — *MAN O' WAR* 4, Friar's Carse 1
          - Liz F — Bubbling Over 8, Weno 8
        - My Recipe
          - *DISCOVERY* — Display 2, Ariadne 23
          - Perlette — Percentage 18, Escarpolette 5
      - Aspidistra (1954)
        - Better Self
          - **Bimelech** — Black Toney 10, *LA TROIENNE* 1
          - Bee Mac — War Admiral 11, Baba Kenny 20
        - Tilly Rose
          - Bull Brier — *BULL DOG* 16, Rose Eternal 4
          - Tilly Kate — Draymont 2, Teak 1
  - Sharon Brown (1980)
    - Al Hattab (1966)
      - The Axe II (1958)
        - *MAHMOUD*
          - *BLENHEIM II* — *BLANDFORD* 3, Malva 1
          - **Mah Mahal** — Gainsborough 2, *MUMTAZ MAHAL* 9
        - Blackball
          - Shut Out — *EQUIPOISE* 5, Goose Egg 16
          - **Big Event** — *BLUE LARKSPUR* 8, *LA TROIENNE* 1
      - Abyssinia (1953)
        - Abernant
          - Owen Tudor — **Hyperion** 6, Mary Tudor II 10
          - **Rustom Mahal** — Rustom Pasha 2, *MUMTAZ MAHAL* 9
        - Serengeti
          - Big Game — Bahram 16, Myrobella 6
          - Mercy — *FAIR TRIAL* 9, Pip Emma 7
    - Agathea's Dawn (1970)
      - Grey Dawn II (1962)
        - Herbager
          - Vandale — Plassy 13, Vanille 3
          - Flagette — Escamillo 14, Fidgette 16
        - Polamia
          - *MAHMOUD* — *BLENHEIM II* , **Mah Mahal** 9
          - Ampola — Pavot 10, Blue Denim 16
      - Agathea (1955)
        - I Will
          - Roman — *SIR GALLAHAD III* 16, Buckup 20
          - Breathless — Haste 23, Entwine 1
        - Alxanth
          - *QUESTIONNAIRE* — Sting 2, Miss Puzzle 2
          - Xanthina — **My Play** 4, Killimick 16
- **Set Them Free ()**
  - Stop The Music (1970)
    - Hail To Reason (1958)
      - Turn-To (1951)
        - Royal Charger
          - *NEARCO* — *PHAROS* 13, Nogara 4
          - **Sun Princess** — **Solario** 26, *MUMTAZ BEGUM* 9
        - **Source Sucree**
          - **Admiral Drake** — Craig An Eran 16, *PLUCKY LIEGE* 16
          - *LAVENDULA II* — *PHAROS* 13, Sweet Lavender 1
      - Nothirdchance (1948)
        - Blue Swords
          - *BLUE LARKSPUR* — Black Servant 8, Blossom Time 8
          - Flaming Swords — *MAN O' WAR* 4, Exalted 7
        - Galla Colors
          - *SIR GALLAHAD III* — *TEDDY* 2, *PLUCKY LIEGE* 16
          - Rouge Et Noir — **St Germains** 16, Baton Rouge 4
    - Bebopper (1962)
      - Tom Fool (1949)
        - Menow
          - **Pharamond II** — *PHALARIS* 1, Selene 6
          - Alcibiades — Supremus 32, Regal Roman 8
        - Gaga
          - *BULL DOG* — *TEDDY* 2, *PLUCKY LIEGE* 16
          - Alpoise — *EQUIPOISE* 5, **Laughing Queen** 3
      - Bebop II (1957)
        - *PRINCE BIO*
          - Prince Rose — Rose Prince 11, Indolence 10
          - Biologie — Bacteriophage 25, Eponge 1
        - Cappellina
          - Le Capucin — Nimbus 5, Carmen 2
          - Bellina — Belfonds 3, Edwina 11
  - Valseuse ()
    - Tyrant (1966)
      - Bold Ruler (1954)
        - **Nasrullah**
          - *NEARCO* — *PHAROS* 13, Nogara 4
          - *MUMTAZ BEGUM* — *BLENHEIM II* 1, *MUMTAZ MAHAL* 9
        - Miss Disco
          - *DISCOVERY* — Display 2, Ariadne 23
          - Outdone — **Pompey** 3, Sweep Out 8
      - Anadem (1954)
        - My Babu
          - *DJEBEL* — Tourbillon 13, Loika 5
          - **Perfume II** — **Badruddin** 9, *LAVENDULA II* 1
        - Anne Of Essex
          - Panorama — Sir Cosmo 6, Happy Climax 1
          - Queen Of Essex — Essexford 8, Queen Cole 2
    - Barbarossa (1968)
      - Cambremont (1962)
        - Sicambre
          - *PRINCE BIO* — Prince Rose 10, Biologie 12
          - Sif — Rialto 7, Suavita
        - Djebellica
          - *DJEBEL* — Tourbillon 13, Loika 5
          - Nica — Nino 17, Canalette 1
      - Barbara (1947)
        - *FAIR TRIAL*
          - **Fairway** — *PHALARIS* 1, Scapa Flow 13
          - **Lady Juror** — Son-In-Law 5, Lady Josephine 9
        - Mistress Ford
          - *BLANDFORD* — Swynford 1, Blanche 3
          - Polly Flinders II — *TEDDY* 2, Polloia 2

Giacomo 1999

Chapter 25

Almost Forgotten: John P. Grier

The thoroughly game John P. Grier, after running neck and neck with Man O' War throughout the race. Man O' War is seen here bounding ahead in the last stretch after his jockey gave him the whip. This race proved to be one of the most outstanding races in all of track history. The great Man O' War, whose power and ability was so massive that he was regularly rated by his jockey in all his races, so no one really knew how good he was. This particular race is the only one of his twenty-one races where he actually had to extend himself to beat a horse, and it was this little horse—John P. Grier—who made Man O' War finally earn one of his victories. —1920

Upset, a close relative to John P. Grier, gave Man O' War his only defeat—he was a decent sire as well—Thoroughbred Types.

Man O' War and John P. Grier raced against each other three times. Little John certainly gave 'Big Red' (Man O' War) a run for the money in all of them, but none more than in the contest pictured above, as he ran neck and neck with him for most of the race, once actually nosing ahead until close to the finish when the jockey finally took the whip to Man O' War causing him to bound forward. Man O' War then won by two lengths. This was the 1920 running of the Dwyer Stakes, and it is still being talked about today. Little John gave his all and almost took it all, and according to Man O' War's jockey it was the first time that his horse had ever extended himself. The race set two new records: 1:19 ½ for six furlongs and then 1:49 ⅛ for the entire 1⅛ mile. For once Man O' War knew he had met a true opponent. Instead of being broken by the defeat given to him by Big Red, John P. Grier went on that same season to win four stakes races. This is a classy horse.

[Note: Man O' War actually lost one of his races; however it is not considered a true defeat as he was bumped severely, then blocked and interfered with, and when finally free he charged forward but just ran out of track before he caught the aptly named Upset. Because of the circumstances of this meet, the race with Upset is considered a fluke, plus Upset's jockey acknowledged that if he had just moved over a little Man O' War would have won easily. With clear running in their next contest Man O' War easily won over Upset. With Little John it was different, as he ran right alongside of the Big Guy, staying with him and making him work for it. I agree with the ranking of Man O' War as far and away higher class than most of his opponents—he was a phenomenon and a marvel of his time and still is now—possibly the greatest horse ever. However, as a pedigree studier, I could not help but notice that Upset, like John P. Grier, was a son of Whisk Broom II, and in addition he is out of a mare who is closely related to John's dam, making them virtual ¾ siblings. It is also notable that the difference between the two of them is that imported Voter is more powerful in Upset's dam, while Domino is the leading element in John P. Grier's dam (see pedigrees). Once again we find that the Domino factor makes the difference. Upset is found as second dam-sire of Rough n' Tumble—he can be used as a line to build complexity.]

John P. Grier was a son of Whisk Broom II out of Wonder by Disguise II. It is interesting that his strongest inbreeding is provided by his dam and his sire's dam. Whisk Broom II's dam Audience is inbred to Maggie B. B. RH, sex-balanced 4x4. His dam Wonder is inbred to Domino, sex-balanced 2x3. Whisk Broom II was not always rated as a key genetic element, but now we recognize his enduring contribution, and as breeders we should aim for his lines, as he is inbred to one of the greatest broodmares of our Heroic Age: Maggie B. B. RH. For this alone, he is an important bloodline (see how significant he was in Rough n' Tumble's pedigree in Chapter 24), and as we saw above, Little John was a top-class racer (John P. Grier physically resembles his sire Whisk Broom II—see his photo for comparison in Chapter 24).

John P. Grier 1917—a talented, tough and durable racehorse and a sire of importance. —photo by W. A. Rouch

His record at stud, like his sire, is underappreciated, yet he keeps turning up in the very best of the generations after him. John P. Grier's stud record is a study in what actually promotes racing class and potency. Here are a few of his most notable offspring:

His daughter Marching Home 1932 is now rated a *reine* for her produce record. Out of Warrior Lass (a Man O' War daughter) she was bred by Walter Armstrong. Combining Man O' War with John P Grier has proven to be a good breeding strategy. Marching Home (pedigree) was a good racer, winning twenty races, and then she produced five offspring, three of them stakes-winning full siblings by Espino. Her daughter Bounding Home won the Belmont but very little else and unfortunately has the distinction of being one of the worst horses to win a classic. Espino was an American-bred of strictly French and English bloodlines—a fair racer

winning nine of thirty-seven starts, and this design puts Bounding Home line-bred 4x5x5 to Voter 1894, a stallion bred by Foxhall Keene in England and later imported in the US. At four he was sent back to England to race again and had a lackluster campaign, so he was brought back to New York and did reasonably well again.

Mr. Keene had a strong belief that English lines were needed to add into the American Thoroughbred for its continual improvement, and besides the stallion Voter he often purchased and imported English mares to breed to his stallions (Domino, Commando, etc.). Voter was therefore used extensively, but he is also one of those the TRA has pointed out as not breeding on—what I think they mean is that he actually downgraded the racing class. His best offspring was Ballot. Bounding Home produced little of note in her progeny. Her durable and useful gelding full brother Breezing Home was raced one hundred seventy-eight times with twenty-four wins, thirty-two seconds, and twenty-four thirds, and her sister Romping Home also won some stakes starting fourteen times winning four. Romping Home produced little at stud. As we can see illustrated here during the Jersey Act, we find strongly demonstrated that **American lines needed occasional outcrossing of course, but very few of the imports actually improved racing class, and they most certainly diluted these mare's ability to pass racing class on**.

However their ¾ sister Sailing Home did better at stud, and her daughter Reason to Earn is the dam of Bold Reasoning, the sire of Seattle Slew. The difference in their pedigrees is Sailing Home is by a son of Espino—and that son's dam brings in **more of Domino**—therefore giving the outcross hybrid vigor factor but continuing the dominance in speed. The influence of Domino for racing class cannot be denied.

The siblings had a ½ sister Flaring Home by Flares, who raced fourteen times with three wins/eight seconds/one third, and had a fair record at stud producing the resilient but poor racing filly Near Home—one hundred thirty-five starts with one win. Other descendants are Fast Gun who did better as he ran ninety times with sixteen wins, and the Near Home daughter Tudor Mistress ran fifty-nine times with four wins, eight seconds, and seven thirds. Tudor Mistress was a decent broodmare producing the stakes winner Shore Patrol, who with ninety-four starts had twelve wins, eleven seconds, and twenty thirds—he was 4x4 to Pharos. These are 'good' horses but lacking greatness in class; however, do not miss the soundness and durability here and in the other siblings—for whether they won their races or not they raced an astounding number of times **sound.**

Marching Home had a full sister in Little Rebel who was dam of Bold, a Preakness winner who unfortunately died at age four after being hit by lightning before he stood at stud.

In contrast, notice the upgrade in racing and breeding performance that comes through John P. Grier's daughter Appeal 1927, who was out of the *reine* Sweetheart, an Ultimus daughter (dam of Case Ace and **inbred to Domino**). This mare was a good stakes winner, and she produced three stakes winners: Plea, The Finest (eighty starts/fifteen wins), and the good broodmare Invoke. Her daughter Invoke by Teddy in-turn produced stakes winners such as Wildlife by Easton, Manipur by Mahmoud, and Admiral Drake by War Admiral—he earned $145,000 with sixty-eight starts/seventeen wins/fifteen seconds/eleven thirds.

Another good John P. Grier daughter is the champion filly Dini 1936 out of Quivera by Display. She was bred by Mr. Roebling, who then lost her in a claiming race to Willie Winfrey for whom she won twenty-seven races. She has an interesting pedigree, as she carries a strong filly factor of **Hindoo daughters 4x4**. Notice the upgrade from the Hindoo daughters. She is also a notable broodmare as she is dam of the champion Dedicate, a major stakes winner who won the Champion-Older-Horse title as well Co-Horse of Year in 1957. He is by Princequillo and is an important sire, as he produced winners such as the champion Smart Deb and he is also sire of the *reines* Mock Orange and Natashka. (Mock Orange is the second dam of the good modern sire Cryptoclearance—his pedigree in previous chapter).

Hindoo 1878, sire of Hanover, was a founder of a dynasty; building up his lines has a proven record of success in performance.—Library of Congress

One of John P. Grier's best sons was Jack High, a notable racer winning fifteen of thirty-four; he was second in nine and third in six. His wins included the Belmont and Withers stakes, and he was still racing and winning at six years old. He is line-bred 5x6x5 to Domino and his full sister Correction, and he is 6x4x5 to Hermit/Chamioness—an equally powerful configuration—an indication of potency. He did well at stud; in 1947 he was rated number fifteen in leading sires. His daughter High Fleet out of Armada by Man O' War won the prestigious Coaching Club American Oaks and was voted Champion-Filly of 1936. She is described as being a very courageous and game racer (like both her grandsires), and she won nine of thirteen races against good company. She had only four foals, but they included stakes-winning steeplechasers: Fleetown and Fleet Command. Notice the upgrade that occurs when Domino lines are made dominant and the Fair Play line in brought in.

High Fleet's full sister Flota produced the stakes winner and good sire Sailor—with twenty-one starts he won twelve, was second in three, and third in one more—a very good record, winning $321,000. Sailor was 3x4 to Man O' War through daughters—this dominance once again proves success in the production of high-class racers—the top broodmare Nothird-chance is also 3x4 to Man O' War through daughters (see Chapter 13). Sailor was a good and solid sire, and his first-class daughter Bowl of Flowers ran sixteen races—winning ten, placing second in three, third in three, plus she was the dam of Whiskey Road, an important sire in Australia. Sailor's son Crewman raced very well also; with twenty-nine starts he was first in nine, second once, and third three times, and Sailor's son Ahoy was the 1964 Champion Sprinter. It is interesting that Ahoy's dam carries Lady Josephine 4x5—another source of speed. Sailor's daughter Gay Sonnet is third dam of important modern sire Distorted Humor (see Chapter 27).

Another daughter of Jack High was Noodle Soup, out of a Supremus dam (Domino again)—she is dam of Kentucky Derby and Belmont stakes winner Needles and the stakes winner Menolene. Another good broodmare by Jack High was Highclere out of Rosebloom by Chicle (Hamburg dam). She is dam of the stakes winner Sopranist.

Jack High's sons overall seemed to be lesser animals than his daughters, and while Andy K won some stakes (six)—and had racing class as he was often second to the great Bimelech—he also had extremely straight pasterns that curtailed his career. He stood in California.

In contrast, his daughter Jack's Jill was able to race sixty-three times and win seventeen while remaining sound. Her pedigree is interesting, as it has Whisk Broom II and his full sister Matinee 3x4, which of course means four lines of Maggie B. B. RH. Building up Maggie B. B. RH is another successful strategy.

The multiple champion Lucky Draw with his trainer W.F. Mulholland. —image from *Who's Who in Thoroughbred Racing*

Perhaps his most famous son (unfortunately a gelding) was the phenomenal stakes winner Lucky Draw who raced thirty-five times—won sixteen, placed second in six and third in four—winning $287,000 while beating the likes of Stymie, Pavot, and Polynesian. He raced until he was seven and set six track records, plus he equaled the world record of 1:54 for 1 3/16 miles in the Narragansett Special. He was a wonderful racer trained by a gifted manager: W.F. Mulholland.

But back to John P. Grier, because his story is not over, and I saved the best for last. His son El Chico 1936 was a good racer but had to be put down with a fractured seismoid at age three. Bred by the Walter Armstrong/Leslie Combs II partnership, he was voted best Two-Year-Old in 1938 when he won all seven of his starts, and they were all stakes races. He is 4x3 to Pink Domino. What he could have produced at stud is surely a huge loss that is plainly illustrated for us by the stud career of his full sister El Chica who produced the great mare Miyako—the granddam of Native Dancer. According to the pedigree experts Alan Porter and Anne Peters, the genetic power in Native Dancer is coming from his second dam Miyako, which they attribute to her lines of Sweep and Whisk Broom II close-up and that she is inbred to Ben Brush (*Patterns of Greatness II*).

While looking at her pedigree, also take a moment to see the strong female element in this mare. She has three powerful filly factors through sons and daughters of the following mares: Pink Domino 3x2, Clemence 6x5, and Queen Mary 6x5x5. There is also another filly factor of Woodbine through daughters 6x6. Surely these strong female factors worked to her advantage in transmitting sex-linked genes.

Fortunately Miyako was bred repeatedly to the great stayer and weight carrier Discovery (more Hamburg/Fair Play). Her son Columbus was a stakes winner, but it was his full sister Geisha who produced Native Dancer. Geisha was a good producer also and had six full sibling offspring; one which was Native Dancer. These siblings demonstrate the variance possible in gene transmission. The sire Polynesian was 4x3 to Polymelus, and the dam Geisha was 4x5 Pink Domino and 5x6x6 to Domino, and it is interesting to students of genetics that all of them could be considered moderate horses except Native Dancer and his sister Teahouse. Although she was unraced, Teahouse became a significant broodmare; of her eight foals, six of them raced, and all of those were winners. Native Dancer needs no introduction as he is one of the greatest racers and sires of all time, but the other three are moderate in ability and at stud—indicating there is some high-class dominance, but it is not reinforced enough to throw consistently to the offspring—obviously Native Dancer and Teahouse got the better distribution of the genes.

However, there is a half-sister that was remarkable, and that is Orientation. A fair racer, with three wins out of twenty-two starts, she is an important broodmare, as out of fourteen foals, twelve ran with ten of them winners, and three of those were stakes winners. Her sire is Questionnaire, who is also the grandsire of Rough n' Tumble (Chapter 23), who is descended from the Spendthrift full brother Fellowcraft. This gives her a strong filly factor of Disguise II daughters 2x4, surely an element in her success at stud and an obvious reinforcement of the Domino lines from Miyako—a validation of the theory proposed by Peters and Porter above.

The legacy of John P. Grier is interesting for several reasons—he clearly was a high-class racer, one of the best of his time, and his stud record is overall super with a propensity to produce very sound and durable racers. However, his stud career is also very instructive to us, as it plainly shows us that his best offspring were created when he was given an strong injection of additional Heroic Era genes from his mate—especially Domino, but also Fair Play, Hindoo, Maggie B. B. RH, and Ben Brush. We can use Little John's stud history as a compass to lead us to victory by pointing to the benefits of concentrating the Heroic Era genetics.

If someone were to ask me what they could do to improve the racing performance of their horses, I would say look at history—it has told us the answer: add more Domino! I realize this is a little too simplistic, but traditionally this has been what has made the difference in the majority of great performers in this country—which we can see clearly demonstrated in the offspring of Dr. Fager and John P. Grier for instance. Domino as we discovered is the most powerful deliver of Lexington RH et al, and in our modern day his genetics have received a tremendous reinforcement when the background power of Diomed was dynamically increased with the fortunate blend of La Troienne with those focused carriers of Domino (Lexington)—there can be no denying the results of this combination. The tremendous genetic reach of War Admiral and Blue Larkspur and Buckpasser—all now considered some of the greatest broodmare sires of the last century can be attributed to this power. The descendants of Domino, and his close relatives: Americus, Beaming Beauty, Hamburg, Durban and Blackstock etc. will all provide these proven genetic boosts, which when multiplied and combined with pedigree patterns that bring this power to the fore, will give us the performance we are looking for.

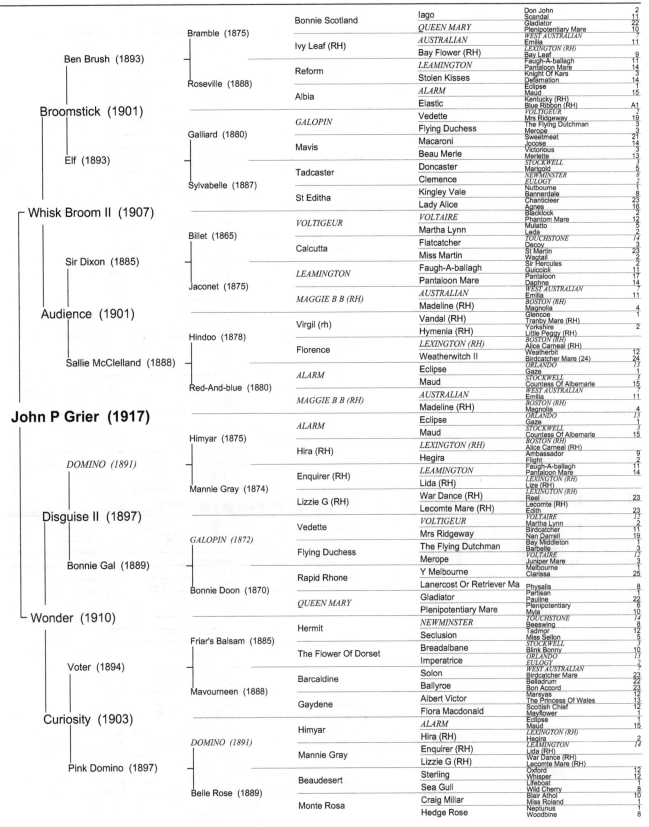

John P Grier (1917)

- **Whisk Broom II (1907)**
  - **Broomstick (1901)**
    - **Ben Brush (1893)**
      - Bramble (1875)
        - Bonnie Scotland
          - Iago
            - Don John [2]
            - Scandal [11]
          - QUEEN MARY
            - Gladiator [22]
            - Plenipotentiary Mare [10]
        - Ivy Leaf (RH)
          - AUSTRALIAN
            - WEST AUSTRALIAN [7]
            - Emilia [11]
          - Bay Flower (RH)
            - LEXINGTON (RH)
            - Bay Leaf [9]
      - Roseville (1888)
        - Reform
          - LEAMINGTON
            - Faugh-A-ballagh [11]
            - Pantaloon Mare [14]
          - Stolen Kisses
            - Knight Of Kars [3]
            - Defamation [14]
        - Albia
          - ALARM
            - Eclipse [1]
            - Maud [15]
          - Elastic
            - Kentucky (RH)
            - Blue Ribbon (RH) [A1]
    - **Elf (1893)**
      - Galliard (1880)
        - GALOPIN
          - Vedette
            - VOLTIGEUR [2]
            - Mrs Ridgeway [19]
          - Flying Duchess
            - The Flying Dutchman [3]
            - Merope [3]
        - Mavis
          - Macaroni
            - Sweetmeat [21]
            - Jocose [14]
          - Beau Merle
            - Victorious [3]
            - Merlette [13]
      - Sylvabelle (1887)
        - Tadcaster
          - Doncaster
            - STOCKWELL [3]
            - Marigold [5]
          - Clemence
            - NEWMINSTER [8]
            - EULOGY [2]
        - St Editha
          - Kingley Vale
            - Nutbourne [1]
            - Bannerdale [8]
          - Lady Alice
            - Chanticleer [23]
            - Agnes [16]
  - **Audience (1901)**
    - **Sir Dixon (1885)**
      - Billet (1865)
        - VOLTIGEUR
          - VOLTAIRE
            - Blacklock [2]
            - Phantom Mare [12]
          - Martha Lynn
            - Mulatto [5]
            - Leda [2]
        - Calcutta
          - Flatcatcher
            - TOUCHSTONE [14]
            - Decoy [3]
          - Miss Martin
            - St Martin [23]
            - Wagtail [2]
      - Jaconet (1875)
        - LEAMINGTON
          - Faugh-A-ballagh
            - Sir Hercules [11]
            - Guiccioli [11]
          - Pantaloon Mare
            - Pantaloon [17]
            - Daphne [14]
        - MAGGIE B B (RH)
          - AUSTRALIAN
            - WEST AUSTRALIAN [7]
            - Emilia [11]
          - Madeline (RH)
            - BOSTON (RH)
            - Magnolia [4]
    - **Sallie McClelland (1888)**
      - Hindoo (1878)
        - Virgil (rh)
          - Vandal (RH)
            - Glencoe [1]
            - Tranby Mare (RH)
          - Hymenia (RH)
            - Yorkshire [2]
            - Little Peggy (RH)
        - Florence
          - LEXINGTON (RH)
            - BOSTON (RH)
            - Alice Carneal (RH)
          - Weatherwitch II
            - Weatherbit [12]
            - Birdcatcher Mare (24) [24]
      - Red-And-blue (1880)
        - ALARM
          - Eclipse
            - ORLANDO [13]
            - Gaze [1]
          - Maud
            - STOCKWELL [3]
            - Countess Of Albemarle [15]
        - MAGGIE B B (RH)
          - AUSTRALIAN
            - WEST AUSTRALIAN [7]
            - Emilia [11]
          - Madeline (RH)
            - BOSTON (RH)
            - Magnolia [4]

- **Wonder (1910)**
  - **Disguise II (1897)**
    - **DOMINO (1891)**
      - Himyar (1875)
        - ALARM
          - Eclipse
            - ORLANDO [13]
            - Gaze [1]
          - Maud
            - STOCKWELL [3]
            - Countess Of Albemarle [15]
        - Hira (RH)
          - LEXINGTON (RH)
            - BOSTON (RH)
            - Alice Carneal (RH)
          - Hegira
            - Ambassador [9]
            - Flight [2]
      - Mannie Gray (1874)
        - Enquirer (RH)
          - LEAMINGTON
            - Faugh-A-ballagh [11]
            - Pantaloon Mare [14]
          - Lida (RH)
            - LEXINGTON (RH)
            - Lize (RH)
        - Lizzie G (RH)
          - War Dance (RH)
            - LEXINGTON (RH)
            - Reel [23]
          - Lecomte Mare (RH)
            - Lecomte (RH)
            - Edith [23]
    - **Bonnie Gal (1889)**
      - GALOPIN (1872)
        - Vedette
          - VOLTIGEUR
            - VOLTAIRE [12]
            - Martha Lynn [2]
          - Mrs Ridgeway
            - Birdcatcher [11]
            - Nan Darrell [19]
        - Flying Duchess
          - The Flying Dutchman
            - Bay Middleton [1]
            - Barbelle [3]
          - Merope
            - VOLTAIRE [12]
            - Juniper Mare [3]
      - Bonnie Doon (1870)
        - Rapid Rhone
          - Y Melbourne
            - Melbourne [1]
            - Clarissa [25]
          - Lanercost Or Retriever Ma
            - Physalis [8]
            - Partisan [1]
        - QUEEN MARY
          - Gladiator
            - Pauline [22]
            - Plenipotentiary [6]
          - Plenipotentiary Mare
            - Myla [10]
  - **Curiosity (1903)**
    - **Voter (1894)**
      - Friar's Balsam (1885)
        - Hermit
          - NEWMINSTER
            - TOUCHSTONE [14]
            - Beeswing [8]
          - Seclusion
            - Tadmor [12]
            - Miss Sellon [5]
        - The Flower Of Dorset
          - Breadalbane
            - STOCKWELL [3]
            - Blink Bonny [10]
          - Imperatrice
            - ORLANDO [13]
            - EULOGY [2]
      - Mavourneen (1888)
        - Barcaldine
          - Solon
            - WEST AUSTRALIAN [7]
            - Birdcatcher Mare [23]
          - Ballyroe
            - Belladrum [22]
            - Bon Accord [23]
        - Gaydene
          - Albert Victor
            - Marsyas [12]
            - The Princess Of Wales [13]
          - Flora Macdonald
            - Scottish Chief [12]
            - Mayflower [1]
    - **Pink Domino (1897)**
      - DOMINO (1891)
        - Himyar
          - ALARM
            - Eclipse [1]
            - Maud [15]
          - Hira (RH)
            - LEXINGTON (RH) [2]
            - Hegira [14]
        - Mannie Gray
          - Enquirer (RH)
            - LEAMINGTON
            - Lida (RH)
          - Lizzie G (RH)
            - War Dance (RH)
            - Lecomte Mare (RH)
      - Belle Rose (1889)
        - Beaudesert
          - Sterling
            - Oxford [12]
            - Whisper [12]
          - Sea Gull
            - Lifeboat [1]
            - Wild Cherry [8]
        - Monte Rosa
          - Craig Millar
            - Blair Athol [10]
            - Miss Roland [1]
          - Hedge Rose
            - Neptunus [1]
            - Woodbine [8]

John P. Grier 1917

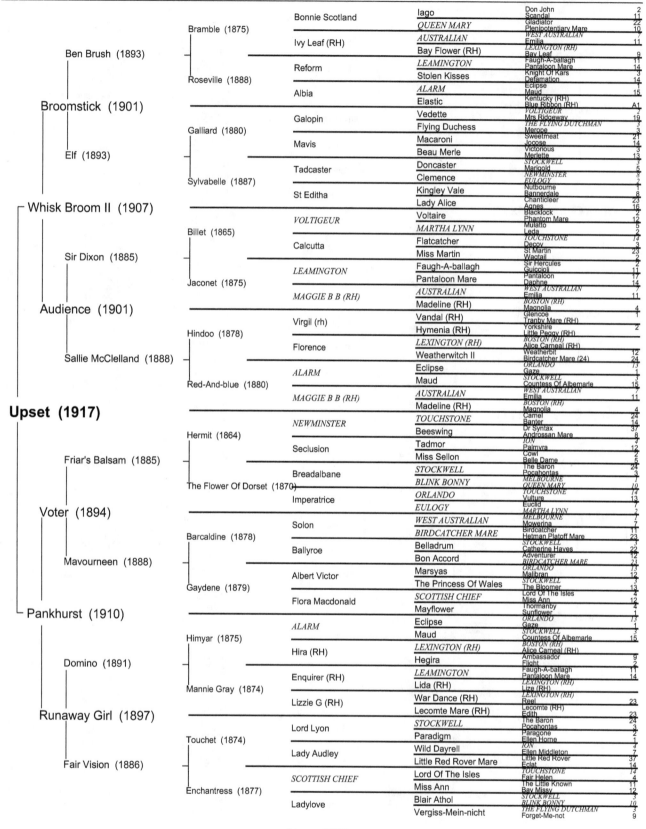

Upset 1917

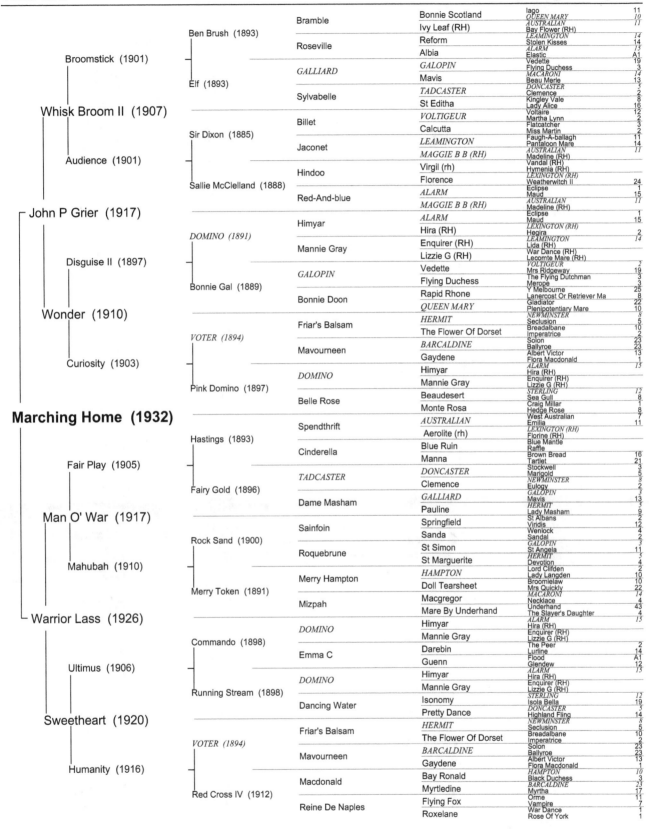

Marching Home 1932

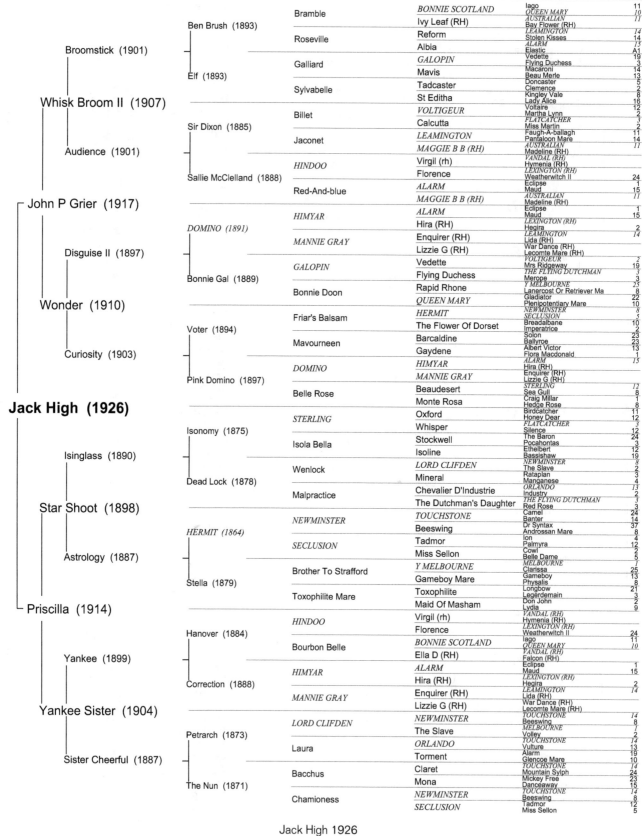

Broomstick (1901)

Whisk Broom II (1907)

Audience (1901)

John P Grier (1917)

Disguise II (1897)

Wonder (1910)

Curiosity (1903)

Jack High (1926)

Isinglass (1890)

Star Shoot (1898)

Astrology (1887)

Priscilla (1914)

Yankee (1899)

Yankee Sister (1904)

Sister Cheerful (1887)

Ben Brush (1893)

Bramble	*BONNIE SCOTLAND*	Iago	11
		QUEEN MARY	10
	Ivy Leaf (RH)	*AUSTRALIAN*	11
		Bay Flower (RH)	
Roseville	Reform	*LEAMINGTON*	14
		Stolen Kisses	14
	Albia	*ALARM*	15
		Elastic	A1

Elf (1893)

Galliard	*GALOPIN*	Vedette	19
		Flying Duchess	3
	Mavis	Macaroni	14
		Beau Merle	13
Sylvabelle	Tadcaster	Doncaster	5
		Clemence	2
	St Editha	Kingley Vale	8
		Lady Alice	16

Sir Dixon (1885)

Billet	*VOLTIGEUR*	Voltaire	12
		Martha Lynn	2
	Calcutta	*FLATCATCHER*	3
		Miss Martin	2
Jaconet	*LEAMINGTON*	Faugh-A-ballagh	11
		Pantaloon Mare	14
	MAGGIE B B (RH)	*AUSTRALIAN*	11
		Madeline (RH)	

Sallie McClelland (1888)

HINDOO	Virgil (rh)	*VANDAL (RH)*	
		Hymenia (RH)	
	Florence	*LEXINGTON (RH)*	
		Weatherwitch II	24
Red-And-blue	*ALARM*	Eclipse	1
		Maud	15
	MAGGIE B B (RH)	*AUSTRALIAN*	11
		Madeline (RH)	

DOMINO (1891)

HIMYAR	*ALARM*	Eclipse	1
		Maud	15
	Hira (RH)	*LEXINGTON (RH)*	
		Hegira	2
MANNIE GRAY	Enquirer (RH)	*LEAMINGTON*	14
		Lida (RH)	
	Lizzie G (RH)	War Dance (RH)	
		Lecomte Mare (RH)	

Bonnie Gal (1889)

GALOPIN	Vedette	*VOLTIGEUR*	2
		Mrs Ridgeway	19
	Flying Duchess	*THE FLYING DUTCHMAN*	3
		Merope	3
Bonnie Doon	Rapid Rhone	*Y MELBOURNE*	25
		Lanercost Or Retriever Ma	8
	QUEEN MARY	Gladiator	22
		Plenipotentiary Mare	10

Voter (1894)

Friar's Balsam	*HERMIT*	*NEWMINSTER*	8
		SECLUSION	5
	The Flower Of Dorset	Breadalbane	10
		Imperatrice	2
Mavourneen	Barcaldine	Solon	23
		Ballyroe	23
	Gaydene	Albert Victor	13
		Flora Macdonald	1

Pink Domino (1897)

DOMINO	*HIMYAR*	*ALARM*	15
		Hira (RH)	
	MANNIE GRAY	Enquirer (RH)	
		Lizzie G (RH)	
Belle Rose	Beaudesert	*STERLING*	12
		Sea Gull	8
	Monte Rosa	Craig Millar	1
		Hedge Rose	8

Isonomy (1875)

STERLING	Oxford	Birdcatcher	11
		Honey Dear	12
	Whisper	*FLATCATCHER*	3
		Silence	12
Isola Bella	Stockwell	The Baron	24
		Pocahontas	3
	Isoline	Ethelbert	12
		Bassishaw	19

Dead Lock (1878)

Wenlock	*LORD CLIFDEN*	*NEWMINSTER*	8
		The Slave	2
	Mineral	Rataplan	3
		Manganese	4
Malpractice	Chevalier D'Industrie	*ORLANDO*	13
		Industry	2
	The Dutchman's Daughter	*THE FLYING DUTCHMAN*	3
		Red Rose	3

HERMIT (1864)

NEWMINSTER	*TOUCHSTONE*	Camel	24
		Banter	14
	Beeswing	Dr Syntax	37
		Androssan Mare	8
SECLUSION	Tadmor	Ion	4
		Palmyra	12
	Miss Sellon	Cowl	2
		Belle Dame	5

Stella (1879)

Brother To Strafford	*Y MELBOURNE*	*MELBOURNE*	1
		Clarissa	25
	Gameboy Mare	Gameboy	13
		Physalis	8
Toxophilite Mare	Toxophilite	Longbow	21
		Legerdemain	3
	Maid Of Masham	Don John	2
		Lydia	9

Hanover (1884)

HINDOO	Virgil (rh)	*VANDAL (RH)*	
		Hymenia (RH)	
	Florence	*LEXINGTON (RH)*	
		Weatherwitch II	24
Bourbon Belle	*BONNIE SCOTLAND*	Iago	11
		QUEEN MARY	10
	Ella D (RH)	*VANDAL (RH)*	
		Falcon (RH)	

Correction (1888)

HIMYAR	*ALARM*	Eclipse	1
		Maud	15
	Hira (RH)	*LEXINGTON (RH)*	
		Hegira	2
MANNIE GRAY	Enquirer (RH)	*LEAMINGTON*	14
		Lida (RH)	
	Lizzie G (RH)	War Dance (RH)	
		Lecomte Mare (RH)	

Petrarch (1873)

LORD CLIFDEN	*NEWMINSTER*	*TOUCHSTONE*	14
		Beeswing	8
	The Slave	*MELBOURNE*	1
		Volley	2
Laura	*ORLANDO*	*TOUCHSTONE*	14
		Vulture	13
	Torment	Alarm	19
		Glencoe Mare	10

The Nun (1871)

Bacchus	Claret	*TOUCHSTONE*	14
		Mountain Sylph	24
	Mona	Mickey Free	23
		Danceaway	15
Chamioness	*NEWMINSTER*	*TOUCHSTONE*	14
		Beeswing	8
	SECLUSION	Tadmor	12
		Miss Sellon	5

Jack High 1926

KATHLEEN H. KIRSAN

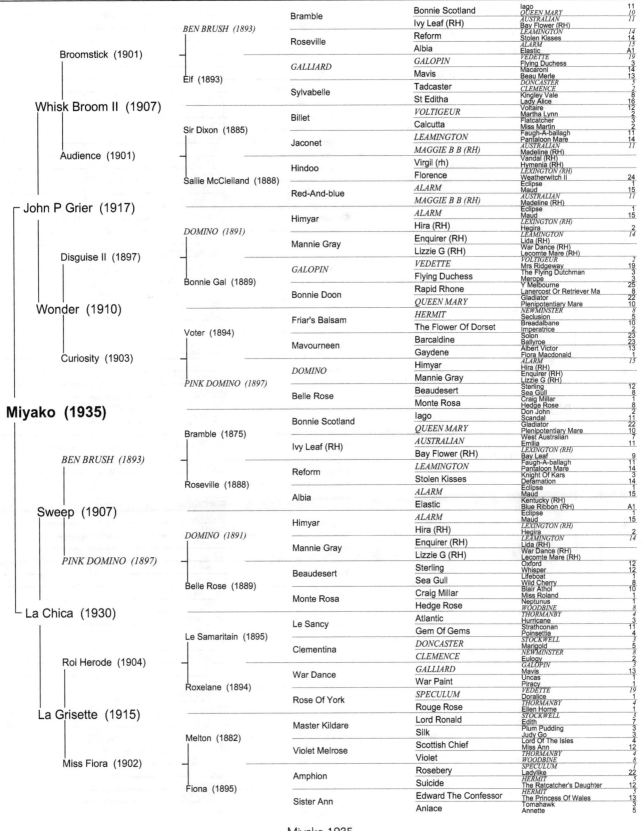

Miyako 1935

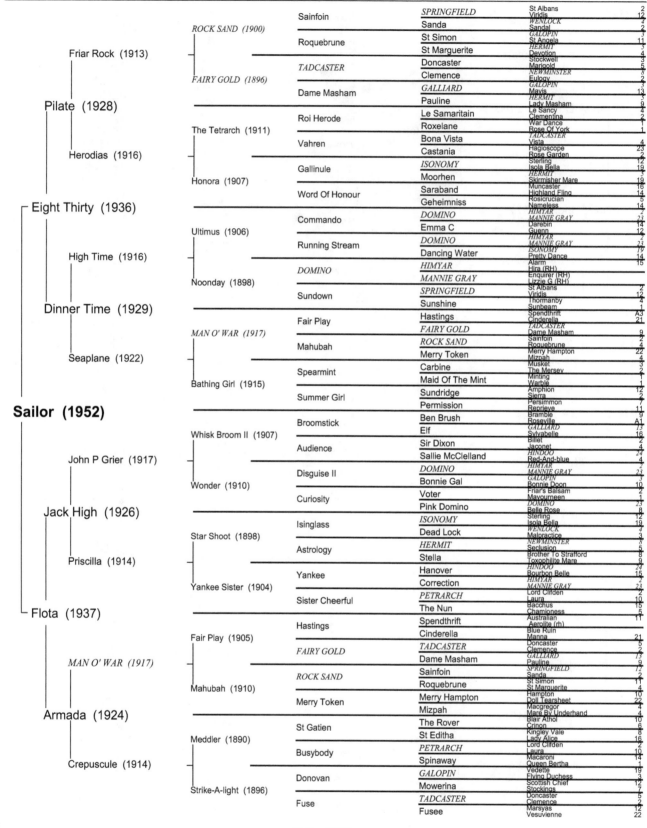

		Sainfoin	*SPRINGFIELD* — St Albans 2 / Viridis 12
	ROCK SAND (1900)		Sanda — *WENLOCK* 4 / Sandal 2
		Roquebrune	St Simon — *GALOPIN* 3 / St Angela 11
Friar Rock (1913)			St Marguerite — *HERMIT* 3 / Devotion 4
		Doncaster	Stockwell 3 / Marigold 5
	FAIRY GOLD (1896)	Clemence	*NEWMINSTER* 8 / Eulogy 2
Pilate (1928)		Dame Masham	*GALLIARD* — *GALOPIN* 3 / Mavis 13
			Pauline — *HERMIT* 3 / Lady Masham 9
		Roi Herode	Le Samaritain — Le Sancy 4 / Clementina 2
	The Tetrarch (1911)		Roxelane — War Dance 1 / Rose Of York 1
Herodias (1916)		Vahren	Bona Vista — *TADCASTER* / Vista 4
			Castania — Hagioscope 23 / Rose Garden 2
		Gallinule	*ISONOMY* — Sterling 12 / Isola Bella 19
	Honora (1907)		Moorhen — *HERMIT* 3 / Skirmisher Mare 19
		Word Of Honour	Saraband — Muncaster 16 / Highland Fling 14
			Geheimniss — Rosicrucian 5 / Nameless 14

Sailor (1952)

		Commando	*DOMINO* — *HIMYAR* 2 / *MANNIE GRAY* 23
	Ultimus (1906)		Emma C — Darebin 14 / Guenn 12
Eight Thirty (1936)		Running Stream	*DOMINO* — *HIMYAR* 2 / *MANNIE GRAY* 23
			Dancing Water — *ISONOMY* 19 / Pretty Dance 14
		DOMINO	*HIMYAR* — Alarm 15 / Hira (RH)
High Time (1916)	Noonday (1898)		*MANNIE GRAY* — Enquirer (RH) / Lizzie G (RH)
		Sundown	*SPRINGFIELD* — St Albans 2 / Viridis 12
Dinner Time (1929)			Sunshine — Thormanby 4 / Sunbeam
		Fair Play	Hastings — Spendthrift A3 / Cinderella 21
	MAN O' WAR (1917)		*FAIRY GOLD* — *TADCASTER* / Dame Masham 9
Seaplane (1922)		Mahubah	*ROCK SAND* — Sainfoin 2 / Roquebrune 22
			Merry Token — Merry Hampton / Mizpah 4
		Spearmint	Carbine — Musket 3 / The Mersey 2
	Bathing Girl (1915)		Maid Of The Mint — Minting 1 / Warble 1
		Summer Girl	Sundridge — Amphion 12 / Sierra 2
			Permission — Persimmon 7 / Reprieve 11
		Broomstick	Ben Brush — Bramble 9 / Roseville A1
	Whisk Broom II (1907)		Elf — *GALLIARD* 13 / Sylvabelle 16
John P Grier (1917)		Audience	Sir Dixon — Billet 2 / Jaconet 4
			Sallie McClelland — *HINDOO* 24 / Red-And-blue 4
		Disguise II	*DOMINO* — *HIMYAR* 2 / *MANNIE GRAY* 23
Jack High (1926)	Wonder (1910)		Bonnie Gal — *GALOPIN* 3 / Bonnie Doon 10
		Curiosity	Voter — Friar's Balsam 2 / Mavourneen 1
			Pink Domino — *DOMINO* 23 / Belle Rose 8
		Isinglass	*ISONOMY* — Sterling 12 / Isola Bella 19
	Star Shoot (1898)		Dead Lock — *WENLOCK* 4 / Malpractice 3
Priscilla (1914)		Astrology	*HERMIT* — *NEWMINSTER* 8 / Seclusion 5
			Stella — Brother To Strafford 6 / Toxophilite Mare 8
		Yankee	Hanover — *HINDOO* 24 / Bourbon Belle 15
	Yankee Sister (1904)		Correction — *HIMYAR* 2 / *MANNIE GRAY* 23
		Sister Cheerful	*PETRARCH* — Lord Clifden 2 / Laura 10
			The Nun — Bacchus 15 / Chamioness 11

		Hastings	Spendthrift — Australian / Aerolite (rh)
	Fair Play (1905)		Cinderella — Blue Ruin / Manna 21
		FAIRY GOLD	*TADCASTER* — Doncaster 5 / Clemence 2
Flota (1937)		Dame Masham	*GALLIARD* 13 / Pauline 9
		Sainfoin	*SPRINGFIELD* 12 / Sanda 2
	ROCK SAND (1900)	Roquebrune	St Simon 11 / St Marguerite 4
MAN O' WAR (1917)	Mahubah (1910)	Merry Hampton	Hampton 10 / Doll Tearsheet 22
		Merry Token	Mizpah — Macgregor 4 / Mare By Underhand 4
		St Gatien	The Rover — Blair Athol 10 / Crinon 6
Armada (1924)	Meddler (1890)		St Editha — Kingley Vale 8 / Lady Alice 16
		Busybody	*PETRARCH* — Lord Clifden 2 / Laura 10
			Spinaway — Macaroni 14 / Queen Bertha 1
		Donovan	*GALOPIN* — Vedette 19 / Flying Duchess 3
Crepuscule (1914)	Strike-A-light (1896)		Mowerina — Scottish Chief 12 / Stockings 7
		Fuse	*TADCASTER* — Doncaster 5 / Clemence 2
			Fusee — Marsyas 12 / Vesuvienne 22

Sailor 1952

Chapter 26

Two Black Horses Turn to Gold

I t was another upset to the status quo when two horses seemingly came out of nowhere, with little to recommend them in their pedigrees, yet they took the best races and then became two of the most enduring sources of racing class in the modern racehorse. These two horses were ignored, shunned, and discarded by the people who should have known better. This kind of thing keeps us all humble, because just when we think we know it all, along comes a lesson demonstrating that we really don't know as much as we thought.

Sunday Silence 1986

Avalyn Hunter in her wonderful work *American Classic Pedigrees 1914-2002* describes Sunday Silence 1986 as a horse that no one wanted. He was a medium-sized, gangly colt who was high-strung and so irritable that he often would strike out and bite those near him; these are personality traits inherited from his sire Halo who was so nasty he had to wear a muzzle to protect the stable hands from his cobra-fast attacks. Sunday Silence was not good-looking, and he had an unfashionable pedigree, so he was rejected at the sales even though his sire was already a leading stallion in stakes winner production. The Halo offspring in spite of their irascible temperament were already proven racers of high class and very competitive—Halo's progeny won races.

Sunday Silence. —image courtesy of Wiki Commons public domain photos

Sunday Silence was a late bloomer, having trouble getting control of his limbs at two, but by his third year he finally had possession of himself and was showing his excellent talent. His races against the gifted Easy Goer became media events, especially their nose-to-nose battle in the Preakness that Sunday Silence won only by an inch. Sunday Silence won both the Kentucky Derby and Preakness; Easy Goer took the Belmont. When Sunday Silence won the Breeders' Cup Classic from Easy Goer he was declared Champion-Three-Year-Old and Horse-of-the-Year. In fourteen starts he won nine with five seconds.

When he was retired to stud his managers still had trouble selling his shares and booking his breedings—even with his stellar race record. The racing establishment just didn't like his pedigree, and many thought he would not do well, and he had hind leg faults—being both cow- and sickle-hocked. Yet he led the sires list in 1983 and 1989. It was not everyone who ignored his promise, because there was Shadai Farm who believed in him from the start, and they already owned a quarter interest in him. It wasn't long then that they were able to purchase him outright; they took him to Japan to stand stud. In Japan he has rewritten the studbooks, leading the sires list from 1995 through 2002. Part of this sensational success can be attributed to the fact that Japan had a broodmare band that was already loaded with Northern Dancer strains, and when bred to Sunday Silence a key inbreeding to the *reine* Almahmoud was formed. Other writers point out that most of his winners have multiple lines of

Mahmoud (sire of Almahmoud) and explain this gain in class which arrives with Mahmoud is delivered by the presence of the great Sundridge, who is the sire of Lady Josephine—his third-dam—and that it is he who is responsible for this talent. Sundridge is a wonderful line and a potent one—possibly because he is 5x5x6x5 to the full brothers Rataplan/Stockwell—but that is not the full story with Lady Josephine, and actually if you do the math it takes second place in dominance to the dam-sire's contribution. Lady Josephine's dam-sire is Americus who is 2x2 to the full siblings Norfolk RH/The Nun RH—by Lexington RH—who are themselves out of an inbred mare; this is dominance. Another clue to this importance in Lady Josephine is that she is possibly the greatest consistent conduit of speed in the modern English Thoroughbred, and then she had remarkable success when her lines were returned to the US. It was here in America where they met their near relatives in Domino/Hamburg and others, creating for her descendants, Mahmoud/Royal Charger/Nasrullah, one of the greatest nicks of modern time.

Sunday Silence has one hundred eighteen lines of Lexington RH in his background, and he has the concentrated focuses of this power to the front—Lady Josephine being just one of them. His sire Halo contributes forty-seven of those lines, which is significant; however it is Sunday Silence's dam-sire Understanding—a practically 'unknown' sire who is overloaded with sixty-seven lines of Lexington RH, and they are funneled forward right to the fore through his Domino/Ben Brush/Whisk Broom II lines. Understanding's genes combined with those of Halo's who is 4x4 to Blue Larkspur and Mumtaz Mahal/Mumtaz Begum 4x5, plus his fourth dam Mother Goose (Hamburg/Ben Brush/Domino), has critical mass in Lexington RH influence. There is also an unusual buildup of the ¾ brothers Chance Shot and Man O' War who are 6x7x7x6x6x6.

Seattle Slew 1974

Maybe I am just reaching at straws here—seeing what I want to see: Lexington RH dominance in the background of these lineages. But then there is Seattle Slew—another horse that they couldn't give away, yet he pulled off an even bigger display of racing class and stallion potency. Seattle Slew carries one hundred forty lines of Lexington RH in his background; any way you slice it this concentration is certainly at critical mass level.

Bred by Ben Castleman, this is a colt that was also rejected at the Keeneland yearling sales and sold instead at the lesser Fasig-Tipton sales for a pittance to the partnership of Taylor and Hill. Like Sunday Silence this colt was not a picture; he was coarse, raw boned, big (16.2 hands), muscular and slow to mature. Luckily he was trained by Billy Turner, who understood he needed to give the colt time to grow into himself, for once he got out there at the Belmont track Seattle Slew won his maiden by five lengths. He loved to run, and in his races he wanted to lead. By the end of his abbreviated season (began in September) he had earned the Champion-Two-Year-Old title and set a record for the fastest mile by a two-year-old; with his definitive display of class he snatched the title Horse-of-the-Year from racers who had run the entire season. The fans and bettors loved him; however the racing industry still wasn't very impressed.

It was his three-year-old season that beat all, as he began by setting a track record at Hialeah for seven furlongs. By the time he got to the classics he was still an undefeated horse, and then he did it all: **he won the Triple Crown—still undefeated**; this record is better than those of Tesio's masterpieces Ribot and Nearco. He was awarded his **second** Horse-of-the-Year title. He then had a few losses, a trainer change, and an illness, but he came back at four to do it again earning the Champion-Older-Horse award. When retired to stud he was syndicated for $300,000 per share/forty shares. In all, he had run seventeen races with fourteen wins and two seconds earning $ 1,208,726.

Seattle Slew is prepotent for his type: large, plain, coarse horses, so buyers hung back in the beginning because of this. Of course it wasn't long before they realized how wrong they were; once his stock got to the track his worth as a sire was established. He was leading freshman sire in 1982, top sire in 1984, leading sire of two-year-olds in 1988, and leading broodmare sire in 1995 and 1996.

It wasn't all rosy with his offspring either, as he seems to carry a recessive trait for off-set knees and toeing out especially on the right, which appears in some of his progeny. Also his stock is slow maturing—as he was—requiring time to grow into itself, with open joints—so if they are trained too early or too hard then soundness can be an issue. But those trainers who wait are rewarded, because by three his stock shows its talents: their speed and acceleration, versatility for different racing surfaces, and generally very good racers for a mile to 1 ¼ miles; like their dad they love to run in front.

Seattle Slew is prepotent; he carries a Nasrullah sex-balance 3x3 and the full sisters Striking/Busher 4x4, plus the great broodmare Frizeur through Myrtlewood and Black Curl 5x6. He carries Sweep, Bubbling Over, John P. Grier, Black Toney, and Man O' War in multiples—his pedigree hums with our American bloodlines of significance; he is a treasure for breeders now and will be for years to come.

As Thoroughbred pedigree expert Edwin Anthony put it: "If you are not convinced that the Ben Brush/Domino concentration is significant, check out the pedigree of Triple Crown winner Seattle Slew, as it combines the genes of **Black Toney**, **Sweep** and **John P Grier**" (*The American Thoroughbred vol 1*).

I am sure some of these names in this partial list of Seattle Slew's winners will ring a bell with you as they all had their place in the racing headlines:

Swale—winner of Kentucky Derby and Belmont—Champion-Three-Year-Old

Digression—Champion-Two-Year-Old in England

Capote—Champion-Two-Year-Old

Slew O' Gold—Champion-Three-Year-Old and Champion-Older-Horse the next year

Tomahawk—Champion-Two-Year-Old in Ireland

A P Indy—Horse-of-the-Year—winner of Belmont and Breeder's Cup Classic

Landaluce—Champion-Two-Year-Old filly

Surfside—Champion-Three-Year-Old filly

Vindication—Champion-Two-Year-Old

A.P. Indy

Well, we would have to blind not to see from just the partial list above that Seattle Slew is prepotent for the best racing genes, so he is an active transmitter for our breeding goals. For our example of his progeny we will use A.P. Indy, as he is usually rated the best of his fifty-five stallion sons. A.P. Indy is an instance of what is called now the Seattle Slew/Buckpasser cross. This combination has proven extremely powerful, as it builds on the lines of War Admiral, Domino, Ben Brush, Bubbling Over, and Hamburg—all strong conduits of our Heroic Era genes. "You can see how the past continues to influence the future, when the same superior genes are reinforced over and over" (Edwin Anthony—*The American Thoroughbred*). As the pedigree experts have pointed out, whenever you cross Black Toney and Sweep in a pedigree you produce a sex-balanced presence of Domino/Ben Brush such as in Seattle Slew and Buckpasser; this combo worked in the greats John P. Grier and Hildene as well. The success of the La Troienne family (Chapter 22) is based on this cross as well (Black Toney/War Admiral). Surely a portion of the success of this stallion is the ¾ sister Busanda found in his dam to the full sisters Busher and Striking found in the sire—this puts this potent filly factor 5x5x4.

One of A.P. Indy's offspring who continued to build on these potencies is the Horse-of-the-Year recipient Mineshaft 1999, who has three lines of both War Admiral (Sweep, Ben Brush, Fair Play) and Black Toney (Domino). Ellen Parker, who keeps her eye out for good sires who do not carry Mr. Prospector or Native Dancer recommends A.P. Indy's excellent son Stephen Got Even, as he is overrun with lines of Domino and Hamburg, and he even carries the rare lines of Blackstock and Ariel as well. Stephen Got Even won five of eleven races, earning $1 million.

Cigar 1990—one of the greatest racers of modern times—is out of a Seattle Slew daughter (Solar Slew); unfortunately Cigar proved entirely sterile and eventually this racing legend was retired to the Kentucky Horse Park —image courtesy of Wiki Commons

Seattle Slew's record as a broodmare sire is impressive also, with greats like Cigar, who earned the Horse-of-the-Year title twice as his sire did—perhaps an indication that sex-linked genes were in play. He was also Champion-Older-Horse twice, and he was the leading North American money earner. It is a tragedy that Cigar was entirely sterile. Sterile or not, we want what this horse carries, so his pedigree is worthy of our study. His sire Palace Music adds more Blue Larkspur/Mahmoud but also brings Princequillo and Turn-To to the foreground.

Seattle Slew proved his status as broodmare sire of note with other champions such as Lemon Drop Kid who earned the Champion-Older-Male title, and of Golden Attraction who was named Champion-Two-Year-Old filly.

Seattle Slew's dam My Charmer (fifty-two Lexington RH lines—see Chapter 22) also produced the significant sires Lomond, Seattle Dancer, and the Irish champion Argosy, who should be targets for our line-breeding exercises in building up our four-miler genes. Argosy has clear potency in full siblings Fighting Fox/Gallant Fox 4x6 from the sire and Striking/Busher 4x4 from the dam.

These two black sheep are an important lesson for breeders, in that fashion does not always produce the winner—it is the bloodlines and the pedigree design that win out time and again—sometimes much to the surprise of everyone.

Easy Goer 1986

Sunday Silence's chief opponent Easy Goer was closely matched in performance to him. It should not surprise us then to find that Easy Goer, who earned his share of honors (US Champion-Two-Year-Old and winning the Belmont Stakes) is also a warehouse for Lexington RH, as he carries one hundred forty-eight lines of him! He also set records for speed, such as the fastest three-year-old mile in America, which actually was a second faster than what Secretariat did at 1:32 ⅛ (Another 'unfashionable' horse, Dr. Fager, holds the world record for that same distance at just ⅛ second faster—we are talking here about 40 mph—extraordinary). Easy Goer won fourteen of twenty starts, but he did not like a muddy track. He is the only horse to win the combination of the Travers, Whitney, Woodward, and Jockey Club Gold—he was a tremendous athlete and one of the greatest racehorses of his day, and he kept racing at four, earning a career total of over $4.8 million!

His pedigree shows us he has multiples of the full siblings Bull Dog/Sir Gallahad 6x7x6x5x7 and Pharamond/Sickle 6x5x6x6, but his front breeding is the ¾ sisters Big Hurry and Businesslike 4x4 involving his dam-line and the genetic ¾ sisters Two Lea and Real Delight 5x5, providing two strong filly factors.

His rivalry with Sunday Silence produced dramatic and exciting events, and the truth is very seldom do we see so closely matched champions—a class act. Easy Goer died suddenly at eight years old from an allergic reaction. In his short time at stud he proved to be a very good broodmare sire.

KATHLEEN H. KIRSAN

California Chrome

There is a post script on this story; after this book was sent to the publisher, but still in the editing stage, the magnificent California Chrome was attempting to win the Triple Crown. It was thirty-six years since Affirmed took the title—a long spell where we have seen many great horses almost catch the ultimate prize, but agonizing as they come up short in one race. California Chrome got pretty close: Kentucky Derby and Preakness wins, and was the favorite for the Belmont, but got blocked in at the rail and just didn't have the acceleration left in him once he got free. This is a reoccurring scene of late (see Chapter 27—Funny Cide). Nonetheless, this is a horse of significant genetic interest to us, of the highest class, and more importantly he carries dominance in his good racing genetics and so he will be able to pass it on to his progeny.

When I looked up his breeding I was immediately struck by its uncanny resemblance to that of Seattle Slew. Both of these top racehorses have an outstanding dam, with tight inbreeding to mares. I think you might find the similiarity in these pedigree patterns interesting and instructive, and so I have included his pedigree (and that of Numbered Account—the mare inbred to) here for your study and comparison with Seattle Slew and Easy Goer, along with a portion of an article I wrote about this point for my website (see complete article in Appendix E, #7). Here is a portion of that article:

"Now if we look at California Chrome's pedigree we find it is very similar. We not only see the same basic pattern, with a dam that is inbred to ¾ siblings 3x3, who are out of the same mare: Numbered Account. But it turns out this inbreeding goes straight back to these same sources of power that created Seattle Slew. For example, Numbered Account's sire Buckpasser is out of a dam that is by War Admiral, out of a Blue Larkspur dam (Businesslike) who is out of La Troienne. Further, the second dam of this mare is Glamour, a daughter of Striking (also found in Seattle Slew), Striking and Businesslike are ¾ sisters and they are 8x8x7x7x7x7, building on the dominance. There are additional lines of Buckpasser, Jet Pilot and other carriers throughout as well. Other pedigree strengths strong in the genetics of California Chrome: a sex-balanced double of Mr. Propspector 3x4, Northern Dancer 4x5, ¾ brothers Secretariat/Sir Gaylord—all these racing bloodlines of the highest class, but these wonderful lines are expected to be found in the top American Thoroughbred in our day as the breed is saturated in them. What makes this pedigree shine is the extraordinary concentration of genes coming from the mare's inbreeding. This type of pedigree pattern is one that is found in the best stallions, both Seattle Slew and Easy Goer (who died young at eight from an allergic reaction) were top sires and their bloodlines are genetic gold in your pedigrees today. Now we find the new super-star, California Chrome, with his pedigree structure that is powerful in America's best genetics, which will insure he will be a legendary sire as well. We have waited a long time for a horse this wonderful."

California Chrome has picked up the genetic torch that powered Seattle Slew and Easy Goer and has carried it to the winner's circle again. He carries eight hundred six lines of Lexington RH—more than half (458) come through the above mentioned conduits, and the power is increased by the close inbreeding at the front of the pedigree causing it to be expressed in the horse's performance. This is a good amount, but at this era there could be horses bred easily that have one thousand to fifteen hundred Lexington lines in their lineage, and California Chrome's offspring, with careful selection could reach the two thousand mark.

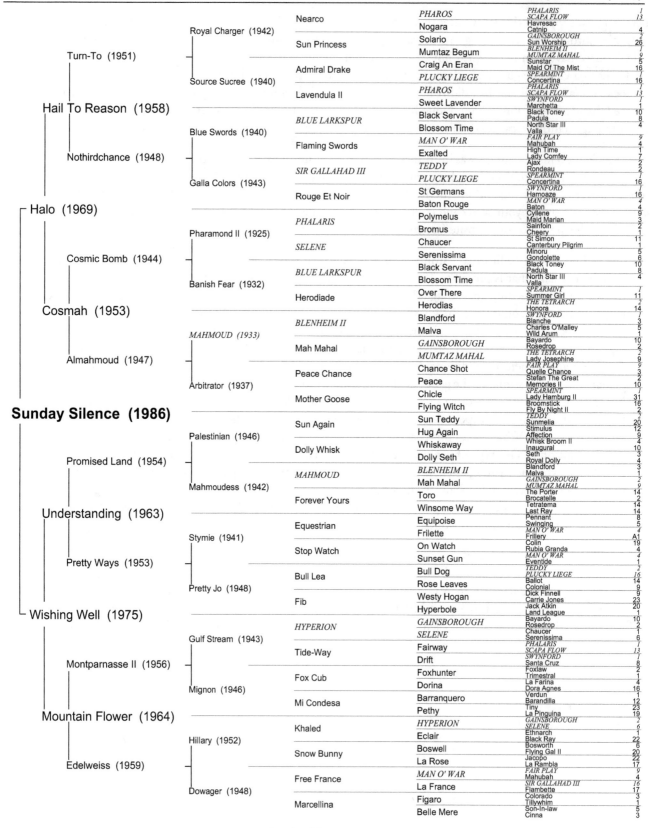

		Nearco	*PHAROS*	*PHALARIS* 1
	Royal Charger (1942)			*SCAPA FLOW* 13
			Nogara	Havresac
Turn-To (1951)		Sun Princess	Solario	Catnip 4
				GAINSBOROUGH 2
				Sun Worship 26
			Mumtaz Begum	*BLENHEIM II* 1
				MUMTAZ MAHAL 9
	Source Sucree (1940)	Admiral Drake	Craig An Eran	Sunstar 5
				Maid Of The Mist 16
Hail To Reason (1958)			*PLUCKY LIEGE*	*SPEARMINT* 1
				Concertina 16
		Lavendula II	*PHAROS*	*PHALARIS* 1
				SCAPA FLOW 13
			Sweet Lavender	*SWYNFORD* 1
				Marchetta 1
		BLUE LARKSPUR	Black Servant	Black Toney 10
				Padula 8
	Blue Swords (1940)		Blossom Time	North Star III 4
				Valla
		Flaming Swords	*MAN O' WAR*	*FAIR PLAY* 9
Nothirdchance (1948)				Mahubah 4
			Exalted	High Time 1
				Lady Comfey 7
		SIR GALLAHAD III	*TEDDY*	Ajax 2
				Rondeau 2
	Galla Colors (1943)		*PLUCKY LIEGE*	*SPEARMINT* 1
				Concertina 16
		Rouge Et Noir	St Germans	*SWYNFORD* 1
				Hamoaze 16
			Baton Rouge	*MAN O' WAR* 4
				Baton 4
		PHALARIS	Polymelus	Cyllene 9
				Maid Marian 3
	Pharamond II (1925)		Bromus	Sainfoin 2
				Cheery 1
		SELENE	Chaucer	St Simon 11
Halo (1969)				Canterbury Pilgrim 1
			Serenissima	Minoru 5
				Gondolette 6
		BLUE LARKSPUR	Black Servant	Black Toney 10
				Padula 8
	Banish Fear (1932)		Blossom Time	North Star III 4
				Valla
		Herodiade	Over There	*SPEARMINT* 1
				Summer Girl 11
			Herodias	*THE TETRARCH* 2
				Honora 14
		BLENHEIM II	Blandford	*SWYNFORD* 1
				Blanche 3
Cosmic Bomb (1944)			Malva	Charles O'Malley 5
	MAHMOUD (1933)			Wild Arum 1
		Mah Mahal	*GAINSBOROUGH*	Bayardo 10
				Rosedrop 2
			MUMTAZ MAHAL	*THE TETRARCH* 2
				Lady Josephine 9
		Peace Chance	Chance Shot	*FAIR PLAY* 9
				Quelle Chance 3
			Peace	Stefan The Great 2
	Arbitrator (1937)			Memories II 10
		Mother Goose	Chicle	*SPEARMINT* 1
Cosmah (1953)				Lady Hamburg II 31
			Flying Witch	Broomstick 16
				Fly By Night II 2
		Sun Again	Sun Teddy	*TEDDY* 2
				Sunmelia 20
	Palestinian (1946)		Hug Again	Stimulus 12
				Affection 9
		Dolly Whisk	Whiskaway	Whisk Broom II 4
				Inaugural 10
			Dolly Seth	Seth 3
				Royal Dolly 4
Almahmoud (1947)		*MAHMOUD*	*BLENHEIM II*	Blandford 3
				Malva 1
	Mahmoudess (1942)		Mah Mahal	*GAINSBOROUGH* 2
				MUMTAZ MAHAL 9
		Forever Yours	Toro	The Porter 14
				Brocatelle 2
			Winsome Way	Tetratema 14
				Last Ray 14

Sunday Silence (1986)

		Equestrian	Equipoise	Pennant 8
				Swinging 5
	Stymie (1941)		Frilette	*MAN O' WAR* 4
				Frillery A1
		Stop Watch	On Watch	Colin 19
Promised Land (1954)				Rubia Granda 4
			Sunset Gun	*MAN O' WAR* 4
				Eventide 1
		Bull Lea	Bull Dog	*TEDDY* 2
				PLUCKY LIEGE 16
	Pretty Jo (1948)		Rose Leaves	Ballot 14
				Colonial 9
		Fib	Westy Hogan	Dick Finnell 9
				Carrie Jones 23
			Hyperbole	Jack Atkin 20
Understanding (1963)				Land League 1
		HYPERION	*GAINSBOROUGH*	Bayardo 10
				Rosedrop 2
	Gulf Stream (1943)		*SELENE*	Chaucer 1
				Serenissima 6
		Tide-Way	Fairway	*PHALARIS* 1
				SCAPA FLOW 13
			Drift	*SWYNFORD* 1
Pretty Ways (1953)				Santa Cruz 8
		Fox Cub	Foxhunter	Foxlaw 2
				Trimestral 1
	Mignon (1946)		Dorina	La Farina 4
				Dora Agnes 16
		Mi Condesa	Barranquero	Verdun 1
				Barandilla 12
			Pethy	Tiny 23
				La Pinguina 19
		Khaled	*HYPERION*	*GAINSBOROUGH* 2
				SELENE 6
Wishing Well (1975)			Eclair	Ethnarch 1
				Black Ray 22
	Hillary (1952)	Snow Bunny	Boswell	Bosworth 6
				Flying Gal II 20
			La Rose	Jacopo 22
Montparnasse II (1956)				La Rambla 17
		Free France	*MAN O' WAR*	*FAIR PLAY* 9
				Mahubah 4
			La France	*SIR GALLAHAD III* 16
Mountain Flower (1964)				Flambette 17
	Dowager (1948)	Marcellina	Figaro	Colorado 1
				Tillywhim 1
			Belle Mere	Son-In-law 5
Edelweiss (1959)				Cinna 3

Sunday Silence 1986

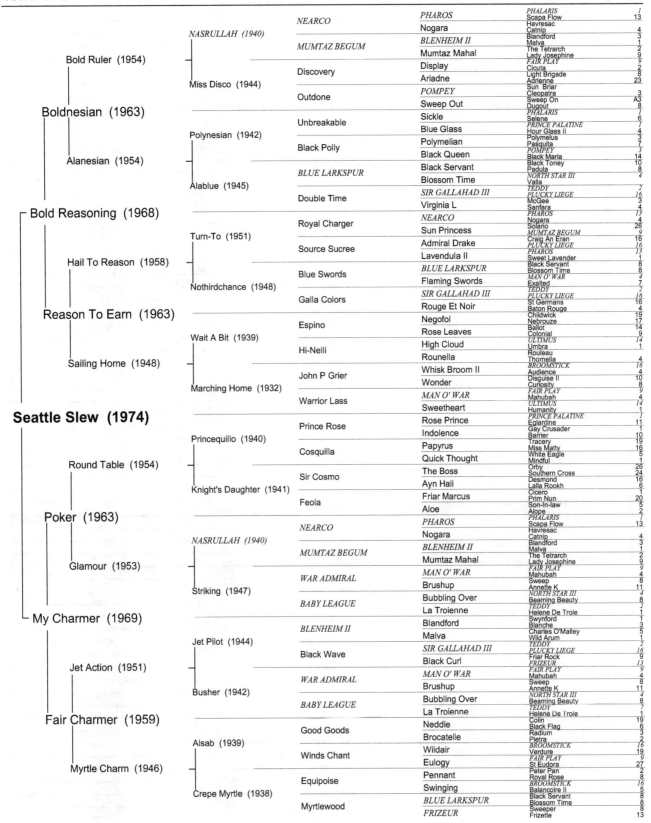

Seattle Slew 1974

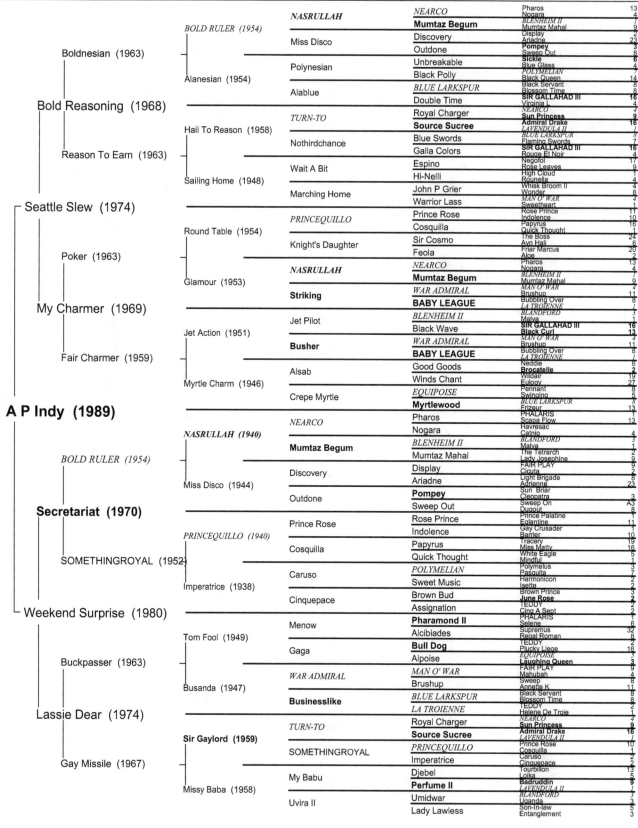

A P Indy 1989

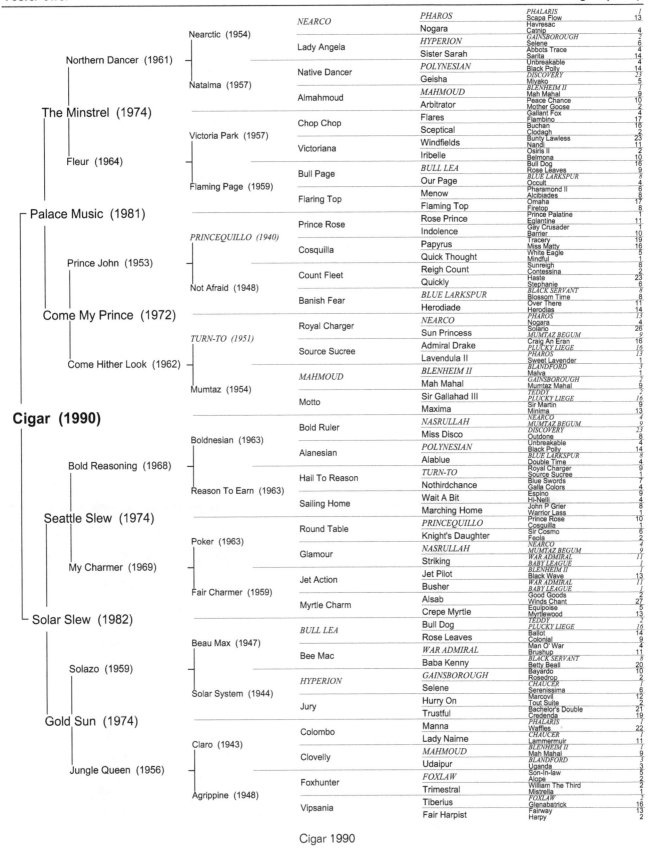

			PHAROS	PHALARIS	1
		NEARCO		Scapa Flow	13
			Nogara	Havresac	4
	Nearctic (1954)			Catnip	
			HYPERION	GAINSBOROUGH	2
		Lady Angela		Selene	6
			Sister Sarah	Abbots Trace	4
Northern Dancer (1961)				Sarita	14
			POLYNESIAN	Unbreakable	4
		Native Dancer		Black Polly	14
			Geisha	DISCOVERY	23
	Natalma (1957)			Miyako	5
			MAHMOUD	BLENHEIM II	1
		Almahmoud		Mah Mahal	9
The Minstrel (1974)			Arbitrator	Peace Chance	10
				Mother Goose	2
			Flares	Gallant Fox	4
		Chop Chop		Flambino	17
			Sceptical	Buchan	16
	Victoria Park (1957)			Clodagh	2
			Windfields	Bunty Lawless	23
		Victoriana		Nandi	11
			Iribelle	Osiris II	2
Fleur (1964)				Belmona	10
			BULL LEA	Bull Dog	16
		Bull Page		Rose Leaves	9
			Our Page	BLUE LARKSPUR	8
	Flaming Page (1959)			Occult	4
			Menow	Pharamond II	6
		Flaring Top		Alcibiades	8
			Flaming Top	Omaha	17
				Firetop	8
			Rose Prince	Prince Palatine	1
		Prince Rose		Eglantine	11
			Indolence	Gay Crusader	1
	PRINCEQUILLO (1940)			Barrier	10
			Papyrus	Tracery	19
		Cosquilla		Miss Matty	16
Palace Music (1981)			Quick Thought	White Eagle	5
				Mindful	1
			Reigh Count	Sunreigh	8
		Count Fleet		Contessina	2
			Quickly	Haste	23
Prince John (1953)				Stephanie	6
	Not Afraid (1948)			BLACK SERVANT	8
			BLUE LARKSPUR	Blossom Time	8
		Banish Fear		Over There	11
			Herodiade	Herodias	14
				PHAROS	13
			NEARCO	Nogara	4
		Royal Charger		Solario	26
			Sun Princess	MUMTAZ BEGUM	9
Come My Prince (1972)				Craig An Eran	18
			Admiral Drake	PLUCKY LIEGE	16
		Source Sucree		PHAROS	13
	TURN-TO (1951)		Lavendula II	Sweet Lavender	1
				BLANDFORD	3
			BLENHEIM II	Malva	1
		MAHMOUD		GAINSBOROUGH	2
			Mah Mahal	Mumtaz Mahal	9
Come Hither Look (1962)				TEDDY	2
			Sir Gallahad III	PLUCKY LIEGE	16
	Mumtaz (1954)	Motto		Sir Martin	9
			Maxima	Minima	13
				NEARCO	4
			NASRULLAH	MUMTAZ BEGUM	9
		Bold Ruler		DISCOVERY	23
			Miss Disco	Outdone	8
	Boldnesian (1963)			Unbreakable	4
			POLYNESIAN	Black Polly	14
		Alanesian		BLUE LARKSPUR	8
			Alablue	Double Time	4
Bold Reasoning (1968)				Royal Charger	9
			TURN-TO	Source Sucree	1
		Hail To Reason		Blue Swords	7
			Nothirdchance	Galla Colors	4
	Reason To Earn (1963)			Espino	9
			Wait A Bit	Hi-Nelli	4
		Sailing Home		John P Grier	8
			Marching Home	Warrior Lass	1
Seattle Slew (1974)				Prince Rose	10
			PRINCEQUILLO	Cosquilla	1
		Round Table		Sir Cosmo	6
			Knight's Daughter	Feola	2
	Poker (1963)			NEARCO	4
			NASRULLAH	MUMTAZ BEGUM	9
		Glamour		WAR ADMIRAL	11
			Striking	BABY LEAGUE	1
My Charmer (1969)				BLENHEIM II	1
			Jet Pilot	Black Wave	13
		Jet Action		WAR ADMIRAL	11
			Busher	BABY LEAGUE	1
	Fair Charmer (1959)			Good Goods	2
			Alsab	Winds Chant	27
		Myrtle Charm		Equipoise	5
			Crepe Myrtle	Myrtlewood	13
Cigar (1990)				TEDDY	2
			Bull Dog	PLUCKY LIEGE	16
		BULL LEA		Ballot	14
			Rose Leaves	Colonial	9
	Beau Max (1947)			Man O' War	4
			WAR ADMIRAL	Brushup	11
		Bee Mac		BLACK SERVANT	8
			Baba Kenny	Betty Beall	20
				Bayardo	10
			GAINSBOROUGH	Rosedrop	2
		HYPERION		CHAUCER	1
			Selene	Serenissima	6
Solar Slew (1982)				Marcovil	12
			Hurry On	Tout Suite	2
	Solar System (1944)	Jury		Bachelor's Double	21
			Trustful	Credenda	19
				PHALARIS	1
			Manna	Waffles	22
		Colombo		CHAUCER	1
			Lady Nairne	Lammermuir	11
Solazo (1959)				BLENHEIM II	1
			MAHMOUD	Mah Mahal	9
		Clovelly		BLANDFORD	3
	Claro (1943)		Udaipur	Uganda	3
				Son-In-law	5
			FOXLAW	Alope	2
		Foxhunter		William The Third	2
Gold Sun (1974)			Trimestral	Mistrella	1
				FOXLAW	2
			Tiberius	Glenabatrick	16
	Agrippine (1948)	Vipsania		Fairway	13
			Fair Harpist	Harpy	2

Cigar 1990

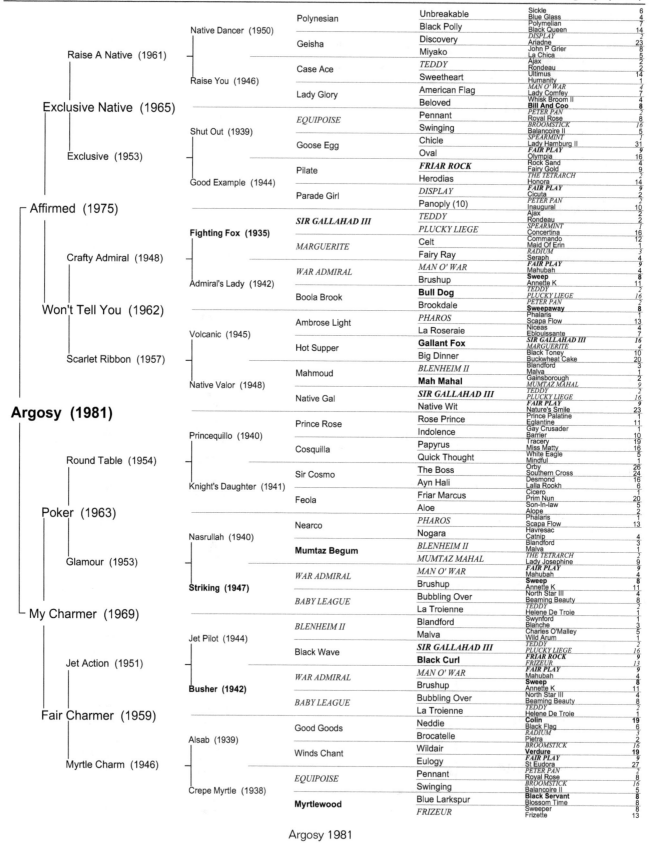

Argosy (1981)

- **Affirmed (1975)**
  - Exclusive Native (1965)
    - Raise A Native (1961)
      - Native Dancer (1950)
        - Polynesian
          - Unbreakable — Sickle 6, Blue Glass 4
          - Black Polly — Polymelian 7, Black Queen 14
        - Geisha
          - Discovery — *DISPLAY* 2, Ariadne 23
          - Miyako — John P Grier 8, La Chica 5
      - Raise You (1946)
        - Case Ace
          - *TEDDY* — Ajax 2, Rondeau 14
          - Sweetheart — Ultimus 1, Humanity
        - Lady Glory
          - American Flag — *MAN O' WAR* 4, Lady Comfey 7
          - Beloved — Whisk Broom II 4, **Bill And Coo** 8
    - Exclusive (1953)
      - Shut Out (1939)
        - *EQUIPOISE*
          - Pennant — *PETER PAN* 2, Royal Rose 8
          - Swinging — *BROOMSTICK* 16, Balancoire II 5
        - Goose Egg
          - Chicle — *SPEARMINT* 1, Lady Hamburg II 31
          - Oval — *FAIR PLAY* 9, Olympia 16
      - Good Example (1944)
        - Pilate
          - *FRIAR ROCK* — Rock Sand 4, Fairy Gold 9
          - Herodias — *THE TETRARCH* 2, Honora 14
        - Parade Girl
          - *DISPLAY* — *FAIR PLAY* 9, Cicuta 2
          - Panoply (10) — *PETER PAN* 2, Inaugural 10
  - Won't Tell You (1962)
    - Crafty Admiral (1948)
      - **Fighting Fox (1935)**
        - *SIR GALLAHAD III*
          - *TEDDY* — Ajax 2, Rondeau
          - *PLUCKY LIEGE* — *SPEARMINT* 1, Concertina 16
        - *MARGUERITE*
          - Celt — Commando 12, Maid Of Erin 1
          - Fairy Ray — *RADIUM* 3, Seraph 4
      - Admiral's Lady (1942)
        - *WAR ADMIRAL*
          - *MAN O' WAR* — *FAIR PLAY* 9, Mahubah 4
          - Brushup — **Sweep** 8, Annette K 11
        - Boola Brook
          - **Bull Dog** — *TEDDY* 2, *PLUCKY LIEGE* 16
          - Brookdale — *PETER PAN* 2, **Sweepaway** 8
    - Scarlet Ribbon (1957)
      - Volcanic (1945)
        - Ambrose Light
          - *PHAROS* — Phalaris 1, Scapa Flow 13
          - La Roseraie — Niceas 4, Eblouissante 7
        - Hot Supper
          - **Gallant Fox** — *SIR GALLAHAD III* 16, *MARGUERITE*
          - Big Dinner — Black Toney 10, Buckwheat Cake 20
      - Native Valor (1948)
        - Mahmoud
          - *BLENHEIM II* — Blandford 3, Malva 1
          - **Mah Mahal** — Gainsborough 2, *MUMTAZ MAHAL* 9
        - Native Gal
          - *SIR GALLAHAD III* — *TEDDY* 2, *PLUCKY LIEGE* 16
          - Native Wit — *FAIR PLAY* 9, Nature's Smile 23
- **My Charmer (1969)**
  - Poker (1963)
    - Round Table (1954)
      - Princequillo (1940)
        - Prince Rose
          - Rose Prince — Prince Palatine 11, Eglantine 1
          - Indolence — Gay Crusader 1, Barrier 10
        - Cosquilla
          - Papyrus — Tracery 19, Miss Matty 16
          - Quick Thought — White Eagle 5, Mindful
      - Knight's Daughter (1941)
        - Sir Cosmo
          - The Boss — Orby 26, Southern Cross 24
          - Ayn Hali — Desmond 16, Lalla Rookh 6
        - Feola
          - Friar Marcus — Cicero 1, Prim Nun 20
          - Aloe — Son-In-law 5, Alope 2
    - Glamour (1953)
      - Nasrullah (1940)
        - Nearco
          - *PHAROS* — Phalaris 1, Scapa Flow 13
          - Nogara — Havresac, Catnip 4
        - **Mumtaz Begum**
          - *BLENHEIM II* — Blandford 3, Malva 1
          - *MUMTAZ MAHAL* — *THE TETRARCH* 2, Lady Josephine 9
      - **Striking (1947)**
        - *WAR ADMIRAL*
          - *MAN O' WAR* — *FAIR PLAY* 9, Mahubah 4
          - Brushup — **Sweep** 8, Annette K 11
        - *BABY LEAGUE*
          - Bubbling Over — North Star III 4, Beaming Beauty 8
          - La Troienne — *TEDDY* 2, Helene De Troie 1
  - Fair Charmer (1959)
    - Jet Action (1951)
      - Jet Pilot (1944)
        - *BLENHEIM II*
          - Blandford — Swynford 3, Blanche 5
          - Malva — Charles O'Malley 1, Wild Arum
        - Black Wave
          - *SIR GALLAHAD III* — *TEDDY* 2, *PLUCKY LIEGE* 16
          - **Black Curl** — *FRIAR ROCK* 9, *FRIZEUR* 13
      - **Busher (1942)**
        - *WAR ADMIRAL*
          - *MAN O' WAR* — *FAIR PLAY* 9, Mahubah 4
          - Brushup — **Sweep** 8, Annette K 11
        - *BABY LEAGUE*
          - Bubbling Over — North Star III 4, Beaming Beauty 8
          - La Troienne — *TEDDY* 2, Helene De Troie 1
    - Myrtle Charm (1946)
      - Alsab (1939)
        - Good Goods
          - Neddie — **Colin** 19, Black Flag 6
          - Brocatelle — *RADIUM* 3, Pietra 2
        - Winds Chant
          - Wildair — *BROOMSTICK* 16, **Verdure** 19
          - Eulogy — *FAIR PLAY* 9, St Eudora 27
      - Crepe Myrtle (1938)
        - *EQUIPOISE*
          - Pennant — *PETER PAN* 2, Royal Rose 8
          - Swinging — *BROOMSTICK* 16, Balancoire II 5
        - **Myrtlewood**
          - Blue Larkspur — **Black Servant** 8, Blossom Time 8
          - *FRIZEUR* — Sweeper 8, Frizette 13

Argosy 1981

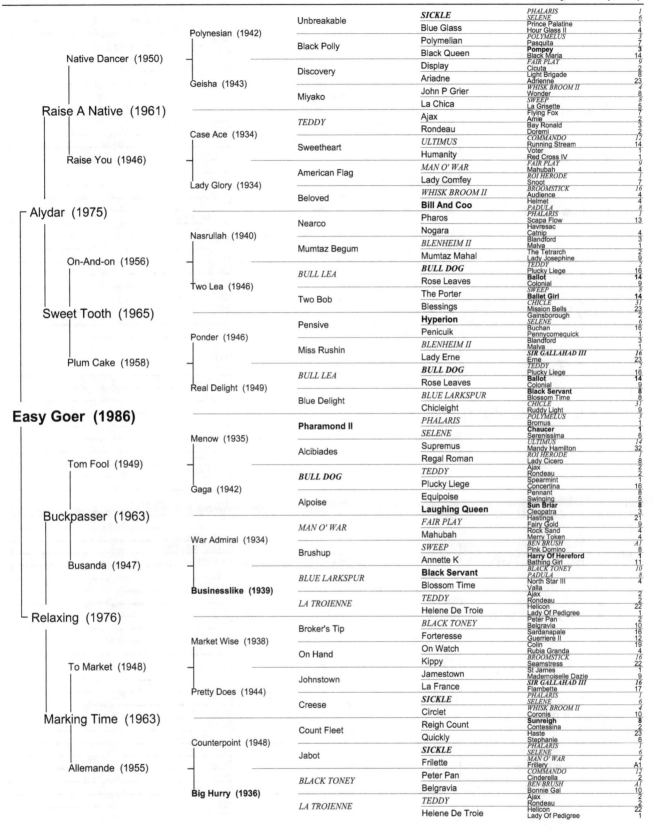

Easy Goer 1986

California Chrome (2011)

Pulpit (1994)

A P Indy (1989)

- Seattle Slew (1974)
  - Bold Reasoning
    - Boldnesian — BOLD RULER 8 / Alanesian 4
    - Reason To Earn — Hail To Reason 4 / Sailing Home 1
  - My Charmer
    - **Poker** — Round Table 2 / *GLAMOUR* 1
    - Fair Charmer — Jet Action 1 / Myrtle Charm 13
- Weekend Surprise (1980)
  - **Secretariat**
    - BOLD RULER — *NASRULLAH* 9 / Miss Disco 8
    - *SOMETHINGROYAL* — *PRINCEQUILLO* 2 / Imperatrice 2
  - Lassie Dear
    - *BUCKPASSER* — Tom Fool 3 / Busanda 1
    - Gay Missile — *SIR GAYLORD* 2 / Missy Baba 3

Preach (1989)

- *MR PROSPECTOR (1970)*
  - Raise A Native
    - *NATIVE DANCER* — Polynesian 14 / Geisha 5
    - Raise You — Case Ace 1 / Lady Glory 1
  - Gold Digger
    - Nashua — *NASRULLAH* 9 / Segula 3
    - Sequence — *COUNT FLEET* 6 / Miss Dogwood 13
- Narrate (1980)
  - Honest Pleasure
    - What A Pleasure — BOLD RULER 8 / Grey Flight 5
    - Tularia — Tulyar 22 / Suntop 11
  - State
    - Nijinsky II — *NORTHERN DANCER* 2 / Flaming Page 8
    - **Monarchy** — *PRINCEQUILLO* 7 / Knight's Daughter 1

Lucky Pulpit (2001)

Cozzene (1980)

- Caro (1967)
  - Fortino II
    - Grey Sovereign — *NASRULLAH* 9 / Kong 6
    - Ranavalo — Relic 8 / Navarra 4
  - Chambord
    - Chamossaire — Precipitation 2 / Snowberry 6
    - Life Hill — Solario 26 / Lady Of The Snows 3
- Ride The Trails (1971)
  - Prince John
    - *PRINCEQUILLO* — Prince Rose 10 / Cosquilla 1
    - Not Afraid — *COUNT FLEET* 6 / Banish Fear 14
  - Wildwook
    - *SIR GAYLORD* — Turn-To 1 / *SOMETHINGROYAL* 1
    - Blue Canoe — Jet Pilot 13 / Portage 4

Lucky Soph (1992)

- Lucky Mel (1954)
  - Olympia
    - Heliopolis — *HYPERION* 6 / Drift 8
    - Miss Dolphin — Stimulus 12 / Tinamou 4
  - Royal Mink
    - *ROYAL CHARGER* — *NEARCO* 4 / **Sun Princess** 9
    - Madeh — *MAHMOUD* 9 / Via Media 1
- Incantation (1965)
  - Prince Blessed
    - *PRINCEQUILLO* — Prince Rose 10 / Cosquilla 1
    - Dog Blessed — *BULL DOG* 16 / Blessed Again 21
  - Magic Spell
    - Flushing II — *MAHMOUD* 14 / Callandar 14
    - Subterranean — By Jimminy 20 / U-Boat 4

Lucky Spell (1971)

California Chrome (2011)

Not For Love (1990)

MR PROSPECTOR (1970)

- Raise A Native (1961)
  - *NATIVE DANCER*
    - Polynesian — Unbreakable 4 / Black Polly 14
    - Geisha — Discovery 23 / Miyako 5
  - Raise You
    - Case Ace — Teddy 2 / Sweetheart 1
    - Lady Glory — American Flag 7 / Beloved 8
- Gold Digger (1962)
  - Nashua
    - *NASRULLAH* — *NEARCO* 4 / Mumtaz Begum 9
    - Segula — Johnstown 17 / Sekhmet 3
  - Sequence
    - *COUNT FLEET* — Reigh Count 2 / Quickly 6
    - Miss Dogwood — *BULL DOG* 16 / Myrtlewood 13

Dance Number (1979)

- *NORTHERN DANCER (1961)*
  - Nearctic
    - *NEARCO* — Pharos 13 / Nogara 4
    - Lady Angela — *HYPERION* 14 / Sister Sarah 14
  - Natalma
    - *NATIVE DANCER* — Polynesian 14 / Geisha 5
    - Almahmoud — *MAHMOUD* 9 / Arbitrator 2
- NUMBERED ACCOUNT (1969)
  - *BUCKPASSER*
    - Tom Fool — **Menow** 8 / Gaga 3
    - Busanda — War Admiral 11 / Businesslike 1
  - **Intriguing**
    - Swaps — Khaled 22 / Iron Reward A4
    - *GLAMOUR* — *NASRULLAH* 9 / Striking 1

Love The Chase (2006)

Polish Numbers (1987)

- Danzig (1977)
  - *NORTHERN DANCER*
    - Nearctic — *NEARCO* 4 / Lady Angela 14
    - Natalma — *NATIVE DANCER* 5 / Almahmoud 2
  - Pas De Nom
    - Admiral's Voyage — Crafty Admiral 8 / Olympia Lou 4
    - Petitioner — Petition 16 / Steady Aim 7
- NUMBERED ACCOUNT (1969)
  - *BUCKPASSER*
    - Tom Fool — **Menow** 8 / Gaga 3
    - Busanda — War Admiral 11 / Businesslike 1
  - **Intriguing**
    - Swaps — Khaled 22 / Iron Reward A4
    - *GLAMOUR* — *NASRULLAH* 9 / Striking 1

Chase It Down (1997)

- Sir Ivor (1965)
  - *SIR GAYLORD*
    - Turn-To — *ROYAL CHARGER* 9 / Source Sucree 1
    - *SOMETHINGROYAL* — *PRINCEQUILLO* 7 / Imperatrice 1
  - Attica
    - Mr Trouble — *MAHMOUD* 9 / Motto 13
    - Athenia — Pharamond II 6 / **Salaminia** 8

Chase The Dream (1984)

- La Belle Fleur (1977)
  - Vaguely Noble
    - Vienna — Aureole 2 / Turkish Blood 14
    - Noble Lassie — *NEARCO* 4 / Belle Sauvage 1
  - Princess Ribot
    - Ribot — Tenerani 6 / Romanella 4
    - Princess Matoaka — *PRINCEQUILLO* / Judy-Rae A4

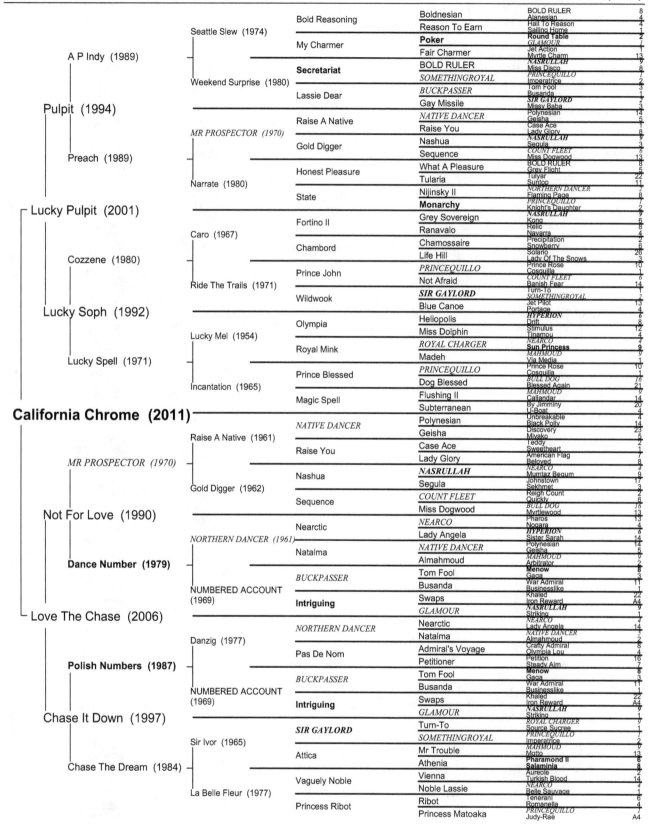

California Chrome 2011

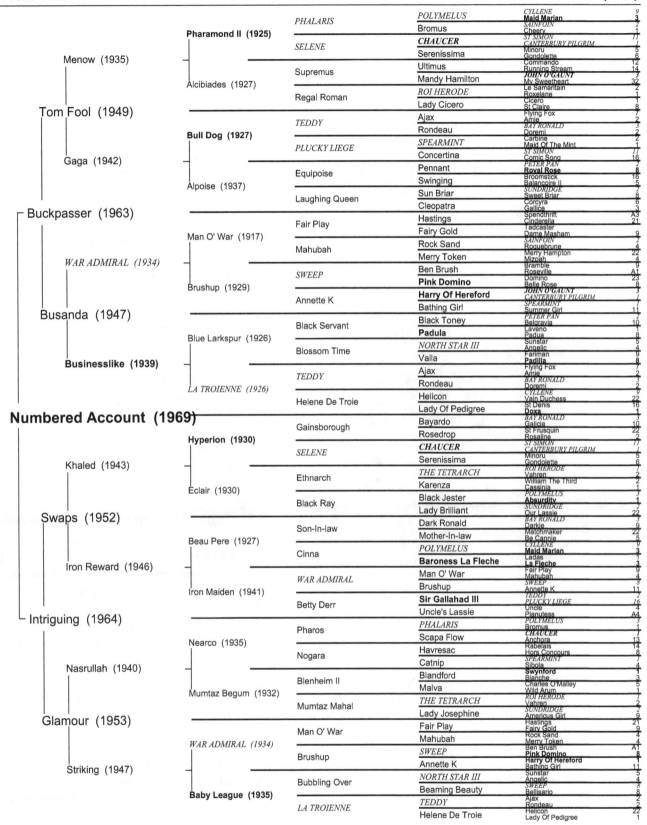

Numbered Account 1969

Chapter 27

Beacon of Hope: Funny Cide

"On May 3, 2003, a narrowly built, New York-bred, long shot gelding, owned by ten inexperienced and uninitiated owners, won the running of the 129th Kentucky Derby, and in the space of 2:01.19, changed everybody's idea of what was possible and what was not" (*Funny Cide* by the Funny Cide Team and Sally Jenkins).

The relaxed Funny Cide, letting it hang out at his stall at Kentucky Horse Park in 2009. —image courtesy of Wiki Commons, photographer sWrightOsment

If you were watching the 2003 running of the Kentucky Derby you were treated to an example of the 'impossible dream' American-style. It couldn't have been more unexpected, for seemingly out of nowhere came a gelding named Funny Cide with odds of thirty-to-one, and he won the Derby handily. His trainer was a fellow named Barclay Tagg who had once been a steeplechase jockey and whose training career was more in the lesser leagues, but after thirty-two years of relentless work he finally had a classic horse in his stable, and this try was his first at the Derby. Seeing his success gave us the satisfaction that hard work does pay off. But it was way better than this—not only was the jockey struggling for a comeback, but the owners of this superb horse were ten guys, most of whom had been friends since high school in upstate New York, who had pooled their money to buy this colt at $75,000. He was priced lower than he might have been otherwise as he was gelded because he was a ridgling (had a retained testicle). Plus he was no oil painting either, being gangly and narrow, especially when he was compared to those sleek and glossy high-priced entries he was racing against. He was certainly not the typical Derby contender, and he was not taken very seriously—the press almost completely ignored him in the pre-race hoopla. The plebian aura around him was increased as his owners, their families, and supporters from upstate New York arrived at Churchhill Downs in a chartered school bus—a vivid contrast to all the celebrities and gentry in their Derby-day displays of opulence and glitz. His owners were just a group of regular guys, like you and me, who had a dream and the nerve to reach for it. We loved them for that.

Funny Cide did not disappoint them; he won decisively. It was bedlam, the improbable goal of a group of buddies was realized, and the joy and the emotion of the moment produced shouts of surprise and delight from the crowd. It was a stunner; the horse no one noticed had ran a strong race against the royally bred, and he had won. It was wonderful. Here was a true 'people's horse', like Seabiscuit had been for American public seventy years before; Funny Cide raised the hopes and joy of us all that day, reminding us that maybe we can win too.

Further, Funny Cide carried the honor of being the first New York-bred to win the Kentucky Derby, and then just a few weeks later he won the Preakness in very fast time. However the coveted Triple Crown was not to be his, as the well-rested Empire Maker took the Belmont in heavy going, with Funny Cide coming in a game third. But by the time of the Belmont the racing public was so enamored with him, his hard knocks trainer, his has-been Jockey, and his middle-class owners, that they gave him a standing and cheering ovation as he walked off the track and back to the stable—for the crowd at Belmont it was Funny Cide who was the winner, he surely and truly owned their hearts.

Funny Cide raced into his seventh year, with a total of thirty-six starts, eleven wins, six seconds, and eight thirds earning a cash total of $3,529,412. Funny Cide was a gelding, so there would be no second chapter in his fairy tale story. The pundits wondered if he was a 'freak' or whether his siblings could run also. His sire Distorted Humor was undervalued at the time, but Funny Cide's performance changed all that, and today he is rated the second-best stallion of the last twenty years.

Funny Cide's sire Distorted Humor 1993 has two hundred thirty-four lines of Lexington RH—that is a lot. Funny Cide's dam-sire Slewacide has one hundred eighty-five, with an additional sixty-eight from the second dam, which makes Funny Cide the carrier of four hundred sixty-seven lines of Lexington RH! There may be more lines beyond my search criteria that I missed, but you can be certain any horse with four hundred plus lines of Lexington RH in the early twenty-first century is at critical mass.

The brilliant racer and sire Turn-To delivers tremendous speed with the ability to accelerate more than once in a race, but unfortunately unsound front legs come along for the genetic ride in many of his progeny as well. —photo by Skeet Meadors, courtesy of Keeneland Library

Looking at Distorted Humor's lineage to see what is dominant we find an overriding Phalaris influence. Besides the unusual and powerful double of Unbreakable (Phalaris grandson) sitting on both the sire and dam-line, which is a strong position and is sex-balanced, there are also eight additional lines of Phalaris—including the rarely seen sex-balanced double of Turn-To—rare because he is most usually present through his sons. However, the brilliant sire Turn-To was one of the Phalaris-line stallions who did pass on foreleg problems—he is 3x3 to Pharos (Phalaris son), sex-balanced. So with Turn-To you get the breath-taking speed and the ability to accelerate more than once in a race and the gameness, but also the bulky frame perched on delicate legs. Further genetic power is demonstrated in the fact that the Turn-To double acts as a funnel forward of the background lines of the ⅞ brothers Nasrullah/Royal Charger—once again Phalaris-line stallions.

There is a fortunate dominance also in Distorted Humor in the relatively sound lines of Sir Gallahad/Bull Dog, who are full brothers found 6x6x7x7, surely providing some solidity, but this factor is not as powerful as the Turn-To double upfront. Looking at this we see a recipe for unbelievable brilliance and class, but with serious weakness in the forelegs, providing ample opportunity for breakdowns.

As we saw from his career, Funny Cide dodged the unsoundness bullet here; however not all of Distorted Humor's progeny will, and many have retired early with problems. It all depends on what the dam brings to the design, or how the genes divide and recombine (See Appendix B). In Funny Cide's case she added more Native Dancer, Polynesian, and Phalaris, but also through Hail to Reason, Seattle Slew, and even Bold Ruler there is also a strong Fair Play element building up (sturdy genotype), and the double of the sound Ribot helps this along. Also, it is obvious by his resiliency that he lucked out on getting the good half of many genes—if he had a full sibling they may not have been as lucky in this. For to me, this slight build up of sturdy elements is not a whole lot of correction, but Funny Cide is the proof of the pudding, for there is no denying he was a sound horse and a fantastically talented and resilient racer—not retiring until he was seven. We can all take heart from this fact—that the task before us (to make our gene pool sounder) is possible, for with only the slight bolstering he received genetically (potency in Ribot and Fair Play), it turned the potential away from disaster. Surely then, in the future, whether we breed Thoroughbreds or Sport Horses, we can design our matings to return to sound offspring.

Born a few years after Funny Cide in 2002 was another great racer by Distorted Humor named Flower Alley, who won the Travers Stakes and others for a total of $2,533,910, and raced until he was four—this son of Distorted Humor is a stallion. His pedigree is 3x3 Mr. Prospector, 4x5x4 Northern Dancer, and 5x5 to the stout broodmare Goofed. He has become a good sire, proving his worth with his son the Kentucky Derby and Preakness winner I'll Have Another. Flower Alley carries five hundred twenty-two lines of Lexington RH. His winning son I'll Have Another has nine hundred eighty-seven lines of Lexington RH, and close to the front he has five lines of Northern Dancer and four of Raise a Native, and he retired at three with tendonitis. So we can see that the superb racing class in this gene pool seems to be riding a very fine line in soundness and is easily tipped into breakdown.

One of Distorted Humor's winningest sons is Drosselmeyer, who won the Belmont Stakes and Breeders' Cup Classic among others to earn a total of $3,728,170—that is more than Funny Cide, and he is a stallion—what is his Lexington RH line total? It is six hundred seventy-three! This stallion has additional Northern Dancer, Bold Ruler, and Seattle Slew with Buckpasser.

Distorted Humor's progeny can run just about anything into the ground—that is established beyond doubt—but for how long? Funny Cide was a sound horse able to race into his seventh year, but others have not done as well—they are all fast, but many breakdown. Surely Funny Cide's body structure, including his lightness and narrow frame on top, contributed to his staying sound. This is our modern-day dilemma. If you breed sport horses for any length of time you cannot be smug about this problem. **It is not a Thoroughbred problem; it is a breeder's problem.** The sport horse and warmblood breeders are faced with the same issues, as very few of the regally bred sport horses or warmbloods make the big show before they blow out a stifle or hock or ankle or knee. We also have found that bigger is not necessarily better, as those huge warmbloods we have bred do not stay sound either—bulk and height mixed with speed causes immense torque on the joints, and contributes to tendon tears and broken limbs. All equine breeds have faults and weaknesses, adding massiveness only increases the odds for breakdowns. We can all learn to get better at our trade.

Clearly, just the fact of having Lexington RH in multiples is not the only factor in the horse's success, but it is an indication that a well-designed pedigree with a critical mass level in the background is a road to victory. We have traveled a long way from our supreme sport athlete of the 1800s and have picked up many flaws in the gene pool, and we have not culled them out. Our sport horse of today—whether racers, jumpers, or dressage horses—are all displaying tragic genetic flaws. We have the talent in the genes, no matter the discipline, but we must reduce the weakness when we build up the talent.

Soundness in the Modern TB—Is Native Dancer to Blame?

The burning issue in the modern Thoroughbred: soundness.

This is something that has been cooking in the breed since the four-mile heat race standard was abolished and substituted with the dash race contest performed with young horses not finished growing. It is at a level now that it cannot be ignored, and it appears to some prognosticators that the breed and industry will destroy itself.

Native Dancer—is he to blame for the unsoundness in our modern racers? —photo by Skeet Meadors, courtesy of Keeneland Library

Up until the Civil War we had the soundest, fastest, and most stamina-loaded racehorse there has ever been. But with the continual use of imported English sires—classic race length specialists, many with soundness issues—this less sound element was brought into our stout gene pools and sped up the decline. If we had continued with the heat-racing standard those weaker strains would have been culled out. The faults added have remained in our lines because a milder performance standard equals horses with lesser abilities and soundness, and unless some sort of economic and attitude miracle happens in the structure of this industry, we will never again see wonderful athletes like those on a large scale. This is just the reality of the industry's financial and philosophic structure.

We, as enlightened breeders, have an opportunity to recapture dominance found in the genes of the horses from that era, and with careful selective breeding we can lessen and possibly eliminate the unsound strains.

What can we do as breeders when we have a very talented line but which displays faults? Here are our options:

1. We can ignore the faults and hope they won't manifest in our sport performers

2. We can cull the line—don't breed from it or to it

3. We can work the unsoundness out of the bloodline

I think you will agree that the first option is what the industry has been employing, and we are now at point where this is really not a viable option any longer. The second option we can use of course, and probably will in some cases where the seriousness of the faults outweighs the benefits we would receive. The third option will take some work and dedication on our part, but the gain will be in preserving the background talent and hopefully cleaning the gene pool of the weaknesses it picked up along the way.

Modern genetic science gives us some hope for success in the clean-up method. Here is a basic primer: we have learned that the genes travel down through the generations basically unchanged, and that they also travel in clusters—therefore the talented and sound base our domestic racer was built on is still there in the genotype of our horses. Plus we have learned that in conception of a foal that a half gene from one parent combines with the corresponding half gene from the other parent. So, there are two halves of a gene, and not all of them carry the same elements, which means a fault can be attached to a gene, but in a mating it may or may not be passed on to the foal (this works the same way with all the traits—good and bad). This natural process is why even full siblings can vary in talent and soundness. We can see this genetic reality in Native Dancer and his family, as he was one of six full siblings. Of those six, only he and his sister Teahouse showed extraordinary talent and potency—the other four were good but not great horses. Now, when we build up background strength in our lineages of a superior ancestor (or two or three) and their close relatives, we are stacking our genetic decks with a multitude of superior and similar genes—this is the principle that selective breeding is based upon, that we can set a 'type'. Therefore if we load up the background of our pedigrees with the best individuals from our Heroic Era, eventually we will achieve what is called critical mass, and the progeny will start demonstrating a type that is reminiscent of our great stayers of yesteryear on a consistent basis. These are the basic principles of breeding that can point us to success.

That's the easy part. The difficulty will be to cull the individual who does display the weaknesses. With mares producing only one foal a year—and that is if we are very lucky—then it can take quite a while to achieve our goals, plus recessive genes can be passed down for quite a few generations before they surface; there is no guarantee we will see them in the first generation. We can speed up the process by inbreeding on purpose to the talented but flawed line, because inbreeding concentrates whatever is there and increases our chance of seeing the faults show up right away. Do we have the determination and patience to do this?

Let's look at our modern day scapegoat: Native Dancer.

Native Dancer was a racing machine, a superb and rare racehorse of tremendous vitality and talent. Powerful and game, he usually won decisively. He raced twenty-two times and won all but one. He won all three of his four-year-old starts as well, and he won at distances from five furlongs to 1¼ miles—therefore he is actually a far sounder creature than the majority of the racers out there today. He had a few physical drawbacks: first he was thickly muscled and heavy, and therefore when racing he put stress on his legs and joints. His ankles sometimes swelled and developed calcium deposits (osslets), although they say he usually was not lame from them, and lastly, he had a tendency to sore feet, and his sole bruises would often abscess. It was this last ailment that brought on his retirement at age four (This fault is also in the Domino line; it caused Domino's retirement and the early death of Commando—septic hoof.)

We must face the fact that some of these joint problems occur because we are racing or competing two-year-olds (see Chapter 26—Seattle Slew progeny). Thoroughbreds are not finished growing until their fourth year. With sport horses and warmbloods it takes even longer, usually until they are six or even seven—I have a gelding who actually grew his final inch when he was nine. To change this practice of racing babies would take a philosophical sea-change.

The Thoroughbred scholar Avalyn Hunter reports that Native Dancer was a "heavily-topped" racehorse with "suspicious" ankles that he inherited from his sire Polynesian (*Classic Pedigrees*). We, the sport horse breeders, know from experience also that a tall or heavy horse is prone to damage, especially in speed sports.

Polynesian was a good racer overall, but he did have crooked front legs; and he did seem pass on weak ankles to some of his offspring. Where did this come from? He is 5x5x5x6x6 to the full siblings Sainfoin/Sierra but is also 4x3x6 to Polymelus through his sons Polymelian, Phalaris, and Corcyra. I am not aware of soundness issues coming via Sainfoin/Sierra (I could just be uninformed also, and it is also possible that while these horses were sound themselves they could be carrying a negative recessive that magnifies the problems); what I do know is that two of the three Polymelus sons in him are notorious for passing on faults, plus Cyllene the sire of Polymelus is notorious for contracted and/or small hooves. Phalaris of course transmits a heavily muscled body mounted on delicate legs, with a tendency to tendon problems and brittle bones. Pompey (Corcyra is his dam-sire) is a purveyor of weak forelegs—especially the ankles. Between these two sire-lines we can account for much of the unsoundness mentioned above (I am not an expert in this diagnosis, and many of you will be able to locate sources of unsoundness better than I.)

Polynesian is fairly sound himself, but is believed to be the carrier of unsoundness to the line. — photo by Skeet Meadors, courtesy of Keeneland Library

It appears other sires with Pompey have these exhibited faults as well as Native Dancer, such as Boldnesian (second sire of Seattle Slew), who carries a double dose of Pompey, and he also had bad ankles—worse than Native Dancer. The great Bold Ruler (who also carries the Pompey line) was never entirely sound, nor was his full brother Independence, a top steeplechaser—they suffered with bone chips, foot problems, and ankles again. But the great sire Tom Fool carries Pompey's full sister Laughing Queen, and his ankles were fine, and aside from brittle hooves and occasionally passing on weak knees, he was remarkably sound and tough for a Phalaris-line stallion. (I have included a copy of Pompey's pedigree for your study—his strongest dominance is the full brothers Rataplan/Stockwell 6x6x7x6x7x6x7 and the full sisters Feronia/Violet 6x5—are either of these groups the origin of the weaknesses? I don't know the answer.) We see something like this in the Domino line, which can pass on sore feet and occasionally tendon issues, but his full sister Correction had none of those weaknesses, nor did she pass them on. Native Dancer might well have inherited his sore feet from Domino as he has four lines of him in eight generations, and perhaps the four lines he has of Cyllene compounded this problem. Native Dancer's dam Geisha is by the sound Discovery (Fair Play and Hamburg), and she has the sound John P. Grier as her second dam-sire, and the sound Sweep as her third dam-sire, so unless you look at the buildup of the bulky Ben Brush in her as contributing to the ankle problem, there is really nothing there to suggest she had anything to do with ankle unsoundness, and while Ben Brush was bulky he was also extremely sound—with short, stout legs.

More clues on this trail come when we see the soundness in the line actually got worse with Native Dancer's most successful son Raise a Native, as he was not particularly sound (noticeably less sound than his sire Native Dancer who raced until he was four), and he was retired after a brilliant juvenile campaign (at two-years-old) with unsound ankles, although some say he otherwise had strong forelegs. (In Raise a Native's case I am not saying his ankle problem arose from being trained too young—he obviously inherited this weakness, but the early hard racing surely brought it on.) Another portion of his structural problems certainly was that he was of that top-heavy quarter-horsey type and was so very fast that it put undue strain on his joints. At stud Raise a Native was a brilliant sire as well, churning out champion after champion: Mr. Prospector, Exclusive Native (sire of Triple Crown winner Affirmed), Majestic Prince, Alydar—this is pretty heady company. Please note also that Exclusive Native and Alydar were very sound, but Majestic Prince was definitely not a sound horse, and he also passed on ankle and knee problems.

In the case of Native Dancer's prolific, brilliant son Raise a Native we can see that more flawed lines were added to the mix as we find his dam has the less-than-sound Case Ace as her sire. A son of Teddy, this sire's dam-sire is Ultimus, a stallion inbred to Domino, and he is noted as one that passed on sore feet—a condition that caused Domino to retire. But Raise a Native retired with an ankle injury—an indication that the Pompey defect was dominant instead and we see he passed it on to his son Majestic Prince.

Pompey—is he the source of the weak ankles? Many believe so, he was a good racer himself but did produce many offspring with ankle problems; his full sister Laughing Queen appeared to be sounder. —image *Thoroughbred Types*

Majestic Prince was a magnificent racer, and it sure looked like he would win the Triple Crown, but his delicate frame could not stand up to the test, and he broke down right before the Belmont, with splints and poor ankles and enflamed tendons they say. Like the rest of this line he became a tremendous sire producing brilliant racers, but often unsound ones, especially in the ankles and knees. What did his dam add to the genetics that tipped the balance to such a dominant factor of unsoundness? Here is what I found as his dominances, and really I cannot find a smoking gun here. The dam brought in a powerful filly factor of the ¾ siblings Mahmoud/Mumtaz Begum through daughters 3x3—this easily explains his outstanding racing class and his success as a sire. Blenheim, the sire of Mumtaz, can pass on weak knees to some of his progeny. Majestic Prince also has two Ajax daughters: Hors Concours in Nearco and Hermosita the sixth dam, which is a strong placement affecting the X chromosome material. His dam also brings in Sierra, the full sibling to Sainfoin, who is dam-sire of Phalaris. Are any of these new strengths responsible for the unsoundness becoming dominant? Most probably the knee weakness can be explained by the doubling up of Charles O'Malley who is associated with this trait (found in Blenheim). Also Majestic Prince's dam-sire is Royal Charger who had crooked legs, but possibly more telling is the line of Alibhai—his second dam-sire who bowed a tendon before he even got to the races. Perhaps Majestic Prince just got the unlucky shuffle of the defect deck and got the eight ball in each division, for not all the offspring of Raise a Native are unsound. This is an illustration for us, the breeders, in that not all the offspring will carry the defect—which means we can save some of these talented lines by breeding on from the soundest of them.

Raise a Native's sound and talented son Exclusive Native was 5x4 to the Fair Play son Display. Exclusive Native's Triple-Crown-winning son Affirmed was 5x5x6x7x6 Teddy and 7x7x6x6 Fair Play, so there was a strong dominance in the sound elements—I think we can find a lesson here on how to bypass weaknesses and produce soundness in our flawed gene pools. None of our gene pools will be 'clean'; our task will be to create dominance in the sound elements while eliminating the progeny who carry the faults.

Then there is Mr. Prospector, who is one of the greatest sires of modern times; experts liken his career to that of Nearco, but he retired from racing with sore shins, bone chips, and a fractured seismoid. He passes on his racing brilliance reliably but also some of his problems, brought out in some of his offspring by their inherited crooked legs or small feet. Yet he is way sounder than his sire, and his record of sound progeny is far better. He possessed tremendous vitality—he lived to 29. He has become a legendary sire of sires: Miswaki, Fappiano, Gulch, Machivellian, Woodman, Conquistador Cielo, Kingmambo, Gone West, Forty-Niner (sire of Distorted Humor), and Seeking the Gold to name a few. This is a staggering list of top horses.

Nashua seen with his groom, trainer, and owner Leslie Combs was surprisingly sound and produced sound tough offspring. —photo by Skeet Meadors, courtesy of Keeneland Library

Now his grandsire Native Dancer is pointed to by many as the source of the unsoundness that Mr. Prospector passes to some of his offspring, but Mr. P also is notable for some extremely sound progeny. So we can see there are some faults in the line, but in Mr. P's case (and Native Dancer's) it is not always dominant enough to go to the next generation—therefore there is a large measure of hope in this situation.

Mr. Prospector has the strong, sturdy, sound Nashua as his dam-sire. Nashua is a puzzle as he is loaded with the known carriers of faults, but he appears to have completely ducked the axe, as not only was he very sound, but his offspring are sound and tough as well, which is an indication that the faults did not travel down to him. He carries lines of Blenheim, which can pass on knee problems (inherited from his dam-sire Charles O'Malley—an unsound horse), and there is The Tetrarch who

One of the toughest American racers in modern times was a horse named Johnstown; he is a very sound bloodline. —sketch by C.W. Anderson from *Who's Who in Thoroughbred Racing*

retired with front leg problems, and of course Phalaris with his tendon and brittle bone issues, and there is also Sardanapale with crooked legs, yet this solid horse passed none of it on nor displayed it. Perhaps it is because he is throwing genetically completely to his dam-sire Johnstown—a talented stakes winner who was tough and sound and is known as producing the same. Johnstown is loaded with sound lines: Fair Play, Hanover 5x6, Ajax 4x3, the talented mare Clemence 7x6x7x7, plus seven lines of St. Simon and his full sister Angelica and seven lines of Lexington RH in ten generations. Here is the demonstration of the positive possible, that some of the offspring of these very talented but unsound lines will still produce foals with not only the talent but the sturdy frame to carry it. Besides possessing the known sound lines of Fair Play and Teddy, his dam Sequence was by the sound Count Fleet, and her second dam-sire was Bull Dog. She also carries the very sound full sister to Domino: Correction, and traces tail-female to the sound and talented Hamburg daughter Frizette. Therefore Mr. P did not get unsoundness from his dam, and this may be why he can sire so many sound youngsters along with the occasional flawed ones. So in Mr. P's case I believe we should carefully breed on from his best and target his sound lines for dominance—to waste the top sport talent manifested in this line would be foolish.

Native Dancer has numerous successful descendants worldwide, for instance his grandson Sharpen Up 1969 raced in England where he won his share of races including the prestigious Middle Park Stakes. He went on to be a marvelous sire there, becoming the leading freshman sire in 1976 and earning the title of Champion-Sire-of-Two-Year-Olds in England in 1982. Northern Dancer, whose dam-sire is Native Dancer, also carries Blenheim, and while he is fairly sound, his son Danzig throws foals with brittle bones and poor knees.

Showing the Native Dancer body type is his grandson Sharpen Up, a champion sire in England with a heavy buildup of Pharos/Phalaris. —image courtesy of Wiki Commons

So how does all this apply to Funny Cide's sire Distorted Humor? He has Raise a Native in the third generation, Danzig in the second, but he also adds a new influence in the unsound Turn-To who is doubled 5x5 and sex-balanced—a very powerful pattern in suspect lines. Turn-To is 3x3 to Pharos, and he is notorious for transmitting the Phalaris weakness of the forelegs with tendon problems, bulky frame, and brittle bones. Turn-To's son Hail to Reason can pass on knee problems on occasion—but is notable also for soundness in some of his offspring—is it a coincidence that Hail to Reason's dam is inbred to Man O' War?

So here we have this fantastic modern sire for brilliance and class—Distorted Humor—who has critical mass in Lexington RH, but whose lineage is married to transmitters of leg faults. His grandson, the spectacular I'll Have Another, who with nine hundred eighty-seven lines of Lexington RH is beyond anything we have seen so far in background stacking of Lexington RH, is grafted to even more of the unsound lines: Turn-To 7x7x8x6, Raise a Native 5x5x6, and Danzig 4x4. It is significant that he also is 4x4 Mr. Prospector and 6x7x6x8x9x7x7x7x8x7 Native Dancer. He blazed through the Kentucky Derby and the Preakness like a train, but then broke down with 'tendonitis' before the Belmont; his frame could not sustain his massive talent.

[Note: on unsoundness, many, many bloodlines have a strain of unsoundness—not just the few we have visited here. Here are a few others: the icon St. Simon transmitted sickle hocks; Spearmint, crooked front legs; John O'Gaunt—sire of Swynford—unsound joints; Charles O'Malley, weak knees; the great mare Clemence, bad temperament; Hastings also transmitted bad temperament, as well as osselets and sickle hocks; Spendthrift, thin-soled feet; Rock Sand, contracted feet; King Tom fostered delicate, fragile constitution; North Star III, delicate, fragile frames; Ultimus broadcast hoof problems; Ormonde, roarer and over at knee; Cyllene gave small hooves; St. Albans, bad legs; Sardanapale, crooked legs; and Tourbillon-sickle hocks—this is a partial list, and obviously, like most faults, only some of the offspring of these carriers received the fault. For instance the great Nasrullah and his ⅞ brother Royal Charger sometimes pass on knee problems (Blenheim—Charles O'Malley), but not always.]

Can we ever reclaim the soundness, talent, and resiliency that were present in our gene pool one hundred years ago? Strange as it may seem we can—it is not impossible. Because of the way genetics work, especially in that the genes travel through the generations unchanged unless there is a mutation (a very rare event), and that the genes also cluster, so that groups of them come down unchanged through the generations (Ann Bowling *Horse Genetics*), then there is some hope for us. Over the decades the sport fabric of those fabulous racers has been adulterated with lesser genetics, so that very few modern racers even show a hint of their ancestor's talent and durability. It will be our task to separate the wheat from the chaff in our pedigree designs until we accomplish our goal—this may take many generations, but for those with patience and perseverance there is a reward waiting.

What does soundness look like?

The American racehorse of the 1800s had achieved the pinnacle of speed, durability and stamina in the world—then and now. Many of our horses today are directly descended from those superstars—not just our Thoroughbred either, but many of our saddle breeds as well, and the horses that made up the Standardbred breed not only carry many of the Heroic Era stars, but they also raced themselves in heat races in this same time frame—often five-heat races—winner three of five; they just did it at the trot or pace rather than the gallop, so in their background there is also a reserve of those incredible genetics as well. America has a reservoir of sport depth that we have not yet begun to tap. When we do build up the background genes of that era (by accident in most cases), we come up with a horse that shocks us all, seemingly freakish in its level of ability in comparison to its peers. Funny Cide was our example in this chapter, but we saw Sunday Silence, Seattle Slew, Easy Goer, Dr. Fager, In Reality, and Holy Bull also, and the English have been stunned by the superlative Sadlers Wells, Never Bend, and Mill Reef.

Imp 1894—this is what soundness looks like, folks, one hundred seventy-one lifetime starts. At first glance the long legs with long pasterns look like a possible source of weakness, but her frame is equally fine—a balanced high class racer. —image from *Racing in America*

Let's take a look back at a filly who raced into the early 1900s, for our example of 'the way it was'. She was a seemingly common mare, born in Ohio in 1894, but very soon she was to be an equine celebrity; she was feted as the "Coal Black Lady", named for a popular song of the era, which became her anthem the band would play and the crowd would sing when she won her races. She started off as an unremarkable black filly bred by D. R. Harness and trained by C. E. Brossman. She was named Imp because she was a playful, good-natured youngster, but she ended up being one of the greatest racehorses of all time, having a lifetime total of one hundred seventy-one races (that is not a typo), with sixty-two wins, thirty-five seconds, and twenty-nine thirds in five seasons. She retired at age seven and then had five foals—one of them a stakes winner (Faust). Compare that to Native Dancer above—he had twenty-two starts in four years—or to our subject Funny Cide who did race into his seventh year like this mare, but with thirty-six starts, which seems quite a bit

until you compare it to Imp's one hundred seventy-one. Funny Cide is about as good as it gets lately—we sure have come a long way down the hill of decline.

Imp had an extremely low, fluid stride, and she ran with her head down, making it look like she was going slower than she was. She had a good two-year-old season winning four of eleven, but like a true stayer she got better with age. At three she ran in fifty(!) races winning fourteen, then at four she won nineteen of her thirty-four starts. At five she ran thirty-one races, winning thirteen. At age six in a 1¾ miles race she set an American record while winning by **thirty lengths** at 2:59 ⅕. She raced and won at distances from four furlongs up to 1¾ mile, and she set records for speed at 1 1/16, 1 ¼, 1½, and the 1¾ mentioned above. She was Horse-of-the-Year in 1899, and of course she has been inducted into the Hall of Fame.

What does her pedigree show us? Her sire is an English Thoroughbred: Wagner and his dominance is found in the full brothers Stockwell/Rataplan 4x4x5. Her dam is the American-bred Fondling who is 3x4 to Lexington RH. We have seen this type of pattern in many great horses—equal strength in the parents of strong line-breeding or inbreeding to different superior ancestors coming together in the foal. Here we have a template of excellence, the soundest, fastest lines from both England and the US ruling the lineage, and what was the result: it was a mare who could go and go, day after day—fifty races in one year means she averaged one race a week, and yet she remained sound and successful—these were races against the best colts of her time as well. We need to think about this, it is what is possible if we really try. It is a lot to strive for, but how can we not?

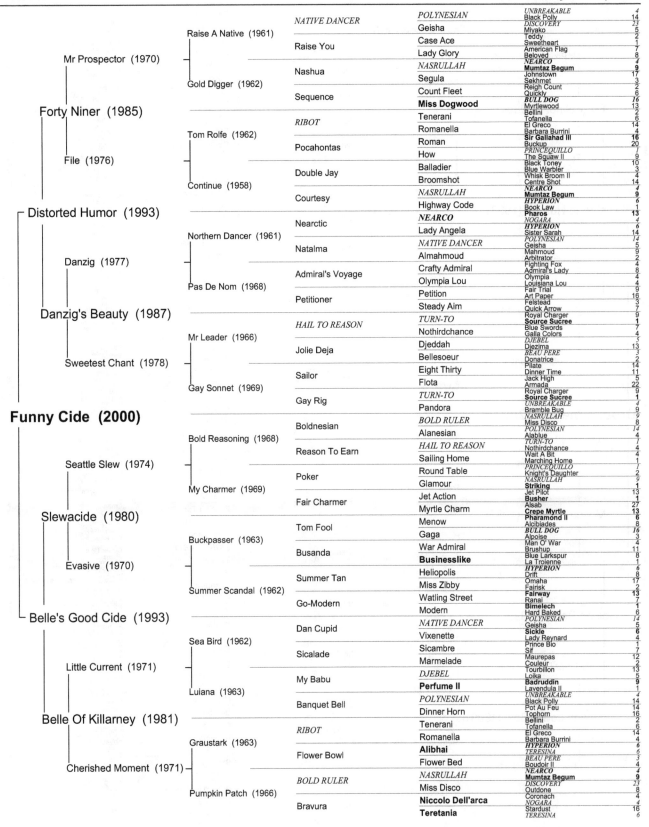

Funny Cide (2000)

Distorted Humor (1993)

Forty Niner (1985)

- Mr Prospector (1970)
  - Raise A Native (1961)
    - NATIVE DANCER
      - POLYNESIAN — Unbreakable 4 / Black Polly 14
      - Geisha — DISCOVERY 23 / Miyako 5
    - Raise You
      - Case Ace — Teddy 2 / Sweetheart 1
      - Lady Glory — American Flag 7 / Beloved 8
  - Gold Digger (1962)
    - Nashua
      - NASRULLAH — NEARCO 4 / Mumtaz Begum 9
      - Segula — Johnstown 17 / Sekhmet 3
    - Sequence
      - Count Fleet — Reigh Count 2 / Quickly 6
      - Miss Dogwood — BULL DOG 16 / Myrtlewood 13

File (1976)

- Tom Rolfe (1962)
  - RIBOT
    - Tenerani — Bellini 2 / Tofanella 6
    - Romanella — El Greco 14 / Barbara Burrini 4
  - Pocahontas
    - Roman — Sir Gallahad III 16 / Buckup 20
    - How — PRINCEQUILLO 1 / The Squaw II 9
- Continue (1958)
  - Double Jay
    - Balladier — Black Toney 10 / Blue Warbler 3
    - Broomshot — Whisk Broom II 4 / Centre Shot 14
  - Courtesy
    - NASRULLAH — NEARCO 4 / Mumtaz Begum 9
    - Highway Code — HYPERION 1 / Book Law 1

Danzig's Beauty (1987)

Danzig (1977)

- Northern Dancer (1961)
  - Nearctic
    - NEARCO — Pharos 13 / NOGARA 4
    - Lady Angela — HYPERION 6 / Sister Sarah 14
  - Natalma
    - NATIVE DANCER — POLYNESIAN 14 / Geisha 5
    - Almahmoud — Mahmoud 9 / Arbitrator 2
- Pas De Nom (1968)
  - Admiral's Voyage
    - Crafty Admiral — Fighting Fox 4 / Admiral's Lady 8
    - Olympia Lou — Olympia 4 / Louisiana Lou 4
  - Petitioner
    - Petition — Fair Trial 9 / Art Paper 16
    - Steady Aim — Felstead 3 / Quick Arrow 7

Sweetest Chant (1978)

- Mr Leader (1966)
  - HAIL TO REASON
    - TURN-TO — Royal Charger 9 / Source Sucree 1
    - Nothirdchance — Blue Swords 7 / Galla Colors 4
  - Jolie Deja
    - Djeddah — DJEBEL 5 / Djezima 13
    - Bellesoeur — BEAU PERE 3 / Donatrice 2
- Gay Sonnet (1969)
  - Sailor
    - Eight Thirty — Pilate 14 / Dinner Time 11
    - Flota — Jack High 5 / Armada 22
  - Gay Rig
    - TURN-TO — Royal Charger 9 / Source Sucree 1
    - Pandora — UNBREAKABLE 4 / Bramble Bug 1

Belle's Good Cide (1993)

Slewacide (1980)

- Seattle Slew (1974)
  - Bold Reasoning (1968)
    - Boldnesian
      - BOLD RULER — NASRULLAH 9 / Miss Disco 8
      - Alanesian — POLYNESIAN 14 / Alablue 4
    - Reason To Earn
      - HAIL TO REASON — TURN-TO 1 / Nothirdchance 4
      - Sailing Home — Wait A Bit 4 / Marching Home 4
  - My Charmer (1969)
    - Poker
      - Round Table — PRINCEQUILLO 2 / Knight's Daughter 1
      - Glamour — NASRULLAH 9 / Striking 1
    - Fair Charmer
      - Jet Action — Jet Pilot 13 / Busher 1
      - Myrtle Charm — Alsab 27 / Crepe Myrtle 13

Evasive (1970)

- Buckpasser (1963)
  - Tom Fool
    - Menow — Pharamond II 6 / Alcibiades 8
    - Gaga — BULL DOG 16 / Alpoise 3
  - Busanda
    - War Admiral — Man O' War 4 / Brushup 11
    - Businesslike — Blue Larkspur 8 / La Troienne 1
- Summer Scandal (1962)
  - Summer Tan
    - Heliopolis — HYPERION 6 / Drift 8
    - Miss Zibby — Omaha 17 / Fairisk 2
  - Go-Modern
    - Watling Street — Fairway 13 / Ranai 7
    - Modern — Bimelech 1 / Hard Baked 6

Belle Of Killarney (1981)

Little Current (1971)

- Sea Bird (1962)
  - Dan Cupid
    - NATIVE DANCER — POLYNESIAN 14 / Geisha 5
    - Vixenette — Sickle 6 / Lady Reynard 4
  - Sicalade
    - Sicambre — Prince Bio 1 / Sif 7
    - Marmelade — Maurepas 12 / Couleur 2
- Luiana (1963)
  - My Babu
    - DJEBEL — Tourbillon 13 / Loika 5
    - Perfume II — Badruddin 9 / Lavendula II 1
  - Banquet Bell
    - POLYNESIAN — UNBREAKABLE 4 / Black Polly 14
    - Dinner Horn — Pot Au Feu 14 / Tophorn 16

Cherished Moment (1971)

- Graustark (1963)
  - RIBOT
    - Tenerani — Bellini 2 / Tofanella 6
    - Romanella — El Greco 14 / Barbara Burrini 4
  - Flower Bowl
    - Alibhai — HYPERION 6 / TERESINA 6
    - Flower Bed — BEAU PERE 3 / Boudoir II 4
- Pumpkin Patch (1966)
  - BOLD RULER
    - NASRULLAH — NEARCO 4 / Mumtaz Begum 9
    - Miss Disco — DISCOVERY 23 / Outdone 8
  - Bravura
    - Niccolo Dell'arca — Coronach 4 / NOGARA 4
    - Teretania — Stardust 16 / TERESINA 6

Funny Cide 2000

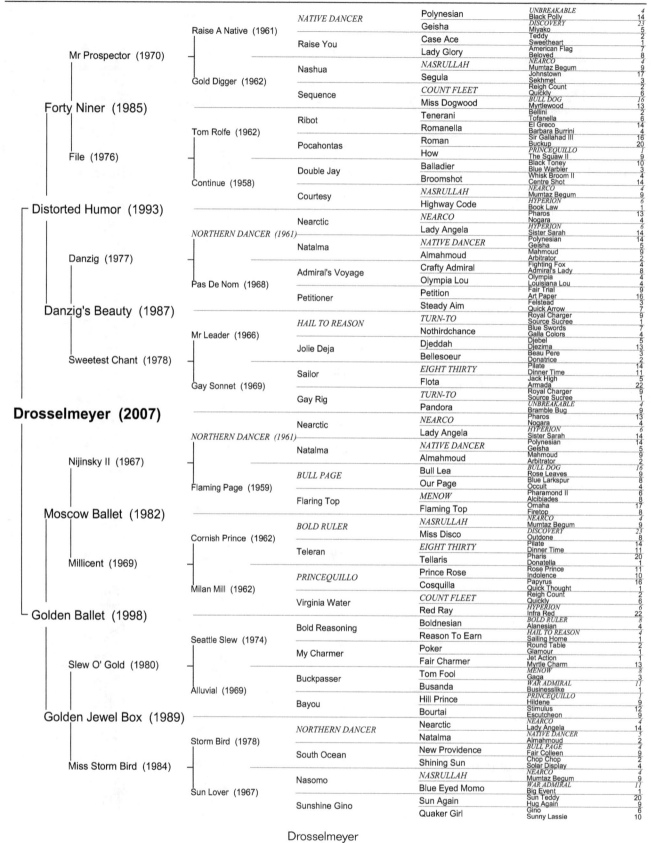

Drosselmeyer

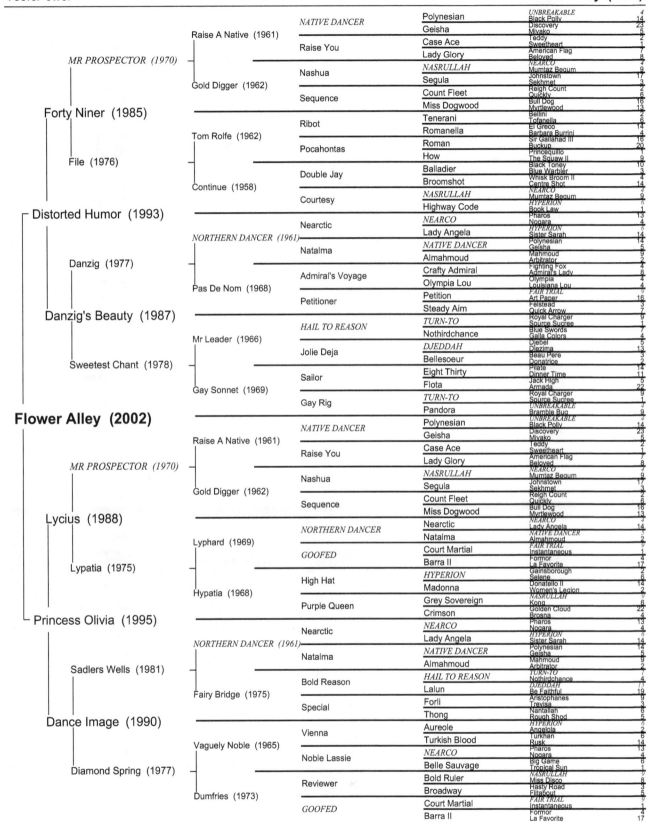

Flower Alley 2002

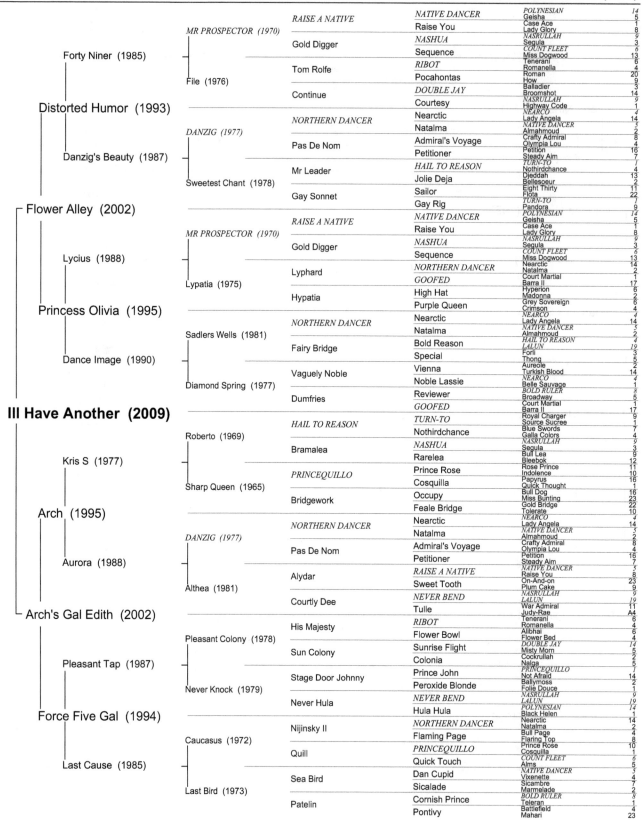

Ill Have Another (2009)

Flower Alley (2002)

Distorted Humor (1993)
- Forty Niner (1985)
  - MR PROSPECTOR (1970)
    - RAISE A NATIVE
      - NATIVE DANCER — POLYNESIAN 14 / Geisha 5
      - Raise You — Case Ace 1 / Lady Glory 8
    - Gold Digger
      - NASHUA — NASRULLAH 9 / Segula 3
      - Sequence — COUNT FLEET 6 / Miss Dogwood 13
  - File (1976)
    - Tom Rolfe
      - RIBOT — Tenerani 6 / Romanella 4
      - Pocahontas — Roman 20 / How 9
    - Continue
      - DOUBLE JAY — Balladier 3 / Broomshot 14
      - Courtesy — NASRULLAH 9 / Highway Code 1
- Danzig's Beauty (1987)
  - DANZIG (1977)
    - NORTHERN DANCER
      - Nearctic — NEARCO 4 / Lady Angela 14
      - Natalma — NATIVE DANCER 5 / Almahmoud 2
    - Pas De Nom
      - Admiral's Voyage — Crafty Admiral 8 / Olympia Lou 4
      - Petitioner — Petition 16 / Steady Aim 7
  - Sweetest Chant (1978)
    - Mr Leader
      - HAIL TO REASON — TURN-TO 1 / Nothirdchance 4
      - Jolie Deja — Djeddah 13 / Bellesoeur 2
    - Gay Sonnet
      - Sailor — Eight Thirty 11 / Flota 22
      - Gay Rig — TURN-TO 1 / Pandora 9

Princess Olivia (1995)
- Lycius (1988)
  - MR PROSPECTOR (1970)
    - RAISE A NATIVE
      - NATIVE DANCER — POLYNESIAN 14 / Geisha 5
      - Raise You — Case Ace 1 / Lady Glory 8
    - Gold Digger
      - NASHUA — NASRULLAH 9 / Segula 3
      - Sequence — COUNT FLEET 6 / Miss Dogwood 13
  - Lypatia (1975)
    - Lyphard
      - NORTHERN DANCER — Nearctic 14 / Natalma 2
      - GOOFED — Court Martial 17 / Barra II 1
    - Hypatia
      - High Hat — Hyperion 6 / Madonna 2
      - Purple Queen — Grey Sovereign 6 / Crimson 4
- Dance Image (1990)
  - Sadlers Wells (1981)
    - NORTHERN DANCER
      - Nearctic — NEARCO 4 / Lady Angela 14
      - Natalma — NATIVE DANCER 5 / Almahmoud 2
    - Fairy Bridge
      - Bold Reason — HAIL TO REASON 19 / LALUN 3
      - Special — Forli 5 / Thong 2
  - Diamond Spring (1977)
    - Vaguely Noble
      - Vienna — Aureole 2 / Turkish Blood 14
      - Noble Lassie — NEARCO 4 / Belle Sauvage 1
    - Dumfries
      - Reviewer — BOLD RULER 8 / Broadway 5
      - GOOFED — Court Martial 17 / Barra II

Arch's Gal Edith (2002)

Arch (1995)
- Kris S (1977)
  - Roberto (1969)
    - HAIL TO REASON
      - TURN-TO — Royal Charger 9 / Source Sucree 7
      - Nothirdchance — Blue Swords 1 / Galla Colors 4
    - Bramalea
      - NASHUA — NASRULLAH 9 / Segula 3
      - Rarelea — Bull Lea 9 / Bleebok 12
  - Sharp Queen (1965)
    - PRINCEQUILLO
      - Prince Rose — Rose Prince 11 / Indolence 10
      - Cosquilla — Papyrus 16 / Quick Thought 1
    - Bridgework
      - Occupy — Bull Dog 16 / Miss Bunting 23
      - Feale Bridge — Gold Bridge 22 / Tolerate 10
- Aurora (1988)
  - DANZIG (1977)
    - NORTHERN DANCER
      - Nearctic — NEARCO 4 / Lady Angela 14
      - Natalma — NATIVE DANCER 5 / Almahmoud 2
    - Pas De Nom
      - Admiral's Voyage — Crafty Admiral 8 / Olympia Lou 4
      - Petitioner — Petition 16 / Steady Aim 7
  - Althea (1981)
    - Alydar
      - RAISE A NATIVE — NATIVE DANCER 5 / Raise You 8
      - Sweet Tooth — On-And-on 23 / Plum Cake 9
    - Courtly Dee
      - NEVER BEND — NASRULLAH 9 / LALUN 19
      - Tulle — War Admiral 11 / Judy-Rae A4

Force Five Gal (1994)
- Pleasant Tap (1987)
  - Pleasant Colony (1978)
    - His Majesty
      - RIBOT — Tenerani 6 / Romanella 4
      - Flower Bowl — Alibhai 6 / Flower Bed 4
    - Sun Colony
      - Sunrise Flight — DOUBLE JAY 14 / Misty Morn 5
      - Colonia — Cockrullah 2 / Nalga 5
  - Never Knock (1979)
    - Stage Door Johnny
      - Prince John — PRINCEQUILLO 14 / Not Afraid 2
      - Peroxide Blonde — Ballymoss 1 / Folie Douce 2
    - Never Hula
      - NEVER BEND — NASRULLAH 9 / LALUN 19
      - Hula Hula — POLYNESIAN 14 / Black Helen 1
- Last Cause (1985)
  - Caucasus (1972)
    - Nijinsky II
      - NORTHERN DANCER — Nearctic 14 / Natalma 2
      - Flaming Page — Bull Page 4 / Flaring Top 8
    - Quill
      - PRINCEQUILLO — Prince Rose 10 / Cosquilla 1
      - Quick Touch — COUNT FLEET 6 / Alms 5
  - Last Bird (1973)
    - Sea Bird
      - Dan Cupid — NATIVE DANCER 5 / Vixenette 4
      - Sicalade — Sicambre 7 / Marmelade 2
    - Patelin
      - Cornish Prince — BOLD RULER 8 / Teleran 1
      - Pontivy — Battlefield / Mahari 23

I'll Have Another 2007

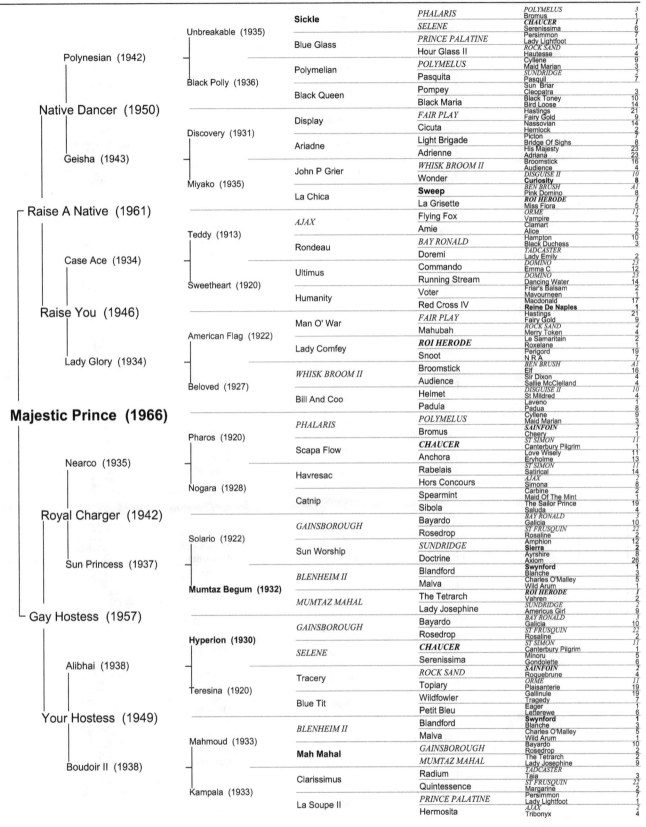

Majestic Prince 1966

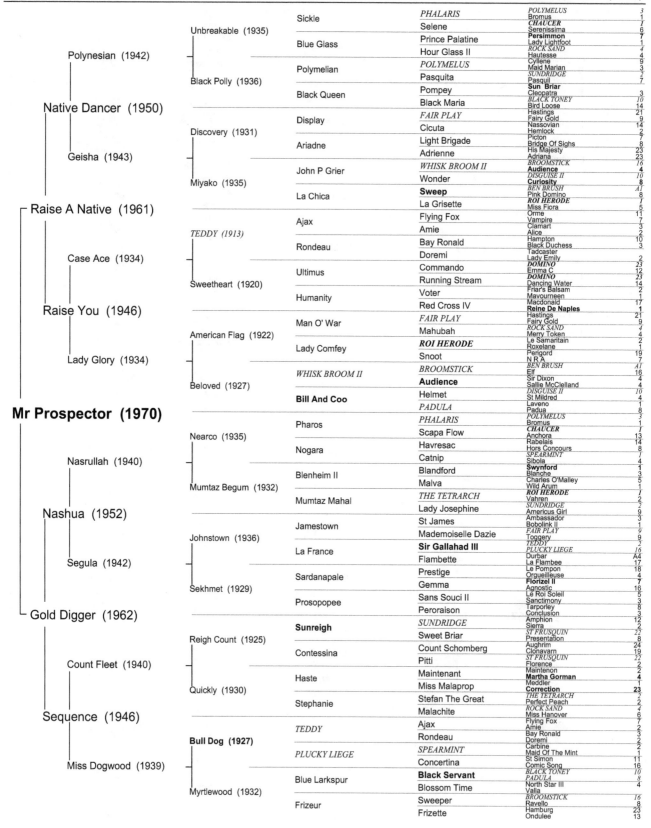

Mr. Prospector 1970

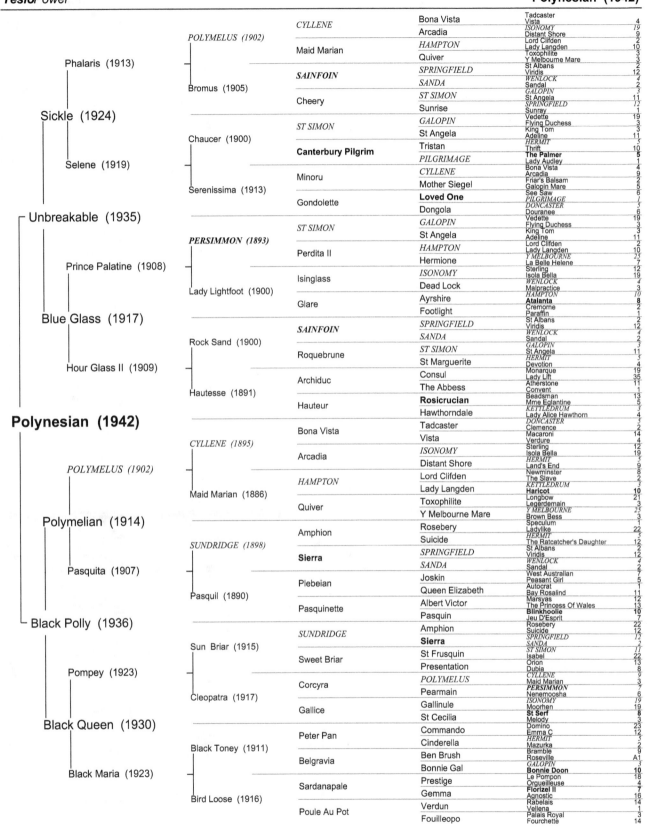

Left-hand lineage (ascending to Polynesian 1942)

- Phalaris (1913)
  - Sickle (1924)
  - Selene (1919)
- Unbreakable (1935)
  - Prince Palatine (1908)
  - Blue Glass (1917)
  - Hour Glass II (1909)
- **Polynesian (1942)**
  - POLYMELUS (1902)
  - Polymelian (1914)
  - Pasquita (1907)
- Black Polly (1936)
  - Pompey (1923)
  - Black Queen (1930)
  - Black Maria (1923)

Expanded pedigree

POLYMELUS (1902)
- *CYLLENE*
  - Bona Vista — Tadcaster / Vista 4
  - Arcadia — *ISONOMY* 19 / Distant Shore 9
- Maid Marian
  - *HAMPTON* — Lord Clifden 2 / Lady Langden 10
  - Quiver — Toxophilite 3 / Y Melbourne Mare 3

Bromus (1905)
- *SAINFOIN*
  - *SPRINGFIELD* — St Albans / Viridis 12
  - *SANDA* — *WENLOCK* 4 / Sandal 2
- Cheery
  - *ST SIMON* — *GALOPIN* 3 / St Angela 11
  - Sunrise — *SPRINGFIELD* 12 / Sunray 1

Chaucer (1900)
- *ST SIMON*
  - *GALOPIN* — Vedette 19 / Flying Duchess 3
  - St Angela — King Tom 3 / Adeline 11
- **Canterbury Pilgrim**
  - Tristan — *HERMIT* 5 / Thrift 10
  - *PILGRIMAGE* — **The Palmer** 5 / Lady Audley 1

Serenissima (1913)
- Minoru
  - *CYLLENE* — Bona Vista 4 / Arcadia 9
  - Mother Siegel — Friar's Balsam 2 / Galopin Mare 5
- Gondolette
  - **Loved One** — See Saw 6 / *PILGRIMAGE* 1
  - Dongola — *DONCASTER* / Douranee 6

PERSIMMON (1893)
- *ST SIMON*
  - *GALOPIN* — Vedette 19 / Flying Duchess 3
  - St Angela — King Tom 3 / Adeline 11
- Perdita II
  - *HAMPTON* — Lord Clifden 2 / Lady Langden 10
  - Hermione — *Y MELBOURNE* 25 / La Belle Helene 7

Lady Lightfoot (1900)
- Isinglass
  - *ISONOMY* — Sterling 12 / Isola Bella 19
  - Dead Lock — *WENLOCK* 4 / Malpractice 3
- Glare
  - Ayrshire — *HAMPTON* 10 / **Atalanta** 8
  - Footlight — Cremorne 2 / Paraffin 1

Rock Sand (1900)
- *SAINFOIN*
  - *SPRINGFIELD* — St Albans 2 / Viridis 12
  - *SANDA* — *WENLOCK* 4 / Sandal 2
- Roquebrune
  - *ST SIMON* — *GALOPIN* 3 / St Angela 11
  - St Marguerite — *HERMIT* 5 / Devotion 4

Hautesse (1891)
- Archiduc
  - Consul — Monarque 19 / Lady Lift 35
  - The Abbess — Atherstone 11 / Convent 1
- Hauteur
  - **Rosicrucian** — Beadsman 13 / Mme Eglantine 5
  - Hawthorndale — *KETTLEDRUM* 3 / Lady Alice Hawthorn 4

CYLLENE (1895)
- Bona Vista
  - Tadcaster — *DONCASTER* 2 / Clemence
  - Vista — Macaroni 14 / Verdure 4
- Arcadia
  - *ISONOMY* — Sterling 12 / Isola Bella 19
  - Distant Shore — *HERMIT* 5 / Land's End 9

Maid Marian (1886)
- *HAMPTON*
  - Lord Clifden — Newminster 6 / The Slave 2
  - Lady Langden — *KETTLEDRUM* / **Haricot** 10
- Quiver
  - Toxophilite — Longbow 21 / Legerdemain 3
  - Y Melbourne Mare — *Y MELBOURNE* 25 / Brown Bess 3

SUNDRIDGE (1898)
- Amphion
  - Rosebery — Speculum 1 / Ladylike 22
  - Suicide — *HERMIT* 5 / The Ratcatcher's Daughter 12
- **Sierra**
  - *SPRINGFIELD* — St Albans 2 / Viridis 12
  - *SANDA* — *WENLOCK* 4 / Sandal 2

Pasquil (1890)
- Plebeian
  - Joskin — West Australian 7 / Peasant Girl 5
  - Queen Elizabeth — Autocrat 1 / Bay Rosalind 11
- Pasquinette
  - Albert Victor — Marsyas 12 / The Princess Of Wales 13
  - Pasquin — **Blinkhoolie** 10 / Jeu D'Esprit 7

Sun Briar (1915)
- *SUNDRIDGE*
  - Amphion — Rosebery 22 / Suicide 12
  - **Sierra** — *SPRINGFIELD* 12 / *SANDA* 2
- Sweet Briar
  - St Frusquin — *ST SIMON* 11 / Isabel 22
  - Presentation — Orion 13 / Dubia 8

Cleopatra (1917)
- Corcyra
  - *POLYMELUS* — *CYLLENE* 9 / Maid Marian 3
  - Pearmain — *PERSIMMON* 7 / Nenemoosha 6
- Gallice
  - Gallinule — *ISONOMY* 19 / Moorhen 19
  - St Cecilia — **St Serf** 8 / Melody 3

Black Toney (1911)
- Peter Pan
  - Commando — Domino 23 / Emma C 12
  - Cinderella — *HERMIT* 5 / Mazurka 2
- Belgravia
  - Ben Brush — Bramble / Roseville A1
  - Bonnie Gal — *GALOPIN* 3 / **Bonnie Doon** 10

Bird Loose (1916)
- Sardanapale
  - Prestige — Le Pompon 18 / Orgueilleuse 4
  - Gemma — **Florizel II** 7 / Agnostic 16
- Poule Au Pot
  - Verdun — Rabelais 14 / Vellena 1
  - Fouilleopo — Palais Royal 3 / Fourchette 14

Polynesian 1942

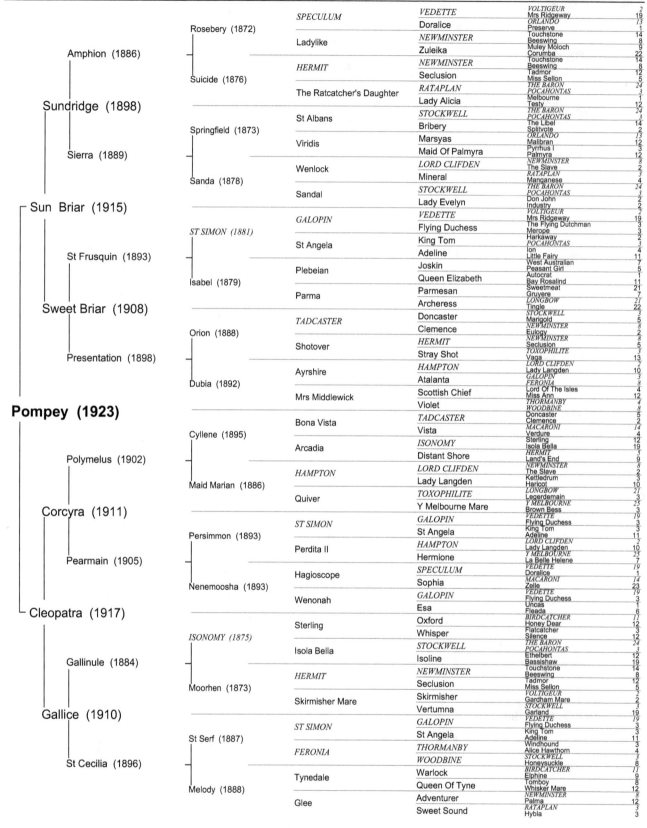

Pompey 1923

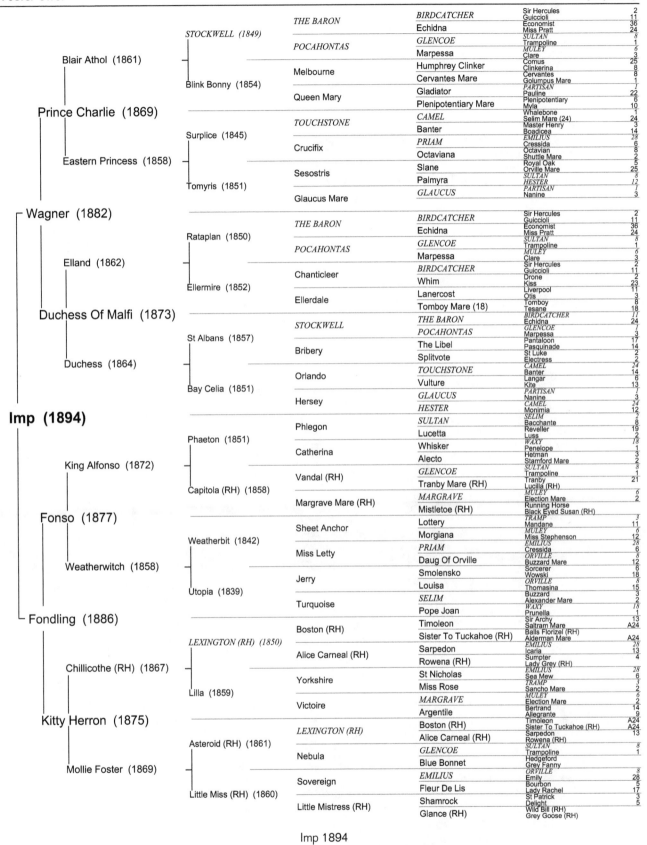

Imp (1894)

- **Wagner (1882)**
  - **Prince Charlie (1869)**
    - **Blair Athol (1861)**
      - STOCKWELL (1849)
        - THE BARON
          - BIRDCATCHER — Sir Hercules 2 / Guiccioli 11
          - Echidna — Economist 36 / Miss Pratt 24
        - POCAHONTAS
          - GLENCOE — SULTAN 8 / Trampoline 1
          - Marpessa — MULEY 6 / Clare 3
      - Blink Bonny (1854)
        - Melbourne
          - Humphrey Clinker — Comus 25 / Clinkerina 8
          - Cervantes Mare — Cervantes 8 / Golumpus Mare 1
        - Queen Mary
          - Gladiator — PARTISAN 1 / Pauline 22
          - Plenipotentiary Mare — Plenipotentiary 6 / Myla 10
    - **Eastern Princess (1858)**
      - Surplice (1845)
        - TOUCHSTONE
          - CAMEL — Whalebone 1 / Selim Mare (24) 24
          - Banter — Master Henry 3 / Boadicea 14
        - Crucifix
          - PRIAM — EMILIUS 28 / Cressida 6
          - Octaviana — Octavian 8 / Shuttle Mare 2
      - Tomyris (1851)
        - Sesostris
          - Slane — Royal Oak 5 / Orville Mare 25
          - Palmyra — SULTAN 8 / HESTER 12
        - Glaucus Mare
          - GLAUCUS — PARTISAN 1
          - Nanine 3
  - **Duchess Of Malfi (1873)**
    - **Elland (1862)**
      - Rataplan (1850)
        - THE BARON
          - BIRDCATCHER — Sir Hercules 2 / Guiccioli 11
          - Echidna — Economist 36 / Miss Pratt 24
        - POCAHONTAS
          - GLENCOE — SULTAN 8 / Trampoline 1
          - Marpessa — MULEY 6 / Clare 3
      - Ellermire (1852)
        - Chanticleer
          - BIRDCATCHER — Sir Hercules 2 / Guiccioli 11
          - Whim — Drone 2 / Kiss 23
        - Ellerdale
          - Lanercost — Liverpool 11 / Otis 3
          - Tomboy Mare (18) — Tomboy 8 / Tesane 18
    - **Duchess (1864)**
      - St Albans (1857)
        - STOCKWELL
          - THE BARON — BIRDCATCHER 11 / Echidna 24
          - POCAHONTAS — GLENCOE 1 / Marpessa 3
        - Bribery
          - The Libel — Pantaloon 17 / Pasquinade 14
          - Splitvote — St Luke 2 / Electress 2
      - Bay Celia (1851)
        - Orlando
          - TOUCHSTONE — CAMEL 24 / Banter 14
          - Vulture — Langar 6 / Kite 13
        - Hersey
          - GLAUCUS — PARTISAN 1 / Nanine 3
          - HESTER — CAMEL 24 / Monimia 12
- **Fondling (1886)**
  - **Fonso (1877)**
    - **King Alfonso (1872)**
      - Phaeton (1851)
        - Phlegon
          - SULTAN — SELIM 2 / Bacchante 8
          - Lucetta — Reveller 19 / Luss 2
        - Catherina
          - Whisker — WAXY 18 / Penelope 1
          - Alecto — Hetman 3 / Stamford Mare 2
      - Capitola (RH) (1858)
        - Vandal (RH)
          - GLENCOE — SULTAN 8 / Trampoline 1
          - Tranby Mare (RH) — Tranby 21 / Lucilla (RH)
        - Margrave Mare (RH)
          - MARGRAVE — MULEY 6 / Election Mare 2
          - Mistletoe (RH) — Running Horse / Black Eyed Susan (RH)
    - **Weatherwitch (1858)**
      - Weatherbit (1842)
        - Sheet Anchor
          - Lottery — TRAMP 3 / Mandane 11
          - Morgiana — MULEY 6 / Miss Stephenson 12
        - Miss Letty
          - PRIAM — EMILIUS 28 / Cressida 6
          - Daug Of Orville — ORVILLE 8 / Buzzard Mare 12
      - Utopia (1839)
        - Jerry
          - Smolensko — Sorcerer 6 / Wowski 18
          - Louisa — ORVILLE 8 / Thomasina 15
        - Turquoise
          - SELIM — Buzzard 3 / Alexander Mare 2
          - Pope Joan — WAXY 18 / Prunella 1
  - **Kitty Herron (1875)**
    - **Chillicothe (RH) (1867)**
      - LEXINGTON (RH) (1850)
        - Boston (RH)
          - Timoleon — Sir Archy 13 / Saltram Mare A24
          - Sister To Tuckahoe (RH) — Balls Florizel (RH) / Alderman Mare A24
        - Alice Carneal (RH)
          - Sarpedon — EMILIUS 28 / Icaria 13
          - Rowena (RH) — Sumpter 4 / Lady Grey (RH)
      - Lilla (1859)
        - Yorkshire
          - St Nicholas — EMILIUS 28 / Sea Mew 6
          - Miss Rose — TRAMP 3 / Sancho Mare 2
        - Victoire
          - MARGRAVE — MULEY 6 / Election Mare 2
          - Argentile — Bertrand 14 / Allegrante 9
    - **Mollie Foster (1869)**
      - Asteroid (RH) (1861)
        - LEXINGTON (RH)
          - Boston (RH) — Timoleon A24 / Sister To Tuckahoe (RH) A24
          - Alice Carneal (RH) — Sarpedon 13 / Rowena (RH)
        - Nebula
          - GLENCOE — SULTAN 8 / Trampoline 1
          - Blue Bonnet — Hedgeford / Grey Fanny
      - Little Miss (RH) (1860)
        - Sovereign
          - EMILIUS — ORVILLE 28 / Emily 5
          - Fleur De Lis — Bourbon 17 / Lady Rachel 3
        - Little Mistress (RH)
          - Shamrock — St Patrick 5 / Delight
          - Glance (RH) — Wild Bill (RH) / Grey Goose (RH)

Imp 1894

Part IV

The American Thoroughbred and
The International Sport Horse

Chapter 28

The American Thoroughbred and its Relation to the American Sport Horse

"The great object of encouraging the breed of racehorse is to produce the stout and enduring horse, from which we can from time to time draw upon to improve the other breeds"(Thoroughbred Record, July 1, 1882).

Our modern non-racing sport roster has expanded since the mid-1800s to include international competition. This began with occasional show jumping contests in England and France, with our Hunter Horse traveling to participate with its riders, owners, and trainers or through our American racing stables that had branches established in those countries that provided stock for those contests. Then after the turn of the century, first the idea of international tests, and then the enjoyment of them by the participating countries, resulted in the organization of structured international competitions. In 1909 the Nations Cup series was opened and held in participating countries. America hosted theirs at Madison Square Garden in NY, and foreign entrants competed there. Our competitors traveled to Europe to participate in the Nations Cup contests held in various countries there as well. After 1912 the 'Olympic' style sports of eventing, show jumping and dressage were introduced to the general public but were restricted to cavalry teams. Despite the constraints these sports slowly began to be adopted by the civilian sport enthusiast, and finally—when turned over to civilian control here in the United States in 1950—they have then grown steadily in popularity, until in our day these forms are pervasive in our domestic and international sports (see *North American Sport Horse Breeder* for more on the development of these international sports).

Diana ~1907, a ½ TB American Hunter bred in Virginia, by the Thoroughbred Gonzales. A beautifully balanced 16-hand bay mare, she was a champion field hunter, and winner of several steeplechases as well, and a lovely example of the quality sport horse that our American breeders were producing at the dawning of international sport. She is seen here with her owner/rider/trainer Mr. Stevenson, who was Master of the Hounds on Long Island, NY —photo by W.A. Rouch

The Thoroughbred, of necessity, played a prominent part in the breed base of the horses that participated in these sport forms—both then and now. In our day, the 'Olympic style' sports of show jumping, dressage, and three-day-eventing now dominate the non-racing sport spectrum internationally, with a lesser role played by driving, endurance, vaulting, and reining.

The American Thoroughbred and the American Sport Horse are a North American product—which includes both Canadian and American operations; their bloodlines have been linked since colonial days, and this has never changed, so the term 'American' is to be understood here to be 'North American' (see *North American Sport Horse Breeder* for a more full history). It is a recognizable and distinct type—our Hunter Horse has been our sport horse breed since

1700, and its breed components and breeding philosophy have never changed. Racehorse was always its base, whether our original racehorse, the Running Horse, or later its derivatives of American Thoroughbred, Quarter Horse, and Standardbred. The Hunter Horse is the American brand of sport horse and has always been so.

Sport horses have never been limited to 'purebred' breeding—this is also by necessity, as each discipline requires talents that sometimes can only be provided by mixing of several breed populations. Hunter breeding relies on the purebred breeds to provide the concentrated elements they are seeking to combine for the ultimate sport performer. Some will argue that a Hunter Horse is not a breed, rather it is a type. But that will not fly in our modern-day world, especially since our European neighbors have been pushing forward their 'warmbloods,' which they certainly define as breeds, and as national breeds at that, and none of those 'breeds' are 'purebred'.

Civilian rider Ralph Coffin is seen here in 1917 performing a 'broad jump,' on his talented hunter Rabbit. During the Jersey Act the civilian sport horse culture in America continued on enjoying the athletic gifts of their full- and part-bred Thoroughbreds. —photo by Harris & Ewing, Library of Congress

So then, our Hunter Horse has always been a breed of horse, because it was **selectively bred** from our racehorse base with bloodlines of our Saddle Horse, Morgan, Trotter, and sometimes foreign coach stock added for substance; therefore it is a breed because it was selectively bred for participation in the Hunter sports, and since 1912 in the new Olympic form sports. This concept is one North Americans have been blind to—that they have been breeding their own 'warmblood' for three hundred plus years. It is not something new, or something that the Europeans discovered or originated. The reality today is whether you call it a 'warmblood' or a sport horse, it is nothing more or less than a Hunter-bred horse—it is all the same design, and in sport horse breeding it is still the bloodline that matters, not the breed designation (see Appendix D – North American Breed Designation Explanation).

Sport Horse definition– a population of horses selectively bred to perform in a particular sport or group of sports. Selection choices are usually determined by bloodline, conformation, and sport performance.

The European versions are usually government-controlled breeding populations and are identified by a national title: Royal Dutch Warmblood, Swedish Warmblood, Irish Sport Horse, etc. Germany, perhaps the largest producer in Europe and exporter worldwide, has several breeds identified by regions: Trakehner, Hanoverian, Holstein, Westphalen, Hessen, etc. Most of those breeds were established only by sport selection since the mid-1900s and are bred from a base of their former agricultural or coach breeds—the sport selection process did not begin until the twentieth century. Before the mid-1900s they were still being performance tested for their ability to pull a plow and cart. There is a resident false assumption in the American sport horse breeder regarding the European Sport Warmblood and its history. This is especially so in the many warmblood breeds from Germany, where their studs of Hanover, Holstein, Trakehner, and the others do have a centuries-old tradition of equine breeding. The misconception is that these programs were horses bred for sport participation, which they were not, except for the Trakehner which was a combination cavalry/light agricultural breed since the mid-1800s, they were actually the opposite: farm horses that were bred at those organized studs (we call that type breed a 'cold blood'). So then, at the time of the photo of the Hunter Diana (beginning of chapter) the Hanoverian was still pulling a plow and cart—it was a draft horse, not a sport horse.

The Germans have a centuries-old tradition of the state standing stallions for the use of the populace at centralized studs. When they switched the focus from a farm and coach breed in the mid-1900s to breed sport horses, they used the same system they had always used, but the breed was different. Unfortunately the uninformed North American has mistaken the centuries-old system to mean they have centuries of sport horse breeding experience as well, an incorrect notion that the marketers of those horses have capitalized on. However, the modern European warmblood—that was formed especially in the last twenty years, no matter the origin—is now largely of Hunter type in that it has become a lighter, faster, more agile horse usually through continual addition of Thoroughbred blood, than the earlier, heavier model. In contrast, France, Ireland, and England have had a continuous Hunter Horse breeding program for centuries—an unbroken tradition, and surprise, so have we here in North America.

English artist Henry Aiken was an celebrated illustrator of the Hunter Horse in England in the early 19th century; here is a copy of 'Mounted Sportsmen' which clearly demonstrates the versatility, courage, and athleticism expected of the Hunter-bred horse in the early 1800s.

In our North American Sport Horse, specific bloodlines have been identified as superior producers of these performers since colonial days; early on the Wildair line, and then the Fearnought line was preferred before our Revolution; later lines of Medley, Goodes Twigg RH, Blackburns Whip RH, Mountain Slasher RH, Bald Stockings RH and Diomed were some of the hot ones, and later of course Lexington RH and the other four-milers. The favored horses originally came from our Running Horse breed and in the mid-1700s they were also from imported English Thoroughbreds; both these closely related breeds were great racehorses and superior saddle horses. From the mid-1800s on it was the individual sires from our Running Horse descendant breeds of Thoroughbred, Saddle Horse, and Trotter that provided the key genetic components.

By the time the concept of international Olympic-style competition became an organized reality—1900s—the North American Sport Horse was largely of Thoroughbred blood with lines of Saddlebred, Morgan, Quarter Horse, and Standardbred a significant portion of its genes as well—the proportion was usually ½ to ⅞ Thoroughbred. (You will find a more comprehensive detailing of the development of the American Sport Horse in *North American Sport Horse Breeder*).

This brings us to a basic recipe for our modern American Sport Horse:

Sport Horse Recipe

Racehorse: traditionally the larger portion of our Hunter Horse is Thoroughbred, but Standardbred is an underappreciated and forgotten source that we may employ as well—and is actually closer genetically (that is a less-diluted source) to our original Running Horse genes. Our racehorse-based formula for performance in these sports has not changed since 1700—racehorse with other breeds added for adjustments of temperament, substance, and style. The American racehorse therefore—in all its forms—is our base sport horse breed; it has always been so.

The American Thoroughbred. —sketch by C. W. Anderson found in *Who's Who in Thoroughbred Racing*

Saddlehorse: these are the breeds added for style, specialized talent, and good temperament—in our modern day they are often called 'improvers.' Our American sources for these are primarily Saddlebred and Morgan, but can also be provided by Tennessee Walker, Missouri Fox Trotter, and Quarter Horse—all these can be the providers of specific talents and movement, along with good dispositions, as the modern Thoroughbred often is high-strung. Our native saddle breeds usually have retained the docile, agreeable temperament of the parent Running Horse. Also all our native breeds share a genetic affinity because of their common roots, so they nick together well—this factor is something just awaiting the modern breeder to recognize and exploit in their programs through specific line-breeding to background targets.

Coach: these breeds can be a source of substance in our Hunter Sport Horse, although it was never a necessity; however, if a heavier hunter was desired, then to add Cleveland Bay, Irish Draught, Canadian Horse, or the then available (1800s—but now extinct) French or German Coach horses to our Running Horse or Thoroughbred-based Hunter would add height and substance (weight carrying ability) to our smaller breeds—even George Washington occasionally added some coach to his Hunter brew, probably because he was six feet tall, and our domestic racehorse was at that time under 15 hands. In our modern day, Cleveland Bay, Irish Draught, and Canadian Horse are still available, but the European old-style Warmbloods (thudmonsters) can provide this as well. As I mentioned above, the modern day Warmblood is usually a Hunter Horse already, so can be crossed in for an outcross, with your best result coming from a tightly bred stallion or mare. To outcross with loosely-bred stock, no matter its country or breed origin, will result in less of the desired talent being passed down to your foal. This is why so many of you are disappointed with your warmblood breeding adventures—most of the stallions imported here were loosely bred—outcrosses already—so may have added the substance you wanted but little of their talent came through. A good example of this occurence is the breeding career of the imported Starman (see Chapter 30), a horse just inducted into the Show Jumper Hall of Fame; obviously he was a superior performer, but he was a poor stallion because his bloodline found little in our mare base to connect with and because he was of good but rather loose-breeding, then to cross him on American horses, an outcross design as well, left very little dominance in the sport traits to travel to his offspring and diluted those resident in our own product.

———————————

The American Thoroughbred is still the chief ingredient in our modern **successful** Olympic style sport horse. When I evaluated our Hall of Fame inductees in 2011 I discovered the Thoroughbred was far and away the dominant breed; even in the dressage representatives it turned out 25% of their genetics were Thoroughbred; the eventers were 75% Thoroughbred, and the Show Jumpers were 82.5% Thoroughbred.

Therefore it is crucial to the success of the North American breeder that they recognize and understand the important sources of true sport talent that resides in our American Thoroughbred, and because our Thoroughbred was banned from the international gene pool for so long, and that fact combined with the last forty years of sport horse indoctrination (which we have allowed) that has arrived via the Europeans who have no real knowledge of our lines, we have dumbed down dramatically in our understanding of our own bloodlines. A lamentable portion of this scenario is that our domestic genetic base has far more sport talent and orientation than that of Europe—so we have actually been in most cases adulterating the very sport ability we need to succeed with, by mixing them with excessive amounts of coach and farm horse breeds and foreign, and usually more unsound, Thoroughbred lines.

Also, we need to wake up to the fact that we cannot rely on the European view to direct our own breeding projects—their system is based on government supervision and support (state studs, breeder subsidies, state-provided training of horse and rider). Because the American breeder has none of that provision, we will be playing a game that is structured against us, so we are bound to fail. The American breeder needs to be conscious of the fact that if you follow the European program of breeding, then it is **they** (registry administrators) who will make the decision if your proposed mating will be accepted in their studbook, not you, and if you breed a stallion, it can only get a breeding license from them if **they** want to give it to you. So, you have in effect handed over your sport horse-breeding program to the European governments.

[Please note: Some of you really appreciate the structure these warmblood registry systems employ, and I am not suggesting you abandon the warmblood registry or European breeding program that you enjoy; only that you recognize what it is, but more importantly respect the American breeder who chooses to do it the American way. This respect would include making sure that the European system is not allowed to dictate our American sport agendas and rules. This is America, and their participation is welcomed, but we must not allow their success and their organized might to overrun the rights of the typical American breeder, who is after all, an individual.]

The combination of the ban on our racehorse followed by the foreign governments' planned and controlled Warmblood invasion into our domestic sport horse market has resulted in the European horses' bloodlines, mindset, and system threatening our native talent and way of doing things. Yet, here we have been the whole time sitting on a genetic fountain of superior sport ability, and we have forgotten what we have.

We have here in our domestic horses, not just the Thoroughbred, but all our quality light horse breeds, the genes that were built by our two hundred years of a heat-racing performance test—a practice which produced a breed of horse that was so sound, athletic, strong, fast, and stamina-loaded that it could regularly run heat races, week after week, into its teens, and in most cases retire sound, many going on to second careers as show, carriage, or utility horses. There has never been on this earth anything to equal them, and we have their genotype right here and now in our domestic breeds—waiting for you to recognize it and bring it back to the dominance.

Quality foals in a sketch by C. W. Anderson for *Who's Who in Thoroughbred Racing*.

The genetics are still here, they have not changed; genes rarely mutate anyway, but are able to travel down through the generations unchanged, and most usually are clustered with other similar genes, straight down to the foals (Bowling *Horse Genetics*). But over the years other strains have been repeatedly added in with those superior genetics, so they then fade into the background and manifest less and less in our current product (see Appendix B).

So what can we do to bring them back to dominance? We can do what every 'foundation movement' has done before us, that is, we can identify the lines that carry those traits and reinforce them every time we breed—until we have re-created our Heroic Era horse. Far-fetched? No, it is not—it is the principles of genetics combined with selective breeding practices. Fortunately, we already have individuals in our current pedigrees who are concentrated carriers of those genes, although some of them have picked up faults along the way (Domino line is an example), but this too can be dealt with intelligent selection procedures.

Lexington RH is far and away the most prevalent bloodline of this era—and I have used him throughout this text as a benchmark to identify the carriers of the four-mile heat genetics by counting how many lines of him they contain. For instance we saw the elite broodmare Fairy Bridge carries eighty-three lines. Seattle Slew has one hundred forty, Easy Goer has one hundred forty-four, Singspiel has one hundred ninety-six, Holy Bull has one hundred eighty-eight, Distorted Humor has two hundred thirty-four, and so on.

Further, our American-bred resources for sport use is much wider and richer than the Thoroughbred, whose gene pool has since our Revolution has been weakened by generations of imported Thoroughbred lines. For instance, we can look to our Standardbred breed as well to identify sport genes, as it is a much less polluted population—closer to our original Running Horse. Plus our quality Saddle breeds have multiples lines of our premier heat-racing era. Our native breeds are a treasure chest of top sport sources for the sport horse breeder to identify and exploit. The North American sport horse genetic base is the richest respository of true sport performance in the world. You, the intelligent breeder, can capitalize on those genetic components easily to create the greatest modern international sport horse.

Chapter 29

The Invisible American Sport Sources

The effects of the 'Warmblood Invasion' in this country, following on the heels of the Jersey Act, has certainly taken its toll on the American bloodlines and their rightful place in sport history to the point that they are virtually invisible to the North American breeder.

Mrs. John Hay (Liz) Whitney on her magnificent hunter Primprillis, seen here taking a jump at the inter-American Horse Show in Washington D.C. October 26, 1935. Mrs. Whitney and her husband Colonel Whitney were avid breeders of show jumpers, steeplechasers, as well as flat racers, and they enjoyed personally participating in the sports as well. —photo by Harris & Ewing from the Library of Congress collection

The student of sport horse breeding is in the dark almost completely about the history and excellence of their native sources in Olympic style sport. During the duration of the Jersey Act many of the American lines of our Heroic Era that made it into the European gene pool faded in influence from lack of genetic reinforcement—you cannot have dominance in a bloodline if you do not increase the presence of it over the generations. It was Europe's loss as well as our own, which we can see vividly demonstrated in those select few that were concentrated, because they have powered some of the strongest sport dynasties in our modern era worldwide.

Recap of 'European' Lines that have American four-mile heat racer genes powering them:

European Families

Catnip: From this humbly bred mare came a sport dynasty that has ringed the globe. Through her daughter Nera di Bicci and granddaughter Nella de Gubbio there has been made an indelible presence in Germany and into the international gene pool from there. It was through Catnip's daughter Nogara the premier sport stallions Niccolo dell'Arca and the 'sire of the century' Nearco arrived, whose dynasty has no end as his genetic gifts are powering the international sport horse everywhere. His son Nasrullah, who carries more American lines on his dam-line (Americus), is rated the #1 line in sport horses in the world.

Americus: Imported into Ireland by their native son Croker, Americus is inbred 3x3 to Lexington RH/Glencoe/Sir Archy/Transport RH, and he is found today principally through the descendants of Lady Josephine through whom he has spread his power all over the world, and to a lesser extend the mare Alabama and his powerful Trakehner branch thorough his son Bachus, especially through his granddaughter Saaleck TR, who heads a maternal dynasty in Germany.

Rhoda B: Another Croker import to Ireland, she is found today mostly in the Orby descendants, although she is also the dam of Alabama mentioned above. She is a source of Hanover and Boston RH, and she provides a strong filly factor from Alice Carneal RH in Europe first, but now internationally.

The new American Thoroughbred seen flat racing in a lithograph of 1883; this illustration is from the era of the first American invasion into England and France, and from there to all Europe—Library of Congress collection.

Grave and Gay: A TB mare imported by W.C. Whitney to England, but later she ended up in Germany as a broodmare where she created a massive record of success. A daughter of Henry of Navarre out of a dam who carries the Lexington RH son Duke of Magenta, she is found continually in the German warmblood product as well in as in their racing population. Her famous offspring include Graf Ferry and Graf Nicht, whose progeny includes the German Derby winner Graf Isolani and great race mare Nereide—both of whom have an extraordinary presence in the German Warmblood.

Frizette: An American Thoroughbred and a daughter of the key sire Hamburg, this mare has become an international genetic giant; classified as a *reine* and a 'blue hen' from her blood in France through her full sister progeny Durban and Heldifann, she has created a dynasty with the likes of Djeddah, Tourbillon, Djebel, and on this continent through the *reines* Myrtlewood and Black Curl—her international influence continues to expand even today. She is truly one of the greatest mares of the twentieth century.

Durban (and her full and ¾ sisters), bred by Herman Duryea in France by Durbar out of Banshee, she and her sisters carry eight lines of Lexington RH in seven generations—a concentration equally that of Hamburg, Beaming Beauty, Americus and Domino. These mares have created a maternal dynasty which has proved to be one of the best sport and racing sources in Europe.

Chicle (and to a lesser extent Dis Donc, half-brothers, both out of the *reine* Lady Hamburg) Chicle especially has become a steady line in the production of talent, both in Europe and in North America.

Relic: his bloodline appears all over Europe through especially through his daughter Relance who produced three top stallions: Relko (*chef*), Match II, and Reliance (*chef*), and through his son Pericles a strong presence in the Dutch Warmblood. Relic is by War Relic, an inbred son of Man O' War out of a mare who also carries the top sport line of Black Toney (Domino). Naturally crossing the Pericles line with that of Relance will provide dominance in Relic.

So, here we are breeding Warmbloods and sport horses and not recognizing our own bloodlines that are powering some of them, and even if the commonly proclaimed bloodlines of top show jumpers found in the European 'warmblood' don't appear to contain American lines, many of you may be shocked to realize that Courville, Lucky Boy, Pluchino, and even Ladykiller all carry American lines.

Of course, after 1970 the American lines began flooding the modern European sport horse, and before too long they will dominate the Thoroughbred contribution to the sport gene pool in Europe as well; there is not much they can do about it, as they have imported our racers in droves from the 1970s on, and their success has made them the leading bloodlines. So in the next few decades you will find, even if the top stallion lines are not identified as American (Sadlers Well, Mill Reef, Never Bend, etc.), that is what they are, and the best of them are saturated in our Heroic Era genes.

Recap of domestic American lines that have powered our sport horses to this day:

American Sources

An evaluation of the top international level sport horses produced in North America (Birdsall, Kirsan) has revealed that they are powered by our own home-bred lines—and surprisingly even the European lines found in them are not those that are heralded as the sport sources in current popular literature in magazines, books, and on the internet (read more on this in Chapter 32). It is our American lines that have provided the genetic power that propelled our horses to Olympic medals regularly. Here are a few of the basic American lines that may have been undervalued by you as a top sport source, but are truly overflowing in our best sport genetics and should be line-breeding targets for the breeder who wants to succeed:

Fair Play: Fair Play and his sire Hastings are premier sources of jump, stamina, and soundness. Found most often through Fair Play's son Man O' War, his daughter Etoile Filante, and his grandson Intent and War Admiral, Discovery, these indi-

Domino—probably the greatest sport bloodline in the world, yet mysteriously absent in popular sport horse writing on bloodlines. —from painting by Henry Stull

viduals and more are all sound and immensely talented hereditary transmitters. Their descendants are a who's who of sport bloodlines: Chance Play, War Glory, War Relic, Annapolis, Battleship, Great War, Hard Tack, and Valkyr (a *reine* whose second dam is the legendary Frizette). A variation on the Fair Play family is through his ½ brother Plaudit (read more in Chapter 33 and 34). This line is sound, and Man O' War transmits the large heart gene to his daughters.

Domino: Although never mentioned in the discussion of Olympic style sport lines, **Domino is actually the most pervasive line in sport; that is in racing and non-racing sport alike**. Talk about invisible! This attitude is also indefensible as he and his close relatives are the bedrock of sport in America although there is a strain of unsoundness in some of them: Blue Larkspur (large heart gene and sound), Black Toney (sound), High Time, The Porter, Celt, Ultimus (front feet), Hippodrome, Supremus, etc. Perhaps the squeamishness obviously in play in mention-

ing this **genetic giant** in regard to sport horse production is because he is a speed line, and of course the dogma is that sprint lines (speed) are not suitable in the production of proper sport horses and warmbloods—yet he is there everywhere you look, powering the best of the best. Domino is inbred 3x4x4 to Lexington RH, with an additional line of his ½ brother Lecomte RH. He is the most concentrated source of Lexington RH and Diomed blood in America. However, there is a massive misconception concerning Domino and his genetic gifts. He was a pure sprinter, and possibly the best there ever was, but he produced classic and even what we would classify today as stamina racing sires (Les Brinsfield). The truth is he the greatest overall transmitter of speed for any distance in the twentieth century.

Ben Brush: This bloodline is an extremely sound and talented line, and he is spread far and wide in the best sporting stock especially through his sons Broomstick and Sweep. Ben Brush is 4x5 Lexington RH, and he has proven invaluable in tempering the Domino lines, giving them a sturdy frame with equally stout legs for their invincible speed. Sweep is not only by Ben Brush but he is also out of Pink Domino, a sound Domino source; he is noted also as a transmitter of the large heart gene. These lines are found everywhere is the successful domestic-bred sport horses.

Whisk Broom II: A son of Broomstick, he is out of the *reine* Audience who is 3x3 to Maggie B. B. RH, and he is found consistently in top sport horses, especially through his sons John P. Grier and Diavolo, plus he is the dam-sire of the famous Seabiscuit. He is 6x7x4 Lexington RH but also carries his ½ sister Madeline RH 5x5 through Maggie B. B. RH. This is an important line to include in your recipes.

Hanover-Hamburg: this father and son are sources of extreme talent, soundness, and resilience, and are key bloodlines in our preserving of the Heroic Era genes, as Hanover is 3x3 to Vandal RH, and his son Hamburg is out of Lady Reel—a daughter of Mannie Gray, the dam of Domino, plus her sire is Fellowcraft a full brother to Spendthrift the grandsire of Fair Play—therefore sex-balancing and fortifying those other key bloodlines. Look for them to include in your recipes. Both these sires, even while classified as 'half-bred' during the Jersey Act, have left a legacy in Europe and will be found in many international pedigrees. Hamburg is a contender for the greatest broodmare sire of all time, as his daughters are all genetic gold, especially on the dam-line.

In our day when everyone is decrying the lack of soundness and stamina in our racer and sport horse, we have the genes that could be the remedy for these weaknesses, right here, right now. There is no better source of sport talent and soundness then these American-bred bloodlines.

For our examples let's look at a few of the top show jumpers from the era right before the 'warmblood invasion' happened here, while noticing the preponderance of both American and European branches of our Heroic Era genes in these stellar sport horses.

Brother Sam 1969 is a Thoroughbred gelding; he had a grand career domestically at Grand Prix level and as a member of the Canadian Team where he racked up an impressive international record--an individual bronze medal and a team silver medal win at Pan Am Games in 1979, and in 1980 when he was on the alternate Olympic gold-medal-winning Canadian team for the Show Jumping Festival in the Netherlands, plus he won the Nations Cup that year also. His pedigree is dominated by the full brothers Chance Play/Chance Shot by Fair Play out of Quelle Chance 3x4, with reinforcement from a double of Friar Rock 5x5 and the full brothers Fairway/Pharos. Also present are the lines of Catnip, Lady Josephine twice, Chicle, along with Broomstick and Himyar on the dam-line.

Then there is the amazing Sympatico 1965, another Thoroughbred gelding, who was the top Grand Prix jumper in the USA for four years: 1972-75. But that is not all this talented sport horse could do, as he won the Puissance at the National Horse Show in 1973 while setting a new indoor record of 7'4", and in 1978 he was on the silver-medal-winning team at the Pan Am Games in Puerto Rico, where he also won one of the classes. Through My Babu he carries ten lines of Lexington RH—eight coming from Durban, who is one of the most concentrated carriers of Lexington RH in our modern day (her full sister is Heldifann)—and there is the Lady Josephine line as well. His strongest concentrations are present through his dam War Tear with Fair Play, a double of Sweep and Black Toney, for a total of twenty-four lines of Lexington RH. This might have something to do with his durability displayed by the length of his career at top level: eight years.

An intriguing individual is The Iron Duke 1966, because he specialized as a high jumper—winning at 7' to 7'5"—extraordinary. Once again, he is a full Thoroughbred gelding; his sire is largely Argentinian Thoroughbred, but still bringing back a line of Tracery to America through Copyright. In pedigree design this lineage is sort of similar to that of Sympatico, as his heaviest concentrations are from the dam, where he has the ¾ siblings Ouch/Questionnaire 3x3. Questionnaire is one of those lines that, while not very common, keeps popping up in the horses that count—such as Rough n' Tumble (see Chapter 24). Questionnaire and his ¾ sister descend from that other Cinderella son, Plaudit, with plenty of Domino and Ben Brush added. So there is some complexity here, as Plaudit's ½ brother Fair Play is present also—an unusual pedigree. But the principle elements are still there, and forty-three lines of Lexington RH in the background.

Better and Better 1969 put in a stellar performance in the 1976 Olympics earning individual silver and team gold in Eventing. What is this horse powered by? You guessed it, huge amounts of our principle sport bloodlines. His sire Saidam is 4x4 to the full siblings Masda/Man O' War, plus he adds multiples of Domino/Ben Brush and Mannie Gray through Equipoise and Chicle. His dam also brings in an extraordinary five lines of the top English mare Canterbury Pilgrim through Swynford/Chaucer 6x6x5x6x5—making almost an equal balance to the Man O' War/Masda grouping in the mare; this is a pedigree design we have seen multiple times in the great horses.

Now that covers lines that are found in jumpers (eventers and steeplechasers also). What about the dressage horse? Can our American bloodlines produce top dressage talent? Yes they can and have, although the sources are extremely underutilized—see Chapter 31 for more on this.

Internationally, the line of Nearco has made its mark indelibly in dressage performers. For instance, the top Hanoverian dressage sire Lauries Crusador has multiple American lines through Nearco and others. Nearco was noted in his race career as being so fluid and agile in movement that he resembled the motion of the big cats (tigers, leopards etc). Did he get all this from his sire Pharos? No, some of it surely comes that way, but there are many Pharos offspring who don't have or pass on top movement, but what put him in a class of his own, was what he got from his dam Nogara the daughter of Catnip, who is remarkable for her balanced, fluid movement. Her action was superlative according to Tesio. Nogara has an American dam-line; her fourth dam Perfection is a full sister to the world beater Parole, with Lexington RH right there, but probably more important to her perfect movement was the presence of the pacing racer and top sire of saddle horses: Blackburns Whip RH. He keeps showing up in horses notable for their action or gaits, and he was himself of superb action at all gaits.

In America our fine saddle breeds were often the product of a pacing Running Horse stallion used on a good saddle mare; the pacer was recognized in that era as the source of lovely movement and pure, clean gaits. Entire saddle breeds bred to perform in horse shows displaying their extreme grace, agility, and smoothness in motion spring from individuals like Blackburns Whip RH, and his co-typesetters Cockspur RH and Tom Hal RH—all were pacing racehorses who were bred in the Maryland/Virginia Plantation Horse movement, and they were used to produce saddle horses as well as racehorses. It turns out the dressage star Keen (Chapter 31) has a strong background in these same root sources. Which brings me to the underrated source of dressage talent in our own backyard: our fine saddle breeds, —horses that can piaffe and passage with ease. Many do so in the natural, plus they are light and responsive and have pure correct gaits, as well as passing on in most cases their lovely dispositions, and they stay sound. It is astounding to me that we have not exploited this resource for this use—we actually have the best genetic base for this sport right here and don't recognize it. Not only that, our Standardbred received all the pacing Running Horse stock into their register in 1891—which means that the root source is right there in that breed also. In just one or two generations we could have world beaters in multiples, instead of pouring our money and dreams into breeds that have little potency for the traits we desire.

Here's my point, we have sitting here all the elements for top sport performance in these disciplines, and in a concentrated form—that means it is able to be passed on (dominance)—all available for us to use, at a cost that would allow all of us to participate—an issue that is important for the majority of small scale (and unsubsidized) American breeders. Plus we have the genetics abounding, awaiting our commitment to concentrate them again, of the greatest overall sport horse there has ever been—**there has never been a better, sounder, or more talented sport horse than our four-mile heat racers**—never. So we have the specialized breeds, racers and saddle horses both, from which we can select the proper bloodlines—and they even already have a great similarity—so if you cross a Saddlebred with a American Thoroughbred for instance, then you would be bringing back a background strength—this is called a nick, and because they have been separated for so long, there would also be the hybrid vigor factor, but without the dissipation of talent that usually occurs when we crossbreed, because if we are selective we can end up adding to the background talent of the key lines as well. Note that crossbreeding, if done intelligently, can actually increase potency. The geneticist Ann Bowling has pointed out that crossing strongly line-bred or inbred individuals can give both potency and vigor, "Diversity can be maintained within a large (breed) context by establishing several inbred lines"(*Horse Genetics*). A Standardbred with a Morgan, a Morgan with a Quarter Horse, etc.—they all spring from some common and important background individuals. It is a recipe for sport success as long as there is a selection procedure of intelligence in play. If we did this, no one in the world could compete with us.

In contrast, when we crossbreed to a Warmblood, or a Arabian, or now the popular fad of Spanish breeds, it is a true outcross—that is unless there are enough common lines in the background, and this will only succeed in a better or even marginally good horse if the sire and dam both are strongly bred in their own sport lines; otherwise it will result in a foal that is less than the parents in talent—this is a basic principle of breeding. Outcrossing is an important tool, and often a good or sometimes a great performer can be produced. International greats such as Landgraf I and Contender are crossbreeds, with both sides of their pedigrees providing powerful sport genetics. If a crossbreeding is not designed properly, then it will result in less of the talent being able to be passed on, no matter the stud's own sports performance record. However, if you have a well line-bred stallion, line-bred in top sport lines, and a mare also well line-bred in top sport lines—then crossing the two should be a successful endeavor. But if the stallion is well line-bred, and the mare of the other breed is not, then you have produced a foal with 50% less potency in sport talent than the sire. Conversely, if you have a mare that has good lines but she is not concentrated in those lines, if a stallion is found for her that carries a potency in those lines, or a full sibling or the sex-balance, then you have improved the outcome of the mating and the foal could actually be an equal or better horse than either parent. We need to crossbreed selectively, not being swayed by glossy stallion promotions, because even a good sire is not necessarily suitable for every mare. I am not suggesting you breeders of warmbloods stop breeding—only that when you do you employ these proven methods to build the dominance in the type you desire. Anyone, in any discipline, can improve their results if they take the time to verify and research their pedigrees and apply Tesio Methods in designing their dream horse.

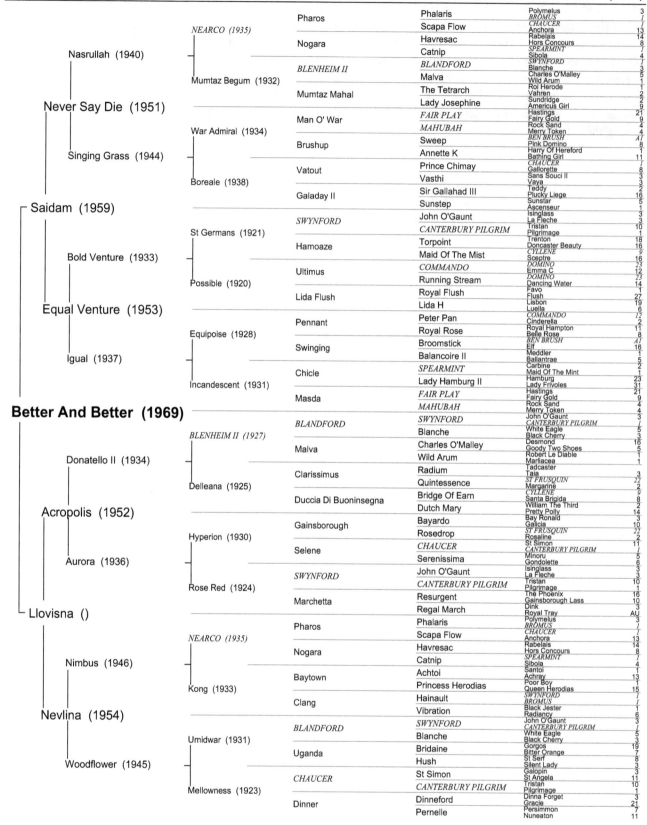

		Pharos	Phalaris	Polymelus 3
				BROMUS 1
	NEARCO (1935)		Scapa Flow	*CHAUCER* 1
				Anchora 13
		Nogara	Havresac	Rabelais 14
Nasrullah (1940)				Hors Concours 8
			Catnip	*SPEARMINT* 1
				Sibola 4
		BLENHEIM II	*BLANDFORD*	*SWYNFORD* 1
				Blanche 3
	Mumtaz Begum (1932)		Malva	Charles O'Malley 5
				Wild Arum 1
		Mumtaz Mahal	The Tetrarch	Roi Herode 1
				Vahren 2
Never Say Die (1951)			Lady Josephine	Sundridge 2
				Americus Girl 9
		Man O' War	*FAIR PLAY*	Hastings 21
				Fairy Gold 9
	War Admiral (1934)		*MAHUBAH*	Rock Sand 4
				Merry Token 4
		Brushup	Sweep	*BEN BRUSH* A1
				Pink Domino 8
Singing Grass (1944)			Annette K	Harry Of Hereford 1
				Bathing Girl 11
		Vatout	Prince Chimay	*CHAUCER* 1
				Gallorette 8
	Boreale (1938)		Vasthi	Sans Souci II 3
				Vaya 3
		Galaday II	Sir Gallahad III	Teddy 2
				Plucky Liege 16
Saidam (1959)			Sunstep	Sunstar 5
				Ascenseur 1
		John O'Gaunt	Isinglass 3
		SWYNFORD		La Fleche 3
	St Germans (1921)		*CANTERBURY PILGRIM*	Tristan 10
				Pilgrimage 1
		Hamoaze	Torpoint	Trenton 18
				Doncaster Beauty 16
Bold Venture (1933)			Maid Of The Mist	*CYLLENE* 9
				Sceptre 16
		Ultimus	*COMMANDO*	*DOMINO* 23
				Emma C 12
	Possible (1920)		Running Stream	*DOMINO* 23
				Dancing Water 14
		Lida Flush	Royal Flush	Favo 1
				Flush 27
Equal Venture (1953)			Lida H	Lisbon 19
				Luella 6
		Pennant	Peter Pan	*COMMANDO* 12
				Cinderella 1
	Equipoise (1928)		Royal Rose	Royal Hampton 11
				Belle Rose 8
		Swinging	Broomstick	*BEN BRUSH* A1
				Elf 16
Igual (1937)			Balancoire II	Meddler 1
				Ballantrae 5
		Chicle	*SPEARMINT*	Carbine 2
				Maid Of The Mint 1
	Incandescent (1931)		Lady Hamburg II	Hamburg 23
				Lady Frivoles 31
		Masda	*FAIR PLAY*	Hastings 21
				Fairy Gold 9
Better And Better (1969)			*MAHUBAH*	Rock Sand 4
				Merry Token 4
		BLANDFORD	*SWYNFORD*	John O'Gaunt 3
	BLENHEIM II (1927)			*CANTERBURY PILGRIM* 1
			Blanche	White Eagle 5
				Black Cherry 3
		Malva	Charles O'Malley	Desmond 16
				Goody Two Shoes 5
Donatello II (1934)			Wild Arum	Robert Le Diable 1
				Marliacea 1
		Clarissimus	Radium	Tadcaster 3
				Taia 23
	Delleana (1925)		Quintessence	*ST FRUSQUIN* 22
				Margarine 2
		Duccia Di Buoninsegna	Bridge Of Earn	*CYLLENE* 9
				Santa Brigida 8
Acropolis (1952)			Dutch Mary	William The Third 2
				Pretty Polly 14
		Gainsborough	Bayardo	Bay Ronald 3
				Galicia 10
	Hyperion (1930)		Rosedrop	*ST FRUSQUIN* 22
				Rosaline 2
		Selene	*CHAUCER*	St Simon 11
				CANTERBURY PILGRIM 1
Aurora (1936)			Serenissima	Minoru 5
				Gondolette 6
		SWYNFORD	John O'Gaunt	Isinglass 3
				La Fleche 3
	Rose Red (1924)		*CANTERBURY PILGRIM*	Tristan 10
				Pilgrimage 1
		Marchetta	Resurgent	The Phoenix 16
				Gainsborough Lass 10
Llovisna ()			Regal March	Dink 3
				Royal Tray AU
		Pharos	Phalaris	Polymelus 3
				BROMUS 1
	NEARCO (1935)		Scapa Flow	*CHAUCER* 1
				Anchora 13
		Nogara	Havresac	Rabelais 14
				Hors Concours 8
			Catnip	*SPEARMINT* 1
				Sibola 4
		Baytown	Achtoi	Santoi 1
Nimbus (1946)				Achray 13
			Princess Herodias	Poor Boy 1
	Kong (1933)			Queen Herodias 15
		Clang	Hainault	*SWYNFORD* 1
				BROMUS 1
			Vibration	Black Jester 1
				Radiancy 6
Nevlina (1954)			*SWYNFORD*	John O'Gaunt 3
		BLANDFORD		*CANTERBURY PILGRIM* 1
			Blanche	White Eagle 5
				Black Cherry 3
	Umidwar (1931)		Bridaine	Gorgos 19
		Uganda		Bitter Orange 7
			Hush	St Serf 8
				Silent Lady 3
Woodflower (1945)			St Simon	Galopin 3
		CHAUCER		St Angela 11
	Mellowness (1923)		*CANTERBURY PILGRIM*	Tristan 10
				Pilgrimage 1
		Dinner	Dinneford	Dinna Forget 3
				Gracie 21
			Pernelle	Persimmon 7
				Nuneaton 11

Better and Better 1969

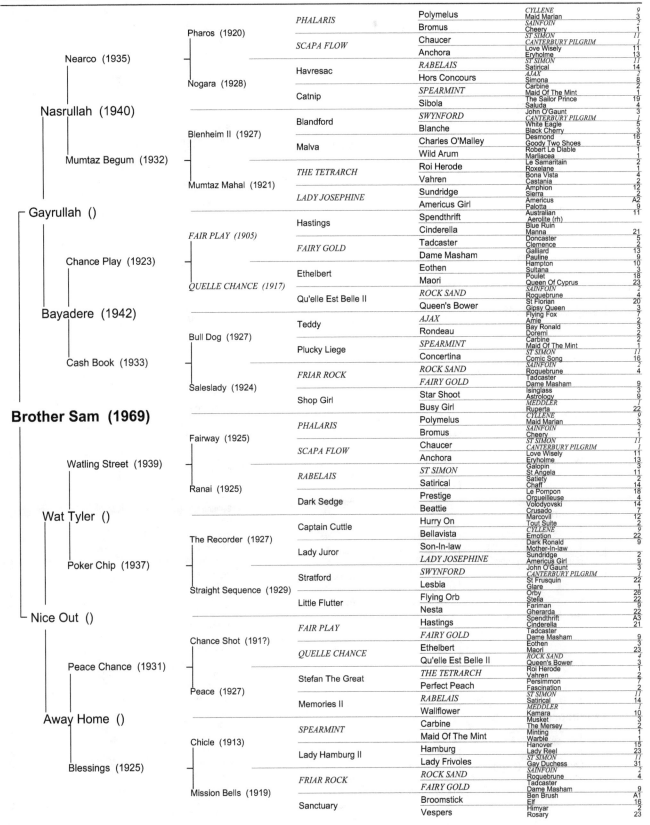

Brother Sam (1969)

- Gayrullah ()
  - Nasrullah (1940)
    - Nearco (1935)
      - Pharos (1920)
        - *PHALARIS*
          - Polymelus — *CYLLENE* 9 / Maid Marian 3
          - Bromus — *SAINFOIN* 2 / Cheery 1
        - *SCAPA FLOW*
          - Chaucer — *ST SIMON* 11 / *CANTERBURY PILGRIM* 1
          - Anchora — Love Wisely 11 / Eryholme 13
      - Nogara (1928)
        - Havresac
          - *RABELAIS* — *ST SIMON* / Satirical 14
          - Hors Concours — *AJAX* 8 / Simona 2
        - Catnip
          - *SPEARMINT* — Carbine 2 / Maid Of The Mint 1
          - Sibola — The Sailor Prince 19 / Saluda 4
    - Mumtaz Begum (1932)
      - Blenheim II (1927)
        - Blandford
          - *SWYNFORD* — John O'Gaunt 3 / *CANTERBURY PILGRIM* 1
          - Blanche — White Eagle 5 / Black Cherry 3
        - Malva
          - Charles O'Malley — Desmond 16 / Goody Two Shoes 5
          - Wild Arum — Robert Le Diable 1 / Marliacea 1
      - Mumtaz Mahal (1921)
        - *THE TETRARCH*
          - Roi Herode — Le Samaritain 2 / Roxelane 1
          - Vahren — Bona Vista 4 / Castania 12
        - *LADY JOSEPHINE*
          - Sundridge — Amphion 2 / Sierra A2
          - Americus Girl — Americus 9 / Palotta 11
  - Bayadere (1942)
    - Chance Play (1923)
      - *FAIR PLAY (1905)*
        - Hastings
          - Spendthrift — Australian / Aerolite (rh)
          - Cinderella — Blue Ruin / Manna 21
        - *FAIRY GOLD*
          - Tadcaster — Doncaster 5 / Clemence 2
          - Dame Masham — Galliard 13 / Pauline 9
      - *QUELLE CHANCE (1917)*
        - Ethelbert
          - Eothen — Hampton 10 / Sultana 3
          - Maori — Poulet 18 / Queen Of Cyprus 23
        - Qu'elle Est Belle II
          - *ROCK SAND* — *SAINFOIN* 2 / Roquebrune 4
          - Queen's Bower — St Florian 20 / Gipsy Queen 3
    - Cash Book (1933)
      - Bull Dog (1927)
        - Teddy
          - *AJAX* — Flying Fox 7 / Amie 2
          - Rondeau — Bay Ronald 3 / Doremi 2
        - Plucky Liege
          - *SPEARMINT* — Carbine 2 / Maid Of The Mint 1
          - Concertina — *ST SIMON* 11 / Comic Song 16
      - Saleslady (1924)
        - *FRIAR ROCK*
          - *ROCK SAND* — *SAINFOIN* 2 / Roquebrune 4
          - *FAIRY GOLD* — Tadcaster / Dame Masham 9
        - Shop Girl
          - Star Shoot — Isinglass 3 / Astrology 9
          - Busy Girl — *MEDDLER* 1 / Ruperta 22
- Wat Tyler ()
  - Watling Street (1939)
    - Fairway (1925)
      - *PHALARIS*
        - Polymelus — *CYLLENE* 9 / Maid Marian 3
        - Bromus — *SAINFOIN* 2 / Cheery 1
      - *SCAPA FLOW*
        - Chaucer — *ST SIMON* 11 / *CANTERBURY PILGRIM* 1
        - Anchora — Love Wisely 11 / Eryholme 13
    - Ranai (1925)
      - *RABELAIS*
        - *ST SIMON* — Galopin 3 / St Angela 11
        - Satirical — Satiety / Chaff 14
      - Dark Sedge
        - Prestige — Le Pompon 18 / Orgueilleuse 4
        - Beattie — Volodyovski 14 / Crusado 7
  - Nice Out ()
    - Poker Chip (1937)
      - The Recorder (1927)
        - Captain Cuttle
          - Hurry On — Marcovil 12 / Tout Suite 2
          - Bellavista — *CYLLENE* 9 / Emotion 22
        - Lady Juror
          - Son-In-Law — Dark Ronald 9 / Mother-In-Law
          - *LADY JOSEPHINE* — Sundridge 2 / Americus Girl 9
      - Straight Sequence (1929)
        - Stratford
          - *SWYNFORD* — John O'Gaunt 3 / *CANTERBURY PILGRIM* 1
          - Lesbia — St Frusquin 22 / Glare 1
        - Little Flutter
          - Flying Orb — Orby 26 / Stella 22
          - Nesta — Fariman 9 / Gherarda 22
    - Away Home ()
      - Peace Chance (1931)
        - Chance Shot (191?)
          - *FAIR PLAY*
            - Hastings — Spendthrift A3 / Cinderella 21
            - *FAIRY GOLD* — Tadcaster / Dame Masham 9
          - *QUELLE CHANCE*
            - Ethelbert — Eothen 3 / Maori 23
            - Qu'elle Est Belle II — *ROCK SAND* 4 / Queen's Bower 3
        - Peace (1927)
          - Stefan The Great
            - *THE TETRARCH* — Roi Herode 1 / Vahren 2
            - Perfect Peach — Persimmon 7 / Fascination 2
          - Memories II
            - *RABELAIS* — *ST SIMON* 11 / Satirical 14
            - Wallflower — *MEDDLER* 1 / Kamara 10
      - Blessings (1925)
        - Chicle (1913)
          - *SPEARMINT*
            - Carbine — Musket 3 / The Mersey 2
            - Maid Of The Mint — Minting 1 / Warble 1
          - Lady Hamburg II
            - Hamburg — Hanover 15 / Lady Reel 23
            - Lady Frivoles — *ST SIMON* 11 / Gay Duchess 31
        - Mission Bells (1919)
          - *FRIAR ROCK*
            - *ROCK SAND* — *SAINFOIN* 2 / Roquebrune 4
            - *FAIRY GOLD* — Tadcaster / Dame Masham 9
          - Sanctuary
            - Broomstick — Ben Brush A1 / Elf 16
            - Vespers — Himyar 2 / Rosary 23

Brother Sam 1969

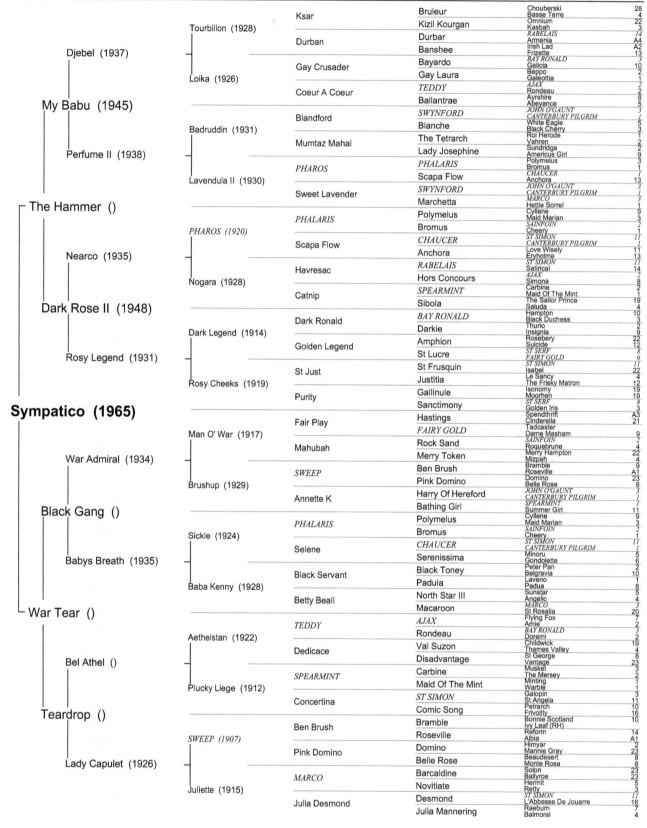

Sympatico (1965)

My Babu (1945)
Djebel (1937)
Perfume II (1938)

The Hammer ()
Nearco (1935)
Dark Rose II (1948)
Rosy Legend (1931)

Sympatico (1965)

War Admiral (1934)
Black Gang ()
Babys Breath (1935)

War Tear ()
Bel Athel ()
Teardrop ()
Lady Capulet (1926)

Tourbillon (1928)
Ksar — Bruleur — Chouberski 28 / Basse Terre 4
Ksar — Kizil Kourgan — Omnium 22 / Kasbah 3
Durban — Durbar — RABELAIS 14 / Armenia A4
Durban — Banshee — Irish Lad A2 / Frizette 13

Loika (1926)
Gay Crusader — Bayardo — BAY RONALD 3 / Galicia 10
Gay Crusader — Gay Laura — Beppo 2 / Galeottia 1
Coeur A Coeur — TEDDY — AJAX 2 / Rondeau 8
Coeur A Coeur — Ballantrae — Ayrshire 5 / Abeyance

Badruddin (1931)
Blandford — SWYNFORD — JOHN O'GAUNT / CANTERBURY PILGRIM 1
Blandford — Blanche — White Eagle 5 / Black Cherry 3
Mumtaz Mahal — The Tetrarch — Roi Herode 1 / Vahren 2
Mumtaz Mahal — Lady Josephine — Sundridge 2 / Americus Girl 9

Lavendula II (1930)
PHAROS — PHALARIS — Polymelus 3 / Bromus 1
PHAROS — Scapa Flow — CHAUCER 1 / Anchora 13
Sweet Lavender — SWYNFORD — JOHN O'GAUNT / CANTERBURY PILGRIM 1
Sweet Lavender — Marchetta — MARCO 3 / Hettie Sorrel 1

PHAROS (1920)
PHALARIS — Polymelus — Cyllene 9 / Maid Marian 3
PHALARIS — Bromus — SAINFOIN 2 / Cheery 1
Scapa Flow — CHAUCER — ST SIMON 11 / CANTERBURY PILGRIM 1
Scapa Flow — Anchora — Love Wisely 11 / Eryholme 13

Nogara (1928)
Havresac — RABELAIS — ST SIMON 11 / Satirical 14
Havresac — Hors Concours — AJAX 2 / Simona 8
Catnip — SPEARMINT — Carbine 2 / Maid Of The Mint 1
Catnip — Sibola — The Sailor Prince 19 / Saluda 4

Dark Legend (1914)
Dark Ronald — BAY RONALD — Hampton 10 / Black Duchess 3
Dark Ronald — Darkie — Thurio 2 / Insignia
Golden Legend — Amphion — Rosebery 22 / Suicide 12
Golden Legend — St Lucre — ST SERF 8 / FAIRY GOLD 9

Rosy Cheeks (1919)
St Just — St Frusquin — ST SIMON 11 / Isabel 22
St Just — Justitia — Le Sancy 4 / The Frisky Matron 12
Purity — Gallinule — Isonomy 19 / Moorhen 19
Purity — Sanctimony — ST SERF 8 / Golden Iris 3

Man O' War (1917)
Fair Play — Hastings — Spendthrift A3 / Cinderella 21
Fair Play — FAIRY GOLD — Tadcaster / Dame Masham 9
Mahubah — Rock Sand — SAINFOIN 2 / Roquebrune 4
Mahubah — Merry Token — Merry Hampton 22 / Mizpah 4

Brushup (1929)
SWEEP — Ben Brush — Bramble 9 / Roseville A1
SWEEP — Pink Domino — Domino 23 / Belle Rose 8
Annette K — Harry Of Hereford — JOHN O'GAUNT / CANTERBURY PILGRIM 1
Annette K — Bathing Girl — SPEARMINT / Summer Girl 11

Sickle (1924)
PHALARIS — Polymelus — Cyllene 9 / Maid Marian 3
PHALARIS — Bromus — SAINFOIN 2 / Cheery 1
Selene — CHAUCER — ST SIMON 11 / CANTERBURY PILGRIM 1
Selene — Serenissima — Minoru 5 / Gondolette 6

Baba Kenny (1928)
Black Servant — Black Toney — Peter Pan 2 / Belgravia 10
Black Servant — Padula — Laveno 1 / Padua 8
Betty Beall — North Star III — Sunstar 5 / Angelic 4
Betty Beall — Macaroon — MARCO 3 / St Rosalia 20

Aethelstan (1922)
TEDDY — AJAX — Flying Fox 7 / Amie 2
TEDDY — Rondeau — BAY RONALD 3 / Doremi 2
Dedicace — Val Suzon — Childwick 19 / Thames Valley 4
Dedicace — Disadvantage — St George 8 / Vantage 23

Plucky Liege (1912)
SPEARMINT — Carbine — Musket 3 / The Mersey 2
SPEARMINT — Maid Of The Mint — Minting 1 / Warble
Concertina — ST SIMON — Galopin 3 / St Angela 11
Concertina — Comic Song — Petrarch 10 / Frivolity 16

SWEEP (1907)
Ben Brush — Bramble — Bonnie Scotland 10 / Ivy Leaf (RH)
Ben Brush — Roseville — Reform 14 / Albia A1
Pink Domino — Domino — Himyar 2 / Mannie Gray 23
Pink Domino — Belle Rose — Beaudesert 8 / Monte Rosa 8

Juliette (1915)
MARCO — Barcaldine — Solon 23 / Ballyroe 23
MARCO — Novitiate — Hermit 5 / Retty 3
Julia Desmond — Desmond — ST SIMON 11 / L'Abbesse De Jouarre 16
Julia Desmond — Julia Mannering — Raeburn 7 / Balmoral 4

Sympatico 1965

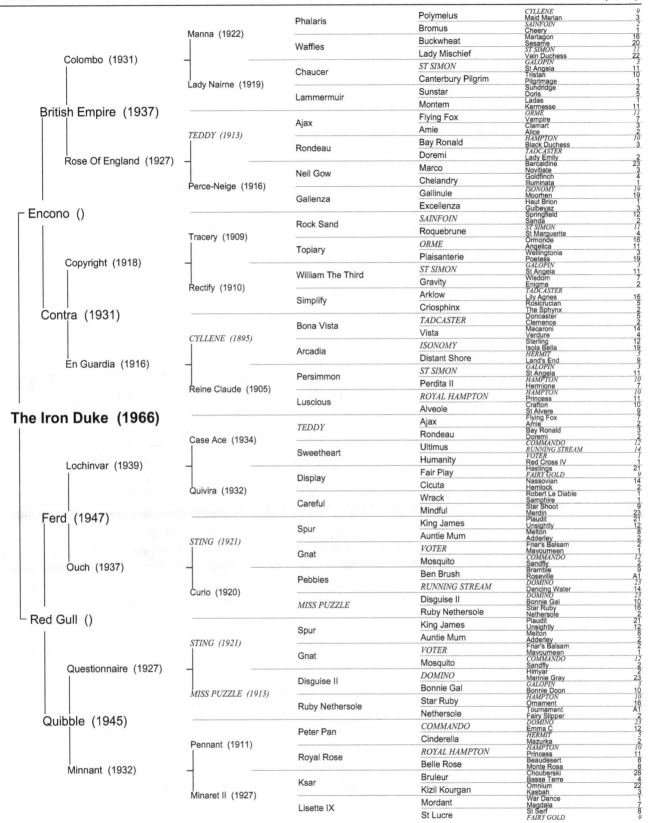

Pedigree tree (left):

- Colombo (1931)
  - British Empire (1937)
    - Rose Of England (1927)
- Encono ()
  - Copyright (1918)
    - Contra (1931)
      - En Guardia (1916)
- **The Iron Duke (1966)**
  - Lochinvar (1939)
    - Ferd (1947)
      - Ouch (1937)
  - Red Gull ()
    - Questionnaire (1927)
      - Quibble (1945)
        - Minnant (1932)

Expanded ancestry:

Generation	Sire/Dam	Parent	Grandparents
Manna (1922)	Phalaris	Polymelus	*CYLLENE* 9 / Maid Marian 3
		Bromus	*SAINFOIN* 2 / Cheery 1
	Waffles	Buckwheat	Martagon 16 / Sesame 20
		Lady Mischief	*ST SIMON* 11 / Vain Duchess 22
Lady Nairne (1919)	Chaucer	*ST SIMON*	*GALOPIN* 3 / St Angela 11
		Canterbury Pilgrim	Tristan 10 / Pilgrimage 1
	Lammermuir	Sunstar	Sundridge 2 / Doris 5
		Montem	Ladas 1 / Kermesse 11
TEDDY (1913)	Ajax	Flying Fox	*ORME* 11 / Vampire 7
		Amie	Clamart 3 / Alice 2
	Rondeau	Bay Ronald	*HAMPTON* 10 / Black Duchess 3
		Doremi	*TADCASTER* / Lady Emily 2
Perce-Neige (1916)	Neil Gow	Marco	Barcaldine 23 / Novitiate 3
		Chelandry	Goldfinch 4 / Illuminata 1
	Gallenza	Gallinule	*ISONOMY* 19 / Moorhen 19
		Excellenza	Haut Brion 1 / Gulbeyaz 3
Tracery (1909)	Rock Sand	*SAINFOIN*	Springfield 12 / Sanda 2
		Roquebrune	*ST SIMON* 11 / St Marguerite 4
	Topiary	*ORME*	Ormonde 16 / Angelica 11
		Plaisanterie	Wellingtonia 3 / Poetess 19
Rectify (1910)	William The Third	*ST SIMON*	*GALOPIN* 3 / St Angela 11
		Gravity	Wisdom 7 / Enigma 2
	Simplify	Arklow	*TADCASTER* / Lily Agnes 16
		Criosphinx	Rosicrucian 5 / The Sphynx 2
CYLLENE (1895)	Bona Vista	*TADCASTER*	Doncaster 5 / Clemence 14
		Vista	Macaroni 4 / Verdure 12
	Arcadia	*ISONOMY*	Sterling 12 / Isola Bella 19
		Distant Shore	*HERMIT* 9 / Land's End 3
Reine Claude (1905)	Persimmon	*ST SIMON*	*GALOPIN* 3 / St Angela 11
		Perdita II	*HAMPTON* 10 / Hermione 7
	Luscious	*ROYAL HAMPTON*	*HAMPTON* 10 / Princess 11
		Alveole	Crafton 10 / St Alvere 9
Case Ace (1934)	*TEDDY*	Ajax	Flying Fox 7 / Amie 2
		Rondeau	Bay Ronald 3 / Doremi 2
	Sweetheart	Ultimus	*COMMANDO* 12 / *RUNNING STREAM* 14
		Humanity	*VOTER* 1 / Red Cross IV
Quivira (1932)	Display	Fair Play	Hastings 21 / *FAIRY GOLD* 9
		Cicuta	Nassovian 14 / Hemlock 2
	Careful	Wrack	Robert Le Diable 1 / Samphire 1
		Mindful	Star Shoot 9 / Merdin 23
STING (1921)	Spur	King James	Plaudit 21 / Unsightly 12
		Auntie Mum	Melton 8 / Adderley 2
	Gnat	*VOTER*	Friar's Balsam 2 / Mavourneen 1
		Mosquito	*COMMANDO* 12 / Sandfly 2
Curio (1920)	Pebbles	Ben Brush	Bramble 9 / Roseville A1
		RUNNING STREAM	*DOMINO* 23 / Dancing Water 14
	MISS PUZZLE	Disguise II	*DOMINO* 23 / Bonnie Gal 10
		Ruby Nethersole	Star Ruby 16 / Nethersole 2
STING (1921)	Spur	King James	Plaudit 21 / Unsightly 12
		Auntie Mum	Melton 8 / Adderley 2
	Gnat	*VOTER*	Friar's Balsam 2 / Mavourneen 1
		Mosquito	*COMMANDO* 12 / Sandfly 2
MISS PUZZLE (1913)	Disguise II	*DOMINO*	Himyar 23 / Mannie Gray 3
		Bonnie Gal	*GALOPIN* 3 / Bonnie Doon 10
	Ruby Nethersole	Star Ruby	*HAMPTON* 10 / Ornament 16
		Nethersole	Tournament A1 / Fairy Slipper 2
Pennant (1911)	Peter Pan	*COMMANDO*	*DOMINO* 23 / Emma C 12
		Cinderella	*HERMIT* 5 / Mazurka 2
	Royal Rose	*ROYAL HAMPTON*	*HAMPTON* 10 / Princess 11
		Belle Rose	Beaudesert 8 / Monte Rosa 8
Minaret II (1927)	Ksar	Bruleur	Chouberski 28 / Basse Terre 4
		Kizil Kourgan	Omnium 22 / Kasbah 3
	Lisette IX	Mordant	War Dance 1 / Magdala 7
		St Lucre	St Serf 8 / *FAIRY GOLD* 9

The Iron Duke 1966

Chapter 30

New Inductees to Show Jumping Hall of Fame

I n May of 2013 two new horses were inducted into the American Show Jumping Hall of Fame. When I did my evaluation of those bloodlines back in 2011, I found that Thoroughbred makes up 82.5% of the top jumper bloodlines—an amount that is shocking for those of us who have been sitting under European Warmblood tutorship for the last four decades and were instructed repeatedly that Thoroughbred should only be used sparingly—they recommended only using 20%—with those lines back in the second or third generations. What astounded me the most was that the facts were so contrary to the dogma, and then I wondered why the heck I hadn't checked this before? Accepting false pronouncements as truth is what happens when we rely on the 'conventional wisdom' in our industry.

Starman WE

The Westphalen stallion Starman 1979 was entered into the Hall of Fame, along with his rider Anne Kursinski, for their wonderful performances in international jumping—team silver at 1988 Olympics, and they won the Grand Prix in Aachen. Anne won honors several times in 'firsts' for woman riders during their partnership, which is part of the glamour of this pair. A beautiful horse, Starman was not just a great jumper, as he excelled as a hunter in the ring as well.

Sport talent does not drop out of the air, and Starman's pedigree demonstrates enough concentration in top performance lines to show us where his jump originated. His strongest poteny is the ¾ brothers Alexander HA and Almfuerst HA 4x5 through both a son and a daughter. These lines are strong conduits of a background build up of the Fling/Ferda/Flirt family, which are full siblings of excellence that are seen so often in the background of successful Hanoverians that they are called a 'standard pattern'. These brothers found in Starman's 'engine room' are 3x3 to Ferda and Fling, so they carry a strong potency in this factor and bring it forward; further, there is a nice reinforcing design of a filly factor of Feiner Kerl (Fling son) daughters 5x5x6. Feiner Kerl is an important jump transmitter in Hanover, and is an excellent sport horse line. Of course there is a good measure of the dreaded Thoroughbred lines as well, as there is also a Phalaris sex balance that certainly added to the athleticism, elegance and speed of this stallion. This is a fairly potent pedigree is some very nice sport bloodlines. However, if you are planning a breeding for a stallion you want to serve as a cross breed sire, then you will need to build a more potent structure than what you see here, so that it can stand up to the dilution that occurs with crossbreeding.

Starman is a nicely bred horse, but his stud record is relatively poor. Part of this reality is surely because of the time frame in which he stood here, as in the 1980s there were few mares that would have been able to genetically build on his strengths—if he had been standing in the late 1990s his career might have been better. This is a reoccurring experience of our domestic breeders when using imported warmblood sires, or the frozen semen of those stationed across the pond, with our domestic mares.

When we breed our American mares to a European warmblood it is crossbreeding and in some cases an outcross. For a stallion used for cross breeding to be successful he needs to be very tightly bred, Starman would have done better if he was inbred to Alexander/Almfuerst—that is if they were in the second and third generation rather than the fourth and fifth, because then it would a stronger delivery of this power. With the duplications, nice as they are in the engine room, crossed on mares that did little to build on it, then this power would present in the foals as 50% less than the sire. Cross breeding is a very valuable tool for us, and we can look to superior examples of this in stallions like Landgraf I HO, however we must also consider the mare base we are breeding to, Starman would have done better standing in Germany with a compatable mare base. He did not establish a family of significance here in the States.

Nautical QH

It is the other 2013 inductee who tickles me as he provides a example for us of the sport power that resides not only in our Thoroughbred, but also the genetic treasures that reside in our other sport breeds. This is Nautical QH 1944, a member of seven Nation's Cup teams with wins in Toronto, Rome, London, Lucerne, and New York, winning by a clear round in his 1960 Nations Cup victory in Rome. At home he cleaned up—the Stone Trophy two years in a row (1957-58), multiple other championships, even in Puissance at Toronto, and in 1959 the team gold in the Pan Am Games. He missed the 1956 Olympics because of a lame left front hoof, and then he came down with pneumonia while in transit for the 1960 Rome Olympics, so he was sidelined for that contest also.

Nautical's real name is Pelo De Oro, and he is a registered Quarter Horse. A beautiful palomino with a distinctive jumping style: he would throw his tail straight up in the air as he cleared the jumps. He was a crowd favorite as much for his color as for his performance flair. Eventually his career along with his charismatic presence earned him the interest of Walt Disney, who did a successful feature documentary on him: *The Horse With The Flying Tail*, which was watched with adoration by most of my generation.

So this horse with the 'it' factor is a humbly bred American Horse, a Quarter Horse no less, and he was a star international jumper of the 1950s and 60s, and now he is being honored again today. What fun!

Evidentially he was a difficult horse to ride, although he did very well jumping under the name Injun Joe when ridden by the future Hall of Fame riders Pat Dixon, Cappy Smith, and Joe Green. But it was later when paired with Hugh Wiley his career went over the top, helped along by coaching from the USET *chef d'equipe* Bert de Nemethy—a master trainer. Nautical QH was a gelding, so you will not be finding him as a head of any jump dynasty either.

> "Nautical was a highly intelligent, very gentle horse when not being ridden, but he could certainly be a problem under saddle; what made him so challenging was that he had overwhelming power and maneuverability and could jump enormous fences with hardly any preparation"(Hugh Wiley *Great Horses of the United States Equestrian Team*- used by permission of the USET).

It is his pedigree that should fascinate you breeders, as it tells the story of our international team horses before the warmblood invasion to this country, and if you bother to evaluate our wins and loss ratios from back then you will see that our modest home-bred products were fully able to compete at the highest level and bring home the medals—the difference is we did it on our own bloodlines. Talent sources have not changed, the same lines produce winners, but we have allowed ourselves to become blinded to what is sitting right in front of us.

Nautical's sire is a Quarter Horse: Muchacho De Oro 1939, whose second sire is the inbred Cotton Eyed Joe QH 1925—he is 2x2 to Jenny QH, aka Old Jennie 1891, a mare by Sykes Rondo QH out of May Mangum QH—reinforced by the presence of her half-brother Captain Sykes; these bloodlines are getting to the base rock of the breed, and both Sykes Rondo QH and May Mangum QH lines were known for producing top sprint racers. Quarter Horses are not usually considered a valid source for the Olympic-style sports, as their conformation often acts against their success in them, as many have an upright shoulder, short pasterns, and a hind end structure that drops so excessively that their femur is shorter than their ilium—a structure that surely helps with the 'dig-in' and short stops that is required in stock horses, but it works against collection, which is needed in all Olympic venues. What you sport horse breeders probably did not know is that this conformation is not universal in the Quarter Horse and has been developed over time by selection for performance in ranch work with cattle and the sports that spring from those activities, however in contrast to this stock type we find that often the best foundation stock of this breed was of a very athletic type, very suitable for our modern Olympic style sports.

The Quarter Horse is an equine that is suitable for many disciplines—it is renowned for its versatility. Further, the American Thoroughbred and the Quarter Horse were the same breed until 1868, so there are strains in our modern Quarter Horse that are conformed perfectly for Olympic-style sports. As you will see, Nautical is not just a 'freak' or an exception that proves the rule; he is one of several Quarter Horses who have operated at international level in these sports. (We will look at this a little more below as Almost Persuaded QH and her full brother Flying Joe QH were noted international jumpers also—and they too are QHs). So how is this possible?

Peter McCue—a Quarter Horse foundation sire is a good racehorse who is found continually in QH sport horses in multiples. Peter carries jumping traits as well as speed. —image at Wiki Commons

The roots of the Quarter Horse are the very same as those of our American Thoroughbred and Standardbred. They all came from our original Running Horse stock—a talented and fast racehorse breed that also excelled as comfortable and gentle saddle horses. When I reached the back of Nautical's sire's lines I found a buildup of a few significant typesetters. He seems to be overloaded with Steel Dust RH and his sisters—all by the Running Horse Harry Bluff. Harry is inbred to Blackburns Whip RH 2x3, the pacing RH sire who was a proven source of speed and exceptional movement and athleticism, and Harry's dam—all go back to the Quarter racing studs of the colonial period. Nautical QH also carries a double of the QH foundation sire Peter McCue QH, whose sire is inbred to Harry Bluff RH 5x4x4x3, and he is out of a Running Horse dam Nora M who has Glencoe 4x4. Her dam-line also goes straight back to the Virginia Quarter racing studs through the famous taproot mare Maria West RH (Chapter 6) and another good mare Irbys Calypso RH. There is also a full sister configuration of the Running Horse mares Margrave Mare RH/Margravine RH 4x3—a strong filly factor. Peter McCue will be found in Quarter Horses who have a jump as well as speed, and he is one of the main speed lines found in the best sprint racers. He is also an example of pedigree error (Appendix C) because originally he was entered into the Thoroughbred studbook as a Thoroughbred, with an incorrect sire. However, his true sire, the Quarter Horse Dan Tucker, is loaded with the best Running Horse bloodlines of our Heroic Era. Nautical's dam also carries the jump transmitter Vandal RH. So Nautical's QH lines were actually a warehouse for the racing stock lines of an earlier era, and therefore he carries dominance in them. He is actually 50% Thoroughbred anyway.

Now here I am going to give you some information that may surprise you. The noted twentieth century writer and historian of the Quarter Horse, Nelson C. Nye, has pointed out there are four American Thoroughbred families that can be counted on to deliver speed to the sprint racer: Himyar-Domino, Ben Brush (Broomstick/Sweep), Hastings-Fair Play, and Glencoe-Hanover. He also mentioned the French-bred Chicle as supplying a strong sprint racing family in the QH. Are these not the same families that are warehouses for our Heroic Era genes: Lexington RH et al? So, it seems that they can be relied on to deliver **the very best in speed and athleticism no matter the distance or form.**

Our cavalry came to the same conclusion also, as said by Colonel William A. Ranck: "Since the sprinter and speed trait apparently have had the greatest development in America, it is logical that we find in the four famous American bloodlines of running horses the most significant material for historical study of the influence of ancestry on the modern short distance running horses. The four American bloodlines in question are Glencoe-Hanover line, the Bonnie Scotland-Ben Brush line, the Himyar-Domino line and the Fair Play line" (*Speed and the Quarter Horse*).

This meshes with the findings of the modern day geneticists, who found that the speed gene is also a sprint gene, and the pedigree expert and scientist Clive Harper discovered that often sprint speed is created by inbreeding to fast horses, no matter the distance they excelled at, and that stamina is found when the background is loaded with strength in those lines. As breeders we need to keep abreast of the findings and test the conventional wisdom that has been handed down to us, because it is often contrary to the facts.

It is Nautical's dam side that I find so typical of our international sport horse of the earlier time, as it was formed by our Remount. Our Remount program, lasting from 1910 until 1950, perfected the American international sport horse—winning multiple Olympic medals in the contests of their era (see more information in Chapter 31 on this and in *North American Sport Horse Breeder*). It also provided stock that dramatically upgraded the horse of the western states, and many of the best QH, Paints, and other western breeds carry significant amounts of Remount stock. Nautical's dam Lula Lee was a Remount bred mare—her sire Toyland was a Thoroughbred that stood for the Remount, also Nautical's second dam: SS Reno and her sire Reno Dart are named 'Reno' because they were bred at the Reno Remount station. We also see concentrations of the usual English contributors of sport talent present here from the St. Simon/Galliard as well as the American powerhouse of Domino. The stallions placed into the Remount program were of top quality.

"In order to encourage the production of horses suitable for cavalry and light artillery uses, the Department of Agriculture in cooperation with the War Department, has placed in selected localities good, sound stallions of proper type and offered some mare owners special endorsements to make use of them…the plan consists

KATHLEEN H. KIRSAN

primarily in placing stallions of merit registered in proper studbooks and belonging to the Thoroughbred, American Saddle, Standard-bred and Morgan breeds in suitable locations…."(Department of Agriculture 1913).

Notice also the Standardbred contribution, as this is the most often overlooked and forgotten source of sport, even though it has a history of providing tremendous talent—even at international level—including high-profile Olympic medal winners such as Halla (½ Standardbred) and Jenny Camp (¼ Standardbred). The trotter lines also seem to be a source of jump mechanics behind not only our sport horses, but those of Europe as well, and they are found to be in the base of many breeds that can jump well. The 'jumper' breeds of Europe, such as the Selle Francais, were developed from a base of French Trotter, Norman, and Standardbred blood. In the German warmblood we find a huge influx of the trotting Yorkshire Coach Horse especially in the Holstein, a breed notable for its jumping talent. What you probably were not aware of is that many of the trotter breeds of Europe, like the Belgian, German and Italian are largely of American Standardbred bloodlines.

In Nautical QH we find the Trotter line of Belmont AT through his best son Nutwood ST. Belmont AT is such a reservoir of

The American Trotter Belmont—a source of jump talent and talented saddle horses. —from a painting by R. Dickey

high-class athleticism that he was named the 'finest trotting stallion in Kentucky', and he was also a great sire of talented saddle horses. He was remembered as a horse with considerable nervous energy, but possessing tremendous stamina and a strong will to win. His line has become known as one of those that transmit physical elegance, and very many of his offspring ended up in the show ring as saddle horses. Some of his line also became prized show carriage horses in England; his grandson Lord Brilliant ST regularly defeated the best Hackneys in the ring on their own soil. Belmont's son Nutwood ST is also a major line for speed, and he imparted elegance and good gaits to those of them who went into the show ring as saddle horses. In our modern day we don't usually picture our Standardbred as a saddle horse, but it always was a good one, and originally it raced under saddle, not in harness. Our Standardbred is found in the background of a surprising number of European breeds—as they were imported in huge numbers by France, Belgium, Italy, Russia, Scandinavia, and Germany. There is no breed in the world that can equal our Standardbred for pacing or trotting speed—none—and so it is the Standardbred that is imported to improve all other mid-gait racing breeds.

Nautical QH has over a dozen lines of Lexington RH in his background, so he is humming along with the best racing stock—flat, trotting, and four-mile racers. No wonder he could jump so well—he had the right mechanical structure, and he was supercharged.

Midnight—a grandson of Peter McCue—was a noted sire of short runners. He was called Midnight because he was born black, but like most grays he ended up almost pure white. This is a line found in many QHs who have a great jump.—Wiki Commons public domain images

Now let's take a quick look at those other exceptions, the full sibling international jumpers Almost Persuaded and Flying John, both Quarter Horses. The Quarter Horse people call the TB/QH cross an Appendix QH as they are out of a Thoroughbred dam—we in the sport horse world would call them Hunters or sport horses. These two full siblings have very similar lines to Nautical QH in the QH half, as they are dominated by a double of the Peter McCue QH grandson Midnight QH; also notice the buildup of Domino from Pennant and the two lines of Disguise—particularly notice the Pennant son Valorous as I will discuss him below. In the Thoroughbred portion of these siblings it is the lines of Ben Brush, Hanover (Hamburg), and Domino (Pennant) dominating and a very interesting triple of the English sire Polymelus—we saw a double of him in the eventer Better and Better. Polymelus is the sire of Phalaris and is found tripled in the sire of the major line Native Dancer, and as an aside, he is believed to have something to do with the ankle problem of that line (see Chapter 27). Further we find the Frizette son Frizzle here through a daughter, Help, who is the fifth dam.

Domino is everywhere there is excellence in sport, yet he is never mentioned when the lists of lines that consistently produce sport horses are published, whether jumpers or eventers. This is just one demonstration on why we need to take the control of the reporting on our own history and not let others tell us what works—the facts don't lie. Domino is a constant in sport excellence, as well as his contemporaries Ben Brush and Fair Play, and they are found as often, if not more, than the likes of Swynford, Gainsborough, Spearmint, Teddy, and Roi Herode, which are the foreign lines that I found in multiples in the sport stars—they are all roughly of the same period, the turn of the last century. Before you blame the Europeans for intentionally omitting our lines in their literature, remember also, they had little first-hand knowledge of these amazing American sport lines because England had banned them internationally, so they are seldom seen in the European sport gene pool, that is until recently, but now they are so far back most fail to recognize where their power is coming from, and obviously neither do we. Therefore when we take our instruction from a population of 'experts' who have no real knowledge of our sport history or bloodlines they are only going to promote what they know about—that is their lines, not ours. And if you just listen to them without a balance of input from American sources, you will be buying and breeding only to their lines—a losing proposition for you, and you will certainly not recognize that all the while you have the very best sport source for your projects looking you right in the face—it is both tragic and comical. By the way, the Man O' War line is far and away the greatest producer of modern hunters and jumpers in North America—not Bonne Nuit, not Nearco, it is our own Man O' War bloodline.

Valorous

To illustrate the issue let's look at the stallion Valorous. A stallion of the Domino line whom I had never heard of until I began studying the pedigrees found in Peter Birdsall's important work: *Bloodlines of Hunters and Jumpers in North America*. Yet Valorous is a significant sire of top jumpers, not just here in these examples, but he has fifteen top hunter/jumper/eventer listed in Birdsall's lists. He is a major player in the career of the international stars Riviera Wonder 1950 (1957 gold medal in Pan Am Games, 1960 team silver medal in Rome Olympics. plus Nations Cup wins in Lucerne and London) and Miss Budweiser aka Circus Rose, on the USET at the Helsinki Olympics, plus in Unusual a jumper champion who was on the gold-medal team in Pan Am Games and more. Often Valorous appears in conjunction with the Man O' War son Great War or with the French jump line of Bonne Nuit.

Valorous 1924 obviously transmitted some jump talent. He is 4x4x4 to Mannie Gray and her ½ brother Inspector B, plus he is out of a Hamburg daughter, and he has ten lines of Lexington RH in eight generations. He is found in some of the greatest international level performers of the 1940-60s, yet he is never mentioned in lists of show jump lines—not any I ever saw anyway.

One reason for this may be found in our international sport history. Our original sport horse was racehorse based. From 1700 on we always bred a horse for sport—our Hunter Horses—other forms came later on. Our Hunter Horse was based on our racehorse blood with other breeds added for style or substance. Our sport horses were exclusively privately bred from 1700 until 1910, which is when the cavalry Remount was formed. Modern Olympic Equestrian sports only began in 1912—and they were only ridden and fielded by each country's cavalry. There were 'international' sport horses before this time as American breeders and owners brought their stock or stables over to England, Ireland, and France to compete in racing and the hunter sports beginning in the mid-1800s. For example, private American citizen Charles Kohler shipped his Thoroughbred stable to France in the early 1900s, and because of the Jersey Act he had them retrained as steeplechasers, as they were barred from the flat by France. They exceeded all expectations, winning against seasoned and established steeplechasers. "The above mentioned (Fitz Herbert, Novelty, Zeus) trio of winners jumped admirably in their earliest attempts and experienced horsemen declared that they were the equal of any steeplechasers or hurdlers abroad…"(Thoroughbred Record). It is a rare American Thoroughbred that does not possess a jump.

Our private domestic sport horse breeders continued on of course, but were barred from Olympic competition until 1950. International sport grew outside of the Olympic venue however, and the Nations Cup competitions were begun in 1909 and were open to all sport horses. When the Olympic regulation of cavalry-only teams dissolved, then in this country the USET was put back in civilian hands.

In contrast, this was not the case in Europe—as most of the European participating countries kept the control of sport horse breeding, training, and fielding under their respective governments' management, which included the State standing stallions and providing financial subsidies for the breeders and a training system for horse and rider. This is a distinct difference from the American experience, whereas the private breeder, rider, and trainer were responsible for all the programing and the cost of competing for their country. It is only in recent times that the USEF was formed and acts as an overseer of these tasks, but still the funding for our competitions is not provided by our government; instead it is from private individuals and company sponsorship in some cases if they are fortunate.

Our domestic Thoroughbred, because it was banned internationally until 1949, is rarely found in the pedigrees abroad. While at home, because our sport horse is racehorse-bred, it was the Thoroughbred racehorse studs who were providing the raw stock for our sport horse recipes, so their bloodlines were promoted and the Remount stock—even though it had proven itself to be a world-class contender—was largely forgotten. For instance, I knew how surprised I was when I began building out pedigrees of sport stars to see how prominent our Saddlebred, Morgan, and Standardbred were in international sport—a wonderful resource that is just dying on the vine here—unused, unrecognized.

With the huge influx of foreign sport stock into our continent since 1970—along with their registries, which ban—**still**—American sport breeds from their 'allowed' lines, in concert with their massive sales promotions with publications and propaganda, the American sport enthusiast has been overwhelmed into thinking that they must breed the European way to succeed (see Chapter 35 for further discussion on this).

For example, while taking a quick look at sport articles on the internet the other day I found that the current creed given to the American breeder is that you **need** a European Warmblood horse to win in International Sport. The article I found didn't even equivocate—it was stated like it is a fact!

But forty years later, many breeders with a history of these warmblood bloodlines in their stock and those who were relying on 'inspection' scores to lead their breeding choices, are finding the results in actual sport performance do not in any way match the investment in time, money, and emotion. A high score in the 'warmblood' inspection process does not and cannot replace a true sport horse performance testing, and many of those equines who scored high in those inspections never produced a credible record in sport. This is how far we have let foreign interests dictate to us, to the point we have forgotten our various performance tests with which we guided how we bred our international champions.

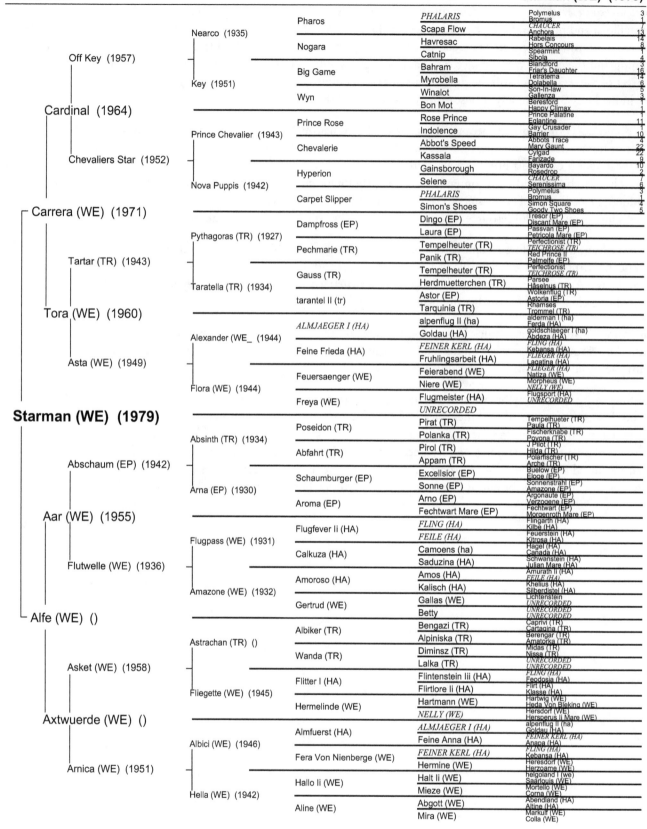

Starman (WE) (1979)

- **Cardinal (1964)**
  - **Off Key (1957)**
    - **Nearco (1935)**
      - Pharos
        - *PHALARIS* — Polymelus 3 / Bromus 1
        - Scapa Flow — *CHAUCER* / Anchora 13
      - Nogara
        - Havresac — Rabelais 14 / Hors Concours 8
        - Catnip — Spearmint 1 / Sibola 3
    - **Key (1951)**
      - Big Game
        - Bahram — Blandford / Friar's Daughter 16
        - Myrobella — Tetratema 14 / Dolabella 6
      - Wyn
        - Winalot — Son-In-law 5 / Gallenza 3
        - Bon Mot — Beresford 1 / Happy Climax 1
  - **Chevaliers Star (1952)**
    - **Prince Chevalier (1943)**
      - Prince Rose
        - Rose Prince — Prince Palatine / Eglantine 11
        - Indolence — Gay Crusader / Barrier 10
      - Chevalerie
        - Abbot's Speed — Abbots Trace 4 / Mary Gaunt 22
        - Kassala — Cylgad 22 / Farizade 9
    - **Nova Puppis (1942)**
      - Hyperion
        - Gainsborough — Bayardo 10 / Rosedrop 2
        - Selene — *CHAUCER* 7 / Serenissima 6
      - Carpet Slipper
        - *PHALARIS* — Polymelus 3 / Bromus 1
        - Simon's Shoes — Simon Square 4 / Goody Two Shoes 5

- **Carrera (WE) (1971)**
  - **Tartar (TR) (1943)**
    - **Pythagoras (TR) (1927)**
      - Dampfross (EP)
        - Dingo (EP) — Tresor (EP) / Discant Mare (EP)
        - Laura (EP) — Passvan (EP) / Petricola Mare (EP)
      - Pechmarie (TR)
        - Tempelheuter (TR) — Perfectionist (TR) / *TEICHROSE (TR)*
        - Panik (TR) — Red Prince II / Palmelfe (EP)
    - **Taratella (TR) (1934)**
      - Gauss (TR)
        - Tempelheuter (TR) — Perfectionist / *TEICHROSE (TR)*
        - Herdmuetterchen (TR) — Parsee / Haselnus (TR)
      - tarantel II (tr)
        - Astor (EP) — Wolkenflug (TR) / Astoria (EP)
        - Tarquinia (TR) — Rhamses / Trommel (TR)
  - **Tora (WE) (1960)**
    - **Alexander (WE_) (1944)**
      - *ALMJAEGER I (HA)*
        - alpenflug II (ha) — alderman I (ha) / Ferda (HA)
        - Goldau (HA) — goldschlaeger I (ha) / Abdeza (HA)
      - Feine Frieda (HA)
        - *FEINER KERL (HA)* — *FLING (HA)* / Kebansa (HA)
        - Fruhlingsarbeit (HA) — *FLIEGER (HA)* / Lagatina (HA)
    - **Flora (WE) (1944)**
      - Feuersaenger (WE)
        - Feierabend (WE) — *FLIEGER (HA)* / Natiza (WE)
        - Niere (WE) — Morpheus (WE) / *NELLY (WE)*
      - Freya (WE)
        - Flugmeister (HA) — Flugsport (HA) / *UNRECORDED*
        - *UNRECORDED*

- **Abschaum (EP) (1942)**
  - **Absinth (TR) (1934)**
    - Poseidon (TR)
      - Pirat (TR) — Tempelhueter (TR) / Paula (TR)
      - Polanka (TR) — Fischerknabe (TR) / Povona (TR)
    - Abfahrt (TR)
      - Pirol (TR) — J Pilot (TR) / Hilda (TR)
      - Appam (TR) — Polarfischer (TR) / Arche (TR)
  - **Arna (EP) (1930)**
    - Schaumburger (EP)
      - Excellsior (EP) — Buelow (EP) / Eloge (EP)
      - Sonne (EP) — Sonnenstrahl (EP) / Amazone (EP)
    - Aroma (EP)
      - Arno (EP) — Argonaute (EP) / Verzogene (EP)
      - Fechtwart Mare (EP) — Fechtwart (EP) / Morgenroth Mare (EP)

- **Aar (WE) (1955)**
  - **Flutwelle (WE) (1936)**
    - **Flugpass (WE) (1931)**
      - Flugfever Ii (HA)
        - *FLING (HA)* — Flingarth (HA) / Kilbe (HA)
        - *FEILE (HA)* — Feuerstein (HA) / Kitrosa (HA)
      - Calkuza (HA)
        - Camoens (ha) — Hagel (HA) / Canada (HA)
        - Saduzina (HA) — Schwanstein (HA) / Julian Mare (HA)
    - **Amazone (WE) (1932)**
      - Amoroso (HA)
        - Amos (HA) — Amurath Ii (HA) / *FEILE (HA)*
        - Kalisch (HA) — Khelius (HA) / Silberdistel (HA)
      - Gertrud (WE)
        - Gallas (WE) — Lichtenstein / *UNRECORDED*
        - Betty — *UNRECORDED* / *UNRECORDED*

- **Alfe (WE) ()**
  - **Asket (WE) (1958)**
    - **Astrachan (TR) ()**
      - Albiker (TR)
        - Bengazi (TR) — Caprivi (TR) / Cartagina (TR)
        - Alpiniska (TR) — Berengar (TR) / Amatorka (TR)
      - Wanda (TR)
        - Diminsz (TR) — Midas (TR) / Nissa (TR)
        - Lalka (TR) — *UNRECORDED* / *UNRECORDED*
    - **Fliegette (WE) (1945)**
      - Flitter I (HA)
        - Flintenstein Iii (HA) — *FLING (HA)* / Feodosia (HA)
        - Flirtlore Ii (HA) — Flirt (HA) / Klasse (HA)
      - Hermelinde (WE)
        - Hartmann (WE) — Hartwig (WE) / Heda Von Bleking (WE)
        - *NELLY (WE)* — Hersdorf (WE) / Hersperus Ii Mare (WE)
  - **Axtwuerde (WE) ()**
    - **Albici (WE) (1946)**
      - Almfuerst (HA)
        - *ALMJAEGER I (HA)* — alpenflug II (ha) / Goldau (HA)
        - Feine Anna (HA) — *FEINER KERL (HA)* / Anapa (HA)
      - Fera Von Nienberge (WE)
        - *FEINER KERL (HA)* — *FLING (HA)* / Kebansa (HA)
        - Hermine (WE) — Heresdorf (WE) / Herzoame (WE)
    - **Hella (WE) (1942)**
      - Hallo Ii (WE)
        - Halt Ii (WE) — helgoland I (we) / Saarlouis (WE)
        - Mieze (WE) — Mortello (WE) / Corna (WE)
      - Aline (WE)
        - Abgott (WE) — Abendland (HA) / Altine (HA)
        - Mira (WE) — Markulf (WE) / Colla (WE)

Starman HA 1979

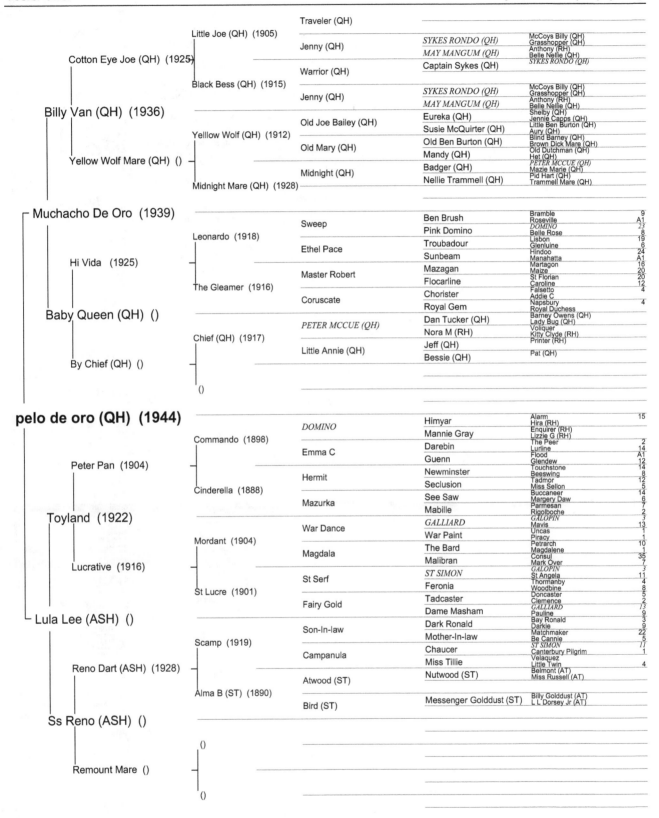

pelo de oro (QH) (1944)

Billy Van (QH) (1936)
- Cotton Eye Joe (QH) (1925)
  - Little Joe (QH) (1905)
    - Traveler (QH)
    - Jenny (QH)
      - SYKES RONDO (QH) — McCoys Billy (QH), Grasshopper (QH)
      - MAY MANGUM (QH) — Anthony (RH), Belle Nellie (QH)
  - Black Bess (QH) (1915)
    - Warrior (QH)
      - Captain Sykes (QH) — SYKES RONDO (QH)
    - Jenny (QH)
      - SYKES RONDO (QH) — McCoys Billy (QH), Grasshopper (QH)
      - MAY MANGUM (QH) — Anthony (RH), Belle Nellie (QH)
- Yellow Wolf Mare (QH) ()
  - Yelllow Wolf (QH) (1912)
    - Old Joe Bailey (QH)
      - Eureka (QH) — Shelby (QH), Jennie Capps (QH)
      - Susie McQuirter (QH) — Little Ben Burton (QH), Aury (QH)
    - Old Mary (QH)
      - Old Ben Burton (QH) — Blind Barney (QH), Brown Dick Mare (QH)
      - Mandy (QH) — Old Dutchman (QH), Het (QH)
  - Midnight Mare (QH) (1928)
    - Midnight (QH)
      - Badger (QH) — PETER MCCUE (QH), Mazie Marie (QH)
      - Nellie Trammell (QH) — Pid Hart (QH), Trammell Mare (QH)

Muchacho De Oro (1939)

Hi Vida (1925)
- Leonardo (1918)
  - Sweep
    - Ben Brush — Bramble 9, Roseville A1
    - Pink Domino — DOMINO 23, Belle Rose 8
  - Ethel Pace
    - Troubadour — Lisbon 19, Glenluine 6
    - Sunbeam — Hindoo 24, Manahatta A1
- The Gleamer (1916)
  - Master Robert
    - Mazagan — Martagon 16, Maize 20
    - Flocarline — St Florian 20, Caroline 12
  - Coruscate
    - Chorister — Falsetto, Addie C 4
    - Royal Gem — Napsbury 4, Royal Duchess

Baby Queen (QH) ()

By Chief (QH) ()
- Chief (QH) (1917)
  - PETER MCCUE (QH)
    - Dan Tucker (QH) — Barney Owens (QH), Lady Bug (QH)
    - Nora M (RH) — Voliquer, Kitty Clyde (RH)
  - Little Annie (QH)
    - Jeff (QH) — Printer (RH)
    - Bessie (QH) — Pat (QH)
- ()

pelo de oro (QH) (1944)

Peter Pan (1904)
- Commando (1898)
  - DOMINO
    - Himyar — Alarm 15, Hira (RH)
    - Mannie Gray — Enquirer (RH), Lizzie G (RH)
  - Emma C
    - Darebin — The Peer 2, Lurline 14
    - Guenn — Flood A1, Glendew 12
- Cinderella (1888)
  - Hermit
    - Newminster — Touchstone 14, Beeswing 8
    - Seclusion — Tadmor 12, Miss Sellon 5
  - Mazurka
    - See Saw — Buccaneer 14, Margery Daw 6
    - Mabille — Parmesan 7, Rigolboche 2

Toyland (1922)

Lucrative (1916)
- Mordant (1904)
  - War Dance
    - GALLIARD — GALOPIN 3, Mavis 13
    - War Paint — Uncas 1, Piracy 1
  - Magdala
    - The Bard — Petrarch 10, Magdalene 1
    - Malibran — Consul 35, Mark Over 7
- St Lucre (1901)
  - St Serf
    - ST SIMON — GALOPIN 3, St Angela 11
    - Feronia — Thormanby 4, Woodbine 8
  - Fairy Gold
    - Tadcaster — Doncaster 5, Clemence 2
    - Dame Masham — GALLIARD 13, Pauline 9

Lula Lee (ASH) ()

Reno Dart (ASH) (1928)
- Scamp (1919)
  - Son-In-law
    - Dark Ronald — Bay Ronald 3, Darkie 9
    - Mother-In-law — Matchmaker 22, Be Cannie 5
  - Campanula
    - Chaucer — ST SIMON 11, Canterbury Pilgrim 1
    - Miss Tillie — Velaquez, Little Twin 4
- Alma B (ST) (1890)
  - Atwood (ST)
    - Nutwood (ST) — Belmont (AT), Miss Russell (AT)
  - Bird (ST)
    - Messenger Golddust (ST) — Billy Golddust (AT), L L Dorsey Jr (AT)

Ss Reno (ASH) ()

Remount Mare ()
- ()
- ()

Pelo de Oro QH 1944

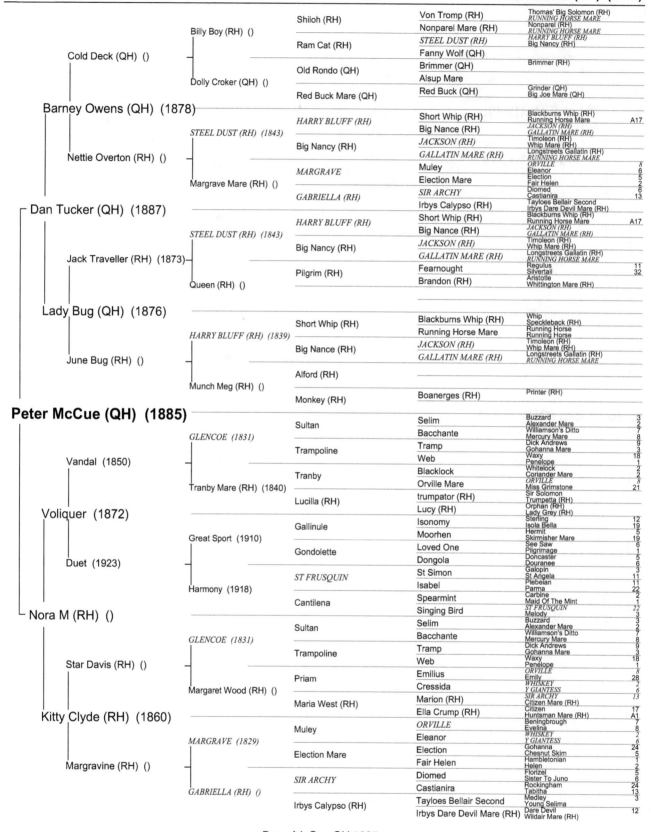

Peter McCue QH 1895

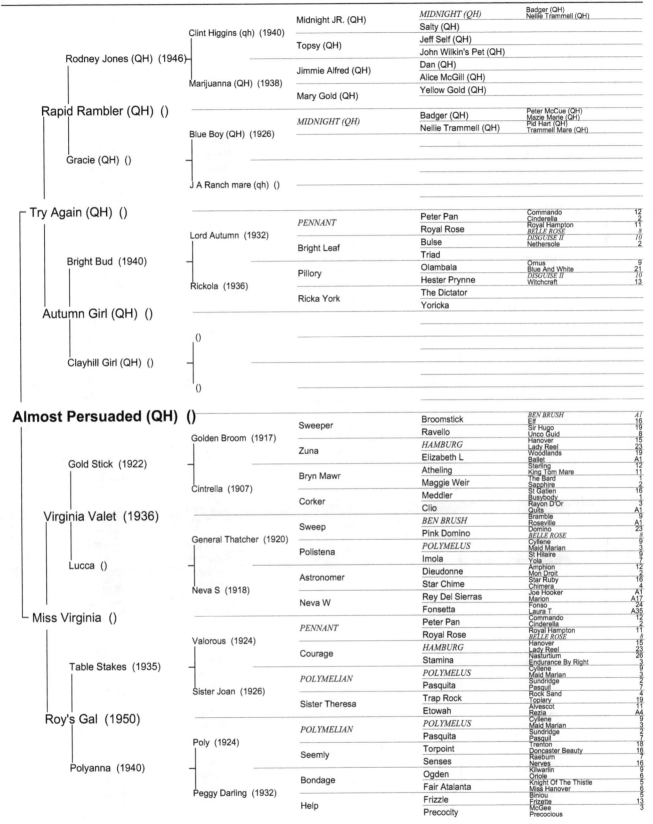

Almost Persuaded QH

Top pedigree (Rapid Rambler section):

- Rapid Rambler (QH) ()
  - Try Again (QH) ()
    - Rodney Jones (QH) (1946)
      - Clint Higgins (qh) (1940)
        - Midnight JR. (QH)
          - MIDNIGHT (QH) — Badger (QH), Nellie Trammell (QH)
          - Salty (QH)
        - Topsy (QH)
          - Jeff Self (QH)
          - John Wilkin's Pet (QH)
      - Marijuanna (QH) (1938)
        - Jimmie Alfred (QH)
          - Dan (QH)
          - Alice McGill (QH)
        - Mary Gold (QH)
          - Yellow Gold (QH)
    - Gracie (QH) ()
      - Blue Boy (QH) (1926)
        - MIDNIGHT (QH)
          - Badger (QH) — Peter McCue (QH), Mazie Marie (QH)
          - Nellie Trammell (QH) — Pid Hart (QH), Trammell Mare (QH)
      - J A Ranch mare (qh) ()
  - Autumn Girl (QH) ()
    - Bright Bud (1940)
      - Lord Autumn (1932)
        - PENNANT
          - Peter Pan — Commando 12, Cinderella 2
          - Royal Rose — Royal Hampton 11, BELLE ROSE 8
        - Bright Leaf
          - Bulse — DISGUISE II 10, Nethersole 2
          - Triad
      - Rickola (1936)
        - Pillory
          - Olambala — Ornus 9, Blue And White 21
          - Hester Prynne — DISGUISE II 10, Witchcraft 13
        - Ricka York
          - The Dictator
          - Yoricka
    - Clayhill Girl (QH) ()
      - ()
      - ()

Almost Persuaded (QH) ()

- Gold Stick (1922)
  - Virginia Valet (1936)
- Lucca ()
- Miss Virginia ()
  - Table Stakes (1935)
- Roy's Gal (1950)
  - Polyanna (1940)

Golden Broom (1917)	Sweeper	Broomstick	*BEN BRUSH*	A1
			Elf	16
		Ravello	Sir Hugo	19
			Unco Guid	8
	Zuna	*HAMBURG*	Hanover	15
			Lady Reel	23
		Elizabeth L	Woodlands	19
			Ballet	A1
Cintrella (1907)	Bryn Mawr	Atheling	Sterling	12
			King Tom Mare	11
		Maggie Weir	The Bard	1
			Sapphire	2
	Corker	Meddler	St Gatien	16
			Busybody	1
		Clio	Rayon D'Or	3
			Quits	A1
General Thatcher (1920)	Sweep	*BEN BRUSH*	Bramble	9
			Roseville	A1
		Pink Domino	Domino	23
			BELLE ROSE	8
	Polistena	*POLYMELUS*	Cyllene	9
			Maid Marian	3
		Imola	St Hilaire	9
			Yola	
Neva S (1918)	Astronomer	Dieudonne	Amphion	12
			Mon Droit	2
		Star Chime	Star Ruby	16
			Chimera	4
	Neva W	Rey Del Sierras	Joe Hooker	A1
			Marion	A17
		Fonsetta	Fonso	24
			Laura T	A35
Valorous (1924)	PENNANT	Peter Pan	Commando	12
			Cinderella	2
		Royal Rose	Royal Hampton	11
			BELLE ROSE	8
	Courage	*HAMBURG*	Hanover	15
			Lady Reel	23
		Stamina	Nasturtium	26
			Endurance By Right	3
Sister Joan (1926)	*POLYMELIAN*	*POLYMELUS*	Cyllene	9
			Maid Marian	3
		Pasquita	Sundridge	2
			Pasquil	7
	Sister Theresa	Trap Rock	Rock Sand	4
			Topiary	19
		Etowah	Alvescot	11
			Rezia	A4
Poly (1924)	*POLYMELIAN*	*POLYMELUS*	Cyllene	9
			Maid Marian	3
		Pasquita	Sundridge	2
			Pasquil	7
	Seemly	Torpoint	Trenton	18
			Doncaster Beauty	16
		Senses	Raeburn	7
			Nerves	16
Peggy Darling (1932)	Bondage	Ogden	Kilwarlin	9
			Oriole	6
		Fair Atalanta	Knight Of The Thistle	6
			Miss Hanover	6
	Help	Frizzle	Biniou	5
			Frizette	13
		Precocity	McGee	3
			Precocious	

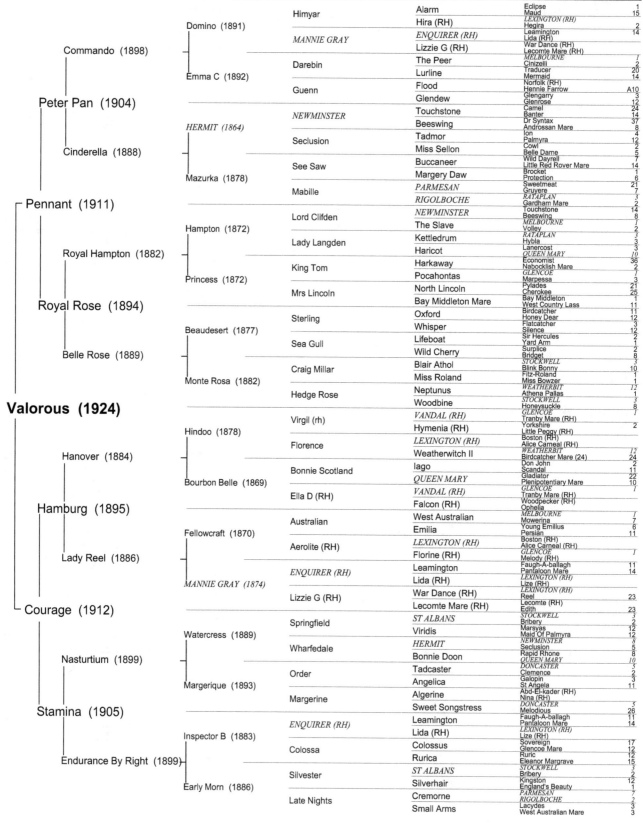

Valorous (1924)

Peter Pan (1904)
- Commando (1898)
  - Domino (1891)
    - Himyar
      - Alarm — Eclipse 1 / Maud 15
      - Hira (RH) — *LEXINGTON (RH)* / Hegira 2
    - *MANNIE GRAY*
      - *ENQUIRER (RH)* — Leamington 14 / Lida (RH)
      - Lizzie G (RH) — War Dance (RH) / Lecomte Mare (RH)
  - Emma C (1892)
    - Darebin
      - The Peer — *MELBOURNE* 1 / Cinizelli
      - Lurline — Traducer 20 / Mermaid 14
    - Guenn
      - Flood — Norfolk (RH) / Hennie Farrow A10
      - Glendew — Glengarry 3 / Glenrose 12
- Cinderella (1888)
  - *HERMIT (1864)*
    - *NEWMINSTER*
      - Touchstone — Camel 24 / Banter 14
      - Beeswing — Dr Syntax 37 / Androssan Mare 8
    - Seclusion
      - Tadmor — Ion 4 / Palmyra 12
      - Miss Sellon — Cowl 2 / Belle Dame 5
  - Mazurka (1878)
    - See Saw
      - Buccaneer — Wild Dayrell 7 / Little Red Rover Mare 14
      - Margery Daw — Brocket 1 / Protection 6
    - Mabille
      - *PARMESAN* — Sweetmeat 21 / Gruyere 7
      - *RIGOLBOCHE* — *RATAPLAN* 3 / Gardham Mare 2

Pennant (1911)
- Royal Hampton (1882)
  - Hampton (1872)
    - Lord Clifden
      - *NEWMINSTER* — Touchstone 14 / Beeswing 8
      - The Slave — *MELBOURNE* 1 / Volley 2
    - Lady Langden
      - Kettledrum — *RATAPLAN* 3 / Hybla 3
      - Haricot — Lanercost 3 / *QUEEN MARY* 10
  - Princess (1872)
    - King Tom
      - Harkaway — Economist 36 / Nabocklish Mare 2
      - Pocahontas — *GLENCOE* 1 / Marpessa 3
    - Mrs Lincoln
      - North Lincoln — Pylades 21 / Cherokee 25
      - Bay Middleton Mare — Bay Middleton 1 / West Country Lass 11
- Royal Rose (1894)
  - Belle Rose (1889)
    - Beaudesert (1877)
      - Sterling
        - Oxford — Birdcatcher 11 / Honey Dear 12
        - Whisper — Flatcatcher 3 / Silence 12
      - Sea Gull
        - Lifeboat — Sir Hercules 12 / Yard Arm 1
        - Wild Cherry — Surplice 2 / Bridget 8
    - Monte Rosa (1882)
      - Craig Millar
        - Blair Athol — *STOCKWELL* 3 / Blink Bonny 10
        - Miss Roland — Fitz-Roland 1 / Miss Bowzer 1
      - Hedge Rose
        - Neptunus — *WEATHERBIT* 12 / Athena Pallas 1
        - Woodbine — *STOCKWELL* 3 / Honeysuckle 8

Hanover (1884)
- Hindoo (1878)
  - Virgil (rh)
    - *VANDAL (RH)* — *GLENCOE* 1 / Tranby Mare (RH)
    - Hymenia (RH) — Yorkshire / Little Peggy (RH) 2
  - Florence
    - *LEXINGTON (RH)* — Boston (RH) / Alice Carneal (RH)
    - Weatherwitch II — *WEATHERBIT* 12 / Birdcatcher Mare (24) 24
- Bourbon Belle (1869)
  - Bonnie Scotland
    - Iago — Don John 2 / Scandal 11
    - *QUEEN MARY* — Gladiator 22 / Plenipotentiary Mare 10
  - Ella D (RH)
    - *VANDAL (RH)* — *GLENCOE* 1 / Tranby Mare (RH)
    - Falcon (RH) — Woodpecker (RH) / Ophelia

Hamburg (1895)
- Lady Reel (1886)
  - Fellowcraft (1870)
    - Australian
      - West Australian — *MELBOURNE* 1 / Mowerina 7
      - Emilia — Young Emilius 6 / Persian 11
    - Aerolite (RH)
      - *LEXINGTON (RH)* — Boston (RH) / Alice Carneal (RH)
      - Florine (RH) — *GLENCOE* 1 / Melody (RH)
  - *MANNIE GRAY (1874)*
    - *ENQUIRER (RH)*
      - Leamington — Faugh-A-ballagh 11 / Pantaloon Mare 14
      - Lida (RH) — *LEXINGTON (RH)* / Lize (RH)
    - Lizzie G (RH)
      - War Dance (RH) — *LEXINGTON (RH)* / Reel 23
      - Lecomte Mare (RH) — Lecomte (RH) / Edith 23

Courage (1912)
- Nasturtium (1899)
  - Watercress (1889)
    - Springfield
      - *ST ALBANS* — *STOCKWELL* 3 / Bribery 2
      - Viridis — Marsyas 12 / Maid Of Palmyra 12
    - Wharfedale
      - *HERMIT* — *NEWMINSTER* 8 / Seclusion 5
      - Bonnie Doon — Rapid Rhone 8 / *QUEEN MARY* 10
  - Margerique (1893)
    - Order
      - Tadcaster — *DONCASTER* 5 / Clemence
      - Angelica — Galopin 3 / St Angela 11
    - Margerine
      - Algerine — Abd-El-kader (RH) / Nina (RH)
      - Sweet Songstress — *DONCASTER* 5 / Melodious 26
- Stamina (1905)
  - Endurance By Right (1899)
    - Inspector B (1883)
      - *ENQUIRER (RH)*
        - Leamington — Faugh-A-ballagh 11 / Pantaloon Mare 14
        - Lida (RH) — *LEXINGTON (RH)* / Lize (RH)
      - Colossa
        - Colossus — Sovereign 17 / Glencoe Mare 12
        - Rurica — Ruric 12 / Eleanor Margrave 15
    - Early Morn (1886)
      - Silvester
        - *ST ALBANS* — *STOCKWELL* 3 / Bribery 2
        - Silverhair — Kingston 12 / England's Beauty 1
      - Late Nights
        - Cremorne — *PARMESAN* 7 / *RIGOLBOCHE* 2
        - Small Arms — Lacydes 3 / West Australian Mare 3

Valorous 1924

Chapter 31

Keen 1966 and the Unsuitable American Thoroughbred

Throughout the decade when I was participating in the 'warmblood' fad in this country (roughly 1993-2003) I read, heard, and was personally advised repeatedly that the Thoroughbred, especially the American Thoroughbred, was a poor choice as an Olympic-style sport horse, and that it was particularly unsuitable to breed warmbloods from. It was explained to me, very patiently multiple times, that the American Thoroughbred did not have the proper riding horse conformation; the registry representatives said this was because it was built downhill and was **a sprinter-only breed**. But they did let me know it was okay to use a German, Irish, or Australian TB, as those strains were truly stamina-bred and therefore were built correctly, but an American Thoroughbred—was I serious? But of course, that was what I had for breeding, and not just one, but two American Thoroughbred mares—poor me. I guess I was fortunate in that they would still let me breed, although my foals of course would not be allowed into the main studbook, because of their shameful dam-line. According to their rules, maybe after four or five generations of breeding back to proper German horses, eventually my product could be elevated into the main studbook. Wow.

What an innocent I was! Who can stand up to the European government-organized marketing genius? They are fabulous at presentation, promotion, and subtle manipulation of the brain-dead Americans. We were such easy prey for them! It took me another decade after dropping out of their 'lose-lose' game for me to clearly see what had occurred here.

So let me quickly address the propaganda perpetrated against the American TB:

Criticism of the American Thoroughbred Commonly Heard in Sport Horse Circles

It is a sprint only breed. Contrary to this bold-faced misrepresentation, the American Thoroughbred is third worldwide in the production of stamina-bred horses (see Appendix E). Based on the *chefs-de-race* list (an accepted industry standard), which identifies which sire-lines produce stakes level horses, divided into sprint, classic, and stamina categories (see *North American Sport Horse Breeder* and www.sport-horse-breeder.com for more on this issue), the leading countries in the production of stamina-bred horses are:

France, world leader with 34%

England, second in the world with 30%

America, third in the world with 25%

Ireland and Germany tied for fourth with 4%.

As you can see, not only is the good ole USA right up there in world production of stamina horses, the critics of our American TB are more than 20% behind us. America also produces great classic length and sprinter horses—the fact is America is a leading producer of **all** varieties of quality Thoroughbreds in the world. Further, it is our original racehorse breed, the American Running Horse, that perfected the **true stamina racehorse** (four-mile heat racer)—not the TB—and its genes are unchanged and behind our modern Thoroughbred and Standardbred as well as in our Saddle Horses. (After writing most of the content here I decided to revisit some of the stamina sources with my new knowledge of the European branches of our Heroic Era race-lines, and just in the French category alone, seven of their 34% of the stamina lines are powered by our American Running Horse bloodlines—pretty funny.)

As an interesting study of human nature and the growth of false 'conventional wisdom' in our industry, we can see this 'sprint-only' classification was already being spread far and wide in the 1960s as one of the top Kentucky equine geneticists of the time, Dewey G. Steele, spoke out on it:

> "Pedigree 'experts' in England still go to great lengths to point out the probable limitation in staying capacity of a Thoroughbred tracing even remotely to American ancestry."

Is this a remnant of the campaign to ban the American Thoroughbred? It is certainly shocking in its deviation from the facts. The originators of the 'dash race' standard claiming the premier distance racing breed of American Thoroughbred will limit the staying ability of their breed is startling. This should alert you that we need to not accept industry wisdom without checking it out. The facts then, and still now, are in the American-bred **we have the very best lines of speed for all distances**.

It is built downhill—not saddle horse conformation. Carriage horses generally have a high head set but many do not have the proper shoulder and hip angles for saddle sports, saddle horses generally have a high to moderate head set and usually have proper saddle horse angles in their shoulder and hip, and some sprinter horses do have a low head set (as do some stamina horses).

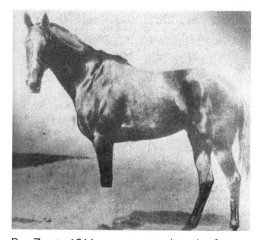

Pan Zareta 1911—no one can claim this famous racehorse was anything but a pure sprinter—perhaps the best there ever was—as she set three world records; would you rate her conformation downhill? —photo from the Thoroughbred Record

[It is advantageous to have elevation of the front end in Olympic-style sport horses—especially those used in jumping and dressage to have a neck set above the point of shoulder. It is just as, and maybe more important, to have the correct hind end conformation, so proper collection can be achieved (see www.jwequine.com on Functional Conformation by Judy Wardrope for more on this).]

The Continental Warmbloods are based on a coach/farm horse breed, not a saddle horse breed. Over the years they have had to add copious amounts of Thoroughbred to get a proper shoulder and hip angle and saddle horse conformation—it is not the other way around. The Thoroughbred is a saddle horse and a sport horse from the get-go; it doesn't need to add farm horse bloodlines to achieve saddle horse conformation—it comes that way naturally.

Other criticisms—high-strung, poor feet, conformation faults—these are usually leveled across the board at all Thoroughbreds, and yes, some are high-strung—what do you expect in a racehorse? Also some may have poor feet and possess some other conformation faults, but guess what? Those wonderful warmbloods all have these same issues; for example the Trakehner as a breed is avoided by some for its high-strung, flighty temperament that is common in some strains; the Don Carlos line in the Hanoverian is one that is famous for its terrible temperament; the Drabant line in the Swedish Warmblood is another with poor disposition. And bad feet and conformation faults, the Warmbloods are loaded with them: weak knees, bad ankles, upright pasterns, club feet, poor hoof wall, sickle hocks, swayback, hock and stifle issues, and on. Conformation faults are not a breed problem; rather they are a breeder problem (see Chapter 27).

Since international sport came about—mid-1800s—Americans have always used their Hunter Horse and won at top international level. Before the Olympics (1912), it was American horses like The Virginian ½ TB and his stable mates Keswick ¾ TB and David Gray ½ TB (see his picture in Chapter 35) who went abroad and won. The Remount-bred, Thoroughbred-based Hunter Horse won well also, and after the Olympics were turned back to the civilians here, horses such as Bold Minstrel (¾ TB), Jet Run (full TB), and Gem Twist (full TB) are superstars of the past in international sport, and they are just a few of the successful horses who come to mind easily—the American tradition of top-quality Hunter Horses is a three-hundred-year-old practice—they are our national breed of sport horse. The world wide equestrian community was well aware of our formidable equine sport product, as they always had a real contest when they came against us.

388

KATHLEEN H. KIRSAN

"For years authorities have maintained that the American Thoroughbred possesses a superb potential for international dressage, provided that the individual has good gaits, enough substance, and a sound temperament. However, relatively few Thoroughbreds have been given a fair chance to prove this; usually they are tried for racing first, and then converted into show-ring jumpers or hunters if that fails" (quotation from *Great Horses of the United States Equestrian Team*, used by permission of the United States Equestrian Team).

This anti-American Thoroughbred 'company-line' is spread far and wide in sport horse circles—and the subtle campaign of the put-down of the Thoroughbred, **especially the American Thoroughbred**, in sport horse breeding has never stopped or been reasonably challenged. For instance, I just got off the net with a Dutch breeder who was searching for a suitable Thoroughbred to breed into her sport product, but she says no one is breeding Thoroughbreds in Holland, and further she said that the sport horse authorities have advised all of them to stay away from Thoroughbreds, as they will—you guessed it—bring in downhill frame, conformation faults, and bad temperament—so the campaign lives on. All Continental Warmblood breeds are based on a farm-coach source, and if they do not add periodic doses of racehorse into their gene pool they revert back to type. My Dutch correspondent was fully aware of this truth, and it was why we were having the dialogue in the first place. Who can say when this all began? But it is important for us, as breeders, to test 'conventional wisdom', for in just the minor research I have done this dogma has been revealed to be blatantly untrue in the case of our wonderful American Thoroughbred. **The harm this false teaching has done to the American breeder is incalculable.**

Keen—International Dressage Champion

This chapter is meant to introduce you to a first-class international champion dressage horse, the Hall of Famer and Olympic medalist Keen, who is a full American Thoroughbred.

Hilda Guerney and Keen, delighting all that watched their grace, precision, and beauty. —photo by Tish Quirk, used by permission

Keen was born in 1966. His stellar career spanned the 1970s and most of the 1980s; he is one of the greatest dressage performers of all time, and he won all over the USA, Canada, and Europe. Keen was the poster child, not only for the sport of dressage in America, but for the suitability of the American Thoroughbred for this sport. Coincidently this powerful, living symbol of what the Thoroughbred was capable of was performing in the same time period that the European Warmblood Registries were planting their outposts here in the USA.

The story of Keen and his gifted rider/trainer Hilda Guerney is one of those that epitomize the equestrian ideal: a perfect partnership between horse and rider, and the heights they reached were based on affection, respect, and the sheer joy of performing their best. Keen and Hilda were the spark that ignited the American equestrian's passion with the sport of dressage. Riding to victories at home and abroad, at times astounding the foreign judges with their perfect movements, they blazed a path through the top events in the 1970-80s, and Keen was still performing at age nineteen!

On the whole, the American sport horse tradition was more Hunter-oriented before this; participation in cross-country and show jumping was a natural for us, and dressage was not a widespread sport here, and there were not the trainers or competitions in place to allow its expansion. It is fitting that our modern day jump into this sport came from our racehorse breed of Thoroughbred—it is after all the main ingredient in our Hunter Horse, which is our domestic 'warmblood'.

Our unlikely horse, California-bred Keen, was extremely tall: 17.2 hands—he had been rejected as a racer because of this; he could not fit in the start box. He was bought by a young schoolteacher named Hilda Guerney; she was an amateur with limited resources, but she was possessed of a pronounced vision, combined with a large amount of natural talent and determination. Keen, even with his immense size, was light on his feet and was agile and graceful, and the 'passage' was his easiest exercise. With an admirable dedication to her goal, every summer on her break from school Hilda would trailer Keen all the way to New York (3500 miles), so she could be coached by Bengt Ljungiest at the American Dressage Institute. The quintessential groundbreakers: Keen and Guerney, through hard work, commitment, and love of the sport reached the heights of dressage—and they did it on their own; there is no government support here—the full credit for their achievement rests on Hilda and her marvelous horse. Their display of spirit and performance awoke in the North American equestrian a passion for dressage, and they truly began the modern day dressage movement in the USA. What an accomplishment!

> "I have always felt the future of American dressage lies with American-bred horses and American trained riders, and was thrilled that Keen and I could show that the idea has real merit. Keen is almost my dream horse—his temperament is very friendly and willing, yet easily stimulated, and he has tremendous power and freedom of movement. All of his gaits are good, but his power at the extended trot, piaffe and passage are exceptional, and these are critical movements in the scoring. Important, too, is the fact that he has a very sound basic structure and has always been a very healthy horse and a good doer" (Hilda Guerney—from *Great Horses of the United States Equestrian* Team—permission to quote granted by the USET).

Synopsis of their career:

> 1974 – USDF Horse of the Year
>
> 1975 – Individual silver and team gold at the Pan Am Games
>
> 1976 – Montreal Olympics, team bronze, individual 4th place, USDF Horse of the Year
>
> 1977 – USDF Horse of the Year
>
> 1978 – World Championship—4th place, Aachen Grand Prix—4th place, USDF Horse of the Year
>
> 1979 – Pan Am Games, individual and team gold, US Champion Grand Prix, US Champion Intermediate II, USDF Horse of the Year
>
> —— – Injury: neck severely damaged—out of commission for 3 years
>
> 1984 – at age 18, Olympic Team—6th place, North American Championship—2nd
>
> 1985 – at age 19 USET Championship—1st
>
> 1989 – death at age 23 from stroke
>
> 1997 – induction into Dressage Hall of Fame

Pedigree Analysis—Keen

Keen's pedigree is interesting also. His sire is English lines, the usual: Canterbury Pilgrim 6x7, the full siblings Sainfoin/Sierra 7x7, and St. Frusquin 6x6x6 sex-balanced—a nice pedigree but nothing special to indicate his level of talent.

His dam provides a sex-balance for Sir Gallahad 5x5, and a line of the rare Harry of Hereford—the full brother to the ever present Swynford 6x6—and she also provides another line of The Tetrarch 5x6 and of Sunstar 5x6 that connect with the sire's lines of those; once again a very nice construction with strong interactions between the lines of the sire and the dam—this is a solid design. In addition we find a Man O' War sex-balance 6x5 and a line of the great Beaming Beauty—very nice, but it is the dam-line itself that provides the surprises. First of all it is **extremely inbred**. Notice Farmer Jim—who is he by the way? He is a son of Abe Frank, a Hanover son who sired the greatest sprinting filly ever: Pan Zareta (see Chapter 10 and photo in this chapter). His son Farmer Jim is the sire of the fifth dam and of the sixth dam—that means his daughter was bred back to him. But that isn't the half of it; flip to the pedigree of Odd Foot (fourth dam), and you will see that the dam of Farmer Jim is Miss Breeze, and right on the dam-line you find her again through a daughter—yowza. Realize that this means that Miss Breeze supplied both the X chromosomes—the one coming from Farmer Jim to his daughter and the dam was also Miss Breeze, there is no question at all then where the mtDNA and sex-linked material arrive from—this is extraordinary! Miss Breeze is 3x4x4 to Lexington RH---just like Domino!

But there is more, as Odd Foot's sire is out of a mare named Hand Bell, and she is a daughter of Hanover, and who is Farmer Jim's grandsire? Yes, you are seeing correctly, it is Hanover. So Farmer Jim is doubled 1x2 in Panic Girl and then is reinforced on both sides of his pedigree, and it all comes in through Odd Foot, the fourth dam. So Odd Foot is 2x3 Farmer Jim, 3x4x5 Hanover, and 3x4x5 Miss Breeze—this is an extremely concentrated gene pool, probably more than you have ever seen before, and it is in American Heroic Era genes. The rest of Keen's pedigree is in good and solid performance lines, but with little refocusing closer than the fifth and sixth. It is the dam-line that provides the laser beam of talent in the fourth, and then the third dam brings in more with a Beaming Beauty dam-line (fifteen lines of Lexington RH in ten generations) and a Fair Play top-line. His dam Mable Victory picks up the power with an injection of more Man O'War, a dam-line to the taproot Frizette, and the Lexington RH warehouse: Commando. But make no mistake—it is the inbreeding in Odd Foot that sets this design above the average good performer; Keen's mtDNA was off the charts.

Now I mentioned that Abe Frank sired a very fast filly, but once again that is only a clue to what lies behind these lines. I only extended the pedigree this far because I was curious about Farmer Jim—a horse I knew nothing about—but what I found behind him has dazzled me. You can see on the Odd Foot pedigree how loaded it is with Lexington RH and the other Heroic Era stars; for instance Miss Breeze (seventh dam x3) is 2x3 to the ¾ siblings Monarchist/Nevada (by Lexington RH)—this is concentrated power again (even with a strictly English sire, Keen has forty lines of Lexington RH). But I decided to take a look behind all that inbreeding as well, and the thirteenth dam Mary Hunt RH brought me right to the root of this tree. The top ¾ is the usual English Thoroughbred contributors, but the bottom quarter is remarkable as it takes us right back to Virginia to the dawn of the Plantation Horse movement. What fun this is, and what a remarkable pedigree!

This background is significant for a horse that needs proper gaits and movement. The Plantation Horse movement began around 1800, when the breeders in the northern North Carolina region and the southern Virginia area became alarmed enough from the changes that were occurring in our native Running Horse from the continual breeding in of English Thoroughbred, and it was that which prodded them to begin a 'foundation movement'. They determined that they would stay the downward slide they perceived in their herds and preserve the original Running Horse traits that were fast disappearing, so they chose a few sires who were strong in the characteristics that they wanted to preserve, sprint speed, gaited-ness (all good saddle horses of the day were gaited), and the sweet temperament of the Running Horse, for use in breeding to the population of pacing and sprinting Running Horse mares that were centered in this area. The continual crossing in of Thoroughbred had caused the gaits to disappear in some strains along with the sweet disposition, which was being replaced with the high-strung and nervous Thoroughbred disposition, plus the emphasis was for distance, and they found they were losing their blistering sprint speed. These breeders, gentleman like Gen. Cocke and John Goode, wanted to produce comfortable saddle horses with stamina and resiliency that could still race when they wanted them to. Goodes Twigg RH is the principal sire of this experiment; he was such a remarkable racehorse and sire that he is rated second only to Janus as the best Quarter Running Horse foundation sire, and he also imparted gaits to his foals. Another Running Horse sire, Roebuck, was used in this program, but he is not in Keen's pedigree. The third sire they used was imported Bedford. In Bedford's day many of the English Thoroughbreds still were more dominant in their English Running Horse characteristics than the newer Oriental traits, and Bedford was one of those (like Janus before him). But unlike Janus, Bedford did not produce many good racers; instead he was highly valued for the exceptional quality of his saddle horses (gaits), and he gave great beauty and docility to his foals consistently, as well as gaits when bred to the Running Horse mares—he was noted for the perfect movement he impated.

The first Kentucky Derby winner Aristides carries the same dam-line as Keen. Artist. — Harry Lyman, Lithograph by Caulfield and Shook 1881, found in "Thoroughbred Record"

Looking at Mary Hunt's pedigree you can see those stars of the Plantation movement, who were the greats of sprint racing as well—most of these racers were gaited and could race at both the pace and the gallop. Here we see the bedrock of Keen is born from our Plantation Horse movement. No wonder he did so well in dressage, his taproot ancestors were bred to have beautiful gaits and great athleticism, and these traits were not smothered over time, instead they were kept dominant by the continual and extreme refocusing (inbreeding) that occurred generation after generation. His abundant energy level, his amazing movement, and resiliency are surely a reflection of this maternal strength.

It is interesting that the first winner of the Kentucky Derby—1875—was a Lexington RH son named Aristides; he won the race easily in 2:37 ¾. His dam is The Greek Slave, who is also the twelfth dam of Keen.

_____

Louise Robson

Louise Robson is a current Thoroughbred trainer and dressage competitor using OTTBs with great success. It is highly appropriate that she is a British trainer, as she is promoting the exceptional sport traits of the breed that England developed. Louise can address some of the other arguments that have arisen on occasion against the Thoroughbred being a suitable choice for the sport of dressage. These usually begin by stating that every once and awhile a Thoroughbred may do well in dressage—but it would be an 'odd' one—that is, untypical. I am not a dressage enthusiast myself, although I think all horses should be trained in basic dressage (and all riders also), and it is an intrinsic portion of my own favorite sport of combined training (eventing). We are never too old to learn, and while searching for other examples of Thoroughbreds that do well in dressage I was enchanted by the work done by Louise Robson in England. She takes OTTBs (Off the Track Thoroughbreds) and retrains them for dressage, and wins on them—consistently. She has established a business based on retraining OTTBs for dressage.

> "A stable dedicated to the retraining of ex-racehorses from the racetrack to the dressage arena" (www.thoroughbreddressage.com).

Louise has regularly demonstrated that the ability to excel in dressage is in many Thoroughbreds. She has a stable full of OTTBs in various stages of retraining and competition, and she, along with other gifted riders/trainers, have what they call "Team Thoroughbred"—a group of them that now compete in open competitions (that means against those expensive warmbloods) and they give them a real challenge, winning their share of top honors.

With fifteen years behind her of retraining Thoroughbreds for dressage I thought it would be valuable if Louise would share with us why she prefers to use Thoroughbreds instead of warmbloods for dressage, and this is what she said:

> "I have always found the Thoroughbred to be a very sensitive creature in terms of riding and daily life. My mum described them to me as an onion. They have many layers, but unlike most horses they are missing the first two layers so are sensitive to everything. In everything that I do with my Thoroughbreds I always have this in mind.

> "They are receptive to education and work and most thrive on it. They are intelligent creatures that learn and understand new things very quickly, especially when the correct foundations of training are in place to start with. Due to their high sensitivity you, as a rider, can ride in an effective yet quiet way, one typical of classical riding. They are on the aid, on the seat and still have the desire to move forward. They may find things such as sitting behind a little more difficult than the warmbloods, mainly because their conformation does not allow for it; however, their trainability and quick understanding means that you can train them to do so. Once in the correct frame and achieve thoroughness the Thoroughbred is a truly elegant horse, one typical of Dressage in the 1950's. They are graceful and make the work look effortless."

KATHLEEN H. KIRSAN

Louise had retired her first dressage star Mr. Glum in 2012, and one of those she is bringing along now is a six-year-old OTTB named Quadrille. This horse, as well as her first star, was originally owned by the Queen of England. Quadrille is not just a cull off the track either, for he was a stakes winner at Ascot, but now with only 1½ years of training he has not only won his first class at Novice level, but he has been evaluated as a "Grand Prix" prospect. He possesses both top movement and a wonderful mind.

Quadrille's breeding is typical of what we will find now in the top racehorses in England. Since the second influx of American Thoroughbreds (see Chapters 19 and 20) the English Thoroughbred has not only French and English lines, but a significant amount of the American product, but when I examined Quadrille's pedigree I was really astonished at what his chief potency turns out to be.

Quadrille is 4 x4 to Northern Dancer sons—in the international Thoroughbred this is a very common design. But where this gelding differs is in the notable reinforcement I find behind this pattern, it turns out that his true power is a little further back. Northern Dancer's dam Natalma (see Chapter 21) is one of the great modern reservoirs of Lexington RH blood, and we find her here not just in her famous son Northern Dancer, but she is also present twice through daughters. Building up lines of significant mares is one of the strongest practices we can do for our success, and here we find Natalma is 5x5x5x5—sex-balanced, as the other two lines of her are daughters—this makes what is called a filly factor, and this gives us the full genetic spectrum of Natalma in multiples. But that is not the end of it, for Natalma's sire is Native Dancer, and her dam is Almahmoud (both genetic giants), and we find that Native Dancer is not just present through the four lines of this daughter, but also from two of his sons (colt factor- see Appendix B), which puts Native Dancer 6x6x5x5x6x6—sex-balanced. But there is even more potency as close to its power is his dam Almahmoud who is also reinforced with another daughter. These are the most powerful designs in the pedigree because they are reinforced again and again. This design already had proven its excellence as it is the leading dominance not only in the sire Danehill Dancer, but also in the dam-sire Machiavellian—both top-of-the-line Thoroughbreds. I don't know about you, but I never considered that Natalma, Almahmoud and Native Dancer could be considered dressage lines, but I guess I will have to rethink things because there they are in dominance.

Criticism of US Army Remount Horses

US Army Remount Horses—Captain Tuttle and Olympic on left received the individual bronze medal, and the entire team received the team bronze medal in Dressage, 1932 Olympics— a Army archive photo.

When I was researching some of this material on the internet, I came across some articles written on the US Army Equestrian Team, which were critiquing the American Remount program and their performance in the Olympics. The thrust of one of these articles was that the Remount horses were really inferior to those of Europe. For instance, the writer said that our wonderful wins of five equestrian medals in the 1932 Olympics were only possible because so few other countries traveled here to participate because of the Depression. The slant was that the European Teams had better horses, so they would have won if more of them could have got here. First of all, many of them did make the trip. Second, if our team was so deficient than why was the humbly bred Jenny Camp able to repeat her silver medal win again in 1936?

In every Olympics there are some teams that can't make it—disaster, government overthrows, wars, depressions and so on. For instance both of the equestrian Olympics in the 1920s were poorly attended for a good reason. World War I had decimated the European horse populations along with their talented riders—it was a cavalry war, and those countries that participated did so with their equine resources, and therefore lost a great portion of their product, horses and riders—remember, until 1950 all Olympic teams were cavalry. By the way, America was involved with both our

Captain Hiram Tuttle with his Olympic string, horses left to right: Vast, Olympic (Individual Bronze), and Si Murray. —army archive picture

men and our horses in a big way in that one too, supporting our allies France and England—so our equine resources were wasted also. Sweden however, which dominated Olympic dressage in the decade after WWI, was a 'neutral' country during that war, so they did not expend their equine resources, nor their best riders, therefore their competition for the medals in those two Olympics was greatly reduced. Does this make their medals invalid? Or would you rate the Swedish Horse as lesser horses because the events were poorly filled out?

Seeing dressage is our focus in this chapter it might interest you to know that when our Remount fielded a dressage team—which was not until 1932—gosh darn if we didn't win a team bronze medal first time out. On our team Captain Hiram Tuttle riding his Remount-bred Olympia came in third in the individual competitions, therefore they too won a bronze medal. In the 1936 Olympics our dressage team placed ninth.

There were no 1940 or 1944 Olympics (World War II), but in 1948 our team took the silver medal in dressage—so how do you explain that?

Colonel Earl F. Thompson is seen here jumping one of the American Remount's horses, Masquerader, over a substantial obstacle at the inter-American Horse Show on October 26, 1935. Obviously this horse can fly—certainly an international level equine. Colonel Thomson was one of America's top equestrians; in his career he won five Olympic medals, for instance it was he who rode Jenny Camp to her two individual Olympic silver medals in eventing in 1932 and 1936, and he also racked up team gold in Eventing in 1932 and 1948, plus team silver in dressage in 1948. —photo by Harris & Ewing from the Library of Congress collection

Let me put the Army Remount breeding program into focus for you. We just examined the dressage superstar Keen's pedigree. We saw that his strongest genetic elements traveled up the dam-side. His second dam-sire War Bam was a Thoroughbred that stood for our Remount and Keen's strongest dominance as we saw involves Abe Frank, the sire of Farmer Jim---he was also the Thoroughbred that sired the greatest sprinting filly in the world (Pan Zareta—better even than Mumtaz Mahal) and surprise, he too was an Army Remount stallion. All our TB stallions that stood in our Remount program were bred by our private citizens and donated to the Army's use.

When the breeding and the fielding of our Olympic equestrian team was turned over to civilians, America repeated our win of five equestrian medals in the 1984 and the 2004 Olympics. What excuse was there for this? America has never been a sideline competitor; whether through her Remount or by her civilians she has always fielded excellent teams and always provides competition for the other contenders. Since World War II, the equestrian Olympics have returned to the amateur citizen—at least in this country. However, we are playing today against entries from countries that still have a government-subsidized and -structured equine product—is this playing field level? Take away those countries' government support and promotion, the training they provide, the state studs, the subsidies for the breeder, the structured program to bring their horses and riders along, and the full marketing campaign their government provides, and then make them handle it all as individuals and what would happen then?

Americans, shake off the sense of inferiority you are carrying around—you have the greatest riders, breeders, owners, and horses in the world; they are able to compete **individually** against the full might of foreign governments and prevail.

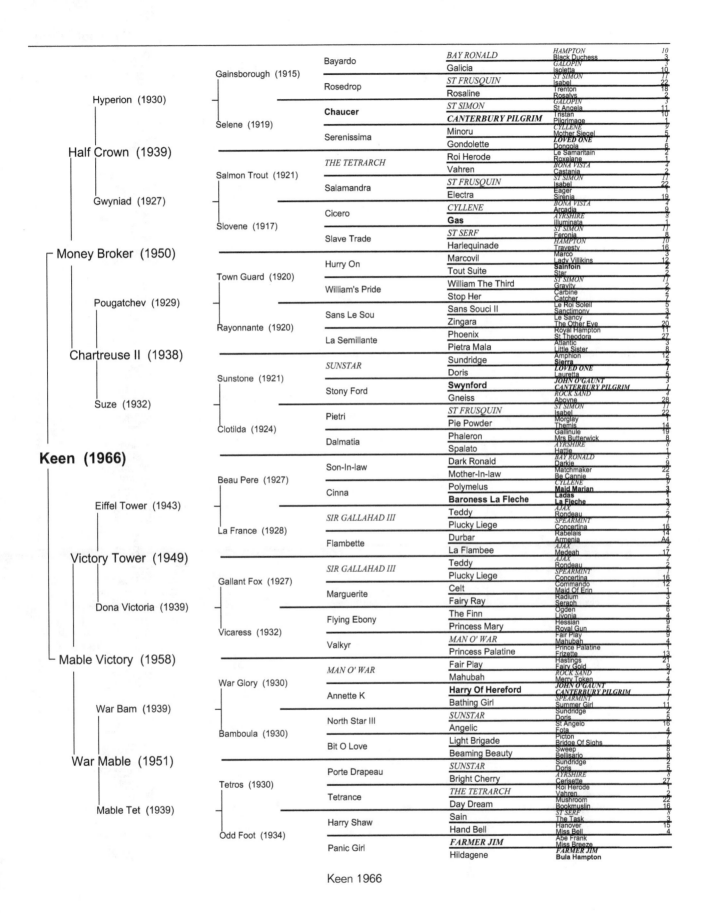

Keen 1966

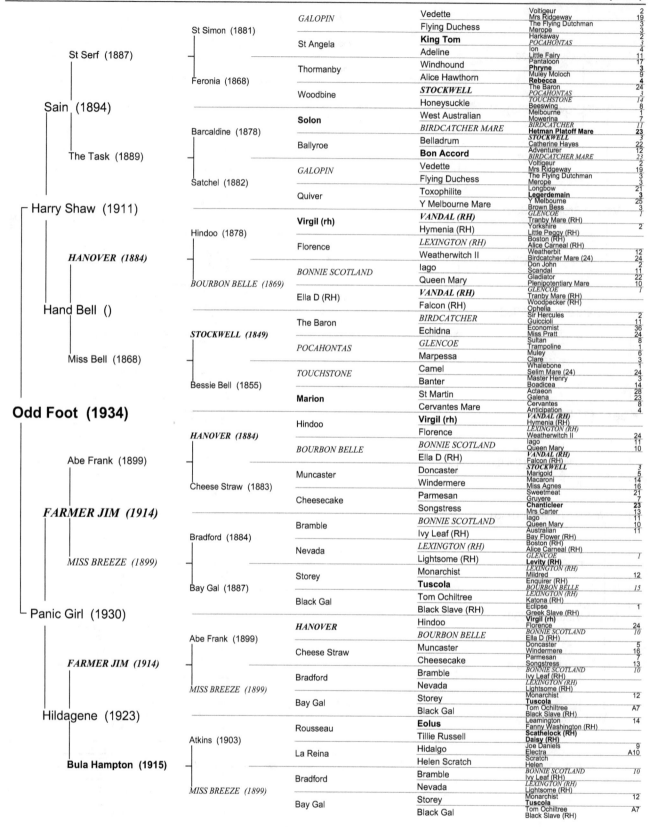

Odd Foot 1934

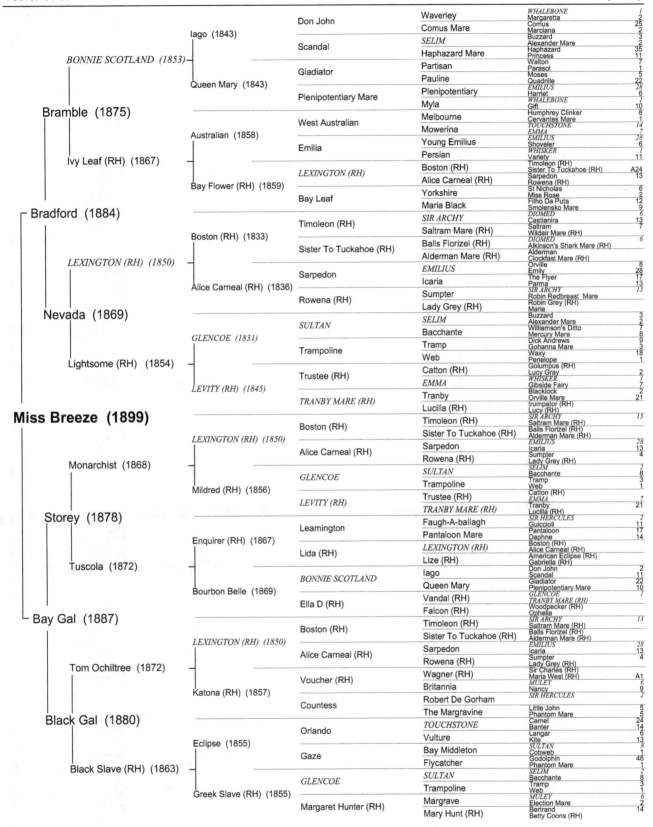

Miss Breeze 1897

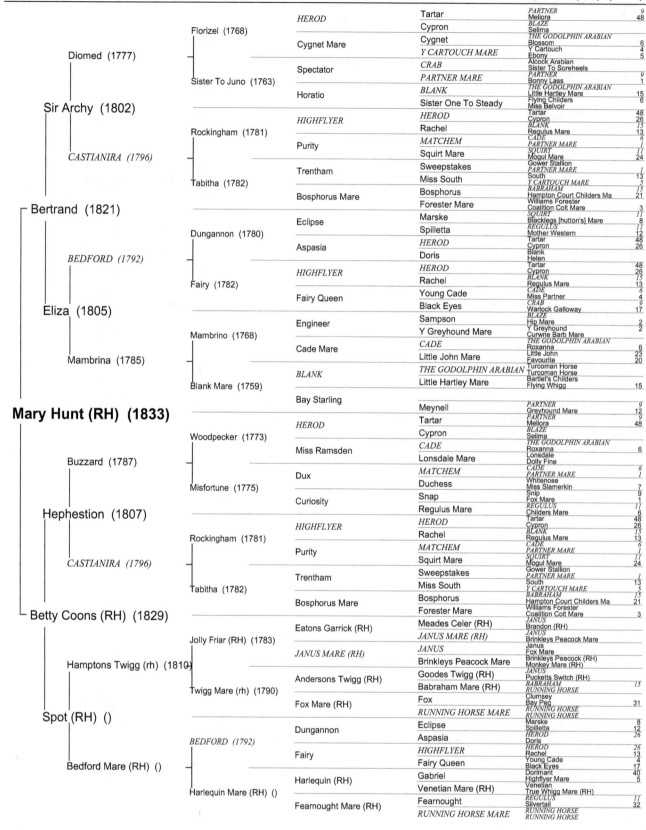

			Tartar	*PARTNER*	9
		HEROD		Meliora	48
	Florizel (1768)		Cypron	*BLAZE*	
				Selima	
		Cygnet Mare	Cygnet	*THE GODOLPHIN ARABIAN*	
				Blossom	6
Diomed (1777)			*Y CARTOUCH MARE*	Y Cartouch	4
				Ebony	5
		Spectator	*CRAB*	Alcock Arabian	
				Sister To Soreheels	
	Sister To Juno (1763)		*PARTNER MARE*	*PARTNER*	9
				Bonny Lass	1
		Horatio	*BLANK*	*THE GODOLPHIN ARABIAN*	
				Little Hartley Mare	15
Sir Archy (1802)			Sister One To Steady	Flying Childers	6
				Miss Belvoir	
			HEROD	Tartar	48
		HIGHFLYER		Cypron	26
	Rockingham (1781)		Rachel	*BLANK*	15
				Regulus Mare	13
		Purity	*MATCHEM*	*CADE*	6
				PARTNER MARE	1
CASTIANIRA (1796)			Squirt Mare	*SQUIRT*	11
				Mogul Mare	24
		Trentham	Sweepstakes	Gower Stallion	
				PARTNER MARE	1
	Tabitha (1782)		Miss South	South	13
				Y CARTOUCH MARE	5
		Bosphorus Mare	Bosphorus	*BABRAHAM*	15
Bertrand (1821)				Hampton Court Childers Ma	21
			Forester Mare	Williams Forester	
				Coalition Colt Mare	3
		Eclipse	Marske	*SQUIRT*	11
				Blacklegs [hutton's] Mare	8
	Dungannon (1780)		Spilletta	*REGULUS*	11
				Mother Western	12
		Aspasia	*HEROD*	Tartar	48
BEDFORD (1792)				Cypron	26
			Doris	Blank	
				Helen	
		HIGHFLYER	*HEROD*	Tartar	48
	Fairy (1782)			Cypron	26
			Rachel	*BLANK*	15
				Regulus Mare	13
Eliza (1805)		Fairy Queen	Young Cade	*CADE*	6
				Miss Partner	4
			Black Eyes	*CRAB*	9
				Warlock Galloway	17
		Engineer	Sampson	*BLAZE*	
				Hip Mare	2
	Mambrino (1768)		Y Greyhound Mare	Y Greyhound	2
				Curwne Barb Mare	
		Cade Mare	*CADE*	*THE GODOLPHIN ARABIAN*	
				Roxanna	6
Mambrina (1785)			Little John Mare	Little John	23
				Favourite	20
		BLANK	*THE GODOLPHIN ARABIAN*	Turcoman Horse	
	Blank Mare (1759)			Turcoman Horse	
			Little Hartley Mare	Bartlet's Childers	
				Flying Whigg	15
		Bay Starling			

				PARTNER	9
Mary Hunt (RH) (1833)			Meynell	Greyhound Mare	12
		HEROD	Tartar	*PARTNER*	9
	Woodpecker (1773)			Meliora	48
			Cypron	*BLAZE*	
				Selima	
		Miss Ramsden	*CADE*	*THE GODOLPHIN ARABIAN*	
				Roxanna	6
Buzzard (1787)			Lonsdale Mare	Lonsdale	
				Dolly Fine	
		Dux	*MATCHEM*	*CADE*	6
				PARTNER MARE	1
	Misfortune (1775)		Duchess	Whitenose	
				Miss Slamerkin	7
		Curiosity	Snap	Snip	9
				Fox Mare	1
Hephestion (1807)			Regulus Mare	*REGULUS*	11
				Childers Mare	6
		HIGHFLYER	*HEROD*	Tartar	48
	Rockingham (1781)			Cypron	26
			Rachel	*BLANK*	15
				Regulus Mare	13
		Purity	*MATCHEM*	*CADE*	6
				PARTNER MARE	1
CASTIANIRA (1796)			Squirt Mare	*SQUIRT*	11
				Mogul Mare	24
		Trentham	Sweepstakes	Gower Stallion	
				PARTNER MARE	1
	Tabitha (1782)		Miss South	South	13
				Y CARTOUCH MARE	5
		Bosphorus Mare	Bosphorus	*BABRAHAM*	15
				Hampton Court Childers Ma	21
			Forester Mare	Williams Forester	
				Coalition Colt Mare	3
		Eatons Garrick (RH)	Meades Celer (RH)	*JANUS*	
				Brandon (RH)	
	Jolly Friar (RH) (1783)		*JANUS MARE (RH)*	*JANUS*	
				Brinkleys Peacock Mare	
		JANUS MARE (RH)	*JANUS*	Janus	
				Fox Mare	
Betty Coons (RH) (1829)			Brinkleys Peacock Mare	Brinkleys Peacock (RH)	
				Monkey Mare (RH)	
		Andersons Twigg (RH)	Goodes Twigg (RH)	*JANUS*	
				Pucketts Switch (RH)	
	Twigg Mare (rh) (1790)		Babraham Mare (RH)	*BABRAHAM*	15
				RUNNING HORSE	
		Fox Mare (RH)	Fox	Clumsey	
Hamptons Twigg (rh) (1810)				Bay Peg	31
			RUNNING HORSE MARE	*RUNNING HORSE*	
				RUNNING HORSE	
		Dungannon	Eclipse	Marske	8
				Spilletta	12
			Aspasia	*HEROD*	26
Spot (RH) ()				Doris	
	BEDFORD (1792)	Fairy	*HIGHFLYER*	*HEROD*	26
				Rachel	13
			Fairy Queen	Young Cade	4
				Black Eyes	17
		Harlequin (RH)	Gabriel	Dorimant	40
				Highflyer Mare	5
Bedford Mare (RH) ()			Venetian Mare (RH)	Venetian	
				True Whigg Mare (RH)	
	Harlequin Mare (RH) ()	Fearnought Mare (RH)	Fearnought	*REGULUS*	11
				Silvertail	32
			RUNNING HORSE MARE	*RUNNING HORSE*	
				RUNNING HORSE	

Mary Hunt RH 1833

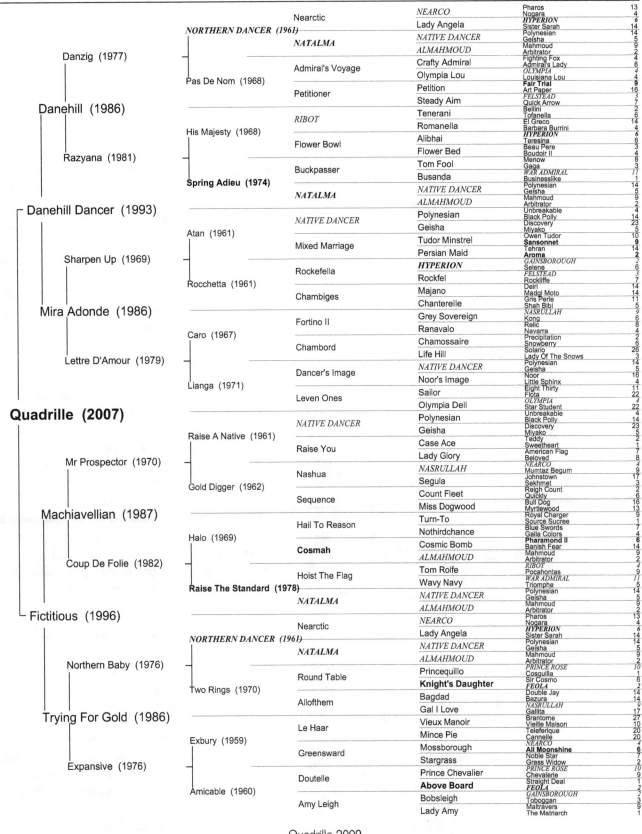

			Nearctic	*NEARCO*	Pharos 13
					Nogara 4
		NORTHERN DANCER (1961)		Lady Angela	*HYPERION* 6
					Sister Sarah 14
			NATALMA	*NATIVE DANCER*	Polynesian 14
	Danzig (1977)				Geisha 5
				ALMAHMOUD	Mahmoud 9
					Arbitrator 2
		Pas De Nom (1968)	Admiral's Voyage	Crafty Admiral	Fighting Fox 4
					Admiral's Lady 8
				Olympia Lou	*OLYMPIA* 4
Danehill (1986)					Louisiana Lou 4
			Petitioner	Petition	**Fair Trial** 9
					Art Paper 16
				Steady Aim	*FELSTEAD* 7
					Quick Arrow 5
			RIBOT	Tenerani	Bellini 2
	Razyana (1981)				Tofanella 5
		His Majesty (1968)		Romanella	El Greco 14
					Barbara Burrini 4
			Flower Bowl	Alibhai	*HYPERION* 6
					Teresina 6
				Flower Bed	Beau Pere 3
Danehill Dancer (1993)					Boudoir II 4
			Buckpasser	Tom Fool	Menow 8
					Gaga 3
				Busanda	**WAR ADMIRAL** 11
		Spring Adieu (1974)			Businesslike 1
			NATALMA	*NATIVE DANCER*	Polynesian 14
					Geisha 5
				ALMAHMOUD	Mahmoud 9
					Arbitrator 2
			NATIVE DANCER	Polynesian	Unbreakable 4
					Black Polly 14
		Atan (1961)		Geisha	Discovery 23
					Miyako 5
			Mixed Marriage	Tudor Minstrel	Owen Tudor 10
	Sharpen Up (1969)				Sansonnet 9
				Persian Maid	Tehran 14
					Aroma 2
			Rockefella	*HYPERION*	*GAINSBOROUGH* 2
					Selene 6
		Rocchetta (1961)		Rockfel	*FELSTEAD* 3
					Rockliffe 7
			Chambiges	Majano	Deiri 14
Mira Adonde (1986)					Madqi Moto 14
				Chanterelle	Gris Perle 11
					Shah Bibi 5
			Fortino II	Grey Sovereign	*NASRULLAH* 6
					Kong 6
		Caro (1967)		Ranavalo	Relic 8
					Navarra 4
			Chambord	Chamossaire	Precipitation 2
	Lettre D'Amour (1979)				Snowberry 6
				Life Hill	Solario 26
					Lady Of The Snows 3
			Dancer's Image	*NATIVE DANCER*	Polynesian 14
					Geisha 5
		Lianga (1971)		Noor's Image	Noor 16
					Little Sphinx 4
			Leven Ones	Sailor	Eight Thirty 11
					Flota 22
				Olympia Dell	*OLYMPIA* 4
Quadrille (2007)					Star Student 22
			NATIVE DANCER	Polynesian	Unbreakable 4
					Black Polly 14
		Raise A Native (1961)		Geisha	Discovery 23
					Miyako 5
			Raise You	Case Ace	Teddy 2
	Mr Prospector (1970)				Sweetheart 1
				Lady Glory	American Flag 7
					Beloved 8
			Nashua	*NASRULLAH*	*NEARCO* 4
					Mumtaz Begum 9
		Gold Digger (1962)		Segula	Johnstown 17
					Sekhmet 3
			Sequence	Count Fleet	Reigh Count 2
					Quickly 6
Machiavellian (1987)				Miss Dogwood	Bull Dog 16
					Myrtlewood 13
			Hail To Reason	Turn-To	Royal Charger 9
					Source Sucree 9
		Halo (1969)		Nothirdchance	Blue Swords 7
					Galla Colors 4
			Cosmah	Cosmic Bomb	**Pharamond II** 6
	Coup De Folie (1982)				Banish Fear 14
				ALMAHMOUD	Mahmoud 9
					Arbitrator 2
			Hoist The Flag	Tom Rolfe	*RIBOT* 4
					Pocahontas 11
		Raise The Standard (1978)		Wavy Navy	*WAR ADMIRAL* 9
					Triomphe 5
			NATALMA	*NATIVE DANCER*	Polynesian 14
					Geisha 5
				ALMAHMOUD	Mahmoud 9
					Arbitrator 2
Fictitious (1996)			Nearctic	*NEARCO*	Pharos 13
					Nogara 4
		NORTHERN DANCER (1961)		Lady Angela	*HYPERION* 6
					Sister Sarah 14
			NATALMA	*NATIVE DANCER*	Polynesian 14
					Geisha 5
	Northern Baby (1976)			*ALMAHMOUD*	Mahmoud 9
					Arbitrator 2
		Two Rings (1970)	Round Table	Princequillo	*PRINCE ROSE* 10
					Cosquilla 1
				Knight's Daughter	Sir Cosmo 6
					FEOLA 2
			Allofthem	Bagdad	Double Jay 14
					Bazura 14
				Gal I Love	*NASRULLAH* 4
Trying For Gold (1986)					Gallita 17
			Le Haar	Vieux Manoir	Brantome 27
					Vieille Maison 10
		Exbury (1959)		Mince Pie	Teleferique 20
					Cannelle 20
			Greensward	Mossborough	*NEARCO* 4
					All Moonshine 6
	Expansive (1976)			Stargrass	Noble Star 7
					Grass Widow 2
		Amicable (1960)	Doutelle	Prince Chevalier	*PRINCE ROSE* 10
					Chevalerie 9
				Above Board	Straight Deal 1
					FEOLA 2
			Amy Leigh	Bobsleigh	*GAINSBOROUGH* 2
					Toboggan 3
				Lady Amy	Maltravers 9
					The Matriarch 1

Quadrille 2009

Chapter 32

Do American Show Jump Lines Exist?

If you read and believe what you find on the internet nowadays, you would have to say the answer to my question—"Do American show jump lines exists?" —is NO. I am looking right at a print out from a respected TB information site, and the article is on 'the' Thoroughbred show jumper sire lines. They list three main ones: Le Sancy from France (we are familiar with Roi Herode and his son The Tetrarch), the Marco line—warmblood breeders know this line through Cottage Son, then there is the Prince Chevalier—this one surprised me, and then it annoyed me when I discovered the writer inaccurately credited the talent of our American superstar Gem Twist to this line. In the body of the article they mention Orange Peel and Furioso of course. But then there is another more comprehensive article on this same site that writes about "…the most important thoroughbreds who have shaped the modern showjumper;" this one is by the repected equine writer Andreas Haberbeck; both of these articles are posted on the tbheritage.com website, a beautifully presented and valuable resource for the Thoroughbred enthusiast—this is a site I personally value and refer to quite often. This second article goes into much more detail and names the predominant show jumper lines as: Orange Peel, Alme, Furioso, Ultimate, Fra Diavolo, Rantzau, Corde la Bryere, Cottage Son, Marlon, Anblick, Uppercut, Lucky Boy, Der Lowe, and Pluchino.

Untouchable and Kathy Kusner clearing a jump in Holland, this OTTB is jumping on the American lines of Man O'War, Domino, and Hamburg. — photo courtesy of USET

But I ask you Americans where is Fair Play? His line is every bit as, and probably more successful, than those promoted lines listed in the article; he produced the highest quality steeplechase, timber jumpers, and show jumpers on a regular basis, and his sons Man O' War, Chance Play, and Display have continued right on with this tradition, as have their descendants, and are still in our day a rich and reliable resource of jumper talent. The article is about sire-lines, so how can they dismiss Fair Play's massive line—tail-male—to such greats as Annapolis, Neji, War Admiral, War Glory, Great War, Battleship, and Holystone, as well as in a series of winning international jumpers (see Chapters 33 and 34)?

How about the Domino line—have you ever seen it even mentioned in regard to top show jumpers? Black Toney or Blue Larkspur for instance? Does Bold Minstrel ring a bell? How about Idle Dice—he won thirty-one Grand Prix and was still jumping at age twenty-one?

You will find part of the answer in the article construction, as it is divided by studbook—European studbook, that is, warmbloods, so it covers the Selle Francais, the Holstein, Anglo-Arab, and the Hanover-Westphalen. Now a few American show jumping superstars are wedged into the last paragraph: Good Twist, Gem Twist, and Riveria Wonder; however, it seems they are only there to call attention to the French line of Bonne Nuit, which of course is where the credit is given for the amazing career of these international champions.

I covered this issue briefly in my web article, "Hall of Fame Show Jumping Bloodlines" (see Appendix E), but if we want to be successful breeders of show jumpers in this country we better learn what really powers the good jumpers and not rely on our European friends instructing us, because obviously they are unaware of our bloodlines, and of course they are only going to promote their own product anyway.

So let's visit some of these Hall of Famers again and see if all the top jumping lines really reside in Europe. Gem Twist 1979—this is the horse whose jump talent is credited to Prince Chevalier and to Bonne Nuit in the Internet articles (above), and indeed, his career is outstanding: winner of the individual and team silvers at the 1988 Seoul Olympics, and he won the Grand Prix Association's "Horse of the Year" title three times—1987, 1989, 1992, plus he has been inducted in the Show Jumper Hall of Fame. No wonder the Europeans want the endorsement for this horse, he is one of the greatest show jumpers anywhere, anytime.

This horse is also an oddity as he is the third in a line that were all top international jumpers; a very rare occurrence because most jumpers in our country are gelded. Gem Twist's grandsire, the stallion New Twist—a top International jumper and sire of International level jumpers, he is 1x2 to a son (Bonne Nuit) and a daughter (Brave Bonne) of the mare Bonne Cause, and looking at her pedigree to see what powers her we find it is the sex-balanced lines of The Flying Dutchman 3x4 that rules her genetics, who in-turn is 5x4 to the full brothers Don Quixote and Alexander, by Eclipse out of Grecian Princess—these are English Thoroughbred lines of excellence. Well, you can't do much better than Eclipse, and there is also a buildup of the foundation sire Partner behind those siblings as well, so the mare Bonne Cause is one of the potencies in this star. New Twists dam-sire is Great War, a son of Man O' War who has a double of Maggie B. B. RH on his dam-line, so another significant buildup of a mare, and he is found repeatedly in the great jumpers of North America. Also his second dam-sire is Valorous—that Domino-line stallion we discussed in Chapter 30. That means then that the Bonnie Cause double, powered by The Flying Dutchman, plus Man O' War/Maggie B. B. RH/Domino—our warehouses of Lexington RH/Boston RH et al are the essence of this top jumper and sire. The build up of mare lines has been proven statistically to be a factor in both a stallion and a mare's breeding success. In New Twist's case we see this plainly—he is a potent carrier of both Bonne Cause and Maggie B.B. RH.

[Note: In this country certain top breeders of flat racers and steeplechasers also turned their talents to producing show jumpers and fielded many notable horses into the international arena. In the next chapter we will visit one of these (Marion DuPont Scott) and her Montpelier Farm operation; however Great War, the dam-sire of New Twist, was a prolific sire of international show jumpers for his owners the Whitneys (Colonel and Liz), celebrated breeders and competitors (see photo in Chapter 29).]

Now New Twist's son Good Twist, also a stallion and top show jumper, brought in a double of The Tetrarch, making Roi Herode sons 3x4x5, so now we finally have a dominance showing in the Le Sancy line, but only through sons. I have found the line of Roi Herode and his great son The Tetrarch are a constant in the best sport horses, and even though this is not an American line, it is one to welcome in our sport recipes. They nick dynamically with our line of Fair Play, because when brought together they provide a buildup of the important mare Clemence as The Tetrarch has her full sibling's offspring Clementina/Tadcaster present through son lines, while Fair Play is out of Fairy Gold who is a Tadcaster daughter, thereby creating a dynamic sex-balance when they are combined. Clementina and Tadcaster are by Doncaster out of the important mare Clemence. So here in this pedigree is brought together the multiple sex-balanced lines of Clemence, creating once again a strong filly factor (see Appendix B). This is three lines of yet another significant mare—so Clemence/Bonne Cause/Maggie B.B. RH are all mare lines in dominance—very unusual.

So what happened when Good Twist was mated with Coldly Noble to produce the legendary Gem Twist? He is clearly the best this line produced—a star among superstars. What we see then is that the genetic reinforcement came from two additional lines of Man O' War to add to the Great War line, plus three sex-balanced lines of Black Toney, including one on the dam-line, and another inbred line of Maggie B. B. RH in Whisk Broom II through full sisters Audience/Martha Gorman. So then, on top of the already vigorous genetics of Good Twist, came a particularly strong saturation of our Heroic Era genes. This makes a total in Gem Twist of two lines of Marco, six of Le Sancy, one of Prince Chevalier, one of Bonne Nuit, but on the other hand we see there are seven of Domino, five of Hastings, and three of his son Fair Play, and then there are forty-three lines of Lexington RH in the background that have been refocused to the front. Not quite the Prince Chevalier and Bonne Nuit dominance that was claimed is it?

Gem Twist, an American superstar, seen jumping here for double silver, powered by the great American sport lines of Fair Play, Domino, and Whisk Broom II, with forty-three lines of Lexington RH in his background. —this photographic masterpiece is by Tish Quirk, used by permission

KATHLEEN H. KIRSAN

One of the most important lessons we can learn is that our American sport lines are not the same as Europe's, and because of the Jersey Act they will not be found there in great quantities in the European stars of the 1900-1980s, but that fact does not make them any less valuable, and we must clearly examine our own winners to determine what really is powering them, rather than relying on slanted reasoning brought to us by the European Warmblood point of view. For us to ignore our own top quality resource is the height of stupidity.

Let's look then at what is powering the Hall of Famer Idle Dice 1962. An OTTB with a record that testifies not only of excellence in sport, but of stamina, soundness, and vitality—as this star, Idle Dice, was still competing and winning at age twenty-one—sound. He won a total of thirty-one Grand Prix; the last three were when he was twenty-one. He won the American Gold Cup three times and the Presidents Cup twice.

> "Even as a green hunter, Idle Dice appeared to have enormous scope and jumped exceptionally cleanly, and he quickly matured into the best all-around jumper I've ever sat on. He's got great strength, along with great balance and agility, and a marvelous attitude. He's just like a businessman in his attitude toward jumping—he knows his job and he does it. I don't think I've ever seen a horse that could *consistently* make the turns he can down to big oxers, or jump walls around the seven-foot level week after week. He is truly a super athlete"(Rodney Jenkins—Idle Dice's rider, from *Great Horses of the United States Equestrian Team*— used by permission of the USET).

We want whatever is powering this superb athlete and sound horse in our herds. We see his sire-line is Phalaris, a great source of athletic talent, but for breeding jumpers it is a prudent practice if you make sure your Phalaris lines are bolstered with tougher lines, as it is notorious for weak front legs—not the best idea in jumpers. In Idle Dice we see he is 4x5 to Black Toney, a sound Domino line. This line is also much more dominant then it appears at quick glance. Notice Adargatis, she is the ¾ sister to La Troienne, and if you remember from Chapter 22, La Troienne and her ¾ sister Adargatis are a warehouse for the female Diomed lines, and Lexington RH is the warehouse for the male Diomed lines. When La Troienne and Adaragatis lines are bred to those containing Domino, who is inbred to Lexington RH, a powerful genetic event occurs. Further, Black Toney's dam Belgravia meets her brother Broomstick here 5x7, and Halcyon is actually a ¾ brother to Black Toney, putting them 4x4x7. This is dominance. There is also an interesting buildup of Hastings (we saw this in Holy Bull also in Chapter 24) through his son Fair Play and daughter Pyramid 7x5x4. In Idle Dice there are no lines of Le Sancy, none of Marco, none of Prince Chevalier, but there are thirty-one lines of Lexington RH, brought right to the front from this wonderful Black Toney/Halcyon (Domino) focus.

Another Hall of Fame jumper is Sinjon 1951; he is also an OTTB, who was retrained for the jumper discipline and excelled. In 1957 he was loaned to the USET. Sinjon was on nineteen winning Nations Cup teams and while placing fourth in the 1960 Olympics, he helped his team earn a silver medal, then a team gold in the 1963 Pan Am Games, and he earned multiple international Grand Prix titles in England and Canada, as well as at home.

> "Johnny's was not an easy temperament, but he was extraordinarily honest and brave; he hated to hit fences, yet would never think of stopping, even when fences were raised right to the limit of his ability. He had a twinkle in his eye and a pink nose, a peculiar habit to several outstanding jumpers I have known—he crossed his hind legs in jumping. In speed classes he was like a rabbit—his great agility and promptness, coupled with his desire to jump cleanly even when he was going fast, made him a consistent winner against the clock" (George Morris, quotation found in *Great Horses of the United States Equestrian Team*, used by permission of the USET).

Sinjon is actually from the Le Sancy line, and here we see why this line is so prevalent: it carries Clementina—she is the full sister to Tadcaster—and he, as has been proven, is that ringer for Bend Or, a fraud that was just uncovered definitively by the geneticists Bower and Hill, which is causing us to rewrite our pedigrees (see Appendix C). This mare is a factor in the excellence of Good Twist mentioned previously, and we will find she is one of the best Thoroughbred contributions to Olympic-style sport worldwide. Clemence—who, even with her temperament issues, had to be a fantastic mare, as she is also the second dam of the great Carbine—no Doncaster this time, so there she is powering all these top sport lines with or without Doncaster. As we detailed above she is also the second dam of Fair Play, which is why these lines all go together so well; with three of the greatest bloodlines in sport in the world directly descended from her (Carbine/Fair Play/Roi Herode) we should be consciously targeting her line. Sinjon has seven lines of these full siblings 6x6x7x6x6x6x7, making a total of nine lines of the same mare: Clemence.

Sinjon's dam-sire War Glory is a ¾ brother to War Admiral, whose dam-sire is Sweep, as they are close brothers to Great War; obviously they are important jump lines of their own as they are found continually in the Olympic-style sport horses (see Gem Twist above—he is 4x5x5 to War Admiral/Great War) and they carry dominance in the full siblings Sainfoin/Sierra 4x5. His second dam, Toro Helen, brings in more Sweep—which is another sound line of the Domino/Ben Brush combination like Black Toney, plus a double of Bramble sex-balanced; his fourth dam Frizette is by Hamburg. Even with just strictly English bloodlines coming from the sire, there are still no lines of Marco, just one of Le Sancy, none of Prince Chevalier, but there is also one of Domino and one of Fair Play; significantly there are also thirteen lines of Lexington RH coming from the dam. So it is the Lexington RH/Clemence grouping powering this sport hero also.

Hall of Famer Touch of Class 1975 is a mare that more than won it all: team and individual golds in the 1984 Olympics, 1983 Nations Cup gold also, and multiple Grand Prix wins. Her genetic dominance is in the full siblings Fairway/Pharos—all son lines 4x6x5. Her sire carries a Sir Gallahad double 5x5; her dam brings in two Fair Play lines 5x6 and adds three lines of Swynford to two in the sire, making him 6x7x5x6x5. Domino is represented by his inbred son Ultimus twice. There are no lines of Marco, none of Le Sancy, none of Prince Chevalier, but there are thirty-three of Clemence (see Sinjon); there are four of Fair Play, eight of Domino, and forty-three of Lexington RH. So it is Clemence/Lexington RH again; as you can see the same bloodlines are in dominance over and over, and the American lines are strongly present.

Untouchable 1952, another OTTB who earned a position in the Hall of Fame, was owned by Benny O'Meary who rode him to several wins in jumping, but then was turned over to the USET as a mount for Kathy Kusner, and this team jumped just about everything in sight with success. Some highlights of the Kusner/Untouchable team: 1964 Grand Prix in Dublin (and repeat next year), 1964 Tokyo Olympics fourth place team, 1965 Nations Cup first place, and 1967 silver medal Pan Am Games, plus he held the American High Jump title. When the tally was done this pair had been on twelve winning Nations Cup teams, and Untouchable won individually in Belgium, England, Switzerland, Ireland, and Holland, and he even won the high jump (puissance) in Aachen, Germany.

He has a powerful pedigree, with some key full siblings groupings such as Sainfoin/Sierra, but most of his dominance is actually in American lines. The full siblings Domino/Mannie Himyar 7x7x6x6, the ¾ brothers Hamburg/Blackstock 5x6, and the ¾ brothers Friar Rock/Man O' War 4x5 are the focus points for the background dominances of thirty-four lines of Lexington RH, and nine lines of the jump transmitter Vandal RH.

So let's leave the Hall of Famers and visit a more recent star: the *Dutch Warmblood* Authentic 1995, whom Beezie Maddon rode to team gold in the 2004 Olympics, was second in the WEG in 2006, and team gold and individual Bronze in the 2008 Olympics. His sire is a registered Selle Francais, his dam is ¾ TB, and he does carry two lines of Le Sancy, eight of Marco, none of Prince Chevalier, but there are also twenty lines of Lexington RH in this 'dutch' horse. With three lines of Nearco, plus a double of Gold Bridge who is inbred to Orby, and then there is Mumtaz Mahal and a line of Fair Play, plus Bubbling Over, it appears that this sport star is being powered by his English/American background, and here you thought he was Dutch.

Authentic is a registered Dutch Warmblood, but he is 60% Thoroughbred, 30% Selle Francais, and 10% Dutch. He was registered Dutch because he was bred in Holland for a performance horse in the Dutch Warmblood Association. He can stand for us as an example of the true nature of our international sport horse breeds—for rarely are they 'purebred,' and the breed designation has more to do with a particular registry than the breed components. This has always been the toughest concept for the North American breeder to understand. However, it should not be, because this is how we have always bred our own Hunter Horse (see Chapter 28 and Appendix D and E).

One of our problems is that we have not made the intellectual leap to connect our selective breeding program of Hunter Horse to the European Warmblood fad. What we used to call 'Thudmonsters' back in the 1980s was a warmblood horse that had a large percentage of their base coach-farm stock. However, in their modern warmbloods they are generally a much lighter, more agile sport horse—that is, a true Hunter Horse model without identifying it as such, so the mystique of their breed remains in the mind of most North Americans because they fail to identify what they really are—the same type sport horse the Americans have been breeding since 1700, and winning internationally on them since the mid-1800s when we brought some of our strings to England and France, which is one hundred years longer experience in international sport breeding than our continental warmblood counterparts can brag of. Check out the National Hunt records of the British

Gold-medal Show Jumper American Team for the 2008 Olympics—Authentic ridden by Beezie Madden in the foreground and Will Simpson on Carlsson von Dach in background. — photo by Craig Maccubbin, courtesy of Wiki Commons

Isles, and you will see how often and how well our American TB and part-TB has done in competition in international non-racing sport (C.M. Prior *Half Bred Stud Book)* in France, Ireland, and England.

Well here is Authentic, and it should be plain to any breeder if they open their eyes to what he really is: a Hunter. His leading dominance is the closely related Tanagra (SF)/Artilier (SF) 4x4—carrying Furioso TB and Jus de Pomme ½ TB close up. This configuration sets the type of Authentic and provides a lot of his sport ability. He carries a triple of Nearco in his dam of sons 5x5x4, and this Nearco sex-imbalance is tempered by the Jus de Pomme double through daughters 5x6 and two daughter lines of Gold Bridge 6x6. It is also interesting to see a double of Plassy sex-balanced 5x6; this lovely Thoroughbred is one who was seized by the Nazis in WWII and was never seen again, so it is nice to see a few

lines of him here. Authentic was a top international level jumper. It is the Hunter model horse—based on racehorse genetics—that is the premier design for success in our international sports.

The Thoroughbred is the constant in show jumping stars—even those bred in other countries, and not only do the American lines in show jumping exist, the fact is that the American lines excel at this sport (read more on jumper and eventing bloodlines in the next two chapters) and have been winning internationally for one hundred forty plus years.

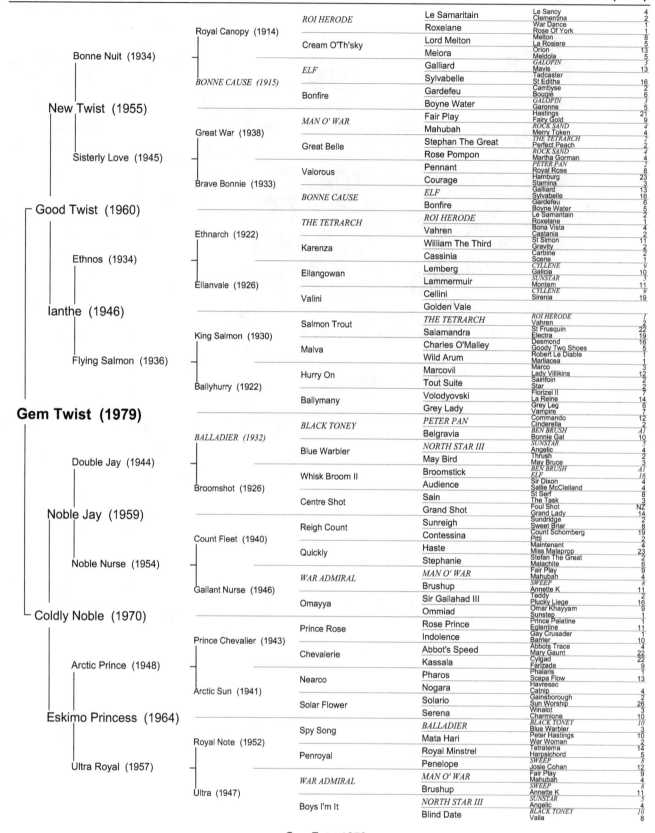

The pedigree of **Gem Twist (1979)** as charted:

- Bonne Nuit (1934)
- New Twist (1955)
- Sisterly Love (1945)
- Good Twist (1960)
- Ethnos (1934)
- Ianthe (1946)
- Flying Salmon (1936)
- **Gem Twist (1979)**
- Double Jay (1944)
- Noble Jay (1959)
- Noble Nurse (1954)
- Coldly Noble (1970)
- Arctic Prince (1948)
- Eskimo Princess (1964)
- Ultra Royal (1957)

Sire/Dam line			Family no.
Royal Canopy (1914)	*ROI HERODE*	Le Samaritain — Le Sancy	4 / Clementina 2
		Roxelane — War Dance	1 / Rose Of York 1
	Cream O'Th'sky	Lord Melton — Melton	8 / La Rosiere 5
		Melora — Orion	13 / Meldola 5
BONNE CAUSE (1915)	*ELF*	Galliard — *GALOPIN*	3 / Mavis 13
		Sylvabelle — Tadcaster / St Editha	16
	Bonfire	Gardefeu — Cambyse 2 / Bougie	6
		Boyne Water — *GALOPIN* 3 / Garonne	5
Great War (1938)	*MAN O' WAR*	Fair Play — Hastings 21 / Fairy Gold	9
		Mahubah — *ROCK SAND* 4 / Merry Token	4
	Great Belle	Stephan The Great — *THE TETRARCH* 2 / Perfect Peach	2
		Rose Pompon — *ROCK SAND* 4 / Martha Gorman	4
Brave Bonnie (1933)	Valorous	Pennant — *PETER PAN* 2 / Royal Rose	8
		Courage — Hamburg 23 / Stamina	3
	BONNE CAUSE	*ELF* — Galliard 13 / Sylvabelle	16
		Bonfire — Gardefeu 6 / Boyne Water	2
Ethnarch (1922)	*THE TETRARCH*	*ROI HERODE* — Le Samaritain 1 / Roxelane	1
		Vahren — Bona Vista 4 / Castania	2
	Karenza	William The Third — St Simon 11 / Gravity	2
		Cassinia — Carbine 2 / Scene	1
Ellanvale (1926)	Ellangowan	Lemberg — *CYLLENE* 9 / Galicia	10
		Lammermuir — *SUNSTAR* 5 / Montem	11
	Valini	Cellini — *CYLLENE* 9 / Sirenia	19
		Golden Vale	
King Salmon (1930)	Salmon Trout	*THE TETRARCH* — *ROI HERODE* 1 / Vahren	2
		Salamandra — St Frusquin 22 / Electra	19
	Malva	Charles O'Malley — Desmond 16 / Goody Two Shoes	5
		Wild Arum — Robert Le Diable 1 / Marliacea	1
Ballyhurry (1922)	Hurry On	Marcovil — Marco 3 / Lady Villikins	12
		Tout Suite — Sainfoin 2 / Star	2
	Ballymany	Volodyovski — Florizel II 14 / La Reine	6
		Grey Lady — Grey Leg 6 / Vampire	7
BALLADIER (1932)	*BLACK TONEY*	*PETER PAN* — Commando 12 / Cinderella	1
		Belgravia — *BEN BRUSH* A1 / Bonnie Gal	10
	Blue Warbler	*NORTH STAR III* — *SUNSTAR* 5 / Angelic	4
		May Bird — Thrush 2 / May Bruce	3
Broomshot (1926)	Whisk Broom II	Broomstick — *BEN BRUSH* A1 / *ELF*	16
		Audience — Sir Dixon 4 / Sallie McClelland	4
	Centre Shot	Sain — St Serf 8 / The Task	3
		Grand Shot — Foul Shot NZ / Grand Lady	14
Count Fleet (1940)	Reigh Count	Sunreigh — Sundridge 2 / Sweet Briar	8
		Contessina — Count Schomberg 19 / Pitti	1
	Quickly	Haste — Maintenant 4 / Miss Malaprop	23
		Stephanie — Stefan The Great 2 / Malachite	6
Gallant Nurse (1946)	*WAR ADMIRAL*	*MAN O' WAR* — Fair Play 9 / Mahubah	4
		Brushup — *SWEEP* 8 / Annette K	11
	Omayya	Sir Gallahad III — Teddy 2 / Plucky Liege	16
		Ommiad — Omar Khayyam 9 / Sunstep	1
Prince Chevalier (1943)	Prince Rose	Rose Prince — Prince Palatine 1 / Eglantine	11
		Indolence — Gay Crusader 1 / Barrier	10
	Chevalerie	Abbot's Speed — Abbots Trace 4 / Mary Gaunt	22
		Kassala — Cylgad 22 / Farizade	9
Arctic Sun (1941)	Nearco	Pharos — Phalaris 13 / Scapa Flow	
		Nogara — Havresac 4 / Catnip	2
	Solar Flower	Solario — Gainsborough 26 / Sun Worship	3
		Serena — Winalot / Charmione	10
Royal Note (1952)	Spy Song	*BALLADIER* — *BLACK TONEY* 10 / Blue Warbler	3
		Mata Hari — Peter Hastings 10 / War Woman	2
	Penroyal	Royal Minstrel — Tetratema 14 / Harpsichord	5
		Penelope — *SWEEP* 8 / Josie Cohan	12
Ultra (1947)	*WAR ADMIRAL*	*MAN O' WAR* — Fair Play 9 / Mahubah	4
		Brushup — *SWEEP* 8 / Annette K	11
	Boys I'm It	*NORTH STAR III* — *SUNSTAR* 5 / Angelic	4
		Blind Date — *BLACK TONEY* 10 / Vaila	8

Gem Twist 1979

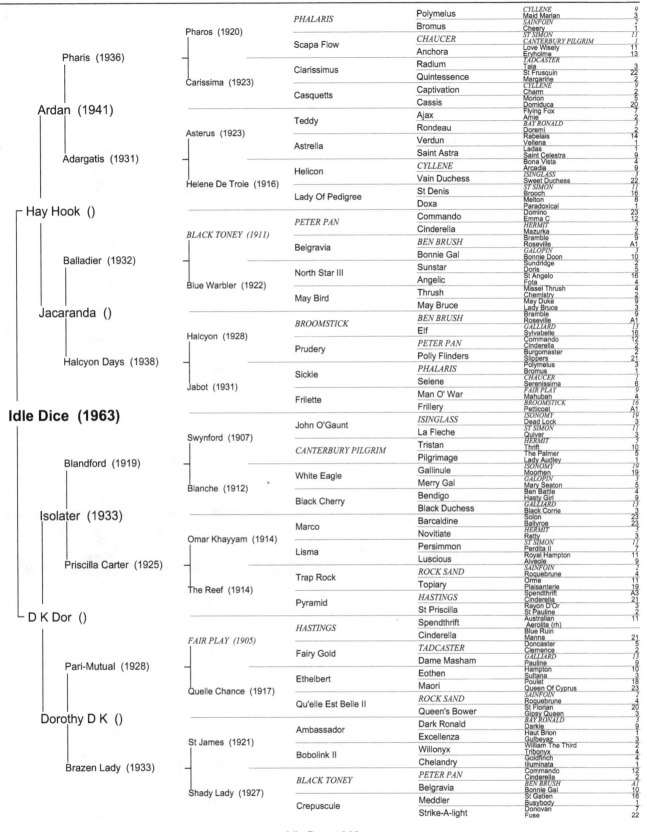

		PHALARIS	Polymelus	CYLLENE 9 / Maid Marian 3
	Pharos (1920)		Bromus	SAINFOIN 2 / Cheery 1
Pharis (1936)		Scapa Flow	CHAUCER	ST SIMON 11 / CANTERBURY PILGRIM 1
			Anchora	Love Wisely 11 / Eryholme 13
		Clarissimus	Radium	TADCASTER / Taia 3
	Carissima (1923)		Quintessence	St Frusquin 22 / Margarine 2
		Casquetts	Captivation	CYLLENE 9 / Charm 2
			Cassis	Morion 5 / Domiduca 20
Ardan (1941)		Teddy	Ajax	Flying Fox 7 / Amie 2
	Asterus (1923)		Rondeau	BAY RONALD 3 / Doremi 2
		Astrella	Verdun	Rabelais 14 / Vellena 1
			Saint Astra	Ladas 1 / Saint Celestra 9
Adargatis (1931)		Helicon	CYLLENE	Bona Vista 4 / Arcadia 9
	Helene De Troie (1916)		Vain Duchess	ISINGLASS 3 / Sweet Duchess 22
		Lady Of Pedigree	St Denis	ST SIMON 11 / Brooch 16
			Doxa	Melton 8 / Paradoxical 1
Hay Hook ()		PETER PAN	Commando	Domino 23 / Emma C 12
	BLACK TONEY (1911)		Cinderella	HERMIT 5 / Mazurka 2
		Belgravia	BEN BRUSH	Bramble 9 / Roseville A1
			Bonnie Gal	GALOPIN 3 / Bonnie Doon 10
Balladier (1932)		North Star III	Sunstar	Sundridge 2 / Doris 5
	Blue Warbler (1922)		Angelic	St Angelo 16 / Fota 4
		May Bird	Thrush	Missel Thrush 4 / Chemistry 2
			May Bruce	May Duke 9 / Lady Bruce 3
Jacaranda ()		BROOMSTICK	BEN BRUSH	Bramble 9 / Roseville A1
	Halcyon (1928)		Elf	GALLIARD 13 / Sylvabelle 16
		Prudery	PETER PAN	Commando 12 / Cinderella 2
			Polly Flinders	Burgomaster 2 / Slippers 21
Halcyon Days (1938)		Sickle	PHALARIS	Polymelus 3 / Bromus 1
	Jabot (1931)		Selene	CHAUCER 1 / Serenissima 6
		Frilette	Man O' War	FAIR PLAY 9 / Mahubah 4
			Frillery	BROOMSTICK 16 / Petticoat A1
Idle Dice (1963)		John O'Gaunt	ISINGLASS	ISONOMY 19 / Dead Lock 3
	Swynford (1907)		La Fleche	ST SIMON 11 / Quiver 3
		CANTERBURY PILGRIM	Tristan	HERMIT 5 / Thrift 10
			Pilgrimage	The Palmer 5 / Lady Audley 1
Blandford (1919)		White Eagle	Gallinule	ISONOMY 19 / Moorhen 19
	Blanche (1912)		Merry Gal	GALOPIN 3 / Mary Seaton 5
		Black Cherry	Bendigo	Ben Battle 4 / Hasty Girl 9
			Black Duchess	GALLIARD 13 / Black Corrie 5
Isolater (1933)		Marco	Barcaldine	Solon 23 / Ballyroe 23
	Omar Khayyam (1914)		Novitiate	HERMIT 5 / Retty 3
		Lisma	Persimmon	ST SIMON 11 / Perdita II 7
			Luscious	Royal Hampton 11 / Alveole 9
Priscilla Carter (1925)		Trap Rock	ROCK SAND	SAINFOIN 2 / Roquebrune 4
	The Reef (1914)		Topiary	Orme 11 / Plaisanterie 19
		Pyramid	HASTINGS	Spendthrift A3 / Cinderella 21
			St Priscilla	Rayon D'Or 3 / St Pauline 2
D K Dor ()		HASTINGS	Spendthrift	Australian 11 / Aerolite (rh)
	FAIR PLAY (1905)		Cinderella	Blue Ruin / Manna 21
		Fairy Gold	TADCASTER	Doncaster 5 / Clemence 2
			Dame Masham	GALLIARD 13 / Pauline 9
Pari-Mutual (1928)		Ethelbert	Eothen	Hampton 10 / Sultana 3
	Quelle Chance (1917)		Maori	Poulet 18 / Queen Of Cyprus 23
		Qu'elle Est Belle II	ROCK SAND	SAINFOIN 2 / Roquebrune 4
			Queen's Bower	St Florian 20 / Gipsy Queen 3
Dorothy D K ()		Ambassador	Dark Ronald	BAY RONALD 3 / Darkie 9
	St James (1921)		Excellenza	Haut Brion 1 / Gulbeyaz 2
		Bobolink II	Willonyx	William The Third 4 / Tribonyx 4
			Chelandry	Goldfinch 1 / Illuminata
Brazen Lady (1933)		BLACK TONEY	PETER PAN	Commando 12 / Cinderella 2
	Shady Lady (1927)		Belgravia	BEN BRUSH A1 / Bonnie Gal 10
		Crepuscule	Meddler	St Gatien 16 / Busybody 1
			Strike-A-light	Donovan 7 / Fuse 22

Idle Dice 1963

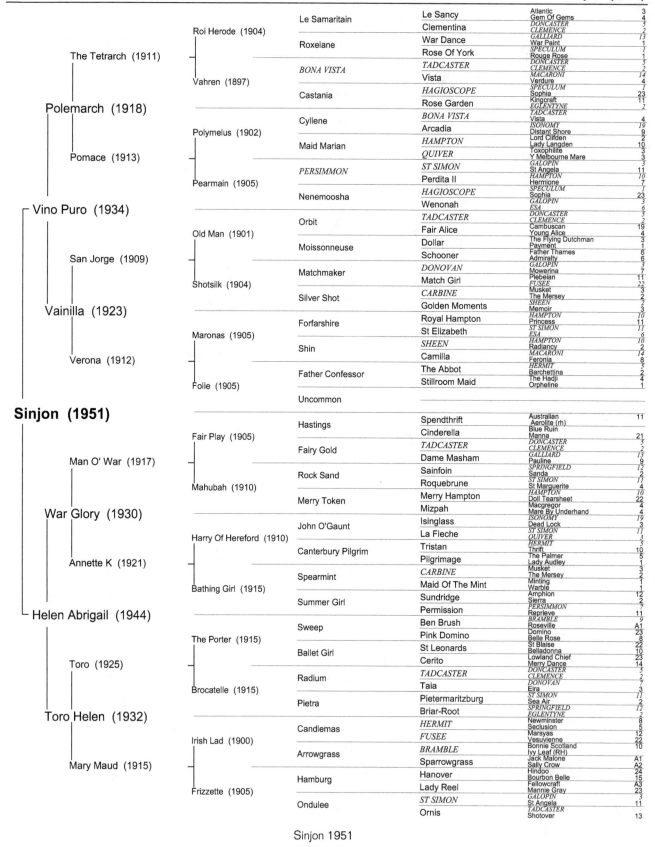

Sinjon 1951

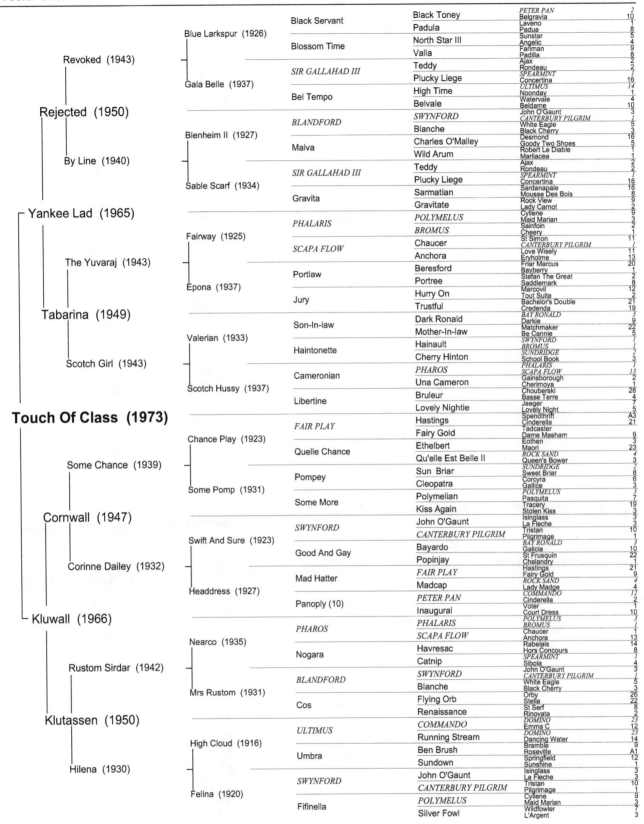

Touch Of Class (1973)

- **Yankee Lad (1965)**
  - **Rejected (1950)**
    - **Revoked (1943)**
      - Blue Larkspur (1926)
        - Black Servant
          - Black Toney — *PETER PAN* /2, Belgravia /10
          - Padula — Laveno /1, Padua /8
        - Blossom Time
          - North Star III — Sunstar /5, Angelic /4
          - Valla — Fariman /9, Padilla /8
      - Gala Belle (1937)
        - *SIR GALLAHAD III*
          - Teddy — Ajax /2, Rondeau /2
          - Plucky Liege — *SPEARMINT* /1, Concertina /16
        - Bel Tempo
          - High Time — *ULTIMUS* /14, Noonday /1
          - Belvale — Watervale /4, Beldame /10
    - **By Line (1940)**
      - Blenheim II (1927)
        - *BLANDFORD*
          - *SWYNFORD* — John O'Gaunt /3, *CANTERBURY PILGRIM* /1
          - Blanche — White Eagle /5, Black Cherry /3
        - Malva
          - Charles O'Malley — Desmond /16, Goody Two Shoes /5
          - Wild Arum — Robert Le Diable /1, Marliacea /1
      - Sable Scarf (1934)
        - *SIR GALLAHAD III*
          - Teddy — Ajax /2, Rondeau /2
          - Plucky Liege — *SPEARMINT* /1, Concertina /16
        - Gravita
          - Sarmatian — Sardanapale /16, Mousse Des Bois /8
          - Gravitate — Rock View /9, Lady Carnot /2
  - **Tabarina (1949)**
    - **The Yuvaraj (1943)**
      - Fairway (1925)
        - *PHALARIS*
          - *POLYMELUS* — Cyllene /9, Maid Marian /3
          - *BROMUS* — Sainfoin /2, Cheery /1
        - *SCAPA FLOW*
          - Chaucer — St Simon /11, *CANTERBURY PILGRIM* /1
          - Anchora — Love Wisely /11, Eryholme /13
      - Epona (1937)
        - Portlaw
          - Beresford — Friar Marcus /20, Bayberry /1
          - Portree — Stefan The Great /2, Saddlemark /8
        - Jury
          - Hurry On — Marcovil /12, Tout Suite /2
          - Trustful — Bachelor's Double /21, Credenda /19
    - **Scotch Girl (1943)**
      - Valerian (1933)
        - Son-In-law
          - Dark Ronald — *BAY RONALD* /3, Darkie /9
          - Mother-In-law — Matchmaker /22, Be Cannie /5
        - Haintonette
          - Hainault — *SWYNFORD* /1, *BROMUS* /1
          - Cherry Hinton — *SUNDRIDGE* /2, School Book /3
      - Scotch Hussy (1937)
        - Cameronian
          - *PHAROS* — *PHALARIS* /1, *SCAPA FLOW* /13
          - Una Cameron — Gainsborough /2, Cherimoya /1
        - Libertine
          - Bruleur — Chouberski /28, Basse Terre /4
          - Lovely Nightie — Jaeger /7, Lovely Night /5
- **Kluwall (1966)**
  - **Cornwall (1947)**
    - **Some Chance (1939)**
      - Chance Play (1923)
        - *FAIR PLAY*
          - Hastings — Spendthrift /A3, Cinderella /21
          - Fairy Gold — Tadcaster /9, Dame Masham /3
        - Quelle Chance
          - Ethelbert — Eothen /9, Maori /23
          - Qu'elle Est Belle II — *ROCK SAND* /4, Queen's Bower /3
      - Some Pomp (1931)
        - Pompey
          - Sun Briar — *SUNDRIDGE* /2, Sweet Briar /8
          - Cleopatra — Corcyra /6, Gallice /3
        - Some More
          - Polymelian — *POLYMELUS* /7, Pasquita /7
          - Kiss Again — Tracery /19, Stolen Kiss /3
    - **Corinne Dailey (1932)**
      - Swift And Sure (1923)
        - *SWYNFORD*
          - John O'Gaunt — Isinglass /3, La Fleche /3
          - *CANTERBURY PILGRIM* — Tristan /10, Pilgrimage /1
        - Good And Gay
          - Bayardo — *BAY RONALD* /3, Galicia /10
          - Popinjay — St Frusquin /22, Chelandry /7
      - Headdress (1927)
        - Mad Hatter
          - *FAIR PLAY* — Hastings /21, Fairy Gold /9
          - Madcap — *ROCK SAND* /4, Lady Madge /4
        - Panoply (10)
          - *PETER PAN* — *COMMANDO* /12, Cinderella /2
          - Inaugural — Voter /1, Court Dress /10
  - **Klutassen (1950)**
    - **Rustom Sirdar (1942)**
      - Nearco (1935)
        - *PHAROS*
          - *PHALARIS* — *POLYMELUS* /3, *BROMUS* /1
          - *SCAPA FLOW* — Chaucer /1, Anchora /13
        - Nogara
          - Havresac — Rabelais /14, Hors Concours /8
          - Catnip — *SPEARMINT* /1, Sibola /4
      - Mrs Rustom (1931)
        - *BLANDFORD*
          - *SWYNFORD* — John O'Gaunt /3, *CANTERBURY PILGRIM* /1
          - Blanche — White Eagle /5, Black Cherry /3
        - Cos
          - Flying Orb — Orby /26, Stella /22
          - Renaissance — St Serf /8, Rinovata /2
    - **Hilena (1930)**
      - High Cloud (1916)
        - *ULTIMUS*
          - *COMMANDO* — *DOMINO* /23, Emma C /12
          - Running Stream — *DOMINO* /23, Dancing Water /14
        - Umbra
          - Ben Brush — Bramble /9, Roseville /A1
          - Sundown — Springfield /12, Sunshine /1
      - Felina (1920)
        - *SWYNFORD*
          - John O'Gaunt — Isinglass /3, La Fleche /3
          - *CANTERBURY PILGRIM* — Tristan /10, Pilgrimage /1
        - Fifinella
          - *POLYMELUS* — Cyllene /9, Maid Marian /3
          - Silver Fowl — Wildfowler /7, L'Argent /3

Touch of Class 1973

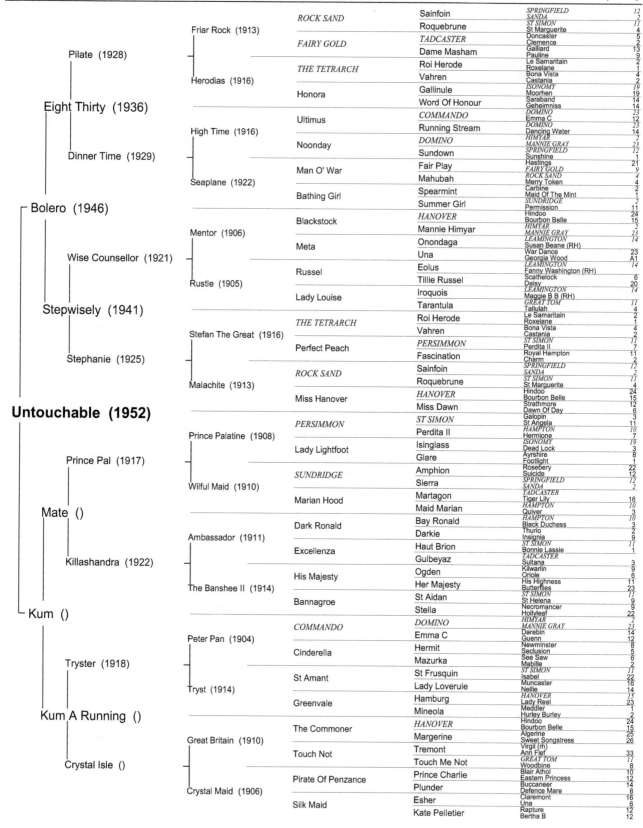

		ROCK SAND	Sainfoin	SPRINGFIELD	12
				SANDA	2
	Friar Rock (1913)		Roquebrune	ST SIMON	11
				St Marguerite	4
Pilate (1928)		FAIRY GOLD	TADCASTER	Doncaster	5
				Clemence	13
			Dame Masham	Galliard	9
				Pauline	
		THE TETRARCH	Roi Herode	Le Samaritain	2
				Roxelane	1
	Herodias (1916)		Vahren	Bona Vista	4
				Castania	2
Eight Thirty (1936)		Honora	Gallinule	ISONOMY	19
				Moorhen	19
			Word Of Honour	Saraband	14
				Geheimniss	14
		Ultimus	COMMANDO	DOMINO	23
				Emma C	12
	High Time (1916)		Running Stream	DOMINO	23
				Dancing Water	14
Dinner Time (1929)		Noonday	DOMINO	HIMYAR	2
				MANNIE GRAY	23
			Sundown	SPRINGFIELD	12
				Sunshine	1
		Man O' War	Fair Play	Hastings	21
				FAIRY GOLD	9
	Seaplane (1922)		Mahubah	ROCK SAND	4
				Merry Token	4
		Bathing Girl	Spearmint	Carbine	2
				Maid Of The Mint	1
			Summer Girl	SUNDRIDGE	2
				Permission	11
Bolero (1946)		Blackstock	HANOVER	Hindoo	24
				Bourbon Belle	15
	Mentor (1906)		Mannie Himyar	HIMYAR	2
				MANNIE GRAY	23
		Meta	Onondaga	LEAMINGTON	14
				Susan Beane (RH)	
Wise Counsellor (1921)			Una	War Dance	23
				Georgia Wood	A1
		Russel	Eolus	LEAMINGTON	14
				Fanny W Washington (RH)	
	Rustle (1905)		Tillie Russel	Scathelock	6
				Daisy	20
		Lady Louise	Iroquois	LEAMINGTON	14
				Maggie B B (RH)	
Stepwisely (1941)			Tarantula	GREAT TOM	11
				Tallulah	4
		THE TETRARCH	Roi Herode	Le Samaritain	2
				Roxelane	1
	Stefan The Great (1916)		Vahren	Bona Vista	4
				Castania	2
Stephanie (1925)		Perfect Peach	PERSIMMON	ST SIMON	11
				Perdita II	7
			Fascination	Royal Hampton	11
				Charm	2
		ROCK SAND	Sainfoin	SPRINGFIELD	12
				SANDA	2
	Malachite (1913)		Roquebrune	ST SIMON	11
				St Marguerite	4
		Miss Hanover	HANOVER	Hindoo	24
				Bourbon Belle	15
			Miss Dawn	Strathmore	12
				Dawn Of Day	6

Untouchable (1952)

		PERSIMMON	ST SIMON	Galopin	3
				St Angela	11
	Prince Palatine (1908)		Perdita II	HAMPTON	10
				Hermione	7
		Lady Lightfoot	Isinglass	ISONOMY	19
				Dead Lock	3
Prince Pal (1917)			Glare	Ayrshire	8
				Footlight	1
		SUNDRIDGE	Amphion	Rosebery	22
				Suicide	12
	Wilful Maid (1910)		Sierra	SPRINGFIELD	12
				SANDA	2
		Marian Hood	Martagon	TADCASTER	
				Tiger Lily	16
			Maid Marian	HAMPTON	10
Mate ()				Quiver	3
		Dark Ronald	Bay Ronald	HAMPTON	10
				Black Duchess	3
	Ambassador (1911)		Darkie	Thurio	2
				Insignia	9
		Excellenza	Haut Brion	ST SIMON	11
				Bonnie Lassie	1
			Gulbeyaz	TADCASTER	
Killashandra (1922)				Sultana	3
		His Majesty	Ogden	Kilwarlin	9
				Oriole	6
	The Banshee II (1914)		Her Majesty	His Highness	11
				Butterflies	23
		Bannagroe	St Aidan	ST SIMON	11
				St Helena	9
			Stella	Necromancer	9
				Hollyleaf	22
Kum ()		COMMANDO	DOMINO	HIMYAR	2
				MANNIE GRAY	23
	Peter Pan (1904)		Emma C	Darebin	14
				Guenn	12
		Cinderella	Hermit	Newminster	8
				Seclusion	5
			Mazurka	See Saw	6
Tryster (1918)				Mabille	2
		St Amant	St Frusquin	ST SIMON	11
				Isabel	22
	Tryst (1914)		Lady Loverule	Muncaster	16
				Nellie	14
		Greenvale	Hamburg	HANOVER	15
				Lady Reel	23
			Mineola	Meddler	1
Kum A Running ()				Hurley Burley	2
		The Commoner	HANOVER	Hindoo	24
				Bourbon Belle	15
	Great Britain (1910)		Margerine	Algerine	25
				Sweet Songstress	26
		Touch Not	Tremont	Virgil (rh)	
				Ann Fief	33
			Touch Me Not	GREAT TOM	11
Crystal Isle ()				Woodbine	8
		Pirate Of Penzance	Prince Charlie	Blair Athol	10
				Eastern Princess	12
	Crystal Maid (1906)		Plunder	Buccaneer	14
				Defence Mare	8
		Silk Maid	Esher	Claremont	16
				Una	6
			Kate Pelletier	Rapture	12
				Bertha B	12

Untouchable 1952

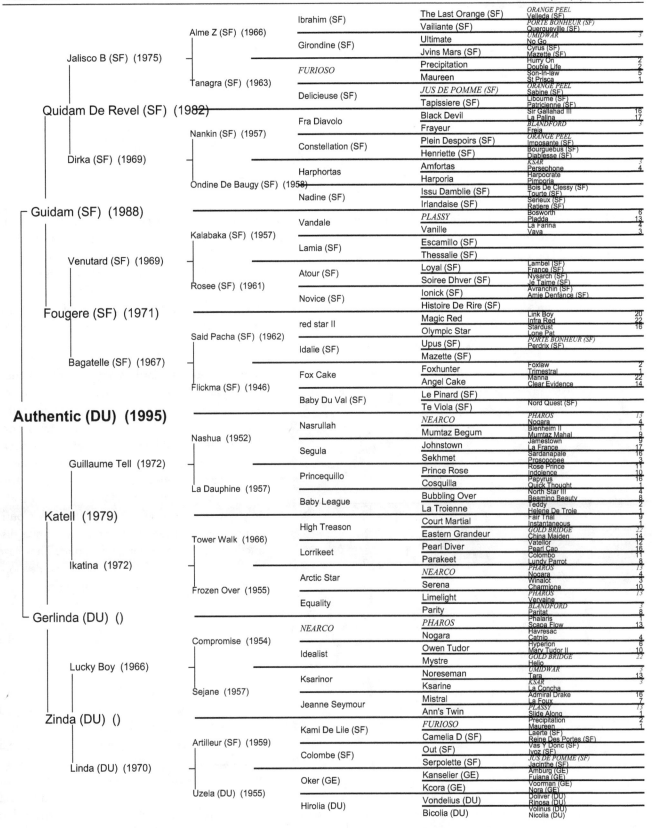

Authentic DU 1995

Chapter 33

Marion Loved Man O' War

America's sport horse has always been based on our racehorse—always.

The top breeders of horses that can hunt and jump chose their breeding stock from the flat racing studs. In this country most steeplechasers, hunt horses, and show jumpers are geldings, and they are bred either as purebred Thoroughbreds or part-bred depending on the breeder's goals. The traditional area for this specialized breeding of horses that jump in America has been until very recent time centralized on the Atlantic Coast area, where hunting and its associated contests (steeplechase, cross country, hunter trials, point-to-points, show jumping) are a way of life. Since the mid-1800s those breeders have maintained a presence not only at home but abroad as well, and many of the choice-bred Thoroughbreds of this region traveled abroad to the British Isles to race and breed, and some of these competed in hunter, jumping, and steeplechase contests as well as flat racing, and several bred on there.

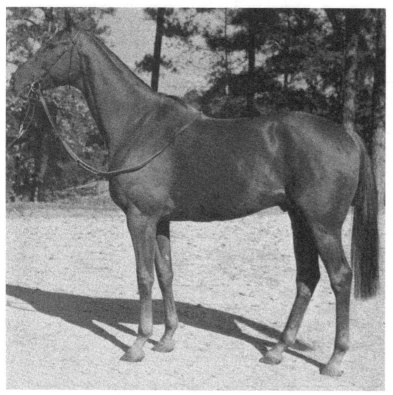

A masterpiece of intelligent breeding, the super-horse Neji, bred by Marion DuPont Scott, is the prototypical Fair Play: full of speed, stamina with heart, and a tremendous jump; he thoroughly owned steeplechasing in this country in the 1950s. —photo by Bert Morgan, courtesy of Keeneland Library

Today's breeder in North America needs to understand which of our native bloodlines produce excellence in sport. Our heritage is rich and long in this pursuit, but it is distinctly different in form from that of Continental Europe. Because of the infiltration of the European method in sport horse breeding in recent decades, the average equestrian here now believes that the 'warmblood' program is the only way to success in Olympic-style sports. Continental Europe is historically and culturally a distinctly different horse culture than ours. They have long ago lost much of their open land to development, and many of their equestrian pursuits are in closed areas, therefore sports such as 'high school' dressage, urban coach driving, and stadium equine sports were more prevalent there, while here in the US the cross-country contests and other open air events were and still are part of our culture. Further, in Europe the breeding of horses was a state-overseen project, with stallions standing at centralized studs, and even after World War II it remained under the government's control as it switched to a sport focus from its farm/coach orientation. In contrast, America's early breeders were English subjects, but 'freemen', and their pursuit of equine sport and its breeding was an individual pursuit, and it has remained so also to this day—this is massive difference in tradition, structure, and philosophy.

Horse racing is in our blood, it is the oldest sport in the Americas, and for most of our history it is the only equine sport that provided purse money—an important consideration to individual breeders operating without government subsidies.

Our sport horses are based on our racehorse of course, too, not a farm or coach horse as is the case in Continental Europe. We appreciated the coach horse in our sport horse recipes for heavy Hunters, but they were never our base stock.

The breeding of Hunters (the true American warmblood) has continued unabated from 1700 to the present day, especially in the 'old dominion' of Virginia and Maryland. Over the years many farms and breeding programs have been in existence that specialized in those flying horses—perhaps none as grand and famous as that of Marion DuPont Scott.

Mrs. Scott was an accomplished horsewoman and held the 'Master of the Hunt' position at the celebrated Montpelier Hunt. She was also an important member of the National Steeplechase and Hunt Association. An heiress, she had the means to build a splendid establishment in Virginia: The Montpelier Farm, which has produced national and international champions. She also was a strong supporter of the Remount Service, donating several broodmares and the stallion Tourist II to the cause, and it was her idea that formed the syndicate to purchase the English stallion Blenheim, which brought him to this country.

Montpelier Farm stud advertisement 1946.

An astute breeder, Marion determined to breed only excellent jumpers, and her produce stood above most of her peers and has provided strong, proven bloodlines for the breeder today. Montpelier Farm was a showcase for the breeding and development of the Steeplechaser and Hunter Horse, with its one-mile, flat racetrack, and a full steeplechase course, where she not only trained her young horses, but she also allowed the Montpelier Hunt to use her facility; her generosity contributed greatly to the enrichment of equine sport in the region.

Marion DuPont Scott loved the bloodline of Man O' War—its stamina, its soundness, and its intrinsic talent for jumping. And she made a point of developing it in her herd.

"But it is not the tracks, nor the meetings of the riding set, that are paramount here. It is also the standing ground of those two famous sires, Battleship and Annapolis; both of whom are now established as two of the best timber-toppers in the country…Today Annapolis and Battleship are producing foals of the highest class and as sire have gained considerable attention from the more astute breeders, especially so, as sire of steeplechasers…The 'get' of Annapolis in 1945 won 10 races of 32 and earned $86,747, while the children of the internationally famous Battleship entered the winner's circle 8 times out of 27 races and accounted for $53,440" (Ned Welch *Who's Who in Thoroughbred Racing*).

The amounts won in the above quotation may seem meager to us today, but in the 1940s this was a huge amount of winnings in steeplechase, as there were no cash prizes for Hunter competitions. Annapolis and Battleship are Man O' War sons.

Steeplechase, point-to-point, hunt races, and show jumping were sports that grew out of our native fox-hunting culture—these were the means we employed in the conditioning of our Hunter Horses, and Hunt Clubs and racetracks were often where these events took place. These sports were generally centered in the Atlantic coast area, especially in the mid-Atlantic states, and were also limited because there was no financial compensation for much of its history—no prize money—no subsidies, and therefore these sports were usually conducted by those who had the means to do so. In Marion's part of the country (Virginia), hunter sports of all kinds were an important part of the culture, and a whole industry arose from this favorite pastime.

General definitions of hunter-related sports:

Steeplechases are often run on racecourses—this meet is at Raceland.
—photo by Boston Herald

Steeplechase: usually run on an oval course, over hurdles 4' 6" (in times past they were called 'hurdle races'), or they were run over brush up to 5' high with ditches and water obstacles as well, and the riders are professional jockeys—the horses are registered Thoroughbreds.

Hunt Race: usually held in late spring or fall, before and after the hunt season, over 'timber' (post and rails), brush, and hurdle fences, it can be ridden by both pros and amateurs, and there is usually a trophy for the winner, occasionally a small cash prize.

Point-to-point: held in early spring after hunt season, this is a cross-country contest over timber, and is open only to those horses who hunted in the previous season; it is ridden by amateurs, and the horses are home-bred.

Montpelier Farm Stallions:

Annapolis 1926 was one of the first of the Man O' War offspring to make a big name in jumping. Bred by master breeder Walter J. Salmon, who also bred Display and Discovery, this stallion was a champion steeplechaser many times over, winning eleven of his forty starts. His pedigree reveals a Fair Play sire-line, and the dam-sire is Peter Pan (Domino). Also of interest is the strong buildup of the English mare Queen Mary, with the third dam Court Dress having five lines of her. There is a double of Hermit through daughters 6x4 and a double of Hampton 5x5—this is the pedigree of a potent stallion—fully able to set type. Purchased by Mrs. DuPont, Annapolis was set up as a stallion at her farm where he produced a remarkable record of top jumping horses. For instance, his son Benguala was also the Champion Steeplechaser in 1960—his third dam is a daughter of Fair Play: Etoile Filante, putting Fair Play 3x4 sex-balanced in this jumper. Annapolis is also dam-sire of the phenomenal Hall of Famer Neji, who was three times the National Steeplechase Champion, and he won while carrying the heavy weight of 178 lbs—the Fair Play line is known for its weight-carrying ability—Neji was 15.3 hands. Neji was physically and performance-wise a Fair Play clone—he was a great weight carrier, with speed, stamina, and a tremendous jump—he earned the Steeplechase-Horse-of-the-Year a record three times: 1955, 1957, 1958.

Annapolis's daughters were especially prolific as dams of jumpers; Accra, herself a winning steeplechaser, produced not only the legend Neji, but the champion hunter Emmett Kelly. Accra not only carries a double of Fair Play, she is 5x5x5 to his sire Hastings, and his sister Slippers is on his dam-line—this is very potent design. Annapolis's daughter Swan Boat produced the top show jumper and stallion Danuji. His daughter Seaborne is the second dam of the top steeplechaser Soothsayer, who is by Mystic II, a top French-bred jumper producer who is actually a grandson of War Relic, putting Man O' War 4x4 and Peter Pan (Domino line) 5x5. Seaborne also is dam of the champion jumper and Grand Prix winner Nanticoke, as well as the champion steeplechaser Shipboard who is by Battleship—which puts Man O' War 2x3, and even though he was competing during the reign of the invincible Neji, he still holds the Champion Steeplechase title for 1956—obviously he was of the highest class. Annapolis's daughter Sea Pies is dam of the champion hunter Seagirt, who is 3x4x4 Man O' War.

The Hall-of-Famer Neji sailing over the brush obstacle while carrying heavy weight, winning the Brook Steeplechase. —photo by Bert Morgan, courtesy of Keeneland Library

Battleship 1927, bred also by Walter J. Salmon, raced for him on the flat and won nine of twenty, after which he was sold to Marion DuPont Scott. He was retrained over fences, and when he was six he began winning for her, three out of four in 1933. In 1934 he won the Grand National at Belmont Park, and three other races out of six. He was shipped to England to be put in training for the Aintree Grand National, but developed a bowed tendon, so he was rested and then slowly brought back into shape, racing in English hunt races. Referred in the British press as the 'American Pony', Battleship, finally at age eleven, made the 'big show' there, and this 15.2-hand son of Man O' War won the Aintree Grand National. It was a close and exciting finish, as Battleship took the lead only at the final obstacle, but win it he did. In England, where this contest was held, Battleship was classified as a half-bred, as it was during the Jersey Act.

Battleship is also by Man O' War and is out of imported Quarantine by Sea Sick. Sea Sick is by Elf, a son of Galliard out of a mare by Tadcaster. We have seen in previous chapters how building up Tadcaster and his dam Clemence is a key element in top athletes—flat or jump. Elf is a key component, as he is the ¾ brother to Fairy Gold, the dam of Fair Play, creating a wonderful ¾ sibling design 3x3. These inbred siblings funnel forward all the power of the background lines—the result was an international champion and a notable sire. By any standard we have to regard the English mare Clemence as one of the top hereditary transmitters of sport ability (see Sinjon in Chapter 32).

Battleship came home a national hero and stood stud at DuPont's farm. He sired fifty-seven foals. Shipboard mentioned before was one of his best, with inbreeding to Man O' War 2x3; another is War Battle, the Champion Steeplechaser of 1947. Another son Sea Legs won the American Grand National. Battleship's stallion son Battlewick, who has a nice buildup of Tadcaster 4x5x4x5 (corrected pedigree), also carries the RH jump sire Virgil RH in the fifth, and he became a noted sire of jumpers and hunters. Battlewick field hunted until he was seventeen, and his sire Battleship also hunted with the Old Dominion Hunt (Virginia). These lines are sound as well as extremely athletic, fully able to compete for years—into their teens—and even while some of them are what we would call small (15.1 to 15.3 hands) they are able to win carry weights that would cripple other horses.

Other noted offspring of Battleship are the champion jumpers Salem and Nanticoke, plus steeplechasers Navigate, Tip Rips, Cap-a-Pie, Eolus, Mighty Mo, Westport Point, and Floating Isle. His stallion son Navy Gun was also a significant sire of hunters and jumpers.

Marion DuPont Scott with her champion Battleship—a son of Man O' War, international Champion and great sire—he stood at Marion DuPont's Montpelier Farm. Compare his conformation to that of Neji; notice the Fair Play front end on both of them. —photo by C.C. Cook, courtesy of the Keeneland Library

Marion's brother William DuPont Jr. was a lifelong participant in hunter sports, is seen here with his then twenty-year-old premier gelding Shapright, who hunted sixteen seasons with his owner. —photo by Haas

The American tradition of the Hunter Horse and the hunter sports is almost as old as our country. The first documented selective breeding of the Hunter Horse was in the Old Dominion, Maryland-Virginia colonies, and it has been continued ever since, an unbroken tradition. Almost Marion's entire family was devotees of these sports, and they bred both racehorse and jumping stock, and personally participated in these sports.

In our recent day, we find the DuPont family tradition is still powerful, as Marion's granddaughter, Lana DuPont Wright was the first woman rider to appear in the Olympics; she competed in eventing—winning the team silver medal in Tokyo in 1964. She has been inducted into the Eventing Hall of Fame.

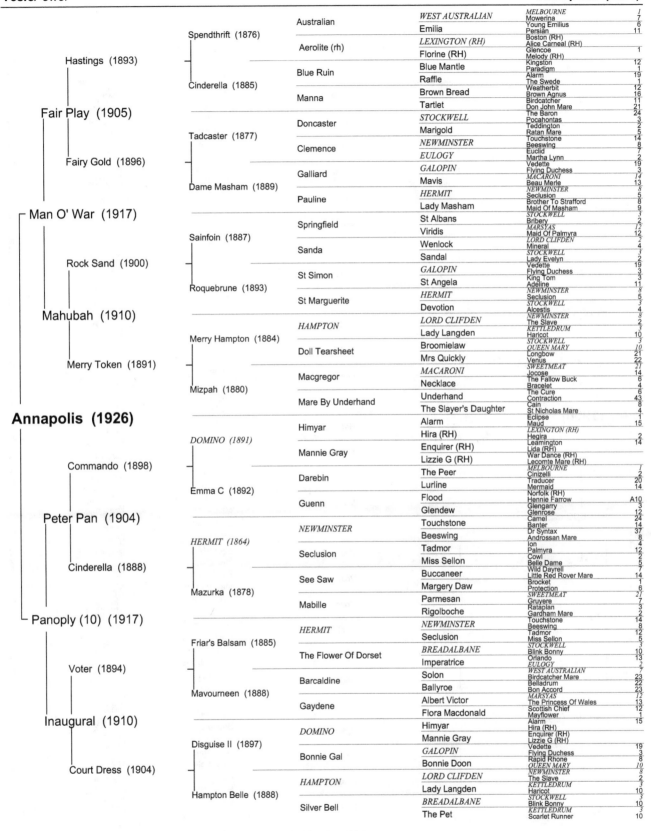

Pedigree chart — left lineage:

Annapolis (1926)

- Man O' War (1917)
  - Fair Play (1905)
    - Hastings (1893)
    - Fairy Gold (1896)
  - Mahubah (1910)
    - Rock Sand (1900)
    - Merry Token (1891)
- Panoply (10) (1917)
  - Peter Pan (1904)
    - Commando (1898)
    - Cinderella (1888)
  - Inaugural (1910)
    - Voter (1894)
    - Court Dress (1904)

Detailed ancestry:

Spendthrift (1876)	Australian	WEST AUSTRALIAN	MELBOURNE 1 / Mowerina 7
		Emilia	Young Emilius 6 / Persian 11
	Aerolite (rh)	LEXINGTON (RH)	Boston (RH) / Alice Carneal (RH) 1
		Florine (RH)	Glencoe 1 / Melody (RH)
Cinderella (1885)	Blue Ruin	Blue Mantle	Kingston 12 / Paradigm 1
		Raffle	Alarm 19 / The Swede 1
	Manna	Brown Bread	Weatherbit 12 / Brown Agnus 16
		Tartlet	Birdcatcher 11 / Don John Mare 21
Tadcaster (1877)	Doncaster	STOCKWELL	The Baron 24 / Pocahontas 3
		Marigold	Teddington 2 / Ratan Mare 5
	Clemence	NEWMINSTER	Touchstone 14 / Beeswing 8
		EULOGY	Euclid 7 / Martha Lynn 2
Dame Masham (1889)	Galliard	GALOPIN	Vedette 19 / Flying Duchess 3
		Mavis	MACARONI 14 / Beau Merle 13
	Pauline	HERMIT	NEWMINSTER 8 / Seclusion 5
		Lady Masham	Brother To Strafford 8 / Maid Of Masham 9
Sainfoin (1887)	Springfield	St Albans	STOCKWELL 3 / Bribery 2
		Viridis	MARSYAS 12 / Maid Of Palmyra 12
	Sanda	Wenlock	LORD CLIFDEN 4 / Mineral 4
		Sandal	STOCKWELL 3 / Lady Evelyn 2
Roquebrune (1893)	St Simon	GALOPIN	Vedette 19 / Flying Duchess 3
		St Angela	King Tom 3 / Adeline 11
	St Marguerite	HERMIT	NEWMINSTER 8 / Seclusion 5
		Devotion	STOCKWELL 3 / Alcestis 4
Merry Hampton (1884)	HAMPTON	LORD CLIFDEN	NEWMINSTER 8 / The Slave 2
		Lady Langden	KETTLEDRUM 3 / Haricot 10
	Doll Tearsheet	Broomielaw	STOCKWELL 3 / QUEEN MARY 10
		Mrs Quickly	Longbow 21 / Venus 22
Mizpah (1880)	Macgregor	MACARONI	SWEETMEAT 21 / Jocose 14
		Necklace	The Fallow Buck 6 / Bracelet 4
	Mare By Underhand	Underhand	The Cure 6 / Contraction 43
		The Slayer's Daughter	Cain 8 / St Nicholas Mare 4
DOMINO (1891)	Himyar	Alarm	Eclipse 1 / Maud 15
		Hira (RH)	LEXINGTON (RH) / Hegira 2
	Mannie Gray	Enquirer (RH)	Leamington 14 / Lida (RH)
		Lizzie G (RH)	War Dance (RH) / Lecomte Mare (RH)
Emma C (1892)	Darebin	The Peer	MELBOURNE 1 / Cinizelli 2
		Lurline	Traducer 20 / Mermaid 14
	Guenn	Flood	Norfolk (RH) A10 / Hennie Farrow
		Glendew	Glengarry 3 / Glenrose 12
HERMIT (1864)	NEWMINSTER	Touchstone	Camel 24 / Banter 14
		Beeswing	Dr Syntax 37 / Androssan Mare 8
	Seclusion	Tadmor	Ion 4 / Palmyra 12
		Miss Sellon	Cowl 2 / Belle Dame 5
Mazurka (1878)	See Saw	Buccaneer	Wild Dayrell 7 / Little Red Rover Mare 14
		Margery Daw	Brocket 1 / Protection 6
	Mabille	Parmesan	SWEETMEAT 21 / Gruyere 7
		Rigolboche	Rataplan 3 / Gardham Mare 2
Friar's Balsam (1885)	HERMIT	NEWMINSTER	Touchstone 14 / Beeswing 8
		Seclusion	Tadmor 12 / Miss Sellon 5
	The Flower Of Dorset	BREADALBANE	STOCKWELL 3 / Blink Bonny 10
		Imperatrice	Orlando 13 / EULOGY 2
Mavourneen (1888)	Barcaldine	Solon	WEST AUSTRALIAN 7 / Birdcatcher Mare 23
		Ballyroe	Belladrum 22 / Bon Accord 23
	Gaydene	Albert Victor	MARSYAS 12 / The Princess Of Wales 13
		Flora Macdonald	Scottish Chief 12 / Mayflower 1
Disguise II (1897)	DOMINO	Himyar	Alarm 15 / Hira (RH)
		Mannie Gray	Enquirer (RH) / Lizzie G (RH)
	Bonnie Gal	GALOPIN	Vedette 19 / Flying Duchess 3
		Bonnie Doon	Rapid Rhone 8 / QUEEN MARY 10
Hampton Belle (1888)	HAMPTON	LORD CLIFDEN	NEWMINSTER 8 / The Slave 2
		Lady Langden	KETTLEDRUM 3 / Haricot 10
	Silver Bell	BREADALBANE	STOCKWELL 3 / Blink Bonny 10
		The Pet	KETTLEDRUM 3 / Scarlet Runner 10

Annapolis 1926

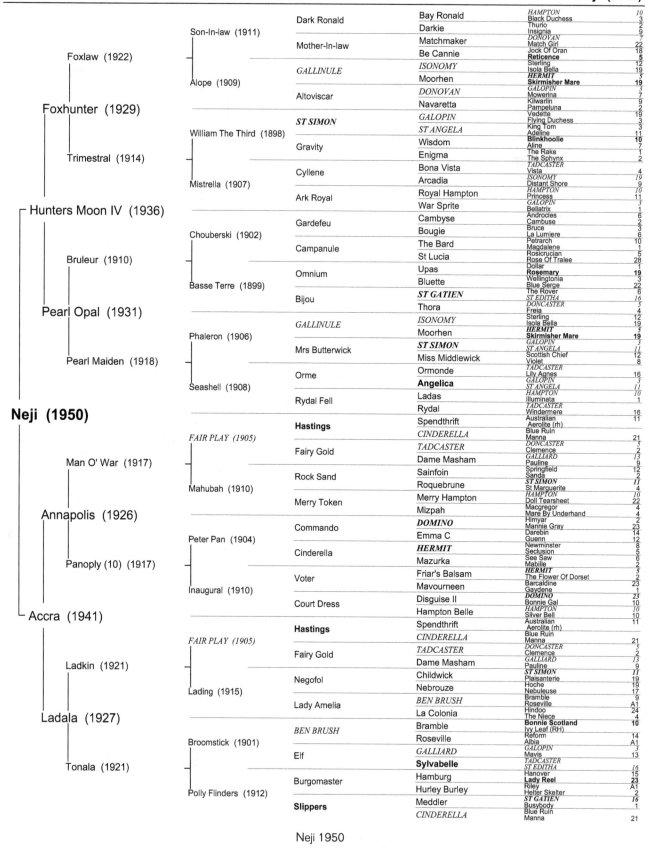

Neji (1950)

- **Hunters Moon IV (1936)**
  - Foxhunter (1929)
    - Foxlaw (1922)
      - Son-In-law (1911)
        - Dark Ronald
          - Bay Ronald — *HAMPTON* 10 / Black Duchess 3
          - Darkie — Thurio 2 / Insignia 9
        - Mother-In-law
          - Matchmaker — *DONOVAN* 7 / Match Girl 22
          - Be Cannie — Jock Of Oran 18 / **Reticence** 5
      - Alope (1909)
        - *GALLINULE*
          - *ISONOMY* — Sterling 12 / Isola Bella 19
          - Moorhen — **HERMIT** 5 / **Skirmisher Mare** 19
        - Altoviscar
          - *DONOVAN* — *GALOPIN* 3 / Mowerina 7
          - Navaretta — Kilwarlin 9 / Pampeluna 2
    - Trimestral (1914)
      - William The Third (1898)
        - *ST SIMON*
          - *GALOPIN* — Vedette 19 / Flying Duchess 3
          - *ST ANGELA* — King Tom 3 / Adeline 11
        - Gravity
          - Wisdom — **Blinkhoolie** 10 / Aline 1
          - Enigma — The Rake 7 / The Sphynx 2
      - Mistrella (1907)
        - Cyllene
          - Bona Vista — *TADCASTER* 4 / Vista 19
          - Arcadia — *ISONOMY* 9 / Distant Shore 10
        - Ark Royal
          - Royal Hampton — *HAMPTON* 10 / Princess 11
          - War Sprite — *GALOPIN* 3 / Bellatrix 1
  - Pearl Opal (1931)
    - Bruleur (1910)
      - Chouberski (1902)
        - Gardefeu
          - Cambyse — Androcles 6 / Cambuse 2
          - Bougie — Bruce 3 / La Lumiere 6
        - Campanule
          - The Bard — Petrarch 10 / Magdalene 1
          - St Lucia — Rosicrucian 5 / Rose Of Tralee 28
      - Basse Terre (1899)
        - Omnium
          - Upas — Dollar 1 / **Rosemary** 19
          - Bluette — Wellingtonia 3 / Blue Serge 22
        - Bijou
          - *ST GATIEN* — The Rover 6 / *ST EDITHA* 16
          - Thora — *DONCASTER* 5 / Freia 4
    - Pearl Maiden (1918)
      - Phaleron (1906)
        - *GALLINULE*
          - *ISONOMY* — Sterling 12 / Isola Bella 19
          - Moorhen — **HERMIT** 5 / **Skirmisher Mare** 19
        - Mrs Butterwick
          - *ST SIMON* — *GALOPIN* 3 / *ST ANGELA* 12
          - Miss Middlewick — Scottish Chief 12 / Violet 8
      - Seashell (1908)
        - Orme
          - Ormonde — *TADCASTER* / Lily Agnes 16
          - **Angelica** — *GALOPIN* 3 / *ST ANGELA* 11
        - Rydal Fell
          - Ladas — *HAMPTON* 10 / Illuminata 1
          - Rydal — *TADCASTER* 16 / Windermere 11

- **Accra (1941)**
  - Annapolis (1926)
    - Man O' War (1917)
      - **Hastings**
        - Spendthrift — Australian / Aerolite (rh)
        - *CINDERELLA* — Blue Ruin / Manna 21
      - Fairy Gold
        - *TADCASTER* — *DONCASTER* 5 / Clemence 2
        - Dame Masham — *GALLIARD* 13 / Pauline 9
    - Mahubah (1910)
      - Rock Sand
        - Sainfoin — Springfield 12 / Sanda 2
        - Roquebrune — *ST SIMON* 11 / St Marguerite 4
      - Merry Token
        - Merry Hampton — *HAMPTON* 10 / Doll Tearsheet 22
        - Mizpah — Macgregor 4 / Mare By Underhand 4
    - FAIR PLAY (1905)
  - Panoply (10) (1917)
    - Peter Pan (1904)
      - Commando
        - *DOMINO* — Himyar 2 / Mannie Gray 23
        - Emma C — Darebin 14 / Guenn 12
      - Cinderella
        - *HERMIT* — Newminster 5 / Seclusion 5
        - Mazurka — See Saw 6 / Mabille 2
    - Inaugural (1910)
      - Voter
        - Friar's Balsam — *HERMIT* 5 / The Flower Of Dorset
        - Mavourneen — Barcaldine 23 / Gaydene 1
      - Court Dress
        - Disguise II — *DOMINO* 23 / Bonnie Gal 10
        - Hampton Belle — *HAMPTON* 10 / Silver Bell 10
  - Ladala (1927)
    - Ladkin (1921)
      - FAIR PLAY (1905)
        - **Hastings**
          - Spendthrift — Australian / Aerolite (rh) 11
          - *CINDERELLA* — Blue Ruin / Manna 21
        - Fairy Gold
          - *TADCASTER* — *DONCASTER* 5 / Clemence 2
          - Dame Masham — *GALLIARD* 13 / Pauline 9
      - Lading (1915)
        - Negofol
          - Childwick — *ST SIMON* 11 / Plaisanterie 19
          - Nebrouze — Hoche 19 / Nebuleuse 17
        - Lady Amelia
          - *BEN BRUSH* — Bramble 9 / Roseville A1
          - La Colonia — Hindoo 24 / The Niece 4
    - Tonala (1921)
      - Broomstick (1901)
        - *BEN BRUSH*
          - Bramble — **Bonnie Scotland** 10 / Ivy Leaf (RH)
          - Roseville — Reform 14 / Albia A1
        - Elf
          - *GALLIARD* — *GALOPIN* 3 / Mavis 13
          - **Sylvabelle** — *TADCASTER* 16 / *ST EDITHA*
      - Polly Flinders (1912)
        - Burgomaster
          - Hamburg — Hanover 15 / **Lady Reel** 23
          - Hurley Burley — Riley A1 / Helter Skelter 2
        - **Slippers**
          - Meddler — *ST GATIEN* 16 / Busybody 1
          - *CINDERELLA* — Blue Ruin / Manna 21

Neji 1950

		WEST AUSTRALIAN	Melbourne 1 / Mowerina 7
	Australian	Emilia	Young Emilius 6 / Persian 11
Spendthrift (1876)		Lexington (RH)	Boston (RH) / Alice Carneal (RH)
	Aerolite (rh)	Florine (RH)	Glencoe 1 / Melody (RH)
		Blue Mantle	Kingston 12 / Paradigm 1
	Blue Ruin	Raffle	Alarm 19 / The Swede 1
Cinderella (1885)		Brown Bread	Weatherbit 12 / Brown Agnus 16
	Manna	Tartlet	Birdcatcher 11 / Don John Mare 21

Fair Play (1905) — Hastings (1893), Fairy Gold (1896)

	Doncaster	STOCKWELL	The Baron 24 / Pocahontas 3
TADCASTER (1877)		Marigold	Teddington 5 / Ratan Mare 1
	Clemence	NEWMINSTER	Touchstone 14 / Beeswing 8
		Eulogy	Euclid 7 / Martha Lynn 2
Dame Masham (1889)	GALLIARD	GALOPIN	Vedette 19 / Flying Duchess 3
		Mavis	MACARONI 14 / Beau Merle 13
	Pauline	HERMIT	NEWMINSTER 8 / Seclusion 6
		Lady Masham	Brother To Strafford 8 / Maid Of Masham 9

Man O' War (1917) — Rock Sand (1900)

	Springfield	St Albans	STOCKWELL 3 / Bribery 2
Sainfoin (1887)		Viridis	Marsyas 12 / Maid Of Palmyra 12
	Sanda	Wenlock	LORD CLIFDEN 2 / Mineral 4
		Sandal	STOCKWELL 3 / Lady Evelyn 1
Roquebrune (1893)	St Simon	GALOPIN	Vedette 19 / Flying Duchess 3
		St Angela	KING TOM 1 / Adeline 11
	St Marguerite	HERMIT	NEWMINSTER 8 / Seclusion 5
		Devotion	STOCKWELL 3 / Alcestis 4

Mahubah (1910) — Merry Token (1891)

	Hampton	LORD CLIFDEN	NEWMINSTER 8 / The Slave 2
Merry Hampton (1884)		Lady Langden	Kettledrum 10 / Haricot 3
	Doll Tearsheet	Broomielaw	STOCKWELL 3 / Queen Mary 10
		Mrs Quickly	Longbow 21 / Venus 22
Mizpah (1880)	Macgregor	MACARONI	Sweetmeat 21 / Jocose 14
		Necklace	The Fallow Buck 6 / Bracelet 4
	Mare By Underhand	Underhand	The Cure 6 / Contraction 43
		The Slayer's Daughter	Cain 8 / St Nicholas Mare 1

Battleship ()

	GALOPIN	Vedette	Voltigeur 2 / Mrs Ridgeway 19
GALLIARD (1880)		Flying Duchess	The Flying Dutchman 3 / Merope 3
	Mavis	MACARONI	Sweetmeat 21 / Jocose 14
		Beau Merle	Victorious 3 / Merlette 13
Sylvabelle (1887)	TADCASTER	Doncaster	STOCKWELL 3 / Marigold 5
		Clemence	NEWMINSTER 8 / Eulogy 2
	St Editha	Kingley Vale	Nutbourne 1 / Bannerdale 8
		Lady Alice	Chanticleer 23 / Agnes 16

Sea Sick (1905) — Elf (1893)

	Atlantic	Thormanby	Windhound 3 / Alice Hawthorn 4
Le Sancy (1884)		Hurricane	WILD DAYRELL 3 / Midia 1
	Gem Of Gems	Strathconan	NEWMINSTER 8 / Souvenir 11
		Poinsettia	Y Melbourne 25 / Lady Hawthorn 4
Athalie (1881)	Caterer	STOCKWELL	The Baron 24 / Pocahontas 3
		Selina	Orlando 13 / The Ladye Of Silverkeld W 7
	Stella	WEST AUSTRALIAN	Melbourne 1 / Mowerina 7
		Mon Etoile	Fitz Gladiator 32 / Hervine 19

Saf Saf (1896) — Quarantine (19??)

	GALOPIN	Vedette	Voltigeur 2 / Mrs Ridgeway 19
GALLIARD (1880)		Flying Duchess	The Flying Dutchman 3 / Merope 3
	Mavis	MACARONI	Sweetmeat 21 / Jocose 14
		Beau Merle	Victorious 3 / Merlette 13
War Paint (1878)	Uncas	STOCKWELL	The Baron 24 / Pocahontas 3
		Nightingale	Mountain Deer 24 / Clarinda 1
	Piracy	Buccaneer	WILD DAYRELL 3 / Little Red Rover Mare 14
		Newminster Mare	NEWMINSTER 8 / Lanercost Mare 1

War Dance (1887) — Queenie (1904), Quilda (1894)

	HERMIT	NEWMINSTER	Touchstone 14 / Beeswing 8
Gamin (1883)		Seclusion	Tadmor 12 / Miss Sellon 5
	Grace	Scottish Chief	Lord Of The Isles 4 / Miss Ann 12
		Virtue	STOCKWELL 3 / Patience 12
Quick Thought (1884)	Forerunner	The Palmer	Beadsman 13 / Mme Eglantine 5
		Preface	STOCKWELL 3 / Prelude 19
	Magnolia	Lecturer	Colsterdale 18 / Algebra 2
		Mahonia	KING TOM 1 / Blooming Heather 10

Battleship

Chapter 34

American Thoroughbred Lines That Jump

As we saw in Chapter 32, American sport bloodlines are left out of the majority of writings found in our current equine literature, but I have discovered that is only a portion of what is missing in these studies—there is actually another side to all this. In most articles on the show jump lines of significance in the world, you will find these Thoroughbreds listed: Rantzau, Fra Diavolo, Ladykiller, Cottage Son, Courville, Lucky Boy, Furioso, Orange Peel, and the deep root lines of Le Sancy and Marco. These are wonderful jumper sires; however they are all of European origin, and they are found in the warmblood program breeding of jumpers. Here is one of the surprises: contrary to the authoritative presentation (see Chapter 32), this list does not account for all the world's jump sources—not even close, just their own European lines—and even then **it is limited to the ones used in warmblood breeding**, it doesn't even cover the European jump sources that come from the flat racing stock judiciously at all—therefore these lists that you take as gospel are in fact, just an arm of the overall warmblood sales promotion scheme. There is nothing wrong with endorsing one's product, and more power to them for their well-thought-out dominance in sport horse advertisement in all its forms. But if you are like me, a breeder in North America, you were fooled as I was—thinking these were all-inclusive and democratic lists—but they are not.

Discovery—he was not called the 'iron horse' for nothing—a winner carrying top weight, he transmits not only speed combined with stamina, but the ability to win while carrying heavy weight, and he brings a tremendous jump as well. He is rated a *chef-de-race* for stamina, and he is also one of the best broodmare sires of recent times. —photo by Bert Morgan, courtesy of Keeneland Library

I already knew from the research for this book into the hidden American lines in the European Thoroughbred that many of those listed above already had American lines in them, such as Ladykiller, Courville, Lucky Boy, etc. (see Chapter 29). But where are the American jumper lines of Fair Play, Domino, Ben Brush, Whisk Broom II, and Hanover? Well, now we know that the Jersey Act kept most of our lines out of Europe from 1913 to 1949, which covers the birth dates of those European sources above, plus until the raids of the American yearlings sales in the 1970-80s, the American lines were not leaving home much either, mainly because we had no reason to, as America had the high purses and biggest races here, with a very healthy industry. For instance, by 1945 the average winnings per horse in America was 30 to 50% higher than what was found in comparable racehorses in England/France and Australia, and this includes the earnings of their superstars Isonomy and Phar Lap.

However, America has been producing a **winning international show jumper since the mid-1800s**, and those same lines that powered those stars have never lost their sport traits and still today produce the highest quality sport performers. Peter Birdsall's *Bloodlines of Hunters and Jumpers in North America* is useful for a starting point of pedigree review in our sport horses. However it is limited by necessity, first by its date of publication—1981—and also in that it lists the top sport horses with a four-generation pedigree, so some lines are aging out, or others are too new to show their potency in his list of occurrence. But it was there that I first found that yes, indeed, the American lines were right there in force, not only in our in North American stars, but in the international champions as well.

When studying bloodlines of sport horses a couple of things need to be remembered, one is the great majority of top performers in non-racing sport are geldings, so we have to go back to their root sire or dam to find current carriers, usually found in the stallions who race on the flat, as the steeplechasers are usually gelded also. America never banned foreign Thoroughbreds, so we will find the top sire-lines of the English and French racers in our product. What I did find interesting is that the jump sire lines listed in the first paragraph, those who are supposed to be the "important" worldwide jump lines (Ladykiller, Cottage Son, Courville, Lucky Boy, Furioso, Orange Peel etc.) were **not** found in the North American-bred international champions either—none of them—really, they are not there.

This of course leads to the realization that those lists of show jump lines and the lovely articles on the Thoroughbred lines that produce jumpers that appear on the internet and elsewhere are very limited in their scope and have never really considered American-bred champions in their statistics, not even the ones who had beat their horses to the medals—they couldn't have or Fair Play and his son Man O' War would have surfaced. Part of this problem is cultural, the European way of producing equines is a national program, their respective governments oversee and in most cases structure and supply the resources for the production of their national products. In America we are still on the free enterprise system, and it is the individual who produces our equine product. I believe this has resulted in a basic lack of understanding—that goes both ways, indeed this may be a portion of the reason that the Europeans appear to view us a 'uncultured' (see Chapter 35), because we are not in a socialist mode as they are—so there is a basic lack of comprehension and of course respect—we don't do it they way they do. This difference in culture results in a mindset that falsely reasons: if we are not organized as a government in equine breeding, then we are not really organized in breeding. History however has demonstrated the opposite is in fact true, and the North American continent is responsible for not only a continual production of top international-level Hunter and Olympic-style sport equines spanning one hundred seventy-years (over one hundred years longer than those warmblood breeders can rightfully claim), but in addition, we have also produced the top international sport horse breeds of American Thoroughbred, Standardbred, and Quarter Horse—and they are the highest rated in the world in their respective catagories. All was accomplished without the government supervising our every move—and one might then reason then our success in all matters equine occurred **because** we were at liberty to develop our own programs—so maybe our friends across the pond should give that some thought.

But there is much more to this issue than this, because evidently **none of their special show jump lines got here either**, so that is the extra wrinkle: horses with those special lines were never imported here for breeding. So there you have it, while we have competed against each other since the beginning of Olympic-style sport (1912), we have maintained separate breeding populations through the 1980s.

Nasrullah—he has been rated #1 sport horse sire by Peter Birdsall; he is found continually in the best sport horse of the last fifty years. —photo by Skeet Meadors—courtesy of Keeneland Library

Nonetheless, North America has always incorporated the top foreign flat racing lines, such as Blenheim, The Tetrarch, Nasrullah, Mahmoud etc.— but not these special European jump sources (found in warmbloods). Of course, one result of the Warmblood fad here is saturation in our country with their bloodlines since the 1980s, as they are sometimes powering the sport horses bred by the members of their very exclusive registries, but still, they usually are not the ones the average American breeder is breeding on with consistently. Dominance in a talent or type requires building up the lines that carry those traits, so having a line of a European sport star in our horses does not equal dominance—unless that horse is very strongly bred in European lines—which is unfortunately seldom seen; most are of outcross breeding.

Instead, here in North America once again, it is still the racehorse base that is accessed continually for our fresh blood. And Peter Birdsall after a modern day re-evaluation of current jumper bloodlines has stated in a more recent article that even now the top sport horse bloodlines are: Nasrullah, Man O' War, Native Dancer, and Princequillo—in that order. So still it is the Thoroughbred that is leading our domestic gene pool. When I did my studies on the Hall of Fame inductees (see Appendix E) I found the Thoroughbred was the consistent factor in all of them, and the only place where it wasn't the leading breed was in the Dressage Horse, where it was a Hanoverian line that dominated. This is not surprising either since the dressage competitors here were emulating their European gurus in this sport, which was a relatively new discipline for the majority of Americans (see Chapter 31- Keen). The dedicated Warmblood breeders here are usually attempting to breed 'pure warmbloods', which is of course a misnomer—as there is no purebred warmblood, but most of those breeders here are attempting to do so. In their breeding populations then of course we will find foreign lines almost exclusively. But that is a very expensive game for the typical American to play—remember we do not have government subsidies here, nor the state studs. Nevertheless while we don't make the big headlines, the small scale and backyard breeders are still supplying the majority of sport horses on this continent.

In the mean time we, the breeders here in North America, need education in which of our native bloodlines are top sport sources for our programs, especially those that are based here at home that are accessible and affordable for all of us. And contrary to the common wisdom, the breeders also need to be reminded that those home-lines are actually a far better sport source, as their genetics are truly sport based, rather than the slower, less athletic farm-coach based genetics they are importing in order to play the Warmblood game. However, I don't expect this revelation to come to our breeders quickly, as they have been instructed in their craft for forty years now by our European cousins; therefore I am just putting all this out there for those of you that are ready to hear it (see Chapter 35).

Man O' War of course is a premier jump line, but this talent did not begin with him, even in the limited time frame in Birdsall's work, I found his grandsire Hastings, the Spendthrift son (Australian/Aerolite RH), is still well represented not just in the Fair Play dynasty but through a daughter and in the line of his ½ brother Plaudit as well. Plaudit is the line behind that relatively uncelebrated sire Questionnaire, who is the sire of Rough n' Tumble (see Chapter 24), but it turns out this sire is also found in several top international jumpers, such as Jet Run—an individual gold medal earner in the Pan Am Games—who was rated in the top ten jumpers in the world. Another example is in the Canadian Equestrian team star Merchant of Venice, who also carries the less celebrated John P. Grier line as well. Plaudit acts as a connecting genetic bridge between Hastings (sire of Fair Play—out of Cinderella) and Domino (by Himyar) as Plaudit is by Himyar out of Cinderella.

Chance Play—an excellent sire—is sometimes forgotten in the shadow of Man O' War, but he and his full brothers Chance Shot and Pari-Mutual are found consistently in the top hunters and jumpers in this country. —TB Record

The Fair Play line however is a massive supplier of the best in sport horses, especially in jumping and eventing. His son Display usually through his son Discovery is a solid source (Discovery's dam brings in the Hamburg line). For instance, Bold Ruler—whose dam-sire is Discovery—is found in top jumpers, plus his full brother Independence was a successful steeplechaser and sire of steeplechasers, hunters, and jumpers. They are out of a Discovery dam, as is Native Dancer, who is rated the #3 sport bloodline in the world by Birdsall. Therefore, the number two and three highest rated sport lines are, one a grandson of Fair Play and the other is out of a dam by a grandson of Fair Play—surely this is something we should take note of.

"Fair Play is a name that will forever hold an exalted place in American turfdom…leading winners include Man O' War, Seabiscuit, War Admiral, Display, Crusader, Discovery, Chance Play, Chance Shot, Some Chance, Four Freedoms and many others…There can be little doubt but these lines have held their own, or actually increased in influence, against a continuing stream of importations of horses from England" (Ned Welch 1946).

Fair Play produced a trio of full brothers that I also found repeatedly in the best show jumpers; these are Chance Play/Chance Shot/Pari-Mutual. His daughters are well represented also, especially Etoile Filante and Ilna.

Man O' War is the fountainhead of a never-fading source of sport, even today; to build up his presence in our back lines is a proven recipe for success. Three of Man O' War's full siblings has surfaced as top jump producers also, his sister Masda, his brothers Playfellow and especially My Play, who is found consistently in top jumpers, often along with his son Head Play.

War Admiral—a top sport bloodline—then and now.
—photo from Thoroughbred Record

The Man O' War son War Admiral is far and away the best producer of this line, but close behind him is his ¾ brother War Glory. Then there is their close relative Great War, who is a premier source of international jumpers, and he is also a source of Maggie B. B. RH—he, like Whisk Broom II, carries a double of her on their dam-side. (Line-breeders take note—War Admiral had five full sisters: Admiralette, War Hysteria, Our Colors, Military Brush, and War Brush—plus the ¾ sisters Marching Along and Harranette.)

But then there is War Relic, already an international force through his grandson Relic who, in spite of the Jersey Act being in force is still found in European performers such as through his son Pericles in the Dutch horse, and he is found also through his French *chef* grandsons Relko, Match, and Reliance. In our American-bred jumpers he is often seen through his son imported Mystic II, a noted sire of show jumpers—who interestingly carries a double of Durban in the dam, making the background presence of Lexington RH the dominant genetic force in this French-bred stallion.

Man O' War daughters are big transmitters of jumper talent as well—Salaminia, Spotted Beauty, Jean Bart, and Anchors Ahead are just a few who have multiple presences in the top performers.

Of course we already devoted a chapter (33) to the Man O' War sons Battleship and Annapolis, jumping dynasty sires.

So if you are a breeder here in North America, and you want to insure you have a jump along with speed, stamina, and soundness you will not be disappointed if you stack the background of your pedigrees with this American world-class jump line.

But Fair Play is not the whole American contribution to top sport performance. The rest of our four-mile era conduits are found strongly in the best horses also, such as the Whisk Broom II dynasty through his son John P. Grier and then his son Jack High (see Chapter 25), and he is also dam-sire of the good jump sire Double Jay who is by a Black Toney sire. The Whisk Broom II son Diavolo has left a significant legacy of top jumpers such as San Lucas, who competed in forty-three Nations Cups, an international jumper of the highest quality, earning gold and silver in Pan Am Games, but also with several High Jump wins.

> "I've never seen a horse that could jump big vertical fences so easily, or had a bigger heart, and riding this superhorse was one of the greatest thrills of my riding career" (Frank Chapot—quotation from *Great Horses of the United States Equestrian Team*, used by permission of the USET).

Domino is everywhere, combined with Fair Play, Ben Brush lines of Broomstick and Sweep, with Whisk Broom II and Hanover. His principle modern conduits of sport talent are Black Toney as he is found in the good sire Double Jay (previously), he is 4x4 in the great Idle Dice (Chapter 32), and he is the dam-sire of one of the greatest steeplechasers of all time: Elkridge, who was national champion in 1942 and 1946. The Black Toney grandson Blue Larkspur, with thirty-four appearances in Birdsall's tabulations, is the second sire of the incomparable international star Bold Minstrel, who has the distinction of representing the USA in both jumping and eventing at international level, appearing in two Pan Am Games and one Olympics in Eventing, but then he also won the medal in jumping at Winnipeg. We already covered the Domino line Valorous in Chapter 30, but then there are the inbred Ultimus and High Time—all are well represented in international performers. Perhaps the poster child for Domino is the international Grand Prix winner Triple Crown, with wins in Germany and France, and he carries both the highly inbred Ultimus and High Time. Ultimus—2x2 to Domino—is a prime jumper sire, and one of the USET's winners, Master William is 4x4 to him.

A tough stayer, Eight Thirty transmits a tremendous jump as well. He is a first class sport horse line. —photo by Skeet Meadors, courtesy of Keeneland Library

Surprisingly, the intensely inbred High Time, who is 2x3x3 to Domino, is found continually in the jumpers—I found twenty-four in Birdsall's book who carry him—not quite what you would expect from an strongly inbred sire. For example, he is found in the USET horse Out Late (along with Man O' War and Broomstick) who won in Holland, Canada, and Ireland; he is also found in The Jones Boy who was rated in the top ten jumpers in the world in 1979, but perhaps his greatest presence is through the sire Eight Thirty, an important jumper line that is inbred not just through his dam-sire High Time (three Domino lines) but he is also 2x3 to the ¾ brothers Man O' War/Friar Rock—you will find him in thirty-four of Birdsall's top jumpers, perhaps most notably as the second sire of the Hall-of-Famer Untouchable (Chapter 33).

I guess it should not be a surprise that our top four-mile heat racing families (Chapter 10) are still powering the athleticism, stamina, speed, and soundness in our top sport horses of today, but here you have their modern families, still providing the essence of sport to the next generation. We, as thoughtful breeders, can exploit this source today, it is our heritage, and the genetics are still here with us; we just need to make them dominant by using proper selective breeding techniques (Appendix B) to see them live again in our herds.

KATHLEEN H. KIRSAN

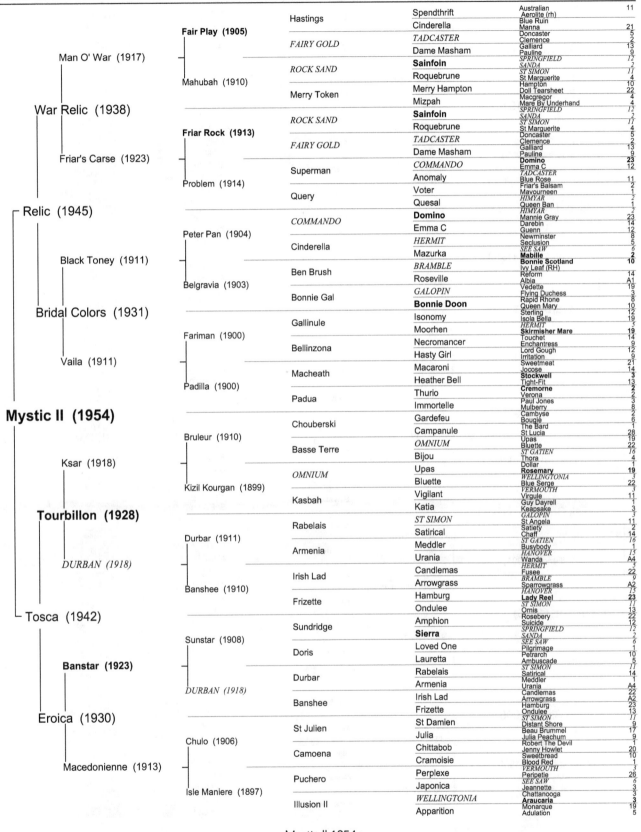

War Relic (1938)

- Man O' War (1917)
- Friar's Carse (1923)

Relic (1945)

- Black Toney (1911)
- Vaila (1911)

Bridal Colors (1931)

Mystic II (1954)

- Ksar (1918)
- *DURBAN (1918)*

Tourbillon (1928)

Tosca (1942)

Banstar (1923)

Eroica (1930)

- Macedonienne (1913)

Fair Play (1905)	Hastings	Spendthrift	Australian / Aerolite (rh) 11
		Cinderella	Blue Ruin / Manna 21
	FAIRY GOLD	*TADCASTER*	Doncaster 5 / Clemence 13
		Dame Masham	Galliard / Pauline 9
Mahubah (1910)	*ROCK SAND*	**Sainfoin**	*SPRINGFIELD* 12 / *SANDA* 2
		Roquebrune	*ST SIMON* 11 / St Marguerite 4
	Merry Token	Merry Hampton	Hampton 10 / Doll Tearsheet 22
		Mizpah	Macgregor 4 / Mare By Underhand 4
Friar Rock (1913)	*ROCK SAND*	**Sainfoin**	*SPRINGFIELD* 12 / *SANDA* 2
		Roquebrune	*ST SIMON* 11 / St Marguerite 4
	FAIRY GOLD	*TADCASTER*	Doncaster 5 / Clemence 2
		Dame Masham	Galliard 13 / Pauline 9
Problem (1914)	Superman	*COMMANDO*	**Domino** 23 / Emma C 12
		Anomaly	*TADCASTER* / Blue Rose 11
	Query	Voter	Friar's Balsam 1 / Mavourneen 2
		Quesal	*HIMYAR* 1 / Queen Ban 1
Peter Pan (1904)	*COMMANDO*	**Domino**	*HIMYAR* 2 / Mannie Gray 23
		Emma C	Darebin 14 / Guenn 12
	Cinderella	*HERMIT*	Newminster 8 / Seclusion 5
		Mazurka	*SEE SAW* 2 / Mabille 6
Belgravia (1903)	Ben Brush	*BRAMBLE*	**Bonnie Scotland** 10 / Ivy Leaf (RH)
		Roseville	Reform 14 / Albia A1
	Bonnie Gal	*GALOPIN*	Vedette 19 / Flying Duchess 3
		Bonnie Doon	Rapid Rhone 8 / Queen Mary 10
Fariman (1900)	Gallinule	Isonomy	Sterling 12 / Isola Bella 19
		Moorhen	*HERMIT* 5 / **Skirmisher Mare** 19
	Bellinzona	Necromancer	Touchet 14 / Enchantress 9
		Hasty Girl	Lord Gough 12 / Irritation 9
Padilla (1900)	Macheath	Macaroni	Sweetmeat 21 / Jocose 14
		Heather Bell	**Stockwell** 3 / Tight-Fit 13
	Padua	Thurio	**Cremorne** 2 / Verona 3
		Immortelle	Paul Jones 8 / Mulberry 2
Bruleur (1910)	Chouberski	Gardefeu	Cambyse 6 / Bougie 1
		Campanule	The Bard 28 / St Lucia 19
	Basse Terre	*OMNIUM*	Upas 22 / Bluette
		Bijou	*ST GATIEN* 16 / Thora 4
Kizil Kourgan (1899)	*OMNIUM*	Upas	Dollar / **Rosemary** 19
		Bluette	*WELLINGTONIA* 3 / Blue Serge 22
	Kasbah	Vigilant	*VERMOUTH* 3 / Virgule 11
		Katia	Guy Dayrell 1 / Keapsake 3
Durbar (1911)	Rabelais	*ST SIMON*	*GALOPIN* 3 / St Angela 11
		Satirical	Satiety 2 / Chaff 14
	Armenia	Meddler	*ST GATIEN* 16 / Busybody 1
		Urania	*HANOVER* 15 / Wanda A4
Banshee (1910)	Irish Lad	Candlemas	*HERMIT* 5 / Fusee 22
		Arrowgrass	*BRAMBLE* 9 / Sparrowgrass A2
	Frizette	Hamburg	*HANOVER* 15 / **Lady Reel** 23
		Ondulee	*ST SIMON* 11 / Ornis 13
Sunstar (1908)	Sundridge	Amphion	Rosebery 22 / Suicide 12
		Sierra	*SPRINGFIELD* 12 / *SANDA* 2
	Doris	Loved One	*SEE SAW* 6 / Pilgrimage 1
		Lauretta	Petrarch 10 / Ambuscade 5
DURBAN (1918)	Durbar	Rabelais	*ST SIMON* 11 / Satirical 14
		Armenia	Meddler 1 / Urania A4
	Banshee	Irish Lad	Candlemas 22 / Arrowgrass A2
		Frizette	Hamburg 23 / Ondulee
Chulo (1906)	St Julien	St Damien	*ST SIMON* 11 / Distant Shore 9
		Julia	Beau Brummel 17 / Julia Peachum 9
	Camoena	Chittabob	Robert The Devil 1 / Jenny Howlet 20
		Cramoisie	Sweetbread 10 / Blood Red 1
Isle Maniere (1897)	Puchero	Perplexe	*VERMOUTH* 3 / Peripetie 26
		Japonica	*SEE SAW* 6 / Jeannette 3
	Illusion II	*WELLINGTONIA* 3	Chattanooga 3 / **Araucaria**
		Apparition	Monarque 19 / Adulation 5

Mystic II 1954

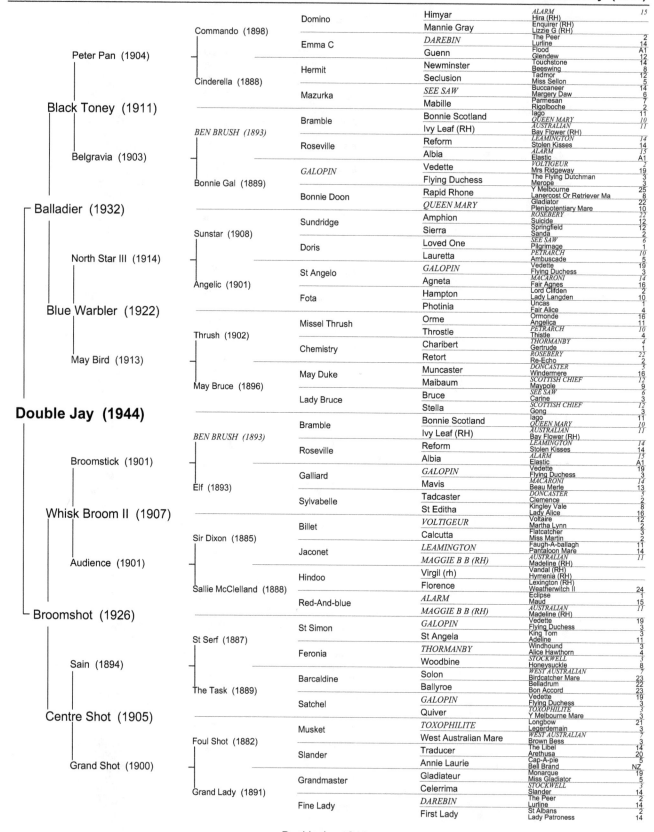

Left-hand pedigree columns:

- Peter Pan (1904)
- Black Toney (1911)
- Belgravia (1903)
- Balladier (1932)
- North Star III (1914)
- Blue Warbler (1922)
- May Bird (1913)
- **Double Jay (1944)**
- Broomstick (1901)
- Whisk Broom II (1907)
- Audience (1901)
- Broomshot (1926)
- Sain (1894)
- Centre Shot (1905)
- Grand Shot (1900)

		Sire / Dam	Grandsire / Granddam	Great-grandparents	No.
Commando (1898)		Domino	Himyar	*ALARM* / Hira (RH)	15
			Mannie Gray	Enquirer (RH) / Lizzie G (RH)	
		Emma C	*DAREBIN*	The Peer / Lurline	2 / 14
			Guenn	Flood / Glendew	A1 / 12
Cinderella (1888)		Hermit	Newminster	Touchstone / Beeswing	14 / 8
			Seclusion	Tadmor / Miss Sellon	12 / 5
		Mazurka	*SEE SAW*	Buccaneer / Margery Daw	14 / 6
			Mabille	Parmesan / Rigolboche	7 / 2
BEN BRUSH (1893)		Bramble	Bonnie Scotland	Iago / *QUEEN MARY*	11 / 10
			Ivy Leaf (RH)	*AUSTRALIAN* / Bay Flower (RH)	11
		Roseville	Reform	*LEAMINGTON* / Stolen Kisses	14 / 14
			Albia	*ALARM* / Elastic	15 / A1
Bonnie Gal (1889)		*GALOPIN*	Vedette	*VOLTIGEUR* / Mrs Ridgeway	2 / 19
			Flying Duchess	The Flying Dutchman / Merope	3 / 3
		Bonnie Doon	Rapid Rhone	Y Melbourne / Lanercost Or Retriever Ma	25
			QUEEN MARY	Gladiator / Plenipotentiary Mare	22 / 10
Sunstar (1908)		Sundridge	Amphion	*ROSEBERY* / Suicide	22 / 12
			Sierra	Springfield / Sanda	12 / 2
		Doris	Loved One	*SEE SAW* / Pilgrimage	6 / 1
			Lauretta	*PETRARCH* / Ambuscade	10 / 5
Angelic (1901)		St Angelo	*GALOPIN*	Vedette / Flying Duchess	19 / 3
			Agneta	*MACARONI* / Fair Agnes	14 / 16
		Fota	Hampton	Lord Clifden / Lady Langden	2 / 10
			Photinia	Uncas / Fair Alice	1 / 4
Thrush (1902)		Missel Thrush	Orme	Ormonde / Angelica	16 / 11
			Throstle	*PETRARCH* / Thistle	10 / 4
		Chemistry	Charibert	*THORMANBY* / Gertrude	1
			Retort	*ROSEBERY* / Re-Echo	22 / 2
May Bruce (1896)		May Duke	Muncaster	*DONCASTER* / Windermere	5 / 16
			Maibaum	*SCOTTISH CHIEF* / Maypole	12 / 9
		Lady Bruce	Bruce	*SEE SAW* / Carine	6 / 3
			Stella	*SCOTTISH CHIEF* / Gong	12 / 3
BEN BRUSH (1893)		Bramble	Bonnie Scotland	Iago / *QUEEN MARY*	11 / 10
			Ivy Leaf (RH)	*AUSTRALIAN* / Bay Flower (RH)	11
		Roseville	Reform	*LEAMINGTON* / Stolen Kisses	14 / 14
			Albia	*ALARM* / Elastic	15 / A1
Elf (1893)		Galliard	*GALOPIN*	Vedette / Flying Duchess	19 / 3
			Mavis	*MACARONI* / Beau Merle	14 / 13
		Sylvabelle	Tadcaster	*DONCASTER* / Clemence	5 / 2
			St Editha	Kingley Vale / Lady Alice	8 / 16
Sir Dixon (1885)		Billet	*VOLTIGEUR*	Voltaire / Martha Lynn	12 / 2
			Calcutta	Flatcatcher / Miss Martin	2 / 3
		Jaconet	*LEAMINGTON*	Faugh-A-ballagh / Pantaloon Mare	11 / 14
			MAGGIE B B (RH)	*AUSTRALIAN* / Madeline (RH)	11
Sallie McClelland (1888)		Hindoo	Virgil (rh)	Vandal (RH) / Hymenia (RH)	
			Florence	Lexington (RH) / Weatherwitch II	24
		Red-And-blue	*ALARM*	Eclipse / Maud	1 / 15
			MAGGIE B B (RH)	*AUSTRALIAN* / Madeline (RH)	11
St Serf (1887)		St Simon	*GALOPIN*	Vedette / Flying Duchess	19 / 3
			St Angela	King Tom / Adeline	3 / 11
		Feronia	*THORMANBY*	Windhound / Alice Hawthorn	3 / 4
			Woodbine	*STOCKWELL* / Honeysuckle	3 / 8
The Task (1889)		Barcaldine	Solon	*WEST AUSTRALIAN* / Birdcatcher Mare	7 / 23
			Ballyroe	Belladrum / Bon Accord	22 / 23
		Satchel	*GALOPIN*	Vedette / Flying Duchess	19 / 3
			Quiver	*TOXOPHILITE* / Y Melbourne Mare	3 / 3
Foul Shot (1882)		Musket	*TOXOPHILITE*	Longbow / Legerdemain	21 / 3
			West Australian Mare	*WEST AUSTRALIAN* / Brown Bess	7 / 3
		Slander	Traducer	The Libel / Arethusa	14 / 20
			Annie Laurie	Cap-A-pie / Bell Brand	5 / NZ
Grand Lady (1891)		Grandmaster	Gladiateur	Monarque / Miss Gladiator	19 / 5
			Celerrima	*STOCKWELL* / Slander	3 / 14
		Fine Lady	*DAREBIN*	The Peer / Lurline	2 / 14
			First Lady	St Albans / Lady Patroness	2 / 14

Double Jay 1944

Chapter 35

It's Our Own Fault

Overall, the North American sport horse breeder requires a 'reset' in perspective regarding our own past record in sport horse production. We have been listening for forty years now to a skewed version of our own equine history fed to us by what I call the 'European Warmblood Marketing Machine', through which our European cousins have carried out the planned and organized conquest of not only our sport horse market, but the worldwide one. We cannot put the blame on them for promoting their agriculture business—although we may be angered by some of the methods used—we have to assume the blame ourselves, and truly on the whole, we all have enjoyed our experience with warmblood breeding. What we have to do is recognize what has occurred and remedy the situation, sanely—which means not to overreact and somehow penalize our European cousins.

European Criticism of American Sport Horse Breeding

I was heavily invested in the warmblood breeding fad when my eyes were opened to the subtle manipulation of the American breeder that had been going on for decades. This revelation happened for me only when an industry spokesperson slipped up and published how the European government warmblood federations really perceived us. This occurred in an editorial published in April of 2003 in a sport horse trade journal ("Breeding News for Sport Horses") published in Switzerland (and Canada!) just after the onset of the Iraq War. This trade journal is supposed to be a resource for all breeders of sport horses and to represent all sport horse breeds that participate in the Olympic-style sports, but the reality is it is only concerned with the promotion of the European Warmblood product. The Iraq War was the stressor, and the event which psychologically gave the editors (in their own estimation) the moral high ground and therefore it seems the permission to really let us have it—telling us not only are we warmongers but were uncultured as well, and that we do little breeding of consequence; mainly they say because we are strictly materialistic and being driven by money we just buy what we want—yes, they really said that. They went on to say the American breeder has not developed the wisdom in breeding that comes only from centuries of selective breeding ("that's called philosophy, and goes hand-in-hand with culture"). In other words, we—the Americans—don't know how to breed good horses, but 'they' (Europeans) do. The confidently delivered judgment of us was that we were both unrefined as a people, and too young a country (therefore unable to rise to their level) to ever reach the heights of the breeding art form that they have come to occupy.

In this tirade the British were included, but they got off a little easier, not quite the complete dismissal we received, as they said that the British "...do breed, even if they are currently not the best organized in this field"—I kid you not, the British not organized in breeding?—the inventor of the Thoroughbred and Cleveland Bay and Hackney—not to mention a four-hundred-year-old Hunter tradition, but according to the far more learned Europeans the Brits don't really know how to breed sport horses either! Remember, this is a sport horse journal stating this—not a farm journal. The whole harangue was pretty insulting, as it was meant to be. But for us, the Americans,

American Thoroughbred foals having a 'chat' over the fence.
—sketch by C. W. Anderson for Who's Who in *Thoroughbred Racing*

they reserved the biggest slice of their vitriol, and there was no attempt to even disguise their utter distain for us in all matters—equine or as a country. And here we are, all the while, lapping up their sport horse product—so in my opinion we deserve it; because if we don't value our own horse—which is so far superior to theirs in sport genetics it isn't even a close call—then we have reached a level of stupidity and naivety where we rate all the condescension they are shoveling at us.

Here is a reality check for you from an unimpeachable source. Contrary to the common knowledge out there in the sport horse world, Alexander MacKay-Smith (editor of Chronicle of the Horse for 30 years, equine scholar and author, superb horseman) has provided us with two pertinent **facts**. His research has revealed that two-thirds of the registered horse breeds **worldwide** originated in English speaking countries, and the leading three breeds of horses—based on studbook registrations, are racehorses: the Thoroughbred, which was developed in England, and the Quarter Horse and the Standardbred, which were developed in the USA.

Plus, the truth of the matter in America is that our original breed of horse is a sport horse—selectively and continually bred from 1624 (see Chapter 1 and Appendix D). From that sport base we created the American Thoroughbred, the Standardbred, the Quarter Horse (that's three racehorse breeds created by us, the Neanderthals!), as well as the greatest light horse breeds in the world: Morgan, Saddlebred, and Tennessee Walker—not to mention our North American 'warmblood': the Hunter Horse, all accomplished breeds in sport performance. And our Hunter Horse, our Thoroughbred, and Standardbred were truly already 'international' sport horses by the late-1800s, as they competed successfully against the best England, Ireland, France, and really all Europe could provide. It was our horse that traveled to these events, not the foreign interests coming here. But we didn't remember this, nor did our critics, so they truly believed they had the vast experience in breeding sport horses.

The international champion and American-bred show jumper and hunter David Gray 1902, owned by Julian Morris. He was a winner domestically and abroad. He traveled to England in 1910-11 and with his stable mates The Virginian and Keswick, won consistently at the Olympia grounds in England; David Gray individually won five blue ribbons and a championship while there. He is half Thoroughbred, and his career totals are ninety-seven blue ribbons, ten reserve championships, and ten championships. —photo by Haas, found in *Thoroughbred Types 1900-1925*

In the mid-1800s, while America already had two hundred years of racehorse development and one hundred fifty years of Hunter Horse breeding behind them, most of Europe was using the farm horse and later the coach horse, and it is only since WWII that they got organized in sport horse breeding (which by the way, would not have occurred at all if these very same 'uncultured' Brits and Yankees did not step in and rescue their European breeds from starvation and slaughter at the close of World War II—see *North American Sport Horse Breeder* for more on this). But the most important issue here is that they have been listening to their own propaganda so long they believe it, and more importantly and tragically, so do many of us. Part of the problem is that their equine writers are mostly from the post-war generation and have forgotten their own history, for they have no high moral ground to stand on (especially in the warmonger category), **nor do they have vast experience in sport horse production.** And we, idiotically, have forgotten that we have been breeding our own 'warmblood' sport horse for three hundred years—see what I mean—we have earned their distain.

But to be fair, that editorial, even though put out by a sport horse trade journal, was written a decade ago in 2003. And while we have not only a one-hundred-seventy-year-old tradition of producing winning **international sport horses**, we have also graciously hosted the government breed societies of our critics here in our country since the 1970s. So what has been going on since 2003—because maybe that editorial was just an emotional response to the fear of being involved in a war? So, since then have they acknowledged our ability to breed medal winners out of our own stock (historically a longer record then theirs) and allowed our sport breeds into the 'allowed' breeds to cross with their warmbloods? No, they have not. Actually, the intent of their presence here, which is to sell their product and control the market, has never skipped a beat.

I didn't have to look far or hard to find the answer to my own question on whether the attitude climate had changed either. I just received a sport horse trade journal in the mail yesterday, which we can fairly use as a current barometer of the industry attitude toward the American breeder. So I present this to you as a recent example of the extremely sly manipulation that is continually being directed to you, the North American sport horse breeder. Here is a seemingly innocuous statement from it:

"The first warmblood stallion approvals date back into the early 1500s, when the state stud in Baden-Wurt-temberg was founded in Marbach" (Engelhardt).

The above quotation is from an article entitled "Stallion Inspections—history and perspective" written by Dr. Maren Engelhardt, Germany, for *Warmblood Stallions of North America 2014*—which is subtitled: "the premier magazine for jumping, dressage, hunter, and eventing sires." This magazine is published in Wisconsin by the way. It sure sounds like the Germans have carefully been breeding sport 'warmbloods' for five hundred years!

The article was demonstrating their superior inspection process system—which indeed did begin in the later 1500s (not early 1500s as stated). But you are being subtlety misled by this presentation—for the horses being inspected and bred then through the early 1900s were draft breeds—selectively bred to pull a plow and cart. The Germans did not start breeding sport 'warmbloods' until after WWII. It was then they used the base of their cavalry (Trakehner and East Prussian) and farm-coach breeds (Holstein/Hanoverian/Oldenburg etc) to accomplish this task, and then added the true sport breeds—such as the Thoroughbred— until their breed could perform in sport. So, what were they breeding in the 1500s at the Baden-Wurttenberg stud? It was the Schwere Warmbluter—or heavy warmblood, which is a farm horse, one designed to pull a plow and cart—in other words a draft horse; we call them cold bloods here. So, semantics is a portion of the confusion for the American breeder in this: the classifying of draft horses as 'warmbloods' whereas we classify them as 'cold bloods'. There is nothing similar between the Schwere Warmbluter of the 1500s and the twenty-first century sport warmblood, and the inspection process for the two types of horse is diametrically opposed in practice and philosophy. Draft horses (plow and cart) are not meant to be saddle horses; they are designed to pull heavy loads at slow speed, whereas a sport horse is meant to be ridden and to perform at speed—totally different genotypes.

American Hunter Horse and his rider watching a point-to-point circa 1800; by this time Hunt Clubs and their performance tests were in most settled areas of the States as Hunter sports were an American passion. —wood engraving by Alexander Anderson, Library of Congress

By its nature, an inspection process is subjective and therefore more liable to corruption and manipulation, whereas a performance test is a much more objective test of true sport ability. From the colonial days in America, the breeders and owners of Hunter Horses not only hunted their horses, but they participated in point-to-points, jumping contests, and steeplechases to test their horse's abilities and to keep it in condition for the hunting season. These performance exercises and tests became sports of their own through this process.

Even as early as 1780 organized hunt clubs were common across settled America, and they were constructed and maintained as testing centers for Hunter Horses, complete with a jumping ring, a steeplechase course, and a cross-country course. Plus the majority of racetracks also set aside portions of their calendar to host hurdling races. Our steeplechase industry, our Hunt Clubs, and our combined training programs of today are preserving our centuries-old tradition of sport horse testing. And America has been fielding an **international** racehorse and Hunter since the mid-1800s.

How far the European campaign has moved in its conquest of the worldwide sport horse market is illustrated plainly in this same magazine where I found the above article, because it showcases seventy-four selected sport sires standing in North America (plus three ponies). The vast majority of those stallions are of European descent, although there was one Russian horse, and three American Thoroughbreds, and even an Appaloosa. However it is sad to see that still a full 75% of those stallions were bred in Europe, which means the American breeder of warmbloods is being bypassed by those buying stallions in this country. Are there no high-quality American-bred stallions available to the North American purchaser? Of course there are, but evidently the buying public has succumbed to the massively successful siren song of Europe. It is apparent then, that our task ahead for the American sport horse industry is first and foremost one of education. With 75% of the stallion purchasers being seduced into buying European by the hype spun out by the European Warmblood Marketing Machine, there is a lot of work ahead for this organization.

[Note: The aim of this book is to provide you, the American breeder, with your own domestic sport history and genetic heritage, which has become hidden or forgotten over the years. The stallions showcased in this magazine are not all the stallions available to the sport horse breeder on this continent, rather they are those that have qualified under the European system; therefore this magazine is an arm of the European Warmblood industry. This is not a criticism; I mention it for your awareness.]

Thoroughbred Industry Silence on Dominant American Lines

I covered our true equine sport history in *North American Sport Horse Breeder,* and in this book I am concerned with the Thoroughbred bloodline—which is just one of our own world-class **sport** breeds. With the heavy influx of the European government-bred breeds into this country since 1970, also came their version of equine history and their view of our domestic Thoroughbred, the base of many of our international level sport horses (see Chapter 31 and Thoroughbred article in Appendix E). The reality is that our Thoroughbred, even with the organized attempt by Britain to eliminate it, is so superior, that in just a few decades after the Jersey Act ban was lifted, it became the greatest Thoroughbred in the world, and has remained so since the 1970s. Indeed, when the experts rated the greatest and most influential Thoroughbreds in our recent times, it is Native Dancer and Mr. Prospector here in the States, and in Europe it is Mill Reef and Sadlers Wells. What do these world dynasty-building stallions have in common? They are not only **all American Thoroughbreds**, but they carry huge amounts of the five families born of our Heroic Era; therefore they are loaded with lines of our native Running Horse (see Appendix D). Therefore the original source of sport talent is still providing the best genetics in competitive equine sport. The way genes work and travel does not change, therefore the genes of our sport equine ancestors are still there in the background of our horses and still travel down to our product today unchanged (Bowling, *Horse Genetics*). The task before us is to consciously reconcentrate those important genes and to eliminate the unsound strains in our herds.

But once again there is a need for re-education on what our stock descends from, for I have found in investigating the great carriers of our Heroic Era genes, here and abroad, they seem to be deliberately overlooked, not just by the warmblood authorities, but by the Thoroughbred gurus as well. See if you agree.

In studying our bloodlines, and reading about the ones that traveled to Europe since the repeal of the Jersey Act and those that set up dynasties there—such as Sadlers Wells and Mill Reef—I have become truly distressed by the almost total ignoring of our native American lines in the explanations of the amazing class these horses possess and their awesome ability to pass it on. Over and over I have read, sometimes from the pens of my personal heroes in pedigree evaluation, that the genetic credit must be placed at the feet of the Nasrullah/Princequillo cross, or the background lines of Sundridge/Hermit/Maid of Masham etc.—seldom did I read about the American lines, which are mentioned by some but generally are bypassed in explaining where the power in the line arises from.

The Water Jump—a lithograph of 1884. At the time period of this print three American sport horse breeds: American Thoroughbred, Standardbred, and Hunter Horse were already established as top international performers. —Library of Congress

Even the power of Mumtaz Begum is given to her being an 'agent of Sundridge/Feronia/Violet.' This may be correct, but it is only a portion of her genetic power, and the rest is mysteriously missing time and again. Is Americus invisible? He is really close up in Mumtaz Begum, and he is tremendously inbred (therefore potent) to Lexington RH/Glencoe/Sir Archy/Transport RH. Why is this not mentioned as possibly contributing to her talents? Those same experts mention Durban/Heldifann as a significant power in the modern horse, but again the fact that these mares have eight lines of Lexington RH in seven generations is not counted.

son and daughters further back. However, after revisiting texts written by experts that I admire greatly, I was disappointed once again to find almost no mention of Hanover; it is like he is not there—how can this be? He is in the front of the pedigree, doubled and sex-balanced—how can he be missed and glossed over?

Those experts (two different texts) attribute the power in Durban, one, to the sire of her dam-sire: Candlemas, and the other, to the three lines of Bonnie Scotland 6x5x6 (½ siblings). Bonnie Scotland, while a fair transmitter of sprint speed, also brings in unsoundness. However, he is a son of the potent mare Queen Mary, and many American pedigrees have multiples of this fine mare not only through her son, but also usually with one of his ½ sisters as well, thereby building a nice dominance in her. (In my opinion, it is the dam, Queen Mary, who is the valuable portion of his lineage.)

So I did some additional research on Durban's pedigree to see what I could determine about her true genetic strengths. I already mentioned the eight background lines of Lexington RH in seven generations, but are they just sitting there, or do they have a closer refocus point? Because maybe those experts are right and her true dominance comes through to the front from Bonnie Scotland rather than Lexington RH. The statistics (Harper) have shown that it is possible to have a strong background power, but have it not manifest in the phenotype because of lack of closer reinforcement (see Appendix B).

Now her sire Durbar 1911 (whom the English judge as a 'poor' Derby winner—I guess that means he is lacking class), has a pair of ¾ siblings sitting in his sixth generation: Crinon/Lord Clifton, so that is a nice power in classic English lines, but it is back in the sixth. Nothing much else is going on except the Stockwell and the Lexington RH multiples in the fifth and sixth generations.

Let me use the modern French foundation mare Durban as an example. Normally with a quick look at Durban's pedigree you would take note that St. Simon is 3x4 and Hanover is 4x4, as I did in Chapter 16; the offspring of these greats are ½ siblings. You will find multiples of the ½ siblings King Tom and Stockwell (Pocahontas sons), as well as the multiple Lexington RH

Durban, bred by Herman Duryea in France, became one of the greatest French broodmares of modern times, a potent carrier of Heroic Era genes.—Wiki Commons public domain images

But then Durbar was mated to Banshee 1910 (both bred by Duryea), and it is their combined produce that really shakes things up. Herman Duryea bred Banshee while he was in France from his American-bred Irish Lad out of the great mare Frizette—also American-bred (Keene). When he put

Durbar to Banshee, the resulting full sibling daughters were spectacular (Durban, Sheba, Heldifann). So what changed to make such a powerful shift in pedigree design?

The mare Slander (Rabelais's fourth dam) found her ¾ brother Touchstone in Candlemas 6x6x7, so here we have the Candlemas reinforcement. Closer to the front however is the ¾ sisters Minnie Minor RH and Aerolite RH 5x6—and they are sitting in positions that would influence both X chromosomes. These sisters are daughters of Lexington RH out of Glencoe mares.

But just a little closer to the front 5x5, are the ¾ siblings Fellowcraft and Ivy Leaf RH by the good English sire Australian out of Lexington RH daughters—this is a reinforcing design.

Close siblings are the single most potent design we can create to build dominance. And the important elite mares Durban/Heldifann are most potent in the lines of Lexington RH/Australian/Glencoe—in the order of their dominance. The Lexington RH daughter lines rule three of the four X chromosome avenues in these mares, so their maternal power resides in them. So, Lexington RH and his premier performance genes are given a clear and powerful pathway to the front of the pedigree and with the Hanover double refocusing this power yet closer.

This then is once again a demonstration that we, the American breeders, need to not only target our own Heroic Era genes for sport performance, but also to stop believing everything we read. Obviously we need to educate ourselves in the field of sport bloodlines, but we need to **think for ourselves**, because we are paying a high price for our lethargy.

If this text does nothing else, it is my hope that it clarifies for the sport horse breeder where sport ability originates. Many different breeds can provide skeletal changes, slight or great, that may improve the performance for a particular sport, but without a strong dose of the speed, stamina, and athletic prowess transferred by the racehorse genes that horse will not go far in sport.

The native horse of the British Isles: the Irish Hobby, Scottish Galloway, and the English Running Horse were the original genetic carriers of those sport traits (see Chapter 1 and Appedix D), and the so-called uncultured American breeders managed with two hundred years of selection to improve those traits until their breed was able to perform four-mile heat races week after week into their teens. This is **the highest pinnacle of stamina racing and soundness ever achieved in the world**. Wherever top sport performance is found in a modern breed you can be sure it possesses some of those essential genes.

In Crisis—the American Breeder

The modern-day American breeder of sport horses is experiencing a crisis, both organizational, financial, and of identity. This level of distress was painfully brought home to me when I visited a few blog spots while surfing for thoughts on the American Thoroughbred in sport horse breeding, and found that most of our equestrians are totally unaware of the quality in our American-bred sport horse breeds, having swallowed the 'conventional industry wisdom' on the American Thoroughbred: sprint only, built downhill, of lesser quality then the foreign brands. This level of misinformation cannot be allowed to go on (see Chapter 31 for more on this).

Others were lamenting the inability to find good sport-type Thoroughbred stallions at stud, or that their financial level prevented them breeding their own, because the cost and logistics of breeding to a good stallion was holding them back, or the problem of how were they to register them if they had bred through AI. Then if they had bred one, they worried that they probably would have no place to register it, nor did they have a showcase to promote it, and on and on.

There is now a prevailing atmosphere in the sport horse industry that you must breed European to succeed. Indeed, our European cousins are very organized in the pursuit of promoting their breeds and methods, succeeding in their quest to a point that the average American equestrian now believes this is the only way they can go, and many are in crisis then because what they want to breed will not be accepted in those foreign registries.

KATHLEEN H. KIRSAN

But things are not always as they seem. Americans need first and foremost to remember they live in a free country and that they do not need a foreign government's breed registry to approve their product for them to be successful. This is America, and we have been breeding our own warmblood sport horse for over three hundred years without the supervision of foreign interests telling us how to do it. Think what would have happened in France if Marcel Boussac paid attention to the British Jockey Club when they banned our Thoroughbred, and responded by not breeding from American lines, because then (Chapter 16) there would be no Tourbillon, no Djedbel, no Djeddah, no Tourzima, no Darshaan, and we probably would not be honoring him as one of the 'greats' today, and obviously, the international Thoroughbred would have been a far poorer specimen without his genius.

If you are one of the American breeders who is discouraged with the present state of things, and you have a vision of how to create a superior sport horse, then get out there and do it—we need your input and product. You may register your Thoroughbred or sport horse with the PHR, and breed whatever you like—no inspection, no one telling you don't qualify. Some of us have already been doing this for a while and are competing our horses successfully without a warmblood brand on its hip—really, it is easy. The PHR by the way is a continuation of our original sport horse registry that began in 1918—yes, America has been registering our Hunter Horse for over one hundred years, and our Canadian siblings have been doing the same since 1926. The task before us is to re-educate the American equestrian public to the benefits of the American-bred, and to present a unified voice in the international marketplace—we don't have to become European clones to do this either.

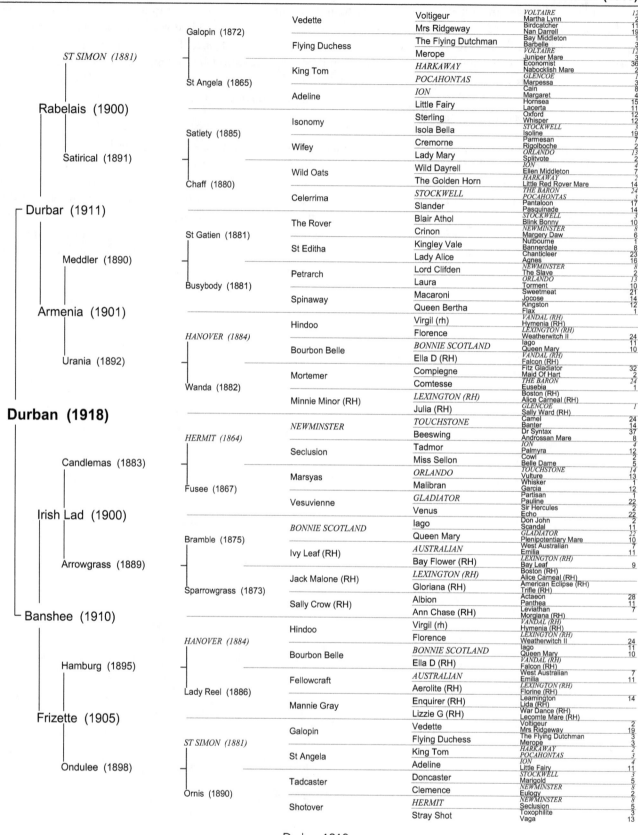

Durban (1918)

Left lineage column:

- ST SIMON (1881)
- Rabelais (1900)
- Satirical (1891)
- Durbar (1911)
- Meddler (1890)
- Armenia (1901)
- Urania (1892)
- **Durban (1918)**
- Candlemas (1883)
- Irish Lad (1900)
- Arrowgrass (1889)
- Banshee (1910)
- Hamburg (1895)
- Frizette (1905)
- Ondulee (1898)

Gen 3	Gen 4	Gen 5	Gen 6	
Galopin (1872)	Vedette	Voltigeur	*VOLTAIRE*	12
			Martha Lynn	2
		Mrs Ridgeway	Birdcatcher	11
			Nan Darrell	19
	Flying Duchess	The Flying Dutchman	Bay Middleton	1
			Barbelle	3
		Merope	*VOLTAIRE*	13
			Juniper Mare	3
St Angela (1865)	King Tom	*HARKAWAY*	Economist	36
			Nabocklish Mare	2
		POCAHONTAS	*GLENCOE*	1
			Marpessa	3
	Adeline	*ION*	Cain	8
			Margaret	4
		Little Fairy	Hornsea	15
			Lacerta	11
Satiety (1885)	Isonomy	Sterling	Oxford	12
			Whisper	12
		Isola Bella	*STOCKWELL*	3
			Isoline	19
	Wifey	Cremorne	Parmesan	7
			Rigolboche	2
		Lady Mary	*ORLANDO*	13
			Splitvote	2
Chaff (1880)	Wild Oats	Wild Dayrell	*ION*	4
			Ellen Middleton	7
		The Golden Horn	*HARKAWAY*	2
			Little Red Rover Mare	14
	Celerrima	*STOCKWELL*	*THE BARON*	24
			POCAHONTAS	3
		Slander	Pantaloon	17
			Pasquinade	14
St Gatien (1881)	The Rover	Blair Athol	*STOCKWELL*	3
			Blink Bonny	10
		Crinon	*NEWMINSTER*	8
			Margery Daw	6
	St Editha	Kingley Vale	Nutbourne	1
			Bannerdale	8
		Lady Alice	Chanticleer	23
			Agnes	16
Busybody (1881)	Petrarch	Lord Clifden	*NEWMINSTER*	8
			The Slave	2
		Laura	*ORLANDO*	13
			Torment	10
	Spinaway	Macaroni	Sweetmeat	21
			Jocose	14
		Queen Bertha	Kingston	12
			Flax	1
HANOVER (1884)	Hindoo	Virgil (rh)	*VANDAL (RH)*	
			Hymenia (RH)	
		Florence	*LEXINGTON (RH)*	
			Weatherwitch II	24
	Bourbon Belle	*BONNIE SCOTLAND*	Iago	11
			Queen Mary	10
		Ella D (RH)	*VANDAL (RH)*	
			Falcon (RH)	
Wanda (1882)	Mortemer	Compiegne	Fitz Gladiator	32
			Maid Of Hart	2
		Comtesse	*THE BARON*	24
			Eusebia	1
	Minnie Minor (RH)	*LEXINGTON (RH)*	Boston (RH)	
			Alice Carneal (RH)	
		Julia (RH)	*GLENCOE*	1
			Sally Ward (RH)	
HERMIT (1864)	*NEWMINSTER*	*TOUCHSTONE*	Camel	24
			Banter	14
		Beeswing	Dr Syntax	37
			Androssan Mare	8
	Seclusion	Tadmor	*ION*	4
			Palmyra	12
		Miss Sellon	Cowl	2
			Belle Dame	5
Fusee (1867)	Marsyas	*ORLANDO*	*TOUCHSTONE*	14
			Vulture	13
		Malibran	Whisker	1
			Garcia	12
	Vesuvienne	*GLADIATOR*	Partisan	1
			Pauline	22
		Venus	Sir Hercules	2
			Echo	22
Bramble (1875)	*BONNIE SCOTLAND*	Iago	Don John	2
			Scandal	11
		Queen Mary	*GLADIATOR*	22
			Plenipotentiary Mare	10
	Ivy Leaf (RH)	*AUSTRALIAN*	West Australian	7
			Emilia	11
		Bay Flower (RH)	*LEXINGTON (RH)*	
			Bay Leaf	9
Sparrowgrass (1873)	Jack Malone (RH)	*LEXINGTON (RH)*	Boston (RH)	
			Alice Carneal (RH)	
		Gloriana (RH)	American Eclipse (RH)	
			Trifle (RH)	
	Sally Crow (RH)	Albion	Actaeon	28
			Panthea	11
		Ann Chase (RH)	Leviathan	7
			Morgiana (RH)	
HANOVER (1884)	Hindoo	Virgil (rh)	*VANDAL (RH)*	
			Hymenia (RH)	
		Florence	*LEXINGTON (RH)*	
			Weatherwitch II	24
	Bourbon Belle	*BONNIE SCOTLAND*	Iago	11
			Queen Mary	10
		Ella D (RH)	*VANDAL (RH)*	
			Falcon (RH)	
Lady Reel (1886)	Fellowcraft	*AUSTRALIAN*	West Australian	7
			Emilia	11
		Aerolite (RH)	*LEXINGTON (RH)*	
			Florine (RH)	
	Mannie Gray	Enquirer (RH)	Leamington	14
			Lida (RH)	
		Lizzie G (RH)	War Dance (RH)	
			Lecomte Mare (RH)	
ST SIMON (1881)	Galopin	Vedette	Voltigeur	2
			Mrs Ridgeway	19
		Flying Duchess	The Flying Dutchman	3
			Merope	2
	St Angela	King Tom	*HARKAWAY*	2
			POCAHONTAS	3
		Adeline	*ION*	4
			Little Fairy	11
Ornis (1890)	Tadcaster	Doncaster	*STOCKWELL*	3
			Marigold	5
		Clemence	*NEWMINSTER*	8
			Eulogy	2
	Shotover	*HERMIT*	*NEWMINSTER*	5
			Seclusion	3
		Stray Shot	Toxophilite	3
			Vaga	13

Durban 1918

Chapter 36

Bringing it Home

Do we want the qualities of the four-mile-heat racers (stamina, speed, soundness, athletic versatility) in our sport horse today? Of course we do.

Our task as sport horse breeders is a different one from the purebred breeder, and this gives us some advantages and some disadvantages both. Because our breeding focus is on the bloodline (or should be if we want to successful) rather than the breed, we have the advantage to go outside our base breed and bring in the carrier of whatever trait we need for our ideal sport horse. But also because we are dealing with multiple sources of sport talent, the danger of dilution of the genes is far greater in our programs. This means that if we really want to succeed or even excel we need to use all the tools available to us with intelligence in our breeding choices.

Man O' War and his best friend Will Harbut coming in for the day—photo by World Wide Photos.

Those who have gone before us have shown us the way—the evidence is in their horses—and we just need to discover the breeding keys they have demonstrated and then put them to work. What we call 'Tesio Methods' (see Appendix B) is a group of principles that were developed not just by the breeding genius Tesio, but by the scholars who studied his work to determine what it was he did that functioned so well, and those coming after who built on this labor, even giving us statistics—hard science—on these practices. I cannot over stress to you how precious this gift of knowledge is for us.

These methods allow us first of all, to evaluate our stock to determine its own genetic strengths, and to be able to interpret the pedigree power of others we might buy, and then we can apply these same principles in choosing the mates for our stock in order to build excellence into our product. Incorporating the latest genetic advances into our decisions is important also, and thankfully we are living at a time where many of the mysteries of the breeds are being revealed by DNA studies. The riches of knowledge for the modern breeder are increasing daily, and if we use what is out there we can only triumph in our quest.

The DNA of those four-mile heat racers is still with us, it has not changed, and it is in the background of all our domestic breeds and some of the foreign ones as well. However, over the years they have faded in potency from lack of reinforcement, and rarely manifest in the foals—when they do, we get a miracle like the undefeated Triple Crown winner Seattle Slew, and we are then astounded with his display of class and perfection. Yet, Seattle Slew is just a shadow of what ran on our racetracks in the mid-1800s (see Chapters 5 and 26).

Because of the way genetics work, the DNA of those super horses is still with us, and it comes down unchanged through the generations (Bowling, *Horse Genetics*). However, if it is not reinforced and added to, then its influence is halved with each generation, until its expression is not seen in the foal at all. The physical manifestation of genes in the horse—what we call phenotype—is a portion only of the total genetics of the horse (genotype). It is the pedigree of the horse, if it is accurate, that will show us what that genotype consists of.

A horse conceived from loosely-bred parents, but with some good lines in it, may express the good genes, but more likely will not—it is a 'crap-shoot' in which of the genes will dominate. If the horse is bred from closely bred parents or those with a strong dominance in them, then it is much more certain that the horse will express this 'type'. This is the principle from which all breeds spring from—setting of type, which is usually achieved through inbreeding or strong line-breeding.

When we target specific bloodlines for increasing potency in our herds, we are aiming to see that bloodline's type in our foals. Because the Heroic Era lines are far back in our lineages, we will want to increase their number and richness every time we breed until we have achieved critical mass. This is the point in which the preponderance of the background genes overwhelms the lesser genes, and like a water tap that is turned on, the resulting superior stock pours out. The scientist Clive Harper, right before his death and after a lifetime of pedigree evaluation, was emphasizing to us that the factor of critical mass (that is the stacking of the background of our pedigrees with the right individuals) is by far the most important practice we can do. For us here in North America it is the good news we have been waiting for, that first all it is possible to bring it all back, and secondly, that we have the goods to build up right here. We have the greatest genetic treasure chest of first class sport bloodlines right here; we should be rejoicing.

For us the goal is the foal. —sketch of Thoroughbred dam and foal by C. W. Anderson, for *Who's Who in Thoroughbred Racing*

Outcrossing and crossbreeding are essential tools for the sport horse breeder, but they should be used intelligently; otherwise we will lose some of the talent we have labored to build up in our stock—remember what happened with the offspring of Fashion, or the disaster of Richard's Arabian experiments. So it is crucial to our success that when we crossbreed or outcross that we are doing so with individuals who are strong in other important lines we want to incorporate. This is why so few of you are succeeding in your warmblood pursuits; it is not because the warmblood breeds do not have good individuals to breed to, or to cross into your herds; rather, it is because you are not identifying those potent in the traits your admire, or ones who have the genetics that compliment or improve what you have already. If you learn to interpret pedigrees correctly you should have no problem increasing your rate of accomplishment in this field.

Harry Bassett RH 1868—the greatest heat-racer after the Civil War was a poor sire—he is a Lexington RH son but has a performance pedigree rather than that of a potent stallion. —image from *Racing in America*

Your goal is to build dominance in the sport bloodline that you want to manifest in your foals—so choose your stock from those who are already powerful in those traits. Performance horses and breeding stock often have different pedigree structures, and many great performance stars are loosely bred. Unless the great performer carries potency in those factors they are demonstrating, then they cannot pass it on consistently—it is not possible. Sport performance, however, is the proof of our correct breeding decisions as well as our goal. A loosely-bred sire can work for you if the mating with your mare creates a dominance that neither of them had alone; for instance, if your horse has one line of a top horse that you would love to make your type, then find a mate that carries a line or multiple lines of that same horse, or its full or ¾ sibling, especially with a sex-balance (see Appendix B), and you will have provided a dominance and upgrading in your foal. Always judge a mating possibility by the combined pedigree that will occur in your foal before you decide on it. Just having two good horses mate does not guarantee a good foal—it is the design illustrated in the foal's lineage that tells the story.

Inbreeding and line-breeding are our tools to create dominance, but they too must be used intelligently with knowledge of the lines we are aiming to concentrate. There is no shortcut for a successful breeder—we all have to do our homework, know our lines—their strengths, their weaknesses—and this takes study and experience.

We have the greatest sport genetics in the world—realize that we are not second rate; we have the best of the best, proven and tested for two hundred years by the four-mile heat race standard. No other country has this in their background—none, not even England, as they gave this performance test up after a century. Luckily for us over the generations there have been bold breeders who were not afraid to concentrate those elements (Duryea, Whitney, Baldwin, Thomas, Boussac, Bradley, etc) and their success is undeniable. Therefore we already have the refocusing of those genes we desire, coming down to us, and our challenge today is to build them up once again.

Our current Thoroughbred gene pool has been diluted over and over with lesser lines or those that had soundness issues. But we find time and again, both big breeder and small, that when someone concentrates the four-mile elements, whether by chance or design, then out comes a world beater with the potency to set type for generations: Seattle Slew, Sunday Silence, Easy Goer, Dr. Fager, In Reality, and Holy Bull are just the ones I highlighted—realize there are others. None of those great performers comes to us with a clean gene pool—and it is to our advantage to reinforce the sound portions of our modern pedigrees, and thereby lessen the risks of bringing down faults to our foals. Those that have gone before us have shown us the way—let's follow it.

Appendices

Appendix A

The Jersey Act

Historically Significant Articles and Announcement

This appendix comprises three articles that illustrate for us the impact of the Jersey Act.

1. **"The Jersey Act" written by Thoroughbred Racing Association 1944**

2. **"The Jersey Act" written by Ned Welch 1947**

3. **Jersey Act Repeal as announced in British Press in 1949**

The first two articles are historically valuable because they were written while the infamous edict was still in force and after the experience of thirty years of its effects on our industry. The third is a portion of the English announcement of the repeal of the Jersey Act. During this period of time 1913-1949 virtually no American Thoroughbreds were allowed into the General Stud Book, which thereby diminished the international worth and marketability of our product. This ruling effectively banned the American Thoroughbred worldwide, because any other foreign country breeding Thoroughbreds could no longer use our mares or stallions as breeding stock, for if they did their own horses would not be able to be registered either. Its intention was to eliminate the only real competition the English had in racing superiority: our native strains of racehorse, and at the same time to insure their worldwide monopoly in international Thoroughbred sales. It was immediately successful, making the American Thoroughbred a prisoner in its own continent, and it raised the worth of the English-bred worldwide. The American sporting institution, the Thoroughbred Racing Association (TRA), calculated and then published the fact that just between 1921 and 1936 over 17,771 stallions, mares, foals, and horses in training were exported from Britain all over the world. Whereas in this same period the American horse was basically worthless in the international market, and fewer than 200 were sold abroad.

---

1. TRA—The Jersey Act (found in *Thoroughbred Racing and Breeding 1944*)

"By an edict published in Volume XXII of the General Stud Book (1913) it is decreed that:

'...in the interests of the English Stud Book, no horse or mare can, after this date, be considered as eligible for admission unless it can be traced without flaw on both sire's and dam's side of its pedigree to horses and mares themselves already accepted in the earlier volumes of the book.'

"This edict resulted from a suggestion made by Lord Jersey at a meeting of the English Jockey Club.

"By a single paragraph England placed the stamp "half-bred" on many American-bred and other horses which, though eligible for registration in the studbooks of their own countries, could not be traced back in unbroken line to Thoroughbred stock exported from England. The General Stud Book (English) was first published in 1791.

"The stigma 'half-bred' has had a full effect in the markets of the world and the issue has been debated for thirty years. The necessity for maintaining purity is recognized but a not-unreasonable suggestion that an animal able to trace his genealogy for eight generations, say, be eligible, has been turned down.

"Embarrassing incidents, such as the defeat of the best English 'Thoroughbreds' by American and other 'half-breds,' have occurred in increasing numbers. Such American horses as Man O' War, Omaha, Sun Beau, Battleship, Gallant Fox, Seabiscuit, and others are taboo—as are good English horses like the mare Quashed, which won the 1935 Epsom Oaks and the 1936 Ascot Gold Cup…Quashed is ineligible because her dam, Verdict, is by Shogun out of Finale, both of whom rank as half-breds. Finale's pedigree has been traced back for over a hundred years.

"It is interesting to note that being a 'half-bred' does not bar a horse from competing in races in England whereas in this country only registered Thoroughbreds are permitted to race.

"The first edition of the American Stud Book was published in 1868, by S.D. Bruce. Bruce's requirements for admission to the American Stud Book were that animals must have "an uncontaminated pedigree for five generations."

---

2. "The Jersey Act" by Ned Welch, presented in his *Who's Who in Thoroughbred Racing* 1947, 2nd edition.

This work has fallen in the public domain (copyright not renewed as was obligatory in the copyright law of the day which required renewal at the twentieth-eight year after publication), but I believe this article is a valuable historical reference, as it is a fascinating accounting of the American breeder's mindset and experience two years before the Jersey Act was emasculated. The author, Ned Welch, was certainly a respected spokesman for the American Thoroughbred Industry, and his own words can tell the story of this rule from the American perspective far better than I can—he and his peers had been living it.

"From every point of the compass and quarter of the globe whence anything of the kind can be requisitioned, Thoroughbreds are being imported into the United States of America.

"They come by shiploads and carloads; they come by sail, by steam, by airplane and all known methods of modern conveyances. They have been got hold of by all manner of means—bought, traded for, leased, or taken over as flotsam and jetsam from the spoils of war, or they have come as invaders looking for conquest.

"They are being publicized with a similar extent and reclaim. Whether they are callow colts and fillies of tender age without reputation, or venerable stallions acclaimed as great progenitors, or incipient brood-mares with 'purple' pedigrees and lineage, or stakes winners in their own lands intended to compete for the stakes of this one, they come accompanied by the sounding of trumpets and the beating of drums…One and all they are going to improve our breed of horses, or our racing scheme, or our net-work of bloodlines, or any and everything else that such priceless acquisitions very naturally are fitted to do.

"It's wonderful—perfectly wonderful! Everybody says so, even though some of them have not as yet received their naturalization papers, and there is grave doubt that they ever will. But, what everybody says, —it was long since established, —necessarily must be true.

"Meanwhile—has anybody heard of even one American Thoroughbred having been exported by a foreign buyer eager, like our own, to improve his home-breds?

"Silence…Not even a whisper, not even a ghost of one, in reply.

"What an extraordinary state of affairs! How can it be accounted for? Especially when it is unequivocally stated that the American Thoroughbred, the English parental one only excepted, is the oldest in the world and that, a direct offshoot of the English breed, we have been breeding him here practically as long as he has been bred in Britain.

"'As every schoolboy knows,' every Thoroughbred in the world today, in every part of it, descends in the direct male line from some one of three Oriental progenitors that, over two hundred years ago, virtually created the British Thoroughbred—to wit: the Darley Arabian, the Godolphin Arabian and the Byerley Turk.

"Well—the 'get' of all three of these great family founders were among the founders of the American Thoroughbred. While their grandsons and granddaughters and other descendants, imported in profusion from 1730 onwards, carried on the great work, which ultimately was to result in our present breed of racehorses.

"Yet, this breed of racehorses is today virtually a prisoner within its own hemisphere—and the Northern half of that, to boot. Throughout the entire globe, otherwise, it is strictly taboo. Nobody will touch it, for either racing or breeding purposes. Like Cain, it has been branded with the leprous stigma of the outcast; like the 'untouchables' of India, any commerce or relation with it is retaliated by expulsion from all contact with the other branches of the great international Thoroughbred network that now girdles the globe.

"Truly, a strange thing! How could it ever have come about?

"Only three words are required to provide the answer. They are: THE JERSEY ACT.

"And what, pray, is the Jersey Act, that it could have such world-wide influence and produce such tremendous results?

"Well—let us take a look at the record:

"Thirty-four years ago, which should have been in the year 1913, it looked as if the breeding and racing of the Thoroughbred in America was headed for early and complete extinction. Years of active 'reform' crusading had resulted in the prohibition of the sport in almost every state of the Union. The gates of the principal tracks had been nailed up since 1910; in some instances never again to reopen. Most of our great racing stables had been disbanded or else shipped abroad to be raced in England and France. Most of our great breeding establishments had been either dispersed or else reduced to mere shadows of their former self. Many of our best stallions and broodmares had also been shipped abroad either for breeding purposes or for sale. Highly successful sires were standing in Kentucky at fees as low as $50.00; high-bred matrons changed hands for as little as $100.00. In 1911 only 390 yearlings had been offered at public sale and their prices averaged but $230.00. Bankruptcy stared those breeders in the face that still hung on, hoping against hope for a turn in the tide.

"It was at this crucial moment that the Jersey Act was passed by the English Jockey Club.

"Up to that time there had always been a reciprocal agreement by the English and American Stud Books that horses registered in one were eligible to the other. The English Stud Book, however, had passed into the ownership of the Jockey Club, from the private hands in which it long had remained after its foundation by James Weatherby in 1791.

"The Jockey Club was founded anterior to the Stud Book, which for nearly one hundred years remained in the Weatherby family, until, realizing its great strategic importance, that body took it over and Weatherby's became merely the compilers and publishers.

"The Jockey Club is composed almost exclusively of members of the oldest and most widely known of the British noble families. In membership, it consists chiefly of Dukes, Marquises, Earls, Barons, Viscounts, Lords and the younger members of their tribes, as yet untitled but in future apt to become so. There is sprinkling of Sirs and Misters—the Ford of Royalty—outside the 'sacred band,' but they are few in numbers and have little or no influence in the conduct of the affairs of the Club or the policies which it follows.

"These Dukes, Marquises, Earls, Barons, Viscounts, Lords, Sirs etc., are further reinforced by the fact that numerous male members of the Royal family are honorary members, headed by the King himself; while—in the past at least—others in this classification included a number of foreign nobles, also of Royal blood.

"The aforesaid collection of titled members of the Jockey Club are also owners of many of the most famous of the great English racecourses, racing stables and breeding studs. The Jockey Club virtually 'runs' the entire British turf scheme, as without a license from it no meeting can be held, no trainer can train, no jockey can ride at a recognized meeting etc., etc., and the and so forth. Its handicapper assigns the weights in all the great fixed events and the officials that preside must be O.K.'d by it.

"Now, in addition to all this, it remains to be said that the British House of Lords, to which 90 per cent of the members of the Jockey Club belong, is known as the most reactionary, selfish, snobbish and egotistical body of men in the world. So extreme did it become in its manifestations of these attributes that whereas in former times it was the most powerful political body in England, some years ago it was found necessary, for the welfare of the nation, to strip it of its power and reduce it to an auxiliary position, principally ornamental, in the administration of the government. Its illiberality, narrow-mindedness, blind adherence to obsolete traditions and customs, left no other way if the British Empire was to go full steam ahead.

"All these things are to be borne in mind in giving studious consideration to the abortive Jersey Act, its inspiration and its enforcement.

"…Up to about one hundred years ago the British turf was practically 100 per cent British in its constitution. All the horses that raced there were bred and owned by Britons, the only exceptions being now and then one or two that belonged to some Continental 'mogul,' such as a Russian Grand Duke, a German or Hungarian Prince or Count, etc., etc. But these were indeed few and far between.

"In what was to eventually prove a luckless hour, an American owner, Richard Ten Broeck, just prior to 1860, decided to ship a stable of American Thoroughbreds to England and race them against the British cracks in its great fixed events. Their success was sensational and set a pattern destined to be of far-reaching influence, for it was to be followed in later years by a number of American owners that, between them, were to carry off, at one time and another, practically every one of the historic 'classics' of the British calendar, from the Derby down, also the great handicaps, cups, plates, etc., etc., until in sum total their showing became really wonderful when it was considered that they were just little groups of invaders opposed by the entire strength of the British turf organization.

"These horses, moreover, were American bred, with very few exceptions, and their pedigrees showed elements that the British breeders had allowed to die out at home and affected to look down upon as inferior…just as members of the Jockey Club and House of Lords looked down upon their owners as plebeian 'Yankees,' whom they utterly despised and hated despicably.

"Time passed and the resentment of the Jockey Club toward the horses from across the Atlantic and their prowess became deep-seated and embittered. It began, therefore, to cast about for means to rid itself of their unwelcome presence—made doubly unwelcome because a good many American strains of blood were being taken up by less snobbish British breeders and beginning to crop up in the pedigrees of British-bred stakes horses and 'classic winners,' thus demonstrating beyond fear of successful contradiction their value as outcrosses for the fashionable British blood-lines.

"It was a process, however, that necessarily called for much wiliness, misrepresentation, the quintessence of chicanery, and a great amount of caution, in order to go over with the necessary forcefulness and effect. The movement therefore began on what were assumed as 'high moral' grounds. Namely, it was announced that the pedigrees of the American horses were many of them doubtful, many more of them short and obscure and, that to protect the 'purity' of the British breed it must be safeguarded against any admixture of 'impure' blood. What a fallacy!

"In the promotion of this dishonest, contemptible and larcenous procedure—for the English Stud Book is replete with doubtful pedigrees and absolutely impure ones as well, which modern investigation has fully established—it was decided not to admit any American horses to it that could not show a required number of orthodox British crosses in its pedigree. This egregiously stupid gesture failed because practically all American horses could show the required number of such crosses. A second rule was passed by the 'holier than thou' Jockey Club and then a third, in each of which the number of crosses required were increased—but these prohibitions also failed to their purpose; the allegedly short-bred American interlopers kept right on qualifying in the most annoying way.

"In the meanwhile, the anti-racing crusade had virtually wiped out the sport in the United States and in consequence of which, breeding there seemed upon the point of dying an unnatural death—especially as a whole coterie of our breeders had transferred their studs bodily to England and France where they maintained their activities. This being like the traditional 'red flag to a bull' to the proprietary Lords and anemic patricians of Johnny Bull's sanctified Thoroughbreds.

"They therefore decided to take the American Taurus by the horns and put him off the reservation, once and for all, and without further preliminaries.

"Result!—the passage of the Jersey Act of 1913, which provided that no horse would therefore be recorded in the English Stud Book unless it traced in *every remove* of its ancestry, no matter how far back, to animals already appearing in that book.

"Behind this act, however, was a double motive. The first object was the getting rid of American Thoroughbreds, lock, stock and barrel, by declaring them of 'impure' blood, —to wit, 'half-breds,' or in plain, unadulterated language, mongrels unfit to be interbred with the true 'pur sang' animal. In this way the influence of American blood, so exasperating to the pietistical fakirs of the Jockey Club through its striking success in England, would be eliminated outright.

"The second object was the elimination of America from the foreign markets of the world, which England had completely monopolized until, just previous to 1913, after the debacle in America set in, American horseman had started the exportation and sale in Europe, South America and the Antipodes of considerable numbers of animals which were offered at auction there.

"This process had even been carried so far as to include shipments to England itself—and while at the sales the American horses were slaughtered, this had infuriated the English commercialists to frenzy; including the hallowed Jockey Club, which despite its 'noble' status, is a grindingly commercialistic as everything else in the English scheme of trade, import, export, or what have you.

"It might be interposed, however, takes no account that all other racing countries had, like America itself, originally derived its breeding stock from England, was still in the habit of importing many animals from there, and in consequence found it to its interest to maintain close relations with her—whereas America, especially in 1913, appeared practically 'down and out' so far as the future was concerned. (Parenthetically speaking, it may be interjected that still another of the ulterior motives behind the Jersey Act was the hope and belief in England that if a revival in America ever did occur, it would be necessary for this country to obtain the bulk of her new material from British owners and breeders. This, however, proved an illusion. The recovery in America came far more quickly than the British schemers had supposed possible. It in reality found us with a comparatively large body of horses still intact and we were in a very few years going ahead again 'on our own' with relatively little outside assistance.)

"Since 1913, however, as above said the American Thoroughbred has been to all intents and purposes a prisoner in his own country, with no outlet abroad in the way of a foreign market. This because of the reasons set forth, plus the additional one of the effectiveness of British diplomacy in international relations, whereas our own is notoriously blundering, inept, unsuccessful and in many cases just plain stupid. There is hardly a member of the British Jockey Club that is not engaged in politics and of influence in many ways, individually if not collectively as the House of Lords was once. This diplomacy has taken as one of its aims the thwarting of any and all attempts to open foreign countries of American blood, and has pursued it relentlessly with complete success to date.

"As an illustration of how this works, and the miserable, puny efforts to offset it that American thus far has made, it may now be stated—we believe for the first time in any published article on the subject—that during the prolonged negotiations between this country and England held at Bretton Woods and Dumbarton Oaks, about two years ago, friends of the American Thoroughbred made efforts to have the Jersey Act brought into the discussions which took place, with the view of its repeal as a slight concession to the United States of America, not out of place, in the view of the enormous financial aid and other forms of support which at the time we were extending to England, to the tune of billions of dollars in hard cash plus commodities of all kinds.

"At the time the American diplomats—such as they are—assured the representatives of our Thoroughbred interests that with little doubt the desired object would be attained—BUT—when it 'came to the showdown,' these funeral-garbed diplomats knuckled to the shifty Britons, and consideration of the Jersey Act was given the merry 'heave-ho' into the circular steel file under the desk.

"Such, in brief compass, is the history of the foul and contemptible Jersey Act up to date; to which it may truthfully added that last summer, when the organized Kentucky breeders presented an appeal to the English Jockey Club asking for repeal of the mercenary Act, the request was treated with the most disdainful contempt, while, only recently, one of the leading members of the English Jockey Club, Lord Roseberry, long known for his bitter hatred of the American Thoroughbred and American blood, which he has displayed on innumerable occasions by frequent tirades against them, indulged in still another one, couched in the most insulting terms.

"Make no mistake about it, the day is not too far away when the American breeders will be rudely shaken off their high horses, upon which they are pleasantly riding, and then we will hear the yowls to high Heaven about the ramifications of this miserable, contemptible, mercenary act, which actually portrays and likens the sportsmanship of the British snobs akin to a bum shooting a pheasant at mealtime."

As you can see, this ruling placed a heavy punishment on the American breeder, and the above article was written thirty years into this cruel act. Welch's attitude and sarcasim surely brings home to us the bitterness felt by the breeders, and not only the gross unfairness of the rule, but of the obscentity of keeping this unsportmanlike edict in place while our men and women spent their lives defending their country. The Jersey Act is surely one of the ugliest actions seen in sporting history.

---

3. Repeal Announcement June 16, 1949, from the English Racing Calendar

"The English Racing Calendar announced on June 16, 1949, the General Stud Book has decided to 'enlarge to include strains which have hitherto been barred.'

'As from this date conditions which have governed admission continuously since volume 22 was rescinded. Any animal claiming admission from now on must be able to prove satisfactorily some eight or nine crosses of pure blood, to trace back for at least a century, and to show such performance of its immediate family on the turf as to warrant belief in the purity of its blood.'"

All of a sudden the rule was rescinded. Canceled and repealed, not for the unfairness levied on their American cousins, but because their own industry was suffering—see Part One for the full story. The Jersey Act has far reaching consequences for the modern day sport horse breeder in America, who not seeing American TB bloodlines in the international sport horse has assumed that our horse must not be any good, and that only Europe produces top sport sources. When in fact the truth is our own sport genetics are the best that can be found on any continent—this absence of knowledge found in the common sport culture lore needs to be rectified.

Appendix B

Understanding Pedigrees

The pedigree is the map of the genetics. It becomes a powerful tool for our use in understanding dominance and in the designing of our breedings **if it is accurate**, and if we know **how to read it** (interpret).

Importance of Accuracy

Accuracy in pedigrees, as you will learn through reading this book is not guaranteed. Over the years many mistakes were made in building out lineages, plus illustrious ancestors were invented by owners and breeders to advance their horses with motives to help sell them, to qualify for studbook requirements, or to elevate their stud fees. Therefore, we must do our best to verify our pedigrees. It is only a powerful tool when it is accurate—a road map of the genetics—but all that positive potential is lost if the lineage is false.

The most comprehensive way to evaluate the pedigree is found in what is called **Tesio Methods**, especially when we combine it with the latest scientific findings. A step-by-step instruction on how to use these methods in presented in *North American Sport Horse Breeder* in Section II, so I will not go into great detail here, but will provide a simple outline on its main points for your reference use for this volume.

Definitions:

It is necessary to understand some common terms used in evaluating pedigrees. Below are definitions of common terms and pedigree patterns that you will find throughout the book. Many of the pedigree designs were identified by a series of scholars over many years, who took the effort to evaluate which designs were producing the best performers and breeding stock (see Tesio Methods below).

Inbreeding: common ancestors three generations or closer (1x3, 2x2, 3x6, etc.)

Linebreeding: common ancestors in the fourth through tenth generation (5x4, 6x6, 5x9, etc.)

Outcrossing: no common ancestors in six generations

Crossbreeding: sire and dam from different breeds (Saddlebred/Holstein, Thoroughbred/Morgan, Standardbred/Dutch)

Standard Pattern: a combination of ancestors that are seen more often than not in a breed (Mansfield and Ulysses in the Morgan, Ali and Falb in the Holstein, Web/Whalebone/Whisker in the Thoroughbred, etc.)

Nick: a combination of ancestors that has proven to produce exceptional offspring (Fair Play/Rock Sand, Lexington RH/Glencoe)

Engine room: title given for the important pedigree position of the fourth through sixth generation (4x6, 5x7, 3x5), which scholars have identified as the key place for refocusing background strengths

KATHLEEN H. KIRSAN

Filly factor: a combination of offspring patterns that have proven to produce the best fillies and mares—these can either be sons and daughter lines of a key mare and/or daughters of a key sire (no sons). All breeding stock, stallions and mares, benefit for a strong filly factor or two as well as strong colt factors

Colt factor: a combination of offspring patterns that have proven to produce the best colts and stallions—these can be both sons and daughters of a key sire, and/or sons of a key mare (no daughters), and they are a notable factor in performance in all horses, male or female. While the best performance colts and geldings can get by with just colt factors, the best performance mares also need a filly factor as well

Sex-linked material: traits that travel on the X chromosome—therefore on the dam-lines. Sex–linked traits travel from a sire to his daughters only and from a mare to both sons and daughters (large heart, respiratory efficiency and energy metabolism factors)

Mitochondrial DNA (mtDNA): the DNA material supplied by the dam only that has been determined to contain the respiratory efficiency and energy conversion matter, plus some genetic material related to heart function and fertility. Because energy conversion is so vital for a sport performer, the quality of the mtDNA is an important factor in successful sport horses. The geneticist Ann Bowling referred to it as the 'metabolic power station'.

Phenotype: the appearance and performance of a horse; it does not necessarily represent the whole genetic package carried

Genotype: the full genetic fabric of the horse

Critical mass: term given the point when the genetic concentration of superior traits becomes so great that first-class horses are regularly produced

---

Helpful Genetic Facts:

Genes travel intact down through the generations (unless a mutation occurs), which is why if you build up a background ancestor (and its close relatives) eventually you will see the type strongly in the foals, even if it is far back in the lineage (Bowling, Harper).

Phenotype usually represents a fraction of DNA material found in a horse, and that is why there is sometimes a sire or mare with no racing ability or poor conformation who may be able to produce offspring that far exceeds its own, or conversely, a stallion who is a great performer may not be able to reproduce his talent or type in his offspring because he is not potent in the traits he himself displays (Bowling).

Genotype is the entire DNA spectrum found in the horse, and elements found in the genotype are not necessarily displayed in the phenotype. Building dominance in superior elements found in the genotype by selective breeding results in the superior attributes being seen more regularly in the phenotype. (For a talent to be manifest in the horse it must be first of all be present in the pedigree; therefore if you find a horse that consistently produces offspring that do not reflect its ancestry, it is a clue that the pedigree is wrong (Bowling).)

Inbreeding concentrates whatever is in the pedigree—good as well as bad—and inbreeding can cause recessive genes to appear that were hidden. **Inbreeding of itself does not create negative traits**—it just makes those present more prevalent in the foal. Conversely it does not create positive factors; it just makes them more certain in the foal as well. Inbreeding is the quickest way to set 'type' (Bell, Kleeman).

Genes travel in clusters, so targeting a carrier of a specific trait for duplication can bring down other factors with that trait—if the target ancestor was a superior horse, then this is a very positive thing. Creating full sibling configurations increases this even more, which is why it is one of the strongest designs in pedigree potency (Bowling).

Performance is the ultimate proof of our breeding designs; however proficiency at a sport at **any level** is a strong indicator of superior genotype, and conversely poor performance in sport at any level is an indicator of mediocre genotype (Losey-Morales).

Pedigree Structure

In order to read a pedigree you need to understand its structure. I will use the pedigree of the great stallion Hamburg to demonstrate pedigree design. The placement position of the horses is a standard practice, that is, all equine pedigrees are constructed this way, so this is a universal design.

Here is a three-generation sample pedigree of Hamburg to illustrate the standard pedigree structure:

			Virgil RH
		Hindoo	
			Florence
	Hanover		
			Bonnie Scotland
		Bourbon Belle	
			Ella D RH
Hamburg			
			Australian
		Fellowcraft	
			Aerolite RH
	Lady Reel		
			Enquirer RH
		Mannie Gray	
			Lizzie G RH

Hamburg's sire is Hanover—the sire is always in this position (top of pedigree). His dam is Lady Reel—the dam is always in this position (bottom of pedigree). Therefore you will always see the sire on top/dam on bottom. When you read about the tail-male line, what they are speaking of is seen here in Hanover/Hindoo/Virgil RH and beyond. Just being on the male side of the pedigree is not included in tail-male, so Bonnie Scotland, the sire of the sire's dam is not included in the tail-male line. The 'RH' breed designation appears on all American racehorses (except the Hunter Horse circa 1700, American Saddle Horse ~1800, American Trotter, Morgan and Canadian Pacer which had split off in 1818, 1840 and 1830 respectively) up to and including the year 1868—which was the year the American Thoroughbred was established; the

American Thoroughbred did not exist as a breed until then—it required adopting the classic race length standard along with specific pedigree requirements, which at that time was five generations of English blood to become a "Thoroughbred", a breed originated in England, not here. Naturally not all of our wonderful Running Horses qualified, nor did they want to, as it was a very successful breed of its own in all racing forms and disciplines.

When you read about tail-female lines, this would be represented here as Lady Reel/Mannie Gray/Lizzie G RH/ and so on—it does not include Aerolite RH the dam of the first-dam's sire.

Sex-linked characteristics travel only on the X chromosome pathways. In Hamburg, because he is a stallion, this would be demonstrated as the tail-female line outlined above, plus from Aerolite RH to Fellowcraft to Lady Reel—so Aerolite RH contributes one of the X chromosomes. This is because each mare has two X chromosomes, and she would give one of her two to Hamburg. At this stage of scientific study there is not a way to determine which of the two X chromosomes he would get. Although this may be a mystery that is solved in our lifetimes, as there is work going on about the X chromosome. For instance, one theory is that one of them gets 'turned off,' so only one is manifest—but this is only a theory at this time.

Now if Hamburg were a mare, she would receive one X chromosome from her dam—like he does, but she would also get another X chromosome from his sire. This is why full brothers and sisters always are a little different genetically and one of the reasons that the design of a full brother and sister in a pedigree is so effective, for it provides the entire genetic fabric of the target ancestor—all the sex-linked material as well as the basic DNA. So in this case if Hamburg were a mare he would get one of Bourbon Belle's two X chromosomes, from either Bonnie Scotland's dam or from Ella D RH, and once again we cannot determine at this time which one of them would come down to her.

Being a stallion, Hamburg would get the Y chromosome from his tail-male sire-line—from Hanover. So far in the research it appears that not much more than the sex determination travels on this gene, but perhaps new discoveries will be made on this as well.

Mitochondrial DNA (mtDNA) travels only on the tail-female line to both sons and daughters; therefore it is always supplied by the mother—in this case to Lady Reel from Mannie Gray, not from Aerolite RH. The mtDNA has been identified as controlling energy conversion in the cells, and it has much to do also with respiratory efficiency; these are important factors in any athlete, so the consideration of the quality of the dam-line and the buildup of our broodmare's is always a key factor in our success as sport horse breeders. In this case, Mannie Gray is about as good as it ever gets, as she is dam of Domino et al—the fastest line, therefore the energy conversion factors she possesses and transfers are top rate.

With learning these principles we can make better decisions based on placement of certain ancestors in certain positions in our pedigree designs. With knowledge of the basic pedigree design we can then apply what we call Tesio Methods in both the evaluation of our proposed breeding stock and in design of its breeding.

[Note: when the breeding of a horse is given in text it is in a traditional form also. In this case the writer would say Hamburg is <u>by</u> Hanover and <u>out of</u> Lady Reel.]

Tesio Methods

A group of scholars, historians, and scientists have put their minds and techniques to work in determining what practices are the most productive in designing equine matings. They began this quest by evaluating the pedigrees of the master breeder Federico Tesio, ergo Tesio Methods, and over the years they have tested and added to the findings. [Many of these scholars published works, so you can increase your study by going to the Bibliography and noting the publications by Harper, Glengarry, McLean, Peters, Porter, Anthony, and Brinsfield, and searching out these books and articles—it is worth the effort.]

These methods are very useful for us, as they enable us to read our pedigrees quickly to find the genetic power in them. Once we have become proficient in these techniques, it will allow us to not only recognize dominance and identify the important ancestors for our goals, but also empower us to also design matings that increase dominance in those desired ancestors and their sport traits, therefore improving our sport horse product. The scientist Clive Harper approached this task from the scientist's viewpoint, and he developed statistics that show which pedigree patterns have proven most effective in the production of top performance and breeding stock. Because of the complexity in genetics, these 'ideal pedigree patterns' are best used as guides in our mating decisions; most pedigrees combine several of these factors in the design—none of them can be assumed to guarantee a successful outcome, but they are important to us because they have a higher percentage of success than standard practices. Further, with the continual discoveries coming to us from the field of genetics we can add to these practices and surely come to understand why they are so effective.

Simplified steps for using the Tesio Methods:

1. **Build out** your pedigrees for multiple generations, verifying the ancestry as best you can.

2. **Establish** a breeding goal or direction, so you can identify the ancestors you want to build on.

3. **Research** the ancestors who represent the factors you want in your herd.

4. **Target** an ancestor and find mates who will build on or concentrate its presence using components listed below.

Pedigree Design Components to use in employing Tesio Methods—these practices increase potency and dominance (statistically proven—Harper—*Thoroughbred Breeders Handbook*):

*Multiple lines of an ancestor—this is simplistic, the more related ancestors you have in a pedigree, the closer the horse will be to that ancestor in type.

*Sex-balance in the bloodlines has proven to be of the utmost importance in bringing the full benefits of the target ancestor down to the foal. So you would want a son and daughter line of an important ancestor, or a full or ¾ sister to a sire, or a ¾ brother through a daughter line. Just repeating son lines of a sire begins to deaden the genetic transmission.

*Close Siblings: full and ¾ siblings have proven to be the strongest potency builder—the design of full brother and sister being the very best.

*Complexity in the lines: when targeting an ancestor, it has been demonstrated that to have variation in its expression increases the power. For instance, combining Man O' War with his ¾ genetic brother Friar Rock, or Nasrullah with his ⅞ genetic brother Royal Charger, are proven power combinations, equaling or exceeding the power of just having multiple lines of the same horses.

*Repeat the breeding: once you have designed a mating that is very genetically promising, it is better to repeat it at least once. Full siblings vary in their expression of the genes, and there are many cases of one sibling being a superstar in performance and his full sibling a dud. This discrepancy happens through the way genes divide before they combine, so a full sibling may have gotten the 'wrong' half of the gene for the trait you want.

* Critical Mass: it is important to build up superior ancestors in the background of a pedigree. This not only builds stamina, but it can also create that 'tipping point' in gene saturation where the 'type' of the target ancestors shows up consistently in the descendants. Harper discovered you will receive the best and most consistent results when you create a closer refocus point of that background power—usually by a dominance configuration in the engine room (fourth through sixth generation). For instance closely related siblings in the third through seventh is one engine-room dominance design of critical mass; then the statistics show with this refocus point that those desired traits (type of superior ancestors) show up consistently in the foals and are able to be passed on for generations (dominance).

* <u>Performance vs. Stud</u>: the pedigrees of successful performance horses can be different from great producers—often we find a 'male-leaning' pedigree in top performance, which is a horse with minimal sex-balance in the lines, or a loosely-bred lineage; however these designs have been shown to limit their career as a producer (Harry Bassett is an example used in Chapter 36).

The above is a bare-bones outline of Tesio Methods and how to use them. For a step-by-step explanation with plentiful examples and instruction I refer you to my book: *North American Sport Horse Breeder,* the entire Section II is on these practices, and Section III is expanded discussions on the performance and breeding value of thirty-five real life examples.

Erroneous Parentage

"These statements I do not make invidiously or with the intent to disparage the purity of the blood of these animals—of which I have no doubt; but simply to show the same want of absolute authenticity is apparent, when we go beyond a certain date in both England and America," Henry William Herbert 1857.

This appendix is a compilation of notes on American colonial horses, imported foundation horses, and others of significance with suspected or proven falsified parentage.

Accuracy in our pedigrees count, not just for our understanding of where the traits we admire originate from, but it is crucial in the planning our matings to have correct ancestry assigned. Right from the beginning there was an element of dishonesty in pedigree statements, whether from the desire to qualify for a new studbook, to promote a stallion as a sire, or to be able to increase a sale price—many have succumbed to the temptation to embellish the lineages of certain horses. Some of these frauds have been revealed, so I present them to you for your use.

(Sources: Alexander MacKay-Smith, Fairfax Harrison, Henry William Herbert, John H. Wallace, Dr. Mim Bower, Ellen Parker, Charles Nye, Robert Denhardt)

The following list is not proposed as a complete accounting—falsified pedigrees are rapidly being discovered with the DNA testing now available, and we surely will be adding more names to this category.

Incorrect sire or sire-line is suspect (most are impossible claims because of place or time):

The Godolphin Arabian—not Arabian, believed to be a Turcoman Horse.

The Byerley Turk—not an imported Turk, instead discovered to be a son of Places White Turk out of a Hobby or Running Horse dam.

The Darley Arabian—not an Arabian either, also believed to be a Turcoman Horse.

Leedes Arabian—not an Arabian, but a son of Darcy's Yellow Turk out of a Running Horse dam

Bald Galloway—his lineage is believed to have been improved (John Wallace) to appear more English than Running Horse, while the contemporary evidence reveals him to be a 14.2-hand, pacing Running Horse.

Fancy 1763—sire not Buchephalus

Phoenix 1784—sire not Shadow

Statesman 17?? —sire not Janus

Paddy Whack 1778—sire should be Janus not Jolly Roger

Moggy 1767—impossible Janus lineage—because of time and place

Cripple 1772—Janus four times is impossible

Atkinson's Janus 1780—Janus five times is impossible

Figure 1795 or 1789 (foundation sire of the Morgan breed) —questionable grandsire

Creeping Kate 1745 —sire not Badger

Nancy 176? —sire not Goodes Bahram

Peter McCue QH 1895—sire not the TB Duke of Highlands; it is Dan Tucker QH

Incorrect dam or dam-line made-up:

*It was common practice to invent English TB dam-lines for our best racing stock; the following horses' dams are now known not to be English Thoroughbred or part-TB—instead they were out of good American RH dams.

Peacock 1760, Spider 1764, Budd 1789, Kirkindall 1758, Fancy 1763, Sweet Mary 1766, Caelia 17??, Belle 1764, Madam 1770

---

*Monkey Mares: Monkey 1725 (see below) was an early imported English TB, although his pedigree is incomplete, we can be certain he was bred to American Running Horse mares—not English TB mares. The following are several of his offspring and offspring of his daughters whose traditional lineage was 'improved' with a fraudulent TB dam.

Shad 1761, Jupiter 1776, Smiling Poll 1795, Sting Lilly 1780, Bahram 1774, Bandy Balls 1774, Twickham , Twigg 1778, Poll Pitchard 1780, Byrnes Big Filly, Sweeping Tail 178?, Harmless 1779, Barleysides 17?? (famous racing son of Fearnought).

---

*The imported English TB mare Mary Gray was regularly substituted for true Running Horse mares in many lineages; these are a few that have been proven false:

Blue Boar 1766, Club Foot 1778, Red Baccus 1778, Polly Williams 1774 (found in famous taproot mare Bonnets o' Blue dam-line), Poll Smiling 1774

Another mare whose progeny list was exaggerated is Creeping Kate 1745.

---

*Many imported English Thoroughbred mares and stallions came to this country with 'beefed-up' dam-lines; these are a few that have been proven to be fraudulent:

Jenny Cameron 1742—unknown dam

Kitty Fisher 1756—her dam-sire of record never had a filly foal by her second dam Bald Charlotte, so Somerset Arabian is not her second dam-sire; it is a fabrication. Kitty Fisher is one of the most important English mares imported in Colonial times, and so this fraud is found in many of our pedigrees.

Jenny Dismal 1752—her dam is not Whitefoot Mare

Messenger 1780—(see below) dam-line entirely fictitious

Blaze 1740—has largely unrecorded dam-lines after two generations; however in our day the back parentage of Grey Grantham mare and Brights Roan Mare are being reconstructed with fanciful parentage—it appears to be in an effort to make him qualify as a true TB, in spite of the evidence to the contrary. It is a case of 'this is our story and we are sticking to it!' (See Messenger below).

Calista ERH—unknown parentage; evidence strongly suggests she was of the English Running Horse breed.

Monkey 1725 Mares

Monkey 1725 was one of the earliest imported English Thoroughbreds. Therefore if you find English ancestry is supplied for the mare that Monkey was bred to, be on your guard—Monkey was foaled in 1725, but came to America in 1737—there were only two English mares imported before him—both un-named, one by the Godolphin Arabian, imported by Alex Clarke of VA in 1733, and the other by Whitefoot imported by John Gower of VA in 1735. Monkey is estimated to have produced three hundred foals while standing in Virginia and North Carolina, so the odds are overwhelming that any Monkey Mare you find in your pedigrees is out of an American Running Horse dam, as that is all there was.

Messenger EH 1780

One of the greatest sires ever to be imported to America from England is Messenger EH. Listed in the GSB as a Thoroughbred, he is found not only in our Heroic Era racers—the dam-sire of American Eclipse RH for instance—but his greatest legacy was his ability to transfer trotting form consistently along with substance, and he is the foundation sire of our American Trotter breed (pre-Standardbred breed). And while he has left a legacy in our racing RH, it should be noted that he was used as a sire of stage coach horses and Hunter Horses as well, his coarse substance combined with athleticism made him a sire of significance for the heavier types. His dam-line is entirely made-up, probably first of all to qualify for inclusion in the new GSB, as many early entries were spiffed up and polished to qualify as 'thoroughbred,' but also to make him more marketable to the American buyers. His sire side is not full 'thoroughbred' either, as his sire Mambrino EH, his grandsire Engineer EH, and his great-grandsire Sampson EH all descend from the trotting transmitter Blaze. A great racehorse and sire Blaze is renowned for his dynasty of superior trotting racers, stage coach horses and carriage horses—and his dam-lines are mostly just a name with 'unknown' beyond it, although in our modern day pedigree wizards are 'finding' authentic Thoroughbred lines for them. However, the contemporary pedigree experts admitted that he was not a full Thoroughbred. For example the founder of the Hackney Stud Book Henry Euren said, "There would appear to have been a large proportion of English (native) blood in the dam of Blaze, though no one can say what was its character—whether running, trotting or ambling." The Hackney breed foundation sire is Old Shales—a son of Blaze.

The English Running Horse, like our native Running Horse, was the provider of true speed—which has been proven by modern DNA studies, but it also carried ability for intermediate gait speed (trot and pace) as well as at the gallop, and the English Running Horse was gaited. To qualify as 'thoroughbred' a horse was required to have Oriental lines, originally those of Places White Turk and then later the Godolphin Arabian and the Darley Arabian. Barb lines were already part of the English Running Horse when the new breed—thoroughbred—was first established. Blaze's dam lines did not qualify, and like most Running Horse lines of the day, they were intentionally hidden.

KATHLEEN H. KIRSAN

The son of Blaze, Messenger's great-grandsire Sampson EH, is documented of being out of a ¾-bred Hunter mare. But that mare has been identified by British Thoroughbred scholar James Hardiman as being by an English black cart horse---this breed was later called 'Shire' and it is a heavy draft breed, and so she would be considered a draft cross. I had always assumed that Hunter mare was a Yorkshire Coach Horse cross—but no, it appears she is by a draft horse. This sure puts the 'purity' of the English TB into question. His son Engineer EH drops in another unknown second dam, and Messenger's sire Mambrino EH added two more pacing crosses from the Bald Galloway lines in his dam— and he demonstrated that he produced far better trotters than runners. In Pick's Turf Register of 1805 the compiler said, "Mambrino was likewise sire of a great many excellent hunters and strong useful road horses. And it has been said that from his blood the breed for the coach was brought near to perfection." Plus Mambrino's dam-line ends with 'foreign horse', and the breed is not identified. Which makes you wonder is it foreign as in from another country or is it foreign from another breed?

But there is more to the mystery of Messenger EH, Mambrino EH, Engineer EH, Sampson EH and Blaze—note that they produced stage coach horses, and delievered coarseness and substance to their progeny, and they were immensely large horses for the day as well. The Running Horse and the TB did not convey these traits, so maybe we are missing something here? And I contend that a draft cross seven generations back by the time of Messenger EH does not account for the progeny type and the type of Messenger EH himself. Perhaps those unfilled in lines in Blaze, Sampson EH etc carry another common English breed? So let me drop this theory into the bucket: there was a breed of horse in England called the Chapman horse, and this breed was elegant, large, powerful, docile, trotting horses that possessed great stamina, that either alone or combined with TB became the greatest coach horse breed in the world by the mid-1800s. By the 1800s they were known worldwide as the Yorkshire Coach Horse and along with the TB they were a great export product to Europe. This breed is what was imported by Mecklenberg, Hanover and Holstein studs to elevate their farm horse breed into coach horses. And crossed with TB they made wonderful Hunter Horses. Today we call this breed Cleveland Bay, and although relatively rare, it is renown for its substance and elegant type—they are majestic. Why do we not just stop the foolishness of pretending the early TBs were all 'pure-bred' Orientals, which the recent DNA studies have proven is not true, and accept and welcome that some other domestic breeds, the RH, the Hobby and in this case the Chapman all contributed? It is something to be proud about, not ashamed. Maybe in our time we will see these early, once dishonorable, bloodlines become recognized for the true genetic values they carry.

Cub Mare 1764 – Her Daughters

The Cub Mare herself is probably of truthful lineage (excellent English TB) for what is there—much is blank—but her most significant 'families' are not of purely English ancestry, and seeing that the Cub Mare has been heralded as one of the true roots of our Thoroughbred based on her influence on the later generations (she is behind the great Galopade family), we should take a look at what her reputation rests on.

By far the most important modern branch of the Cub Mare family is Miss Obstinate RH 1829, who is inbred to the Running Horse Jane Hunt 3x4 through her dam Jenny Slamerkin RH, whose second dam is the Cub Mare. Jane Hunt's sire Paragon RH has a RH dam-line going back to a RH named Hunting Squirrel. Plus Jenny Slamerkin's sire is the Running Horse Tiger, a son of the famous pacer Blackburns Whip RH. Not quite as purely "English" as we are led to believe. This is not meant to be a put-down of the English bloodlines, but to get you to 'see' that speed also arose from our native Running Horse.

Bend Or 1877 – The Mystery Horse

The recent revelation of the equine genome scientists Dr. Mim Bower and her team (2012) that published the true ancestry of the great sire Bend Or has rattled the racing world. They have proven by DNA evaluation that he is really a stallion named Tadcaster. Back when Bend Or was racing it was reported to the Jockey Club stewards by his groom that sometime in training Tadcaster was substituted for Bend Or by his owner (I think we used to call these 'ringers'), which was a common fraud that is usually attributed to the lower-class circles, but evidently in this case the English hierarchy were not on the up-and-up either, as the owner denied the charge and the groom was not believed. The result here is the superb racing record and breeding dynasty attributed to Bend Or and his breeding is a lie. Although at the time of the switch the groom alerted the officials at the Jockey Club of the fraud, but they disregarded the statements of this whistle blower—classifying him as a 'disgruntled' employee, and they chose to rely on the word of the English owner instead—even though he was a man of proven unreliability in record keeping, but what he did have was social standing, and the honest groom did not.

Tadcaster, a ringer for Bend Or, definitively proven by DNA.
—Wiki Commons

This fraud has far-reaching effects, as Bend Or has been held up as one of the most influential sires of his time—half of the famous Bend Or/Macaroni nick and his bloodlines are found in many American horses—especially in the Fair Play family (see Chapter 12). The sire of both of these is the same: Doncaster; it is the dam who is different, Tadcaster's dam is Clemence. This discovery explains in part why the influence of The Tetrarch is so strong, because with a corrected pedigree it a reveals a 3x3 design of inbreeding to Clementina and Tadcaster—full siblings by Clemence. This mare is now revealed as one of the greatest broodmares of all time with Tadcaster, Fair Play, and Carbine all descended from her—some of the strongest sport bloodlines from three continents.

Appendix D

North American Breed Designation Explanation

There is a massive and common confusion in our modern day equestrian world about when and how our North American domestic breeds came into being. There are several factors operating in this muddle: one is our 'collective amnesia' about our original sport horse breed (Running Horse); other elements compound the problem, such as our unconscious assumption that a breed is 'purebred' and has a registry—neither of these beliefs are historically correct. Then on top of this mindset comes the effects of the 'warmblood invasion', where their 'breeds' and methods have been superimposed on our preconceptions, the result is an utter disconnect with regard to our own equine history and traditions.

Although this may be tiresome to some of you, let me address these issues, and then provide a short explanation of our domestic sport horse breeds. Realize that it took me years of research and database building to unravel the mess and give myself a clear understanding. I can only hope what I determined will help you as well.

Let's begin with a definition of sport horse: a population of horse selectively bred for performance in a particular sport or group of sports, normally with selection based on specific prepotent bloodlines. Therefore there is a performance standard, a type standard, and a pedigree standard in most sport breeds.

North America is blessed with many established breeds of light horse that are true sport horses. The story of how and when these marvelous breeds came into being has been absent from or slanted in our popular equine literature. Therefore most modern day equestrians are unaware that North America's first domestic breed of horse was a sport horse, and that it did not go extinct until the early twentieth-century, and it is the parent breed of all our best sporting horses of today.

> "The American Running Horse was America's first domestic breed of horse. It was immensely talented and prepotent, prized for its comfortable gaits (pace, rack, amble) and its agreeable temperament, its stamina, toughness and speed. It was both a sport horse and a riding horse. The Running Horse survived as a breed for three hundred years and left a modern day legacy of eight separate quality light horse breeds that are directly descended from it"(*North American Sport Horse Breeder*).

Let me quickly outline some points on the development of our first breed of horse that may not have been conveyed to you. In North America, the early Colonists were avid racehorse enthusiasts. Contrary to most modern-day assumptions the breeders of our first domestic breed of sport horse (racehorse) were extremely intelligent and educated persons who, with the help of huge land grants provided for them, and armed with vast wealth of their own, set about immediately to import the very best racing stock from the 'old country' with the aim of continuing the sport they loved in their new home. They imported from 1611 until 1660 the very best racing horses from Ireland and England, and it was their passion to breed from those imports wonderful racehorses. These horses were not Thoroughbreds—that breed did not exist yet—they were English Running Horse and Irish Hobbies. Happily, our forefathers were very successful in this endeavor, and we, the North American sport horse breeders, four hundred years later are still reaping the harvest from their intelligent breeding procedures.

Because the printing press did not make its way to the new world until 1700, all the earlier colonial records were handwritten or printed with wood block engravings and impressions, and their stud records and correspondence were handwritten. It was the wealthiest settlers who bred racehorses, people of education and means, and they had immense libraries of their own, which they continually built with importations of the best volumes from England. However, even the common folk in our colonies were literate, and the English public school system was in place almost immediately. The New England Puritans and the Pennsylvania Quakers insisted on literacy, and surprisingly we find except on the frontiers, the children who attended those schools were already literate, as their mothers taught them how to read and write before they ever made it to the public school ("Colonial Education in America" by AmericanEducation.org and "The First Hundred Years of Printing in British North America" by Reese). Remember, we even had a school of higher learning (Harvard University) by 1636. (Later immigrants from central Europe often did not have the advantage of a public school system in their own countries so were not always literate—but our early colonial settlers were generally products of the English school system). Therefore the breeding of our early racehorse was not done by 'country bumpkins;' it was done by people of intelligence and education who fully understood how to breed selectively for their goals. And their results were spectacular.

This racehorse birthed in our colonies, the American Running Horse, has been the subject of group memory loss in our equestrian community even though it was still around into the early 1900s. Yet, it was a world-renowned horse in its heyday, both as a top quality racer at both the pace and gallop, and later at the trot (1800s), but in addition it was the most prized saddle horse in the world, as it retained its pace-derived intermediate gaits, and therefore was far more comfortable to ride than a horse that only trotted at the intermediate gait. It also possessed a gentle and willing temperament, and was incredibly hardy, plus it was loaded with both stamina and speed. From this original American sport horse descend our best modern-day light horse breeds. But because we have 'forgotten' about it and assumed all breeding done in colonial times was 'willy-nilly' by idiots, we are at a loss to explain the origin of the excellence found in our modern breeds and when it was they truly emerged. Indeed, most texts state that we had no true 'breed' of horse until the English Thoroughbred arrived. Failure to recognize the original breed has made the starting date of our modern breeds waiver around, instead of clearly identifying our breeds' birth by its true organization time, which would be when there was a conscious selection for type combined with specific performance and bloodline factors; instead most assume they are just birthed out of the colonial primordial soup.

By the 1950-60s most North Americans had adopted the belief that all breeds were 'purebred,' as we had by then long-established registries for all our domestic light horse breeds. So entrenched was this mindset that I remember being instructed that the Hunter Horse (our true American 'warmblood') was a type, not a breed, implying it was a by-product of racehorse breeding rather than a breed established and selected for performance in its own sports. I wonder what Marion DuPont and Liz Whitney would say about this? Do you think they were just mindlessly mixing bloodlines, or do you think they were intentionally choosing stallions and mares that they felt could jump well?

This disconnect is not just an American phenomenon, when I contacted our National Federation of North American Sport Horse (now a defunct organization) in the 1990s to find out why the Irish Sport Horse was not included as approved crosses in the member breeds (European Warmbloods), I was told that the Irish Sport Horse is not a 'true breed', but is considered a cross-breed, while they rated the European Warmblood as true breeds. Here then is more evidence of the 'doublethink' and double standard that has become commonplace in our industry—as the judgement rendered required the warmblood registries viewing their mixed-bred breeds as being somehow more pure than the Irish Sport Horse. Yet, Ireland has been selectively breeding a horse for the hunter sports for hundreds of years and has led the world ratings in 3-day eventing for over sixteen years.

By the 1980s the European Warmblood invasion into our domestic sport market began in earnest, and this caused more disconnect with our heritage, as their 'breeds' are not purebred either, yet they promoted them as true breeds—national breeds—the pride of their countries. These same theorists that say our Hunter Horse is not a true breed, will proclaim the European warmblood however as a true breed—does no one notice the hyprocrisy of this? You can not have it both ways folks, either **all** horses bred by 'recipe', that is part-racehorse with other elements added intentionally for improvements in form and sport performance, are a breed or none of them are. Yet we did not make the intellectual leap that our Hunter Horse—which we have been selectively breeding since colonial days, was every bit as much a breed as their 'warmbloods'. Even though I was part of this generation of equestrians in the late twentieth century, I still am not sure how it was we did not classify our own Hunters as true sport horses—even while they were competing against and often winning the medals in international sport competitions—silly and sad. Registries are a nineteenth century practice—prior to this era breeds were organized by breeding practices and performance standards.

Therefore, for your reference, let me list the emergence date of our sport breeds for you. These dates were arrived at by carefully studying the intent of the breeders of the day and the implication of an organized set of performance standards and consciousness of sport bloodlines (see *North American Sport Horse Breeder* for more on this).

Running Horse (RH): This is our original saddle and racehorse breed, and it is based on the Irish Hobby and English Running Horse imports. It is documented (Hervey) that organized breeding for racing was in place by **1624** in the Virginia Colony. He found in the records that all the members of the Kings Council in Jamestown were already racehorse owners, and most were also breeders; first with sprint racing performance testing in place and standardized, and within fifty years heat-racing as well. The sportsmen in the Rhode Island portion of the Massachusetts Bay Colony were performance testing their branch of this breed about twenty years later—soon after it became known as the 'Narragansett Pacer'. The two populations of racers—New England and Virginia, traveled by ship between the two centers of racing for competing, for sale, and for breeding purposes. This breed spread to all the settled areas along with the sport of racing in all its forms (sprint to four-mile heat racing, at the trot, pace, or gallop), and it continued on until the dawn of the twentieth century, when the last of its members were absorbed into their descendant breeds.

American Sport Horse (ASH)—aka Hunter Horse: The selective breeding of mounts for use in the sport of hunting was in place in the Maryland/Virginia Colonies by **1700**. These horses were either full Running Horse or based on the RH with other breeds added for substance, height, and style. Once again, originally this sport, —and the intelligent selection for this breed—was restricted to the most privileged of our settlers, but by the late 1700s hunt clubs were widespread, and the hunt sport mania had infiltrated the general populace. All those that had access to a fine Hunter-bred horse joyfully participated in these sports. When the new English Thoroughbred arrived in America (mid-1700s) it quickly became a prized cross for our native race-saddle horse because it was fast also, and it provided the bonus of adding height to our much shorter Running Horse. This breed of horse has been continually bred to our day; we called them Hunters until very recently, now we call them Sport Horses or even Warmbloods after the European influence, but the breeding philosophy and selection process is still the same as it was in 1700, and this is the concept that the modern American has been blind to: that we here, the 'uncultured Americans', have been breeding our own 'warmblood' sport horse since 1700 continually to this day—three hundred years. The first Hunter registry was in 1918.

American Saddle Horse (ASA): This breed emerged when the breeders consciously separated a portion of our Running Horse stock and made their breeding choices to preserve the original excellent saddle horse traits of our racehorse that were being lost with excessive crossing in of the English Thoroughbred. This movement—our first foundation movement—began around 1800 by intelligent breeders like General Cocke and John Goode. The first documented performance test (horse show) was in **1817**. The registry for this breed was established in 1891. It gradually went extinct when the Tennessee population separated in 1935, and then the breeders in Kentucky retained the original studbook to develop their own strain separately—this became known as the Saddlebred (see below).

American Trotter (AT): This breed came about from selective breeding from those Running Horses that acquired a mid-gait of the trot, but retained the speed from their pacer roots. The first documented performance test for this strain was in **1818**. Originally they were raced under saddle, but harness racing began to become more popular by 1840, both because a trotter was the preferred harness horse and the northeast bred mostly harness horses for utility use in its urban areas as well as for racing, so that the harness horse was bred there extensively. The

Here is the Champion American Trotter Dexter being ridden in a race. How would you like to race a trotter in saddle, going thirty mph? Currier and Ives print

imported English horse Messenger EH—who is still to this day is purported by the face-saving English to be a full TB, though he was not—is the agreed upon foundation horse of this breed. The first registry was established in 1867. Later in 1879, the fastest of them were organized into the Standard register, and a new breed began; the AT gradually went extinct.

Canadian Pacer (CP): There is tremendous confusion around this breed, because no registry was ever formed, no studbooks have ever surfaced, and it became trendy at one point to call any pacing racehorse a "Canadian"—which has muddied the waters more. However, this population of racehorse was definitely a breed of its own by around 1830-40, and a premier racing breed by 1850, and—the name aside—it raced at both the trot and the pace. For lack of documentation I assigned a 'date of birth' for it in my original book of **1830**. It was formed by importations of Running Horse stock from the Americas and also from the Nova Scotia portion of Canada, sometimes crossed onto its light farm breed of the Canadian Horse, but more often with Morgan horses. This was sporadic at first, with occasional individuals like Old Pilot appearing. But it took the progeny of the foundation sire Tippoo Sultan to jump start a true breed and by the 1830s the Canadian Pacer had emerged. By 1850 it was a top-quality racehorse that competed as an equal with the American Trotter and Pacing Running Horse all across North America, and all three of these racing breeds were absorbed into the later-formed Standardbred Register.

Morgan Horse (MO): The Morgan breeders have been exceptionally organized from the get-go, which according to AMHA is **1840**. Their breeding criterion was to set the type of their foundation sire: Figure RH into their breed based on him. They have succeeded tremendously, and their breed has continued on unabated as one of the oldest sport horse breeds in America. However, not all branches were sport oriented, but through a branch formed from the genetics of the great Black Hawk (trotter) and the lesser-known Copperbottom (pacer)—who is often confusedly labeled a Canadian—the Morgan Horse was and is still today a prime source of true sport genetics. The first studbook was Linsley's in 1857, followed by Battell's in 1894.

American Thoroughbred (TB): The origin of this breed is very muddled, mainly because of the lack of knowledge and recognition of our first-rate Running Horse racehorse breed. However, it was only in **1868** that S. D. Bruce's studbook came out, with its requirement of at least five generations of strictly English Thoroughbred ancestry, and along with the performance breed test of the classic race standard—one- to two-mile 'dash' races; therefore it was only in 1868 that this population of racehorse became a separate breed of its own. Lexington RH 1850 for instance is not a Thoroughbred. The horse that became known as 'Thoroughbred' was an English-organized breed (1670—although the breed name: 'Thoroughbred', was assumed one hundred years later in the mid-1700s, which is when the performance standard of the classic race was also adopted), and we could not call our racehorse a "Thoroughbred" until it met the breed requirements mentioned above. In the text of this book I label all our pre-Thoroughbred racehorses RH—until after 1868 when **some** of them qualified for the newly established American Thoroughbred.

Quarter Horse (QH): The Quarter Horse was always a dual-purpose breed—a sprint racer and a cattle-working stock horse, which specialized from the original sprint and pacing racing stock and the Saddle Horse stock of Virginia. By the time the classic distance branch of our Running Horse fixed its breed criteria to become "Thoroughbred," our sprint-racing branch of Running Horse was centered beyond the Mississippi River, and was, along with its branch that worked on ranches, a breed of its own; therefore **1868** is an appropriate date for the true birth of the Quarter Horse. The registry was formed in 1940.

Standardbred (ST): When John Wallace opened his Standard Register in **1879** to gather all those American Trotters that could go a mile in 2:30 or under, the Standardbred was born. It later absorbed the fast-trotting lines of the Morgan and Canadian Pacer trotters as well, and in **1891** it took in all the fast pacing racers—Running Horse and Canadian.

American Saddlebred (SB): When the Tennessee branch of American Saddle Horse seperated to preserve its 'running walk' gait in **1935**, the American Saddle Horses who could trot as well as do its pace-derivative gaits retained the American Saddle Horse studbook, changing its foundation sire list to those who reflected its own strain, and thus SB became its own breed.

Tennessee Walker (TW): In **1935** the breeders in the Tennessee region removed their strain of horses from the American Saddle Horse registry by forming their own registry to preserve and promote their 'running walk' gait, thereby signaling the separation of strains of American Saddle Horse into its descendant breeds.

KATHLEEN H. KIRSAN

Missouri Fox Trotter (MFT): The breeders in the Missouri region selectively bred their own version of the American Saddle Horse to preserve and promote its 'fox-trotting' gait, so **1935** works for them also—their registry opened in 1948.

[See *North American Sport Horse Breeder* for a full history of our domestic sport horse development.]

The breed list above is those North American breeds that are **directly** descended from our original Running Horse. Most of them also carry large measures of our Heroic Era racers in their background as well, so there is a genetic affinity in these breeds based on the very best sport genetics in the world. Selective breeding by you can bring the power of those sport performers of yesteryear to the fore in each of these breeds quite easily once you understand the genetic importance of specific ancestors. And crossing these breeds, if done judiciously, can also build up tremendous background power in true sport performance.

Appendix E

Reprints of My Articles That Appear on www.sport-horse-breeder.com

American Hunter Horse. —engraving by Alexander Anderson, an American tradition for over 300 years, Library of Congress

In the process of writing and researching the below listed articles, it was revealed to me the unevenness there has been in reporting the sources of true sport performance in popular equine journals and books. My findings led to more research, which is still ongoing, and it impressed upon me the need to publish this story of the American Thoroughbred for the sport horse breeder, especially those in North America. Our much-maligned American Thoroughbred, along with other of our fine domestic sport horse breeds, all stem from our original sport horse, a horse so talented it could race at a pace or gallop in sprints or four-mile heat races, and it was a superb jumper and hunter, and it provided the finest saddle horses in the world. What a heritage we have here! We have the greatest reservoir of true sport talent right in our own native breeds, always bred for sport for almost four hundred years. At the time of writing these articles I had no idea why these bloodlines were not widely recognized, but the research for this book has provided those answers.

[Note: after this manuscript went to the publisher I witnessed a taping of the 2011 Kentucky Derby, won with ease by California Chrome. When I pulled up his pedigree I was surprised to find that it is almost identical in structure and content to that of Seattle Slew and Easy Goer. This discovery resulted in a web article which I have included here for your reference and listed here as #7. I have also included the comparision of the pedigree patterns in the text of this book as I believe it is instructive for us.]

1. **Sport Horse Recipe**

2. **Thoroughbred – the Importance of the Thoroughbred in Warmblood and Sport Horse Breeding**

3. **Real Stayers – Four-Mile-Heat Racers of Yesteryear**

4. **American Hall of Fame Show Jumpers**

5. **Bloodlines of Dressage Champions of the USDF**

1. Sport Horse Recipe

(What Genetic Ingredients Make Up our Sport Horse Recipe?)

Sport horses, those that are used for the Olympic style sports, are usually not purebred, although they can be. The great majority have a significant amount of Thoroughbred in their lineages.

Your goal is success in a particular sport and therefore your selection criteria will vary with the demands of the sport and your expectations and goals. So, most breeders will end up following a rough outline of genetic components to reach their goals—a basic recipe.

Basic Ingredients:

Racehorse — needed for athleticism, proper saddle horse conformation, speed and stamina. Thoroughbred is the major source for these traits, although another option could be the Standardbred.

Fair Play—a champion Thoroughbred, a great sire, and a very good sport horse bloodline. —image from *Thoroughbred Types*

Saddle Horse — these breeds are used for style, movement or elegance and specialized talent. Often called improvers, these breeds are added to adjust the abilities of the horse for each sport. Key providers are Saddlebred, Morgan, Quarter Horse, Missouri Fox Trotter, Tennessee Walker, also breeds to consider the Selle Francais, Anglo-Arab, Swedish Warmblood, Trakehner and Arabian.

Coach Horse — these coach horse derivative breeds contribute height, weight carrying ability or substance. Coach sources: Irish Draught, Cleveland Bay or Canadian Horse as well as the old-style Continental Warmbloods (Hanoverian, Holstein, Oldenburg etc.)

These are the basic ingredients you will commonly find in those horses that succeed in Olympic style sport—either used as a purebred or mixed and matched to produce the sport product you desire.

Your recipe for success will depend on your sport goal. For instance, the heavy coach derivative breeds of Europe were lightened up and made more athletic by the introduction of Thoroughbred, and to a lesser extent with additions of other light saddle breeds. The breeders have found not to periodically inject more Thoroughbred or a light saddle horse source will result in those farm/coach derivative breeds reverting back to the heavy coach-farm form and they become too heavy, slow and un-agile to win.

The sport of dressage can stand a greater proportion of substance and still succeed, but the three-day horse and the show jumper need the speed and agility that only comes from the lighter horses. Your sport goal will determine your ingredients and the amount of each.

You will want to further refine your ingredient list by identifying which particular bloodlines in these types is a source of superior sport ability, good temperament and soundness. And which ones will improve the genetic package you are building into your herd—this in-turn will require a familiarity with the Tesio Methods and also a study of the bloodlines.

Here are a few examples of proven sport bloodlines:

A warmblood example can be the Holstein stallions Calypso I thorugh V, which are crossbred stallions with Selle Francais and Holstein parents, their ingredients are 30% Thoroughbred (Furioso/Rantzau), 50% Holstein, 20% Selle Francais.

In the Thoroughbred the line of Nearco has proven to transmit both the beautiful movement needed in dressage and the sport ability for jump and eventing. Fair Play and his descendants are big winners in jump and eventing.

In the Standardbred the bloodline of Adios and his full sister Adieu produce spectacular balanced movement that succeeds at dressage. These bloodlines are just a few of the proven transmitters of superior sport talent.

As a breeder who wants to succeed you will need to examine your own stock's lineages to determine the important transmitters they already carry and then choose their mates from those that build on or improve the genetic package that will become the foal. You're the creator of your sport product.

2. Thoroughbred – The Importance of the Thoroughbred in Warmblood and Sport Horse Breeding)

The Thoroughbred (or other racehorse) genetic contribution is essential for our sport horse success. Our sport horses are usually not purebred, but instead are a combination of several different breeds brought together in the effort to produce an exceptional equine athlete that can succeed at Olympic style sport of Jumping, Dressage or Eventing. See "Sport Horse Recipe" for the most commonly found ingredients.

Aqua Tom and his rider-owner Helen Hayn, a team with several national titles, have moved up to international level. Tom is ⅝ Thoroughbred and ⅜ Holstein. The brand on Tom's hip is USA in an oval. —cover photo from *North American Sport Horse Breeder*, GRC Photography

KATHLEEN H. KIRSAN

It is time for some plain talk. I may lose a portion of my readers at this point, but if you press on you will discover some interesting and relevant facts about the Thoroughbred and its value to our sport horse goals. We cannot be misled any longer; thirty years after the 'warmblood' invasion into America we still find it is our original sport horse—the Hunter Horse that is winning (racehorse based sport horse). We may not call those horses Hunters anymore, but that is what our modern 'warmblood' and 'sport horse' are, and it is a sport horse we have selectively bred in this country for 300 years (since 1700).

Today, the horses at the top of the sport horse leader boards whether they have a warmblood brand on their hip or not, are consistent for containing Thoroughbred blood with varying amounts of other breeds (a Hunter)—it is the Thoroughbred that is the constant in Olympic style sport horse success, not the warmblood.

What is the Thoroughbred? First and foremost it is a racehorse of the highest excellence—a galloper—its speed at the gallop is unmatched by any other breed. The Thoroughbred is also a magnificent polo horse, a steeplechaser and Hunter Horse, full or part-bred, and it also now excels at the more modern Olympic style sports. Further, it is an 'improver' for just about any other equine breed that needs an injection of athleticism, style or speed, and the proof of this is most other breed studbooks—even if closed studbooks (purebreds) will allow Thoroughbred also.

This makes it all the more confusing when we find the continuing resistance and truly an anti-Thoroughbred culture in the warmblood circles. Having been a participant in the warmblood fad in this country I can say from personal experience that the inclusion of the Thoroughbred in the breeding inspections was grudging and they were looked upon as a lesser animal. I heard comments as 'not more than 20%', or 'it is better if they are two or three generations back'—and the American Thoroughbred was barely tolerated: 'sprint only', 'built downhill', 'not proper saddle horse conformation' were comments I heard continually in the 1990s, the Thoroughbred, especially the American Thoroughbred was treated like something that smelled bad.

Yet the facts don't support these prejudices. The Thoroughbred—full or part-bred, has been a top Olympic style competitor since the 1912 Olympics when 'team equestrian' was begun. And even in modern times, the Thoroughbred still dominates the standings of top equine athletes. I found that in this country 80% of the Show Jumping Hall of Fame inductees are full Thoroughbred. Even in the Dressage stars of the USDF Hall of Fame, of which there are only six Inductees, however 25% of the bloodlines are Thoroughbred. Eventing of course is dominated by Thoroughbred bloodlines: 45% are full Thoroughbred, 50% Thoroughbred/Irish, 5% Thoroughbred/Standardbred. So the facts do not support the attitude.

[see attached articles 4, 5, and 6]

But those are American standings, what about Europe? The recent DNA evaluation of the Hanoverian Horse, which is the most popular of the Warmblood breeds worldwide, is 35% Thoroughbred in the general population and 39% Thoroughbred in the stallions. This is a huge amount of another breed, and it did not get there by accident—the warmblood, a breed derived from coach and light agricultural stock, will revert back to 'type' without periodic infusions of more athletic breeds.

So there appears to be some hypocrisy present in the psyche of the sport horse producers, as there is a strong love-hate relationship with the Thoroughbred horse. The Thoroughbred is needed for the athleticism, elegance and style it delivers but is despised for the temperament issues it may bring along for the ride. Anyone who has ridden Thoroughbreds can attest that some of them can be high-strung. We find with some Thoroughbreds that if there is excitement in the sport that it plays upon their sensitive and high tuned systems, and sometimes that translates into an animal that may be hard to control. And that is something that comes along the genetic trail with the speed and stamina; some of them have a cranked-up disposition, although many do not. This is not something new—the sport horse breeders of the early 1800s in this country were complaining about this same element. However some Thoroughbreds are 'bomb-proof' and forgiving and they always deliver courage and brilliance. And like most traits in the gene pool, intelligent selective breeding practices should provide the remedy for this. It is we, the breeders, which need to take this concentrated sport resource and make the most of it.

Now, let me touch on some other criticisms, such as "the American Thoroughbred is built downhill because it is a sprinter." This myth is one that I have heard in the past repeated like rote, and still do today, but that is just it, people are merely repeating what they were told without proper evaluation, so this assessment may be just one more example of our collective lack of knowledge.

There is a trait for massive high hindquarters that is strong in the Thoroughbred. But it is the powerful early **distance** racing typesetter—the Godolphin Arabian who has been identified as the source of this distinctive trait. (The Godolphin Arabian is not an Arabian Horse, he is a Turcoman Horse). Usually however the high withers of the Thoroughbred, which is an equally present attribute, not only sets saddle position but produces a more uphill frame.

The Thoroughbred is a saddle racehorse—not harness, and is renowned for imparting a good wither and saddle position on the coach stock of Europe, along with proper hip and shoulder angles.

The German Coach Horse, precursor to the sport-type warmblood. This photo was taken around 1910; notice the type—heavy coarse coach with low withers.—found in *Judging Farm Animals*, Plumb

Speed horses often have a slightly straighter shoulder than a stamina racer, but so does most of the top show jumpers. Perhaps the myth of high massive hindquarters and a downhill frame got placed on the American strains, not by observation but by its association with its cousin the Quarter Horse, a breed that often has lower withers along with the powerful hindquarter— a trait produced by the typesetter Printer 1795, and part of the famous 'bull dog' frame in strains. (Note—not all Quarter Horses are conformed this way, for instance the roping and reining strains have perfect riding horse conformation.)

It is horses that have been bred for harness (coach and carriage horses) that usually are the breeds that have a lower wither than a saddle horse, it is just selection, the harness works better this way. I guess we need to be reminded then that the majority of the warmblood breeds we reverence so much were in fact from coach horse stock, and before that farm horse stock. The low wither is part and parcel of those breeds, and was only improved with vast importation of the Thoroughbred and Hunter stock starting in the 1800s and continuing to this day. The critics of the Thoroughbred as breeding stock, especially the American Thoroughbred, are in my experience intent on promoting the heavier breeds of European Warmblood as superior Olympic style sport horse material. But the facts do not support this judgment, the only place where the European Warmblood has actually proven this case is in Olympic style dressage, which often requires a slower more controlled mount. In 'modern' warmblood breeding the breeders discovered that they needed more Thoroughbred to compete successfully at the highest levels in show jumping and of course in eventing— and even then they heavily and successfully campaigned to revise the cross-country test in eventing to a form more suited to their slower and less athletic breeds (steeplechase portion removed).

Now on the subject of the much-maligned American Thoroughbred and its supposed sprinter bent, taking a look at the *chef-de-race* list (created by Dr. Steve Roman) may help you get some true perspective, because once again the facts do not support the anti-American-bred Thoroughbred bias.

The *chef-de-race* list is a tool used by the Thoroughbred racing industry to classify and identify the sires whose offspring dominate the different race lengths. The Brilliant and Intermediate columns are the premier sprinter sires. The classic column is of course those sires that produce the best classic race winners. But the last two columns—Stout and Professional—are the stamina sires—the producers of stayers. Of those 76 listed premier stayer sires 19 are American-breds—that is an even 25% of the best stayer sire-lines in the world are American Thoroughbreds. But that is not all; the only countries that produce more stayers are England (22) and France (27). Here are the American-breds that have made this exclusive list in the stamina catagories: Chiefs Crown, Crème-dela-Crème, Kingmambo, Pia Star, Sadlers Wells, Niniski, Run the Gantlet, Tom Rolfe, Discovery, Fair Play, Man O' War, Mill Reef, Stage Door Johnny, Round Table, Rainbow Quest, Nodouble and Graustark. I found one Canadian-bred: Nijinsky, but surprising there are no New Zealand, no Australian, no Argentina, there are two from Italy (Tesio) and only three Irish and three German. Don't take my word for it—check it out for yourself. We have all been taught the New Zealand, the Irish, the Australian and of course the German Thoroughbred are the best sources of stayers—and that those are the strains we should only be using in sport horse breeding. It

466   KATHLEEN H. KIRSAN

is time for the American breeders to wake-up, and accept the fact that you may have been conned. For it is no contest—America produces far more stamina bloodlines than all those Irish, Australian, New Zealand and German strains combined!

On the other side of this issue you would think that there is something really negative in sprinter bloodlines—that we, the sport horse breeders should be avoiding them like the plague. Maybe then in the sport of eventing, where they have to gallop long distances this possibly could be a valid concern. (Although, if that was the case why would we ever use the slower, less athletic warmbloods at all?)You want a horse with stamina—one that will not tire. Sprint sources have traditionally been providers of impulsion, and many great jumpers have strong sprinter bloodlines as that ability to push off the hind quarter is a help—we all want our jumpers to have a great lift-off. Perhaps what we should really be looking for is a horse that excels at all distances, that has the acceleration of a sprinter, but the wind of a stayer, who can cut seconds off the time in a jump-off, but still be able to go the distance in cross-country.

Even the great Tesio came to the realization that he needed some sprint-speed lines in his program. In the beginning of his project he would only look for stout or professional type sires (stayers), but eventually he came to understand that the sprint lines are essential for speed at all distances. When he used the French-bred sprinter Havresac II with his staying mare Catnip he produced Nogara and when he used the Phalaris son Pharos, a sire of speed horses, to be her mate—the result was Nearco.

The Nearco son Nasrullah is rated the #1 sport horse sire-line in North America by Peter Birdsall, not just has a hunter/jumper sire, but also in eventing and most surprising in dressage and Nasrullah is considered a sprinter sire-line in racing.

As breeders that aspire to produce excellence in sport performance we must do our research and apply our learning to achieving our sport goals. If we want a quiet amateur mount that can do the lower levels in our sports, than truly a nice saddle horse from just about any breed will do. However, if we have aspirations of success at a higher level of competition than the mix we create in our foals can make the difference, and one thing we can depend on is that we will need some high class Thoroughbred to succeed.

3. Real Stayers – Four-Mile-Heat Racers of Yesteryear

There was a time in England and the Colonies (America) when racehorses were being bred that had such immense quantities of both stamina and speed that they were regularly raced four miles several times in one meet. These four-mile-heat racers of yesteryear were the real stayers. What we breed today and call stamina-bred is just a shadow of the athleticism that these amazing creatures possessed.

In England, before the Thoroughbred was a breed, King Charles II decreed that formal racing, with heats was to be carried out every October at Newmarket Heath. The first race was run in 1666. This was the beginning of the performance standards that would create the world's most successful racehorse breed: the Thoroughbred. Racing had been carried on long before this 1500s into the 1600s saw the remarkable English Running Horse being bred and competed widely.

Famous four-mile heat match race between the pride of the north, Fashion, running against the hopes of the south, Peytona, in 1846 at Union racecourse in New York; Peytona won. *Racing in America*

It was in the previous reign of King James that the fad had developed for crossing in of 'Oriental' sires on the English Running Horse to add height and distance speed to the shorter Running Horse. However, it was what King Charles did in formalizing racing, which is, he set standards, with written rules, and this changed everything.

On the Atlantic sea board in the American colonies (English) in that same year (1665) Governor Richard Nicholls of the New York colony also established a two-mile racecourse on Hempstead Plain on Long Island with set performance standards that mimicked those in England; he even named the New York track Newmarket after King Charles's English track. This was not the first racetrack in the colonies, before this

Kingston, Rhode Island had a one-mile track already for the testing of its pacing racer, and racing was already a widespread pastime in all the colonies. Virginia had formalized ¼-mile sprints on straight tracks before this also. But it was the Long Island track which was keeping step with the new English racing form. And this style race course started popping up in the other colonies as well, in Virginia in 1677.

Traditionally it is a stallion born in 1670 and named Spanker that is considered the first real English Thoroughbred horse. In America our racehorse breed was the Running Horse, and we did not see any English Thoroughbred blood added to it until almost one-hundred years after Spanker. Therefore, it was our native Running Horse that ran both sprint and distance races, at both the pace and the gallop.

America's first racehorse breed was gaited- its intermediate gait was not the trot, but the pace and its variations. Our native Running Horse was carefully bred for racing from English Running Horse and Irish Hobby horses that had been import-ed by the wealthiest settlers, who enjoyed horse racing in the New World just as much as they did in the 'old country' (British Isles), and they took great pride in breeding fast horses.

In the mid-1700s we began seeing the first English Thoroughbred imports in America, which coincided with the fad of heat racing was waning in England. At this time heat racing in England was replaced by classic length races (1 to 2 mile races- run once- not heats). America did not adopt this new British test for another 100 years. And it was in that same time frame (1760-1860) that the America breeder developed the greatest distance racehorse the world had ever seen then or now. The world records for 4-mile heat racing were all made and broken during that era, culminating in the record set by the Running Horse Lexington in1855- which has never been broken.

Lexington—the king of stayers—holds the world record of both fastest four-mile and most years heading the sires list: sixteen.—"Spirit of the Times"

As breeders these horses are interesting to us for a number of reasons: one of course is because they are the ultimate stayer, never has then been a faster racehorse for distance then these; also because so much emphasis has been placed on the use of the stamina-bred Thoroughbred as a basis for sport perfor-mance by sport horse societies. And lastly, for the American breeder of sport horses, who has listened to the repeated state-ments from the warmblood 'gurus' who deride our American Thoroughbred as lacking in stamina, this is the last laugh, for it is the American lines that have the real deal, the proven per-formance, a standard that no other country can match, and it is sitting right there in the background of your pedigrees wait-ing for you to activate it.

So let's look at a few of these stamina stars.

Boston (1833) Boston is an American Running Horse found in the Racing Hall of Fame. His excellence as both a racehorse and as a sire puts Boston in that exclusive company of elite horses such as St. Simon, Man O' War and the more recent Nearco (who carries Boston through a Lexington daughter on his dam-line). Boston was not a Thoroughbred, that breed did not exist yet in America. After 1750 the breeders of our domestic racehorse often brought in English Thoroughbred bloodlines, most usually an imported English Thoroughbred stallion was bred to the Running Horse mare, but it would be another one-hundred years before our American Thoroughbred was established as a separate breed. Our Running Horse was our first racehorse breed and had been selectively bred from at least 1624, which is more than one-hundred years before the English Thoroughbred ever made it to this continent. Did our racehorse breed become Thoroughbred as soon as some English bloodlines were added? No, of course not! But there is a confusion that occurs when reading the old records because the term 'thoroughbred' was used extensively in the eighteenth and nineteenth century on all species of livestock that had been carefully bred from superior ancestors to improve its qualities. So there were 'thoroughbred' sheep and cattle and hogs as well as horses. Over time the English racehorse became known as the 'the Thoroughbred'.

Shortly after the first imports of English typesetters (like Janus) to this country, the English breeding took a different direc-tion. Before this, their racehorse (like ours) ran at ¼ mile and 4-mile heat races (King's Plate), but by the 1770s this was

KATHLEEN H. KIRSAN

changing over to what became known as the classic distance races- 1 to 2 miles, run on an oval track and just once; heat racing was abolished. However in America we continued on with heat racing of our distance runner until 1868—when classic racing became more popular and the four-mile form began to phase out.

Our galloping strain of Running Horse, especially those bred for distance racing, made up most of what later became our American Thoroughbred in 1868 when specific racing standards (classic length races) were adopted and specific pedigree qualifications were designated. The setting of separate performance and breeding standards always precedes breed formation.

Boston, the American Running Horse who is considered the best racehorse of the 19th century.—from painting by Troye

Boston was an extreme stamina bred horse, who regularly won at four-mile-heat races, these kinds of races had been run by our Running Horse breed from 1665. Boston then is an example of the high quality found in our native racehorse breed. He has been rated as the greatest racer of the nineteenth century. He ran forty-five races and won forty-one of them. Fifteen of those victories were consecutive, thirty were four-mile-heat races and nine were three-mile-heat races. He was undefeated at age four and five, and lost only once at six, and that to the Running Horse mare Fashion, who set a **world** record for four miles in that race (Fashion will be our other example- discussed below).

He began partial stud duties while he was still racing at eight, and then became a full time stallion at age ten. He stood first in Virginia, then Washington D.C. and finally in Kentucky. In his last year he sired his two best sons: Lecomte and Lexington, both world beaters and founders of racing dynasties. He was the leading sire 1851, 1852 and 1853 and was second in 1854. And as was common in that era, he sired a significant amount of trotting racers also.

[It is interesting that our newly emerged American Trotter (1818—date of first performance standard: three-minute-mile was ridden under saddle in heat races also—sometimes in five-heats of one mile—winner three of five; all our Running Horse derivative breeds possessed speed along with stamina.]

Many of his best progeny and those of his sons were the result of matings with daughters of imported Glencoe- a 'nick' of immense power, and those lines have become the backbone of the modern American Thoroughbred as well as the American Saddle Horse and American Trotter- the precursors to the Standardbred and Saddlebred.

Boston was foaled in Virginia in 1833; the same year as the trotting sensations Black Hawk and Lady Suffolk were born. This era was a remarkable one in American equine history as the strains of our native Running Horse were specializing and would soon become recognized breeds of their own (American Trotter, Morgan, American Saddle Horse and American Thoroughbred.)

But at Boston's birth the Morgan had not yet been organized, the Trotter and Saddle Horse had just emerged (1817/1818 performance standards). And our Thoroughbred had not become a separate breed of its own yet—which occurred in 1868 with the new Classic race standard (one to two-mile races- not heats) was applied in this country to those horses with enough English Thoroughbred bloodlines (five generations) to qualify.

The English Thoroughbred had been the preferred typesetter for our galloping racehorse for the previous one-hundred years to add height and distance speed to our native Running Horse. There was such a strong preference for 'English' blood that it resulted in a great deal of pedigree 'fudging' and advertisement exaggerations. John H. Wallace cited Boston's 'official' pedigree as one of the casualties of this fraud, especially in the dam lines of both the dam and sire. The pedigree you see here reflects the work he did on this.

One of Boston's dam-lines (Balls Florizel) goes straight back to a Running Horse mare that is a documented champion sprint racer: Sweet Mary. In Edgar's Race and Turf Register she is labeled CQHRM= Celebrated Quarter Horse Race Mare.

But in Boston's day and continuing right up through the twentieth-century no one valued those fast gaited mares, so they hid the ancestry when they could, preferring to think that speed came from the more glamorous imports from England.

Mr. Wallace's and Mr. MacKay-Smith's efforts have been vindicated recently with the publishing of various papers on the equine genome that deal with the true ancestry of the Thoroughbred.horse. The scientists have discovered that the speed gene in the Thoroughbred comes not from the 'oriental' sires and dams as long believed but from the native English and Irish racehorse mares that made up the broodmares of the early racehorse studs. Also it surprised the researchers to discover that it is a sprint speed gene—not distance. Therefore, it originated with those pre-Thoroughbred racehorse mares of Running Horse and Hobby blood. It was horses of that same stock that Colonial breeders imported for racing and saddle horses, and this was the genetic base of all our later sport and fine saddle breeds: Quarter Horse, Standardbred, Tennessee Walker, Missouri Fox Trotter, Saddlebred, Morgan and of course our American Thoroughbred.

Boston's son Lexington (1850) still holds the **world** record for four-mile-heat racing. And Lexington- Boston bloodlines possessed such devastating speed combined with stamina that their descendants were sweeping races in England as well. This perceived insult to the British racing establishment ultimately resulted in the backlash of the Jersey Act of 1913 to 1948. There was a monstrous hypocrisy evident in the ban. Not only were American bloodlines producing racers in France and elsewhere that kept winning, those same lines left some legacy in England before the ban that were powering their own fastest racers, especially those from the Lady Josephine family (Mumtaz Mahal and Lady Juror) and those descended from Orby. Even the 'sire of the century' Nearco carried Lexington as his fourth-dam-sire. And many of the best in France, such as Durbar, Tourbillon and others were descended from these same sources.

At the end, the financial realities, and a general lack of class in their racehorse from its isolated breeding policies, plus the French objection to participating in a stud book that barred the fastest horses, it was then that England modified their rule so that most of the barred bloodlines were then acceptable.

Fashion 1837. As spectacular as Boston's athletic talent was, he was not a 'freak', our native racehorse was producing many racers who came close to his ability and even a few that exceeded him occasionally. Competition raged between different racing areas of the country and match races between regional champions were events of great excitement. So it was in May of 1842 that a contest was set up between the southern hero Boston against the northern star Fashion. Fashion was an amazing race mare with 36 races, 32 wins, 4 seconds, most of those 3 and 4 mile races- she also holds a position in the Racing Hall of Fame.

The race mare Fashion retired to stud.—*American Thoroughbred* by Trentham

The race between these two mega-racers was set at Union racecourse on Long Island, and had the fantastic purse of $20,000, and as each heat was finished carrier pigeons were released to bring the news to the New York newspapers—this was an event!

"The race was in four-mile heats and the contest drew another enormous crowd, estimated at seventy thousand people. The grand stand was crowded with a large array of those distinguished in political, social and sporting life, and for more than a quarter of a mile, on both sides of the course, spectators were packed in solid phalanxes. Intense interest prevailed as the heats were run (Lyman Weeks)."

Four-mile-heat races were run in heats—the winner being the best two out of three. Fashion won the first two heats and therefore won the race. Being a mare she was not able to leave near the massive genetic legacy of Boston, but she did produce seven foals, and her daughter Young Fashion proved to be a very good producer as she had ten foals of which six were winners.

Fashion herself was beaten by another great racing mare- Peytona, who beat her in a heat race in 1846 (illustration at beginning of article). Races of this sort were run regularly; the American bred horses had reached the pinnacle in speed combined with stamina. It is ironic that today so many of the critics of our Thoroughbred have been trying to convince us that it is a 'sprint' only breed; it is laughable really, as our breed is based genetically on the best stamina-speed genetics that this planet has ever seen.

4. American Hall of Fame Show Jumpers

(A Brief Analysis of American Show Jump Champions)

This is a brief analysis of those super show jumpers, the select few, which have made it into the American Show Jumper Hall of Fame. After adding a paragraph to my article on Gordon Russell [remount stallion—website article] who produced two hall of famers, it hit me that I should take a closer look at the genetics of the best jumpers we have had in America. Peter Birdsall did an admirable job of cataloging the best hunters and jumpers in his 1980s texts, but I decided to take a look at the genetics of those few that broke all the records and made it to the Hall of Fame. What I found surprised me a little. First of all only twenty horses have made it so far to the list. Two of those (Snowman and Main Spring) are of unknown breeding, and I expected more warmbloods—but found only one Trakehner (Abdullah) and one 'Dutch' warmblood who is actually a ½-American Thoroughbred (Calypso). The rest were all Thoroughbreds.

Now this being the end of 2011, and me being a product of our modern sport breeder experience, I fully expected to see by this time the proven merits of the 'European' warmblood horse in evidence at the very top of the game (although I am sure undisputable greats like American-bred Dutch warmblood Judgement and his rider Beezie Madden will be added shortly). But we in America have been breeding our own heavy type 'warmblood' since the mid-1800s—in that it is part coach horse mixed with racehorse (see Sport Horse Recipe). At that time it was regular practice to add Cleveland Bay, Irish Draught or other coach types to our racehorse to produce our heavy hunters; and of the unknowns in the Hall of Fame it seems likely from his known history and temperament that Snowman was a part Irish horse—a heavy hunter.

That said, the evidence is undeniable that the Thoroughbred has reigned supreme at the very upper levels of achievement seeing that sixteen out of the twenty (80%) are Thoroughbred and significantly for us is that many of those are of American Thoroughbred bloodlines.

It has to be just our lack of knowledge that has allowed us to agree with the 'warmblood' association's view of our domestic TB. And I am ashamed to admit that when I was actively involved in breeding in the 'European' manner and following the warmblood registries' instructions that I accepted their decidedly unfavorable view of our domestic Thoroughbred. But the evidence is clear; our Thoroughbred produces sport horses of the very highest excellence and ability.

Now, as breeders we want to be enlightened to what bloodlines—domestic or foreign, produce the winners—it is a key to our success. And in the Hall of Fame inductees you do see the same bloodlines repeated over and over—such as Nearco/Pharos, Teddy, Black Toney/Domino, Man O' War/Fair Play, Hurry On, Rock Sand, Dollar, Blanford, The Tetrarch/Roi Herode. For example, the magnicent Sinjon carries Roi Herode on his top line through The Tetrarch and his damsire is War Glory a ¾-brother to War Admiral, a Fair Play grandson. And we see that For The Moment descends from Teddy on the sire line through Bull Lea and from Double Jay, a grandson of Black Toney.

I said this would be a brief analysis, and so I will just pull a couple of these top American TBX out for our inspection. Gem Twist, who won individual and team silver at the Seoul Olympics (1988)—he also was the Grandprix Association 'Horse of the Year' a whopping **three times** (1987, 1989, 1992).

Looking at his topline you will see he descends from Bonne Nuit—who is a grandson of Roi Herode and also has the great Dollar line in his dam—these are French jump lines. Notice also the presence of Bonne Nuit's half-sister Brave Bonnie—who is out of a Domino line sire (American sprint line) as well as reinforces the Dollar influence. We find three more lines of Roi Herode through his best son The Tetrarch. Don't miss the Man O' War son Great War, and that the dam carries two lines of War Admiral through daughters, as well as three lines of Black Toney, and another line of The Tetrarch. These are the genetic powers behind this world beater.

I found a curious coincidence when looking at the genetics (pedigrees) of the Hall of Famers. There was another world beater back in the 1950s, this was a mare called 'Miss Budweiser' whose registered name was Circus Rose. She is ¾-sister to Sisterly Love who is the dam of New Twist, the grandfather of Gem Twist. Check out her pedigree and compare to Gem Twist. She is by Great War (Man O' War son) out of a daughter of Valorous, a Pennant son (Domino line).

One other thing before we leave Gem Twist—his father Good Twist, a stallion, also made it to the Hall of Fame list. Described as a speed horse with a tremendous jump, he managed to win an amazing twenty-one international level classes in both Europe and America.

Next let's look at an incredible mare: Touch of Class. In the 1984 Olympics Touch of Class won two Gold Medals! She also had the first double clear rounds in Olympic history. What a mare! Usually teamed with Joe Fargis, she also won on the Nations Cup teams in Aachen, New York and Washington, and she won the Grand Prix of Tampa. After the Olympics she and Fargis continued their winning ways including making first in the World Cup US east coast standings. She then retired to broodmare duties where she also succeeded. Her pedigree can become a blue-print for us, illustrating how to breed top mares—mares that can succeed both in sport and as mothers.

We can see Black Toney/Domino on the sire line through Blue Larkspur, but also through two lines of the inbred Ultimus (Domino). A strong filly factor of Sir Gallahad daughters (Teddy line), the full brothers Fairway/Pharos multiple times on both sides of the pedigree, a strong presence of the ¾-brothers Chance Play/Mad Hatter from the Fair Play line, as well as a beautifully sex balanced Blandford and his ½-sister Felina. There is also a great background buildup of the taproot mare Canterbury Pilgrim through the lines of Chaucer and Swynford. All and all, an extremely strong genetic structure.

For those of you who aspire to breed the best jumpers these are bloodlines that are proven transmitters of jump talent—look for them and build them into your foals.

5. Bloodlines of the Dressage Champions of the USDF

This is second in a series exploring the genetic make-up of our most successful sport horses. The idea is to clear away all the common knowledge and hype about popular bloodlines and breeds in order to truly see for ourselves what genetics are powering the champions of today. Following are the bloodlines of our Dressage champions.

A quick examination of our USDF Hall of Famers reveals that we are on more expected ground with the majority of the dressage inductees being European warmbloods. There are only six horses that have received this honor so far. To be eligible the horses have to near the end of the career or over with it, possibly deceased and to have made a significant contribution to the sport of dressage in the US. Four of the six are warmbloods: Roemer 1975, Gifted 1980, Graf George 1984 and Bretina 1997.

Hanover has perfected the dressage horse, and has often dominated the international standings since the 1980s. But there is something significant that has shown up here in the very top in American dressage that the sport horse breeder might want to know. That is all four of these warmbloods have a prominent daughter line of Duellant, often through his grandson Grande—all of them—even though there is a twenty-two year age difference between them.

Roemer, who is a Westphalen but often identified as a Dutch horse, carries a Duellant daughter—Duela in the second generation--and she is the dam of his sire Pilatus. All the others are Hanoverians and carry Grande who also is out of a Duellant daughter. Graf George and Gifted have him as their second sire, Bretina carries him as the dam sire of her sire in the third, and she is a mare and because of his position in her pedigree, he colors her X-chromosome. In the males the position in the pedigree shows he rules the Y—this is an interesting indicator of the possible transmission of sex linked traits. Duellant is renowned as a dressage line, and we see this is so still, and his grandson Grande continues on with this.

Seeing the very best dressage performers in this country carry this particular line in several different descendants and that it is the consistent theme throughout—this then should be an alert to the line-breeder out there that they will still find dressage success with building up these lines in the engine room (fourth through sixth) and beyond in their prospective dressage foals. Remember to look for the daughter lines of Duellant—all of these are out of his daughters—no sons, and possibly see if you can find some closely related sisters for more genetic punch (Tesio Methods).

Some BIG surprises for warmblood purists will come in the other two: an American Thoroughbred—yeah really, and get ready for the shocker—a pony! That ought to poke a hole in your warmblood balloon. These are not lower level horses—these are the best so far—wow, a pony.

Keen, is an American Thoroughbred—in warmblood circles this is a breed which we have been told not to use because of their supposed sprinter bent—and here is something amusing on this subject: Keen's second dam-sire is War Bam, a good race horse who sired great Quarter Horses as well as Thoroughbreds, that's right, half his progeny are Quarter Horses

So let's look at this Thoroughbred and see where he could possibly have gotten this exceptional movement and sport ability from. We find the full siblings Swynford and Harry of Hereford in the sixth—full siblings are usually an indication of the strongest potency, there is also more strength to this with their half-brother Chaucer in the fifth. Swynford and Chaucer are everywhere in the modern Thoroughbred and have become a standard pattern, and while these are great sport lines, they usually are far enough back to be a vague influence unless they are activated. This is what we find here with the rare full brother Harry of Hereford found in War Glory (a ¾-brother to Triple Crown winner War Admiral). Other contributors to the talents in Keen is the Teddy presence through a strong sex balanced double of his son Sir Gallahad, and reinforcement coming through his sire Ajax, who is here also through a daughter, La Flambee, therefore she is a sister to Teddy. There is also a strong sex balance presence of the Tetrarch and of Man O' War, who are both potent sources of impulsion and sport ability. And those are the strongest elements in this dressage champion. Not quite what you would expect maybe?

Then there is the pony- Seldom Seen 1970, a 14.2-hand Connemara/Tb cross, and his pony lines are incomplete, but he does carry a double of the important pony sire Gil (CSB 43), who in-turn carries a sex balanced double of Cannon Ball (CSB 1), who is one of the early greats of this pony breed. His sire Mitipo is an Argentine bred Thoroughbred—a sprinter by the way, who carries strong Phalaris and St. Simon lines which includes a sex-balance of his son Chaucer. These are ever present lines in the background of the modern Thoroughbred. Phalaris can contribute very nice movement and impulsion, as does St. Simon. However it is clear some of the style must come down the line from the pony sire Cannon Ball.

How can a pony be a sport horse? The Connemara is a superb sport horse, a natural jumper and is renowned for its hardiness, good temperament and stamina. Combined with Thoroughbred it is a winning eventer. The Connemara is closely related genetically to both the Irish Draught and the Thoroughbred (mtDNA studies by Bower and Hill). The ancestors that are common to these breeds is the Irish Hobby, a gaited saddle-racehorse breed that is also found at the base of both the English and the American Thoroughbred, as well as in the American breeds of Standardbred, Saddlebred, Quarter Horse, Tennessee Walker, Morgan and Missouri Fox Trotter, through our original Colonial race-saddle horse, which is based on the Hobby, both English and Irish. So sport is in their DNA. This is no small thing, that is, to be the parent breed of four racehorse breeds—and should be something we in the sport horse world take an interest in.

6. Bloodlines of Eventing Champions

(US Eventing Hall of Fame Inductees)

This is the last in a series of articles looking at the genetics of the best Olympic style horses that have competed in this country. In this article we will be looking at the genetics of the eventing champions that have made it to the ultimate honor of the Hall of Fame.

There are nine Hall of Fame inductees: Jenny Camp 1926, The Grasshopper 1948, Kilkenny and Plain Sailing, Good Mixture 1962, Bally Cor 1965, Irish Cap 1967, Biko 1984, and Custom Made 1985.

Overall we find in these nine that the Thoroughbred is king of the genetics as four are full Tb, and the remaining five are ½ to ¾-Thoroughbred. That is an overwhelming affirmation that the sport genetics of the much maligned Thoroughbred are supreme in the sport of eventing. And the funny thing is we found that they are also the top breed in the best of the show jumpers. And surprisingly we even found they comprise 25% of the genetics of the dressage champions. I hope this helps put to rest the common lore that the Thoroughbred is not the proper ingredient for Olympic sport success; rather the facts and history demonstrate not only the excellence of this sport breed, but that it probably the only constant to be found in the successful sport horses today.

In eventing we find the influence of the Irish Horse, both the Irish Draught and the Connemara Pony are of significant importance. When crossed with the Thoroughbred these horses have led the sport leader boards since the mid-1800s, which is long before anyone thought of having a Hall of Fame. The roots of this successful cross reach back to the 1500s all the way to the racehorse studs of Ireland (pre-Thoroughbred), where a saddle-race horse was perfected, they were known as Irish Hobbies. These horses, alon: the American Running Horse. Our Running Horse was a premier racehorse at all distances from ¼-mile sprints to four-mile-heat stamina contests—all one-hundred years before the English Thoroughbred arrived on our shores. This Running Horse—like those in the British Isles, became the base of our Thoroughbred, Morgan, Standardbred, Saddlebred, Tennessee Walker and Missouri Fox Trotter and several now extinct breeds. These native breeds then are the base of our own sport horses of today (see Sport Horse Recipe). I provide this history lesson so that you may begin to understand why it is the Irish Horse and the English Thoroughbred have such an affinity for own native breeds—it is because they all come from the same base stock.

Now in our Hall of Famers, only four of the nine have full pedigrees (Tbs) and that none of the part-breds have full pedigree information, and unfortunately the only Irish part-bred that has some of its Irish lines known is Custom Made, so we will only be able to partially determine the full genetic strengths of many of these horses. In Custom Made we can see the Galty Boy line is concentrated, but through sons only. Galty Boy is a proven hereditary transmitter of jumping talent, but unfortunately is usually found only by son lines, as he is here. Custom Made's sire line, the Thorughbred Bassompierre, is also a male leaning pedigree, led by a double of Wild Risk sons, who are actually ¾ brothers as their dams are from the Teddy line. There are four lines of Teddy, sex balanced, and we find Pharos and his sister Mirawala. Custom Made won the individual Gold medal at the 2000 Sidney Olympics.

Two of the other Irish/Tb crosses, Plain Sailing and Kilkenny, are out of the same sire: Water Serpent. Water Serpent has a pedigree worthy of study, not only because he was such a wonderful sire of top eventers, but because it is a very strong genetic design. Water Serpent is living proof that we should strive to build up the maternal influences we find in our stock. He was an immensely successful sire of event horses in Ireland. His pedigree reveals a strong filly factor of Gallinule daughters: Lady Drake, Hammerkop, and Joie De Vivre 4x3x4. Further he carries the ever present Swynford with his ¾-brother Chaucer—also through daughters 3x3, but they are then reinforced through their dam Canterbury Pilgrim who finds her brother Loved One here also. These are the lines Lord Derby built his racing empire on—the sound progeny of the mare Pilgrimage. Plain Sailing won team Gold at the 1967 Pan Am Games, team Silver at the 1968 Olympics, team Silver at the 1972 Olympics and in 1979 team Gold at the World Championships—what a horse!

A note on Swynford: He is by the elite mare Canterbury Pilgrim, a daughter of Pilgrimage, as is her brother Loved One. The mare Pilgrimage was the target line that Lord Derby built his racehorse stud on. The presence of Swynford, plus his ¾ brother Chaucer are what is called a 'standard pattern' in the Thoroughbred, because it is more common to find them then not to. Swynford is not an entirely sound line, his sire John O'Gaunt gave unsound joints, although his great-grandson Mahmoud is a sound line. How can a bloodline that has some unsoundness become such a successful sport transmitter? It is because of the way genes divide and combine in a mating—so that the progeny do not get all of its parent's genetics—this can be a positive and a negative. When a bloodline has immense talent but also some unsoundness, then we should pick the descendants who show the talent, but are free from the weakness; in this case you will find Mahmoud is a sound representative of that line.

In more modern lineages we see the same thing with Nasrullah, his   -brother Royal Charger and their ¾-brother Mahmoud. This combination worked so well it became a standard pattern in the modern Thoroughbred. However, being part of a standard pattern does not detract from their importance and several of these stars have a strong concentration of them.

[For American breeders especially, realize War Admiral, plus his five full sisters (Admiralette, Military Brush, Our Colors, War Brush and War Hysteria) and his ¾-brother War Glory or his ¾-sisters Marching Along and Harrannette—all carry Harry of Hereford who is the rarely seen full brother to Swynford, and including these lines will add to the potency in a large way.]

Strong marelines don't just appear in the event sire Water Serpent, as we find three of the top eventers have a tremendous build-up of Pocahontas with significant sources of the often missing daughter lines coming from these sources: Wellingtonia, Teddy, Tracery and Ksar. Pocahontas is a daughter of Glencoe and of course she is the main source of the large heart gene, however Glencoe had many other daughters and we find them in the Gordon Russell the sire of Jenny Camp and through Spearmint progeny Plucky Liege, Chicle, Catnip and Bathing Girl. Other female strength appears from build-ups of Brown Bess who provides impulsion, coming through lines of Quiver and Carbine- also found in Spearmint.

Spearmint is an interesting character, a great race horse (Derby winner), but also unsound in his front legs. However, he established one of the most lasting performance lines in the modern Thoroughbred. We found other unsound individuals such as John O'Gaunt, the sire of Swynford, and Phalaris, all three had poor front legs, but the excellence of the athletic ability still made them great sport bloodlines.

So let's look at few of these full Thoroughbred stars of eventing to see what is powering their amazing careers. Here is Irish Cap, he has Swynford 6x6x5 sex balanced, plus two lines of Gondolette who is a daughter of Loved One 6x7—this is a significant build-up of these siblings who are out of Pilgrimage. Also of interest to us is the perfect symmetry of this performer's sire and dam-lines: Roman and Maimaison who are ¾ siblings, a son and a daughter of Sir Gallahad (Teddy son), with a son and a daughter of Sunstar as the second dam and dam-sire. Irish Cap won the 1974 individual and team Gold at the European Championship.

Another Hall of Famer with a strong pedigree is Good Mixture showing a strong Spearmint concentration of Chicle, Plucky Liege and Petite Marmite 4x5x4x4 (Spearmint is strong in Pocahontas and Brown Bess). The full brother Teddy sons Bull Dog/Sir Gallahad are sex balanced 4x3, Swynford and Chaucer are 4x5, the full siblings Sainfoin/Sierra are 6x6, plus the impulsion lines of Polymelus 5x5. Even as a cull from the race track, this gelding was the USCTA Horse of the Year, he won Silver at the Munich Olympics and in 1974 the individual Silver and team Gold at the World Championship.

Bally Cor is a full Tb with the usual strong Swynford and his relatives, but another theme keeps arising in these stars, which is the reinforcement of the Pocahontas lines. This horse carries a triple of Negofol, who carries Wellingtonia, a stallion who carries two of the rarely seen daughter lines of Pocahontas. Teddy and Tracery are the other most often found carriers of these essential daughter lines. The other Hall of Famers with these key lines are Good Mixture with Teddy, Biko with Teddy and his sire Ajax, Irish Cap with both Teddy and Tracery and Custom Made with Teddy. Other common lines are of course Swynford et al, Sunstar, Gainsborough.

What we can conclude from this series of articles is that overall the **Thoroughbred is the most important sport resource available to us.** No other breed comes close to it in the top performers of eventing and show jumping and it is second only to the Hanoverian line of Duellant in the dressage stars.

7. California Chrome –Mare Power in Action

Everyone here in northern California is abuzz about California Chrome, a product of this area; his owners are from Yuba City, a farming community north of Sacramento. And no one can deny after seeing him run in the Kentucky Derby that this is a horse of the highest class, as he easily won his race, breezing home at the finish.

What I want to share with you is how similar this pedigree design is to Seattle Slew's, and for the illustration of what a good mare can contribute. You will see both of these champions have nice sires, but truly it is the mare in each who is the power factor in their genetics.

Let's review first what it was about Seattle Slew's pedigree structure (which is the map of his genetics) that made such an incredible champion. He was born back in 1974, is proven to be one of the greatest sires in the last fifty years, his power continues to grow even today, and I know personally he is a line I value in my sport horse designs. And Seattle Slew is the fourth sire of California Chrome, so his genetics are already present in our subject. Seattle Slew's dam My Charmer is an inbred horse, as she is inbred 3x3 to the full sisters Busher/Striking. Both of these mares have a tremendous record as broodmares, but combining them together (plus their ¾ genetic sister Nothirdchance sits in the third generation on the sire side) gave us the invincible Seattle Slew. This type of concentration obviously provides dominance. Another example of this same type of pattern can be seen in the champion Easy Goer for instance, as his dam Relaxing, was 3x3 to the ¾ sisters Businesslike/Big Hurry. This is the strongest pedigree feature in both of these super-stars of the past, and now we see this design in the new star California Chrome.

To understand the power in Seattle Slew that was focused through these doubled up mares we need to take a trip back in time to when it was common place in this country to race our horses in <u>four-mile heat races</u>. This period of our racehorse development is unique in the world; for two hundred years the American breeders chose the best genetics for heat racing horses—the result being the soundest, strongest and most stamina loaded racehorse there has ever been. Seattle Slew, Easy Goer, and now California Chrome are demonstrating 'critical mass' in these background genetics.

The second dam of the full sisters in Seattle Slew is the famous La Troienne, an imported French-bred mare who was a mediocre racer, but proved to an astounding broodmare, especially of quality mares—this created a maternal dynasty of excellence in this country. But I found that her pedigree appears to be more male oriented on the surface as she is inbred to the ¾ brothers St Denis/Flying Fox, therefore on the surface it would appear her sons should be better than her daughters—but that was not the case. It took Les Brinsfield to solve the mystery of her power to produce fantastic daughters. He discovered first of all that she is a genetic warehouse of Young Giantess, a Diomed daughter. He found she carries over 40 lines of her, but no other Diomed lines, just this one daughter. This level of concentration we call 'critical mass', and surely reached a tipping point in dominance, enough so that it would strongly set type. But it also is an extreme example of a background filly factor—as this daughter of Diomed is in-turn present through both sons and daughters (see Les' articles on www.pedigreepost.com in the archives section).

But that is just the set-up for what occurred when this mare was imported to America. Les has pointed out that when she was imported here she was bred strictly to stallions who were strong carriers of Domino: Black Toney, Blue Larkspur and Bubbling Over—so stallions dominant in Domino genetics. Domino, who was the fastest sprinter of his time; ironically Domino is inbred to the King of Stayers: Lexington. The Running Horse Lexington set the world record for fastest four-mile heat, and then set a world record as top stallion that has never been broken—he led the sires list for sixteen years. So Lexington is America's super-horse, and to be carrying multiple lines of him is the stacking the genetic deck with fastest, soundest, most stamina loaded racer there has ever been—this is no small thing. Lexington is everywhere in the American Thoroughbred, but is particularly concentrated in Domino who is inbred to him 3x4x4. But the genetic power doesn't stop there as Lexington himself is inbred to Diomed, through sons only—so he and then Domino after him, is a warehouse of the male Diomed lines.

When these two gene pools (Domino/ La Troienne) came together, the long separated daughter lines of Diomed met their male counterparts and it provided a tremendously powerful 'nick' in Diomed lines. Diomed was born in 1777, but imported to this country when he was twenty-one, he is one of the greatest English stallions ever entered the American horse; and he set a strong type in our native racehorse and created a bonanza of top performers; all at a time when his peers were disappointing our breeders. Diomed was bred as a four-mile-heat racer, but as that race standard was being abolished in England at that time. He was raced also in the new 'classic distance' race form. He was a winner in both types. Here in the USA we kept the four-mile-heat standard for another hundred years, so his genetics contributed positively to our domestic distance racer.

When a horse is inbred or tightly line-bred, they are dominant in those bloodlines; therefore inbreeding is an important tool for the breeder, and historically this practice is responsible for the creation of many breeds. In Seattle Slew's case he is inbred 3x3x3 to closely related sisters (Busher/Striking/Nothirdchance) who are powered by Diomed genetics. La Troienne has 46 lines of Diomed (through a daughter), Bubbling Over has 33 male lines of Diomed, Blue Larkspur has 23 male lines and War Admiral carries an additional 16 male lines. The rest of Seattle Slew's pedigree adds even more sources of these genetics throughout, but it is his front inbreeding which acts as a laser beam of this genetic power. Enough so this horse, Seattle Slew, even with crooked hind legs and slow maturing joints, was able to win the Triple Crown while undefeated— an extraordinary achievement.

Now if we look at California Chrome's pedigree we find it is very similar. We not only see the same basic pattern, with a dam that is inbred to ¾ siblings 3x3, who are out of the same dam: <u>Numbered Account</u>. But it turns out this inbreeding goes straight back to these same sources of power that created Seattle Slew. For example Numbered Account's sire Buckpasser is out of a dam who is by War Admiral, out of a Blue Larkspur dam (Businesslike) who is out of La Troienne. Further the second dam of this mare is Glamour, a daughter of Striking (also found in Seattle Slew). Striking and Businesslike are ¾ sisters and they are 8x8x7x7x7x7, building on the dominance. There are additional lines of Buckpasser, Jet Pilot and other carriers throughout as well. Other pedigree strengths play in the genetics of California

Chrome: a sex-balanced double of Mr. Prospector 3x4, Northern Dancer 4x5, ¾ brothers Secretariat/Sir Gaylord—all of these are racing bloodlines of the highest class, but these wonderful lines are expected to be found in the top American Thoroughbred in our day as the breed is saturated in them. What makes this pedigree shine is the extraordinary concentration of genes coming from the mare's inbreeding. This type of pedigree pattern is one that is found in the best stallions, both Seattle Slew and Easy Goer (who died young at eight from an allergic reaction) were top sires and their bloodlines are genetic gold in your pedigrees today. Now we find the new super-star, California Chrome, and surely with his pedigree structure that is powerful in America's best genetics he will be a legendary sire as well. We have waited a long time for a horse this wonderful.

Bibliography

Aldridge, Lynn I. "Genetic Evaluation of Show Jumping Horses in Ireland" 2000

All Breed Database – www.allbreedpedigree.com

American-Education.org "Colonial Education in America – American Education" 2011

Anderson, James Douglas *Making the American Thoroughbred- especially in Tennessee 1800-1845*, 1916

Anthony, Edwin *The 21st Century Handbook- a comprehensive guide to Thoroughbred Pedigrees* 1998

—   *The American Thoroughbred* 2008

Austin, Frank "Memoirs of Old Steeldust" – interview of Meredith 'Bud' Hart Raeburn by Frank Austin 1939

BCM Foundation, *WBFSH International Breeding Guide*

Bell, Jerold S. "The Ins and Outs of Pedigree Analysis, Genetic Diversity and Genetic Disease Control" 1992

Bettingmarket.com "Sadlers Wells 1981-2011"

Birdsall D.V.M., Dr. Peter H. *Bloodlines of Hunters & Jumpers in North America* 1981

Bloodlines.net "Equine Genetic Genealogy" (www.bloodlines.net)

Bowen, Edward l. "The Jockey Club's Illustrated History of the Thoroughbred in America" 1994

—   *Matriachs- Great Mares of the 20th Century* 1999

—   *Matriachs volume II: More Great Mares of Modern Times* 2008

—   *Dynasties- Great Thoroughbred Stallions* 2000

—   *Man O' War* 2000

—   *Legends of the Turf* 2003

—   *War Admiral* 2007

Bower, Dr. Mim et al. "The cosmopolitan maternal heritage of the Thoroughbred racehorse breed shows a significant contribution from British and Irish native mares" 2010.

Bowling, Ann T. *Horse Genetics* 1996

Bowling, Michael. "The Application of mtDNA Research in Horses" 2002

—   "Who's your Momma? New Genetic Research and Old Pedigrees" 2002 published on www.tbheritage.com

Boyd, Eva Joline. *Native Dancer* 2007

KATHLEEN H. KIRSAN

Breeding International Limited. "Breeding News for Sport Horses" editorial on page 1, 4/2003

Brinsfield, Les. "Domino: the Pedigree" (The Pedigree Post)

— "La Troienne: A Distaff Fountainhead" (The Pedigree Post)

— "Domino – Belmont Influence" 2005 (The Pedigree Post)

— "War Admiral/La Troienne" (The Pedigree Post)

Bryant, Jennifer O. *Olympic Equestrian-the sports and stories from Stockholm to Sidney* 2000

Carter, General William H. *The U.S. Cavalry Horse* 1895

Clarke, Celia, and Wallin, Debbie. *The International Warmblood Horse* 1991

Craig, Dennis. *Breeding Race Horses from Cluster Mares* 1964

Culver, Francis Barnum. *Blooded Horses of Colonial Days: Classic Horse Matches in America Before the Revolution* 1922

Curtis, Robert S. *The Fundamentals of Live Stock Judging and Selection* 1925

Darlington, George Eyre. *Fox Hunting in Delaware County, Pennsylvania and Origin and History of the Rose Tree Fox Hunting Club* 1901

Davidge, D. William. "Is the X-factor the Answer" (The Pedigree Post) 2005

Denhardt, Robert M.

— *Foundation Dams of the American Quarter Horse* 1982

— *The Quarter Running Horse* 1979

— *Foundation Sires of the American Quarter Horse* 1976

DiMarco, Lou. "The Army Equestrian Olympic Team" parts Iand II www.militaryhorse.org

— *War Horse, a history of the military horse and rider* 2008

Edgar, Patrick Nesbitt. *The American Race-Turf Register* 1833

Equine Research Publications. *Equine Genetics & Selection Procedures* 1978

Erigero, Patricia. "Ariel" (tbheritage.com)

— "Eternal" (tbheritage.com)

— "Boston (USA)" (bloodlines.net)

— "Glencoe" (tbheritage.com)

— "Hanover" (tbheritage.com)

— "Henry of Navarre" (tbheritage.com)

— "Norfolk" (tbheritage.com)

Erigero, Patricia, and Peters, Anne. "Leamington" (tbheritage.com)

Evans, J. Warren et al. *The Horse* 1976 –revised 1989

Faversham, Rommy. *Samuel Riddle, Walter Jefords and the Dynasty of Man O'War* 2005

— "Rise and Fall of Lexington's Sire Line" 2006 (Thoroughbred Times)

Faversham, Rommy, and Rasmussen, Leon. *Inbreeding to Superior Females- using the Rasmussen Factor to produce better race-horses* 1999

Glengarry, Jack. *Upgrading Thoroughbred Families* 1995

Goebel, Anna. "Warmblood Stallions of North America" 2014

Green, Dr. Ben K. *Horse Conformation, as to Soundness and Performance* 1969

Harper, Clive. *The Thoroughbred Breeders Handbook* 1997

— *The Thoroughbred Broodmare Handbook* 2002

— *Patterns of Patterns* 2006

Harrison, Fairfax. *The Background of the American Stud Book* 1933

   Early American Turf Stock 1730-1830 1934

   The Belair Stud 1747-1761 1929

   The Roanoke Stud, 1795-1883 1930

Harrison, Stephen Paul et al. "Mitochondrial DNA: an important female contribution to Thoroughbred performance" 2005

Haskin, Steve. *Dr. Fager* 2007

Haun, Marianna. *The X Factor- what it is and how to find it, the relationship between inherited heart size and racing perfor-mance* 1997

— *Understanding the Power of the X Factor- patterns of heart score and performance* 2001

Hewitt, Abram S. *Sire Lines* 1977 -updated 2006

Herbert, Henry William. *Frank Forester's Horse and Horsemanship of the United States and British Provinces of North Amer-ica* volumes I and II 1857

Hervey, John. *Racing in America 1665-1865* 1944

Hill, Dr. Emmeline et al. "History and Intregrity of Thoroughbred Dam Lines Revealed in Equine mtDNA Variation" 2002

— "The genetic origin and history of speed in the Thoroughbred racehorse" 2012.

Hunter, Avalyn *American Classic Pedigrees (1914-2002)* 2003

— "Mare Study: Performance vs Pedigree"

— "Soundness of the Modern Racehorse" (The Pedigree Post)

— "Tiznow and Officer" (The Pedigree Post)

Jansen, Thomas et al. "Mitochondrial DNA and the origins of the domestic horse" 2002

Jenkins, Sally and the Funny Cide Team. *Funny Cide 2004*

Jones, Caroline. "Fox Hunting in America" 1973

Jones, Hugh. *The Present State of Virginia* 1724

Kirsan, Kathleen. *North American Sport Horse Breeder 2013*

—   "Sporthorse Pedigree" www.SporthorsePedigree.com 2003- 2005

—   "Sport Horse America" www.sport-horse-america.com 2005- 2007

—   "Sport Horse Breeder" www.sport-horse-breeder.com 2007-

Kleeman, Dr. "Useful Information on Motherlines" 1930

Leimbach, Jay. "Inbreeding in Top Thoroughbreds" (The Pedigree Post)

Livingston, Phil and Roberts, Ed. *War Horse- mounting the cavalry with America's finest horses* 2003

Losey, Robert; Morales, Erradare; Capps, Timothy. "Identifying Broodmare Prospects for an Elite Broodmare Band" 6/2010

Luis, Christina et al. "Iberian Origins of New World Horse Breeds" 2006

Macgregor-Morris, Pamela. *The World's Show Jumpers* 1956

MacKay-Smith, Alexander. *Speed and the Thoroughbred- the complete history* 2000

—   *The Colonial Quarter Race Horse* 1983

—   *American Foxhunting- an anthology* 1970

—   *The Race Horses of America 1832-1872* 1981

Magee, Sean. "Horse Racing: Pride of Ireland" 2007 (The Racing Post)

Manchester, Herbert. *Four Centuries of Sport in America* 1931

Martiniak, Elizabeth. "Hamburg" (tbheritage.com)

—   "Maggie B. B." (tbheritage.com)

—   "Hastings" (tbheritage.com)

—   "Frizette" (tbheritage.com)

—   "Curiosity" (tbheritage.com)

McLean, Ken. *Tesio- Master of Matings* 1984

—   *Quest for a Classic Winner* 1987

—   *Genetic Heritage* 1996

—   *Designing Speed in the Racehorse* 2005

Means, Dan. *Seattle Slew 2007*

Merck & Co. *The Merck Veterinary Manual* 1998

Mitchell, Ph.D., Frank. *Racehorse Breeding Theories* 2004

Milner, Mordaunt. *The Godolphin Arabian: Story of the Matchem Line* 1990

Morris, Tony. *Thoroughbred Stallions* 1990

National Steeplechase Association www.nationalsteeplechase.com

Nevill, Ralph. *Old Sporting Prints* 1900

Nye, Nelson C. *Speed and the Quarter Horse* 1973

Parker, Ellen. "Reines-de-Course" book I and II 2006

—   "Rush Box" (reines-de-course.com)

—   "Catnip" (reines-de-course.com)

—   "A. P. Indy" (reines-de-course.com)

—   "Almahmoud" (reines-de-course.com)

—   "Ruddy Light" (reines-de-course.com)

—   "Beaming Beauty" (reines-de-course.com)

—   "Aspidistra" (reines-de-course.com)

—   "Adargatis" (reines-de-course.com)

—   "Delicacy" (reines-de-course.com)

—   "Rough Shod II" (reines-de-course.com)

—   "Myrtlewood" (reines-de-course.com)

—   "Hildene" (reines-de-coures.com)

—   "Frizette" (reines-de-course.com)

—   "Lady Be Good" (reines-de-course.com)

—   "Maggie B. B. Part I & II" (reines-de-course.com)

—   "Unbridled's Song" (reines-de-course.com)

—   "Seattle Slew" (reines-de-course.com)

—   "Broad Brush" (reines-de-course.com)

—   "Raise a Native" (reines-de-course.com)

—   "The Softening of the Thoroughbred Runner" (reines-de-course.com)

—   "Phalaris 'Disease'" (reines-de-course.com)

Paulick, Ray. "Sunday Silence" 2008

Pedigree.me.uk. "Northern Dancer Inbreeding"

Peters, Anne. "Inbreeding, by Boussac" (The Pedigree Post)

— "Broomstick" (tbheritage.com)

— "Ben Brush" (tbheritage.com)

— "Medley" (tbheritage.com)

— "Durbar" (tbheritage.com)

— "Americus" (tbheritage.com)

— "American Eclipse" (tbheritage.com)

Peters, Anne and Young III, Thomas M. "The Good, the Bad, and the Inbreed" (The Pedigree Post)

Philips, Deane. *Horse Raising in Colonial New England* 1922

Plumb, Charles S. *Judging Farm Animals* 1919

Porter, Alan. *Patterns of Greatness- a pedigree analysis of the leading European Thoroughbreds of the last fifty years* 1992

— "Line-Breeding to Northern Dancer and Nasrullah in Thoroughbred Stallion Pedigrees" 2008

Porter, Alan, and Peters, Anne. *Patterns of Greatness II- The Americans- the careers and pedigrees of the leading American Thoroughbreds from 1940-1995* 1995

Porter & Coates. *Famous Horses of America* 1877

Potts, Allen. *Fox Hunting in America* 1912

Pullen, Nigel. "Rough Shod: Part 1 – Her Dynasty" and "Rough Shod: Part II - Her Legacy" (The Pedigree Post)

Reed, Will. "The South vs. the North – Boston's Challenge to Fashion Accepted" (tbheritage.com)

Reese, William. "The First Hundred Years of Printing in British North America" 1989 (reeseco.com)

Rogers, Byron. "The Real Bend Or" (bloodhorse.com) 2012

Roman, Dr. Steve. www.chef-de-race.com

Robertson, William H.P. *The History of Thoroughbred Racing in America* 1964

Rotterman, Silke. "Keen xx, a Pioneer of American Dressage" 2009 (eurodressage.com)

Royo, L. J. et al. "The Origins of Iberian Horses Assessed via Mitochondrial DNA" 2005

Saylor, Henry H. *Thoroughbred Types 1900-1925- photographic portraits of notable racehorses, steeplechase and cross-country horse, hunters and polo ponies* 1926

Show Jumping Hall of Fame "Untouchable"

— "Idle Dice"

— "Touch of Class"

—   "Sinjon"

Skinner, J.S. "Essay on the American Horse" found in *The Horse* by William Youatt 1847

Sparkman, John. "The Northern Dancer Effect" (pedigreecurmudgeon.blogspot.com)

Spilleta.com. "The Unofficial Thoroughbred Hall of Fame"

—   "Boston: Champion Thoroughbred Racehorse"

—   "Boston"

Sporthorse data website. www.sporthorse-data.com

Sport Morgan Ltd. "Classic Bloodlines" www.sportmorgan.com

Stoneridge, M.A. *Great Horses of Our Time* 1972

Strickland, Charlene. *The Warmblood Guidebook* 1992

Tapp, Ian. "The Sadler's Wells/Mill Reef Nick" 2010 (bloodhorse.com)

Tattersall, George. *The Pictorial Gallery of English Race Horses* 1850

Taunton, Theo. *Famous Horses* 1901

Taunton, Thomas Henry. *Portraits of Celebrated Racehorses* 1888

Taylor, Lewis. "The Horse America Made- the story of the American Saddle Horse" 1961

Tesio, Fredrico. "Breeding the Racehorse"

TesioPower Database. source of pedigrees and notes

The Blood Horse Inc. *Sires and Dams of Stakes Winners 1925-85* vol. I and II 1986

—   *Thoroughbred Champions- top 100 racehorses of the 20th Century* 1999

—   *25 years – 1916 through 1940- A Quarter Century of American Racing and Breeding* 1941

—   *Horse Racing's Top 100 Moments* 2006

—   *Horse Racing Divas 2010*

The Horse Magazine www.horsemagazine.com

Thoroughbred Bloodlines. Nineteenth Century Stallions "Lexington (USA)" (bloodlines.net)

Thoroughbred Genetics. "Thoroughbred Genetics identifies performance genes in racehorses and publishes ground breaking research" www.thoroughbredgenetics.com

Thoroughbred Heritage. www.tbheritage.com

Thoroughbred Racing Association. *Thoroughbred Racing and Breeding* 1945

Trevathan, Charles E. *The American Thoroughbred* 1905

Tsatsaronis, Leo. "Northern Dancer Female Inbreeding" (The Pedigree Post)

United States Equestrian Team and Steinkraus, Bill. *Great Horses of the United States Equestrian Team* 1977

Varola, Franco. *The Tesio Myth* 1984

von Velsen, Dr. Eberland. "Thoughts about the Influence of the Thoroughbred Stallions and Mares in Germany's Oldest Riding Horse Breed" 1981 Trakehner Hefte

Vila, Carlos et al. "Widespread Origins of Domestic Horse Lineages" 2001

Virginia State Archives. newspapers, letters, documents

Vosborough, W. S. *Racing in America 1866-1921*

Waldrope, Judy. *Analyzing the Functional Conformation for the Olympic Disciplines* 2012

Wallace, John H. *The Horse of America in his Derivation, History, and Development* 1897

—   *Wallace's American Stud-Book* vol. I 1867

Washington, George. "The Papers of George Washington" The University of Virginia Press 2009

Weeks, Lyman Horace *The American Turf: an historical account of racing in the United States* 1898

Welch, Ned. *Who's Who in Thoroughbred Racing,* volumes I and II 1946-1947

Willett, Peter. *Makers of the Modern Thoroughbred* 1984

Pedigree Index

Jaconet 1875 128
Janus 1746 10
Jenny Slamerkin RH 1828 42
Jersey Lightening 1905 118
John P. Grier 1917 321
Just-A-Minute 1944 272
Keen 1966 395
Kerala 1958 264
King James 1905 160
Kitty Fisher 1767 67
Lady Be Good 268
Lady Grey RH 1817 18
Lady Josephine 1912 191
La Troienne 1926 284
Lauries Crusador 1985 220
Lexington RH 1850 11
Liz F 1933 265
Macho Uno 1998 314
Maggie B. B. RH 1867 125
Majestic Prince 1966 353
Mannie Gray 1874 78
Marching Home 1932 323
Maria West RH 1827 50
Mary Hunt RH 1833 398
Maskette 1906 119
Mikayo 1935 325
Miss Breeze 1899 397
Miss Obstinate RH 1829 44
Moccasin 1963 193
Monsieur Tonson RH 1822 40
Mother Goose 1922 204
Mr. Prospector 1970 354
Mumtaz Mahal 1921 192
My Charmer 1969 286
Myrtlewood 1932 262
Mystic II 1954 425
Nasrullah 1940 195
Natalma 1957 274
Neasham Belle 1948 218
Nebos 1976 234
Neckar 1948 232
Neji 1950 418
Nella da Gubbio 1924 217
Nereide 1933 231
Never Bend 1960 294
Nixe 1941 233
Noholme II 1956 194
Numbered Account 1969 339
Odd Foot 1934 396
Orby 1904 188
Orphan RH 1810 29
Pan Zareta 1911 120

Parole 1872 92
Pekina ASA 1844 43
Pelo de Oro (Nautical) QH 1944 383
Peter McCue 1885 384
Picric 1914 196
Pilate 1928 162
Planet RH 1855 79
Polynesian 1942 355
Pompey 1923 356
Prayer Bell 1954 269
Quadrille 2007 399
Quiet American 1986 309
Rare Treat 1952 276
Reading 1918 197
Red-and-Blue 1880 129
Reference Point 1984 297
Regret 1912 142
Relaunch 1976 311
Relaxing 1976 287
Riverman 1969 295
Saaleck TR 1940 226
Sadlers Wells 1981 293
Sadlers Wells/Darshaan 212
Sailor 1952 326
Sarazen 1925 179
Seattle Slew 1974 333
Seven Pines 1933 132
Sex Appeal 1970 277
Singspiel 1992 299
Sinjon 1951 408
Sir Dixon 1885 126
Snap 1750 68
Starman HA 1979 382
Stymie 1941 163
Sunday Silence 1986 332
Sweep 1907 144
Sweep On 1916 145
Sympatico 1965 374
Ta Wee 1966 266
The Commoner 1892 115
The Iron Duke 1966 375
The Niece 1882 127
Top Flight 1929 206
Touch of Class 1973 409
Tourzima 1939 207
Trifle RH 1828 45
Ultimus 1906 178
Unbridled 1987 308
Untouchable 1952 410
Upset 1917 322
Valid Appeal 1972 312
Valorous 1924 386

Vandal RH 1850 80
Velasquez 1986 298
Verdict 1920 HB 93
Walk in the Water RH 1813 30
Whisk Broom II 1907 131
Yorkville Belle 1889 155

Horse Index

Aaron Pennington 84
Abe Frank 1899 109-10, 120, 391, 394-6
Abernant 1946 168, 187, 220, 313-5
Acamas 1975 200-1, 210
Accra 1941 414, 418
Ace Card 1942 172
Activate 1951 282
Adam 1902 201, 256, 271-3
Adana 1908 104, 271-2
Adargatis 1931 211, 403, 407
Addi 1928 223, 230
Addie C 1883 147, 383
A Deck 1961 255
Admiral Drake 1947 153, 318
Admiring 1962 154, 282
Adriana 1905 114, 165, 262, 271, 274-5, 277, 310-2, 353-4
Aela 1936 223
Aerolite RH 1861 33, 38, 63, 69-70, 76, 98, 102, 104, 111, 117-19, 138, 142-3, 147-8, 155, 157-59, 165, 165-7, 183, 204-6, 239, 232, 234, 261-5, 323, 336, 373, 386, 407-8, 417-9, 422, 425, 432, 434, 448-9
Affectionately 1960 282
Affirmed 1975 61, 331, 336, 344-5
Agathea's Dawn 1970 304, 313-5
Agnes Star 1928 135
Ahoy 1960 155, 318
Ajax 1901 201, 256, 345-6, 473, 475
Ajhal 152
Alabama 1906 86, 101, 223, 228, 230, 367
Alablue 1945 123, 307, 333-5, 349
Alan-a-Dale 1899 109
Albanella 1944 223
Alleged 1974 247
Al Mundher 195? 251
Anblick 1938 400
Anis 1943 223
Apalachee 1983 183
Alarm 1869 98-100, 104, 122, 146
Alarm Belle 1887 121
Ala Toby 1972 152
Albion 1837 14
Alcibiades 1927 172, 249, 277, 287, 309, 314-6, 334-5, 337, 339, 349-50

Algerine 1873 21, 93, 115, 181, 187-9, 205, 217-8, 223, 229, 230-1, 233, 336, 410
Al Hattab 1966 304, 313-5
Alice Carneal RH 1836 11, 19, 22, 48, 58, 62-3, 76-8, 85-6, 90-4, 109, 115-20, 130-2, 141-5, 155-60, 165, 176-82, 188-92, 196-7, 203, 216, 223, 226-9, 240-1, 263, 289-90, 321-2, 357, 367, 386, 396-7, 417, 419, 434
Allemande 1955 137, 287, 337
Almahmoud 1947 201, 212, 238, 249, 257-9, 273-5, 298-9, 327-8, 332, 335, 339, 349-52, 393, 399, 482
Alme SF 1966 400, 411
Almost Persuaded QH 19?? 113, 377, 385
Always 1943   183
Alydar 1975 61, 139, 172, 201, 283, 337, 345, 352
Amabel 1885 147
American Eclipse RH 1814 37-8, 46, 48-9, 53, 56, 64, 71-2, 76-8, 81, 96, 116-9, 142, 144, 147, 155-9, 170, 176-8, 197, 199, 203, 241, 259, 289, 302, 397, 434, 454, 483
American Flag 1922 172, 270, 298, 309-10, 314, 336-8, 349-51, 353-4, 399
Americus 1892 (aka Rey de Carreras) 62-3, 85-6, 88, 90, 104-5, 115-6, 121, 149, 153, 164, 184-6, 189-94, 199, 210, 215, 220, 222-3, 226, 228, 230, 248, 254, 256-7, 264, 271, 273, 289, 291, 294-5, 320, 328, 339, 367, 372-4, 431, 483
Americus Girl 1905 86, 164, 184-5, 191-3, 195, 210, 220, 240, 264, 271, 273-5, 286, 294-7, 311, 339, 353-4, 372-4
Amicitia 1899 149
Anchors Ahead 1932 150, 153, 423
Andy K 1937 319
Angelica 1879 150, 173, 213
Anna Marrone 1921 184
Annapolis 1926 151, 368, 400, 413-4, 417-9, 423
Annul 1892 301, 304, 306
Another Treat 1972 260
Abdullah TR 1970 471
Admiralette 1938 435, 486
A P Indy 1989 329, 334, 338, 482
Apollo 1953 223, 230
Apollonia 1953 200, 219, 486

Appeal 1927 172, 318

Aqua Tom ASH 2001 464

Araucaria 1862 202, 215, 223

Arbitrator 1937 165, 191-2, 195, 197, 212, 240, 249,
    258, 273-5, 291, 298-9, 332, 335, 338, 349-51, 399,

Arctic Dancer 1963 259

Arctic Tern 1973 258-9

Argosy 1981 330, 336, 486

Ariel 1925 104, 138, 169, 232, 234, 256, 271-2, 329, 491

Ariel RH 1822 38, 49

Aristides 1872 83, 392

Aristophanes 1949 183, 212, 293, 298-9, 351

Armada 1924 318, 326, 349-51

Arromanches 1993 254, 304

Artful 1902 112, 117

Artilier SF 1959 405

Aristocrat 187? 84

Artless 1907 136

Ashado 2001 258

Aspidistra 1954 96, 110, 254-6, 260, 266, 270, 278, 280,
    300-2, 306-9, 313-5, 482

Assault 1943 110, 199

Assert 1979 136, 152, 259

Asteria 1930 200

Asturie 1932 200

Audience 1901 99, 101, 120, 122-4, 130-1, 135, 206,
    214, 265-6, 270, 272, 274, 287, 306-7, 310-2, 317,
    321-6, 333, 337, 353-5, 369, 401, 406, 426

Australian 1858 98-9, 102-3, 147, 253, 387, 432

Authentic DU 1995 404-5, 411

Ayacanora 1854 201, 217, 284

Baby League 1935 139, 253, 277, 280-2, 285-6, 333-6,
    339, 411

Bacchus TR 1910 226, 324, 326

Back Yard 1942 269

Baden-Baden 1874 62

Badruddin 1931 185, 264, 315, 334, 349, 374

Bahram RH 1774 313-5, 382, 453

Baladier 1932 135

Bald Galloway (ERH) ~1703 7, 10, 14, 18, 40-2, 46, 50,
    59-60, 65, 67, 279, 452, 455

Bald Peg ERH (aka Old Morocco Mare) ~1665 6-7, 10,
    65, 68, 279

Bald Charlotte 1721 18, 46, 67, 453

Bald Stockings RH 1837 69, 374

Balls Floziel RH 1801 59, 73

Bally Cor 1965 471, 473

Ballyhoo 1887 103

Ballyhoo Bey 1898 103

Bandy Balls RH 1774 453

Banish Fear 1932 220, 275, 295, 299, 332, 335, 338,
    399

Banshee 1910 113, 136-7, 199-00, 207-11, 264, 293-6,
    302, 311, 367, 374, 410

Banshee Breeze 1995 302

Banstar 1923 200, 425

Barleysides RH 17?? 9, 453

Bar Nothing 1933 139, 253, 264

Barnton 1844 238

Bartlet's Childers 1717 291

Bassompierre 1968 486

Bathing Girl 1915 255, 410, 475

Battleship 1927 152, 370, 402, 415-8, 421, 443

Battlewick 1942 415

Bay Flower RH 1859 63, 74, 102, 131, 134, 141-5, 180,
    197, 203-5, 261-5, 267, 272, 285, 321-5, 396-7, 426,
    434

Bay Maria RH 38

Bayonet RH 1865 84

Bayou 1954 254, 350

Bay Peg 1700 6-7, 10, 41, 65, 68, 398

Bay Ronald 1893 213-4

Beacon RH 1861 84

Beaming Beauty 1917 104, 139, 169, 171, 173, 252-3,
    263-7, 277, 285-6, 310-3, 320, 333, 336, 339, 391,
    395, 411, 482

Bedford 1792 40, 43, 45, 77, 79, 155, 391, 398

Bee Ann Mac 1941 281

Beldame 1901 112, 409

Belgravia 1903 135, 164, 173, 210-1, 219, 234, 249,
    262, 264, 266, 269-70, 274-5, 277, 287, 293-4, 296-7,
    306-7, 309-13, 337, 339, 355, 403, 406-7, 409, 425-6

Be Like Mom 1937 238

Belle Histoire 1945 281

Belle of Troy 1947 281, 299

Belmont AT 1864 383

Bendara 1969 259

Benguala 1954 414

Ben Holladay 1893 111

Believe It 1975 254, 303, 429

Bellisario 1911 114, 252, 263-7, 277, 285-6, 310-2, 339,
    395

Be My Guest 1974 135, 154, 185, 247, 259

Ben Ali 1883 74

Ben Brush 1893 74, 101-2, 105, 114, 120, 122-3, 131,
    134-6, 139, 141-5, 163-4, 167-9, 171, 173-5, 180,
    204-6, 237, 245, 252, 24-6, 258-9, 261-77, 285-7,
    291-3, 295-7, 302, 306-7, 310-2, 319-26, 328-30,
    337, 339, 344, 353-5, 368-9, 373-5, 378-80, 383, 385,
    404, 406-9, 418, 420, 423, 425-6, 483

Bend Or 1877 58, 83, 149-50, 153, 167, 238, 255, 278,
    403, 456, 483

Beningbrough 1791 14

Bernardini 2003 113

Bounamica 1943 215

Bound 1984 195

Bounding Home 1941 317

Bourbon Mist 1959 122

Bourtai 1942 173, 351

Bowl of Flowers 1958 154, 318

Bramble 1875 62-3, 74, 102-3, 120, 131, 141-5, 163, 180, 203-9, 261-9, 271-4, 274-7, 285, 287, 294, 306, 321-6, 339, 349-1, 355, 374-5, 383, 385, 396-7, 404, 407-9, 418, 425-6, 434

Breezing Home 1940 317

Bretina HA 1997 472

Bridal Colors 1931 135, 211-2, 219, 234, 314, 425

Brights Roan Filly ERH~1680 65, 454

Brimmer Quarter Mare RH 18?? 16, 19, 71

Brobinski 189? 75

Broke Even 1941 281

Brokers Tip 1930 135

Brookdale 1921 314, 336

Brother Sam 1969 369, 333

Brown Bess 1876 475

Brown Prince 1874 82

Brush Along 1924 140

Brushup 1929 253

Bubbling Beauty 1961 258-9, 273

Bubbling Over 1923 134, 135, 139-40, 171, 253, 265-7, 277, 280, 285-6, 302-3, 308, 310-5, 329, 333-4, 336, 339, 404, 411, 476

Buckfinder 1974 114

Buckpasser 1963 174, 255-6, 260, 277, 279, 281, 287, 303, 308, 320, 329, 331, 334, 337-9, 342, 349-50, 399, 475

Budd (RH) 1789 9, 443

Buisson Ardent 1953 135

Bull Dog 1927 136, 151, 168, 237, 245, 256, 278, 301-2, 305, 330, 341, 346, 475

Bull Lea 1935 249, 252, 257, 332, 335, 350, 352, 471

Bulse 1913 264, 300, 308-9, 383

Burgomaster 1903 113, 272, 407, 418

Burgoo King 1929 139, 253

Busanda 1947 139, 260, 277, 279-81, 287, 308, 329, 334, 337-9, 349-51, 399

Busher 1942 139, 253-4, 281-6, 329-31, 333-6, 349, 475-6

Businesslike 1939 277, 279-83, 287, 309, 330-1, 334, 337-9, 349-50, 399, 475-6

Bushleaguer 1950 281

Byerley Turk ERH 6, 13, 41, 65, 67-8, 442, 452

By Jiminy 1941 238, 253

Bymeabond 1942 253

Byrds Express ERH ~1750 13

Byrnes Big Filly RH 453

Cade 1734 58, 60

Cadillacing 1984 283

Caelia RH 9

Caerleon 1980 153, 247, 249

Cahill Road 1988 256, 302

California Chrome 2011 139, 283, 331, 338, 462-3, 475, 477

Caixa Elecktona 304

Calista ERH 1758 13, 18, 20, 28, 37, 39, 46, 56, 63, 291, 454

Caluse 190? 109

Calypso DU 1971 464, 471

Candlemas 1883 431-2

Cannon Ball CSB 1904 473

Canterbury Pilgrm 1893 369, 472, 474

Cap and Bells 1898 75

Capitola RH 1858 73, 91, 197, 357

Cap-a-Pie 1949 415, 426

Capote 1984 329

Captain Sykes QH 1906 377, 383

Carbine 1885 168, 255, 258, 403, 456, 475

Carnegie 1991 291

Caro 1967 215, 219, 224, 234, 238 298, 30-9, 313-4, 318, 336-8, 344, 349-54, 375, 399

Caspia 1906 185, 190

Cassius Mare RH ~1775 11, 13, 18, 63

Castianira 1796 47

Castrel 1801 134

Catherine Marrone 1919 184

Catnip 1910 34-5, 69, 123, 153, 164, 182, 193, 195, 210-4, 217-20, 223, 225, 231-4, 238, 240, 249-51, 270-1, 275, 286, 291, 294-9, 309, 315, 332-7, 339, 353-4, 367, 369-71, 372-4, 382, 406, 409, 411, 467, 475, 482

Cee's Tizzy 1987 303

Celt 1905 105, 109-10, 173, 193, 302, 336, 368, 395

Cequillo 1956 270, 302, 307-9

Chamant 1874 82, 201

Champagne Cocktail 1976 259

Charles O' Malley 1907 345

Charles XII 1836 148

Chance Play 1923 151, 369-70, 373, 400, 409, 422, 472

Chance Shot 1924 151, 212, 249, 273-5, 293, 298-9, 313, 328, 332, 369, 373, 422

Chant 1891 147

Chaucer 1900 369, 472-5

Cherokee 1877 82

Cherokee Rose 1910 114, 136, 173, 259, 265-6, 276, 310-2

Cherokee Run 1990 112

Cherry Pie 1920 200

Chicaro 1923 200

Glorious Song 1976 258, 299
Go and Go 1987 259
Godolphin Arabian (TURK) 4-6, 13, 59, 87, 442, 452, 454, 466
Gohanna Mare 1807 174
Gold Bridge 1929 86, 182, 193, 212, 289-90, 2935, 298-9, 352, 404-5, 411
Golden Attraction 1993 330
Golden Boss 1920 187, 193, 212, 293, 298
Golden Broom 1917 114, 136, 385
Golden Fleece 1979 259
Golden Maid 1914 185
Golden Rod 1906 184-5
Golden View 1906 149
Gondolette 1902 475
Gone West 1984 345
Gonzales ~1898 360
Goodes Twigg RH 1778 362, 391, 398
Good Mixture 1962 473, 475
Good Twist 1960 400-1, 403, 406, 472
Goose Egg 1927 114, 201, 311, 313-5, 336
Gordon Russell 1910 471, 475
Graf Ferry 1918 224-5, 229, 231-4, 367
Graf Isolani 1926 224-5, 229, 231-4, 367
Grand Glacier 1923 184, 190
Grand Parade 1916 182, 190, 194, 213-4, 217, 231-4
Grave and Gay 1899 89, 223-4, 227, 229, 231-4, 367
Great Above 1972 254-5, 302, 304-5, 313-5
Great Britain 1910 109, 410
Great Captain 1949 280-2
Great War 1938 151, 368, 380, 400-1, 404, 406, 423, 471-2
Grecian Princess 1770 19, 48, 66, 76-7, 80, 92, 115-6, 128, 130, 156, 401
Grey Diomed RH (Tayloe's) 1785 11, 18-9, 43, 45-6, 48-50, 56, 76, 78, 80
Grey Diomed 59, 280
Grey Grantham Mare ERH 454
Grey Flight 1946 139, 185, 256-7, 271, 339
Grey Whynot ERH ~1790 7, 10, 65, 67
Grindstead 1871 84
Grolleja 1938 224
Grolle Nicht 1917 224
Grossularia 1933 246
Guido Reni 1908 215
Guillotine 1947 223
Gulch 1984 290, 299, 345
Gunfire 1899 149
Habitat 1966 26, 35, 236, 246, 297
Hail to Reason 1958 151-3, 163, 213, 249, 259, 275, 291, 293, 298-9, 315, 332-5, 338, 341, 346, 349-2, 399

Halcyon 1928 137, 403, 407
Halcyon Days 1938 136, 407
Half and Half 1957 151
Halla TT 1945 379
Halma 1892 101, 109, 184, 190
Halo 1969 260-1, 275, 299, 327-8, 332, 399
Hambletonian AT 1849 57
Hamburg 1895 33, 64, 70, 97, 100, 103-5, 109-14, 117-9, 120, 122, 134-7, 139, 142-3, 148, 163, 165, 168-9, 173, 183, 185, 199-2, 204-9, 239-40, 249, 251-2, 254-5, 259-60, 261-7, 270-6, 285-6, 291, 294-5, 296, 301-2, 306, 309-13, 319-20, 329, 332, 336, 344, 346, 367, 369, 372-3, 379-80, 329, 332, 336, 344, 346, 367, 369, 372-3, 379-80, 385-6, 400, 404, 406, 408, 419, 422, 425, 434, 448-9, 481
Hamburg Belle 1901 112
Hammerkop 1900 474
Hamoaze 1911 153
Hampton 1872 414
Hand Bell 1889 391, 395-6
Handsome 1892 133, 149
Handspring 1893 111
Hanover 1884 74, 86, 89, 93, 96, 100-1, 108-11, 114-21, 123, 133-4, 137, 142-3, 152, 163, 165, 170, 181, 183-90, 193-4, 197, 200-1, 204-9, 213, 217-9, 223, 228, 230-3, 252, 261-7, 272-4, 276, 285, 291, 300, 306, 310, 318, 324, 326, 346, 354, 361, 369, 373, 376, 378-9, 385-6, 391, 395-6, 400, 408, 410, 418, 420, 423, 425, 431-2, 434, 448-9, 455, 472, 479
Hard Tack 1926 188, 255, 368
Harmless RH 1779 453
Harriet's Kid 1944 254
Harold 1876 83, 98, 124
Harranette194? 423
Harry Bassett RH 1868 64, 436, 451
Harry Bluff RH 1839 43, 379, 384
Harry of Hereford 1910 390, 473-4
Haste 1923 124, 132-3, 169, 210-1, 219, 270, 287, 295-8, 307-9, 313-5, 335, 337, 354, 406
Hastings 1893 70, 103, 148-9, 163-6, 173-4, 186, 266, 268-9, 271, 273-7, 285-7, 295-6, 301, 304-7, 310-2, 323, 326, 337, 339, 345, 353-4, 369, 372-5, 378, 395, 401, 403, 406-10, 415, 417-9, 422, 425, 481
Hasty Road 1951 148, 259, 273, 351
Hautboy 1690 7, 10, 41, 65, 67-8
Haynies Maria 1808 37
Head Play 1930 422
Heart Breaker TR 198? 223
Heldifann 1921 104-5, 113, 137, 169, 199-2, 207-12, 250-1, 289-98, 303, 311, 368, 369, 431-3
Helmbold 1866 (aka Dublin) 62, 84
Henry RH 1819 37, 47

Norman 1905 87, 379

Northeast 1905 87

Northern Dancer 1961 136, 201, 212, 238, 247, 249, 258-9, 283, 288-90, 293, 298-9, 327, 331, 335, 338, 341, 346, 349-52, 393, 399, 477, 483

North Star III 1914 253

Nothirdchance 1948 152-3, 164, 212, 249, 259, 275, 298-9, 315, 318, 332-5, 349-52, 399, 475-6

Novice RH 1853 85-6, 90, 105, 122, 176, 178, 180, 185, 190-2, 226, 228, 239-42, 393, 411

Number 1979 183

Numbered Account 1969 283, 331, 339-40, 476

Nureyev 1977 183

Nutwood AT 1870 379, 383

Nuvolona 1926 212-4

Octoroon 1899 304

Odd Foot 1934 391, 395-6

Office Wife 1977 259

Ogden 1894 237

Okapi 1930 138

Oktibbena 1911 305, 313

Olambala 1906 100, 385

Old Bald Peg (ERH) 1635 6-7, 10, 68

Olden Times 1958 135, 314

Old Peg (ERH) 1655 (aka Morocco Mare) 6, 10, 59, 6, 67-8

Old Rosebud 1911 99, 112, 122

Old Shales 1755 21, 63, 454

Oleander 1924 223

Ole Liz 1963 122

Olitipa 1872 84

Olympian 1898 151, 166

Olympic ASH ~1926 394

Omar Khayyim 1914 112

Omnium 1892 199

Once Double 1967 123

Ondulation 1920 113, 135-7

On Watch 1917 163, 173, 249, 276, 287, 332, 337

On To Glory 1971 257

Ophelia RH 1831 93, 101, 108, 115-20, 143, 188-9, 197, 229

Orange Peel 1919 400, 411, 420-1

Orby 1904 21, 86, 88, 93, 101, 108-9, 181-3, 185, 187-90, 193-4, 199, 213-5, 217-8, 223, 225, 230-5, 249, 286, 289-90, 333, 336, 367, 373, 404, 409, 470

Orientation 1948 319

Orlass 1914 183, 215, 218, 230

Orme 1889 86, 181

Ormonde 1883 149, 278

Orphan RH 1810 22, 29, 57, 73, 75, 77, 80, 91

Orville Mare 1815 109

Ouch 1937 369, 375

Our Colors 1943 423, 474

Outdone 1936 271, 315, 333-5, 349-50

Out Late 1961 424

Oval 1921 151, 201, 304, 311, 313, 336

Oversight 1906 109

Paddy Whack RH 1778 212, 452

Padua 1896 122, 173, 258

Paintbrush 1911 112

Palace Music 1981 87, 330, 335

Panasette 1928 270, 296, 301, 306-15

Panay 1934 114, 270, 296, 306-15

Panic Girl 1930 391, 395-6

Panique 1881 98

Panoply 1917 173, 336, 409, 417-8

Pan Zareta 1911 109-10, 119, 184, 388, 391, 394

Papillon 1769 11, 17, 44, 48, 60, 62, 66, 76, 80, 92, 128, 279, 291

Papoose 1877 82

Papyrus 1920 213

Paragon RH 1788 34-5, 42, 44, 77, 92, 455

Parasol 1800 102

Pari Mutual 1928 407, 422

Parole 1872 2, 16, 33, 57, 62, 69, 81-4, 92, 112, 213, 238, 270

Partner 1718 401

Pasquinade 1957 134

Passaic 1878 84

Pat Malloy RH 1865 36

Paul Jones 1917 114, 262, 425

Pavot 1942 313-5, 319

Peacock RH 1760 398, 453

Pearl River 1926 113

Pekina ASA 1844 36, 43

Pelo de Oro (see Nautical, Injun Joe) QH 1944

Pennant 1911 114, 151, 163, 168, 173, 249, 259, 276-7, 287, 297, 311-3, 332-3, 336-7, 339, 372, 375, 379, 385-6, 406, 472

Pera 1875 98

Perfection 1875 85, 182, 194, 211, 215-6, 231, 238, 240, 294, 370

Pericles 1958 222, 367, 423

Peroxide 1937 253, 352

Perugino 1991 290

Peter McCue QH 1885 73, 378-9, 383-5, 453

Peter Hastings 1925 173, 311, 406

Peter Pan 1904 120, 136, 163-4, 171, 173, 179, 186, 200-1, 204, 206, 210-1, 219, 234, 238, 249, 252, 255, 258, 264-6, 268-70, 272-7, 286-7, 293-7, 306-7, 309-4, 333, 336-7, 339, 355, 372, 374-6, 383, 385-7, 406-7, 409-10, 414-5, 417-9, 425-6

Petite Marmite 1963 475

Petticoat 1906 122, 137, 163, 276, 287, 407

KATHLEEN H. KIRSAN

General Index

Alexander, Richard A. 5, 12, 171, 429, 462
Aiken, Henry 362
Allison, Mr. 886-7
American Civil War (aka Civil War) 8-9, 23, 31-2, 39, 57, 63-4, 69-71, 81, 84, 96, 146-7, 149, 235, 237, 248, 342, 436
American Dressage Institute 390
American Foundation Movement (see American Saddle Horse) 23, 364, 391, 459
American Gold Cup 403
American Horse Show 366
American Hunter Horse (see also American Sport Horse) 8, 221-2, 360-3, 380, 388, 390, 404, 413, 416, 428-9, 431, 431, 448, 458-9, 463, 465
American invasion 84, 86, 239, 367
American Jockey Club 71
American Remount (aka Remount, US Remount Service) 109-10, 221, 378, 380-1, 383, 389, 393-4, 413, 471
American Revolution 7-8, 13, 16, 25, 32, 57, 362, 365
American Running Horse (aka Native American Woods Horse) 4-9, 12-7, 20-5, 27, 31, 33-7, 39, 51, 58-61, 63, 65, 69, 71-5, 82-3, 85, 90, 98, 100-1, 105-6, 108, 121-2, 134, 170-1, 183, 185, 200, 214, 222-4, 228, 235, 238, 245, 247, 257-8, 279, 288-9, 361-3, 365, 370, 378, 387, 391, 430, 432, 452, 469-70, 474, 476
    Stud Book (aka Edgar's, American Race-Turf Register) 21, 58
American Saddle Horse (aka Plantation Horse) 4, 7-8, 13, 22-3, 34-6, 100, 361-2, 370, 379, 388, 391-2, 448, 459-61, 463, 465-7, 469, 473
American Sport Horse (Hunter Horse) 8, 71, 96, 220-2, 360-2, 380, 388-90, 404, 413, 416, 428-9, 430-1, 433, 448, 458-9, 462, 465
American Stud Book (S. D. Bruce 1868) 4, 35, 97, 441
American Trotter Horse (American Trotter Breed) 21, 25, 63, 72, 97, 100, 224, 361-3, 379, 449, 454, 459-60, 469
American Turf Register 36, 38, 51
American Turf Register and Sporting Magazine 36, 51
Anderson, Alexander 5, 12, 171, 429, 463
Anderson, C.W. 151, 247, 250, 280-1, 346, 363-4, 427, 436
Anglo-Arab 400, 463

Anthony, Edwin 11, 34, 302, 329
Arabian Horse (aka Arab) 6-8, 12, 32, 72, 222, 370, 436, 452, 463, 466
Armstrong, Walter 317
Army Equestrian Team 393
Artificial insemination 247
Baldwin, Lucky 85, 105, 183
Barb 4-7, 12, 22, 31, 58
Bell, Jerold S. 447, 478
Belmont Park 55, 111, 135, 244
    Grand National 415
Beresford, Lord William 85
Birdsall, Dr. Peter 186, 215, 368, 421-3, 467. 471
Blanc, Edmund 199
Bloodhorse Inc (Bloodhorse Magazine, Bloodhorse publications, Bloodhorse.com) 135, 151
Boston Herald 414
Boussac, Marcel 13, 137, 198-02, 246, 433, 437
Bower, Dr. Mim 5, 9, 16, 58, 170, 452, 456, 473
Bowling, Dr. Ann 148, 248, 347, 356, 370, 430, 435, 447
Bradley, Col. 253, 281, 437
Breeding News for Sport Horses 427, 479
Bretton Woods 445
Brinsfield, Les 169, 171, 279-80, 368, 449, 476
British Jockey Club (aka English Jockey Club) 2-3, 12, 62, 71, 86, 88, 112, 172, 181-2, 199, 235-6, 288, 330, 433, 440, 442-5, 456
British House of Lords 443
Brossman, C.E. 347
Bruce, B.G. 4, 62
Bruce, S.D. (aka Greysteel) 35, 70, 97, 441
Canadian Horse 363, 460, 463
Canadian Equestrian Team 422
Carpenter, Rachel 304
Castleman, Ben 328
Caulfield & Snook 392
Chapot, Frank 423
Chef-de-race (aka chef) 104, 124, 133-4, 137, 139-40, 147-53, 172-4, 182-3, 185-7, 199-01, 213-5, 222, 236, 238, 245, 246, 253, 257, 259, 279, 290-2, 302, 367, 377, 420, 423, 466
Cigarette card (Arent's Cigarette Collection) 87, 89, 181

Printed in the USA
CPSIA information can be obtained
at www.ICGtesting.com
LVHW070019221123
764421LV00007B/737

9 780578 503615